McDougal Littell

CLASSZONE

D1366049

Visit **classzone.com** and get connected.

ClassZone resources provide instruction, planning and assessment support for teachers.

Help with the Math

- @Home Tutor enables students to focus on the math and be more prepared for class, using animated examples and instruction.

Games and Activities

- Crossword puzzles, memory games, and other activities help students connect to essential math concepts.
- Math Vocabulary Flipcards are a fun way to learn math terminology.

 Math

- Engaging activities with animated problem–solving graphics support each lesson.
- Online resources include direct correlations to hands–on games and activities at the SHODOR website.

You have immediate access to the the online version of the textbook and ClassZone resources at **www.classzone.com**

M C D T A N T Z M 8 Z Z

Use this code to create your own user name and password.

McDougal Littell
Where Great Lessons Begin

McDougal Littell

Math*Thematics*

NEW EDITION

Senior Authors

Rick Billstein
Jim Williamson

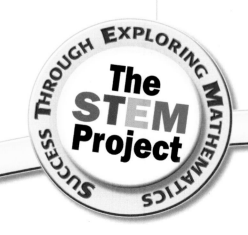

SUCCESS THROUGH EXPLORING MATHEMATICS

The **STEM** Project

BOOK **1**

AUTHORS

SENIOR AUTHORS

Rick Billstein   Department of Mathematical Sciences, The University of Montana, Missoula, Montana

Jim Williamson   Department of Mathematical Sciences, The University of Montana, Missoula, Montana

REVISION WRITERS Lyle Andersen, Jean Howard, Deb Johnson, Bonnie Spence

MATHEMATICS CONSULTANTS Dr. Ira Papick, The University of Missouri, Columbia, Missouri; Dr. David Barker, Illinois State University, Normal, Illinois

PROJECT EVALUATOR Dr. Ted Hodgson, Montana State University, Bozeman, Montana

CONSULTING AUTHORS Perry Montoya, Jacqueline Lowery, Dianne Williams

STEM WRITERS Mary Buck, Clay Burkett, Lynn Churchill, Chris Clouse, Roslyn Denny, William Derrick, Sue Dolezal, Doug Galarus, Paul Kennedy, Pat Lamphere, Nancy Merrill, Perry Montoya, Sallie Morse, Marjorie Petit, Patrick Runkel, Thomas Sanders-Garrett, Richard T. Seitz, Bonnie Spence, Becky Sowders, Chris Tuckerman, Ken Wenger, Joanne Wilkie, Cheryl Wilson, Bente Winston

STEM TEACHER CONSULTANTS Melanie Charlson, Polly Fite, Jean Howard, Tony Navarro, Paul Sowden, Linda Tetley, Marsha Vick, Patricia Zepp

PHOTOGRAPHY ACKNOWLEDGEMENTS

Cover: Coral in Soma Bay, Gorgonian Fan © Settimio Cipriani/Grand Tour/Corbis; *Maze at Hampton Court* © Skyscan Photolibrary/Alamy; *Diplodocus Dinosaur and Human Skeletons* © Louie Psihoyos/Corbis.

Pages T1–T73: **T4** *top* RMIP/Richard Haynes/McDougal Littell/Houghton Mifflin Co., *bottom* Tracey Wheeler/McDougal Littell/Houghton Mifflin Co.; **T6** © Settimio Cipriani/Grand Tour/Corbis; **T7** © Skyscan Photolibrary/Alamy; **T8** © Phil Schermeister/Corbis; **T9** © Frans Lanting/Minden Pictures; **T10** © Jim West/The Image Works; **T11** © Louie Psihoyos/Corbis; **T12** © Jose Fuste Raga/Corbis; **T13** © Chuck Place/Alamy; **T57** Jorge Alban/McDougal Littell/Houghton Mifflin Co.

Further acknowledgements for copyrighted material can be found at the end of the book and constitute an extension of this page.

THE STEM PROJECT   *McDougal Littell Math Thematics*® is based on the field-test versions of The STEM Project curriculum. The STEM Project was supported in part by the

 NATIONAL SCIENCE FOUNDATION

under Grant No. ESI-0137682. Opinions expressed in *McDougal Littell Math Thematics*® are those of the authors and not necessarily those of the National Science Foundation.

ISBN-13: 978-0-618-65609-7   123456789-VJM-11 10 09 08 07
ISBN-10: 0-618-65609-X

Internet Web Site: http://www.mcdougallittell.com

McDougal Littell

Math*Thematics*

BOOK 1

TEACHER'S EDITION

SUCCESS THROUGH EXPLORING MATHEMATICS

The STEM Project

Table of Contents

Program Philosophy

Promoting Student Success

The *Math Thematics* program is a complete mathematics curriculum that promotes student success and engages students in learning by using a thematic approach, active learning, and varied practice and assessment.

- **Thematic Approach** Students learn mathematical concepts and skills through thematic modules that connect mathematical concepts to real-world applications and students' interests.

- **Active Learning** Students are actively engaged in learning as they explore, model, and communicate mathematical ideas using a variety of tools. Direct instruction is also included when appropriate.

- **Varied Practice and Assessment** Teachers and students have a variety of practice and assessment tools that can be used to assure development and mastery of important concepts and skills. Students also learn to assess their own progress.

Unifying Concepts

Four key unifying concepts are used throughout the *Math Thematics* curriculum to make mathematical connections and increase understanding.

- **Proportional Reasoning** The ability to reason proportionally provides the basis for understanding concepts of ratio, rate, percent, proportions, slope, similarity, scale, linear functions, and probability.

- **Multiple Representations** Multiple representations of concepts help students see the connections between topics such as coordinate systems and functions, fraction-decimal-percent representations, and geometric representations of arithmetic concepts.

- **Patterns and Generalizations** Identifying and describing numeric and geometric patterns and making, testing, and applying generalizations about data are tools that students use to develop concepts and construct mathematical thinking.

- **Modeling** By expressing real-world problems using mathematics, finding solutions, and then interpreting the solutions in a real-world context, students become confident problem solvers.

Organization of the Student Edition

The mathematics content for each grade level is presented in one book containing eight thematic modules that connect the mathematical ideas to real-world applications.

Each module contains four to six sections, an *Extended Exploration,* a *Module Project,* and a *Review and Assessment.* A typical module takes about 4 weeks to complete.

The organization of the material in a module is described below.

Module There are 8 modules in each book.

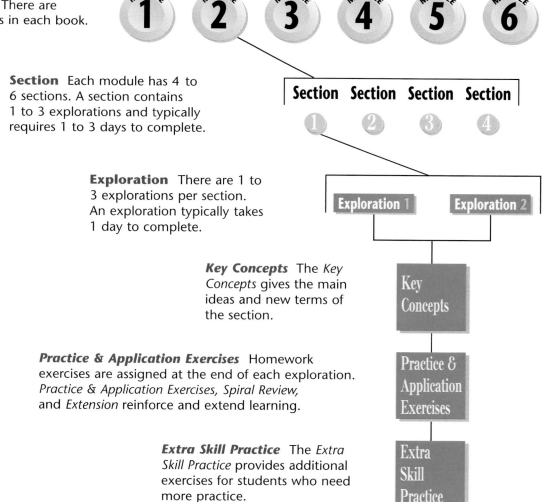

Section Each module has 4 to 6 sections. A section contains 1 to 3 explorations and typically requires 1 to 3 days to complete.

Exploration There are 1 to 3 explorations per section. An exploration typically takes 1 day to complete.

Key Concepts The *Key Concepts* gives the main ideas and new terms of the section.

Practice & Application Exercises Homework exercises are assigned at the end of each exploration. *Practice & Application Exercises, Spiral Review,* and *Extension* reinforce and extend learning.

Extra Skill Practice The *Extra Skill Practice* provides additional exercises for students who need more practice.

Mathematics Students Will Be Learning

Section 1
- learning the order of operations
- estimating answers by rounding
- using compatible numbers to find sums and products mentally

Section 2
- finding rules to extend patterns in sequences
- modeling number sequences with verbal rules, tables, and equations

Section 3
- using the 4-step approach to problem solving
- using problem-solving strategies

Section 4
- writing fractions and mixed numbers to describe situations
- writing fractions greater than 1 as mixed numbers, and vice versa
- writing quotients as mixed numbers

Section 5
- recognizing and finding equivalent fractions
- recognizing and writing fractions in lowest terms
- finding a fraction of a whole number

Pre-Course Features
Scavenger Hunt, p. xx
Pre-Course Test, p. xxii
Test-Taking Skills, p. xxiv

Module Features

MODULE PROJECT
A Puzzling Problem,
pp. 1 and 68–69

EXTENSION
Applying Order of
Operations, p. 13

Assessment Options

PORTFOLIO ASSESSMENT
EXTENDED EXPLORATION (E²):
Estimating Animal
Populations, p. 38
REFLECTING ON THE SECTION:
pp. 13, 25, 36, 51, and 66

ONGOING ASSESSMENT
CHECKPOINTS: pp. 4, 7, 8, 9,
17, 20, 41, 42, 44, 45, 55,
57, 58, 59, and 60
KEY CONCEPTS QUESTIONS:
pp. 10, 11, 21, 33, 46, 47,
61, and 62
STANDARDIZED TESTING:
pp. 14, 37, 52, and 67

MODULE ASSESSMENT
REVIEW AND ASSESSMENT:
pp. 70–71
REFLECTING ON THE MODULE:
p. 71

 Table of Contents

PATTERNS and PROBLEM-SOLVING

MODULE **1**

Connecting the Theme *From tiles to quilts to kites, designers use numbers and geometry to make products sturdy, speedy, or less expensive. You'll discover how patterns in mathematics can be more than just pretty.*

MATH DETECTIVES

72

Connecting the Theme *Detectives use factual information, patterns, past experiences, and different strategies to solve problems. You will see how mathematics can be a tool for solving a variety of problems.*

Module Features

MODULE PROJECT
Pop-Up Art, pp. 73 and 124–125

STUDENT RESOURCE
Student Self-Assessment Scales, p. 87
Using a Protractor, p. 117

EXTENSION
Applying Experimental Probability, p. 83

Assessment Options

PORTFOLIO ASSESSMENT
EXTENDED EXPLORATION (E²):
Pattern Block Angles, p. 123
REFLECTING ON THE SECTION:
pp. 83, 95, 110, and 121

ONGOING ASSESSMENT
CHECKPOINTS: pp. 76, 78, 88, 89, 91, 99, 102, 104, 114, 115, and 117
KEY CONCEPTS QUESTIONS:
pp. 80, 92, 106, 107, and 119
STANDARDIZED TESTING:
pp. 96 and 111

MODULE ASSESSMENT
REVIEW AND ASSESSMENT:
pp. 126–127
REFLECTING ON THE MODULE:
p. 127

Mathematics Students Will Be Learning

SECTION 1
- finding experimental and theoretical probabilities
- identifying impossible and certain events
- plotting probabilities on a number line

SECTION 2
- applying problem-solving strategies
- assessing problem-solving procedures
- generalizing solutions to problems

SECTION 3
- identifying and naming basic geometric figures
- classifying triangles by the lengths of their sides
- determining when triangles can be formed
- identifying types of angles
- classifying triangles by their angle measures

SECTION 4
- identifying and classifying polygons by the number of sides they have
- classifying quadrilateral by pairs of parallel sides and by side lengths and angle measures
- using a protractor to measure and draw angles

Mathematics Students Will Be Learning

SECTION 1
- reading and writing decimals
- comparing and ordering decimals
- understanding place value

SECTION 2
- adding and subtracting decimals

SECTION 3
- using divisibility tests
- finding the factors of a number
- finding the greatest common factor of two or more numbers
- identifying prime and composite numbers
- finding the prime factorization of a number
- evaluating and writing powers of numbers

SECTION 4
- listing the multiples of a number
- finding the least common multiple of two or more numbers

SECTION 5
- renaming fractions and mixed numbers
- multiplying fractions and mixed numbers

SECTION 6
- multiplying decimals
- estimating decimal products

Module Features

MODULE PROJECT
Puzzle Making, pp. 129 and 194–195

CAREER CONNECTION
Choreographer and Dancer, p. 170

EXTENSION
Extending Decimal Place Value, p. 146
Products in Lowest Terms, p. 182

Assessment Options

PORTFOLIO ASSESSMENT
EXTENDED EXPLORATION (E²):
The Cleaning Crew, p. 164
REFLECTING ON THE SECTION:
pp. 136, 146, 162, 169, 182, and 192

ONGOING ASSESSMENT
CHECKPOINTS: pp. 132, 133, 140, 142, 149, 150, 151, 153, 156, 166, 167, 174, 175, 177, 178, and 187
KEY CONCEPTS QUESTIONS:
pp. 134, 143, 158, 168, 178, and 190
STANDARDIZED TESTING:
pp. 137, 147, 163, 171, 183, and 193

MODULE ASSESSMENT
REVIEW AND ASSESSMENT:
pp. 196–197
REFLECTING ON THE MODULE:
p. 197

 Table of Contents

MIND GAMES

128

Connecting the Theme *Most games involve a mix of chance and strategy. How can you develop a strategy for winning? You'll play number games, invent puzzles, and run experiments to find the winning edge.*

STATISTICAL SAFARI

MODULE 4

198

Connecting the Theme *In the field, a biologist watches an animal's movements and records the data. Counting, classifying, and comparing animals can help protect a species. You'll find out how mathematics helps in studying animals.*

Module Features

Assessment Options

Mathematics Students Will Be Learning

SECTION 1
- sorting sets of data
- estimating and measuring metric measures of length and mass
- converting between metric units of length and between metric units of mass

SECTION 2
- drawing and interpreting line plots
- using mean, median, and mode to describe data
- choosing appropriate averages
- writing a fraction as a decimal
- rounding decimal quotients

SECTION 3
- dividing a decimal by a whole number
- writing addition and subtraction equations
- using inverse operations to solve addition and subtraction equations

SECTION 4
- making and interpreting stem-and-leaf plots
- dividing by a decimal
- graphing pairs of values on a coordinate grid

SECTION 5
- making line graphs
- recognizing misleading graphs
- choosing an appropriate average

Mathematics Students Will Be Learning

SECTION 1
- using number sense to compare fractions
- comparing fractions by writing equivalent fractions with a common denominator
- using decimals to compare fractions

SECTION 2
- developing benchmarks to estimate customary lengths
- measuring in fractions of an inch
- converting among customary units of length
- adding and subtracting measurements

SECTION 3
- adding and subtracting fractions

SECTION 4
- adding and subtracting mixed numbers
- estimating mixed number sums

SECTION 5
- using customary units to estimate and measure area
- converting between units of area in the same measurement system
- developing and applying formulas for the areas of parallelograms and triangles
- using equations to find missing dimensions

SECTION 6
- dividing by fractions and mixed numbers

Module Features

MODULE PROJECT
Creating Cubes, pp. 280 and 357–359

EXTENSION
Combining Inequalities, p. 293

Writing Measurements in Mixed Units, p. 305

Making Connections about Regrouping, p. 328

Area of an Irregularly Shaped Figure, p. 343

Assessment Options

PORTFOLIO ASSESSMENT
EXTENDED EXPLORATION (E²):
Add a Square, p. 317

REFLECTING ON THE SECTION:
pp. 293, 304, 314, 327, 342, and 355

ONGOING ASSESSMENT
CHECKPOINTS: pp. 286, 288, 297, 299, 300, 310, 311, 321, 323, 332, 335, 336, 338, 346, 348, 349, 350, and 351

KEY CONCEPTS QUESTIONS:
pp. 290, 301, 302, 312, 324, 339, 340, and 352

STANDARDIZED TESTING:
pp. 306, 316, 329, and 356

MODULE ASSESSMENT
REVIEW AND ASSESSMENT:
pp. 360–361

REFLECTING ON THE MODULE:
p. 361

MODULE 5

CREATING THINGS

280

Connecting the Theme *Designers give an artistic flair to every type of creation. You'll see how people use mathematics to create everyday objects. You'll also give your personal touch to some creations.*

T10

COMPARISONS and PREDICTIONS

362

Connecting the Theme *In news, sports, or weather, reporters like to compare the fastest, strongest, greatest, and longest. You'll see how artists use scale, and how scientists make predictions.*

Module Features

MODULE PROJECT
Mystery Tracks, pp. 362 and 433–435

STUDENT RESOURCE
How to Measure, p. 384

CAREER CONNECTION
Oceanographer, p. 417

EXTENSION
A Doubling Rate, p. 379

Assessment Options

PORTFOLIO ASSESSMENT
EXTENDED EXPLORATION (E²):
The Ideal Chair, p. 395

REFLECTING ON THE SECTION:
pp. 371, 379, 393, 404, and 431

ONGOING ASSESSMENT
CHECKPOINTS: pp. 366, 367, 375, 376, 383, 386, 388, 398, 400, 409, 411, 412, 420, 421, 422, 423, and 427

KEY CONCEPTS QUESTIONS:
pp. 368, 377, 389, 401, 402, 413, 416, 427, and 428

STANDARDIZED TESTING:
pp. 380, 394, 405, 418, and 432

MODULE ASSESSMENT
REVIEW AND ASSESSMENT:
pp. 436–437

REFLECTING ON THE MODULE:
p. 437

Mathematics Students Will Be Learning

SECTION 1
- using ratios to make comparisons
- writing equivalent ratios

SECTION 2
- finding unit rates
- using rates to make predictions

SECTION 3
- writing ratios as decimals to make comparisons
- using "nice" fraction forms of ratios to describe data and make predictions
- making scatter plots
- fitting a line to the data in a scatter plot and using it to make predictions

SECTION 4
- using cross products
- solving proportions

SECTION 5
- identifying similar and congruent figures and their corresponding parts
- applying similarity to solve problems involving scale drawings, scale models, and map scales

SECTION 6
- relating fractions, decimals, and percents
- using fractions to find and estimate percents or percents of a number
- displaying data in circle graphs

Mathematics Students Will Be Learning

SECTION 1
- identifying and drawing prisms
- modeling polyhedra with nets
- identifying the faces, vertices, and edges of a polyhedron
- finding the volume of prisms

SECTION 2
- using customary units to estimate and measure weight
- converting between customary units of weight

SECTION 3
- identifying the parts of a circle
- finding the circumference of a circle

SECTION 4
- finding the area of a circle
- identifying cylinders
- finding the volume of a cylinder

SECTION 5
- estimating and comparing Celsius and Fahrenheit temperatures
- using integers to represent real life situations
- comparing integers
- solving simple inequalities with integers
- graphing on a coordinate grid

Module Features

MODULE PROJECT
Create a World Travel Poster, pp. 438 and 494–495

STUDENT RESOURCE
Interpreting Temperature Scales, p. 483

CAREER CONNECTION
Doctor, p. 458

EXTENSION
Compass Construction, p. 469
Volume of a Cone, p. 480

Assessment Options

PORTFOLIO ASSESSMENT
EXTENDED EXPLORATION (E²):
A Weighty Problem, p. 460
REFLECTING ON THE SECTION:
pp. 450, 457, 468, 479, and 492

ONGOING ASSESSMENT
CHECKPOINTS: pp. 443, 446, 454, 462, 463, 465, 474, 476, 485, and 487
KEY CONCEPTS QUESTIONS:
pp. 447, 448, 455, 466, 477, and 489
STANDARDIZED TESTING:
pp. 451, 459, 470, 481, and 493

MODULE ASSESSMENT
REVIEW AND ASSESSMENT:
pp. 496–497
REFLECTING ON THE MODULE:
p. 497

MODULE 7

WONDERS of the WORLD

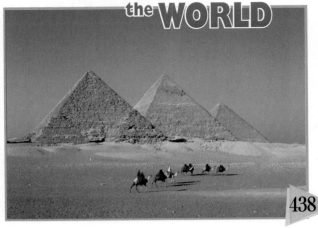

438

Connecting the Theme *Behind the world's greatest construction projects lie legends of love, fame, competition, and glory. You'll look across centuries and continents to see how engineers use mathematics to build a better marvel.*

MATH-THEMATICAL MIX

MODULE 8

498

Connecting the Theme *In this module, you will connect and expand mathematical topics you studied in earlier modules. You will use mathematics to find and compare measurements.*

Module Features

MODULE PROJECT
Play *The Math is Right!*,
pp. 499 and 560–561

CAREER CONNECTION
Chef, p. 510

EXTENSION
Commutative and Associative
Properties, p. 531

Assessment Options

PORTFOLIO ASSESSMENT
EXTENDED EXPLORATION (E²):
Mix It Up, p. 533

REFLECTING ON THE SECTION:
pp. 509, 518, 530, 540, 551,
and 558

ONGOING ASSESSMENT
CHECKPOINTS: pp. 502, 504,
505, 514, 515, 522, 523,
525, 526, 536, 545, 547,
and 554

KEY CONCEPTS QUESTIONS:
pp. 506, 516, 527, 537, 548,
and 556

STANDARDIZED TESTING:
pp. 511, 519, 541, 552, and
559

MODULE ASSESSMENT
REVIEW AND ASSESSMENT:
pp. 562–563

REFLECTING ON THE MODULE:
p. 563

Mathematics Students Will Be Learning

SECTION 1
- estimating capacity in customary units
- converting between customary units of capacity
- relating metric units of capacity and metric units of volume
- estimating capacity in metric units
- converting between metric units of capacity

SECTION 2
- using estimation and mental math strategies

SECTION 3
- adding and subtracting integers

SECTION 4
- using geometric figures to find probabilities

SECTION 5
- performing translations, reflections, and rotations
- using transformations to make designs

SECTION 6
- writing and interpreting numbers in scientific notation

NCTM Standards and Focal Points

The charts below give information about the NCTM Principles and Standards for School Mathematics (2000) and the NCTM Curriculum Focal Points for Prekindergarten through Grade 8 Mathematics (2006).

NCTM Principles and Standards for School Mathematics

CONTENT STANDARDS	PROCESS STANDARDS
1. NUMBER AND OPERATIONS Understand numbers, ways of representing numbers, relationships among numbers, and number systems; understand meanings of operations and how they relate to one another; compute fluently and make reasonable estimates.	**6. PROBLEM SOLVING** Build new mathematical knowledge through problem solving; solve problems that arise in mathematics and in other contexts; apply and adapt a variety of appropriate strategies to solve problems; monitor and reflect on the process of mathematical problem solving.
2. ALGEBRA Understand patterns, relations, and functions; represent and analyze mathematical situations and structures using algebraic symbols; use mathematical models to represent and understand quantitative relationships; analyze change in various contexts.	**7. REASONING AND PROOF** Recognize reasoning and proof as fundamental aspects of mathematics; make and investigate mathematical conjectures; develop and evaluate mathematical arguments and proofs; select and use various types of reasoning and methods of proof.
3. GEOMETRY Analyze characteristics and properties of two- and three-dimensional geometric shapes and develop mathematical arguments about geometric relationships; specify locations and describe spatial relationships using coordinate geometry and other representational systems; apply transformations and use symmetry to analyze mathematical situations; use visualization, spatial reasoning, and geometric modeling to solve problems.	**8. COMMUNICATION** Organize and consolidate their mathematical thinking through communication; communicate their mathematical thinking coherently and clearly to peers, teachers, and others; analyze and evaluate the mathematical thinking and strategies of others; use the language of mathematics to express mathematical ideas precisely.
4. MEASUREMENT Understand measurable attributes of objects and the units, systems, and processes of measurement; apply appropriate techniques, tools, and formulas to determine measurements.	**9. CONNECTIONS** Recognize and use connections among mathematical ideas; understand how mathematical ideas interconnect and build on one another to produce a coherent whole; recognize and apply mathematics in contexts outside of mathematics.
5. DATA ANALYSIS AND PROBABILITY Formulate questions that can be addressed with data and collect, organize, and display relevant data to answer them; select and use appropriate statistical methods to analyze data; develop and evaluate inferences and predictions that are based on data; understand and apply basic concepts of probability.	**10. REPRESENTATION** Create and use representations to organize, record, and communicate mathematical ideas; select, apply, and translate among mathematical representations to solve problems; use representations to model and interpret physical, social, and mathematical phenomena.

NCTM Curriculum Focal Points

GRADE 6 FOCAL POINTS	GRADE 7 FOCAL POINTS	GRADE 8 FOCAL POINTS
1 NUMBER AND OPERATIONS Developing an understanding of and fluency with multiplication and division of fractions and decimals	**1 NUMBER AND OPERATIONS and ALGEBRA and GEOMETRY** Developing an understanding of and applying proportionality, including similarity	**1 ALGEBRA** Analyzing and representing linear functions and solving linear equations and systems of linear equations
2 NUMBER AND OPERATIONS Connecting ratio and rate to multiplication and division	**2 MEASUREMENT and GEOMETRY and ALGEBRA** Developing an understanding of and using formulas to determine surface areas and volumes of three-dimensional shapes	**2 GEOMETRY and MEASUREMENT** Analyzing two- and three-dimensional space and figures by using distance and angle
3 ALGEBRA Writing, interpreting, and using mathematical expressions and equations	**3 NUMBER AND OPERATIONS and ALGEBRA** Developing an understanding of operations on all rational numbers and solving linear equations	**3 DATA ANALYSIS and NUMBER AND OPERATIONS and ALGEBRA** Analyzing and summarizing data sets

SCOPE AND SEQUENCE

Key to Focal Points

Grade 6:	Grade 7:	Grade 8:
Focal Point 1	Focal Point 1	Focal Point 1
Focal Point 2	Focal Point 2	Focal Point 2
Focal Point 3	Focal Point 3	Focal Point 3

The Scope and Sequence chart below correlates *Math Thematics* objectives to the NCTM Principles and Standards for School Mathematics (2000) and to the NCTM Curriculum Focal Points (2006). *Math Thematics* objectives appear as bulleted items beneath each bold-faced NCTM Standard. Columns for the three student editions indicate where an objective is covered and correlate the objective to the relevant NCTM grade-level focal point, as shown in the key to the right.

Number and Operations

	Math Thematics Book 1	Math Thematics Book 2	Math Thematics Book 3
Students should work flexibly with fractions, decimals, and percents to solve problems.			
• Write a fraction or mixed number to compare part of a set or object with the whole.	**1** 1.4.1 *		
• Identify and find equivalent fractions.	**1** 1.5.1, 1.5.2	3.3.1	
• Write fractions in lowest terms.	**1** 1.5.2, 3.3.1	3.3.1, 4.1.1	
• Write a fraction greater than one as a mixed number, and vice versa.	**1** 1.4.2	3.4.1	
• Write a quotient as a mixed number and decide when a mixed number quotient is appropriate to solve a problem.	**1** 1.4.2		
• Write fractions and mixed numbers as decimals, and vice versa.	**1** 3.1.1, 4.2.3, 6.6.1	2.1.1, 4.3.3	4.4.1
• Understand decimal place value and read and write decimal numbers.	3.1.1	2.1.1	
• Round decimals.	4.2.3, 5.1.2		
• Use notation for repeating decimals.		**3** 4.3.3	4.4.1
• Identify rational and irrational numbers.			4.4.1, 7.2.1
• Write fractions and decimals as percents, and vice versa.	6.6.1	**1** 5.5.1	2.4.1
• Use mental math, common fraction/percent equivalents, or percent bar models to estimate percents.	6.6.2	**1** 5.4.1, 5.5.2	2.5.1
• Use mental math to write ratios as percents.		**1** 5.5.1	2.5.2
• Use equations to find the percent, the part, or the total.		**1** 5.5.2, 5.5.3, 8.3.1	2.4.3
• Use a fraction to find a percent of a number.	6.6.2	**1** 5.5.2	2.4.2, 2.4.3
• Estimate a percent of a number.	6.6.2	**1** 5.4.3	2.4.2
Students should compare and order fractions, decimals, and percents efficiently and find their approximate locations on a number line.			
• Compare fractions by writing equivalent fractions with a common denominator, converting to decimals, or by using number sense.	5.1.1, 5.1.2	3.3.1	
• Compare and order decimals.	3.1.2	2.1.1	

* The reference 1.4.1 means Module 1, Section 4, Exploration 1

Number and Operations (continued)

	Math Thematics Book 1	Math Thematics Book 2	Math Thematics Book 3
Students should develop meaning for percents greater than 100 and less than 1.			
• Recognize that the whole is 100%.	6.6.1		
• Find percents greater than 100% and less than 1%.		5.5.3	2.4.3
Students should understand and use ratios and proportions to represent quantitative relationships.			
• Use ratios, rates, and unit rates to compare quantities.	**2** 6.1.1, 6.2.1, 6.3.1, 6.3.2	**1** 2.2.1, 5.1.1	1.1.1
• Express a ratio three ways: using the word *to*, a colon, or fraction form.	**2** 6.1.1	**1** 2.2.1, 5.1.1	
• Recognize and write equivalent ratios and rates.	**2** 6.1.1	**1** 5.1.1	1.1.1
• Use the decimal form of a ratio to make comparisons.	**2** 6.3.1, 6.3.2	**1** 2.2.1	
Students should develop an understanding of large numbers and recognize and appropriately use exponential, scientific, and calculator notation.			
• Write integral powers of 10 in exponential and standard form.	**1** 8.6.1	2.1.2	
• Identify powers and convert between standard and exponential form.	3.3.3	1.1.3, 2.1.2	**3** 6.3.1, 6.3.2
• Write powers with negative exponents in fraction form.		2.1.2	**3** 7.1.2
• Simplify powers with zero and negative exponents.		2.1.2	**3** 7.1.2
• Write numbers in scientific notation.	8.6.1	2.1.3	**3** 3.5.1, 7.1.1, 7.1.2
• Write numbers that are in scientific notation in standard form.	8.6.1	2.1.3	**3** 3.5.1, 7.1.2
Students should use factors, multiples, prime factorization, and relatively prime numbers to solve problems.			
• Use divisibility tests for 2, 3, 5, 9, and 10.	3.3.1	**3** 3.2.2	
• Find all the factors of a number.	3.3.1	**3** 3.2.1	
• Find the greatest common factor (GCF) of two or more numbers.	3.3.1	**3** 3.2.2	
• Identify prime and composite numbers.	3.3.2	**3** 3.2.1	
• Find the prime factorization of a number.	3.3.2	**3** 3.2.1, 3.2.2, 3.2.3	
• List the multiples of a number.	3.4.1	**3** 3.2.3	
• Find the least common multiple of two or more numbers.	3.4.1	**3** 3.2.3	
Students should develop meaning for integers and represent and compare quantities with them.			
• Use integers to represent real life situations.	7.5.1	**3** 1.2.1	
• Compare integers.	7.5.1	**3** 1.2.1	

Number and Operations (continued)

	Math Thematics Book 1	Math Thematics Book 2	Math Thematics Book 3
Students should understand the meaning and effects of arithmetic operations with fractions, decimals, and integers.			
• Use the order of operations to evaluate numerical expressions.	**1** 1.1.1	**3** 1.1.3, 4.5.2	3.2.1
• Interpret the remainder in a division problem.	**1** 1.4.2		
• Interpret division with zero.		4.3.3	
• Use measurement, area, and number-line models to interpret addition, subtraction, and multiplication of fractions and mixed numbers.	**1** 3.5.1, 5.3.1, 5.4.1, 5.4.2	3.3.2	
• Use measurement models and partitioning to interpret division of fractions.	**1** 5.6.1	**3** 4.1.2	
• Interpret the remainder when dividing by a fraction.	**1** 5.6.1		
• Use set union and take-away models to interpret addition and subtraction of decimals.	3.2.1, 3.2.2		
• Use area models and partitioning to interpret multiplication and division of decimals.	**1** 3.6.1, 4.3.1, 4.4.2		
• Multiply decimals by powers of 10.	**1** 3.6.2, 8.6.1	2.1.3	
• Understand the effect of multiplying a positive number by 0, by a number between 0 and 1, and by a number greater than 1.		**3** 4.3.1	
• Understand the effect of dividing a positive number by 1, by a number between 0 and 1, and by a number greater than 1.		**3** 4.3.3	
• Use a chip model to interpret integer addition and subtraction.	8.3.1, 8.3.2		
• Use a number-line to model addition and subtraction of integers.		**3** 1.3.1, 1.3.2, 1.3.3	
• Apply addition properties of 0 and opposites to integer addition.		**3** 1.3.2, 1.5.2, 1.5.3	
• Use repeated addition and a number-line to model and interpret multiplication of integers.		**3** 4.5.1	2.1.3
• Use the missing factor model to interpret division of integers.		**3** 4.5.1	2.1.3
Students should use the associative and commutative properties of addition and multiplication and the distributive property of multiplication over addition to simplify computations with integers, fractions, and decimals.			
• Use the distributive property to multiply a mixed number by a whole number or a fraction.	**1** 3.5.2	4.1.1	
• Apply the commutative and associative properties to integer addition.		**3** 1.3.2	
• Apply the commutative and associative properties to integer multiplication.		**3** 4.5.1	

Number and Operations (continued)

	Math Thematics Book 1	Math Thematics Book 2	Math Thematics Book 3
Students should understand and use the inverse relationships of addition and subtraction, multiplication and division, and squaring and finding square roots to simplify computations and solve problems.			
• Use the inverse relationships between addition and subtraction or multiplication and division to solve equations.	**3** 4.3.3, 5.5.3	**3** 1.5.3, 4.6.6	1.3.2
• Use the inverse relationship between multiplication and division to develop an algorithm for decimal division.		**3** 4.3.2, 4.3.3	
• Multiply by the reciprocal to solve multiplication equations.	**3** 5.5.3		
• Find the reciprocal of a number.	**3** 5.6.1	4.1.1	
• Find principal and negative square roots of perfect squares.		6.3.1	**2** 3.1.1
• Estimate and find square roots.		6.3.1	**2** 3.1.1
• Simplify square roots and expressions involving square roots.			**2** 7.2.1
Students should select appropriate methods and tools for computing with fractions and decimals from among mental computation, estimation, calculators or computers and pencil and pencil, depending on the situation, and apply the selected methods.			
• Decide when to use estimation, mental math, paper and pencil, or a calculator.	**1** 1.1.3		
• Use mental math to find a fraction of a whole number.	**1** 1.5.3		
• Multiply mentally by special multipliers like 0.001 and 1000.	**1** 3.6.2		
Students should develop and analyze algorithms for computing with fractions, decimals, and integers and develop fluency in their use.			
• Use compatible numbers to find sums and products mentally.	**1** 1.1.3		
• Use trading off to find a whole number or decimal sum.	8.2.1		
• Add and subtract fractions and mixed numbers.	5.3.1, 5.4.1, 5.4.2	**3** 3.3.2, 3.4.2	2.2.1, 2.2.2, 2.2.3
• Multiply and divide fractions and mixed numbers.	**1** 1.5.3, 3.5.1, 3.5.2, 5.6.1, 5.6.2	**3** 4.1.1, 4.1.2	
• Add and subtract decimals.	3.2.1, 3.2.2		
• Multiply and divide decimals.	**1** 3.6.1, 4.3.1, 4.4.2	**3** 4.3.1, 4.3.2, 4.3.3	
• Add and subtract integers.	8.3.1, 8.3.2	**3** 1.3.2, 1.3.3	2.1.1, 2.1.2
• Multiply and divide integers.		**3** 4.5.1	2.1.3
• Multiply and divide powers.		2.1.3	7.1.1

Number and Operations (continued)

	Math Thematics Book 1	Math Thematics Book 2	Math Thematics Book 3
Students should develop and use strategies to estimate the results of rational-number computations and judge the reasonableness of the results.			
• Estimate sums, differences, and products of whole numbers by rounding.	1.1.2		
• Use front-end estimation to approximate a whole number or decimal sum.	8.2.1		
• Estimate mixed number sums.	5.4.1		
• Use compatible numbers to check the reasonableness of decimal quotients.	**1** 4.3.1		
• Estimate decimal products and quotients.	**1** 3.6.1, 3.6.2, 4.3.2	4.3.1, 4.3.2	
Students should develop, analyze, and explain methods for solving problems involving proportions, such as scaling and finding equivalent ratios.			
• Make tables of equivalent rates and use patterns to make predictions.	**2** 6.2.1		
• Find unit rates and use them to make predictions.	**2** 6.2.1	**1** 5.1.1	1.1.1
• Use cross products to identify equivalent ratios.	6.4.1	**1** 5.3.1	
• Find equivalent ratios to solve a proportion.	**2** 6.1.1, 6.2.1	**1** 5.1.1	
• Use "nice" fractions to approximate ratios and make predictions.	**2** 6.3.2		
• Use cross products to find a missing term in a proportion.	6.4.1, 6.4.2	**1** 5.3.1, 5.4.2	
• Write and use proportions to solve problems and make predictions.	**2** 6.4.2	**1** 5.1.1, 5.3.1	2.4.2
• Recognize when using a proportion is or is not appropriate.	**2** 6.4.2		
• Use the scale of a drawing or model to find unknown measures.	**2** 6.5.2	**1** 6.5.1, 6.5.2	5.6.1
• Use proportions to find the percent, the part, or the total.		**1** 5.4.2, 5.4.3, 5.5.3	2.4.2
• Use percents to make predictions and solve problems.		**1** 5.5.2	2.5.1, 2.5.2
• Find percent of increase or percent of decrease.		**1** 8.3.1	2.5.2

Algebra

	Math Thematics Book 1	Math Thematics Book 2	Math Thematics Book 3
Students should represent, analyze, and generalize a variety of patterns with tables, graphs, words, and, when possible, symbolic rules.			
• Analyze patterns and find rules to extend patterns.	**3** 1.2.1, 1.2.2, 1.3.3, 2.2.3, 3.4.1	2.3.1	8.1.1, 8.1.2
• Model a number sequence with a verbal rule, a table, a graph, or an equation and predict the nth term.	**3** 1.2.1, 1.2.2, 1.3.3, 2.2.3, 3.4.1, 4.4.3	2.3.1	**1** 8.1.1, 8.1.2
• Identify arithmetic and geometric sequences.			**1** 8.1.1

Algebra (continued)

	Math Thematics Book 1	Math Thematics Book 2	Math Thematics Book 3
Students should relate and compare different forms of representation for a relationship.			
• Use coordinates to identify and plot points in a coordinate plane.	4.4.3, 6.3.3, 7.5.2	1.2.2	2.1.1
• Use exponents to write products and to evaluate expressions.	3.3.3	1.1.3	6.3.1, 6.3.2
• Graph equations and formulas.	4.4.3	**1** 1.4.2, 2.2.1,	**1** 3.2.2, 6.2.1
• Use tables, graphs, and equations to model relationships.		**1** 1.4.1, 1.4.2, 1.5.1, 2.2.1, 4.6.3	**1** 1.5.1, 3.3.1, 3.3.2, 6.2.1
Students should identify functions as linear or nonlinear and contrast their properties from tables, graphs, or equations.			
• Identify linear functions from their graphs.	4.4.3	1.4.2, 2.2.1	**1** 3.2.2, 6.2.1
• Use tables and graphs to model and interpret changes in data.			**1** 6.1.1, 6.3.1, 6.3.2
• Interpret coordinate graphs without scales or labels.			**1** 6.1.1
• Use tables, graphs, and equations to model exponential change.			**1** 6.3.1, 6.3.2
• Use equations to predict the shapes of parabolas.			6.5.1
• Recognize quadratic equations.			**1** 6.5.2
• Use equations, tables, and graphs to represent and identify functions.		1.4.1, 1.4.2	**1** 6.1.2, 6.3.1, 6.5.1
Students should develop an initial conceptual understanding of different uses of variables.			
• Use a variable to represent an unknown value or a quantity that can change.	**3** 1.2.2	**3** 1.4.1	1.3.1
• Evaluate expressions containing variables.	**3** 1.2.2, 4.4.3	**3** 1.4.1, 4.5.2	1.3.1, 3.2.1
• Use opposites to evaluate −*x*.			2.1.1
Students should explore relationships between symbolic expressions and graphs of lines, paying particular attention to the meaning of intercept and slope.			
• Use graphs to explore and compare linear functions.		1.4.2, 2.2.1	**1** 2.1.3, 3.3.1, 4.3.2, 6.2.1
• Find the slope of a line.		**1** 2.2.1, 5.3.2	**1** 3.3.1, 4.3.1, 6.2.1
• Recognize how the slope of a line and its equation are related.		**1** 2.2.1	**1** 2.1.3, 3.3.1, 3.3.2
• Identify slopes of horizontal and vertical lines.			**1** 4.3.1
• Write equations in slope-intercept form.			**1** 3.3.2, 4.3.2, 6.2.1

Algebra (continued)

	Math Thematics Book 1	*Math Thematics* Book 2	*Math Thematics* Book 3
Students should use symbolic algebra to represent situations and to solve problems, especially those that involve linear relationships.			
• Write addition and subtraction equations.	**3** 4.3.2	**3** 1.5.1	1.3.1
• Write multiplication and division equations.	**3** 4.4.3	**3** 1.4.1, 1.5.1	1.3.1
• Write two-step equations involving integers, fractions, or decimals.	4.4.3	**3** 4.6.3	1.3.1, 3.5.2, 4.4.2
Students should recognize and generate equivalent forms for simple algebraic expressions and solve linear equations.			
• Model and solve equations using algebra tiles.	**3** 4.3.2, 4.3.3	1.5.2, 1.5.3	
• Use inverse operations to solve one-step equations.	**3** 4.3.3, 5.5.3	**3** 1.5.3	**1** 1.3.2
• Solve two-step equations involving integers, fractions, or decimals.		**3** 4.6.3	**1** 1.3.2, 3.5.2, 4.4.2, 6.2.2
• Solve equations with variables on both sides or that involve simplifying.			**1** 6.2.2
• Solve equations graphically.			**1** 6.2.1
• Solve systems of linear equations graphically and algebraically.		1.4.2	**1** 6.2.1, 6.2.2
• Identify like and unlike terms.			**1** 1.3.3
• Use properties to simplify expressions.		**3** 2.3.2	**1** 1.3.3, 6.2.2
• Solve equations involving absolute value.			2.1.1
• Simplify quadratic expressions.			6.5.2
• Use algebra tiles to model polynomials.			7.4.1
• Use algebra tiles and tables to multiply binomials.			7.4.1
• Multiply binomials.			7.4.1
• Use algebra tiles to factor quadratics.			7.4.2
• Factor quadratics.			7.4.2
• Simplify radical expressions.			7.2.2
Students should model and solve contextualized problems using various representations, such as graphs, tables, and equations.			
• Use tables, graphs, and equations to model situations and solve problems.	**3** 4.3.3	**3** 1.4.2, 1.5.1	**1** 3.2.2, 3.3.1, 3.3.2, 6.3.1, 6.3.2
• Use equations in slope-intercept form to model real-world situations.			**1** 3.3.2, 4.3.2, 6.2.1
• Write exponential equations to model situations and solve problems.			6.3.2
• Write, graph, and solve inequalities.		6.1.1, 7.3.2	7.3.1, 7.3.2, 7.3.3

Algebra (continued)

	Math Thematics Book 1	Math Thematics Book 2	Math Thematics Book 3
Students should use graphs to analyze the nature of changes in quantities in linear relationships.			
• Interpret the slope of a line.		**1** 2.2.1, 2.2.2, 5.3.2	**1** 3.3.1, 4.3.1
• Use equations, tables, and graphs to solve problems involving linear change.			**1** 3.3.1, 3.3.2, 6.2.1, 6.2.2

Geometry

	Math Thematics Book 1	Math Thematics Book 2	Math Thematics Book 3
Students should precisely describe, classify, and understand relationships among types of two- and three-dimensional objects using their defining properties.			
• Identify, draw, and name basic geometric figures (point, line, segment, ray, angle, etc.)	2.3.1, 2.3.3	1.1.1	
• Recognize parallel and perpendicular lines in a plane.	2.3.1	1.2.2, 3.1.2	
• Identify pairs of angles formed by intersecting lines.		6.4.1	**2** 5.5.1
• Determine the measures of angles formed by parallel lines and a transversal.		6.4.1	**2** 5.5.1
• Classify angles as acute, obtuse, right, or straight.	2.3.3	1.1.1	
• Identify and find the measures of complementary and supplementary angles.		1.1.2	**2** 5.5.1
• Know the characteristics of a polygon.	2.4.1	6.1.2	
• Identify regular polygons.	2.4.1	6.1.2	
• Recognize concave and convex polygons.		6.1.2	8.2.1
• Find the sum of the measures of the interior angles of a convex polygon.		6.4.2	**2** 8.2.1
• Use the sum of the measures of the angles to find unknown angle measures in polygons.		6.4.2	**2** 8.2.1
• Classify triangles as equilateral, isosceles, or scalene.	2.3.2	3.1.2	
• Classify triangles as right, obtuse, or acute.	2.3.3	3.1.2	
• Classify polygons by the number of sides.	2.4.1		
• Classify quadrilaterals.	2.4.1	6.1.2, 8.4.1	8.3.1
• Identify, draw, and name prisms and distinguish between right and oblique prisms.	7.1.1	**2** 6.3.2	4.1.2, 5.1.1
• Identify and count the vertices, edges, and faces of a polyhedron.	7.1.1	**2** 6.3.2	5.2.2
• Identify parts of a circle.	7.3.1	3.1.1, 6.3.3	3.4.2
• Identify cylinders.	7.4.2	**2** 7.2.1	4.1.2
• Recognize a cone.		7.2.1	

Key to Focal Points

Grade 6:	Grade 7:	Grade 8:
Focal Point **1**	Focal Point **1**	Focal Point **1**
Focal Point **2**	Focal Point **2**	Focal Point **2**
Focal Point **3**	Focal Point **3**	Focal Point **3**

Geometry (continued)

	Math Thematics Book 1	Math Thematics Book 2	Math Thematics Book 3
Students should understand relationships among the angles, side lengths, perimeters, areas, and volumes of similar objects.			
• Identify similar and congruent figures and their corresponding parts.	6.5.1	**1** 4.6.2, 6.5.1	**2** 3.4.1, 5.2.1
• Understand and apply properties of similar figures.	6.5.1	**1** 6.5.1, 6.5.2	**2** 3.4.1
• Find unknown measures in similar figures.	**3** 6.5.2	**1** 6.5.2	**2** 3.4.1
• Find perimeters and areas of similar figures.			**2** 3.1.2, 5.6.2
• Recognize the effects of linear dimension changes on area or volume and solve problems involving the relationships.			**2** 3.1.2, 4.1.2
• Find and interpret surface area to volume ratios.			4.2.2
Students should create and critique inductive and deductive arguments concerning geometric ideas and relationships, such as congruence, similarity, and the Pythagorean relationship.			
• Apply the triangle inequality.	2.3.2	3.1.2	5.2.1
• Demonstrate that figures are or are not similar.	6.5.1	**1** 6.5.2	3.4.1
• Apply the side-side-side and side-angle-side congruence rules.			**2** 5.2.1, 5.2.3
• Identify triangles by their side lengths (converse of the Pythagorean theorem).			**2** 5.3.1
• Use the Pythagorean theorem to find an unknown side length of a right triangle.			**2** 5.3.2
Students should use coordinate geometry to represent and examine the properties of geometric shapes.			
• Use coordinates to describe translations and reflections and locate an image after a transformation.		4.6.1	2.1.2, 6.4.1
Students should use coordinate geometry to examine special geometric shapes, such as regular polygons or those with pairs of parallel or perpendicular sides.			
• Use coordinate geometry to identify quadrilaterals and explore the properties of figures.			8.3.2
Students should describe sizes, positions, and orientations of shapes under informal transformations such as flips, turns, slides, and scaling.			
• Identify and perform translations, rotations, and reflections.	8.5.1, 8.5.2	4.4.1, 4.4.2, 4.6.1	2.1.2, 6.4.1
• Use coordinates to describe a stretch or squash transformation of a figure.		4.6.2	
• Write an algorithm to describe a series of transformations.			6.4.1

Geometry (continued)	Math Thematics Book 1	Math Thematics Book 2	Math Thematics Book 3
Students should draw geometric objects with specified properties, such as side lengths or angle measures.			
• Use a compass to draw a circle.	7.3.1	3.1.1	
• Construct triangles.		3.1.2	5.2.1
• Construct perpendicular bisectors of segments.		3.1.2	3.4.2
• Construct angle bisectors.			5.2.3
Students should use two-dimensional representations of three-dimensional objects to visualize and solve problems such as those involving surface area and volume.			
• Create and explore nets for three-dimensional figures and predict the shape a net will form.	7.1.1, 7.1.2	2 6.3.2	5.2.2
• Use nets for polyhedra to explore surface area.		2 6.3.2	5.4.1
• Use isometric dot paper to draw figures made with cubes.			5.1.1
• Explore volumes and surface areas of figures made with cubes.	3 7.1.2	2 7.1.1	5.1.1
• Draw different views of three-dimensional figures.		2 7.1.3	5.1.2
Students should use visual tools such as networks to represent and solve problems.			
• Sort data and organize information using arrays and Venn diagrams.	2.4.1, 4.1.1		3.6.1
Students should use geometric models to represent and explain numerical and algebraic relationships.			
• Use geometric models to model fractions and mixed numbers.	1.4.1		
• Use geometric models to model multiplication of fractions.	3.5.1		
• Construct geometric models for the terms of a sequence.	3 1.2.2	2.3.1	
• Use geometric models to illustrate the expression for the general term of a sequence.	3 1.2.2	2.3.1	
• Use geometric models to model equivalent expressions.		1 2.3.1	
• Use base-ten blocks to model decimal place value.	3.1.1		
• Use base-ten blocks to add and subtract decimals.	3.2.1, 3.2.2		
• Use geometric models to model decimal multiplication.	1 3.6.1		
• Use a geometric model to interpret and find probabilities in a multistage experiment.		6.2.2	
Students should recognize and apply geometric ideas and relationships in areas outside the mathematics classroom, such as art, science, and everyday life.			
• Use transformations to make designs.	8.5.2		
• Create a tessellation.		8.4.2	
• Make a scale drawing.			2 5.6.1
• Solve indirect measurement problems.			2 3.4.1

Measurement

	Math Thematics Book 1	Math Thematics Book 2	Math Thematics Book 3
Students should understand both metric and customary systems of measurement.			
• Select appropriate metric units to measure length and mass.	4.1.2	4.2.2	
• Choose an appropriate customary unit or combination of units to measure length and weight.	5.2.1, 7.2.1		
Students should understand relationships among units and convert from one unit to another within the same system.			
• Convert between metric units of measure.	2 4.1.3, 8.1.2	1 4.2.2, 7.1.2	
• Use the relationship among metric units of volume, capacity, and mass.	2 8.1.2	1 7.1.2	
• Convert between customary units of measure.	2 5.2.2, 7.2.1, 8.1.1	1 3.4.3, 7.3.1	
• Convert between units of area in the same measurement system.	2 5.5.1		
Students should understand, select, and use units of appropriate size and type to measure angles, perimeter, area, surface area, and volume.			
• Measure lengths in metric units.	4.1.2	4.2.2	
• Measure lengths in customary units.	5.2.1		
• Select appropriate customary units to measure area.	5.5.1		
Students should use common benchmarks to select appropriate methods for estimating measurements.			
• Use benchmarks to estimate metric length, mass, and capacity.	4.1.2, 8.1.2	4.2.1	
• Use benchmarks to estimate customary length, weight, and capacity.	5.2.1, 7.2.1, 8.1.1		
• Use models to estimate area in customary units.	5.5.1		
• Use benchmarks to estimate Celsius and Fahrenheit temperatures.	7.5.1		
Students should select and apply techniques and tools to accurately find length, area, volume, and angle measures to appropriate levels of precision.			
• Measure lengths in metric units.	4.1.2	4.2.1	
• Measure the length of an object in customary units.	6.5.2	3.4.3	
• Add and subtract lengths measured in customary units.	5.2.2		
• Use customary units to estimate and measure area.	5.5.1		
• Use a protractor to measure and draw angles.	2.4.2	1.1.1	
• Use an equation to find a missing dimension.	3 6.5.2		

Measurement *(continued)*	Math Thematics Book 1	Math Thematics Book 2	Math Thematics Book 3
Students should develop and use formulas to determine the circumference of circles and the area of triangles, parallelograms, trapezoids, and circles and develop strategies to find the area of more-complex shapes.			
• Develop formulas to find the area of a parallelogram and a triangle.	5.5.2, 5.5.3	**2** 6.1.2	
• Find the areas of parallelograms and triangles.	**3** 5.5.2, 5.5.3	**2** 6.1.2	
• Develop formulas to find the area of a trapezoid.		**2** 6.1.3	
• Find the area of trapezoids.		**2** 6.1.3	
• Find the area of composite shapes.		**2** 6.1.2	
• Develop a formula for finding the circumference of a circle.	7.3.2	**2** 3.1.1	
• Find the circumference of a circle.	**3** 7.3.2	**2** 3.1.1	4.1.1
• Develop a formula for finding the area of a circle.	7.4.1	**2** 6.3.3	
• Find the area of a circle.	**3** 7.4.1	**2** 6.3.3	4.1.1
Students should develop strategies to determine the surface area and volume of selected prisms, pyramids, and cylinders.			
• Understand the concept of volume.	7.1.1, 7.1.2	**2** 7.1.1	3.1.2
• Develop a formula for finding the volume of a prism.	7.1.2	**2** 7.1.1	
• Find the surface area of a prism.		**2** 6.3.2	5.4.1
• Find the volume of a prism.	**3** 7.1.2	**2** 7.1.1	3.1.2, 4.1.2, 5.4.2
• Find the surface area of a cylinder.			4.2.1
• Find the volume of a cylinder.	**3** 7.4.2	**2** 7.2.1	4.1.2
• Find the volume of a cone.		7.2.1	5.4.2
• Find the surface area of a pyramid.			5.4.1
• Find the volume of a pyramid.		7.2.2	5.4.2
• Find the volume of a sphere.			4.1.2
• Find volumes of composite figures.			5.4.2
Students should solve problems involving scale factors, using ratio and proportion.			
• Apply similarity to solve problems involving scale drawings, scale models, and map scales.	6.5.2	**1** 6.5.1, 6.5.2	
• Use sine, cosine, and tangent ratios to find side lengths in a right triangle.			8.5.1, 8.5.2
Students should solve simple problems involving rates and derived measurements for such attributes as velocity and density.			
• Solve problems involving rates.	6.2.1	**1** 1.4.1, 1.4.2, 5.1.1	**1** 1.1.1

Data Analysis and Probability

	Math Thematics Book 1	Math Thematics Book 2	Math Thematics Book 3
Students should formulate questions, design studies, and collect data about a characteristic shared by two populations or different characteristics within one population.			
• Design and conduct a survey.		**1** 5.2.1	2.4.1
• Identify and correct biased survey questions.			2.4.1
Students should select, create, and use appropriate graphical representations of data, including histograms, box plots, and scatterplots.			
• Construct line plots (dot plots).	4.2.1, 4.2.2		
• Construct stem-and-leaf plots and back-to-back stem-and-leaf plots.	4.4.1	5.1.2, 5.2.2	1.2.1
• Make a line graph.	4.5.1	2.2.2	
• Make circle graphs.	6.6.3	**1** 7.4.2	1.1.2
• Choose a scale for a graph and determine how the scale affects the appearance of a graph.	4.2.1, 4.5.1, 6.3.3	1.4.2, 2.2.1, 2.2.2	1.4.1
• Construct a scatter plot.	6.3.3	5.3.2	**3** 1.4.1, 3.3.2
• Construct histograms.		**1** 5.2.2	1.1.2
• Construct box-and-whisker plots.		7.4.1	**3** 1.2.2
• Choose an appropriate data display.		5.2.2	**3** 1.2.3
Students should find, use, and interpret measures of center and spread, including mean and interquartile range.			
• Find the mean, median, mode, and range of a data set.	4.2.1, 4.2.2, 4.2.3, 4.5.2	5.1.2	**3** 1.2.1
• Choose an appropriate average.	4.2.3, 4.5.2	5.1.2, 5.3.3	**3** 1.2.1
• Find and interpret quartiles and the interquartile range.		5.3.3, 7.4.1	**3** 1.2.2

Data Analysis and Probability (continued)

	Math Thematics Book 1	Math Thematics Book 2	Math Thematics Book 3
Students should discuss and understand the correspondence between data sets and their graphical representations, especially histograms, stem-and-leaf plots, box plots, and scatterplots.			
• Interpret data displayed in line plots (dot plots).	4.2.1		
• Interpret data displayed in stem-and-leaf plots and back-to-back stem-and-leaf plots.	4.4.1	5.1.2	1.2.1, 1.2.3
• Interpret data displayed in line graphs.	4.5.1	2.2.2	1.2.3, 4.3.1
• Interpret data displayed in circle graphs and use percents and fractions to estimate angle measures in a circle graph.	6.6.3	**1** 7.4.2	1.1.2, 1.2.3
• Interpret data displayed in a scatter plot.	6.3.3	**1** 5.3.2	**3** 1.2.3, 1.4.1, 4.1.1
• Understand the difference between data displayed in a bar graph and in a histogram and interpret data displayed in histograms.		**1** 5.2.2	1.1.2, 1.2.3
• Interpret data displayed in box-and-whisker plots.		5.3.3, 7.4.1	**3** 1.2.2, 1.2.3
• Recognize trends and identify correlations in data from a scatter plot.			**3** 1.4.2, 4.4.1
Students should use observations about differences between two or more samples to make conjectures about the populations from which the samples were taken.			
• Understand the meanings of population, sample, and representative sample.	1.5.3		**3** 2.4.2
• Summarize and interpret survey results.	6.6.1	**1** 5.2.1	**3** 2.4.2, 2.4.3
• Make predictions from samples.	1.5.3		**3** 2.4.2, 2.4.3
Students should make conjectures about possible relationships between two characteristics of a sample on the basis of scatterplots of the data and approximate lines of fit.			
• Make a scatter plot, fit a line to the data, and use the line to make predictions.	6.3.3	5.3.2	**3** 1.4.2, 3.3.2
• Use an equation of a fitted line to make predictions.			**3** 3.3.2
Students should use conjectures to formulate new questions and plan new studies to answer them.			
• Design and conduct a survey or a study and analyze the results.	4.Project, 6.Project	**1** 2.Project, 5.Project, 8.Project	
Students should understand and use appropriate terminology to describe complementary and mutually exclusive events.			
• Find probabilities of complementary events.	8.4.1	6.2.1	8.4.1

Key to Focal Points

Grade 6:	Grade 7:	Grade 8:
Focal Point 1	Focal Point 1	Focal Point 1
Focal Point 2	Focal Point 2	Focal Point 2
Focal Point 3	Focal Point 3	Focal Point 3

Data Analysis and Probability (continued)

	Math Thematics Book 1	Math Thematics Book 2	Math Thematics Book 3
Students should use proportionality and basic understanding of probability to make and test conjectures about the results of experiments and simulations.			
• Identify outcomes of an experiment.	2.1.1	2.5.1	2.3.1
• Find experimental and theoretical probabilities.	2.1.1, 2.1.2	**1** 2.5.1, 2.5.2	2.3.1, 2.3.2
• Compare the experimental and theoretical probabilities of an event.	2.1.2	**1** 2.5.2	2.3.3
• Use numbers from 0 through 1 to estimate probabilities and identify impossible and certain events.	2.1.1, 2.1.2	**1** 2.5.1	2.3.1, 2.3.2
• Determine if outcomes are equally likely.	2.1.1	**1** 2.5.2	2.3.1, 2.3.2
• Use probabilities to predict.	2.1.1, 8.4.1	**1** 2.5.1, 2.5.2	2.3.1, 2.3.2
• Plot probabilities on a number line.	2.1.2	2.5.1	
• Identify dependent and independent events.			2.3.2
Students should compute probabilities for simple compound events, using such methods as organized lists, tree diagrams, and area models.			
• Find geometric probabilities.	8.4.1	**1** 6.2.1	8.4.1
• Find theoretical probabilities for a multistage experiment.		**1** 6.2.2	2.3.3
• Find all possible arrangements of items.		8.1.1	4.5.1
• Use tree diagrams to model the outcomes of an experiment and to find theoretical probabilities.		6.2.2	2.3.3
• Use the counting principle and tree diagrams to find the number of permutations of a group of items.		8.1.2	4.5.1
• Use the counting principle to determine the probability of an event.			4.6.1
• List and find the number of permutations when items repeat.		8.2.1	
• Use tree diagrams and listing to find the number of combinations of items chosen from a group of items.		8.2.2	4.5.2
• Distinguish a combination from a permutation.		8.2.2	4.5.2

Summary of Assessment

As shown below, *Math Thematics* provides a variety of assessment tools, many of which are built into the student edition. The *Teacher's Edition* and other teaching resources offer additional assessment tools.

Assessment in the Student Edition

Tool	Used to Assess	Purpose	Book 1 Examples
Discussion Questions	• understanding of a concept	• **student** uses for self-assessment	Question 22, p. 79
Checkpoint Questions	• mastery of a skill	• **teacher** assesses student proficiency in content area and makes instructional decisions	Question 7, p. 76 Question 20, p. 91
Try This as a Class Questions	• understanding of a concept or an algorithm • application of concepts and skills	• **student** uses for self-assessment • **teacher** assesses student proficiency in content area and makes instructional decisions	Question 9, p. 76
Practice & Application Exercises (See the *Section Planner* pages in the *Teacher's Edition* for each module.)	• understanding of a concept • mastery of a skill • application of concepts and skills	**teacher** • assesses student proficiency in content area and makes instructional decisions • monitors student progress in problem solving, reasoning, and communication • uses for grading	Exercises 8, 11, 15, 16, 19, 23, and 29, pp. 108 and 109
Reflecting on the Section Questions	• understanding of a concept • application of concepts and skills • problem solving, reasoning, and communication	• **student** uses for self-assessment • **teacher** monitors student progress in problem solving, reasoning, and communication • **teacher** uses for grading	Exercise 11, p. 83 Exercise 10, p. 95 Exercise 12, p. 121
Extended Explorations (E²s)	• problem solving, reasoning, and communication • application of concepts and skills	• **student** uses the *Student Self-Assessment Scales* for self-assessment • **teacher** monitors student progress in problem solving, reasoning, and communication • **teacher** uses the *Teacher Assessment Scales* for grading	"Pattern Block Angles," p. 123
Module Projects	• mastery of specific content • problem solving, reasoning, and communication • application of concepts and skills	• **student** uses the *Student Self-Assessment Scales* for self-assessment • **teacher** monitors student progress in problem solving, reasoning, and communication • **teacher** uses the *Teacher Assessment Scales* for grading	See pp. 73, 124, and 125.

Assessment in the Student Edition *continued*

Tool	Used to Assess	Purpose	Book 1 Examples
Module Review and Assessment	• mastery of specific content • problem solving, reasoning, and communication • application of concepts and skills	**teacher** • assesses student proficiency in content area and makes instructional decisions • monitors student progress in problem solving, reasoning, and communication • uses for grading	See pp. 126 and 127.

Assessment in the Teaching Resources

Tool	Used to Assess	Purpose	Resource
Warm-Ups	• prerequisite skills and concepts for a section	• **teacher** assesses student proficiency in content area and makes instructional decisions	See *Teacher's Resource Books.*
Pre-Course Test	• prerequisite skills and concepts for a course	• **teacher** assesses student proficiency in content area and makes instructional decisions	See the student edition (pp. xxii–xxiii) and the *Teacher's Resource Books.*
Module Diagnostic Tests	• skills and concepts to be taught in a module	• **teacher** assesses student prior knowledge of content and makes instructional decisions	See *Teacher's Resource Books.*
Module Tests, Standardized Tests, Performance Assessments, Cumulative Tests, Mid-Year Test, End-of-Year Test	• mastery of specific content • problem solving, reasoning, and communication • application of concepts and skills	**teacher** • assesses student proficiency in content area and makes instructional decisions • monitors student progress in problem solving, reasoning, and communication • uses for grading	See *Teacher's Resource Books.*
Portfolios	• growth over time and perseverance in problem solving, reasoning, and communication	**teacher** • assesses student proficiency in content area and makes instructional decisions • monitors student progress in problem solving, reasoning, and communication • reports to parents	See *Teacher's Resource Books.*
Test Generator	• mastery of specific content • problem solving, reasoning, and communication • application of concepts and skills	**teacher** • assesses student proficiency in content area and makes instructional decisions • monitors student progress in problem solving, reasoning, and communication • uses for grading	Test Generator CD-ROM

The **Math Thematics Assessment Scales** are designed to help students answer the question "How can I improve my performance in problem solving, reasoning, and communication?" There are five scales—Problem Solving, Mathematical Language, Representations, Connections, and Presentation—which together provide a generalized rubric that defines the various dimensions of mathematical investigation.

The scales can be applied to open-ended questions, *Module Projects, Reflecting on the Section* questions, and especially *Extended Explorations (E²s)*. Students are encouraged to write their solutions to these items using appropriate language and representations to communicate how they solved the problem, the decisions they made as they solved it, and any connections they made.

The key to improving student performance is to actively involve students in assessing their own work. As students become familiar with the *Student Self-Assessment Scales*, they understand what they need to do to improve their problem solving, reasoning, and communication. Teachers assess students' work using the same scales written from a teacher's point of view. The combination of student and teacher assessment provides important feedback to help students improve.

If used consistently, the *Math Thematics Assessment Scales* have the potential to raise the level of students' performance. However, you and your students will not master the use of the assessment scales immediately. This is okay—the more work you and your students assess, the better and more confident you will be with the assessment process. Keep in mind that learning to use the scales is like learning a new language. It requires time and patience. In the end, the effort will pay off, and students' higher-order thinking skills will improve as a result of using the *Math Thematics Assessment Scales*.

Copies of the *Teacher Assessment Scales* and the *Student Self-Assessment Scales* can be found in the *Teacher's Resource Book* for each module. The *Student Self-Assessment Scales* are also shown on page 87 of the student edition.

Descriptions of the scales and facsimiles of the *Teacher Assessment Scales* are provided below. For a detailed discussion of how to interpret each scale, see *The Teacher's Resource Book* for Modules 1 and 2.

Problem Solving Scale

The *Problem Solving Scale* assesses the student's ability to select and use appropriate mathematical concepts and problem solving strategies (guess and check, make a model, look for a pattern, and so on) to solve a problem. The scale emphasizes and reinforces the steps in the *4-Step Approach to Solving Problems*—Understand the Problem, Make a Plan, Carry out the Plan, and Look Back. The related Teacher Assessment Scale gives a range of criteria used for problem solving.

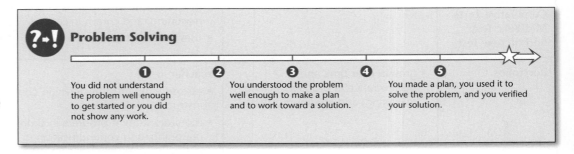

?→! Problem Solving

① You did not understand the problem well enough to get started or you did not show any work.

③ You understood the problem well enough to make a plan and to work toward a solution.

⑤ You made a plan, you used it to solve the problem, and you verified your solution.

Mathematical Language Scale

The *Mathematical Language Scale* assesses the student's use of mathematical vocabulary, notation, and symbols. The scale encourages consistent and accurate use of mathematical language.

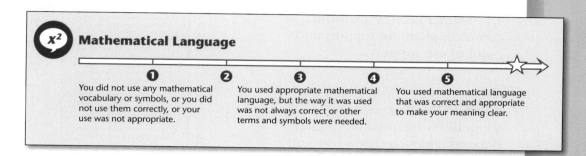

Mathematical Language

1 You did not use any mathematical vocabulary or symbols, or you did not use them correctly, or your use was not appropriate.

2

3 You used appropriate mathematical language, but the way it was used was not always correct or other terms and symbols were needed.

4

5 You used mathematical language that was correct and appropriate to make your meaning clear.

Representations Scale

The *Representations Scale* assesses the student's use of graphs, tables, models, diagrams and equations to solve problems. The scale looks specifically at whether the representations are accurate and appropriate.

Representations

1 You did not use any representations such as equations, tables, graphs, or diagrams to help solve the problem or explain your solution.

2

3 You made appropriate representations to help solve the problem or help you explain your solution, but they were not always correct or other representations were needed.

4

5 You used appropriate and correct representations to solve the problem or explain your solution.

Connections Scale

The *Connections Scale* assesses the student's ability to make connections within mathematics, to real-world situations, and to other disciplines. This scale emphasizes and reinforces the Look Back step in the 4-Step Approach to Solving Problems.

Connections

1 You attempted or solved the problem and then stopped.

2

3 You found patterns and used them to extend the solution to other cases, or you recognized that this problem relates to other problems, mathematical ideas, or applications.

4

5 You extended the ideas in the solution to the general case, or you showed how this problem relates to other problems, mathematical ideas, or applications.

Presentation Scale

The *Presentation Scale* assesses the student's ability to reason logically and to communicate ideas effectively. This scale assesses why students did what they did to solve the problem. Evidence of reasoning is shown by making and testing conjectures, formulating models, explaining why, and gathering and presenting evidence. The differences between levels on the scale reflect both the correctness and the clarity of reasoning.

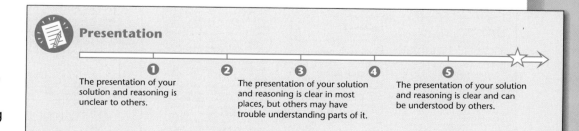

Presentation

1 The presentation of your solution and reasoning is unclear to others.

2

3 The presentation of your solution and reasoning is clear in most places, but others may have trouble understanding parts of it.

4

5 The presentation of your solution and reasoning is clear and can be understood by others.

The *Teacher's Edition* provides complete planning support and point of use support.

Point of Use Support

Suggestions are given for helping students understand new concepts and avoid common errors. Other features include classroom examples, classroom management ideas, and ideas for differentiating instruction.

Complete Planning Support

Module and section planning guides include mathematical overviews, day-by-day planning guides, and homework assignments. Section objectives are keyed to exercises that can be used for embedded assessment.

Exploration 1

CLASSROOM MANAGEMENT
Although students can work on it individually, Exploration 1 is best done in groups of two.

TEACHING NOTES
When working with fractions, some students may not understand that wholes come in various sizes so that one-half of one whole may be different from one-half of another whole. One way to help students visualize this principle is to show them that one-half of a regular-sized candy bar is not the same as one-half of a miniature candy bar, even though they are both halves.

The example below can be used to help students identify fractional parts before beginning **Labsheet 4A**.

CLASSROOM EXAMPLE
Write a fraction for the shaded part of the figure below.

Answer: 9 of the 16 equal-sized parts are shaded.
The fraction is $\frac{9}{16}$.

GOAL

LEARN HOW TO...
• write a fraction and a mixed number

AS YOU...
• use pattern blocks to explore the relationship between part of a design and the whole design

KEY TERMS
• fraction
• numerator
• denominator
• mixed number

3. b. Two of the parts have a given characteristic.

Exploration 1

Fractional **PARTS**

SET UP You will need: • Labsheets 4A and 4B • pattern blocks

Our coins have changed over time. An enlargement of the back of the half-cent coins minted from 1800 to 1808 is shown. The design uses the fraction $\frac{1}{200}$ to show the value of the coin.

▶ Fractions are numbers that can be used to compare part of an object or part of a set with the whole.

EXAMPLE

The square region is the whole.

The numerator tells how many parts to consider.

$$\frac{3}{4}$$

3 of the 4 equal-sized parts are shaded.

The denominator tells how many equal-sized parts the whole is divided into.

3 Suppose the fraction $\frac{2}{5}$ compares part of a shape with the whole shape.
  a. What does the 5 mean? The whole consists of 5 equal parts.
  b. What does the 2 mean?
  c. What is the numerator of the fraction? 2
  d. What is the denominator of the fraction? 5

4 **Discussion** How can fractions help you describe the design of the kite shown at the left? You can use fractions to describe the parts of the kite that are a given color.

40 Module 1 Patterns and Problem Solving

40

Section 4 · Fractions and Mixed Numbers

Section 4 Planner

Section Objectives

Exploration 1
• Write fractions and mixed numbers to describe drawings for situations

Exploration 2
• Write a fraction greater than one as a mixed number and vice versa
• Write a quotient as a mixed number
• Decide when a mixed number quotient is appropriate to solve a problem

Days for Section 4

First Day
Setting the Stage, p. 39
Exploration 1 through Question 5, pp. 40–41

Second Day
Exploration 1 from Question 6, pp. 41–42

Third Day
Exploration 2 through Question 13, pp. 43–44

Fourth Day
Exploration 2 from Example, pp. 44–45
Key Concepts, pp. 46–47

Teaching Resources

Teacher's Resource Book
• Warm-Up
• Labsheets 4A and 4B
• Practice and Applications
• Study Guide
See page 1 for additional teaching resources.

Materials List

Exploration 1
• Labsheets 4A–4B
• pattern blocks

Exploration 2
• pattern blocks
• 1 number cube per group of students

Practice and Applications
• dot paper (Exs. 13–14)

Assessment Options

EMBEDDED ASSESSMENT
• Write fractions and mixed numbers to describe drawings for situations
  Exercises 3, 5, 8, 9
• Write a fraction greater than one as a mixed number and vice versa
  Exercises 21, 23, 25, 27
• Write a quotient as a mixed number
  Exercises 36, 37
• Decide when a mixed number quotient is appropriate to solve a problem
  Exercise 41

PERFORMANCE TASK/PORTFOLIO
• Exercise 6 on p. 48
• Exercises 32–35 on p. 50 (visual thinking)
• Exercise 42 on p. 51 (journal)

QUIZZES/TESTS
• Quick Quiz

TEST GENERATOR

Section 4 Overview

In this section, students will explore different representations of fractions.

Exploration 1
Students begin this exploration by studying how a fraction is incorporated in the design of a half-cent coin to show its value in dollars. Pattern blocks are used to represent fractions and to explore relationships between parts and wholes. Students also work with visual models of fractions and mixed numbers.

Exploration 2
Students play the game *Flex Your Hex* with pattern blocks to see how fractional parts can be traded for a whole. The game is used as a tool for explaining how to convert fractions greater than 1 to mixed numbers and mixed numbers to fractions. Students also explore different ways of writing a quotient: as a fraction, as a mixed number, and as a whole number with an integer remainder. They also examine real life situations and decide when a mixed number is appropriate for answering a question.

Guide for Assigning Homework

REGULAR SCHEDULING (45 MIN CLASS PERIOD)			EXERCISES TO NOTE		
Section/ P&A Pages	Core Assignment	Extended Assignment	Additional Practice/Review	Open-ended Problems	Extended Problems
4 pp. 47–52	**Day 1:** 1–6, SR 44–46 **Day 2:** 7–11, SR 47–51 **Day 3:** 13–18 **Day 4:** 20–38, 40 ROS 42–43	1–6, SR 44–46 7–12, SR 47–51 13–19 20–27, 32–41, ROS 42–43	EP, p. 52		PA 39 Challenge PA 12, 19

Key: PA = Practice & Application; ROS = Reflecting on the Section; SR = Spiral Review; TB = Toolbox; EP = Extra Skill Practice; Ext = Extension; ST = Standardized Testing

Math Background and Teaching Strategies

Classroom Notes

Bulletin board displays for this section include:

• pictures of real life objects that show fractional parts (kites, stained glass windows, art, etc.)

• fractions and mixed numbers shown with pattern blocks

Math Strands

Topic Spiraling and Integration

Exploration 1
For many students, this exploration on fractions will be a review. The

reasoning and writing proportions to change fractions to percents. The relationships among fractions, decimals and percents will be developed in Section 6 of Module 6.

Exploration 2
Students first use pattern blocks and trading to represent fractions greater than 1 as mixed numbers. The concrete model is then used to explain the process of changing a fraction greater than 1 to a mixed number and vice versa.

In *Math Thematics*, the term *improper fraction* is not used for a fraction in which the numerator is greater

form since they are "improper". This is not true and, especially with the slopes of lines and in the case of algebraic fractions containing variables, the fraction form is often preferred over the mixed number form. Teachers choosing to use the term *improper* to describe fractions greater than 1 may want to explain to students that there is nothing wrong with the fraction and that in some situations it is preferable to leave it as a fraction.

Finding equivalent fractions and expressing fractions in lowest terms will be covered in the next section of Module 1. Fraction and mixed

T34

Using the Teaching Resources

The *Teacher's Resource Books* contain a variety of resources for each module:

- *Teaching tools,* including section warm-up exercises, labsheets, additional practice and application exercises, study guide materials, and parent newsletters
- *Assessment tools,* including quizzes, module tests, cumulative tests, pre-course, mid-year, and end-of-year tests, standardized tests, and performance assessments

Teacher's Resource Book for Modules 1 & 2

The **Student Workbook** contains labsheets, additional practice and application exercises, and study guide materials.

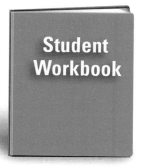

Student Workbook

The **Spanish Resources** book includes practice and applications exercises, assessment, and parent newsletters translated into Spanish, as well as a Spanish glossary.

Spanish Resources

The **Technology Book** provides alternative technology-based explorations designed for use with the modules of *Math Thematics.*

Technology Book

Technology Resources

A variety of technology resources are designed for use with *Math Thematics.*

- **Test Generator (CD-ROM)**
- **@Home Tutor (CD-ROM and online)**
- **Activity Generator (CD-ROM)**
- **Professional Development DVD**
- **ClassZone.com**

CLASSZONE.COM

Professional Development DVD

@Home Tutor

Activity Generator

Test Generator

The *Math Thematics* program was originally developed using National Science Foundation funding over a five-year period that involved extensive field testing. The new edition was developed over a four-year period, and reflects recent thinking from the National Council of Teachers of Mathematics (NCTM) including the Curriculum Focal Points, results from the National Assessment of Educational Progress (NAEP), new state standards, feedback from teachers, and additional field-test results. The *Math Thematics* curriculum has been shown to be particularly effective in promoting strong communication skills and problem solving abilities, as well as positive student attitudes about mathematics.

An Instructional Approach that Works

Research shows that students learn best when they play an active role in instruction. With this observation in mind, *Math Thematics* helps teachers provide a learning environment in which students model real-world situations and see mathematics as a way of thinking about real-world problems. The *Math Thematics* program's hands-on, exploratory approach, combined with its strong offering of varied practice, ensures that students will have a solid underpinning for the concepts and skills they learn. The program's emphasis on problem solving helps students become strong mathematical thinkers. Its use of cooperative learning techniques promotes discussion, so that students learn to justify their thinking. Its use of multiple entry points for mathematical content addresses the needs of all students. And its innovative approach to assessment, which involves not only teacher assessment tools but also student self-assessment tools, encourages students to become active participants in their own progress.

> *During initial development, the* **Math Thematics** *materials underwent extensive field testing by more than 250 teachers with over 35,000 students.*

Development and Field Testing

The *Math Thematics* curriculum was developed using an iterative process that involved many stages of field testing and revision. The writing team consists of mathematics educators from mathematics departments and schools of education as well as mathematicians from departments of mathematics. In addition, many of the *Math Thematics* writers are actual classroom teachers. These teachers were able to provide valuable feedback on their students' success with field-testing materials.

> *Many of the* **Math Thematics** *writers are actual classroom teachers.*

Program Development During initial development, the *Math Thematics* curriculum materials and instructional strategies underwent five years of extensive field testing by more than 250 teachers in 25 states with over 35,000 students. An outside evaluator chose sites to assess the effectiveness of the materials in different types of schools—urban, suburban, and rural—as well as in a variety of classroom settings. *Math Thematics* program staff made frequent visits to field-test sites to observe classes and consult with teachers. Formative evaluation data was collected from the sites by the evaluator, and the teachers met in the summer to give feedback on materials and to prepare for the use of upcoming modules. Data and teacher feedback were used to revise, edit, and rewrite the materials.

Program Evaluation To assess the impact of the *Math Thematics* program, evaluators conducted research on *Math Thematics* students and on control groups of students using other textbooks. At the end of sixth- and seventh-grade field tests, criterion referenced tests (CRTs) were administered to both groups. The CRTs were designed to assess student achievement on content-specific learner outcomes related to one of twelve NCTM Curriculum Standards (2000) for Grades 5–8. (Standard 4: Mathematical Connections was excluded.) The test for each grade level consisted of a combination of short-answer and open-response items, as well as essay questions designed to measure students' ability to communicate with and about mathematics, to do arithmetic, and to solve problems.

The results from the CRTs, which included traditional objectives, showed that sixth-grade students who used *Math Thematics* for one year significantly outperformed control-group students on 11 of the 40 CRT objectives. The control group did not significantly outperform the *Math Thematics* group on any objectives. At the seventh-grade level, *Math Thematics* students achieved a significantly greater mastery level on 12 of the 42 CRT objectives. These results occurred after a statistical correction was applied to make significance more difficult to obtain, thus giving more meaning to the differences.

> *For students who had used* Math Thematics, *the research showed positive shifts in attitude towards problem solving abilities, interest in mathematics, and the perception of the importance of mathematics for their future.*

Student Attitudes The outside evaluator also collected and analyzed data about students' attitudes. For students who had used *Math Thematics*, the research showed positive shifts in attitude toward problem solving abilities, interest in mathematics, and the perception of the importance of mathematics for their future. These shifts were found among both boys and girls and there was evidence to show that *Math Thematics* may have benefited girls by closing a "gap" in attitudes that was evident before the students started using the program.

Other Studies Recent research studies confirm that the *Math Thematics* program is successful when it comes to teaching students basic skills, mathematical concepts, and problem solving approaches. Researchers have compared student performance in school districts using *Math Thematics* for at least two years with the performance of students from similar backgrounds in districts using other materials. The findings indicate that students using *Math Thematics* scored as well as or significantly higher than students using other materials. The *Math Thematics* students scored higher than the control groups in number; geometric and spatial sense; discrete mathematics; algebra; and data analysis, probability, and statistics; as well as on the nationally norm referenced Terra Nova assessment. The researchers also note that, in terms of open-ended problem solving, *Math Thematics* students were both more likely to earn partial credit for each subscale and to excel at the highest level of achievement. These results were consistent across all subgroups of students.

In this study, the control group's eighth graders in all districts studied were enrolled in prealgebra or algebra and most used algebra textbooks. It is worth noting that significant differences occurred across the groups on the algebra portion of the Missouri Assessment Program (MAP) test. In every case, students using *Math Thematics* scored significantly higher on the cluster of algebra items than their comparison groups, a result that demonstrates the effectiveness of the program on students' understanding of algebra.

The *Math Thematics* curriculum was written for a broad range of academic abilities and learning styles, and the goal of the program is to reach all students. This goal is accomplished through the use of cooperative-learning groups, visual representations, manipulatives, discovery learning, and teaching the mathematics content in context. Pages T34–T35 and T48–T54 of the Teacher's Edition describe how the student edition, Teacher's Edition, and ancillary materials support the learning of all students.

Understanding more about the different types of teaching challenges you may have in your classroom, such as working with students who are learning English, students with learning disabilities, or students needing additional challenge, can help you adapt instruction to accomodate all students. The following section identifies areas in which teachers can adjust their teaching method or the curriculum to accommodate all students.

Learning Styles

Students learn by seeing, hearing, and doing. Knowing that some students learn best by one of these means can help you adjust your teaching style to accommodate all learners. The learning styles associated with seeing, hearing, and doing are described in the book *Marching to Different Drummers* (Guild, P. and S. Garger. Alexandria, VA: Association for Supervision and Curriculum Development, 1985).

Visual learners use illustrations, diagrams, tables, and charts to help them understand and remember information. They like to follow what a teacher is presenting with an advanced organizer that outlines the presentation. To accommodate the visual learner, key terms and steps students are to follow are bolded in color within the *Math Thematics* student edition. Written directions are often further supported by photos of students shown engaged in an activity during various steps of a process. In addition, many of the text *example boxes* include visuals of manipulatives and written explanations for each step of a problem. The *Math Thematics* materials also include

labsheets where students can record their work during an exploration or activity. Through introduction of *multiple representations*, students are encouraged to record their work in tables, charts, and diagrams.

Auditory learners love class discussion. They understand by working and talking with others, and they appreciate a teacher taking time to explain something to them. They want to talk through a problem that is difficult to understand. To accommodate the auditory learner, *Math Thematics* materials include embedded *discussion questions* and questions that are worked together as a class (*Try This As a Class*). *Reflecting on the Section* questions and *Module Projects* provide opportunities for oral reports or presentations. In addition, students frequently work in pairs or small groups where discussion is essential.

Kinesthetic learners want to act out a situation or make a product. They find that when they physically do something, they understand it and they remember it. To accommodate the kinesthetic learner, *Math Thematics* materials incorporate games, manipulatives, and other hands-on activities to introduce and teach mathematical concepts. In addition to the exploration activities, the *Module Projects* often allow students to physically construct models related to the mathematics of a module. The active approach in *Math Thematics* promotes "doing" math in place of passively receiving information.

Being aware of your students' learning styles and your teaching method can help you reach all students. Think about these questions as you prepare or teach a lesson:

- Do I write down important ideas as well as say them aloud?
- Do my students have opportunities to act out situations in addition to reading about them?
- Are there other ways I can present this material to appeal to different learners? For example, can I use video or audio tapes, speakers, field trips, plays, skits, poems, stories, or art work?

Instructional Levels

Students at middle-school age, even those at the same grade level, are at a variety of operational levels. Some students are at a concrete level, some at an abstract level, and some at a connecting level. At the connecting level, students begin to write symbols for the physical situation. Students at a concrete level for one concept may be at an abstract level for another concept. To accommodate these various levels, *Math Thematics* uses hands-on, concrete models whenever possible and appropriate. Pictures and symbolic representations are also shown to help students make the transition from the concrete to the symbolic.

For example, in Book 1, students are introduced to integer addition and subtraction using a bean model. Students add and subtract integers intuitively in a game, and then see pictures and symbols to represent integer addition and subtraction. Finally, students formalize the ideas with a set of "rules" for adding and subtracting integers. An example from the student pages showing part of this development is shown at the right.

Language and Cultural Diversity

Students who are learning English can enhance self esteem and build friendships in cooperative-learning groups. There are several ways to actively engage students in the learning process. The following suggestions apply to all students, but they are especially helpful for linguistically or culturally diverse students.

- Encourage students to discuss how the module theme relates to their lives. Many of the *Practice & Application Exercises* can be used to address cultural diversity.
- The hands-on work in *Math Thematics* allows students to explore concrete models. You may want to have manipulatives available for use at home or in later modules.

▶ **The bean models in the Example below show the relationship between the expressions 5 – (–3) and 5 + 3.**

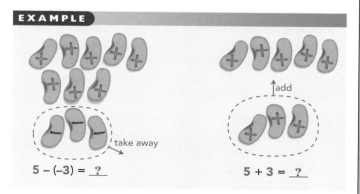

EXAMPLE

$5 - (-3) =$ <u> ? </u> $5 + 3 =$ <u> ? </u>

21 **a.** In the Example, why are 8 positive beans and 3 negative beans used to model 5?

b. How are the expressions 5 – (–3) and 5 + 3 similar?

c. How are the expressions different?

d. Use the beans to find 5 – (–3) and 5 + 3. How do their values compare?

22 **Try This as a Class**

a. Use your answers from Questions 20 and 21 to describe a method for changing a subtraction problem to an addition problem.

b. Use your method to find –2 – 3 by rewriting it as an addition problem.

c. Check your answer to part (b) by using beans to find –2 – 3.

23 Use your method from Question 22(a) to find each difference. Show your steps.

a. 22 – (–12)   **b.** 15 – 72   **c.** –18 – 7

24 ✔ **CHECKPOINT** Find each difference.

a. –17 – (–25)   **b.** 13 – (–7)   **c.** –36 – (–19)

d. –11 – 11   **e.** 49 – 78   **f.** 0 – (–13)

- Create a poster of troublesome mathematical words or English phrases. Review these terms often and try to anticipate other difficult words students may encounter. Try to give a translation of the word or phrase in one of the languages spoken in your class. For Spanish speaking students, see the Spanish Glossary in the *Spanish Resources* book. For speakers of other languages, you may want to use the *Multi-Language Visual Glossary*, also published by McDougal Littell.

Be sure to involve parents through letters or conferences. Clearly state your expectations for your students and describe ways parents can help students succeed in school. The *Math Gazette* parent letter for each module is available in both English and Spanish. The activities and information provided in the newsletter allow parents to communicate with their children about the mathematics that is being studied at school.

Students with Learning Disabilities

The *Math Thematics* program offers many ways to address the needs of all students. For each module, a diagnostic test is provided to help assess students' understanding of concepts to be covered and to identify gaps in students' background knowledge. Each section in a module has an accompanying *Study Guide* which summarizes the mathematical concepts presented in the student edition. The guides give steps, examples, math facts, and definitions necessary for meeting the goal of the lesson. Teachers may use the guides as replacement sections or as reinforcement and review of the section covered in class. Each *Study Guide* comes with its own exercise set. Also, in the student edition, the additional practice provided in the *Spiral Review* and *Extra Skill Practice* help solidify understanding of mathematical concepts for all students, and are extremely helpful for students with learning disabilities.

Some characteristics of students with learning disabilities are hyperactivity, attention deficit, impulsiveness, and reading difficulties. Specific suggestions for these behaviors follow.

Hyperactivity The hands-on activities in *Math Thematics* work well with hyperactive students, but establishing well-defined goals and expectations for the activity and a student's behavior will help the hyperactive student channel his or her energy. Consider posting a class-generated list of rules and goals.

Attention Deficit Students with attention deficit are often distracted by superfluous pictures, designs, or other problems. If students have trouble focusing on one problem at a time, you may want to have them create a "window," as shown below. Students with attention deficit may have less trouble concentrating with such a tool, since all other problems are blocked from view.

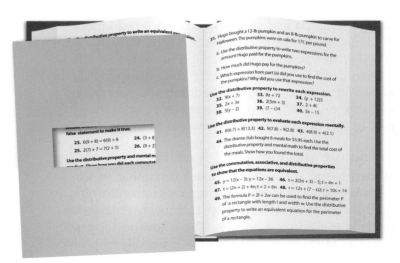

Materials used for activities can also be distracting to students. Materials needed for an activity, such as labsheets, number cubes, pattern blocks, and so on, should be distributed only when students need them.

Students with attention deficit may need to sit in a low-traffic area. Additionally, you may want to seat these students away from bulletin boards or display centers.

Impulsiveness Students who hastily begin activities, games, homework assignments, or tests without reading or listening to directions may need assistance. One technique is to have students read the directions and explain the directions in their own words before you provide the materials for an activity or game. You may also want to go over the directions for tests or homework with students before distributing or assigning them.

Reading Difficulties The reading level in *Math Thematics* is at or below grade level. *Setting the Stage* readings have the flexibility to be read aloud as a class, while the *Think About It* questions give students the opportunity to reflect on a reading. Similarly, students working in small groups can read the directions or instructions for an activity aloud and confirm their understanding before beginning the activity. *Student Resource Pages* as well as step-by-step photos for completing an activity help students understand written instructions.

In *Math Thematics*, key terms and goals are listed at the beginning of each exploration so that students are aware of the main ideas and terms. The *key terms* are bolded within the text and then defined again along with the main ideas of the section in the *Key Concepts Pages*. An organized display of mathematical vocabulary on a wall chart or in a student-created math dictionary can also be helpful.

Gifted Students

Math Thematics provides teachers with many projects and exercises to enrich the learning of gifted students. These projects and exercises can be used in place of, or in addition to, the regular coursework. For each module, teachers are provided with a diagnostic test for assessing students' knowledge of upcoming content, suggestions for extended homework assignments, and a list of open-ended and extended problems. A description of the enrichment and extended learning problems in the *Math Thematics* student edition follows.

- *Challenge* exercises in the *Practice & Application Exercises* are a source of enrichment. Often these exercises build students' problem-solving skills.
- *Open-ended* exercises in the *Practice & Application Exercises* engage students in working on problems that do not have predetermined solutions, thereby encouraging in-depth responses and exploration.
- *Create-your-own* exercises in the *Practice & Application Exercises* encourage student creativity and ingenuity by providing the opportunity to develop unique diagrams, artwork, or problems related to a given math concept.
- *Extensions* take students to a deeper level of understanding of the mathematics in a section or connect to other branches of mathematics.
- *Extended Explorations* (E^2s) may be completed by all students but provide rich opportunities for gifted students. Because most E^2s are open-ended, gifted students can develop creative approaches and solutions to the problem. One component of an E^2 is the presentation of the solution. Gifted students can use their expressive talents to present the solution.
- *Module Projects*, which vary in math content and theme, can be a creative release for many gifted students. Music, artwork, and drama can be incorporated, and creativity and divergent thinking will help students devise unusual solutions. The projects can also be used in place of regular coursework for students who may already have an understanding of material within a module.

A Final Note

Adjusting for students' special needs takes a team of people: the student, parents, general classroom teacher, and possibly the resource teacher, speech therapist, physical therapist, counselor, and others. The suggestions given in this section are limited and do not encompass all special needs cases. We recommend that you consult with your team to decide which teaching ideas are appropriate for your students.

Cooperative Learning

Teachers who use cooperative learning in their classrooms have reported that it produces higher levels of achievement than competitive or individualistic learning.

The Four Parts of Cooperative Learning

Cooperative learning is based on ideas defined by Johnson and Johnson (1984).* These ideas include positive interdependence, individual accountability, cooperative skills, and assessment. Some of these ideas are clearly embedded in the *Math Thematics* curriculum, while others are achieved by teaching students appropriate social skills.

We're All In This Together!

Positive interdependence is sometimes communicated to students as "together you must attain this goal." Fundamentally, it means the group cannot succeed unless all members of the group succeed.

Sometimes positive interdependence means that students need each other to complete a task or understand a concept. Other times it means sharing materials or information.

To help students develop positive interdependence, you can assign a task or role to each group member. The list below gives some ideas for assigning tasks. Remember that not all roles are applicable for all situations.

Roles and Tasks for Group Members

- **Record Keeper** Records the data for the group.
- **Writer** Writes or edits the final report to be turned in.
- **Materials Dispatcher** Gathers and distributes materials needed by the group. This student may also put away all materials at the end of the period.
- **Encourager** Encourages everyone to participate and notes when members have done a good job. (We recommend that you assign this job to all students.)
- **Reader** Reads the directions, story, or problem out loud.
- **Spokesperson** Reports on the group's progress or results.
- **Time Keeper** Monitors how much time the group has left to complete the task.
- **Noise Monitor** Reminds group members to keep the noise level within an acceptable range.

- **Ideas Generator** Asks questions using words like *how*, *why*, and *what else* to help the group come up with ideas.

You Are Responsible

One criticism of cooperative learning is that one student does the work for everyone. In reality, if cooperative learning is implemented correctly, all students are accountable for their learning and for the group results. Individual accountability can be fostered in a number of ways.

- Give points to individuals who demonstrate good social and group skills.
- Test students individually on what they have learned instead of giving a group test.
- Randomly select one group member to explain the problem and solution to the class.
- Give points to groups that demonstrate exceptional cooperation.

Getting Along

An important aspect of cooperative learning is teaching students the social skills needed for interaction. One way to encourage students to think about these skills is to have the class generate a list of behaviors that are acceptable when working within a group. Students should include rules of conduct for listening, talking, giving help, and checking others' work.

Group size and group selection also contribute to the success of cooperative learning. Even the set up of the desks and tables can influence the outcome of group learning. Below are suggestions for each of these concerns based on our work with *Math Thematics* teachers and students.

Group Size In the *Math Thematics* curriculum, groups either have two, three, or four students. Although groups of five or six can use cooperative learning effectively, we feel that teachers and students perform better with smaller groups. We recommend that you use groups of four, and have students pair up with the person on their right or left for partner work. Most activities designed for three students have three obvious roles for students to play. If your class is already set up for groups of four, use one or more of the roles previously listed for the fourth person.

Group Selection At the beginning of the school year, it may be best to have students write down one person they would like to have in their group. You can then randomly select pairs of students to create groups of four. As you get to know your students, you may want to choose the groups. Some things to consider are students' instructional levels, gender ratio, learning disabilities, and behavioral concerns. It is important to remember that some groups work well together and others do not. The personalities of the students will play a major role in how well groups work together.

Classroom Set Up The arrangement of desks or tables should be considered as you implement cooperative learning. Students should be close enough to each other to quietly discuss the problem at hand. The noise level can be an issue if students are too far away from each other or are too close to other groups. Try to have desks or tables situated so that all students can see the overhead or board easily.

How Did We Do?

At various times during a module, students should reflect on how well their group has worked together, both academically and socially. These reflections can take the form of a journal entry or a group discussion. A checklist like the one shown at the right is another way students can assess their group's progress.

You should also give feedback to students on the social interaction you observe. Making the class aware of superior behavior helps all students model appropriate conduct. Many teachers employ a point-reward system when students work in cooperative groups. These points can be added to a test score or counted as a component of the final grade.

Other Common Concerns

How often should I use cooperative groups?

The *Math Thematics* curriculum clearly states when group work is most appropriate. The remaining activities can be done in a variety of ways and their structure is left to the teacher. Although cooperative learning is an excellent teaching tool it should not be used to the exclusion of whole class or individual work.

Should students stay in the same groups for the entire semester?

Students should have a chance to interact with others in the class, so new groups should be formed every 4 weeks or so. Since a typical module in the *Math Thematics* curriculum is approximately 4 weeks long, new groups should be organized for each module.

Take It Slow

There are many facets and layers to cooperative learning, and it may take time to fully incorporate the philosophy into a classroom. When introducing cooperative learning to your class, you may want to focus on one part of cooperative learning, such as positive interdependence, and later bring in the other aspects.

* Johnson, D., R. Johnson, E. Holubec, et al. *Circles of Learning: Cooperation in the Classroom*. Association for Supervision and Curriculum Development, 1984.

Cooperative Learning Evaluation Form			
Comment	**Always**	**Sometimes**	**Never**
Everyone in our group is given a chance to talk.			
My opinions are valued by others in my group.			
I listen to others in my group without interrupting.			
Our group is able to finish the task or solve the problem in the given time.			
I understand the mathematics I learn in my group.			
Other comments:			

Extended Explorations (*E²s*) are open-ended, problem solving tasks designed to be completed independently. Many *E²s* can be assigned to pairs or groups of students. An *E²* should take one or two weeks to complete.

Introducing the *E²*

Some class time should be used to introduce and begin working on the *E²*. Consider the suggestions at the right as you introduce the *E²* to the whole class.

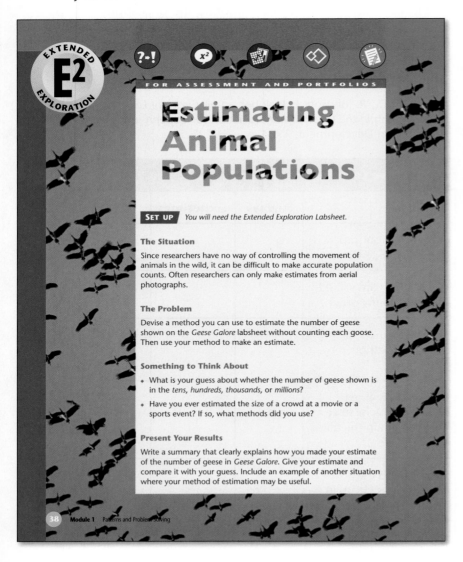

• Discuss the due date. You have some flexibility as to when you assign *E²s*. If you have five classes, do not have all the *E²s* due the same day.

• Use the *Format for an E² Solution* in the *Teacher's Resource Book* for Module 1 to explain to students what is expected in the solution of an Extended Exploration.

• Make sure everyone understands the problem. Discuss what students know about the problem and what they do not know.

• Brainstorm possible approaches to the problem.

As you read through the following discussion, try answering the questions in the shaded boxes. For answers to the questions see the Additional Answers beginning on page A1.

> **1.** How might you introduce the *E²* shown here?
>
> **2.** What approaches do you think would work best?
>
> **3.** Suppose you are a student. Solve the *Estimating Animal Populations E²*.

Monitoring Student Progress

Students often do not fully comprehend a task until they start it. Thus, it is important to discuss the *E²* after students have had a day or two to think about it. If students have difficulty getting started, you may want to:

• Make sure they have identified and collected the information needed to solve the problem.

• Give clues about appropriate problem solving strategies.

• Provide prompts about possible connections.

To help students organize their thinking, you may want to have them turn in an outline of what they plan to do before they venture off on their final product. You may also want to offer to look at students' work in progress.

Before collecting the *E²*, have students assess their own work using the *Student Self-Assessment Scales.* After they have assessed their work, you may want to:

• Have students share parts of their solutions with the class.

• Give students a chance to rework parts of their solution before turning it in.

4. Suppose you are a student. Use the *Student Self-Assessment Scales* in the *Teacher's Resource Books* to assess your work on *Estimating Animal Populations*.

Assessing Solutions

The following are tips for assessing student work on an E^2 using the *Math Thematics Assessment Scales*.

- Give yourself the same amount of time to evaluate the solutions as you gave the students to work on them. Read an entire solution before you begin to assess it.

- Look at the sample solution in the *Teacher's Resource Book* to get ideas about what scales to use and what a solution might contain. Use this information and the *Teacher Assessment Scales* to get an idea of what you might expect a student to do to score at each level on each scale.

- Do not spend too much time deliberating over the scoring on a scale. Use your best judgment and move on. If you are not sure which level a solution scores at on a scale, score it between two levels.

- Be sure to record the mathematical content used and note any calculation errors on the bottom of the *Teacher Assessment Scales*.

- Students are not going to score high at first, but they will improve. The goal is that the final level reflect the student's highest potential.

- Students' solutions give you information about their conceptual understanding. When you recognize a misconception, have a conference with the student to clear it up.

5. Read over the sample solution to *Estimating Animal Populations* given in the *Teacher's Resource Book* for Module 1. How would you score your solution now?

Grading Solutions

The reason for assessing an E^2 is to give students an indication of their current problem solving ability, how it has changed over time, and what they can do to continue to improve. Simply giving each solution a grade based on the total of the ratings on the scales does not achieve this goal. Instead, we recommend using scoring profiles like the ones in the *Teacher's Resource Book* for Module 1 to help assign grades.

The line on a profile indicates the minimum level a student should score at on each scale for each response. The *Excellent* response is a composite of the abilities the *Math Thematics* curriculum strives to develop. The *Good* response reflects the primary objective of the curriculum; most students should eventually reach this level. The *Developing* response indicates progress toward an acceptable level. Anything below the *Developing* level reflects little effort or understanding.

Keep the following in mind as you convert scores into students' grades.

- Be flexible. The profiles are only suggestions. You must determine which procedure is best for converting your students' assessment data into grades.

- If you use the profiles, familiarize your students with them so they know how their grades were determined and what goal to work toward.

6. Read the Student Sample E^2 Solutions in the *Teacher's Resource Book* for Module 1. Use the *Teacher Assessment Scales*. Read, assess, and grade the students' sample work.

Follow-Up

You may want to spend some class time letting students share their results and strategies for solving the problem. You may want to display solutions on a bulletin board.

With the class as a whole you might want to:

- Discuss universal misunderstandings or misconceptions regarding a problem or a mathematical idea.

- Illustrate a variety of solutions, approaches, and connections and highlight exceptional responses.

With the individual student, you may want to:

- Monitor individual growth on the scales.

- Compare the *Student Self-Assessment* with the *Teacher Assessment*.

- Give help or explanations regarding the student's individual solution.

Communicating with Parents

Research has shown that students perform better when there is a strong parental involvement program that includes communicating with parents and other family members on a regular basis. Communication can be achieved through individual conferences, letters to parents, newsletters, and parent workshops. We recommend that you use a variety of methods to reach parents, but adjust the content or delivery to best suit your community.

Letters to Parents

Most parents remember mathematics classes as hours spent doing endless arithmetic problems. Although this teaching strategy is viable for a small number of students, it does not address the learning styles of most students, nor the intellectual needs of our society. It is important to share information about changes in mathematics education and about the advantages of using a program like *Math Thematics*. One way to apprise parents is to send out a general letter describing the textbook their students will be using and the philosophy of the curriculum. A sample letter is shown below.

Dear Family Members,

This year we'll be using the *Math Thematics* curriculum. This curriculum is designed to help all students develop their mathematical understanding and ability. The materials stress not only key mathematical skills, but also the importance of problem solving, reasoning, and critical thinking. One component of this approach is that students will spend time discussing and writing about mathematics.

Math Thematics uses a variety of instructional techniques, including discovery learning and real-world problems, to motivate students. Because the program allows students to discover the mathematics, you will see few step-by-step procedures. This does not mean that students are completely on their own. There are many examples and pages in the textbook that will help you and your child identify the content that is most important. These examples include:

• **Key Concepts pages** that summarize what students have learned in each section.

• **Student Resource pages** that appear throughout the book and give detailed guidance on various mathematical skills, such as using fraction-percent relationships and using a protractor.

• The **Toolbox** at the end of the book to help students review essential skills they need this year but may have forgotten.

You should expect to see homework assignments at least three nights each week. Some of these problems reinforce skills while others require more thought and effort. As part of your child's homework, you may be asked to help conduct an experiment, answer questions for a survey, or play a math game.

I have planned a Math for Parents meeting to familiarize you with the text and to answer questions. The first session will be held on (date). Additional information about this session will be sent home with your child.

Sincerely,

Newsletters

For each module of *Math Thematics*, the *Teacher's Resource Book* includes a *Math Gazette*. This newsletter informs parents about the mathematics, activities, and real-world situations their children will explore in the coming weeks. Questions are provided to help parents discuss the mathematics and themes with their child. The newsletter also lists several activities parents can do at home with their child, and it describes the *Extended Exploration* (*E²*), and the *Module Project*. We encourage you to copy and distribute these newsletters on a regular basis.

Math for Parents Meetings

Meetings with parents provide an opportunity to discuss the concerns of parents and to explore the pedagogical approaches in *Math Thematics*. Depending on the needs of your community, your math department may want to hold a "Math for Parents" meeting or several such meetings throughout the year. For example, four meetings could be scheduled as follows:

- **Meeting 1:** two weeks into the school year
- **Meeting 2:** one month into the school year
- **Meeting 3:** halfway through the school year
- **Meeting 4:** at the end of the school year

For meeting 1, you could give an overview of the *Math Thematics* curriculum and philosophy, emphasizing that it is a challenging curriculum that addresses the needs of a broad range of students, and pointing out that its theme-based approach engages students and encourages them to become expert problem solvers. To introduce the program's hands-on, discovery philosophy, you could have parents work in cooperative groups to complete an exploration that students will be doing in class. For example, they could try doing the integer activity in Module 8, Section 3.

At other meetings, you might want to focus on a particular topic such as "learning the basics," so that parents will understand that each book in the *Math Thematics* program explores and reviews basic computation, mental math, estimation, number ideas, and measurement. Pre-Algebra and technology are other topics that may be of interest to parents.

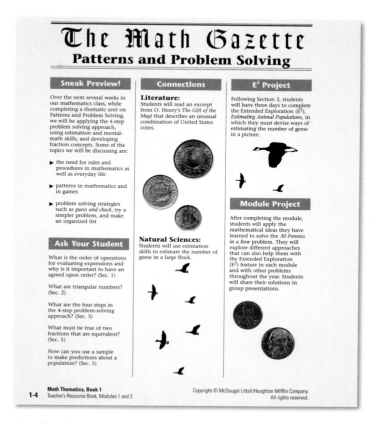

Another important aspect of the *Math Thematics* curriculum that you may want to discuss at a parent meeting is assessment. (See the articles on pages T30–T33.) You might want to have parents try solving an *Extended Exploration*, such as "Estimating Animal Populations" in Module 1. Consider having parents use the assessment scales to critique their own work.

Parent meetings are also a good opportunity to talk about how to help students with homework. You may want to point out textbook features such as the *Key Concepts* pages and the *Toolbox*, which are intended to help students and parents review concepts.

The last meeting of the year could be an orientation for parents of students now in an earlier grade who will be using the *Math Thematics* curriculum in the coming year.

To ensure that all parents hear the same message, we suggest that the entire math department organize and participate in Math for Parents meetings.

ORGANIZATION OF THE BOOK

This book contains eight modules. To get an overview of the modules and their themes, look at the Table of Contents starting on p. iv.

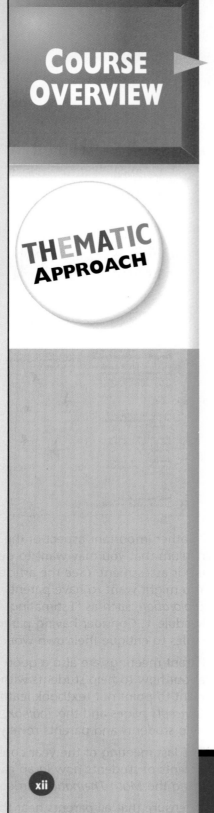

THEMATIC APPROACH

MODULES:
8 per book

MODULE **1**

MODULE **2**

MODULE **3**

MODULE **4**

MODULE **5**

MODULE **6**

MODULE **7**

MODULE **8**

SECTIONS:
4–6 per module

Section ①
Section ②
Section ③
Section ④
Section ⑤
Section ⑥

EXPLORATIONS:
1–3 per section

Exploration 1
Exploration 2
Exploration 3

PRACTICE:
for each exploration

Practice & Application Exercises

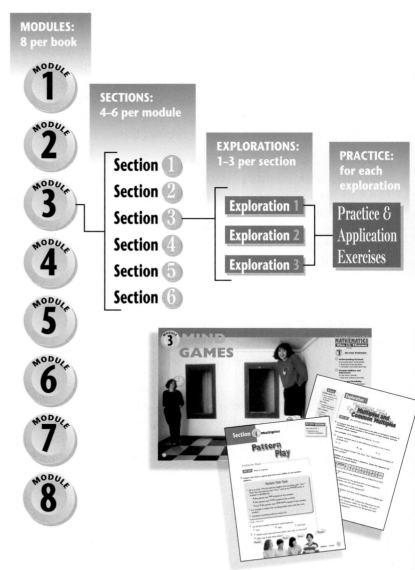

xii

T48

MODULE THEME & PROJECT

Each module's theme connects the mathematics you are learning to the real world. *Mind Games* is the theme of Module 3. At the end of each module is a Module Project that relates to the module theme.

Connecting Mathematics and the Theme
The math topics you'll be learning and the settings in which you'll be learning them.

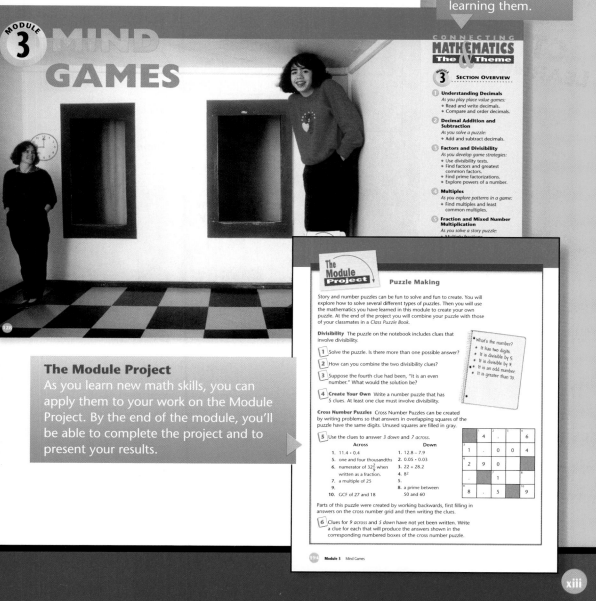

The Module Project
As you learn new math skills, you can apply them to your work on the Module Project. By the end of the module, you'll be able to complete the project and to present your results.

ACTIVE LEARNING

SECTION ORGANIZATION

The diagram below illustrates the organization of a section:

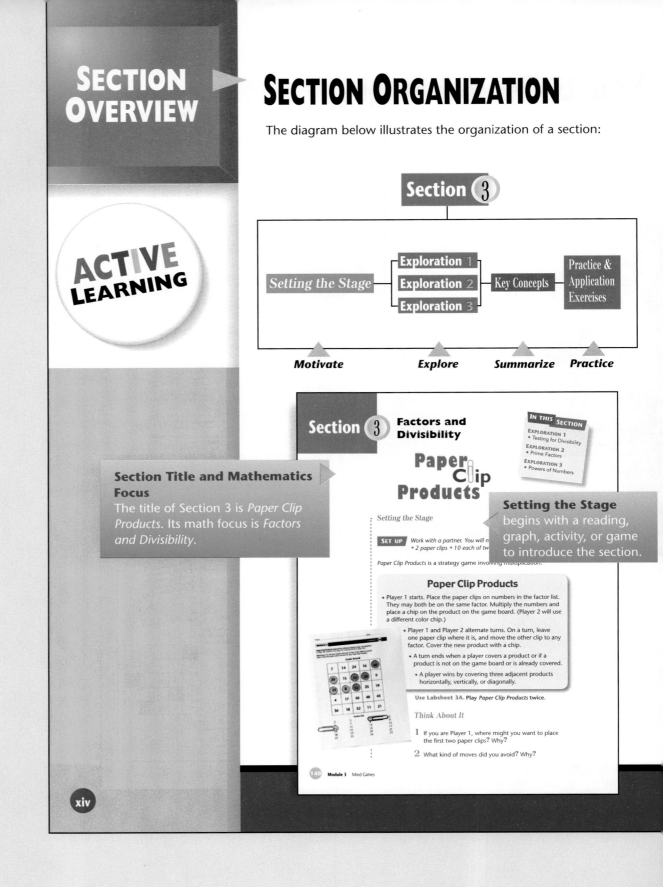

Section ③

Setting the Stage → Exploration 1 / Exploration 2 / Exploration 3 → Key Concepts → Practice & Application Exercises

Motivate   **Explore**   **Summarize**   **Practice**

Section Title and Mathematics Focus
The title of Section 3 is *Paper Clip Products*. Its math focus is *Factors and Divisibility*.

Setting the Stage
begins with a reading, graph, activity, or game to introduce the section.

Section ③ Factors and Divisibility

IN THIS SECTION
EXPLORATION 1
◆ Testing for Divisibility
EXPLORATION 2
◆ Prime Factors
EXPLORATION 3
◆ Powers of Numbers

Paper Clip Products

Setting the Stage

SET UP Work with a partner. You will n
• 2 paper clips • 10 each of tw

Paper Clip Products is a strategy game involving multiplication.

Paper Clip Products

◆ Player 1 starts. Place the paper clips on numbers in the factor list. They may both be on the same factor. Multiply the numbers and place a chip on the product on the game board. (Player 2 will use a different color chip.)

◆ Player 1 and Player 2 alternate turns. On a turn, leave one paper clip where it is, and move the other clip to any factor. Cover the new product with a chip.

◆ A turn ends when a player covers a product or if a product is not on the game board or is already covered.

◆ A player wins by covering three adjacent products horizontally, vertically, or diagonally.

Use Labsheet 3A. **Play** *Paper Clip Products* twice.

Think About It

1 If you are Player 1, where might you want to place the first two paper clips? Why?

2 What kind of moves did you avoid? Why?

148 **Module 3** Mind Games

xiv

EXPLORATIONS & KEY CONCEPTS

In the explorations you'll be actively involved in investigating mathematics concepts, learning mathematics skills, and solving problems.

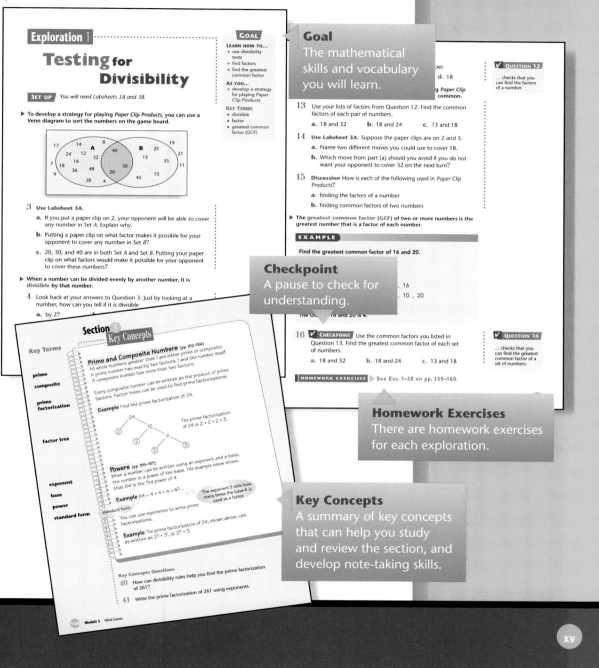

Goal
The mathematical skills and vocabulary you will learn.

Checkpoint
A pause to check for understanding.

Homework Exercises
There are homework exercises for each exploration.

Key Concepts
A summary of key concepts that can help you study and review the section, and develop note-taking skills.

SECTION OVERVIEW

PRACTICE & APPLICATION

Practice and Application Exercises will give you a chance to practice the skills and concepts in the explorations and apply them in solving many types of problems.

VARIED PRACTICE

Balanced Practice
These exercises develop algebra, geometry, numerical, and problem solving skills and help you communicate mathematical ideas.

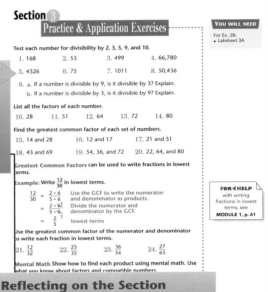

Section 3

Practice & Application Exercises

YOU WILL NEED
For Ex. 28:
• Labsheet 3A

Test each number for divisibility by 2, 3, 5, 9, and 10.

1. 168   2. 53   3. 499   4. 66,780

5. 4326   6. 75   7. 1011   8. 50,436

9. a. If a number is divisible by 9, is it divisible by 3? Explain.
   b. If a number is divisible by 3, is it divisible by 9? Explain.

List all the factors of each number.

10. 28   11. 51   12. 64   13. 72   14. 80

Find the greatest common factor of each set of numbers.

15. 14 and 28   16. 12 and 17   17. 21 and 51

18. 43 and 69   19. 54, 36, and 72   20. 22, 64, and 80

Greatest Common Factors can be used to write fractions in lowest terms.

Example: Write $\frac{12}{30}$ in lowest terms.

$\frac{12}{30} = \frac{2 \cdot 6}{5 \cdot 6}$ Use the GCF to write the numerator and denominator as products.

$= \frac{2 \cdot 6}{5 \cdot 6}$ Divide the numerator and denominator by the GCF.

$= \frac{2}{5}$ lowest terms

FOR HELP
with writing fractions in lowest terms, see
MODULE 1, p. 61

Use the greatest common factor of the numerator and denominator to write each fraction in lowest terms.

21. $\frac{12}{32}$ 22. $\frac{25}{35}$ 23. $\frac{36}{54}$ 24. $\frac{27}{63}$

Mental Math Show how to find each product using mental math. Use what you know about factors and compatible numbers.

Section 3 Factors and Divisibility 159

Reflecting on the Section
exercises help you communicate ideas through oral reports, journal writing, visual thinking, research, and discussion.

$2^5 = 32$
$2^4 = 16$
$2^3 = 8$
$2^2 = 4$
$2^1 = 2$

60. a. What mathematical operation is used to go from 32 to 16? from 16 to 8? Does this pattern continue throughout the sequence 32, 16, 8, 4, 2?

   b. Based on the pattern, what is the value of 2^0?

   c. How does this compare with the number of sections after 0 folds in the paper-folding pattern in Exploration 3 on page 155? Explain.

Oral Report
Exercise 61 checks that you can apply your understanding of divisibility and prime factorization.

Reflecting on the Section

Be prepared to discuss your answer to Exercise 61 in class.

61. a. Write the prime factorization of each number in the table.

   b. What do you notice about the prime factors of the numbers that are divisible by 6?

   c. Use your results from part (b) and the divisibility tests you know. Write a divisibility test for 6.

Divisible by 6	Not Divisible by 6
72	44
30	39
114	175
24	63
138	70

Spiral Review

62. A bag contains 1 red marble, 2 yellow marbles, and 7 blue marbles. What is the theoretical probability of drawing a red marble from the bag? a green marble? (Module 2, p. 80)

63. If possible, sketch a triangle that is both obtuse and scalene. (Module 2, pp. 106–107)

Decide if the given lengths will form a triangle. (Module 2, p. 106)

64. 3 in., 2 in., 6 in.   65. 4 ft, 22 ft, 25 ft

Write an equation for each word sentence in Exercises 66–69. Use t for the term and n for the term number. (Module 1, p. 21)

66. The term is three more than the term number.

67. The term is four times the term number.

68. The term is two more than three times the term number.

69. The term is the term number to the third power.

70. Use your equations from Exercises 66–69 to find the first 4 terms of each sequence.

162 **Module 3** Mind Games

Spiral Review
exercises help you maintain skills by revisiting material from previous sections in the book.

xvi

ADDITIONAL PRACTICE

At the end of every section, you will find Extra Skill Practice. If needed, you can use these exercises for extra practice on important skills before you begin the next section.

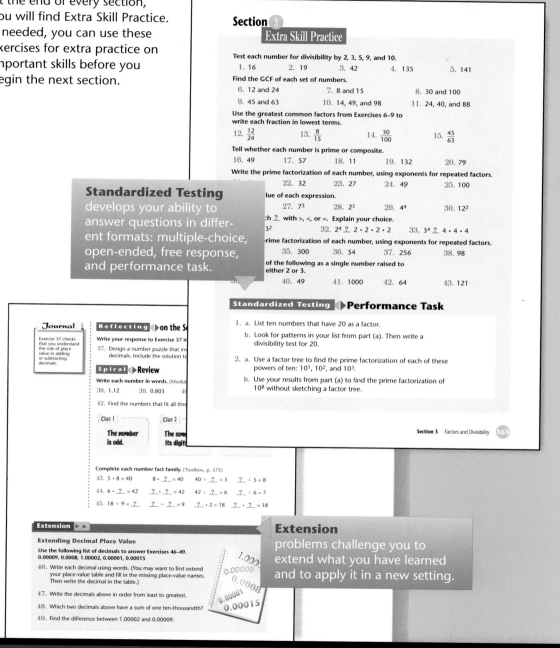

Section 3
Extra Skill Practice

Test each number for divisibility by 2, 3, 5, 9, and 10.

1. 16   2. 19   3. 42   4. 135   5. 141

Find the GCF of each set of numbers.

6. 12 and 24   7. 8 and 15   8. 30 and 100

9. 45 and 63   10. 14, 49, and 98   11. 24, 40, and 88

Use the greatest common factors from Exercises 6–9 to write each fraction in lowest terms.

12. $\frac{12}{24}$ 13. $\frac{8}{15}$ 14. $\frac{30}{100}$ 15. $\frac{45}{63}$

Tell whether each number is prime or composite.

16. 49   17. 57   18. 11   19. 132   20. 79

Write the prime factorization of each number, using exponents for repeated factors.

22. 32   23. 27   24. 49   25. 100

value of each expression.

27. 7^3 28. 2^5 29. 4^4 30. 12^2

ch ? with >, <, or =. Explain your choice.

3^2 32. 2^4 ? $2 \cdot 2 \cdot 2 \cdot 2$ 33. 3^4 ? $4 \cdot 4 \cdot 4$

rime factorization of each number, using exponents for repeated factors.

35. 300   36. 54   37. 256   38. 98

of the following as a single number raised to either 2 or 3.

40. 49   41. 1000   42. 64   43. 121

Standardized Testing ▶ Performance Task

1. a. List ten numbers that have 20 as a factor.

   b. Look for patterns in your list from part (a). Then write a divisibility test for 20.

2. a. Use a factor tree to find the prime factorization of each of these powers of ten: 10^1, 10^2, and 10^3.

   b. Use your results from part (a) to find the prime factorization of 10^8 without sketching a factor tree.

Section 3   Factors and Divisibility   163

Standardized Testing develops your ability to answer questions in different formats: multiple-choice, open-ended, free response, and performance task.

Journal

Exercise 37 checks that you understand the role of place value in adding or subtracting decimals.

Reflecting ◀▶ on the S

Write your response to Exercise 37 i

37. Design a number puzzle that inv decimals. Include the solution t

Spiral ▶ Review

Write each number in words. (Modul

38. 1.12   39. 0.803   40

42. Find the numbers that fit all thr

Clue 1	Clue 2
The number is odd.	The sum its digit

Complete each number fact family. (Toolbox, p. 573)

43. $5 \cdot 8 = 40$ $8 \cdot \underline{?} = 40$ $40 \div \underline{?} = 5$ $\underline{?} \div 5 = 8$

44. $6 \cdot \underline{?} = 42$ $\underline{?} \cdot \underline{?} = 42$ $42 \div \underline{?} = 6$ $\underline{?} \div 6 = 7$

45. $18 \div 9 = \underline{?}$ $\underline{?} \div \underline{?} = 9$ $\underline{?} \cdot 2 = 18$ $\underline{?} \cdot \underline{?} = 18$

Extension ▶▶

Extending Decimal Place Value

Use the following list of decimals to answer Exercises 46–49.
0.00009, 0.0008, 1.00002, 0.00001, 0.00015

46. Write each decimal using words. (You may want to first extend your place-value table and fill in the missing place-value names. Then write the decimal in the table.)

47. Write the decimals above in order from least to greatest.

48. Which two decimals above have a sum of one ten-thousandth?

49. Find the difference between 1.00002 and 0.00009.

1.0002
0.00009
0.0008
0.00001
0.00015

Extension problems challenge you to extend what you have learned and to apply it in a new setting.

CALCULATORS & COMPUTERS

There are many opportunities to use calculators, as well as mental-math and paper-and-pencil methods. Online resources and a Technology Book provide opportunities to use computers and calculators to explore concepts and solve problems.

TOOLS FOR LEARNING

Using Calculators
Calculators can be especially useful as a problem solving tool. The questions on this page help make calculator use meaningful.

GOAL

LEARN HOW TO...
• improve your estimating skills

AS YOU...
• play Target Number Plus or Minus 1

Exploration 2

Estimating Decimal Products

SET UP *Work with a partner. You will need one calculator per pair of students.*

In a new game, *Target Number Plus or Minus 1*, the goal is to find a product that is within 1 of the target number. To play the game, follow the flowchart below. You must use estimation and mental math to decide what numbers to enter in the calculator.

Start

- Player 1 chooses a target number and writes it down.
- Player 2 chooses a number and enters it on the calculator.
- Player 1 takes the calculator and presses ✕, enters a guess, then presses =.
- Is the result within 1 of the target number? —No→ Player 2 takes the calculator and presses ✕, enters a guess, then presses =.
- Is the result within 1 of the target number?
- Yes → The player who entered the last guess wins.

Sample Game

Player 1 chose 196 for the target number.
Player 2 chose the number 7.

Player	Keys pressed	Display
2	7	7.
1	✕ 2 5 =	175.
2	✕ 1 . 1 =	192.5
1	1 . 0 2 =	196.35

Since 196.35 is within 1 of 196, Player 1 wins!

McDougal Littell
@Home Tutor
ONLINE

Map ▶ Main Menu ▶ Chapter Menu ▶ Lesson Menu ▶ **Interactive Instructor**

3.6 **Lesson 3.6 - Interactive Instructor**
Decimal Multiplication
Multiplying Decimals

Find the product.
6.271 × 2.3

$$
\begin{array}{r}
6.271 \\
\times\ 2.3 \\
\hline
18813 \\
12542 \\
\hline
14.4233
\end{array}
$$
  3 decimal places
+ 1 decimal place

  4 decimal places

Our answer must have 4 decimal places. Placing the decimal point between the 4s gives us our product, 14.4233.

Using Computers
The @Home Tutor is an interactive program that provides additional instruction and practice. The tutorial, and other resources, can be accessed at classzone.com.

xviii

ASSESSMENT & PORTFOLIOS

In each module there are a number of questions and projects that help you check your progress and reflect on what you have learned. These pages are listed under *Assessment Options* in the Table of Contents.

E² stands for Extended Exploration—a problem solving project that you'll want to add to your portfolio.

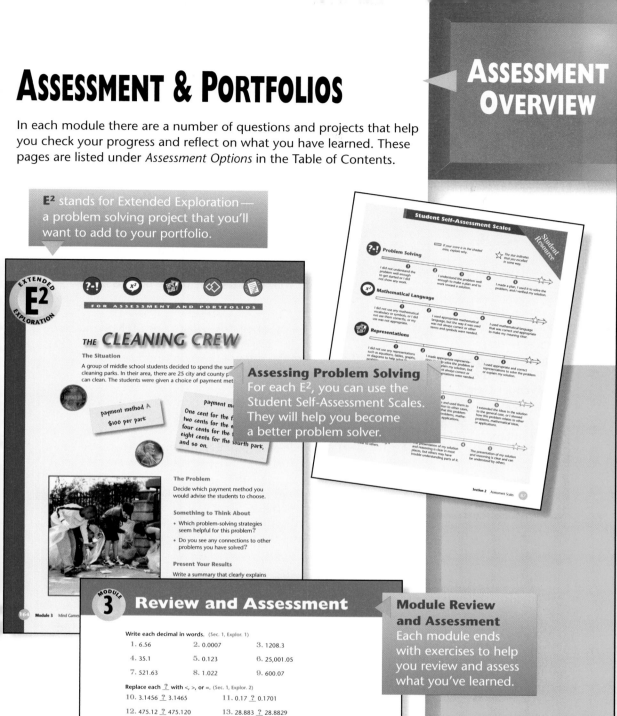

Student Self-Assessment Scales

Student Resource

?-! Problem Solving

If your score is in the shaded area, explain why.

☆ The star indicates that you excelled in some way.

❶ I did not understand the problem well enough to get started or I did not show any work.

❷ I understood the problem well enough to make a plan and to work toward a solution.

❸ I made a plan, I used it to solve the problem, and I verified my solution.

Mathematical Language

❶ I did not use any mathematical vocabulary or symbols, or I did not use them correctly, or my use was not appropriate.

❷ I used appropriate mathematical language, but the way it was used was not always correct or other terms and symbols were needed.

❸ I used mathematical language that was correct and appropriate to make my meaning clear.

Representations

❶ I did not use any representations such as equations, tables, graphs, or diagrams to help solve the problem.

❷ I made appropriate representations to solve the problem or explain my solution, but they were not always correct or other representations were needed.

❸ I used appropriate and correct representations to solve the problem or explain my solution.

Section 2 Assessment Scales

EXTENDED E² EXPLORATION

?-! ⚹ 🖊 ◇ 📝

FOR ASSESSMENT AND PORTFOLIOS

THE CLEANING CREW

The Situation

A group of middle school students decided to spend the sum... cleaning parks. In their area, there are 25 city and county p... can clean. The students were given a choice of payment met...

payment method A
$100 per park

payment me...
One cent for the f...
two cents for the s...
four cents for the t...
eight cents for the fourth park,
and so on.

The Problem

Decide which payment method you would advise the students to choose.

Something to Think About

• Which problem-solving strategies seem helpful for this problem?

• Do you see any connections to other problems you have solved?

Present Your Results

Write a summary that clearly explains

164 **Module 3** Mind Games

Assessing Problem Solving

For each E², you can use the Student Self-Assessment Scales. They will help you become a better problem solver.

MODULE 3 **Review and Assessment**

Module Review and Assessment
Each module ends with exercises to help you review and assess what you've learned.

Write each decimal in words. (Sec. 1, Explor. 1)

1. 6.56   2. 0.0007   3. 1208.3

4. 35.1   5. 0.123   6. 25,001.05

7. 521.63   8. 1.022   9. 600.07

Replace each ? with <, >, or =. (Sec. 1, Explor. 2)

10. 3.1456 ? 3.1465   11. 0.17 ? 0.1701

12. 475.12 ? 475.120   13. 28.883 ? 28.8829

14. sixteen hundredths ? four tenths

15. fourteen and seven hundredths ? fourteen and seventy thousandths

Find each sum or difference without using a calculator. (Sec. 2, Explors. 1 and 2)

xix

Scavenger Hunt

1. In this book mathematics is learned through thematic modules that connect mathematical concepts to real world applications related to a module theme.

The following resources will help you on your Scavenger Hunt:

- Table of Contents
- Test-Taking Skills
- Toolbox
- Tables
- Glossary
- Index
- Selected Answers

---

3. Patterns and Problem Solving, Math Detectives, Mind Games, Statistical Safari, Creating Things, Comparisons and Predictions, Wonders of the World, MATH-Thematical Mix.

6. c. Answers will vary. *Sample Response:* The freezing point of water in degrees Fahrenheit is 32°.

Your textbook will be an important tool in your study of mathematics this year. Complete the scavenger hunt below to learn more about your textbook and its various resources.

1. Why do you think the title of the book is *Math Thematics*?

2. According to the book, what does STEM stand for? **Success Through Exploring Mathematics**

3. What are the titles of the eight modules you will be studying?

4. In which module and section will you learn about "Building with Nets"? **Module 7 Section 1**

5. In Module 5 Section 3, what math will you be learning? **addition and subtraction of fractions**

6. a. On what page does the Student Resources section begin? **page 564**

   b. What is the fifth math topic that is reviewed in the Toolbox? **mental math**

   c. Name one math fact that can be found in the Table of Measures.

   d. In which of the Student Resources can you find the definition of experimental probability? **the glossary**

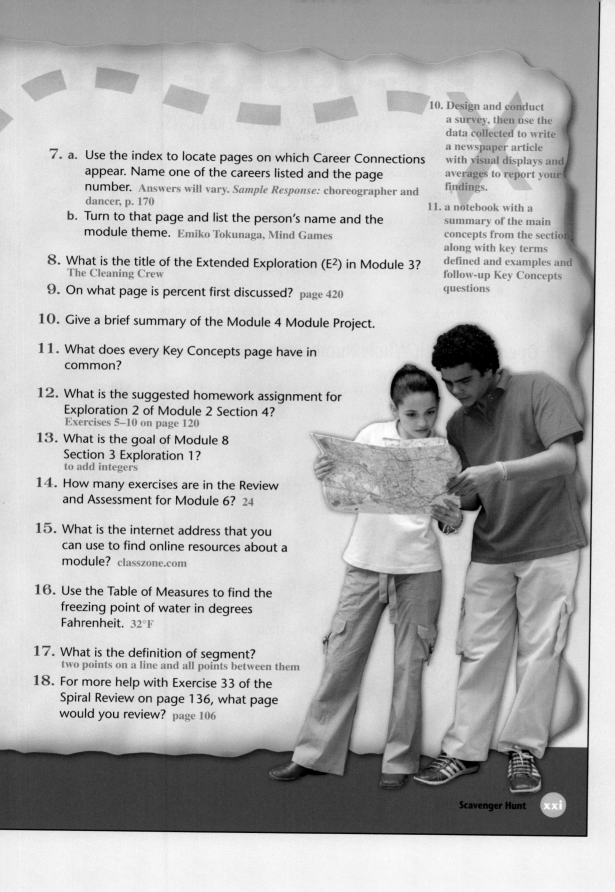

7. **a.** Use the index to locate pages on which Career Connections appear. Name one of the careers listed and the page number. *Answers will vary. Sample Response:* **choreographer and dancer, p. 170**

   b. Turn to that page and list the person's name and the module theme. **Emiko Tokunaga, Mind Games**

8. What is the title of the Extended Exploration (E²) in Module 3? **The Cleaning Crew**

9. On what page is percent first discussed? **page 420**

10. Give a brief summary of the Module 4 Module Project.

10. Design and conduct a survey, then use the data collected to write a newspaper article with visual displays and averages to report your findings.

11. What does every Key Concepts page have in common?

11. a notebook with a summary of the main concepts from the section, along with key terms defined and examples and follow-up Key Concepts questions

12. What is the suggested homework assignment for Exploration 2 of Module 2 Section 4? **Exercises 5–10 on page 120**

13. What is the goal of Module 8 Section 3 Exploration 1? **to add integers**

14. How many exercises are in the Review and Assessment for Module 6? **24**

15. What is the internet address that you can use to find online resources about a module? **classzone.com**

16. Use the Table of Measures to find the freezing point of water in degrees Fahrenheit. **32°F**

17. What is the definition of segment? **two points on a line and all points between them**

18. For more help with Exercise 33 of the Spiral Review on page 136, what page would you review? **page 106**

Scavenger Hunt xxi

PRE-COURSE TEST

NUMBERS AND OPERATIONS

Whole Numbers (Toolbox, pp. 565–567)

Write each number in standard form.

1. three thousand, five hundred ninety-six
   3596

2. one million, forty-one thousand, seven
   1,041,007

Replace each ___?___ with >, <, or =.

3. 220,022 ___?___ 220,220 <

4. 7,360,032 ___?___ 7,359,661 >

Round each number or amount to the given place.

5. 18,623 (nearest ten) 18,620

6. 1,955,014 (nearest ten thousand) 1,960,000

7. $105.66 (nearest hundred dollars)
   $100.00

8. $25.49 (nearest dollar) $25.00

Operations with Whole Numbers (Toolbox, pp. 568–572)

Use mental math to find each sum.

9. 59 + 97 156

10. 281 + 75 356

11. $6.09 + $14.32 $20.41

Add, subtract, multiply, or divide.

12. 4566 + 231 4797

13. 69,304 + 12,999 82,303

14. $45.83 + $22.25 $68.08

15. 5700 − 432 5268

16. 9807 − 1289 8518

17. $60.24 − $49.50 $10.74

18. 56 × 87 4872

19. 334 × 739 246,826

20. 40 × $15.12 $604.80

21. 6557 ÷ 20 327 R17

22. 700 ÷ 16 43 R12

23. 8037 ÷ 99 81 R18

Number Sense (Toolbox, pp. 573–574)

Find each missing number.

24. 9 × ___?___ = 54 6

25. ___?___ + 27 = 35 8

26. 64 − ___?___ = 43 21

Multiply or divide.

27. 7000 × 300 2,100,000

28. 50,000 ÷ 1000 50

29. 31,000 × 800 24,800,000

T58

MEASUREMENT

Perimeter and Area (Toolbox, pp. 575–576)

Find the perimeter of each figure.

30.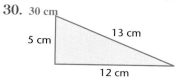
30 cm
5 cm
13 cm
12 cm

31.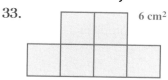
22 in.   7 in.
4 in.   4 in.
7 in.

Find the area of each figure. Each small square is 1 centimeter by 1 centimeter.

32. 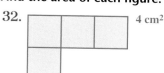   4 cm²

33. 6 cm²

Time Conversions and Elapsed Time (Toolbox, p. 577)

Find how much time has elapsed between the given times.

34. 12:45 P.M. and 7:59 P.M. 7 hr 14 min   35. 10:32 A.M. and 2:10 P.M. 3 h 38 min

DATA DISPLAYS

Reading and Making Graphs (Toolbox, pp. 578–579)

Use the bar graph for Exercises 36–38.

36. How many fish were caught in June? 16

37. In what month were the greatest number of fish caught? August

38. About how many more fish were caught in June than in July? 6

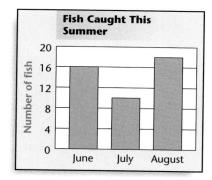

Fish Caught This Summer

39. Make a pictograph to represent the number of players on each team. See Additional Answers.

Team	basketball	football	soccer	baseball
Number of players	15	35	25	20

TEST-TAKING SKILLS

Reading a Word Problem

Before you can solve a word problem, you have to understand the information being given and the question being asked.

- Read quickly through the problem once to get a general sense of what the problem is about.

- Read carefully through the problem a second time, focusing on those things that relate to solving the problem.

Solving a Word Problem

- Underline, jot down, and/or make a quick sketch of any information that can be used to solve the problem.

Problem

Clay bought a shirt, a tie, and a pair of pants at a clothing store. <u>The shirt cost $24, the tie cost $17, and the pants cost $28.</u> Clay also used a coupon for <u>$5 off</u> the total price. What was the total amount of money Clay spent at the clothing store?

- Decide which math topic(s) relate to the problem. Think of procedures, formulas, and definitions related to the topics that can be used to solve the problem.

- Solve the problem, making sure that the question answered is the question asked.

Prices: $24, $17, $28
Coupon: $5

To find the total amount of money spent, add all of the prices and subtract the value of the coupon.

Total without coupon: $24 + 17 + 28 = \$69$
Total with coupon: $69 - 5 = \$64$

Clay spent $64 at the clothing store.

- Use estimation to check the reasonableness of your answer.

$24 + 17 + 28 - 5 \approx 20 + 20 + 30 - 5 = 65$

Keep up with the course.

Ask questions about things you don't understand. Take advantage of extra-help sessions. If you get a problem wrong on a test or on your homework, try to figure out why you got it wrong. If you are absent, find out what material you missed and make up the work.

Become familiar with the test.

Make sure you know the answers to the following questions before you take the test:

- How much time do I have to complete the test?

- How many points are assigned to each type of question?

- About how much time should I spend answering a multiple choice question? a short response question? an extended response question?

- If I can't answer a multiple choice question, is it better to guess, or to leave a blank?

- Am I better off answering the easy, or the more difficult questions first, or should I just answer the questions as they come?

- Is paper provided for scrap work, or should it be done in the white space of the test booklet?

- On which, if any, parts of the test may I use a calculator?

During the Test

- As soon as the test begins, jot down on scrap paper or in the white space of the test booklet any formulas or procedures you're afraid you'll forget.

- Quickly scan the entire test to get an idea of which problems will probably take you the most time to do. Some people prefer to do those problems first. Others do them last.

- Skip over any question you are stuck on. Make a mark next to the question in your test booklet so that you can go back to it later if you have time. Be sure to leave a blank on your answer sheet for the answer to the question.

- Read an entire problem carefully before you start to answer it. Don't assume you know the question that will be asked.

- When answering a multiple choice question, don't assume your answer is correct because it is one of the choices. Always double check your work.

- If you think you can't do a multiple choice question, try substituting each choice back into the problem to see if it is the correct choice.

- If you must guess on a multiple choice question, first try to eliminate any choices that are obviously wrong because they have the wrong units or sign, for example.

- As you write the answer to an extended or short response question, imagine that you are writing an explanation for a fellow student who doesn't know how to solve the problem.

- If you can do part, but not all, of an extended or short response question, write down what you can do. Something written may receive partial credit. Nothing written definitely receives no credit.

Test-Taking Skills xxv

BUILDING TEST-TAKING SKILLS (For use after Module 2.)

Strategies for Answering

Multiple Choice Questions

You can use the 4-step approach to solving problems on page 33 to solve any problem. If you have difficulty solving a problem involving multiple choice, you may be able to use one of the strategies below to choose the correct answer. You may also be able to use these strategies and others to check whether your answer to a multiple choice question is reasonable.

Strategy: Estimate the Answer

Problem 1

Jared is buying cereal that costs $3.20, milk that costs $1.85, and juice that costs $2.79. What is the total cost?

●------ Since the question asks for the *total cost*, you need to *add* the costs of the items.

A. $1.84

B. $6.84

C. $7.84 ●------ Estimate: $3.20 + $1.85 + $2.79 ≈ $3 + $2 + $3 = $8, so the correct answer is C.

D. $17.84

Strategy: Use Visual Clues

Problem 2

The bar graph shows the tickets sold for the school play on three different nights. How many more tickets were sold on Saturday than on Friday?

F. 95

G. 115 ●--- The horizontal lines are 50 units ----● apart, so the difference in the heights of the bars is between 100 and 150.

H. 165

I. 175

115 is the only one of the given numbers that is between 100 and 150, so the correct answer is G.

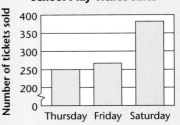

School Play Ticket Sales

Problem 3

Evaluate the expression $67 + (112 \times 17) \times 0$. ●------- Notice that 0 is a factor in the product $(112 \times 17) \times 0$. Use the fact that the product of 0 and any number is 0.

A. 0

B. 67 ●----¬

C. 1971

D. 3043

$67 + 0 = 67$, so the correct answer is B.

Eliminating Unreasonable Choices

The strategies used to find the correct answers for Problems 1–3 can also be used to eliminate answer choices that are unreasonable or obviously incorrect.

Strategy: Eliminate Choices

Watch out for answer choices based on common errors. For example, the length of the garden is 11 + 10 = 21 feet, not 10 feet.

Problem 4

A rectangular garden is 11 feet wide. The length of the garden is 10 feet more than the width. What is the perimeter?

F. 42 feet ●---------- *Not the correct answer:* $11 + 21 + 11 + 21 \approx 10 + 20 + 10 + 20 = 60$.

G. 58 feet ●---------- *Not the correct answer:* In the estimate above, the values were rounded down, so the actual perimeter should be greater than 60 feet.

H. 62 square feet ●--- *Not the correct answer:* perimeter is measured in *linear* units.

I. 64 feet ●--------- I is the correct answer: $11 + 21 + 11 + 21 = 64$.

TRY THIS

Explain why the highlighted answer choice is unreasonable.

1. A ribbon that is 64 centimeters long is cut into 4 pieces of equal length. How many centimeters long is each piece? **72 cm is greater than the length of the ribbon.**

   A. 14 cm   **B.** 16 cm   **C.** 32 cm   ✗ **D.** 72 cm

2. Which expression has the least value? **$10.06 − $ .20 has the greatest value, not the least value.**

   ✗ **F.** $10.06 – $.20   **G.** $5.70 – $2.90   **H.** $2.01 + $1.56   **I.** $3.99 + $4.03

3. A rug is 10 feet long. The width of the rug is 2 feet less than the length. What is the perimeter? **Perimeter is measured in linear units, not square units.**

   A. 18 ft   **B.** 36 ft   ✗ **C.** 18 ft²   **D.** 36 ft²

Multiple Choice

1. A certain airplane can carry 305 passengers. A flight attendant counts 19 empty seats on the plane. How many passengers are on the plane? **B**

   A. 186   B. 286   C. 300   D. 324

2. The heights of wooden pickets in a fence follow the pattern below. What are the heights of the next three pickets? **F**

   4 feet, 4.5 feet, 4 feet, 4.5 feet, . . .

   F. 4 feet, 4.5 feet, 4 feet

   G. 4.5 feet, 4 feet, 4.5 feet

   H. 4 feet, 4 feet, 4.5 feet

   I. 4.5 feet, 4.5 feet, 4 feet

3. Carmen wants to buy a skateboard for $43.50. She has $29.75. How much more money does Carmen need? **B**

   A. $3.75   B. $13.75

   C. $14.00   D. $73.25

4. The bar graph shows how much Sam earned during each month of the summer. How much more did Sam earn in July than in June? **I**

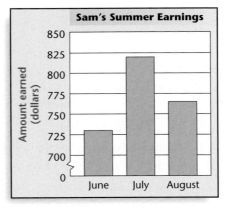

Sam's Summer Earnings

   F. $40   G. $55   H. $75   I. $90

5. What type of polygon is shown? **C**

   A. triangle   B. pentagon

   C. hexagon   D. octagon

6. Raymond bought 5 pounds of apples for $.69 per pound. What is the best estimate for the total cost of the apples? **H**

   F. $.35   G. $3.05

   H. $3.50   I. $35.00

7. Which rule describes the following pattern? **D**

   2, 6, 18, 54, . . .

   A. Add 4 to the previous term.

   B. Multiply the previous term by 4.

   C. Add 3 to the previous term.

   D. Multiply the previous term by 3.

8. Sandra bought the items shown. What is the total cost of the items? **F**

Shampoo	$2.89
Conditioner	$3.73
Hair spray	$1.95

   F. $8.57   G. $9.00

   H. $9.57   I. $857

9. A picture frame has a width of 5 inches. The length is 2 inches more than the width. What is the perimeter of the picture frame? **C**

   A. 10 in.   B. 14 in.

   C. 24 in.   D. 35 in.

BUILDING TEST-TAKING SKILLS (For use after Module 4.)

Strategies for Answering
Short Response Questions

Scoring Rubric

FULL CREDIT
- answer is correct, *and*
- work or reasoning is included

PARTIAL CREDIT
- answer is correct, but reasoning is incorrect, *or*
- answer is incorrect, but reasoning is correct

NO CREDIT
- no answer is given, *or*
- answer makes no sense

Problem

Sara is organizing a 5 kilometer road race. She wants to have 3 water stations along the race route, with equal distances between the start and the first station, between each station, and between the last station and the finish. How many meters apart should the water stations be placed?

FULL CREDIT SOLUTION

The diagram shows that the 3 water stations divide the race route into 4 equal parts. — The reasoning is the key to solving the problem.

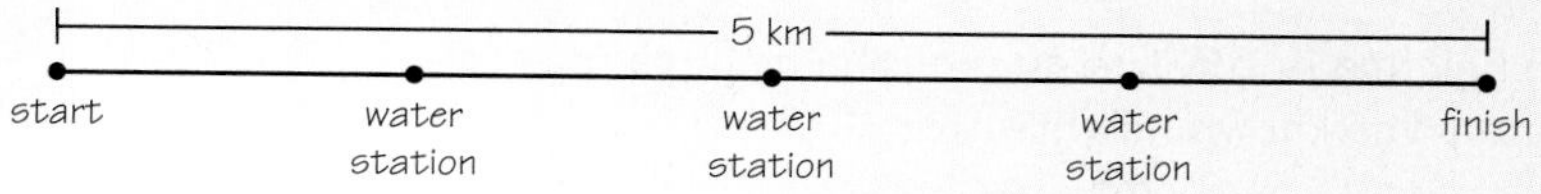

Divide 5 kilometers by 4 to find the length of each part: — The steps of the solution are clearly written.

5 km ÷ 4 = 1.25 km

Convert kilometers to meters:

1 km = 1000 m, so 1.25 km = 1.25 • 1000 m = 1250 m

The water stations should be 1250 meters apart. — The question asked is answered correctly.

PARTIAL CREDIT SOLUTION

First convert 5 kilometers to meters: — The reasoning and the conversion are correct.

1 km = 1000 m, so 5 km = 5 • 1000 m = 5000 m

There are 4 parts, so divide 5000 meters by 4: $4\overline{)5000}$ = 125

The water stations should be 125 meters apart. — The answer is not correct because the quotient was not calculated correctly.

$5 \div 4 \times 1000 = 1250$ •-- Without explanation, the reasoning behind this calculation is unclear.

The water stations should be 1250 meters apart. •---- The answer is correct.

$5 \div 3 = 1\frac{2}{3}$ •-- The wrong divisor is used and no conversion is done.

The water stations should be $1\frac{2}{3}$ meters apart. •------ The answer is not correct.

TRY THIS

Score each solution to the short response question below as *full credit*, *partial credit*, or *no credit*. **Explain your reasoning.**

Watch Out!
If a problem involves measurements, don't forget to include units with your solution.

Problem

The mean of the heights of three brothers is 66 inches. If one brother is 68 inches tall, and another brother is 70 inches tall, how tall is the third brother?

1.   If the mean of the 3 heights is 66, the sum of the heights must be $66 \times 3 = 198$. Subtract the known heights from 198:

$$198 - 68 - 70 = 60$$

The height of the third brother is 60 inches.

Full credit; the reasoning is correct, the steps are clearly written, and the question is answered correctly.

2.   Find the mean of the heights:

$$\frac{66 + 68 + 70}{3} = 68$$

The height of the third brother is 68 inches.

No credit; the calculation does not make sense and the answer is not correct.

3. $68 + 70 = 138$

$198 - 138 = 60$

The height of the third brother is 60 inches.

Partial credit; the answer is correct, but the reasoning behind the calculations is not included.

PRACTICING TEST-TAKING SKILLS

Short Response 1–10. See Additional Answers for explanations.

1. Brian made 48 brownies. He gave $\frac{1}{4}$ of the brownies to his grandmother. Then he gave $\frac{1}{2}$ of the remaining brownies to his father. The rest he kept for himself. How many brownies did Brian keep? Explain how you found your answer. 18

2. The line plot below shows the hours of sleep one person got on each of ten nights. Find the mean, median, and mode of the data. Show your work. mean = 7.9 hours, median = 8 hours, mode = 9 hours

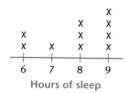

Sleeping Habits Over Ten Nights

Hours of sleep

3. Mark is 5 years younger than twice the age of Laura. Write an expression for Mark's age. If Laura is 15 years old, how old is Mark? Show your steps. $2x - 5$; 25 years old

4. A carpenter wants to saw a board into 6 pieces of equal length. The board is 1.8 meters long. How many centimeters long will each piece be? Show your work. 30 cm

5. A class of 30 students is on a field trip. The teacher wants to divide the students into groups with the same number of students in each group. There must be at least 3 students in each group. What are the possible group sizes? Explain how you found your answer. 1 group of 30, 2 groups of 15, 3 groups of 10, 10 groups of 3, 5 groups of 6, or 6 groups of 5

6. A two-digit number is divisible by 9 and by 5. If the first digit is an even number, what is the two-digit number? Explain how you found your answer. 45

7. Maria's scores on her science tests are 74, 31, 85, 80, 93, 83, and 93. Find the mean, median, and mode of the test scores. Which average best describes Maria's typical test score? Explain your reasoning. mean = 77, median = 83, mode = 93

8. Alvin is buying supplies for a barbecue. He needs 4.75 pounds of hamburger and enough buns for 19 hamburgers. Using the pricing information below, what is the total cost of the supplies that Alvin needs? Show your work. $22.42

Hamburger: $3.40 per pound
Pack of 8 buns: $2.09

9. A paper bag contains a tile for each of the letters in the word *MISSISSIPPI*. Another paper bag contains a tile for each of the letters in the word *OHIO*. From which bag are you more likely to draw a tile for the letter *I*? Explain how you found your answer. from the MISSISSIPPI bag

10. The Venn diagram below shows the number of girls at Highland Middle School on each of three sports teams. What is the total number of girls on each team? Explain how you found your answer. soccer: 27, basketball: 18, track: 42

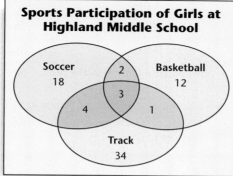

Sports Participation of Girls at Highland Middle School

Strategies for Answering

Context-Based Multiple Choice Questions

Some of the information you need to solve a context-based multiple choice question may appear in a table, a diagram, or a graph.

Problem 1

A coach's playbook contains a scale drawing of a basketball court. The actual width of the basketball court is 50 feet. What is the actual length of the basketball court?

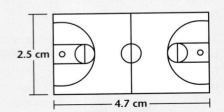

2.5 cm

4.7 cm

A. 4.7 ft   **B.** 87 ft

C. 94 ft   **D.** 135 ft

Solution

1) From the problem and diagram, you know: ●--------------------- Read the problem carefully. Decide what information you are given and how you can use it to solve the problem.

   width on drawing = 2.5 centimeters   actual width = 50 feet

   length on drawing = 4.7 centimeters   actual length = ?

   You can use the width on the drawing and the actual width to find the scale of the drawing. Then use the scale to find the actual length.

2) The scale of the drawing is $\frac{2.5 \text{ cm}}{50 \text{ ft}}$ or $\frac{1 \text{ cm}}{20 \text{ ft}}$. ●-------------------- Find the scale.

3) $\frac{1 \text{ cm}}{20 \text{ ft}} = \frac{\text{Length on drawing}}{\text{Actual length}}$ Write a proportion. ●------------ Write and solve a proportion to find the actual length of the car. Use cross products.

   $\frac{1 \text{ cm}}{20 \text{ ft}} = \frac{4.7 \text{ cm}}{x \text{ ft}}$ Substitute values.

   $1 \cdot x = (20)(4.7)$ The cross products are equal.

   $x = 94$ Multiply.

   The actual length is 94 feet. The correct answer is C.

4) Check to see that your answer is reasonable. For example, ●---- Use one of the strategies on pages xxvi–xxvii.
   because $20 \times 4.7 \approx 20 \times 5 = 100$, the most reasonable answer is C.

Problem 2

A recipe for 8 servings of punch is shown at the right. How many quarts of ginger ale will you need for 4 servings?

F. $\frac{3}{8}$ qt

G. $\frac{3}{4}$ qt

H. 3 qt

I. 6 qt

Punch Recipe

$\frac{1}{2}$ gal sherbet $1\frac{1}{2}$ qt ginger ale

1 pt lemonade

Scoop sherbet into a punch bowl. Pour ginger ale and lemonade over sherbet. Enjoy.

Solution

1) 8 servings ÷ 2 = 4 servings, so you will need half the ● - - - - - - - - - Read the problem amount of each ingredient to make 4 servings.

Read the problem carefully. Understand what you need to do to solve the problem.

2) $1\frac{1}{2} \div 2 = \frac{3}{2} \times \frac{1}{2} = \frac{3}{4}$ ● -

Find the amount of ginger ale needed.

You will need $\frac{3}{4}$ quart of ginger ale for 4 servings.

The correct answer is G .

Watch Out!
Be sure that you know what question you are asked to answer. Some choices given may be intended to distract you.

TRY THIS

1. How many gallons of sherbet would be needed to make 2 servings of the punch in Problem 2? A

A. $\frac{1}{8}$ gal

B. $\frac{1}{4}$ gal

C. $\frac{1}{2}$ gal

D. 1 gal

2. The triangles shown are similar. What is the missing side length? I

F. 8 in.

G. 10 in.

H. 12 in.

I. 15 in.

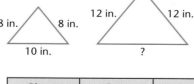

8 in.   8 in.   12 in.   12 in.

10 in.   ?

3. The table gives the free throws made and free throws attempted by four players at a basketball practice. Which player made 68% of her free throws? A

A. Gina

B. Terry

C. Mia

D. Carmen

Player	Free throws made	Free throws attempted
Gina	17	25
Terry	26	40
Mia	9	16
Carmen	20	32

PRACTICING TEST-TAKING SKILLS

Context-Based Multiple Choice

1. A scale drawing of a yoga mat is shown. If the width of the actual yoga mat is 36 inches, what is the length of the actual yoga mat? **D**

$\frac{3}{4}$ in.

$1\frac{1}{2}$ in.

 A. 18 in.   B. 27 in.

 C. $40\frac{1}{2}$ in.   D. 72 in.

2. Which two cans are similar? **H**

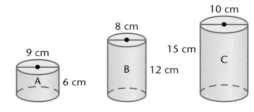

10 cm

8 cm

9 cm

15 cm

C

B

12 cm

A

6 cm

 F. can A and can B   G. can A and can C

 H. can B and can C   I. none

In Exercises 3 and 4, use the diagram below.

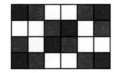

3. What is the ratio of blue squares to red squares? **C**

 A. 1   B. $\frac{1}{2}$ C. $\frac{3}{4}$ D. $\frac{4}{3}$

4. What is the ratio of red squares to white squares? **G**

 F. $\frac{3}{5}$ G. $\frac{4}{5}$ H. $\frac{5}{4}$ I. $\frac{5}{3}$

In Exercises 5 and 6, use the spinners shown below.

5. The spinner on the left is spun once. What is the probability of spinning a 1? **B**

 A. $\frac{1}{3}$ B. $\frac{1}{2}$ C. $\frac{2}{3}$ D. 1

6. The spinner on the right is spun once. What is the probability of spinning a prime number? **H**

 F. 0   G. $\frac{1}{3}$ H. $\frac{2}{3}$ I. 1

In Exercises 7 and 8, use the table of data.

Person	Height
Jared	5 ft 9 in.
Paul	6 ft 2 in.
Greg	5 ft 4 in.

7. How much taller is Paul than Greg? **B**

 A. 2 in.

 B. 10 in.

 C. 1 ft 2 in.

 D. 1 ft 8 in.

8. What is the mean of the boys' heights? **H**

 F. 5 ft 7 in.

 G. 5 ft 8 in.

 H. 5 ft 9 in.

 I. 5 ft 10 in.

BUILDING TEST-TAKING SKILLS (For use after Module 8.)

Strategies for Answering
Extended Response Questions

Scoring Rubric

FULL CREDIT
- answer is correct, *and*
- work or reasoning is included

PARTIAL CREDIT
- answer is correct, but reasoning is incorrect, *or*
- answer is incorrect, but reasoning is correct

NO CREDIT
- no answer is given, *or*
- answer makes no sense

Problem

Peter is starting a lawn mowing business. He buys a lawn mower for $320. Peter has work lined up that will earn him $40 a week. Make a table of values to show the number of weeks in business and the profit for 0, 1, 2, 3, 4, and 5 weeks. Graph the values. Find the number of weeks that Peter has to be in business in order to make back the cost of the lawn mower. Explain how you found your answer.

FULL CREDIT SOLUTION

Let x represent the number of weeks in business. Let y represent profit.

Week, x	0	1	2	3	4	5
Profit, y	−$320	−$280	−$240	−$200	−$160	−$120

●--- The table of values is correct and reflects an understanding of the relationship between the number of weeks and the profit.

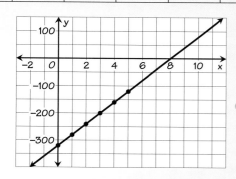

●--- The graph correctly represents the data in the table.

Peter needs to be in business for 8 weeks in order to make back the cost of the lawn mower.

●------ The answer is correct.

I found my answer by drawing a line through the plotted points. I looked to see where the line crosses the x-axis, since that represents a profit of $0. The line crosses the x-axis at x = 8, so it will take 8 weeks.

●--- The explanation is clear and reflects correct mathematical thinking.

The table of values is ------● incorrect. The cost of the lawn mower should be represented as a negative amount, not a positive amount.

Week, x	Profit, y
0	$320
1	$360
2	$400
3	$440
4	$480
5	$520

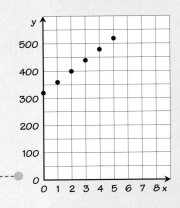

The graph correctly displays the data in the ------------● table, but the data is incorrect.

The answer is correct. ------● **Peter will make back the cost of the lawn mower in 8 weeks.**

The explanation reflects ---● correct mathematical reasoning.

I found my answer by dividing the cost of the lawn mower by the amount earned per week: $320 ÷ $40 = 8.

TRY THIS

Watch Out!
Scoring is often based on how clearly you explain your reasoning.

1. A student's answer to the problem on page xxxv is given below. Score the solution as *full credit, partial credit,* or *no credit*. Explain your choice. If you choose *partial credit* or *no credit*, explain how you would change the answer to earn a score of *full credit*.

   Full credit; the reasoning is correct, the steps are clearly written, and the question is answered correctly.

Week, x	Profit, y
0	−$320
1	−$280
2	−$240
3	−$200
4	−$160
5	−$120

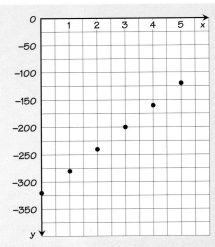

It will take Peter 8 weeks to make back the cost of the lawn mower.

To find my answer, I reasoned that since it took 4 weeks to make back half the cost of the lawn mower, it must take 8 weeks to make back the full cost of the lawn mower.

Extended Response
1–6. See Additional Answers for explanations.

1. The dimensions of two rectangular prisms are shown. Find the volume of each prism. How could you change one of the dimensions of prism A to make the volume equal to the volume of prism B? Show your work. Volume of prism A = 5 · 4 · 6 = 120 in.³, volume of prism B = 5 · 3 · 10 = 150 in.³

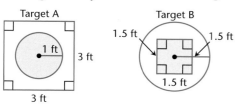

2. The deli at a grocery store sells macaroni salad by weight. Brianna buys 3 pounds of macaroni salad for $8.16. How much would 1 pound 4 ounces of macaroni salad cost? Explain how you found your answer. $3.40

3. The highest daily temperatures for one week are listed below. Find the mean, median, mode, and range of the data. Show your work. Which average does not represent the data well? Why?
mean = 7°F, median = 6°F, mode = −2°F, range = 30°F
−2°F   28°F   6°F   0°F   9°F   10°F   −2°F

4. A carnival game involves throwing a dart on one of the targets shown below. You win by having the dart land within the shaded area of a target. If the dart lands on a chosen random point on a target, on which target is there a better chance of winning? Show your calculations. Target A

Target A

Target B

5. The circle graph shows the results of a survey in which 400 middle school students were asked to name their favorite after-school activity. How many more students said that playing sports is their favorite activity than said playing video games? Show your work. 20

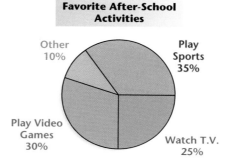

Favorite After-School Activities

Other 10%

Play Sports 35%

Play Video Games 30%

Watch T.V. 25%

6. The table below shows the number of tickets sold to adults, senior citizens, and children at a movie screening. Make a bar graph of the data that makes it appear like the number of tickets sold to children was double the number sold to senior citizens. Explain how you created this impression. See Additional Answers.

Ticket type	adult	senior citizen	child
Number of tickets	126	75	98

MODULE 1

Patterns and Problem Solving

Module 1 Overview

Problem solving is the focus of this module. Estimation, mental math, and a review of whole number computation are woven throughout the module. Students explore the mathematics of patterns and problem solving through such themes as coins, kites, and window designs. Manipulatives and visual models are used to develop an understanding of sequences and fractions.

Module 1 Planner

Day 1: Section 1	Day 2: Section 1	Day 3: Section 1	Day 4: Section 2	Day 5: Section 2
Setting the Stage, *p. 2* Exploration 1, *pp. 3–4*	Exploration 2, *pp. 5–8*	Exploration 3, *pp. 8–9* Key Concepts, *pp. 10–11*	Setting the Stage, *p. 15* Exploration 1, *pp. 16–17*	Exploration 2 *through Example, pp. 18–19*
Day 6: Section 2	**Day 7: Section 3**	**Day 8: Section 3**	**Day 9: Section 3**	**Day 10: E²**
Exploration 2 *from Question 15, p. 20* Key Concepts, *p. 21*	Setting the Stage, *p. 27* Exploration 1, *pp. 28–29*	Exploration 2, *pp. 29–31*	Exploration 3, *pp. 31–32* Key Concepts, *p. 33*	Begin Extended Exploration, *p. 38*
Day 11: Review and Assessment Mid-Module Quiz	**Day 12: Section 4** Setting the Stage, *p. 39* Exploration 1 *through Question 5, pp. 40–41*	**Day 13: Section 4** Exploration 1 *from Question 6, pp. 41–42*	**Day 14: Section 4** Exploration 2 *through Question 13, pp. 43–44*	**Day 15: Section 4** Exploration 2, *from Example, pp. 44–45* Key Concepts, *pp. 46–47*
Day 16: Section 5 Setting the Stage, *p. 53* Exploration 1, *pp. 54–55*	**Day 17: Section 5** Exploration 2, *pp. 56–59*	**Day 18: Section 5** Exploration 3, *pp. 59–60* Key Concepts, *pp. 61–62*	**Day 19: Module Project** Begin Module Project, *pp. 68–69*	**Day 20: Module Project** Work on Module Project, *pp. 68–69*
Day 21: Module Project Present Module Project Solutions, *pp. 68–69* Assign Review and Assessment, *pp. 70–71*	**Day 22: Review and Assessment** Discuss Review and Assessment, *pp. 70–71*	**Day 23: Assessment** Module 1 Test		

Materials List

Section	Materials
1	• Labsheets 1A–1B, 4 number cubes per group of 2 or 3, scissors, calculator
2	• pattern blocks, 20 square tiles or graph paper per student
3	• 9 index cards numbered 1 through 9, graph paper (optional)
4	• Labsheets 4A–4B, pattern blocks, 1 number cube per group of students, dot paper
5	• Labsheets 5A–5B, pattern blocks, calculator
Project	• Project Labsheet A

Module 1 Objectives

Section	Objectives	NCTM Standards 2000*
1	• Follow the order of operations. • Decide when an estimate is appropriate. • Estimate answers by rounding whole numbers. • Use compatible numbers to find sums and products mentally. • Decide when to use mental math, paper and pencil, or a calculator.	1, 6, 7, 8, 9
2	• Find a rule to extend a pattern. • Make a table to organize work. • Model a number sequence with a verbal rule, a table, or an equation. • Predict the nth term of a number sequence.	1, 2, 3, 4, 6, 8, 9, 10
3	• Learn the 4-step problem solving approach—*Understand the Problem, Make a Plan, Carry Out the Plan, Look Back.* • Apply strategies such as *try a simpler problem* and *make an organized list.* • Make an organized list to find the number of possible arrangements.	1, 2, 6, 7, 8, 9, 10
4	• Write fractions and mixed numbers to describe drawings for situations. • Write a fraction greater than one as a mixed number, and vice versa. • Write a quotient as a mixed number. • Decide when a mixed number quotient is appropriate to solve a problem.	1, 3, 4, 6, 7, 8, 9, 10
5	• Recognize and find equivalent fractions. • Write fractions in lowest terms. • Make predictions from samples. • Use mental math to find a fraction of a whole number.	1, 3, 4, 5, 6, 7, 8, 9, 10

* See page T14.

Section 1 Planner

Section Objectives

Exploration 1
• Follow the order of operations

Exploration 2
• Decide when an estimate is appropriate
• Estimate answers by rounding whole numbers

Exploration 3
• Use compatible numbers to find sums and products mentally
• Decide when to use mental math, paper and pencil, or a calculator

Days for Section 1

First Day
Setting the Stage, *p. 2*
Exploration 1, *pp. 3–4*

Second Day
Exploration 2, *pp. 5–8*

Third Day
Exploration 3, *pp. 8–9*
Key Concepts, *pp. 10–11*

Teaching Resources

Teacher's Resource Book
• Warm-Up
• Labsheets 1A and 1B
• Practice and Applications
• Study Guide
See page 1 for additional teaching resources.

Materials List

Setting the Stage
• Labsheet 1A
• 4 number cubes per group of 2 or 3
• scissors
• calculator

Exploration 3
• Labsheet 1B
• calculator

Assessment Options

EMBEDDED ASSESSMENT
• Follow the order of operations
  Exercises 1, 4–8
• Decide when an estimate is appropriate
  Exercise 15
• Estimate answers by rounding whole numbers
  Exercises 17, 18, 19, 21
• Use compatible numbers to find sums and products mentally
  Exercises 24, 27, 28
• Decide when to use mental math, paper and pencil, or a calculator
  Exercises 29, 30

PERFORMANCE TASK/PORTFOLIO
• Exercise 1 on *p. 11*
• Exercise 35 on *p. 13 (oral report)*
• Exercise 40 on *p. 13 (extension)*

QUIZZES/TESTS
• Section 1 Quick Quiz

TEST GENERATOR

Section 1 Overview

In this section, students will decide which computational tools—estimation, pencil and paper, mental math, or calculator—will be best for solving a problem.

Exploration 1
Students learn to simplify numerical expressions using the order of operations. Students then use the order of operations to evaluate the expressions they wrote in the game *A Dicey Problem* from the *Setting the Stage*.

Exploration 2
Students use rounding to estimate sums, differences, and products. For those students who have difficulty rounding, Toolbox Exercises on page 567 provide a review that they should complete before beginning Exploration 2. Checkpoint Exercises in Exploration 2 help students to decide whether their estimates are greater than or less than the exact answer. Students will also learn that in some instances it may not be possible to tell how close an estimate is to the exact answer.

Exploration 3
In Exploration 3, students learn about compatible numbers and how they can be used to find sums of numbers mentally. Strategies for use of compatible numbers in mental multiplication are also developed. Finally students play *The Great Arithmetic Race* to see when it is to their advantage to use mental math, paper and pencil, or a calculator to do a computation.

Guide for Assigning Homework

REGULAR SCHEDULING (45 MIN CLASS PERIOD)			EXERCISES TO NOTE		
Section/ P&A Pages	**Core Assignment**	**Extended Assignment**	**Additional Practice/Review**	**Open-ended Problems**	**Extended Problems**
1 pp. 11–14	**Day 1:** 1–13 **Day 2:** 14–22, SR 36–39 **Day 3:** 23–34, ROS 35	1–13 14–22, SR 36–39 23–34, ROS 35, Ext 40	EP, p. 14 TB, p. 567	PA 15	Ext 40

Key: PA = Practice & Application; ROS = Reflecting on the Section; SR = Spiral Review; TB = Toolbox; EP = Extra Skill Practice; Ext = Extension; ST = Standardized Testing

Math Background and Teaching Strategies

Classroom Notes

Bulletin board display ideas for this section include:

- the order of operations and some worked examples
- show compatible numbers for adding and compatible numbers for multiplying

Math Strands

Topic Integration and Spiraling

Exploration 1
The order of operations for expressions with parentheses, multiplication, division, addition, and/or subtraction is introduced. Students will be expected to apply the order of operations from here on. In Books 2 and 3, order of operations will be extended to include exponents, square roots, fraction bars, and other grouping symbols such as brackets. Order of operations lays a foundation for evaluating expressions and is referred to when using inverse operations to solve equations.

Exploration 2
At this level students should be familiar with rounding whole numbers. Rounding is approached as one possible method for estimating sums, differences, and products. Throughout Book 1 students will estimate computations. In Module 3 they will estimate decimal products. Front-end estimation is explored in Module 8.

Exploration 3
This exploration introduces the use of compatible numbers in mental calculations involving sums and products. Students need to realize that use of compatible numbers requires examining a problem before working on it. There are times when compatible numbers do not exist.

It is important to note that the presentation of compatible numbers is limited to addition and multiplication expressions because these two operations are associative and commutative. Students may question how they can "ignore" the "working left to right" rule of the order of operations. Explain that the rule can only be disregarded when other properties, such as the associative and commutative properties, can be used to reorder and regroup operations. They will learn an exception to parentheses in the order of operations, when the distributive property is introduced in Books 2 and 3.

The trading-off strategy for mental math calculation will be introduced in Module 8.

Section 2   Patterns and Sequences

Section 2 Planner

Section Objectives

Exploration 1
- Find a rule to extend a pattern
- Make a table to organize work

Exploration 2
- Model a number sequence with a verbal rule, a table, or an equation
- Predict the nth term of a number sequence

Days for Section 2

First Day
Setting the Stage, *p. 15*
Exploration 1, *pp. 16–17*

Second Day
Exploration 2 through the Example,
pp. 18–19

Third Day
Exploration 2 from Question 15, *p. 20*
Key Concepts, *p. 21*

Teaching Resources

Teacher's Resource Book
- Warm-Up
- Practice and Applications
- Study Guide
See page 1 for additional teaching resources.

Materials List

Setting the Stage
- pattern blocks

Exploration 1
- pattern blocks

Exploration 2
- 20 square tiles or graph paper

Assessment Options

EMBEDDED ASSESSMENT
- Find a rule to extend a pattern
  Exercises 3, 5, 7
- Make a table to organize work
  Exercises 6, 16(a)
- Model a number sequence with a verbal rule, a table, or an equation
  Exercises 12, 13, 14, 15, 16
- Predict the nth term of a number sequence
  Exercises 14(d), 15(f)

PERFORMANCE TASK/PORTFOLIO
- Exercise 9 on *p. 23 (challenge)*
- Exercise 15 on *p. 24*
- Exercise 18 on *p. 25 (visual thinking)*
- Exercise 19 on *p. 24 (discussion)*

QUIZZES/TESTS
- Section 2 Quick Quiz

TEST GENERATOR

Section 2 Overview

In this section, students will use shapes to create sequences and study the related number patterns.

Exploration 1
Students begin this exploration by looking at sequences and trying to identify patterns that can be used to create or extend the sequence. The key terms *rule, term,* and *term number* are introduced.

Exploration 2
Students continue investigating sequences in this exploration. Geometric models are used to help students visualize the rules for sequences. Tables are used to organize information related to a sequence and help students see relationships between the term numbers and terms of a sequence. Variables are introduced and used to write equations that describe the relationship between the term numbers and the terms. The equations are then used to predict terms in the sequences.

Guide for Assigning Homework

REGULAR SCHEDULING (45 MIN CLASS PERIOD)			EXERCISES TO NOTE		
Section/ P&A Pages	Core Assignment	Extended Assignment	Additional Practice/Review	Open-ended Problems	Extended Problems
2 pp. 22–26	**Day 1:** 1–8 **Day 2:** 10–12, SR 20–31 **Day 3:** 13–16, 18, ROS 19	1–9 10–12, SR 20–31 13–18, ROS 19	EP, p. 26		Challenge PA 9, 17

Key: PA = Practice & Application; ROS = Reflecting on the Section; SR = Spiral Review; TB = Toolbox; EP = Extra Skill Practice; Ext = Extension; ST = Standardized Testing

Math Background and Teaching Strategies

Classroom Notes

Bulletin board displays for this section include:

- history and information about the Pythagoreans

- triangular, square, pentagonal, hexagonal, etc. number sequences

- sequences and patterns that occur in science or nature

Math Strands

Topic Spiraling and Integration

Exploration 1
Sequences provide the venue for exploring and extending patterns. This problem solving skill is essential in the study of mathematics. It is used in developing algorithms, generalizations, and formulas.

In Module 2 students will work with the *Assessment Scales* and in the process use recognition of patterns to solve a problem. This exploration also teaches students the importance of organizing their work in a table so as to be able to study the information in a format that may make it easier to make connections and identify patterns.

Exploration 2
Representation is one of the five *NCTM Process Standards* for mathematics. In Exploration 1, students used geometric designs and tables to represent sequences. In Exploration 2, students learn how to use an equation to represent a sequence. In Module 3, students use sequences to explore multiples and least common multiples.

When students revisit sequences in Book 2 Module 3, the focus will be on algebraic and graphical representations. In Book 3 Module 8, distinctions are made between arithmetic and geometric sequences. Students identify the type of sequence and use generalizations about each type to help them write the equation for the general term of any arithmetic or geometric sequence.

Section ③ A Problem Solving Approach

Section 3 Planner

Section Objectives

Exploration 1
- Learn the first step in the 4-step problem-solving approach–*understand the problem*

Exploration 2
- *Make a plan* to solve a problem
- Apply strategies such as *try a simpler problem* and *make an organized list*
- Use an organized list to find the number of possible arrangements

Exploration 3
- *Carry out the plan* to solve a problem
- *Look back* and reflect on the problem and the solution

Days for Section 3

First Day
Setting the Stage, *p. 27*
Exploration 1, *pp. 28–29*

Second Day
Exploration 2, *pp. 29–31*

Third Day
Exploration 3, *pp. 31–32*
Key Concepts, *p. 33*

Teaching Resources

Teacher's Resource Book
- Warm-Up
- Practice and Applications
- Study Guide
See page 1 for additional teaching resources.

Materials List

Setting the Stage
- 9 index cards numbered 1 through 9

Explorations 1–3
- 9 index cards per group

Practice and Applications
- graph paper (optional)

Assessment Options

EMBEDDED ASSESSMENT
- Learn the first step in the 4-step problem-solving approach–*understand the problem*
  Exercises 2, 3, 4
- *Make a plan* to solve a problem
  Exercises 8, 9
- Apply strategies such as *try a simpler problem* and *make an organized list*
  Exercises 6, 9
- *Make an organized list* to find arrangements
  Exercise 6
- *Carry out the plan* to solve a problem
  Exercises 10, 12
- *Look back* on the problem and the solution
  Exercise 10

PERFORMANCE TASK/PORTFOLIO
- Exercise 9 on *p. 35 (geometry connection)*
- Exercise 14 on *p. 36 (challenge)*
- Exercise 15 on *p. 36 (visual thinking)*
- Standardized Testing on *p. 37 (performance task)*
- Extended Exploration on *p. 38**

* *indicates a problem-solving task that can be assessed using the Assessment Scales*

QUIZZES/TESTS
- Section 3 Quick Quiz
- Mid-Module Quiz

TEST GENERATOR

Section 3 Overview

In this section, a game is used to develop a 4-step approach to problem solving.

Exploration 1
The first step in the 4-step approach to solving problems is to *Understand the Problem*. Students begin the exploration by playing the game *Card Swappers*. This way they become familiar with the game and are able to describe the problem they need to solve to be successful at the game.

Exploration 2
In Exploration 2 students continue to use the game to explore problem solving. They learn to *Make a Plan* and use different problem solving strategies such as *try a simpler problem* and *make an organized list* in the context of the game.

Exploration 3
The *make a table* and *look for a pattern* strategies are employed in this exploration. Students should be able to organize data in a table and recognize patterns in the data. Students who had difficulty with either of these skills in Section 2 should review that section. Students will *Carry out a Plan* to solve the *Card Swappers* problem, and *Look Back* at their work. These are the final two steps in the 4-step problem solving approach.

Guide for Assigning Homework

REGULAR SCHEDULING (45 MIN CLASS PERIOD)			EXERCISES TO NOTE		
Section/ P&A Pages	Core Assignment	Extended Assignment	Additional Practice/Review	Open-ended Problems	Extended Problems
3 pp. 34–38	**Day 1:** 1–5, SR 16–21 **Day 2:** 6–9, SR 22–34 **Day 3:** 10–13, ROS 15	1–5, SR 16–21 6–9, SR 22–34 10–14, ROS 15	EP, p. 37	E², p. 38	Challenge PA 14 E², p. 38

Key: PA = Practice & Application; ROS = Reflecting on the Section; SR = Spiral Review; TB = Toolbox; EP = Extra Skill Practice; Ext = Extension; ST = Standardized Testing

Math Background and Teaching Strategies

Classroom Notes

Bulletin board displays for this section include:

- an enlargement of Key Concepts page 33
- sample format for an E² solution
- student solutions to the E²

Math Strands

Topic Spiraling and Integration

This section introduces the 4-step problem solving approach that students are expected to use throughout Books 1, 2, and 3. It is developed in the context of an on-going problem in the three Explorations.

The *Assessment Scales* that students will use to assess their solutions of problems and to help improve their problem solving and communication skills will be introduced in Module 2. The *Problem Solving, Representations,* and *Connections Scales* will be introduced in Section 2 of Module 2 where students solve a problem and discuss how they applied the 4-step problem solving process.

The introduction of the *Assessment Scales* is completed in Sections 3 and 4 of Module 2 where the last two scales, *Mathematical Language* and *Presentation*, are introduced.

Exploration 1

This exploration focuses on the first step of the 4-step approach: *Understand the Problem*. To understand the problem, students should read it carefully–possibly several times, identify the important information, and restate the problem in their own words.

Exploration 2

This exploration focuses on the second step: *Make a Plan*. It also introduces strategies that students can use in their plans.

Exploration 3

This exploration focuses on the last two steps of the 4-step approach: *Carry out the Plan* and *Look Back*. Once the plan is carried out, students need to present their solutions using appropriate mathematical language and representations.

The *Problem Solving Scale* assesses how well students understand the problem, make and carry out a plan to solve the problem, and look back over their solution. The *Representations, Mathematical Language,* and *Presentation* Scales assess students' ability to use mathematical language and representations and to communicate their solutions effectively.

Section 4 Fractions and Mixed Numbers

Section 4 Planner

Section Objectives

Exploration 1
- Write fractions and mixed numbers to describe drawings for situations

Exploration 2
- Write a fraction greater than one as a mixed number and vice versa
- Write a quotient as a mixed number
- Decide when a mixed number quotient is appropriate to solve a problem

Days for Section 4

First Day
Setting the Stage, *p. 39*
Exploration 1 through Question 5,
pp. 40–41

Second Day
Exploration 1 from Question 6, *pp. 41–42*

Third Day
Exploration 2 through Question 13,
pp. 43–44

Fourth Day
Exploration 2 from Example, *pp. 44–45*
Key Concepts, *pp. 46–47*

Teaching Resources

Teacher's Resource Book
- Warm-Up
- Labsheets 4A and 4B
- Practice and Applications
- Study Guide
See page 1 for additional teaching resources.

Materials List

Exploration 1
- Labsheets 4A–4B
- pattern blocks

Exploration 2
- pattern blocks
- 1 number cube per group of students

Practice and Applications
- dot paper (Exs. 13–14)

Assessment Options

EMBEDDED ASSESSMENT
- Write fractions and mixed numbers to describe drawings for situations
  Exercises 3, 5, 8, 9
- Write a fraction greater than one as a mixed number and vice versa
  Exercises 21, 23, 25, 27
- Write a quotient as a mixed number
  Exercises 36, 37
- Decide when a mixed number quotient is appropriate to solve a problem
  Exercise 41

PERFORMANCE TASK/PORTFOLIO
- Exercise 6 on *p. 48*
- Exercises 32–35 on *p. 50 (visual thinking)*
- Exercise 42 on *p. 51 (journal)*

QUIZZES/TESTS
- Quick Quiz

TEST GENERATOR

Section 4 Overview

In this section, students will explore different representations of fractions.

Exploration 1
Students begin this exploration by studying how a fraction is incorporated in the design of a half-cent coin to show its value in dollars. Pattern blocks are used to represent fractions and to explore relationships between parts and wholes. Students also work with visual models of fractions and mixed numbers.

Exploration 2
Students play the game *Flex Your Hex* with pattern blocks to see how fractional parts can be traded for a whole. The game is used as a tool for explaining how to convert fractions greater than 1 to mixed numbers and mixed numbers to fractions. Students also explore different ways of writing a quotient: as a fraction, a mixed number, and as a whole number with an integer remainder. They also examine real life situations and decide when a mixed number is appropriate for answering a question.

Guide for Assigning Homework

	REGULAR SCHEDULING (45 MIN CLASS PERIOD)		**EXERCISES TO NOTE**		
Section/ P&A Pages	**Core Assignment**	**Extended Assignment**	**Additional Practice/Review**	**Open-ended Problems**	**Extended Problems**
4 pp. 47–52	**Day 1:** 1–6, SR 44–46 **Day 2:** 7–11, SR 47–51 **Day 3:** 13–18 **Day 4:** 20–38, 40 ROS 42–43	1–6, SR 44–46 7–12, SR 47–51 13–19 20–27, 32–41, ROS 42–43	EP, p. 52		PA 39 Challenge PA 12, 19

Key: PA = Practice & Application; ROS = Reflecting on the Section; SR = Spiral Review; TB = Toolbox; EP = Extra Skill Practice; Ext = Extension; ST = Standardized Testing

Math Background and Teaching Strategies

Classroom Notes

Bulletin board displays for this section include:

- pictures of real life objects that show fractional parts (kites, stained glass windows, art, etc.)
- fractions and mixed numbers shown with pattern blocks

Math Strands

Topic Spiraling and Integration

Exploration 1

For many students, this exploration on fractions will be a review. The use of pattern blocks provides an opportunity for students who lack understanding of basic fraction concepts to develop it through concrete activities. The idea of relating a part to the whole provides the foundation for proportional reasoning and writing proportions to change fractions to percents. The relationships among fractions, decimals and percents will be developed in Section 6 of Module 6.

Exploration 2

Students first use pattern blocks and trading to represent fractions greater than 1 as mixed numbers. The concrete model is then used to explain the process of changing a fraction greater than 1 to a mixed number and vice versa.

In *Math Thematics*, the term *improper fraction* is not used for a fraction in which the numerator is greater than or equal to the denominator because the term *improper* implies that something is wrong with the fraction. Often times students believe that "improper fractions" must be changed to mixed numbers and that it is wrong to leave them in fraction form since they are "improper". This is not true and, especially with the slopes of lines and in the case of algebraic fractions containing variables, the fraction form is often preferred over the mixed number form. Teachers choosing to use the term *improper* to describe fractions greater than 1 may want to explain to students that there is nothing wrong with the fraction and that in some situations it is preferable to leave it as a fraction.

Finding equivalent fractions and expressing fractions in lowest terms will be covered in the next section of Module 1. Fraction and mixed number multiplication will be studied in Module 3, and addition, subtraction, and division will be covered in Module 5.

Section 5 Planner

Section Objectives

Exploration 1
• Recognize equivalent fractions

Exploration 2
• Find equivalent fractions
• Write a fraction in lowest terms

Exploration 3
• Make predictions from a sample
• Use mental math to find a fraction of a whole number

Days for Section 5

First Day
Setting the Stage, *p. 53*
Exploration 1, *pp. 54–55*

Second Day
Exploration 2, *pp. 56–59*

Third Day
Exploration 3, *pp. 59–60*
Key Concepts, *pp. 61–62*

Materials List

Exploration 1
• Labsheet 5A
• pattern blocks

Exploration 2
• pattern blocks

Exploration 3
• Labsheet 5B
• 25 pattern blocks for each group of students

Practice and Applications
• pattern blocks (Ex. 8)
• calculator (Exs. 27–29)

Teaching Resources

Teacher's Resource Book
• Warm-Up
• Labsheets 5A and 5B
• Practice and Applications
• Study Guide
See page 1 for additional teaching resources.

Assessment Options

EMBEDDED ASSESSMENT
• Recognize equivalent fractions
  Exercises 1, 4, 7, 9
• Find equivalent fractions
  Exercises 14, 15, 17
• Write a fraction in lowest terms
  Exercises 20, 22, 24
• Make predictions from a sample
  Exercises 41, 43
• Use mental math to find a fraction of a whole number
  Exercises 31, 39, 40

PERFORMANCE TASK/PORTFOLIO
• Exercise 26 on *p. 64 (challenge)*
• Exercise 41 on *p. 65*
• Exercise 47 on *p. 65 (challenge)*
• Module Project on *pp. 68–69*

QUIZZES/TESTS
• Quick Quiz
• Module Tests A and B
• Module Standardized Test
• Module Performance Assessment

TEST GENERATOR

Section 5 Overview

In this section, student will learn to recognize and write equivalent fractions and use these skills to write fractions in lowest terms.

Exploration 1

By covering a portion of a floor design with rhombus pattern blocks and then with triangle pattern blocks, students recognize that the two fractions representing the covered portion are equivalent. Students continue to use pattern blocks to represent and write equivalent fractions.

Exploration 2

After informally learning how to find equivalent fractions in a geometric design, students begin to write statements that show how to obtain an equivalent fraction by multiplying or dividing the numerator and denominator by the same number. Division of the numerator and denominator by the same number is used to express fractions in lowest terms.

Exploration 3

Exploration 3 uses predicting from a sample as a bridge to multiplying a whole number by a fraction. Students are given a sample from a larger population and write a fraction to describe that part of the sample with a given attribute. Then they use the fraction to predict what part of the population has the attribute. Students find fractional parts by counting and by using mental math.

Guide for Assigning Homework

REGULAR SCHEDULING (45 MIN CLASS PERIOD)			EXERCISES TO NOTE		
Section/ P&A Pages	Core Assignment	Extended Assignment	Additional Practice/Review	Open-ended Problems	Extended Problems
5 pp. 62–67	**Day 1:** 1–9, SR 50–59 **Day 2:** 10–25, SR 60–65 **Day 3:** 30–46, ROS 48–49	1–9, SR 50–59 13–29, SR 60–65 30–47, ROS 48–49	EP, p. 67 Review & Assessment, pp. 70–71		Challenge PA 26, 47 Mod Proj, pp. 68–69

Key: PA = Practice & Application; ROS = Reflecting on the Section; SR = Spiral Review; TB = Toolbox; EP = Extra Skill Practice; Ext = Extension; ST = Standardized Testing

Math Background and Teaching Strategies

Classroom Notes

Bulletin board displays for this section include:

- floors with geometric patterns

- key stroke sequence for simplifying fractions on a fraction calculator

- mental math strategies for finding a fraction of a whole number

- module project reports

Math Strands

Topic Spiraling and Integration

Exploration 1
The study of fractions from Section 4 is continued as students use pattern blocks to represent equivalent fractions. The pattern blocks give students a tactile model that can be used to demonstrate equivalence by laying the blocks on top of each other or using them to cover the same figure. They also provide a visual model so that when we say $\frac{3}{6}$ and $\frac{1}{2}$ are equivalent they understand what this means.

Exploration 2
Exploration 2 extends the ideas from Exploration 1 to the use of multiplication and division to find equivalent fractions. A transition is made from use of pattern blocks to an algorithm for creating equivalent fractions. The algorithm works because when the numerator and denominator of a fraction are multiplied by the same number, the fraction is actually being multiplied by $\frac{n}{n}$ which is a form of 1. Since 1 is the identity for multiplication, multiplying a fraction by 1 does not change its value. This is also true when dividing by forms of 1. Division is used to find equivalent fractions that are in lowest terms.

Exploration 3
Using pattern blocks, students learn about samples and populations and use fractions to make predictions about a population. Students learn to use mental math and fraction concepts to find a fraction of a whole number. Students see the term "of", but it is not yet related to the operation of multiplication. Multiplication of a fraction and a whole number will be covered in Module 3 where students will multiply both fractions and mixed numbers.

Module 1

MODULE 1 PATTERNS and Problem Solving

OVERVIEW
Problem solving is the focus of this module. Estimation, mental math, and a review of whole number computation are woven throughout the module. Students explore the mathematics of patterns and problem solving through such themes as coins, kites, and window designs. Manipulatives and visual models are used to develop an understanding of sequences and fractions.

PREREQUISITE SKILLS
Warm-Up Exercises for each section are provided in the *Teacher's Resource Book*. You can use these exercises to review skills and concepts students will need for each section. In addition, the Spiral Review exercises at the end of each section in the student edition provide practice on prerequisite skills.

MODULE DIAGNOSTIC TEST
The Module Diagnostic Test in the *Teacher's Resource Book* can be used to assess students' prior knowledge of skills and concepts that will be taught in each section of this module. You can use test results to help structure your teaching to meet the diverse needs of your classroom.

CONNECTING
MATHEMATICS
The & Theme

MODULE 1 · SECTION OVERVIEW

① Operations, Estimation, and Mental Math

As you look for patterns in number sentences and everyday situations:
- ◆ Learn the order of operations.
- ◆ Estimate by rounding.
- ◆ Decide when to use estimation, mental math, or a calculator.

② Patterns and Sequences

As you explore patterns and model sequences:
- ◆ Find a rule to extend a pattern.
- ◆ Write an equation to find the terms of a sequence.
- ◆ Predict terms of a sequence.

③ A Problem Solving Approach

As you play a card swapping game:
- ◆ Learn a 4-step approach to solve problems.
- ◆ Use several problem-solving strategies.

④ Fractions and Mixed Numbers

As you explore coins and kites:
- ◆ Write fractions and mixed numbers.

⑤ Equivalent Fractions

As you use pattern blocks to make window designs:
- ◆ Recognize and find equivalent fractions.
- ◆ Write fractions in lowest terms.
- ◆ Find a fraction of a whole number.

The Module Project

A Puzzling Problem

You will apply mathematical ideas you have learned as you solve the *30 Pennies in a Row* problem. You will explore different approaches that can also help you with the Extended Exploration (E²) feature in each module and with other problems throughout the year. You will share your solution in a group presentation.

For the Module Project
See pp. 68-69.

INTERNET
Resources and practice at
classzone.com

Module Resources

TEACHER'S RESOURCE BOOK
Resources
- *The Math Gazette* (parent newsletter)
- Warm-Ups
- Labsheets
- Practice and Applications
- Study Guide

Assessment
- Pre-Course Test
- Section Quick Quizzes
- Mid-Module Quiz
- Module 1 Diagnostic Test
- Module 1 Tests A and B
- Module 1 Standardized Test
- Module 1 Performance Assessment

SPANISH RESOURCES
- *The Math Gazette* (parent newsletter)
- Practice and Applications
- Assessment
- Spanish Glossary

STUDENT WORKBOOK

TECHNOLOGY BOOK

TECHNOLOGY RESOURCES
- @Home Tutor
- Test Generator
- Activity Generator
- Professional Development DVD
- Online Activities

ABOUT SETTING THE STAGE
To learn more about the *Setting the Stage* feature, see page 15.

ABOUT LABSHEETS
All labsheets for *Math Thematics* are copymasters in the *Teacher's Resource Book* for the given module.

ABOUT THE THEME
In this module, students will learn to recognize and analyze patterns and to become better problem solvers. In this section, students learn to look for compatible numbers to make mental math computations easier, and learn to choose an appropriate method of calculation.

GETTING STARTED
In this section, students will learn strategies for estimating sums, differences, and products of numbers. Module 1 Section 1 *Warm-Up* has students estimate various real-life measures to assess that they understand the concept of estimating.

Have students read the introductory paragraph and play the game. Then discuss **Question 1**. Be sure students explain how they developed their strategies. Following the discussion, have students complete **Questions 2 and 3**. Discuss the results. Some students may say the greatest possible value is 71. Have them explain how they got this answer. They either did the operations in the expression 6 + 6 • 6 – 1 in order from left to right or they inserted parentheses, (6 + 6) • 6 – 1. The need to agree on an order for performing operations motivates Exploration 1.

Section ① **Operations, Estimation, and Mental Math**

IN THIS SECTION

EXPLORATION 1
♦ Order of Operations

EXPLORATION 2
♦ Estimating with Rounding

EXPLORATION 3
♦ Using Mental Math

The Science of Patterns

KEY TERM
♦ expression

1. Answers will vary. Samples: Multiply large number to get greatest possible product. Add large number. Subtract small number.

FOR ▶ HELP
with *variables*, see
MODULE 1, p. 19

Setting the Stage

SET UP | *Work in a group of two or three. You will need:* • *Labsheet 1A* • *4 number cubes* • *a pair of scissors* • *a calculator*

Mathematics has been described as the science of patterns. In this module, you will begin studying patterns. Recognizing patterns can help you discover new mathematics, solve problems, and create interesting designs. It might even help you win a game!

Use Labsheet 1A. Follow the directions on the labsheet to play *A Dicey Problem*.

Think About It

▶ The problems you recorded as you played *A Dicey Problem* are examples of mathematical *expressions*. An **expression** can contain numbers, variables, and operations.

1 When you played the game, what strategies did you use for choosing the numbers and operations?

2 What is the greatest possible value you could get for an expression in one turn of *A Dicey Problem*? **41 (6 • 6 + 6 – 1)**

3 **a.** Use a calculator to find the value of your expressions.
Answers will vary.
b. Did you get the same answers? If not, why do you think the answers were different? **Answers may vary. If they did not get the same answers, it is because the operations were done in different orders.**

1. Order
2. Of
3. Operations

GOAL

LEARN HOW TO...
◆ follow the order of operations

AS YOU...
◆ look for patterns in number sentences

KEY TERM
◆ order of operations

▶ When they played *A Dicey Problem*, Sarah and Josh used the same numbers and operations but got different answers.

Sarah's solution:

$$4 + 6 \times 5 - 2$$
Answer $= 32$

Josh's solution:

$$4 + 6 \times 5 - 2$$
Answer $= 48$

4 a. $4 + 6 \times 5 - 2$
$= 4 + 30 - 2$
$= 34 - 2$
$= 32$
multiplication first; addition and subtraction in order from left to right

b. $4 + 6 \times 5 - 2$
$= 10 \times 5 - 2$
$= 50 - 2$
$= 48$
operations were done in order from left to right

4 Discussion

  a. In what order did Sarah perform the operations in the expression $4 + 6 \times 5 - 2$ to get her answer?

  b. In what order did Josh perform the operations?

▶ Mathematics would be very confusing if expressions like $4 + 6 \times 5 - 2$ could have more than one value. To understand each other's work, mathematicians have agreed on an order to follow when performing operations. This order is known as the **order of operations**.

To answer Questions 5–8, study the number sentences. Each number sentence follows the order of operations.

5 Describe the order in which addition and subtraction are performed to get the answers shown. The operations were done in order from left to right.
  a. $4 + 5 - 3 = 6$ **b.** $30 - 10 - 8 = 12$ **c.** $16 - 8 + 11 = 19$

6 Describe the order in which multiplication and division are performed to get the answers shown. The operations were done in order from left to right.
  a. $10 \cdot 6 \div 3 = 20$ **b.** $24 \div 6 \cdot 2 = 8$ **c.** $60 \div 10 \div 2 = 3$

> Another way to show multiplication is to use a dot between the factors.
> $10 \cdot 6$ means 10×6.

Exploration 1

ABOUT EXPLORATIONS
A section contains one to three explorations. In an exploration, students may work individually, in small groups, or as a class. Activities range from guided discovery to open-ended investigation, with students doing one or more of the following: collecting, generating, and presenting data; using concrete and/or visual models; applying problem-solving strategies; looking for patterns and relations; exploring alternative methods and solutions; using number sense; and applying prior knowledge. Students observe, analyze, predict, make and test conjectures, draw conclusions, and communicate their ideas orally and in writing.

TEACHING NOTES
Students are naturally inclined to perform the operations in an expression from left to right. However, as **Question 4** shows, this is not the only way to evaluate an expression. If they did not do so in the *Setting the Stage*, students should conclude from this exercise that there has to be an agreement that only one of the two orders of performing the operations is correct.

Monitor students' work on **Questions 5–10** as they begin to realize that multiplication and division always precede addition and subtraction, unless the order is changed by parentheses. Note that the first expression in **Question 6**, $10 \cdot 6 \div 3$, can be performed left to right, or the $\div$ can be done first to produce the given result. All the other expressions in **Question 6** must be performed left to right.

TEACHING NOTES

Try This as a Class Question 9
asks students to formulate a clear description of the order of operations. Write their responses on the board. Then guide them to a version that is correct.

Have students show intermediate steps for simplifying the expressions in **Question 11** to confirm that they have been done correctly. For example, $5 + 3 \cdot 2 = 5 + 6 = 11$.

---

7. First, do the multiplications and divisions in order from left to right. Then, do the additions and subtractions in order from left to right.

9. First, do the operations in parentheses. Then, do multiplications and divisions in order from left to right. Finally, do additions and subtractions in order from left to right.

10. a. $6 + 2 \cdot 9 = 6 + 18$
$= 24$ ft

b. $(6 + 2) \cdot 9 = 8 \times 9$
$= 72$ beads

✔ **QUESTION 11**

...checks that you can follow the order of operations.

---

7 Describe the order in which the operations are performed to get the answers shown.

a. $3 \cdot 6 - 5 = 13$ **b.** $20 - 6 \cdot 2 = 8$

c. $30 \div 10 + 5 = 8$ **d.** $15 - 4 \cdot 3 + 6 = 9$

8 How do parentheses affect the order in which operations are performed? (*Hint*: Compare these number sentences with the ones in Question 7.) The operation in parentheses was performed first.

a. $3 \cdot (6 - 5) = 3$ **b.** $(20 - 6) \cdot 2 = 28$

c. $30 \div (10 + 5) = 2$ **d.** $(15 - 4) \cdot 3 + 6 = 39$

9 **Try This as a Class** Use your results from Questions 5–8. Describe the order of operations in a way that is clear and easy to remember.

10 For each problem, write an expression that uses both addition and multiplication and can be used to solve the problem. Then find the value of the expression.

a. How many feet of fencing are needed to fence the three sides of the garden?   **b.** How many beads are needed to make the necklace?

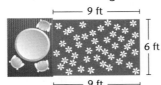

11 ✔ **CHECKPOINT** Find the value of each expression.

a. $5 + 3 \cdot 2$
11
b. $12 - 8 + 5$
9
c. $25 \cdot 4 \div 2$
50

d. $6 \cdot 5 - 18 \div 3$
24
e. $6 \cdot (5 - 2) \div 9$
2
f. $4 + (14 - 6)$
12

12 a. Use order of operations to find the value of the expressions you wrote when you played *A Dicey Problem*. Answers will vary.

b. Compare your answers in part (a) with the answers you got with your calculator in Question 3. Does your calculator follow the order of operations when it does calculations? Explain. Answers may vary, but the answers in part (a) will probably be the same as the answers in Question 3.

HOMEWORK EXERCISES ▶ See Exs. 1–13 on pp. 11–12.

Estimating with Rounding

GOAL

LEARN HOW TO...
- estimate by rounding
- decide when to use an estimate

AS YOU...
- look at everyday situations

KEY TERMS
- estimate
- round

▶ When you played *A Dicey Problem*, you needed to find the exact answer, but sometimes estimating the answer is enough. An **estimate** is an approximate answer that can be found quickly.

13 **Discussion** For each situation, when would you need an exact answer? Samples are given.

    a. the amount you will be paid for babysitting for three hours
      When you are being paid
    b. the time when the spaghetti you are cooking will be ready
      When the spaghetti is cooking
    c. the number of students who attend your school
      When textbooks are being ordered

14 **Discussion** For each situation in Question 13, when would an estimate be useful?

14. Samples are given.
   a. When you are trying to figure out what you will make
   b. When you are planning dinner
   c. When you are describing your school to a friend

▶ **Estimating Sums and Differences** One way to estimate is to **round** numbers before you add or subtract.

EXAMPLE

347 sixth graders, 261 seventh graders, and 493 eighth graders attend West Middle School. Estimate the total number of students.

SAMPLE RESPONSE

FOR ▶ HELP
with *rounding*, see
TOOLBOX, p. 567

First Round the numbers to the nearest hundred.		**Then** Use mental math to add.
347	⟶	300
261	⟶	300
+ 493	⟶	+ 500
		1100

About 1100 students attend West Middle School.

Exploration 2

ALTERNATIVE APPROACH
Ask students to devise two situations that require addition or subtraction. The first situation should be one where an exact answer is important; the second situation should be one where an exact answer is not required. Have students discuss the situations in partner pairs. Then have the entire class discuss **Questions 13 and 14**.

TEACHING NOTES

The additional example below can be used following **Question 15**. Using a simple example allows students to see the reasoning applied to determine whether the exact sum is greater than or less than the rounded sum. In this particular case, the exact sum can easily be found.

CLASSROOM EXAMPLE

Estimate the sum of 17 + 21 + 31. Then discuss how to use the estimate to find the exact sum.

Answer: 20 + 20 + 30 = 70

17 is 3 less than 20, the rounded value. 21 is 1 more than the rounded value 20, and 31 is one more than the rounded value 30, so altogether the exact value is 1 less than the estimated value of 70.

70 − 1 = 69.

TEACHING NOTES

Many students need a model like the one in the example to understand why a particular estimate is greater than or less than the exact answer. They can see that the bar that represents the exact answer is shorter than the bar that represents the estimate.

---

15. b. To round to a given place, look at the digit to the right of that place. If the digit is less than 5, round down. If it is greater than or equal to 5, round up.
c. Since the numbers were rounded down 47 and up 46, the sum is less than 1100.
d. Yes; It is reasonable since two of the numbers were rounded up by a combined total of about 50 and one number was rounded down about 50.
e. Less than; One number will be rounded up by 3, while the other two will be rounded down by 1 and 3. The estimate will be one less than the sum.

16. Sample: When you order food in a restaurant, you want the estimate to be greater than the actual cost to be sure you have enough money.

---

15 Discussion

a. In the Example on page 5, why was 347 rounded down to 300? 47 is less than half of 100, so 347 is closer to 300 than to 400.

b. What rules do you follow to round numbers?

c. Is 1100 *greater than* or *less than* the exact sum? Why?

d. Do you think 1100 is a reasonable estimate? Explain.

e. If all the numbers are rounded to the nearest ten before adding, will the estimated sum be *greater than* or *less than* the exact sum? Explain.

16 Give an example of when you need to know whether your estimate is greater than or less than the exact number.

17 a. Estimate the difference \$362 − \$29 by rounding the numbers to the nearest ten and then using mental math to subtract. about \$330

b. Explain why rounding both \$362 and \$29 to the nearest hundred does not give a reasonable estimate. The estimate, \$400, is greater than the greatest number.

c. Explain why rounding \$362 to \$400 and \$29 to \$30 does not give a reasonable estimate. The estimate, \$370, is greater than the greatest number.

▶ A diagram can help you understand why a subtraction estimate is *greater than* or *less than* the actual difference.

EXAMPLE

To estimate the difference 346 − 104, you can round both numbers to the nearest ten.

SAMPLE RESPONSE

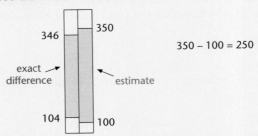

350 − 100 = 250

The estimate is greater than the exact difference. Rounding 346 up and rounding 104 down increased the difference.

18 Decide whether your estimate for Question 17(a) is *greater than* or *less than* the exact difference. Explain your thinking. Less than; Rounding 362 down and 29 up both decrease the difference.

19 ✔ **CHECKPOINT** Estimate each sum or difference. Decide whether the estimate is *greater than* or *less than* the exact answer. Explain your thinking. **Accept reasonable estimates.**

a. 139 + 57

b. 57 − 49

c. 13,968 − 2,117

d. 291 + 513 + 115

e. $38.15 − $6.78

f. $21,281 + $5,260 + $79,346

▶ **Estimating Products** You can also use rounding to estimate products. Here are two ways students estimated 258 × 6.

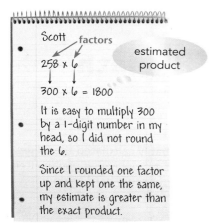

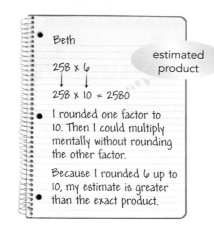

20 **Try This as a Class** Look at Scott's and Beth's work.

a. Predict which estimate is closer to the exact product.

b. Find 258 · 6. Which of the two estimates is closer to the exact product? **1548; Scott's estimate**

c. In which estimate was the smaller factor rounded up? By how much did the size of the factor change? **Beth's estimate; by about $\frac{1}{2}$**

d. In which estimate was the larger factor rounded up? By how much did the size of the factor change? **Scott's estimate; by about $\frac{1}{6}$**

e. Which method of rounding had a greater effect on the estimate? Why do you think this happened? **Beth's method; the change was relatively greater.**

21 **Try This as a Class**

a. Estimate 76 · 43 by rounding both factors to the nearest ten before multiplying. **about 3,200**

b. Is it hard to tell whether your estimate from part (a) is greater than or less than the exact product? Explain. **Yes, because one number was rounded up and the other was rounded down.**

 Section 1 Operations, Estimation, and Mental Math

✔ **QUESTION 19**

...checks that you can estimate sums and differences using rounding.

19. a. about 200; greater; Both numbers were rounded up.

b. about 10; greater; 57 was rounded up more than 49 was, so the difference is greater.

c. about 12,000; greater; Rounding 13,968 up and 2,117 down both increase the difference.

d. about 900; less; One number was rounded up 9, but the other two were rounded down 28.

e. about $31; less; $38.15 was rounded down and $6.78 was rounded up. Both make the difference less.

f. about $105,000; less; All numbers were rounded down.

20. a. Answers may vary. Since one factor was rounded up in each estimate, both estimates are greater than the actual product. Since 1800 < 2580, Scott's estimate is closer to the actual product.

TEACHING NOTES

Before assigning **Checkpoint 19**, you may want to discuss the following Classroom Example.

CLASSROOM EXAMPLE

Estimate the difference 452 − 96. Decide whether your estimate is *greater than* or *less than* the exact difference. Explain your thinking.

Answer: Round both numbers to the nearest ten: 450 − 100 = 350.

My estimate is less than the exact difference. Rounding 452 down and rounding 96 up decreased the difference.

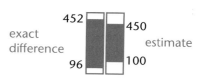

TEACHING NOTES

Emphasize the fact that the answers students get for **Question 19** depend on how the numbers are rounded. For example, in **part (c)**, if the numbers are rounded to the nearest ten, the estimate is 11,850, which is 1 less than the exact answer; if the numbers are rounded to the nearest hundred, the estimate is 11,900, which is 49 greater than the exact answer.

Some students may think that Beth's estimate in **Question 20** is better than Scott's since "Scott increased one of the factors by 42, but Beth increased a factor by only 4". Help them see that rounding the 6 to 10 adds 4 · 258 (or about 1000) to the actual product, whereas rounding 258 to 300 only adds 6 · 42 (or about 240). So Scott's estimate is better than Beth's.

Exploration 2 *continued*

TEACHING NOTES

Question 22 It will often not be possible to tell whether an estimated product is greater than or less than the exact answer if one factor is rounded up and the other is rounded down. Sometimes, you may get better results by rounding only one of the factors to a number that makes the product easy to calculate.

Exploration 3

TEACHING NOTES

In Exploration 2, students estimated answers; that is, their answers were not exact. Mental math can be used both to estimate answers (especially when numbers have been rounded) and to find exact answers. Emphasize that in this section, when mental math is used, it is to find exact sums and products.

DIFFERENTIATED INSTRUCTION

Some students may need to visualize concretely the regrouping of the addends in the **Example**. Write the operations on the board but write the numbers 19, 27, and 11 on memo stickers and position them in place among the operations. Then interchange the stickers. For example, 19 + 27 + 11 will change to 19 + 11 + 27 so that the compatible numbers 19 and 11 can be added and replaced by 30. Then 30 and 27 can be added to get 57. Memo stickers can be used in a similar way to illustrate the regrouping of the compatible factors in the product in the Example on page 9.

22. and 24. See Additional Answers beginning on page A1.

✔ **QUESTION 22**

...checks that you know how to use rounding to estimate products.

22 ✔ **CHECKPOINT** Estimate each product. If possible, decide whether the estimate is *greater than* or *less than* the exact product. Explain your thinking. **a–f. See margin.**

a. 13 · 61   **b.** 63 · 391   **c.** 224 · 7

d. 99 · 55   **e.** 723 · 118   **f.** 3968 · 442

HOMEWORK EXERCISES ▶ See Exs. 14–22 on p. 12.

Exploration 3

Using **Mental** Math

GOAL

LEARN HOW TO...
- use compatible numbers for mental math
- decide when to use mental math, paper and pencil, or a calculator

AS YOU...
- take part in *The Great Arithmetic Race*

KEY TERM
- compatible numbers

SET UP   *Work in a group of four. You will need:*
- *Labsheet 1B* • *a calculator*

▶ When you played *A Dicey Problem*, you probably calculated the value of expressions like 4 + 5 · 6 − 2 in your head. However, if you wanted to find the sum 17 + 31 + 8 + 19 + 25 it might seem hard to do it without using a calculator or paper and pencil.

23   **Discussion** Why is it easy to find the value of 40 + 8 + 2 + 20 + 19 + 1 in your head?

23. Answers may vary; Sample: These numbers may be grouped in ways that give sums that are easy to use in computations.

▶ Checking for *compatible numbers* can help you find the exact answer by adding quickly and easily in your head. **Compatible numbers** have sums or products that are easy to find and to use in computations.

EXAMPLE

Use mental math to find the sum 19 + 27 + 11.

SAMPLE RESPONSE

19 and 11 are compatible because 30 is easy to use in computations.

$$19 + 27 + 11 \quad \longrightarrow \quad 30 + 27 = 57$$

24   Suppose you want to find the sum 17 + 31 + 8 + 19 + 25.
a.–c. See margin.
a. Are 17 and 31 compatible numbers? Explain.

b. Are 31 and 19 compatible numbers? Why?

c. Show how you could find the sum using mental math.

25 ✔ **CHECKPOINT** Use mental math to find each sum.

    a. 40 + 60 + 87 187   **b.** 42 + 24 + 8 + 26 100

    c. 113 + 76 + 74 + 87 350   **d.** 17 + 8 + 30 + 75 130

▶ **Multiplying by Mental Math** Checking for compatible numbers may also help you multiply quickly in your head. Look for numbers with products that are easy to use in computations.

EXAMPLE

Use mental math to find the product 4 · 7 · 5.

SAMPLE RESPONSE

4 and 5 are compatible because it is easy to multiply by 20.

$$4 · 7 · 5 \longrightarrow 20 · 7 = 140$$

You can easily multiply 7 and 20 in your head.

26 Explain how you can use compatible numbers to find the product 4 · 17 · 25 by mental math. **Multiply 4 and 25 to get 100, then multiply 100 by 17 to get 1700.**

27 ✔ **CHECKPOINT** Use compatible numbers to find each product.

    a. 2 · 8 · 15 240   **b.** 9 · 5 · 4 180

    c. 25 · 6 · 4 · 4 2,400   **d.** 5 · 9 · 5 · 4 900

▶ **Choosing a Computational Tool** It is important to know when to use mental math, paper and pencil, or a calculator to do a computation. *The Great Arithmetic Race* will help you see which tool to choose for different problems.

Use Labsheet 1B for Questions 28 and 29.

28 Follow the directions on the labsheet to play *The Great Arithmetic Race.* **Check students' work.**

29 Use your results from *The Great Arithmetic Race* to help answer parts (a) and (b).

    a. Was using a calculator always the quickest method? Explain.

    b. Give an example of when you should use mental math.

HOMEWORK EXERCISES ▶ See Exs. 23–35 on pp. 12–13.

✔ QUESTION 25

...checks that you can use compatible numbers for mental addition.

FOR ▶ HELP

with *multiplying by tens*, see

TOOLBOX, p. 574

✔ QUESTION 27

...checks that you can use compatible numbers for mental multiplication.

29. Answers may vary.
    a. No; It may take longer to enter the numbers than it would to do the operation using mental math.
    b. When compatible numbers make it easy to do the operation in your head.
    5 · 17 · 20 = 100 · 17 = 1,700

TEACHING NOTES

The example below is best presented prior to assigning **Question 26**.

CLASSROOM EXAMPLE

Use mental math to find the product 20 · 9 · 5.

Answer: 20 and 5 are compatible because it is easy to multiply by 100.

So 20 · 9 · 5 = 100 · 9 = 900.

CLASSROOM MANAGEMENT

Before playing the game in **Question 28**, groups should decide who will be Player 1, Player 2, Player 3, and the Record Keeper. One method is to write each role on a card, place the cards in a box, and have group members draw a card to determine their roles. You can use Problem 1 as a practice problem to familiarize students with the game.

The teacher will need to read each problem aloud to the class. Only one problem should be revealed at a time. The problems are listed below. The correct answers can be given and checked at the end of the race.

Problems for the Great Arithmetic Race

1) **2 + 7 + 3**	= 12
2) **1 million + 1 million**	= 2 million
3) **23 · 20**	= 460
4) **30 ÷ 2**	= 15
5) **123 – 96**	= 27
6) **77 · 10 · 0 · 18**	= 0
7) **33 + 17 + 50**	= 100
8) **60,000 ÷ 500**	= 120
9) **3 · 4 · 5**	= 60
10) **99 – 11**	= 88

Key Concepts

Key Terms

About Key Concepts

Students can use the *Key Concepts* to review for a test or as a reference when they have missed a day of class. The *Key Concepts* are also a resource for parents who are helping their child with homework. These pages give a quick overview of the content, illustrate the content with examples, highlight the most important content, and provide a reference to the applicable pages in the explorations. The *Key Concepts* questions reinforce the main ideas from the section.

Absent Students

For students who were absent for all or part of this section, the blackline Study Guide for Section 1 may be used to present the ideas, concepts, and skills of Section 1.

expression

order of operations

Order of Operations (pp. 3–4)

An expression can contain numbers, variables, and operations. When finding the value of an expression, it is important to use the correct order of operations.

The dot is a symbol for multiplication.

Example

$18 - (2 + 4) \cdot 3 + 12$

Order of Operations

First Calculate what is inside parentheses.

$18 - (2 + 4) \cdot 3 + 12$
$= 18 - 6 \cdot 3 + 12$

Next Perform multiplication and division in order from left to right.

$= 18 - 6 \cdot 3 + 12$
$= 18 - 18 + 12$

Then Perform addition and subtraction in order from left to right.

$= 18 - 18 + 12$
$= 0 + 12$
$= 12$

Estimation Using Rounding (pp. 5–8)

An estimate is a reasonable answer that can be found quickly when an exact answer is not needed. Rounding can be used to estimate sums, differences, and products.

estimate

round

Example

$247 \cdot 26$

$\downarrow \qquad \downarrow$ *estimated product*

$250 \cdot 30 = 7500$

Since both factors were rounded up, the estimated product is greater than the actual product.

30 Key Concepts Question Ann wants to buy a 52¢ ruler and three 48¢ pens at the school store. (There is no tax.)

a. How many dollars does she need to bring to school? $2

b. Explain what method you used to solve part (a) and why you chose that method. **Sample Response: I estimated by rounding because I wanted to find a reasonable amount.**
$3 \cdot \$.48 \approx 3 \cdot \$.50 = \$1.50$
$\$1.50 + \$.52 \approx \$1.50 + \$.50 = \$2.00$

Section 1

Key Concepts

Key Term

Mental Math Using Compatible Numbers (pp. 8–9)

Checking for compatible numbers can help you find the exact answer in your head. Compatible numbers are numbers that have sums or products that are easy to find and to use in computations.

compatible numbers

Example

> 5, 5, and 4 are compatible numbers. Their product, 100, is easy to use in computations.

$$5 \cdot 3 \cdot 5 \cdot 4 \cdot 6 = 100 \cdot 18 = 1800.$$

with 100 and 18 marked.

Key Concepts Questions Find the value of each expression.

31 $82 + 37 + 18 + 13$ 150   **32** $2 \cdot 9 \cdot 5 \cdot 6$ 540

CLOSURE QUESTIONS
State the order of operations.

Sample Response:

Order of Operations:
1. Calculate what is inside parentheses.
2. Perform multiplications and divisions in order from left to right.
3. Perform additions and subtractions in order from left to right.

Section 1

Practice & Application Exercises

1. a. 355; The answer is not reasonable because the first hurdle would be at 45 m and, since 45 m + 355 m = 400 m, the second hurdle would be at the finish line.

1. **Sports** The manager of the track team made a sketch and wrote this expression to calculate how far apart to place the hurdles for the 400-meter race.

$$400 - 40 - 45 \div 9$$

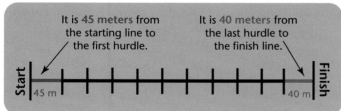

It is **45 meters** from the starting line to the first hurdle.

It is **40 meters** from the last hurdle to the finish line.

Start | 45 m ... 40 m | Finish

a. Follow the order of operations to find the value of the expression. Is the answer reasonable? Explain.

b. Use parentheses to rewrite the expression so that it clearly shows what the manager was thinking. $(400 - 40 - 45) \div 9$

c. How far apart should the hurdles be placed? **35 meters**

Practice & Applications

SUGGESTED ASSIGNMENTS

Core Course
Day 1: Exs. 1–13
Day 2: Exs. 14–22, 36–39
Day 3: Exs. 23–35

Extended Course
Day 1: Exs. 1–13
Day 2: Exs. 14–22, 36–39
Day 3: Exs. 23–35, 40*

Note: Extended Course assignments can be used to differentiate within the regular classroom. In classrooms where students are grouped homogeneously, the material might be covered in fewer days. In this case assignments may be combined.

*denotes Extension Exercises

Practice & Applications

ABOUT PRACTICE & APPLICATIONS

The questions in the *Practice and Applications* exercises range from skill to application and open-ended to single answer. A wide variety of topics are covered, and students may explore how the content relates to other areas of mathematics or other subject areas. The exercises can be used to assess how well students comprehend the content. See the section planner page that appears in the *Teacher's Edition* before each module for a list of exercises that can be used as embedded assessment. (For Module 1, Section 1, see page 1C.)

ADDITIONAL PRACTICE

See the *Teacher's Resource Book* for additional practice and application exercises for this section.

EXERCISE NOTES

In **Exercise 29**, students need to choose a method of calculating. Encourage them to look for a mental math approach before using paper and pencil. (You may want to have them read **Exercise 30** ahead of time.) Mention that if there is no obvious mental math solution, then after they have found a pencil and paper answer, they might be able to use estimation to make a rough check of the exact answer. For example, in **part (a)**, rounding the addends to the nearest hundred gives an estimate of 4900 which is close to the exact answer, 4941.

---

14. b. Yes; I rounded up $0.20 and down $0.09, so my estimate is $0.11 too high. Since the amount I have is $0.20 less than the estimate, I don't have enough.

1 gal lowfat milk	2.95
1 can of soup	.85
wheat bread	1.09
TOTAL	

17. about 14,000; not possible to tell whether estimate is greater than or less than exact product

18. about 1,800; greater than

20. about 60,000; not possible to tell whether estimate is greater than or less than exact product

21. about 9,700; less than

30. b and d;
b. 2 · 8 · 15 = 30 · 8 = 240
d. 24 + 380 + 56 + 120 = 380 + 80 + 120 = 380 + 200 = 580

Find the value of each expression.

2. $7 + 2 \cdot 3$ 13

3. $4 \cdot 6 + 3 \cdot 4$ 36

4. $6 + (18 - 9) \cdot 2$ 24

5. $12 - 8 \div 4$ 10

6. $80 \div 5 \cdot 4$ 64

7. $(12 + 3) \div 3 + 2$ 7

8. $5 \cdot 4 - 2 \div 2$ 19

9. $(11 + 4) \div 5$ 3

10. $6 \cdot (2 + 4) - 3$ 33

In Exercises 11–13, write an expression to show each set of operations in the correct order.

11. Add 11 and 5. Then divide the sum by 4. $(11 + 5) \div 4$

12. Multiply 3 and 5. Then divide 60 by that result. $60 \div (3 \cdot 5)$

13. Start with 50. Then subtract the product of 4 and 6. $50 - (4 \cdot 6)$

14. a. Estimate the total grocery receipt shown to the left. about $5

b. Suppose you have exactly $4.80. Without finding the exact total, can you tell if you have enough money to buy the three items? Explain.

15. **Open-ended** Describe two situations where estimating the answer is appropriate. Explain your reasoning. Answers will vary.

Estimate each answer. If possible, decide whether the estimate is greater than or less than the exact answer.

16. $126 + 72$
about 200; greater than

17. $347 \cdot 42$

18. $58 \cdot 29$

19. $421 - 209$
about 200; less than

20. $61 \cdot 992$

21. $794 + 8932$

22. **Fitness** To lose one pound, you must burn about 3,540 calories. Estimate how many calories must be burned to lose 6 pounds. $3,500 \cdot 6$ is about 21,000 calories.

Use compatible numbers to find each answer by mental math.

23. $7 + 15 + 13 + 5$ 40

24. $210 + 35 + 65 + 90$ 400

25. $2 \cdot 15 \cdot 4$ 120

26. $54 + 29 + 16$ 99

27. $3 \cdot 4 \cdot 25 \cdot 2$ 600

28. $5 \cdot 12 \cdot 2 \cdot 10$ 1200

29. Find the value of each expression.

a. $3678 + 729 + 534$ 4,941

b. $2 \cdot 8 \cdot 15$ 240

c. $7 \cdot 13 \cdot 4$ 364

d. $24 + 380 + 56 + 120$ 580

30. For which expressions in Exercise 29 can you find the value using mental math? Explain how you would do them.

31. Compatible numbers can also be used to estimate products.

Example:

$$26 \cdot 198$$
$$\downarrow$$
$$26 \cdot 200 = 5200$$

or

$$26 \cdot 198$$
$$\downarrow$$
$$25 \cdot 200 = 5000$$

Without using a calculator, explain how you can tell which estimate in the Example is closer to the exact product.

In Exercises 32–34, explain how to use compatible numbers to estimate each answer.

32. $14 \cdot 2 \cdot 39$
$15 \cdot 2 \cdot 40 = 1,200$

33. $24 \cdot 389$
$25 \cdot 400 = 10,000$

34. $325 + 34 + 40$
$325 + 35 + 40 =$
$325 + 75 = 400$

Reflecting ◀▶on the Section

Be prepared to report on the following topic in class.

35. a. Choose from the digits 3, 5, 4, 2, and 8. You may not repeat a digit. Copy and fill in the boxes to make the greatest possible product.

b. Describe how you used estimation, mental math, or a calculator to solve this problem. Answers will vary.

Spiral ◀▶Review

Replace each __?__ with < , >, or =. (Toolbox, p. 566)

36. 84,987 __?__ 85,132
$<$

37. 25 thousand __?__ 2500
$>$

Find the missing number. (Toolbox, p. 577)

38. 50 min = __?__ sec
3,000

39. 3 hours = __?__ min
180

Extension ▶ ▶

Applying Order of Operations Samples are given.

40. Find a sequence of keys that results in each number 1 through 10. You may use only the keys [2], [5], [×], [−], and [=]. You may use each key as many times as you like or not at all.

Example: The keystrokes below result in 8.

$5 - 2 \times 2 = 1$
$2 \times 2 - 2 = 2$
$5 - 2 = 3$
$2 \times 2 = 4$
$5 \times 2 - 5 = 5$

$2 \times 2 \times 2 - 2 = 6$
$2 \times 2 \times 2 \times 2 - 2 \times 2 - 5 = 7$
$5 \times 2 - 2 = 8$
$5 \times 5 - 2 \times 2 \times 2 \times 2 = 9$
$5 \times 2 = 10$

Section 1 Operations, Estimation, and Mental Math **13**

---

31. 26 · 200 is $26 \cdot 2 = 52$ greater than the exact answer. 25 · 200 is $198 - 25 \cdot 2 = 148$ less than the exact answer. So 26 · 200 is closer.

Oral Report

Exercise 35 checks that you can choose an appropriate computational method to solve a problem.

EXERCISE NOTES

In **Exercise 40**, students need to know whether their calculator automatically applies order of operations. If it does, students will have to press the equal button if they want to perform subtraction before multiplication. For example, $5 - 2 \times 2 =$ will result in 1 because the calculator will multiply 2 x 2 first. If the student intended it to equal 6, they will have to press $5 - 2 =$, and then use the result x 2. This can be recorded on paper as either $5 - 2 = \times 2$ or by using parentheses $(5 - 2) \times 2 =$.

ABOUT EXTRA SKILL PRACTICE
The first part of the *Extra Skill Practice* reinforces the concepts students investigated in the section. The exercises are usually skill-based, but sometimes are application-based. The last part of the page usually provides *Standardized Testing* questions relating to the section content. In some sections, an important study skill is presented.

TEACHER NOTES
For each Exploration, the corresponding Extra Skill Practice Exercises are noted.

Exploration 1: 1–12
Exploration 2: 13–24
Exploration 3: 25–32

EXTRA HELP
Teacher's Resource Book
• Practice and Applications
• Study Guide

Technology Resources
• @Home Tutor
• Test Generator

ASSESSMENT
• Section 1 Quick Quiz
• Test Generator

Section 1
Extra Skill Practice

Find the value of each expression.

1. $5 + 7 \cdot 3$ 26

2. $6 \cdot 4 + 7 \cdot 2$ 38

3. $15 - 6 \div 3$ 13

4. $60 \div 15 \cdot 5$ 20

5. $10 + 30 \div 6$ 15

6. $42 - 21 \cdot 2$ 0

7. $(10 + 4) \div 7 + 3$ 5

8. $5 + (12 - 4) \cdot 4$ 37

9. $(19 - 10) \cdot 5 - 8$ 37

10. $16 \div 2 \cdot (5 + 3)$ 64

11. $25 - (14 + 3) + 6$ 14

12. $2 \cdot (5 + 8) - 4 \div 2$ 24

Estimate each answer. If possible, decide whether the estimate is *greater than* or *less than* the exact answer.

13. $229 + 68$
about 300, greater than

14. $323 - 119$
about 200, less than

15. $64 + 42$
about 100, less than

16. $137 + 22$
about 160, not possible to tell

17. $31 \cdot 58$
about 1800, not possible to tell

18. $427 - 212$
about 200, less than

19. $158 + 43 + 78$
about 280, not possible to tell

20. $2362 - 1221$
about 1,200, greater than

21. $193 \cdot 13$
about 2,600, greater than

22. $12 \cdot 62$
about 720, less than

23. $98 \cdot 45$
about 4,500, greater than

24. $22,352 + 1,649$
about 24,000, not possible to tell

Use compatible numbers to find each answer by mental math.

25. $12 + 17 + 8 + 3$ 40

26. $6 + 19 + 14 + 211$ 250

27. $32 + 45 + 5 + 8$ 90

28. $140 + 58 + 60 + 42$ 300

29. $5 \cdot 5 \cdot 12 \cdot 4$ 1,200

30. $2 \cdot 3 \cdot 3 \cdot 25$ 450

31. $15 \cdot 4 \cdot 6 \cdot 5$ 1,800

32. $20 \cdot 8 \cdot 5 \cdot 3$ 2,400

Standardized Testing ◄► Multiple Choice

1. Which expression matches this set of directions? A

   ♦ First multiply 25 by 9.
   ♦ Next add 16 to the product.
   ♦ Then divide the total by 4.

   Ⓐ $(16 + 25 \cdot 9) \div 4$
   Ⓑ $25 \cdot 9 \div 4 + 16$
   Ⓒ $25 \cdot 9 + 16 \div 4$
   Ⓓ $16 + (25 \cdot 9) \div 4$

2. Use mental math to decide which expression is equal to $17 + 46 + 13 + 24$. C

   Ⓐ $20 + 60$
   Ⓑ $46 + 50$
   Ⓒ $30 + 70$
   Ⓓ $30 + 50 + 25$

Section 2 Patterns and Sequences

IN THIS SECTION

EXPLORATION 1
◆ Extending Patterns

EXPLORATION 2
◆ Analyzing Sequences

sHAPELy Numbers

Setting the Stage ▸▸▸▸▸▸▸▸▸▸▸▸▸▸▸▸▸▸▸▸▸▸▸▸▸▸▸▸▸▸▸

SET UP *Work with a partner. You will need pattern blocks.*

Do numbers have geometric shapes? The Pythagoreans and other ancient Greeks thought so. They classified numbers based on the patterns that regularly spaced coins or pebbles formed.

For example, they called 6 a triangular number because six pebbles can be arranged to form an equilateral triangle as shown at the right.

There are other triangular numbers besides 6. The first four are:

1, 3, 6, 10, ...

An ordered list of numbers or objects like this is a **sequence**.

1 pebble
2 pebbles
3 pebbles

KEY TERM
◆ sequence

The Pythagoreans were a society founded by Pythagoras of Samos (c. 500 B.C.). They studied numbers, music, and geometry.
▼

Think About It

1 What does each of the following words mean?

  a. pentagonal
    5 sided (or 5 angled)

  b. hexagonal
    6 sided (or 6 angled)

  c. equilateral
    All sides have the same length

2 Show how the following numbers of pattern blocks can be arranged to form an equilateral triangle.

  a. 3 pattern blocks

  b. 10 pattern blocks

3 What do you think the fifth triangular number is? Why? See margin.

▸ In this section, you will explore patterns in mathematics. Finding patterns and using them to make predictions is an important problem-solving strategy.

Setting the Stage

ABOUT SETTING THE STAGE
Each section in *Math Thematics* begins with a *Setting the Stage* whose purpose is to pique students' interest and relate the mathematics to a real-world situation. The *Setting the Stage* motivates students to learn the mathematics or introduces a problem that will be explored. It may be a reading, activity, visual display, or some combination of these. Students may review a previously learned concept in the *Think About It* questions, but usually they explore an idea they will later investigate in depth. Mental math and estimation are often incorporated into the questions.

GETTING STARTED
In this section students will look for patterns in sequences of geometric shapes to develop rules for creating and extending the sequence. Module 1 Section 2 *Warm-Up* checks that students can recognize whether a set of blocks shows a repeating pattern.

Have students read the *Setting the Stage.* Then discuss **Question 1** as a class. Following the discussion, have students complete **Questions 2 and 3** with their partners. When they have finished, ask some of the students to share their solutions and discuss the results.

3. 15; You will need to add a row of 5 objects to the triangle in 2(b).

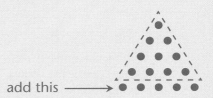

add this ⟶

15

Exploration 1

TEACHING NOTES

The Classroom Example below can be discussed before students start **Question 5**, so that they understand what to do when asked for a rule.

CLASSROOM EXAMPLE

What rule would you use to extend this pattern?

Answer: A rule for repeating this pattern is to repeat one hexagon and two triangles.

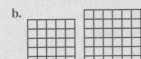

5. a.

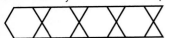

Start with a single block. To get each shape after the first, add a single block on the left side and on top of the previous figure.

b.

Start with a single block. To get each shape after the first, add a row and a column of blocks to the previous figure.

c. ◇◇◇◇ ◇◇◇◇◇

Start with a rhombus. Place 2 triangles together to form a congruent rhombus and place it at the left edge of each figure to get the next figure.

---

6. a. 14, 17; Start with 2. Add 3 to each number to get the next number.

b. 25, 36; 1 · 1, 2 · 2, 3 · 3, 4 · 4, 5 · 5, 6 · 6
Or, square the first counting number. Continue by squaring each consecutive counting number.

c. ten thousand, hundred thousand; Start with 1. Multiply each number by 10 to get the next number, but write it in words.

GOAL

LEARN HOW TO...
- find a rule to extend a pattern
- make a table to organize your work

AS YOU...
- explore patterns using pattern blocks

KEY TERMS
- rule
- term
- term number

Exploration 1

Extending PATTERNS

SET UP *Work with a partner. You will need pattern blocks.*

▶ Pythagoras had a *rule* for finding triangular numbers. He noticed that the third triangular number, 6, was equal to 1 + 2 + 3, and that the fourth triangular number, 10, was equal to 1 + 2 + 3 + 4.

4 a. How would Pythagoras have found the fifth triangular number?
by finding the sum 1 + 2 + 3 + 4 + 5
b. What is the fifth triangular number? How does this compare with your answer to Question 3? 15; It is the same

▶ **Finding a Rule** When you describe how to create or extend a sequence you are giving a **rule** for the sequence.

5 For each of the following sequences: a–c. See margin.
- Look for a pattern.
- Use pattern blocks to build the next two shapes in the sequence.
- Explain the rule you used.

The three dots tell you the pattern continues in the same way.

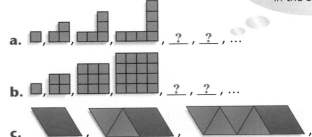

a. ▪ , ▪ , ▪ , ▪ , ? , ? , ...

b. ▪ , ▪ , ▪ , ▪ , ? , ? , ...

c. ▱ , ▱ , ▱ , ? , ? , ...

6 For each of the following sequences:
- Look for a pattern.
- Give the next two entries in the sequence.
- Explain the rule you used.

a. 2, 5, 8, 11, _?_ , _?_ , ...

b. 1, 4, 9, 16, _?_ , _?_ , ...

c. one, ten, hundred, thousand, _?_ , _?_ , ...

7 Discussion

a. What things did you look for when you tried to discover the rules for the patterns in Questions 5 and 6?

b. Are any of the sequences in Question 6 related to sequences in Question 5? If so, which ones? Explain.

c. What do you think the Pythagoreans would have called the numbers in the sequence in Question 6(b)? Why?

▶ Each number or object in a sequence is a **term** and can be labeled with a **term number**. The term number tells you the order or position of the term in the sequence.

The **2nd term** in the sequence is **3**.

1, **3**, 6, 10, 15, …

8 Use Pythagoras' rule to find the next term in the sequence above. What is its term number? $1 + 2 + 3 + 4 + 5 + 6 = 21$; Term number = 6

▶ **Using a Table** You can use a table to help organize the terms and term numbers of a sequence.

Triangular Numbers

Term number	1	2	3	4	5	…
Term	1	3	6	10	15	…

A rule for this sequence is to start with 1. To find each term after the first, add the term number to the previous term. For example,

5th term = 4th term + 5 = 10 + 5 = 15

9 a. Use the rule to find the next term of the sequence in the table. What is its term number? $15 + 6 = 21$; Term number = 6

b. What would the eighth term be? Explain. $21 + 7 = 28$ 7th term
$28 + 8 = 36$ 8th term

10 ✔ **CHECKPOINT** Make a table showing the term numbers and terms of each sequence. Then find the next two terms of each sequence. a–b. See margin.

a. 1, 3, 7, 13, 21, __?__ , __?__ , …

b.  , __?__ , __?__ , …

HOMEWORK EXERCISES See Exs. 1–9 on pp. 22–23.

---

7. a. Answers will vary. Sample: Look for things that repeat; look to see if the same number is added to the preceding number each time.

b. Yes; Each term of the number sequence in 6(b) is the number of squares in the corresponding term of the shape sequence in 5(b).

c. Square numbers; If each term of the sequence was modeled with blocks, the blocks could be arranged in a square.

✔ **QUESTION 10**

…checks that you can set up a table to help examine and extend a sequence.

TEACHING NOTES

Questions 7(b) and (c) You might specifically ask students to compare the patterns in **Questions 5(b) and 6(b)**. Students should notice that the two patterns are essentially the same: the sequence in **Question 6(b)** is just the numerical representation of the one in **Question 5(b)**. Mention that because of this relationship, the terms of the sequence 1, 4, 9, 16, … in **Question 6(b)** are called *square numbers*.

In **Question 10**, have students state the pattern in words. For **part (a)**, they might say that the difference between the terms increases by two each time (+2, +4, +6, +8, …). Some students may be able to use angle rotations to describe the pattern in **part (b)**. Others may need a real-world model. Suggest they use the numbers on a circular clock face to describe the pattern (*Start at midnight with the triangle pointing up at the 12. Adding 2 hours on each move rotates the figure so the triangle points at the 2, then at the 4, then 6, then 8,…*).

TIPS FROM TEACHERS

Since students often confuse *term* and *term number* during this lesson, I leave an example on the board with the terms and term numbers identified. Relating the vocabulary to real world ideas seems to help my students. One example I use is

term number: number of students
1, 2, 3, …
term: admission fee
$3, $6, $9, …

10. a–b. See Additional Answers beginning on page A1.

17

Exploration 2

Developing Math Concepts

The table in **Question 11** and the related **Questions 12–14** provide additional exposure to the ideas of *term number* and *term*. In the table the different block arrangements in the shape sequence are terms. The number of blocks used in each arrangement are the terms of the related number sequence. Students should notice that in the questions, term numbers are indicated by ordinal numbers (like 5th and 6th) that tell *where* you will find the term in the sequence. The terms are the actual shapes or numbers found in those positions.

Question 13(b) Most students can easily see that each term in the number sequence is 2 more than the preceding term. The difficulty arises when they must make connections between the term numbers and the terms of the number sequence. It may help students if you direct them by asking specifically, "How is 2 related to 1? 4 related to 2? 6 related to 3? 8 related to 4?"

12. a.
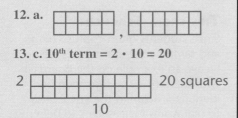

13. c. 10th term = $2 \cdot 10 = 20$

2 [grid] 20 squares
10

LEARN HOW TO...
- write an equation to find the terms of a sequence
- make predictions

AS YOU...
- model sequences
- explore visual patterns

KEY TERMS
- equation
- variable
- evaluate an expression

11. Each term in the number sequence is the number of squares used to make the corresponding term in the shape sequence.

Exploration 2

ANALYZING SEQUENCES

SET UP *You will need 20 square tiles or graph paper.*

▶ Like Pythagoras, you can use patterns to predict the terms in sequences. A table can help you see the relationship between the term numbers and the terms of the sequences.

11 How are the sequence of numbers and the sequence of shapes in the table related?

Term number		1	2	3	4	5	6	...
Term	Shape sequence	▪	▦	▦▦	▦▦▦	?	?	...
	Number sequence	2	4	6	8	?	?	...

12 **a.** Use square tiles (or draw pictures) to model the 5th and 6th terms of the shape sequence. See margin.

b. What are the 5th and 6th terms of the number sequence?
10, 12

13 **a.** What pattern can you use to predict the 10th term of the shape sequence? Each term in the shape sequence is a rectangle 2 squares tall and *n* squares long, where *n* is the term number.

b. How is each term of the number sequence related to its term number? Each term in the number sequence is 2 times its term number.

c. Predict what the 10th term of the number sequence will be. To check, use your pattern from part (a) to model the 10th shape and count the squares in it. See margin.

14 **Try This as a Class**

a. Share your patterns from Question 13(a). Monitor students.

b. Describe the 90th term in the shape sequence. A rectangle 2 squares high and 90 squares long.

c. Predict the 90th term of the number sequence.
90th term = $2 \cdot 90 = 180$

d. Are the numbers in the number sequence even or odd? even

▶ In Question 14, you used a pattern to predict a term of the sequence 2, 4, 6, 8, ... You may have noticed that the number of squares in each term of the shape sequence is equal to 2 times the term number. For example:

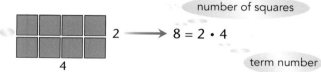

The 4th term of the shape sequence contains 8 squares.

number of squares

$2 \longrightarrow 8 = 2 \cdot 4$

term number

4

▶ An **equation** such as $8 = 2 \cdot 4$ is a mathematical sentence stating that two quantities are equal. Sometimes you can use *variables* to write an equation that gives a rule for finding any term of a sequence. A **variable** is a quantity that is unknown or that changes. It can be represented by a letter, a word, or a symbol. To **evaluate an expression** with one or more variables, you substitute a number for each variable. Then you carry out any operations in the expression using the order of operations.

EXAMPLE

Write an equation for the rule for the sequence 2, 4, 6, 8, ... Use the equation to predict the 90th term of the sequence.

SAMPLE RESPONSE

Because the terms and the term numbers change, you can use variables to represent them. Let t = the term. Let n = the term number.

The term is equal to 2 times the term number.

$$t = 2 \cdot n$$
or $\quad t = 2n$

"2 times n" can be written $2 \cdot n$ or $2n$.

Use this equation to predict the 90th term of the sequence. Evaluate the expression $2 \cdot n$ when $n = 90$.

$$t = 2 \cdot n$$
$$= 2 \cdot 90$$
$$= 180$$

For the 90th term, the term number n is 90.

The 90th term of the sequence 2, 4, 6, 8, ... is 180.

You may want to spend some time discussing variables and giving examples of variables before discussing the **Example**. Students will be using variables to write equations in the homework assignment, so be sure they understand the concept.

Not all students will be able to easily write an equation to represent the rule for a sequence. For those that are frustrated, encourage them to make a table as in **Question 11** and then verbally express the patterns they see. Acknowledge their understanding of the patterns and then help them represent the patterns they notice with an algebraic equation. For example, the pattern 3, 6, 9, 12 can be shown in a table as

n	1	2	3	4
t	3	6	9	12

The student might say, "The terms increase by 3 each time." This is true, but then challenge them to find a pattern relating a term t and its term number n. Students should be able to state, "The term is 3 times the term number." Show how this can be represented with variables to get $t = 3 \cdot n$.

Exploration 2 *continued*

TEACHING NOTES

The Classroom Example below can be used to provide additional practice writing an equation that relates the term number and term of a sequence. This example also shows how an equation might contain a combination of operations. Show students how to analyze the pattern, eventually arriving at an equation with variables.

CLASSROOM EXAMPLE

Organize the sequence 50, 45, 40, 35, 30, 25... in a table to write an equation that can be used to find any term of the number sequence from its term number.

Answer:

Term Number n	Term t
1	50
2	45
3	40
4	35
5	30
6	25

Notice that the terms decrease by 5 each time. The first term does not decrease by 5, the second decreases by one 5, the third by two 5s, the fourth by three 5s.

$50 - 0(5) = 50$
$50 - 1(5) = 45$
$50 - 2(5) = 40$
50 – one less than the term number times 5 = the term

The equation is $50 - (n - 1)(5) = t$

15. See Additional Answers beginning on page A1.

20

---

16. a. The top row of squares will have 19 squares; the bottom row will have 20 squares.
   e. odd; You can tell because there is only one square in the right column of each shape and there are two squares in each of the other columns.

✔ **QUESTION 17**

...checks that you can write a rule for finding the terms of a sequence.

---

15 Copy the table below and extend it to include the next two terms in the shape and number sequences. **See margin.**

Term number		1	2	3	4	5	6	...
Term	Shape sequence	▪	▪▪	▪▪▪	▪▪▪▪	?	?	...
	Number sequence	1	3	5	7	?	?	...

16 Try This as a Class

a. Explain how to sketch the 20th term in the shape sequence.

b. Describe two ways to find the 20th term of the number sequence. $2 \times 20 - 1$ and $2 \times 19 + 1$

c. Write an equation that can be used to find any term of the number sequence from its term number. Use t for the term and n for the term number. $t = 2n - 1$ or $t = 2(n - 1) + 1$

d. Use your equation to find the 75th term of the number sequence. $2 \cdot 75 - 1 = 150 - 1 = 149$

e. Are the numbers in the number sequence *even* or *odd*? How can you tell from the shapes in the shape sequence?

f. How can you tell whether a number is *even* or *odd* without sketching a shape? **A number is odd if the remainder is 1 when the number is divided by 2. It is even if it is divisible by 2.**

17 ✔ **CHECKPOINT**

a. How is each term in the number sequence below related to its term number? **Each term is 3 more than the term number.**

Term number	1	2	3	4	...
Term	4	5	6	7	...

b. Write an equation for the rule for the sequence. Be sure to identify what each variable in the equation represents. $t = n + 3$ where t = term and n = term number.

c. Use the equation to find the 67th term in the sequence. 67th term = $67 + 3 = 70$

HOMEWORK EXERCISES ▶ See Exs. 10–19 on pp. 24–25.

Section 2
Key Concepts

Sequences (pp. 15–17)

A sequence is an ordered list of numbers or objects.

Example

5, 10, 15, 20, 25, ...

> The 3rd term in the sequence is **15**.

Each number or object of a sequence is a term. The position of each term can be labeled with a term number.

A table can help you see how the term numbers and terms of a sequence are related and write a rule for finding the terms of the sequence.

Example

Term number	1	2	3	4	5
Term	5	10	15	20	25

Rule: Start with 5. Add 5 to each term to get the next term.

or

The term is 5 times the term number.

Equations and Variables (pp. 18–20)

You can use variables to write an equation that shows how a term in a sequence is related to its term number. A variable is a letter, word, or symbol used to represent unknown quantities or quantities that change. To evaluate an expression with one or more variables, substitute a number for each variable. Then carry out any operations in the expression.

Example Write an equation for the rule for the sequence 5, 10, 15, 20, ...

The term t is 5 times the term number n.
$$t = 5 \cdot n \text{ or } t = 5n$$

18 Key Concepts Question Make a table for the sequence 3, 5, 7, 9, 11, ... Extend the table to include the next two terms. Then write a rule for the sequence. **See margin.**

Key Terms

sequence

term
term number

rule

equation
variable

evaluate an
expression

Key Concepts

CLOSURE QUESTION

Explain the meanings of the words *sequence, term, term number,* and *rule.*

Sample Response: A sequence is an ordered list of numbers or objects; a term is a number or object in the sequence; the term number tells the position of the term in the sequence; and a rule tells how to continue the pattern or extend the sequence.

ABSENT STUDENTS

For students who were absent for all or part of this section, the blackline Study Guide for Section 2 may be used to present the ideas, concepts, and skills of Section 2.

18. See Additional Answers beginning on page A1.

Practice & Applications

SUGGESTED ASSIGNMENTS

Core Course
Day 1: Exs. 1–8
Day 2: Exs. 10–12, 20–31
Day 3: Exs. 13–16, 18–19

Extended Course
Day 1: Exs. 1–9
Day 2: Exs. 10–12, 20–31
Day 3: Exs. 13–19

Note: Extended Course assignments can be used to differentiate within the regular classroom. In classrooms where students are grouped homogeneously, the material might be covered in fewer days. In this case assignments may be combined.

ADDITIONAL PRACTICE

See the *Teacher's Resource Book* for additional practice and application exercises for this section.

2. 35, 42, 49, 56
Start with 7 and add 7 to each number to get the next number OR multiply the term number by 7.

3. 63, 54, 45, 36
Start with 99 and subtract 9 from each term to get the next term.

4. $\frac{1}{10}, \frac{1}{12}, \frac{1}{14}, \frac{1}{16}$
Each term is a fraction with one in the numerator. The denominator is 2 times the term number.

Section ②
Practice & Application Exercises

In Exercises 1–4, look for a pattern and replace each `?` with the correct term. Describe the rule you used for each sequence.

1. △, ◩, ◪, ◩△ , `?` , `?` , `?` , `?` , ◪◪◪
See margin.

2. 7, 14, 21, 28, `?` , `?` , `?` , `?` , 63

3. 99, 90, 81, 72, `?` , `?` , `?` , `?` , 27

4. $\frac{1}{2}, \frac{1}{4}, \frac{1}{6}, \frac{1}{8}$, `?` , `?` , `?` , `?` , $\frac{1}{18}$

5. At the end of February, Ben began to save for a $240 mountain bike. At the time he had $113 in his savings account. His savings increased to $138 at the end of March and $163 at the end of April. If his savings pattern continues, when will he be able to buy the bike? **end of August**

6. A middle school class schedule forms a sequence. Each period is the same length. The first three periods begin at 7:40 A.M., 8:30 A.M., and 9:20 A.M.

   a. What rule does the class schedule follow? **Classes begin at 7:40 am and every 50 min after that.**
   b. Make a table showing the periods of the day and the times they begin. Using your rule from part (a), extend the table to find what time 7th period will begin. **See margin.**

7. **Science** Plants and animals are made up of tiny cells you can only see under a microscope. The pictures show a new starfish starting to grow from a single cell. The cell divides to form two cells. Then each of the new cells divides into two cells, and so on.

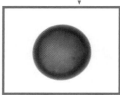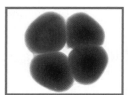

   a. The numbers of cells in the pictures form a sequence. Make a table and record the sequence. **See margin.**

   b. Describe the pattern that develops as the number of cells increases. **Each term is twice the preceding term.**

   c. How many cells would be in the 6th term of the sequence? **32 cells**

1., 6. b., and 7. a. See Additional Answers beginning on page A1.

8. Jimi and Adam both extended the sequence 2, 4, 8, ... Did they both extend the sequence correctly? Explain.

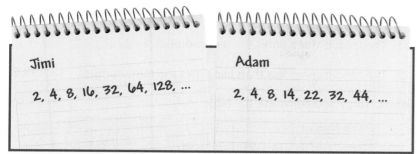

Jimi

2, 4, 8, 16, 32, 64, 128, ...

Adam

2, 4, 8, 14, 22, 32, 44, ...

9. **Challenge**

   a. The following table contains the first four pentagonal numbers. What are the 5th and 6th pentagonal numbers? 35, 51

Term number		1	2	3	4	5	6
Term	Shape sequence	●	●● ●●	(shape)	(shape)	?	?
	Number sequence	1	5	12	22	?	?

   b. The following table contains the first four hexagonal numbers. What are the 5th and 6th hexagonal numbers? 45, 66

Term number		1	2	3	4	5	6
Term	Shape sequence	●	(shape)	(shape)	(shape)	?	?
	Number sequence	1	6	15	28	?	?

   c. How is the shape for each hexagonal number related to the shape for the corresponding pentagonal number? See margin.

8. Yes; Jimi saw the sequence as 2, 2 · 2, 2 · 2 · 2, ... and extended it by multiplying each term by 2. Adam saw it as a sequence that started with 2 and with terms found by adding 2, 4, 6, 8 and so on.

EXERCISE NOTES

In **Exercise 8**, students see that two different sequences can have the same first few terms. In these instances it may be important to continue a sequence through the 4th or 5th term so that there is no confusion as to the pattern used to create it.

9. **c.** Each hexagonal number is the corresponding pentagonal number with the triangle at the top added underneath.

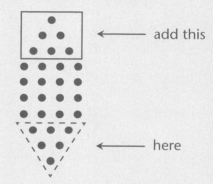

← add this

← here

Practice & Applications

Exercise Notes

Before students attempt **Exercises 10–12** you may want to discuss key words for = and operations such as +, –, and x.

15. a.

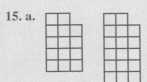

14. b. The term is 100 – term number. Or, term + term number = 100
    c. $t = 100 - n$
    d. $t = 100 - 30 = 70$

15. c. Make rectangle 10 squares tall and 3 squares wide. Remove the square from the top right corner.

Write an equation for each word sentence. Use t for the term and n for the term number.

10. The term is four more than the term number. $t = n + 4$

11. The term is three times the term number. $t = 3 \cdot n$

12. The term is three less than five times the term number. $t = 5 \cdot n - 3$

13. a. Copy and complete the table. **See margin.**

Term number	1	2	3	4	?	?	?	?
Term	12	24	36	48	?	?	?	?

   b. How are the term numbers and terms related?
      The term is 12 times the term number.
   c. Write an equation for the rule for the sequence. Use t for the term and n for the term number. $t = 12 \cdot n$

   d. Use the equation to find the 30th term in the sequence.
      $t = 12 \cdot 30 = 360$

14. Repeat parts (a)–(d) of Exercise 13 for the table below. **a. See margin.**

Term number	1	2	3	4	?	?	?	?
Term	99	98	97	96	?	?	?	?

15. Use the sequence of shapes in the table below.

Term number	1	2	3	4
Term				

   a. Draw a picture of the 5th and 6th terms of the sequence.
      See margin.
   b. Write the number sequence that matches the first six terms of the shape sequence. **See margin.**

   c. Explain how to sketch the 10th term in the shape sequence.

   d. Describe two ways to find the 10th term of the number sequence. **Start with 2 and add 3 to each term to get the next term. Multiply the term number by 3 and subtract 1.**
   e. Write an equation that can be used to find any term of the number sequence from its term number. Be sure to identify what each variable in the equation represents. $t = 3n - 1$
      t = term; n = term number
   f. Use your equation to find the 25th term of the number sequence. $t = 3 \cdot 25 - 1 = 74$

13. a., 14. a., and 15. b. See Additional Answers beginning on page A1.

16. Each shape at the right is made with toothpicks. A sequence can be formed by listing the number of toothpicks in each shape.

   a. Make a table and record the first five terms. *See margin.*

   b. Think about the relationship between the terms and the term numbers. Write an equation that can be used to find any term in the sequence.

   c. How many toothpicks would be needed to build the 12th shape? **61 toothpicks**

17. **Challenge** Look back at Exercise 7 on page 22. Explain how you could find the number of cells in the 25th term.

18. **Visual Thinking** Use the shape sequences on pages 18 and 20 to help answer the following questions.

   a. Is the sum of an even number and an odd number *even* or *odd*? How can you tell?

   b. Is the sum of two odd numbers *even* or *odd*? Explain. **even; The two extra squares can be put together so a rectangle will be formed.**

Reflecting ◀▶ on the Section

Be prepared to discuss your response to Exercise 19 in class.

19. *Start with 3 and add 4 to each term to get the next term*
   and
   the term is 1 less than 4 times the term number

   are both rules for the sequence 3, 7, 11, 15, 19, ….

   For each rule, give an example of a problem that you would use the rule to solve. Explain why you would choose that rule to solve the problem. **See margin.**

Spiral ◀▶ Review

Write each number in words. (Toolbox, p. 565)

20. 3672   21. 671,598   22. 23,856

Find each sum or difference. (Toolbox, pp. 568, 570)

23. 534 + 682 **1216**   24. 291 − 156 **135**   25. 7256 + 873 **8129**

26. 5473 − 598 **4875**   27. 32,567 − 9239 **23,328**   28. 294 + 67 + 141 **502**

Draw a picture of each shape. **29–31. See margin. Sample responses are given.**

29. triangle   30. square   31. rectangle

---

16. b. $t = 5n + 1$
   t = term
   n = term number

17. Sample: Extend the table and multiply each term by 2 to get the next term, until you have 25 terms.

Discussion

Exercise 19 checks that you understand how different kinds of rules can be used to create or extend patterns.

18. a. odd; When you put the shapes for the numbers together, there will still be one column with just one square in it.

20. three thousand six hundred seventy-two

21. six hundred seventy-one thousand five hundred ninety-eight

22. twenty-three thousand eight hundred fifty-six

EXERCISE NOTES

Encourage students to share their observations about the pattern in **Exercise 16**. Instead of only focusing on the total number of toothpicks in each term, focus on how you can build each term. Some may say just add 5 more toothpicks each time. Ask students to explain how to build the 12th or 20th term without building all the terms prior to these terms. Ask how they could use the number of sides on a hexagon to find each term. (*The first term has 1 hexagon, so there are 6 toothpicks. The second has 2 hexagons, so there should be 12 toothpicks, but one side is shared so there are 11. The third term has 3 hexagons, so 3 • 6 is 18, but two sides are shared, so 18 − 2 = 16 toothpicks. The fourth term will have 4 hexagons or 4 • 6, but there will be 3 sides shared, so 4 • 6 − 3 = 21 toothpicks.*) Building the pattern through steps will help students see that the number of hexagons is equal to the term number, but the number of shared sides is one less than the term number, alternatively producing $t = 6n − (n − 1)$ as a possible equation. Encourage students to find other possible ways to describe the pattern.

19. Samples:
   I would use the first rule if asked: "Find the next two terms in the sequence," because it would be easy to calculate. I would use the second rule for: "Find the 317th term of the sequence," because it would be faster than writing out the first 317 terms.

16. a., 29–31. See Additional Answers beginning on page A1.

25

Extra Skill Practice

1. 125, 150, 175, 200, 225
   Multiply the term number by 25. Or, start with 25 and add 25 to each term to get the next term.

2. 25, 28, 31, 34, 37
   Multiply the term number by 3 and add 10. Or, start with 13 and add 3 to each term to get the next term.

3. 96, 84, 72, 60, 48
   Multiply the term number by 12 and subtract the product from 156. Or, start with 144 and subtract 12 from each term to get the next term.

4. $\frac{1}{15}, \frac{1}{18}, \frac{1}{21}, \frac{1}{24}, \frac{1}{27}$
   The term is a fraction with one in the numerator and the denominator is 3 times the term number.

5. 81, 243, 729, 2187, 6561
   Multiply each term by 3 to get the next term.

6.–8. See Additional Answers beginning on page A1.

Section ②

Extra Skill Practice

Look for a pattern and replace each __?__ with the correct term. Describe the rule you used for each sequence. **1.–5. See margin.**

1. 25, 50, 75, 100, __?__ , __?__ , __?__ , __?__ , __?__ , 250

2. 13, 16, 19, 22, __?__ , __?__ , __?__ , __?__ , __?__ , 40

3. 144, 132, 120, 108, __?__ , __?__ , __?__ , __?__ , __?__ , 36

4. $\frac{1}{3}, \frac{1}{6}, \frac{1}{9}, \frac{1}{12}$, __?__ , __?__ , __?__ , __?__ , __?__ , $\frac{1}{30}$

5. 1, 3, 9, 27, __?__ , __?__ , __?__ , __?__ , __?__ , 19,683

For each sequence,
- copy and complete the table,
- write an equation for the rule for the sequence, and
- use your rule to find the 40th term. **6.–8. See margin.**

6.

Term number	1	2	3	4	?	?	?	?
Term	499	498	497	496	?	?	?	?

7.

Term number	10	11	12	13	?	?	?	?
Term	100	110	120	130	?	?	?	?

8.

Term number	1	2	3	4	?	?	?	?
Term	14	16	18	20	?	?	?	?

Study Skills ◀▶ Getting to Know Your Textbook

When you begin a new course, it is helpful to get to know your textbook. Then you will be able to find information you need quickly.

1. Look through pages xii–xix. Describe two features of your textbook that are illustrated in these pages. **Answers will vary.**

2. A section of student resources appears at the back of your textbook. Make a list of all these resources. **Toolbox, Tables, Glossary, Index, Selected Answers**

3. Find the Toolbox. Which page of the Toolbox contains help with rounding whole numbers? **page 567**

Section ③ A Problem Solving Approach

IN THIS SECTION

EXPLORATION 1
◆ Understand the Problem

EXPLORATION 2
◆ Make a Plan

EXPLORATION 3
◆ Carry out the Plan and Look Back

What's the Plan?

Setting the Stage

SET UP *Work as a class. You will need 9 index cards numbered 1–9.*

Knowing how to solve problems is important. There is often a pattern to the way good problem solvers approach problems. As you play a game called *Card Swappers,* you will learn a 4-step approach that can help you become a better problem solver.

▶ As a class, first practice swapping by putting these cards in order from 1 to 9. Try to use as few swaps as possible. Record your swaps.

CARD SWAPPERS

The object of the game is to put nine cards in order from least to greatest in the fewest swaps possible.

A swap is made by exchanging the positions of two cards.

The challenge is that you must predict the number of swaps needed before you see the order of the cards.

1 2 5 4 8 7 6 3 9

Think About It

1 How many swaps were needed to put the cards in order? **Answers will vary.**

2 Will the number of swaps needed for different arrangements of the cards always be the same? Explain. **Answers will vary. Sample Response: No; 321456789 takes just one swap, but 231456789 takes two swaps.**

Setting the Stage

GETTING STARTED

In Module 1 Section 3 *Warm-Up* students informally apply problem solving skills to find the missing digits in an addition and a subtraction problem.

Before starting Section 3, prepare a set of nine cards numbered 1 through 9 that have numbers large enough to be seen from anywhere in the room.

To begin the activity, ask if anyone knows what an auction is. After discussing the role of bidding in an auction, explain to the students that in this section they will be playing a game that involves bidding and that they will be trying to find a strategy for winning the game.

Explain the rules for *Card Swappers.* Then arrange the cards on the eraser tray of the chalkboard or whiteboard in the order shown. Have the class put the cards in numerical order from left to right by making swaps. Remember to record the swaps as the students order the cards. When they finish, discuss **Questions 1 and 2**.

TEACHING NOTES

Question 3 Before playing the game, remind students that a swap is an exchange, not a slide. Thus, it is permissible to swap 2 and 4 in the sequence 1, 4, 3, 2. Shuffle the cards so students can see that they are in random order. Then arrange the cards on the eraser tray of the chalkboard with numbers facing away. Before turning over the cards, ask students to predict how many swaps it will take for the cards to be in order from least to greatest (left-to-right, as they would appear on a number line). Repeat the game with the class a few times until you are sure that the students understand the rules. With the class divided into teams of four, choose one student from each team to be the spokesperson for the team. Before they become involved in their games, discuss the relative advantages and disadvantages of bidding low and bidding high.

GOAL

LEARN HOW TO...
- develop an understanding of a problem

AS YOU...
- play and think about the *Card Swappers* game

Exploration 1

Understand the Problem

SET UP *Work in a group of four. You will need 9 index cards numbered 1–9.*

▶ **You have had some experience swapping cards. Now you will play the game *Card Swappers*.**

You will need two teams. At the start of each game, the cards should be shuffled and placed facing away from both teams.

First

Each team bids the number of swaps they think it may take to put the cards in order.

Next

The cards are turned over so that the numbers can be seen.

Then

The lowest bidding team puts the cards in order from least to greatest.

If the lowest bidding team uses ***no more than*** the number of swaps they bid, then they win. Otherwise the other team wins.

▶ **One way to understand the game better is to play it several times.**

3 Try This as a Class Play *Card Swappers* two times with the whole class divided into two teams. **Check students' work.**

4 Discussion In the *Setting the Stage*, you just needed to put the cards in order from least to greatest in the fewest swaps possible. What new challenges did you face when your class played the game? **Sample Response: My team had to guess the number of swaps it would take without knowing what order the cards were in. Our bid had to be high enough to be reasonable, but low enough to give us a chance to swap the cards when they were turned around and we could see the order.**

► **Now work in your group to think more about bidding.**

5 Split up your group and play *Card Swappers* two times.
  Check students' work.

6 **a.** If you bid 1 swap each time, would you ever win? Why?
  Sample responses are given: You could win if only two cards were out of order.
  b. If you bid 9 swaps and get the bid, will you win? Why?
  I think so. In all the games we played we never had more than 8 swaps.
  c. Discussion A bid is called "safe" if you can be sure of always putting the cards in order using at most that many swaps. What could you do to determine the lowest safe bid?
  Answers will vary.

7 **Try This as a Class** Describe the problem you need to solve to be successful at the *Card Swappers* game.

► To *Understand the Problem* **is the first step in a 4-step approach to solving problems. As you played and thought about** *Card Swappers*, **you developed an understanding of the problem you will solve in Explorations 2 and 3.**

▌ **HOMEWORK EXERCISES** ▶ See Exs. 1–5 on pp. 34–35.

7. Sample Response: You need to decide the lowest safe bid to make when trying to guess how many swaps it will take to put a number of cards in order. Your bid must be low enough to win the chance to swap the cards, but high enough to be reasonable.

Step I

Understand the Problem

Exploration 2 ‣ ‣ ‣ ‣ ‣ ‣ ‣ ‣ ‣ ‣ ‣ ‣ ‣ ‣ ‣ ‣ ‣

Make a **Plan**

GOAL

LEARN HOW TO...
- make a plan to solve a problem
- use several problem solving strategies

AS YOU...
- begin to solve the *Card Swappers* problem

SET UP Work in a group of four. You will need 9 index cards numbered 1–9.

► **Once you understand the problem you have to solve, the next step is to** *Make a Plan* **for solving it. The plan for solving a problem often involves using problem-solving strategies.**

8 **Discussion** List some strategies you remember using to solve problems in mathematics. Answers will vary. Sample Responses: try a simpler problem, make a list, draw a picture, act it out.

TEACHING NOTES
The strategies that students need to have at their command by the end of Explorations 2 and 3 include *trying a simpler problem, making an organized list, making a table,* and *looking for a pattern.* Point out the advantage of organizing information as shown on the notebook page that accompanies **Questions 12–14**.

▶ To find the lowest safe bid in the *Card Swappers* game, you can begin by seeing whether the strategy *try a simpler problem* is helpful. You will explore what happens as you play with fewer cards.

Step 2

Make a Plan

Make an organized list

Try a simpler problem

9 Imagine playing *Card Swappers* with only one card. How many swaps do you have to make? Explain. **None. If there is only one card it must be in the correct position.**

10 Use only the cards numbered 1 and 2.

   a. Play *Card Swappers* several times in your group. **Observe students.**

   b. What seems to be the lowest safe bid for two cards? **1** Remember, this is the least number of swaps you can bid and still be certain of putting the cards in order.

11 Use only the cards 1, 2, and 3. Repeat Question 10. **2**

▶ Your next step is to check your findings. One way to do this is to **make an organized list**.

12 **a.** List all the possible arrangements for cards 1 and 2. **12, 21**

   b. What is the lowest safe bid for two cards? **1**

13 There are six possible arrangements for cards 1, 2, and 3. What are they? **123, 213, 312, 132, 231, 321**

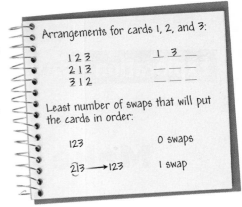

Arrangements for cards 1, 2, and 3:

123   1 3 __
213   __ __ __
312   __ __ __

Least number of swaps that will put the cards in order:

123   0 swaps

213 ⟶ 123   1 swap

14 **a.** For each arrangement found in Question 13, find the least number of swaps that will put the cards in order. Record your swaps.

   b. What is the lowest safe bid for three cards? **2**

14. a. Order	Swaps	No. of Swaps
123	none	0
132	123	1
213	123	1
231	132	2
	123	
312	132	2
	123	
321	123	1

15 **Discussion** Think about your answers to Questions 10 and 11. How does using an organized list help you check your answer? **Sample: It helps you make sure you consider all the possibilities.**

▶ So far you have found the lowest safe bid for three cards. In Exploration 3 you will complete and carry out a plan for bidding successfully in the *Card Swappers* game.

| HOMEWORK EXERCISES | See Exs. 6–9 on p. 35. |

16.

Number of cards	1	2	3	4
Least Number of swaps	0	1	2	?

Exploration 3

Carry Out the Plan and Look Back

GOAL

LEARN HOW TO...
- carry out the plan
- look back

AS YOU...
- complete the 4-step approach to solve the *Card Swappers* problem

SET UP Work in a group of four. You will need 9 index cards numbered 1–9.

To complete the solution of the *Card Swappers* problem, you could **make a table** to organize the information about the number of swaps and **look for a pattern** in the data.

16 Copy the table. Use your results from Exploration 2 to fill in the lowest safe bid for one, two, and three cards.

Number of cards in the game	1	2	3	4
Least number of swaps to safely bid	?	?	?	?

17 **a.** Use your table to predict the lowest safe bid for four cards. Write your prediction in the table. **3**

b. Play the game with four cards. Does it seem as if your prediction was correct? Explain. **Yes; I tried all possible arrangements and couldn't find one that required more than 3 swaps.**

c. Make an organized list to check your prediction. Record your swaps as you did in Question 14(a). **Check students' lists.**

COMMON ERROR
Question 17(c) In making an organized list to find a rule for the safest bid when there are four cards, students may draw an incorrect conclusion because they have not analyzed enough arrangements. Help them list the 24 arrangements systematically by keeping each position fixed until all possibilities have been exhausted. For example, they might begin by putting the 1 in the first position and writing 1234, 1243, 1324, 1342, 1423, and 1432 before putting the 2 in the first position, and so on.

Exploration 3 *continued*

DEVELOPING MATH CONCEPTS

It is important to devote a good amount of class time to **Question 21** since it addresses a major goal of the section, determining a rule for finding the lowest safe bid in the *Card Swappers* game. An even more important goal is to help students to understand two methods of reasoning that lead to the rule that the safest bid is 1 fewer than the number of cards. The first method is to find the underlying pattern revealed by the table in **Question 16** and to generalize the pattern to cover any number of cards. A second method is to generalize the results of several actual games involving various numbers of cards. Students should see that both the analytical approach (method 1) and the experimental approach (method 2) are standard intellectual tools for solving problems.

21. c. **Sample Response:** It takes at most one swap to get the 1 in the correct position. Once the 1 is in the correct position, it takes at most one swap to get the 2 in the correct position, then one swap for the 3, one for the 4, one for the 5, one for the 6, one for the 7, and one for the 8. Once the 8 is in the correct position, the 9 is too, so it takes at most 8 swaps.

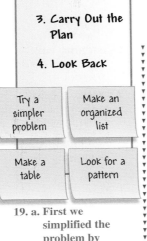

19. a. **First we simplified the problem by seeing what happened with fewer cards. Then we organized the data in a table and made a prediction based on the results. Finally we checked the prediction by making an organized list.**

b. **Look for a pattern in the data in the table from Question 16 to see if we can write a rule to predict the lowest safe bid for *n* cards.**

 32 **Module 1** Patterns and Problem Solving

18 Suppose you have more than four cards. Would you want to use an organized list to examine what happens? Explain. No; The list would be too long and complicated.

19 **Try This as a Class** Think about your work on the *Card Swappers* problem so far.

   a. Describe the plan you have developed.

   b. Explain what you can do now to find the lowest safe bid for nine cards.

Now you are ready for the third and fourth steps of the 4-Step Approach, which are to *Carry Out the Plan* and *Look Back*. You will use these steps to find the lowest safe bid. Then you will use the result to solve the full problem of how to bid successfully in the *Card Swappers* game.

20 Use your strategies from Question 19 to carry out the plan. What is the lowest safe bid for nine cards? 8

21 **Discussion** Look back at your solution to the problem of finding the lowest safe bid in *Card Swappers*. Sample responses are given.

   a. Does your solution seem reasonable? Explain. Yes; I compared my work with the work of the other students.

   b. Do you see any errors in your work? If you do, correct them. Answers will vary.

   c. Try to think of another way to find the lowest safe bid for nine cards. If you can, use this method to check your solution to Question 20. See margin.

   d. Suppose there are 12 cards in the deck. What is the lowest safe bid? 11

   e. What is a rule you can use to find the lowest safe bid? The lowest safe bid is one less than the number of cards.

22 When playing *Card Swappers* with 9 cards, what would you bid? Why? Answers will vary.

The 4-step problem-solving approach will help you tackle other problems. Some problems have many ways to get to a single correct answer. Other problems may have several correct answers.

4-Step Problem-Solving Approach

1. Understand the Problem

2. Make a Plan

3. Carry Out the Plan

4. Look Back

HOMEWORK EXERCISES ▶ See Exs. 10–15 on pp. 35–36.

Section 3 Key Concepts

4-Step Approach to Solving Problems

1. Understand the Problem
- Read the problem carefully, probably several times.
- Restate the problem in your own words.
- Identify the important information in the problem.

2. Make a Plan
- You may try several problem-solving strategies.

> If information is missing, you may need to gather it.

Look for a pattern

Make an organized list

Try a simpler problem

Make a table

Act it out

Use logical reasoning

Work Backward

Guess and check

Make a picture or a diagram

3. Carry Out the Plan
- Solve the problem using the strategies selected.
- You may need to try other strategies.

4. Look Back
- Check that you answered the question being asked.
- Check that your solution seems reasonable.
- Check that your work is accurate.
- Try to find another method. Compare the results.
- Is the problem similar to other problems you have solved?
- Can you generalize your solution or extend it to other situations?

23 **Key Concepts Question** Suppose you play the *Card Swappers* game with 26 cards each showing a letter of the alphabet from A to Z. You must put the cards in alphabetical order. What would be the lowest safe bid? **25**

Key Concepts

CLOSURE QUESTION
State the 4-step approach to problem solving. Briefly explain each step.

Sample Response: (1) understand the problem, (2) make a plan, (3) carry out the plan, and (4) look back; To understand the problem, read the problem carefully and find any important information. To make a plan, select a problem-solving strategy or strategies that will help you solve the problem. To carry out the plan, solve the problem using the selected strategies along with others you may need. To look back, check that your solution is reasonable and complete and that the work is accurate.

ABSENT STUDENTS
For students who were absent for all or part of this section, the blackline Study Guide for Section 3 may be used to present the ideas, concepts, and skills of Section 3.

Practice & Applications

SUGGESTED ASSIGNMENTS

Core Course
Day 1: Exs. 1–5, 16–21
Day 2: Exs. 6–9, 22–34
Day 3: Exs. 10–13, 15

Extended Course
Day 1: Exs. 1–5, 16–21
Day 2: Exs. 6–9, 22–34
Day 3: Exs. 10–15

Note: Extended Course assignments can be used to differentiate within the regular classroom. In classrooms where students are grouped homogeneously, the material might be covered in fewer days. In this case assignments may be combined.

ADDITIONAL PRACTICE

See the *Teacher's Resource Book* for additional practice and application exercises for this section.

EXERCISE NOTES

Exercises 1–4 are assigned following Exploration 1 where students learn to *Understand the Problem.* Reinforce with students that at this time they are only to work on this step of the 4-step process, so they are NOT to solve the problems.

1–3. See Additional Answers beginning on page A1.

YOU WILL NEED

For Ex. 15:
◆ graph paper (optional)

FOR ▶ HELP

with *computing with money,* see
TOOLBOX,
pp. 568, 571

Canoes carry visitors among the islands at the Polynesian Cultural Center. Polynesians crossed the Pacific in giant catamarans to settle Hawaii and other islands centuries before Columbus ever set sail.
▼

Section ③ Practice & Application Exercises

For Exercises 1–4 do parts (a)–(c). **Do not** solve the problems now.
1–3. Sample responses are given. See margin.

    a. Describe the problem you need to solve.

    b. State the important information in the problem.

    c. Identify any information missing from the problem.

1. An on-line computer service offers two monthly service contracts. Suppose you spend 8 to 10 hours a month on line. Which contract should you choose?

Standard Contract	Frequent User Contract
Monthly fee $4.95	Monthly fee..............$19.95
Hours included.................3	Hours included...............20
Additional hours........$2.50	Additional hours........$2.00

* Receive a 10% discount when you use over 50 hours of on-line time.

For Exercises 2–4, use the schedule shown below. This schedule shows some of the daily events at the Polynesian Cultural Center in Hawaii where you can learn about Polynesian culture and traditions. Remember, just do parts (a)–(c) shown at the top of the page.

AFTERNOON EVENTS

Double Hulled Canoe Tour (15 min) 12:30–2:00 and 3:00–7:30
    Tours leave every 15 min with last tour at 7:15.

"Ancient Legends of Polynesia" Canoe Pageant (90 min) 2:30

"The Polynesian Odyssey" (45 min) 3:00 4:00 6:00

"The Living Sea" (45 min) 2:00 5:00 7:00

Ali'i Luaua Buffet Dinner 5:15-7:00

2. Can you attend the activities and shows listed during one visit?

3. How many times a day is the Canoe Tour given if a tour leaves at 2 P.M.?

4. Suppose you plan to arrive at the Polynesian Center at 2:00 P.M. You want at least 45 minutes for the buffet dinner. It takes 15 minutes to get to each event. Can you attend all the events listed on page 34? Explain.

5. Tell whether each problem contains *too much* or *not enough* information. Identify any extra or missing information.

 a. Jon had $25.00. He bought a CD for $12.95 and two pens for $1.75 each. How much money did he spend?
 too much information; Jon had $25.00

 b. The Coles drove from Ashton to Collins with one stop in Bates. The drive from Ashton to Bates took 2.5 hr, and the entire trip lasted 5 hr. How long did it take the Coles to drive from Bates to Collins? not enough information; How long was the stop at Bates?

6. At work Derek must wear a dress shirt, long pants, and a tie. He has three dress shirts (white, blue, and green), two pairs of long pants (tan and black), and two ties (plain and striped). Make an organized list to find how many different outfits he has for work. There are 12 different outfits.

7. Solve the problem in Exercise 1.

For Exercises 8 and 9, choose one or more strategies from the list on page 33. Explain how you could use those strategies to solve each problem. You do not need to actually solve it.

8. Marita has to be at school by 8 A.M. It takes her 40 minutes to get up and get dressed in the morning. She needs at least 20 minutes to eat breakfast. Then she has a 15 minute walk to school. What time does Marita need to get up?

9. **Geometry Connection** How many 1-inch equilateral triangles are needed to make a row of triangles that has a perimeter of 20 inches? See margin.

perimeter = 5 in.

10. Use Exercise 9 to answer parts (a)–(c).

 a. Solve the problem. 18 triangles

 b. Describe the plan you used. (see Ex 9)

 c. Look back: See margin.

 • Did you answer the question asked in the problem?
 • Does your solution seem reasonable? Explain.
 • How can you check your work? Explain.
 • Is the problem similar to other problems you have solved? If so, how is it similar?
 • Can you generalize your solution to a chain of triangles with any perimeter?

Remember, **perimeter** is the distance around a figure.

The Canoe Pageant uses "dance language" and narration to tell the legends of ancient Polynesia.

4. a. Are you able to attend all five events offered at the Cultural Center in a given time period?

 b. arrival time, time between events, amount of time needed for dinner

 c. schedule of events (which can be found in Ex 2)

7. If you are online 8 hr, the standard contract is cheaper. For 9 hr the costs are the same. For 10 hr the frequent user contract is cheaper.

8. Work backward; Start at 8:00 A.M. and work backward allowing time for each activity.

Exercises 8 and 9 Students are to list only the strategies they might use. They are NOT to solve the problems until **Exercise 10** when they will be instructed to solve **Exercise 9** and to look back at their work.

9. Try a simpler problem, make a table, look for a pattern; Draw chains with 1, 2, 3, and 4 triangles. Find the perimeters. Enter the values in a table. Make a prediction.

10. c. ◆ Yes

 ◆ For all the examples in my table, the perimeter was 2 more than the number of triangles. So I think my answer is reasonable.

 ◆ Draw 18 triangles and check the perimeter

 ◆ No

 ◆ Yes—the perimeter is always two more than the number of triangles.

Practice & Applications

EXERCISE NOTES

Exercise 14 Provide hints as required. For example, mention to students that to obtain exactly 5 cups, they will find it necessary to pass water back and forth between the pots and that some of the water will have to be discarded along the way.

Exercise 15 Some students may be more successful if they work with actual chips and one game board rather than making several sketches on graph paper.

15. c.

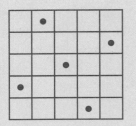

---

12. No; there wouldn't be enough time to attend all the events

13. No later than 6:45 AM

Visual THINKING

Exercise 15 checks that you can use the 4-step approach to solve a problem.

14. Fill the small pot and empty it into the large pot. Fill the small pot again and empty 3 cups into the large pot. There will be 1 cup of water in the small pot. Empty the large pot and pour the 1 cup of water from the small pot into the large pot. Fill the small pot and empty it into the large pot. The large pot now contains 5 cups of water.

15. Samples are given.
   a.

   ![grid]

   b. I used guess and check.

Solve each of these problems from pages 34–35.

11. Exercise 3 25 times 12. Exercise 4   13. Exercise 8

14. **Challenge** Suppose you have two pots. One pot holds 7 cups and the other holds 4 cups. How can you measure exactly 5 cups of water?

Reflecting ◀▶ on the Section

15. a. Solve the following problem. (*Hint*: graph paper can make it easier to sketch the game board.)

   How can five chips be placed on the game board so that each chip does not lie in the same row, column or any diagonal as any other chip?

   b. Describe your plan.

   c. Find at least one other solution. See margin.

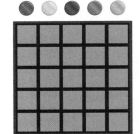

Spiral ◀▶ Review

Round each number to the given place. (Toolbox, p. 567)

16. 5632 (nearest hundred)
   5,600

17. $44.99 (nearest ten dollars)
   $40

18. $6.72 (nearest dollar)
   $7

19. 34,819 (nearest thousand)
   35,000

20. 896 (nearest ten)
   900

21. 45,031 (nearest hundred)
   45,000

Mental Math Multiply. (Toolbox, p. 574)

22. $100 \cdot 100$
   10,000

23. $10,000 \cdot 10$
   100,000

24. $1000 \cdot 6$
   6,000

25. $56 \cdot 10$
   560

26. $300 \cdot 70$
   21,000

27. $726 \cdot 100$
   72,600

28. $80 \cdot 400$
   32,000

29. $2000 \cdot 500$
   1,000,000

30. $900 \cdot 70,000$
   63,000,000

Mental Math Find the value of each expression. (Module 1, p. 10)

31. $15 - 9 \div 3$ 12

32. $32(37 + 13)$ 1600

33. $10 \cdot 6 + 5 \cdot 2$ 70

34. Make a table for the sequence 4, 8, 12, 16, …. Extend it to include the next two terms. Then write a rule for the sequence. (Module 1, p. 21)

Term Number	1	2	3	4	5	6
Term	4	8	12	16	20	24

$t = 4n$ where n is the term number and t is the term

36

Section 3
Extra Skill Practice

Tell whether each problem contains *too much* or *not enough* information. Identify any extra or missing information.

1. Pens cost $1.25, markers $1.50, and pencils $0.75. Bridgit bought three pencils. If there is no tax, how much did she spend?
   too much; the cost of markers and pens

2. Sue earns $25 each week for baby-sitting. In how many weeks will Sue have saved $175? *not enough; whether or not Sue spent any money*

3. The cinema charges a reduced rate for children under 12. If Jose has $14, how many movies can he see this month? *not enough; Jose's age, ticket price*

Solve each problem and describe any strategies you used.

4. Kenesha sold three tickets to the school dance the first day. On each of the next ten days she sold two more tickets than the day before. How many tickets did she sell in all? *143 tickets; make a table and extend pattern*

5. A library is located 5 mi east of a school. A park is 3 mi east of the school and halfway between the library and a deli. How far is it from the deli to the library? *4 mi; make a picture or diagram*

6. Basketball shots are worth one, two, or three points. In how many different ways can a player score 9 points? *12 ways; make a table or organized list.*

7. Giang has $2.50 left after a shopping trip. She spent $58.50 on purchases, $12.50 on lunch, and $10.00 on travel. How much money did she have before her trip? *$83.50; work backward*

8. You saw your friend sorting beads. You asked how many of each color there were and your friend replied this way. "There are 67 beads altogether. There are twice as many white beads as red beads and twice as many green beads as white beads. The number of blue beads is only one more than the number of green beads." How many beads of each color were there?
   25 blue, 24 green, 12 white, 6 red; guess and check

Standardized Testing ▸ Performance Task

Answers will vary. Check students' work.

Choose a problem solving strategy you have learned and write a word problem that can be solved using that strategy.

Then present a solution to your problem. Include an explanation of how the strategy you chose can be used to find the solution.

Extra Skill Practice

TEACHER NOTES
For each Exploration, the corresponding Extra Skill Practice Exercises are noted.

Exploration 1: 1–3
Exploration 3: 4–8

EXTRA HELP
Teacher's Resource Book
- Practice and Applications
- Study Guide

Technology Resources
- @Home Tutor
- Test Generator

ASSESSMENT
- Section 3 Quick Quiz
- Mid-Module Quiz
- Test Generator

Extended Exploration

E² NOTES

When solving the E², students should put into practice the 4-step problem solving approach just covered in this section. Note that the Assessment Scales will not be introduced until Module 2, so it probably is not appropriate to use them to assess this E². Instead you may want to have students identify each step of the 4-step process in an outline of their work.

Labsheet: Each student needs a copy of the Extended Exploration Labsheet, which is found in the *Teacher's Resource Book.*

Using an E²: Suggestions for managing and evaluating an Extended Exploration are available in the *Teacher's Resource Book* for Modules 1 and 2. See also pages T44–T45 in the *Teacher's Edition.*

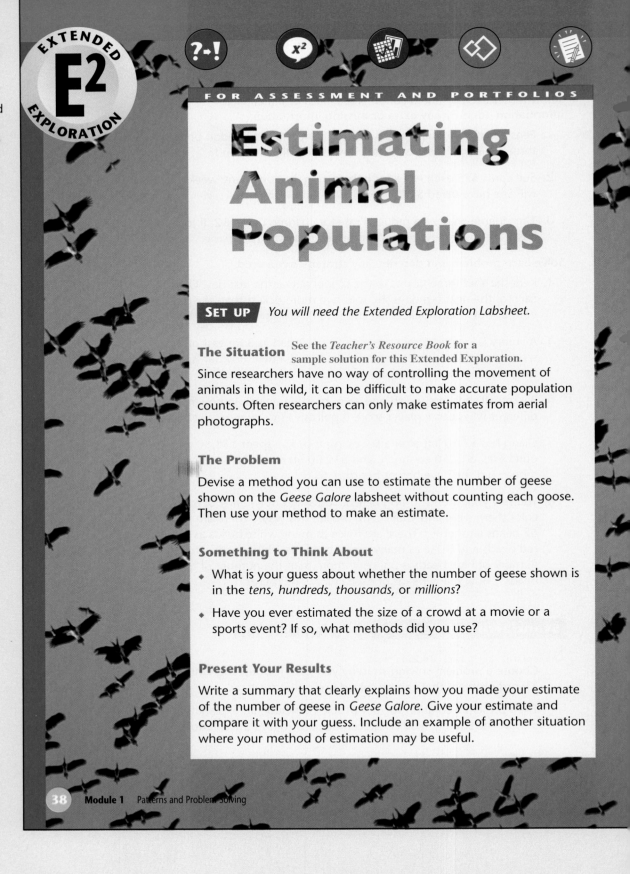

FOR ASSESSMENT AND PORTFOLIOS

Estimating Animal Populations

SET UP *You will need the Extended Exploration Labsheet.*

The Situation See the *Teacher's Resource Book* for a sample solution for this Extended Exploration.

Since researchers have no way of controlling the movement of animals in the wild, it can be difficult to make accurate population counts. Often researchers can only make estimates from aerial photographs.

The Problem

Devise a method you can use to estimate the number of geese shown on the *Geese Galore* labsheet without counting each goose. Then use your method to make an estimate.

Something to Think About

- What is your guess about whether the number of geese shown is in the *tens, hundreds, thousands,* or *millions*?

- Have you ever estimated the size of a crowd at a movie or a sports event? If so, what methods did you use?

Present Your Results

Write a summary that clearly explains how you made your estimate of the number of geese in *Geese Galore*. Give your estimate and compare it with your guess. Include an example of another situation where your method of estimation may be useful.

Section ④ Fractions and Mixed Numbers

IN THIS SECTION

EXPLORATION 1
♦ Fractional Parts

EXPLORATION 2
♦ Mixed Numbers

From Coins to Kites

Setting the Stage ▸▸▸▸▸▸▸▸▸▸▸▸▸▸▸▸▸▸▸▸▸▸▸▸▸▸▸▸▸▸▸▸▸▸

In his short story *The Gift of the Magi,* O. Henry describes the sacrifices a young couple, Della and Jim, make to buy each other a present. The story begins:

> One dollar and eighty-seven cents. That was all. And sixty cents of it was in pennies. ... Three times Della counted it. One dollar and eighty-seven cents.

Think About It

1 a. How much of Della's money did not include pennies? **$1.27**

  b. In the United States today, is it possible to have $1.27 and not have any pennies? Explain. **No, because you have at least 2 pennies in order to make 7 cents.**

2 The *Gift of the Magi* is set in the 1800s. During the nineteenth century, in addition to the familiar quarter, dime, nickel, and penny, the United States also minted twenty-cent, three-cent, two-cent, and half-cent coins. How many different ways could Della have 7¢ if none of the coins were pennies?

▸ **In this section, you will explore how numbers can be used to describe objects and to create patterns and designs.**

2. 10 ways

5¢	3¢	2¢	$\frac{1}{2}$¢
1		1	
1			4
	2		2
	1	2	
	1	1	4
	1		8
		3	2
		2	6
		1	10
			14

Setting the Stage

GETTING STARTED
Module 1 Section 4 *Warm-Up* uses visual diagrams to assess whether students understand the concept of fractional part. This section will use similar shapes to represent fractions and mixed numbers.

Have the students read the *Setting the Stage*. Then discuss **Question 1**. Students should recognize that it is impossible to have $1.27 and not have any pennies unless there are coins with values other than 25¢, 10¢, 5¢, and 1¢. After the discussion, have the students complete **Question 2**.

LITERATURE CONNECTION
Check with the school librarian or English teacher for a copy of the complete story from which the *Setting the Stage* excerpt is taken. Some students may be interested in reading the short story. You may also want to coordinate the reading of the short story in English class prior to the start of Section 4.

Section 4   Fractions and Mixed Numbers   **39**

Exploration 1

CLASSROOM MANAGEMENT

Although students can work on it individually, Exploration 1 is best done in groups of two.

TEACHING NOTES

When working with fractions, some students may not understand that wholes come in various sizes so that one-half of one whole may be different from one-half of another whole. One way to help students visualize this principle is to show them that one-half of a regular-sized candy bar is not the same as one-half of a miniature candy bar, even though they are both halves.

The example below can be used to help students identify fractional parts before beginning **Labsheet 4A**.

CLASSROOM EXAMPLE

Write a fraction for the shaded part of the figure below.

Answer: 9 of the 16 equal-sized parts are shaded.

The fraction is $\frac{9}{16}$.

GOAL

LEARN HOW TO...
- write a fraction and a mixed number

AS YOU...
- use pattern blocks to explore the relationship between part of a design and the whole design

KEY TERMS
- fraction
- numerator
- denominator
- mixed number

3. b. Two of the parts have a given characteristic.

Exploration 1

Fractional PARTS

SET UP   *You will need: • Labsheets 4A and 4B • pattern blocks*

Our coins have changed over time. An enlargement of the back of the half-cent coins minted from 1800 to 1808 is shown. The design uses the fraction $\frac{1}{200}$ to show the value of the coin.

▶ **Fractions** are numbers that can be used to compare part of an object or part of a set with the whole.

EXAMPLE

The square region is the **whole**.

3 of the 4 equal-sized parts are shaded.

The **numerator** tells how many parts to consider.

$\frac{3}{4}$

The **denominator** tells how many equal-sized parts the whole is divided into.

---

3 Suppose the fraction $\frac{2}{5}$ compares part of a shape with the whole shape.

  a. What does the 5 mean?   **b.** What does the 2 mean?
      The whole consists of 5 equal parts.
  c. What is the numerator   **d.** What is the denominator
      of the fraction? 2   of the fraction? 5

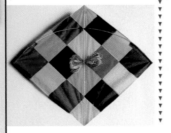

4 **Discussion** How can fractions help you describe the design of the kite shown at the left? You can use fractions to describe the parts of the kite that are a given color.

5 **Use Labsheet 4A.** Use pattern blocks to complete the table *Relating the Part to the Whole.* Then follow the directions to complete the *Fractions of Shapes* problems.

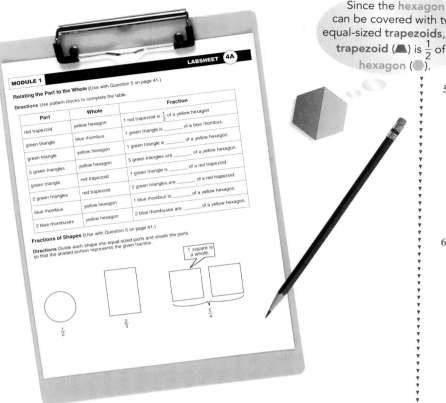

Since the hexagon can be covered with two equal-sized **trapezoids**, one **trapezoid** (▲) is $\frac{1}{2}$ of a hexagon (●).

5. $\frac{1}{2}, \frac{1}{6}, \frac{5}{6}, \frac{1}{3}, \frac{2}{3}, \frac{1}{3}, \frac{2}{3}$

Sketches may vary.

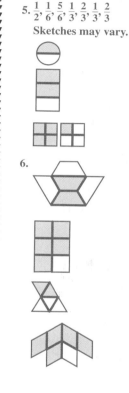

6.

6 **Use Labsheet 4B.** Follow the directions to *Cover Each Shape* with pattern blocks and show the given fraction.

7 ✔ **CHECKPOINT** The drawing at the right shows the design of a kite. What fraction of the design is white? $\frac{6}{18}$

✔ **QUESTION 7**

...checks that you can write a fraction relating a part to a whole.

8 **Discussion** Fractions can also be used to show the value of a coin.

a. How many half cents does it take to make a dollar? 200

b. What fraction of a dollar is one cent? $\frac{1}{100}$

c. A half cent is what fraction of a dollar? How is this shown on the half cent coin on page 40? $\frac{1}{200}$; by the fraction $\frac{1}{200}$ in the circle

Section 4 Fractions and Mixed Numbers **41**

USING MANIPULATIVES

Give students a few minutes for free exploration with the pattern blocks before asking them to complete **Labsheet 4A.** Allowing free time to create designs on their own often avoids problems with students being off task when they begin using the blocks for a structured activity.

TEACHING NOTES

Before students begin **Question 5,** draw attention to the bubble that explains why the trapezoid block is $\frac{1}{2}$ of the hexagon block.

In *Fractions of Shapes* on **Labsheet 4A,** students may be confused when asked to find "$\frac{5}{4}$ of the square" since all fractions up to this point have been less than one. Make sure they realize that they should consider the two squares to be a single shape.

CLASSROOM MANAGEMENT

Students should complete **Question 5** by the end of the period. If they do not, assign it as part of their homework.

TEACHING NOTES

After the students have completed **Question 8,** introduce mixed numbers by discussing their solutions to finding "$\frac{5}{4}$ of the square" in *Fractions of Shapes* on Labsheet 4A. You may want to use the **Example** on page 42 as a guide for discussion.

Exploration 1 *continued*

TEACHING NOTES

You may want to go through another Classroom Example before completing **Question 9**.

CLASSROOM EXAMPLE

  represents the whole.

Write   as a fraction and as a mixed number.

Answer:

5 trapezoids = $2\frac{1}{2}$ hexagons

$\frac{5}{2} = 1 + 1 + \frac{1}{2} = 2\frac{1}{2}$

TEACHING NOTES

In **Question 10**, students are asked to write numbers as fractions where the numerator is greater than the denominator or as mixed numbers. They should understand that whenever the numerator of a fraction is greater than the denominator, the fraction is greater than one and can be written as a mixed number. Likewise, when the numerator is less than the denominator, the fraction is less than one, and when the numerator and denominator are equal, the fraction represents one whole.

▶ **More than a Whole** You have mostly worked with fractions that are less than a whole. When the part is more than a whole, you can describe the relationship in two ways.

EXAMPLE

AS A FRACTION

1 trapezoid is $\frac{1}{2}$ of a hexagon.

3 trapezoids = $\frac{3}{2}$ hexagons

AS A MIXED NUMBER

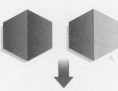

1 whole hexagon and $\frac{1}{2}$ of another hexagon

3 trapezoids = $1\frac{1}{2}$ hexagons

$\frac{3}{2} = 1 + \frac{1}{2} = 1\frac{1}{2}$

▶ A **mixed number** is the sum of a whole number and a nonzero fraction less than one.

9 **Try This as a Class** Four **triangles** (▲) equal how many **trapezoids** (◢)? Write your answer two ways. $\frac{4}{3}$ trapezoids; $1\frac{1}{3}$ trapezoids.

10 ✔ **CHECKPOINT** A rhombus (◢) represents the whole. Use the pattern block pictures to write each part to whole relationship.

a. Write the value of the triangles as a fraction.

5 triangles (▲) = __?__ rhombuses (◢) $\frac{5}{2}$

b. Write the value of the triangles as a mixed number.

5 triangles (▲) = __?__ rhombuses (◢) $2\frac{1}{2}$

✔ **QUESTION 10**

...checks that you can write a fraction that is greater than one whole as a fraction and as a mixed number.

HOMEWORK EXERCISES ▶ See Exs. 1–19 on pp. 47–50.

Mixed Numbers

SET UP *Work in a group. You will need: • pattern blocks • a number cube*

11 Play the game *Flex Your Hex* with your group. **Monitor students.**

Flex Your Hex

◆ Place about 30 triangles and about 15 hexagons in a pile.

◆ On your turn, roll the number cube and take the number of triangles shown on the number cube from the pile. Trade for a hexagon if you have enough triangles.

◆ The winner is the first player to collect five hexagons.

EXAMPLE

First Turn

You roll:

You take 5 triangles.

You cannot trade.

Next Turn

You roll:

You add

to

Trade

You now have

12 **Discussion**

a. What part of a hexagon is one triangle? $\frac{1}{6}$

b. How does this fraction equation represent a roll of 2 on your first turn and a roll of 3 on your next turn?

$$\frac{2}{6} + \frac{3}{6} = \frac{5}{6}$$

c. What fraction equation can you use to represent a first roll of 6 and a second roll of 5? $\frac{6}{6} + \frac{5}{6} = \frac{11}{6}$

d. Will the denominator always be 6 when you add up your rolls? Explain. **Yes; The denominator of the fraction for each roll is 6, so the denominator of any sum is 6.**

12. b. When you roll a 2, you get 2 triangles or $\frac{2}{6}$ of a hexagon. When you roll a 3, you get 3 triangles or $\frac{3}{6}$ of a hexagon. After the second roll, you have 5 triangles or $\frac{5}{6}$ of a hexagon, so $\frac{2}{6} + \frac{3}{6} = \frac{5}{6}$.

Exploration 2

CLASSROOM MANAGEMENT
Exploration 2 is best completed by students working in groups of three to five. Each group will need about 30 triangle and 15 hexagon pattern blocks.

Have students play two rounds of *Flex Your Hex*. If students trade incorrectly, they should retake their turn.

Teaching Notes

The Classroom Example below provides an additional illustration of how to use regrouping with pattern blocks to convert between a fraction and a mixed number.

Classroom Examples

Write $\frac{15}{6}$ as a mixed number.

Answer:
How many groups of 6 in 15?

$$\frac{15}{6} = 15 \div 6$$

Trade:

for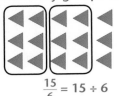

$6)\overline{15}$ $\;^{2\ R3}$ or $2\frac{3}{6}$

Write $4\frac{2}{3}$ as a mixed number.

Answer: $4\frac{2}{3} = 4 + \frac{2}{3}$

$$4\frac{2}{3} = \frac{12}{3} + \frac{2}{3}$$

$$4\frac{2}{3} = \frac{14}{3}$$

---

13 **Try This as a Class** Suppose your first two rolls added up to $\frac{8}{6}$.

  a. How many triangles do you have? **8 triangles**

  b. After trading, how many hexagons and triangles will you have? **1 hexagon, 2 triangles**

  c. How can you use division to find the number of triangles in part (b)? **8 ÷ 6 = 1 R2**

  d. What fractional part of a hexagon do the remaining triangles in part (b) make? Use this fraction to write the number of hexagons as a mixed number. $\frac{2}{6}$; $1\frac{2}{6}$ **hexagons**

▸ **Fractions to Mixed Numbers** You can write fractions greater than 1 as mixed numbers by using division. Pattern block trades can show this process.

EXAMPLE

Write the fraction $\frac{10}{6}$ as a mixed number.

$\frac{4}{6}$ of a hexagon

SAMPLE RESPONSE

How many groups of 6 in 10?

   Trade

$$\frac{10}{6} = 10 \div 6$$ $6)\overline{10}$ $\;^{1\ R4}$ $1\frac{4}{6}$

14 Three blue rhombuses (▰) make one yellow hexagon (⬡).

  a. Use seven blue rhombuses to make $\frac{7}{3}$ yellow hexagons.
  Check students' work.

  b. Use division to write $\frac{7}{3}$ as a mixed number.
  Divide 7 by 3: 7 ÷ 3 = 2 R1 = $2\frac{1}{3}$

✔ **QUESTION 15**

...checks that you can write a fraction as a mixed number.

15 ✔ **CHECKPOINT** Write each fraction as a mixed number if possible. If it is not possible, explain why not.

  a. $\frac{27}{8}$ $3\frac{3}{8}$ **b.** $\frac{3}{4}$ **c.** $\frac{32}{5}$ $6\frac{2}{5}$ **d.** $\frac{3}{3}$

15. **b.** Not possible; $\frac{3}{4}$ is less than 1.
  d. Not possible; $\frac{3}{3} = 1$

▸ You can also write mixed numbers as answers to whole number divisions. The Example above shows that $10 \div 6 = 1\frac{4}{6}$.

16 **Try This as a Class** Complete parts (a)–(d) to write the quotient $17 \div 3$ as a mixed number.

  a. Draw a picture to model $17 \div 3$. See margin.

  b. When you divide 17 by 3, what is the whole number part of the quotient? 5

  c. What is the denominator of the fractional part of the quotient? Why? 3; When you divide 17 by 3, the divisor is 3.

  d. What is the numerator of the fraction? 2

  e. Think about the problem:

> *A bowling league has 3-member teams.*
> *How many teams can be formed from 17 people?*

  Do you think the mixed number in part (a) is an appropriate answer? If not, how would you answer the question? Explain.

16. e. No; The number of teams must be a whole number. I would say there will be five teams, with two people not assigned to a team.

▶ **Mixed Numbers to Fractions** You have learned how to write fractions greater than 1 as mixed numbers. You can also write mixed numbers as fractions.

EXAMPLE

Write the mixed number $2\frac{1}{3}$ as a fraction.

SAMPLE RESPONSE

$$2\frac{1}{3} \quad = \quad 2 + \frac{1}{3} \quad = \quad \frac{6}{3} + \frac{1}{3} = \frac{7}{3}$$

---

17 **Discussion** Look at the Example.

  a. Why was 2 written as $\frac{6}{3}$? To account for the whole-number part of the mixed number

  b. Explain how to write $4\frac{2}{3}$ as a fraction. $4\frac{2}{3} = 4 + \frac{2}{3} = \frac{12}{3} + \frac{2}{3} = \frac{14}{3}$

18 ✔ **CHECKPOINT** Write each mixed number as a fraction.

  a. $1\frac{3}{4}$ $\frac{7}{4}$ **b.** $2\frac{1}{2}$ $\frac{5}{2}$ **c.** $10\frac{2}{3}$ $\frac{32}{3}$ **d.** $3\frac{5}{6}$ $\frac{23}{6}$

✔ **QUESTION 18**

...checks that you can write a mixed number as a fraction.

HOMEWORK EXERCISES ▶ See Exs. 20–43 on pp. 50–51.

TEACHING NOTES
Students may need to review the meaning of division in order to model $17 \div 3$ in **Question 16(a)**. The interpretation needed for **part (a)** is that $m \div n$ means to separate m objects into groups with n objects in each group. The quotient is the number of groups that can be formed.

16. a. Sample Response:

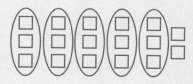

$$17 \div 3 = 5\frac{2}{3}$$

Key Concepts

ABSENT STUDENTS

For students who were absent for all or part of this section, the blackline Study Guide for Section 4 may be used to present the ideas, concepts, and skills of Section 4.

Key Terms

Key Concepts

fraction

mixed number

numerator

denominator

Fractions (pp. 40–42)

A fraction is a number that tells how a part of an object or set compares to the whole.

When a fraction is greater than a whole it can be written as a fraction or as a mixed number. A mixed number is the sum of a whole number and a nonzero fraction less than one.

Example

As a fraction	As a mixed number
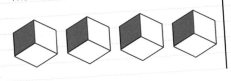	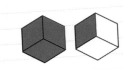
Divide each whole into **thirds**. Then take 4 of the **thirds**.	1 whole and $\frac{1}{3}$ of another whole.

19 Key Concepts Question For each of the following, tell whether the statement is *true* or *false*. If a statement is false, explain why.

a.

$\frac{1}{2}$ of the triangle is shaded. **False; the triangle is not divided into two equal parts.**

b.

$\frac{2}{3}$ of the square is shaded. **True**

c.

$\frac{4}{6}$ of the rectangle is shaded. **True**

Section 4

Key Concepts

Mixed Numbers (pp. 43–45)

- A mixed number can be written as a fraction by rewriting the whole number as a fraction and then combining it with the fractional part.

Example $2\frac{3}{7} = 2 + \frac{3}{7} = \frac{14}{7} + \frac{3}{7} = \frac{17}{7}$

- Fractions greater than 1 can be changed to mixed numbers by dividing.

Example Write $\frac{25}{4}$ as a mixed number.

$$\frac{25}{4} = \frac{24}{4} + \frac{1}{4} = 6 + \frac{1}{4} = 6\frac{1}{4}$$

or $\quad \frac{25}{4} = 25 \div 4 = 6 \text{ R1} = 6\frac{1}{4}$

Quotients as Mixed Numbers (p. 45)

The remainder in a division problem can be written over the divisor to form a fraction.

Example $17 \div 5 = 3 \text{ R2} = 3\frac{2}{5}$

Key Concepts Questions

20 **a.** Write $\frac{37}{12}$ as a mixed number. $3\frac{1}{12}$

b. Write your mixed number as a fraction to check your work.

21 Describe a division situation where a mixed number is an appropriate answer and one where it is not appropriate.

20. b. $3\frac{1}{12} = 3 + \frac{1}{12} =$
$\frac{36}{12} + \frac{1}{12} = \frac{37}{12}$

21. Samples are given. **Appropriate:** dividing a board that is 15 in. long into two pieces of the same length. **Inappropriate:** forming three teams with the same number of members from a group of 19 people.

Section 4

Practice & Application Exercises

Write a fraction for the shaded part of each figure.

1. $\frac{1}{2}$

2. $\frac{2}{3}$

3. 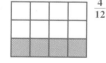 $\frac{4}{12}$

YOU WILL NEED

For Exs. 13-14:
- dot paper

CLOSURE QUESTION

Explain how you can tell if a fraction can be written as a mixed number, and if it can, how to write it as a mixed number.

Sample Response: If the numerator is greater than the denominator, a fraction can be written as a mixed number. To write the mixed number, divide the numerator by the denominator. The quotient is the whole number part of the mixed number. The remainder is the numerator of the fractional part, and the divisor is the denominator.

Practice & Applications

SUGGESTED ASSIGNMENTS

Core Course

Day 1: Exs. 1–6, 44–46
Day 2: Exs. 7–11, 47–51
Day 3: Exs. 13–18
Day 4: Exs. 20–38, 40, 42–43

Extended Course

Day 1: Exs. 1–6, 44–46
Day 2: Exs. 7–12, 47–51
Day 3: Exs. 13–19
Day 4: Exs. 20–27, 32–43

Note: Extended Course assignments can be used to differentiate within the regular classroom. In classrooms where students are grouped homogeneously, the material might be covered in fewer days. In this case assignments may be combined.

Practice & Applications

ADDITIONAL PRACTICE

See the *Teacher's Resource Book* for additional practice and application exercises for this section.

DIFFERENTIATED INSTRUCTION

If available, it may help some students to use fraction circles. These are sold commercially in a set of one whole, two halves, three thirds, four fourths, six sixths, and eight eighths and sometimes ten tenths and twelve twelfths. They can also be made from card stock.

For Exercises 4 and 5, use these sketches of two figures that were built with pattern blocks. Some blocks in each are shaded.

Figure A   Figure B

4. What fraction of Figure A is shaded? $\frac{1}{5}$

5. a. What fraction of Figure B is shaded? $\frac{3}{8}$

   b. What fraction of Figure B is not shaded? $\frac{5}{8}$

   c. What is the sum of the fractions in parts (a) and (b)? Why?
      1; the two fractions together represent the whole.

6. A vase fell and broke into 12 pieces. Jason picked up one of the pieces, but it was not $\frac{1}{12}$ of the vase. How could this be?
   The vase did not break into 12 equal parts.

 represents one whole. Write each part to whole relationship as a fraction and as a mixed number.

7.
   $\frac{4}{3}, 1\frac{1}{3}$

8.
   $\frac{14}{8}, 1\frac{6}{8}$

9.
   $\frac{5}{2}, 2\frac{1}{2}$

The first three terms of a sequence of shapes are shown below. Use the sequence for Exercises 10–12.

10. a.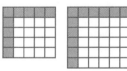

10. a. Draw the fourth and fifth terms.

    b. Describe the rule you used.

    b. Sample: For each new step of the sequence, I added a row and a column to the square. I shaded the first row and first column.

11. Write a fraction for the shaded part of each of the first five terms of the sequences. $\frac{3}{4}, \frac{5}{9}, \frac{7}{16}, \frac{9}{25}, \frac{11}{36}$

12. **Challenge** Predict what fraction of the 10th term will be shaded. $\frac{21}{121}$

13. a. Draw the square below on dot paper.
Check students' work.

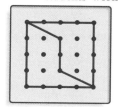

b. Divide the square into two **congruent** parts (parts that have the same shape and size) as shown below.
Check students' work.

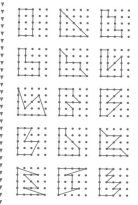

c. What fraction of the square is each congruent part? $\frac{1}{2}$

d. Find five other ways to divide the square into two congruent parts. Sketch your answers on dot paper.

14. a. Draw this rectangle on dot paper.
Check students' work.

b. Divide the rectangle into four congruent parts. Record your answer on dot paper.
See margin.

c. What fraction of the rectangle is each part? $\frac{1}{4}$

d. Find four more ways to divide the rectangle into four congruent parts. Sketch your answers on dot paper. See diagram in part b.

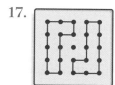

e. Shade each diagram from parts (b) and (d) to show $\frac{3}{4}$ of the rectangle. See diagram in part b.

For each pair, explain why the shapes are or are not congruent.

15.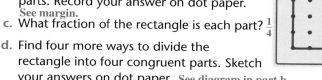
16.
17.

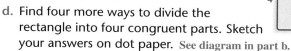
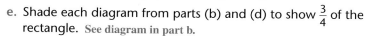

18. Physical Education A running track is $\frac{1}{4}$ of a mile long.

a. How many times must you run around the track in order to run one mile? 4 times.

b. How many miles will you have run if you run around the track twice? If you run around 6 times? $\frac{2}{4}$ mile; $1\frac{2}{4}$ miles.

c. If you run halfway around the track, what fraction of a mile will you have run? $\frac{1}{8}$

---

13. d. Answers will vary. Sample Responses:

15. The figures are congruent because they have the same size and shape.

16. The figures are not congruent; they do not have the same size.

17. The figures are congruent because they have the same size and shape.

EXERCISE NOTES

Before assigning **Exercises 13–17**, you may want to discuss the meaning of *congruent*. Congruent figures must be the same shape and the same size. These exercises can also be represented on geoboards instead of dot paper. The geoboard figures give students another tactile resource in addition to pattern blocks.

14. b. See Additional Answers beginning on page A1.

EXERCISE NOTES
When checking answers to
Exercises 32–35, you may want
to have students verbalize how they
determined where each number
was located on the number line.
Some may have divided each whole
into sixths and counted by sixths
to locate each number. Others
may have converted the first two
fractions into mixed numbers and
estimated where $2\frac{2}{6}$ and $1\frac{3}{6}$ are
located.

19. **Challenge** Mina ran $\frac{3}{5}$ of a cross-country course. If she ran 6 km, how long is the course? **10 km**

Rewrite each fraction as a mixed number.

20. $\frac{21}{4}$ $5\frac{1}{4}$ 21. $\frac{15}{8}$ $1\frac{7}{8}$ 22. $\frac{41}{6}$ $6\frac{5}{6}$ 23. $\frac{14}{3}$ $4\frac{2}{3}$

Rewrite each mixed number as a fraction.

24. $4\frac{1}{5}$ $\frac{21}{5}$ 25. $1\frac{7}{12}$ $\frac{19}{12}$ 26. $11\frac{1}{2}$ $\frac{23}{2}$ 27. $2\frac{2}{3}$ $\frac{8}{3}$

28. $7\frac{4}{5}$ $\frac{39}{5}$ 29. $3\frac{1}{8}$ $\frac{25}{8}$ 30. $6\frac{5}{7}$ $\frac{47}{7}$ 31. $9\frac{9}{11}$ $\frac{108}{11}$

Visual Thinking Copy the number line. Mark and label a point on the line where you think each fraction or mixed number would be.
32.–35. See margin.

32. $\frac{14}{6}$ 33. $\frac{9}{6}$ 34. $2\frac{1}{6}$ 35. $1\frac{2}{3}$

Write each quotient as a mixed number.

36. $26 \div 5$ $5\frac{1}{5}$ 37. $52 \div 7$ $7\frac{3}{7}$ 38. $98 \div 10$ $9\frac{8}{10}$

39. Suppose you roll a 3 on each of your first five turns of *Flex Your Hex*. The sequence below represents the fraction of a hexagon you had after each turn.

$$\frac{3}{6}, \frac{6}{6}, \frac{9}{6}, \frac{12}{6}, \frac{15}{6}, \ldots$$

  a. Write a rule for finding any term in the sequence from its term number. **Let t = the term and n = the term number; $t = \frac{3 \cdot n}{6}$**

  b. If possible, write each term in the sequence as a mixed number to show the results after trading. $\frac{3}{6}, 1, 1\frac{3}{6}, 2, 2\frac{3}{6}$

  c. Suppose you keep rolling a 3 on every turn. In how many more turns will you collect 5 hexagons? **5 more turns**

40. Naomi's class is playing a trading game similar to *Flex Your Hex* using circles. Naomi just finished a turn and has $3\frac{4}{5}$ circles.

  a. How many pieces does it take to make a complete circle in this game? **5**

  b. It takes five complete circles to win the game. Can Naomi win on her next turn? Explain. **Yes; If she rolls a 6, she will take 6 pieces. This will give her exactly 5 circles. $3\frac{4}{5} + 1\frac{1}{5} = 4\frac{5}{5} = 5$**

32–35. See Additional Answers
beginning on page A1.

41. Suppose you are sharing 6 dollars among 4 people. Which form of $6 \div 4$ would you use to describe each share? Explain your choice.

b (1.50); Half of a dollar is $0.50.

a. 1 R2   b. 1.50   c. $1\frac{1}{2}$

Reflecting ◀▶ on the Section

Be prepared to respond to Exercises 42 and 43 in class.

Here is a shortcut for changing a mixed number to a fraction.

- **Multiply** the whole number and the denominator.

- Then **add** the numerator to the product.

- Write the result over the **original denominator, 3.**

$$2 \times 3 + 1 = 7$$

$$2\ \frac{1}{3} + = \frac{7}{3}$$

42. Look back at the Example on page 45. Use the idea of trading pattern blocks to explain each step in the shortcut.

43. Use the shortcut to write each of the following mixed numbers as fractions.

a. $1\frac{7}{8}$ **$\frac{15}{8}$**   b. $3\frac{5}{6}$ **$\frac{23}{6}$**   c. $6\frac{3}{4}$ **$\frac{27}{4}$**

Spiral ◀▶ Review

Describe in words how to find the value of each expression.
(Module 1, p. 10)

44. $4 \cdot (3 + 2)$ **45.** $7 + 10 \div 2$ **46.** $8 - 3 \cdot 2$

Solve each problem. (Module 1, p. 33)

47. Together, a breakfast bar and juice cost $4.00. The breakfast bar costs 90¢ more than the juice. How much does the juice cost?
$1.55

48. Bruno mailed 30 postcards and letters. It cost $.26 each to mail the postcards and $.41 each for the letters. His total cost was $10.65. How many of each did he mail? **11 postcards and 19 letters**

Find each product without using a calculator. (Toolbox, p. 574)

49. 17
      ×20
      ——
      340

50. 300
      × 53
      ——
      15,900

51. 70000
      × 627
      ——
      43,890,000

Journal

Exercises 42 and 43 check that you understand mixed numbers.

42. Multiplying the whole number by the denominator corresponds to writing the whole number as a fraction with the same denominator as in the mixed number. Adding the numerator to the product corresponds to adding the fractional part to the whole number part.

44. Add 3 and 2, then multiply the sum by 4.

45. Divide 10 by 2, then add the quotient to 7.

46. Multiply 3 by 2, then subtract the product from 8.

EXERCISE NOTES

You may want to provide a short lesson on the short cut presented in the **Reflecting on the Section.** It is important that students be able to verify the method with pattern blocks and that they see the relationship between the whole and the parts. Students who just memorize the shortcut often confuse which numbers are multiplied and which are added. You may want to show them that

$$2\frac{1}{3} = 2 + \frac{1}{3}$$
$$= \frac{2}{1} + \frac{1}{3}$$
$$= \frac{2 \cdot 3}{1 \cdot 3} + \frac{1}{3}$$
$$= \frac{2 \cdot 3}{3} + \frac{1}{3}$$
$$= \frac{2 \cdot 3 + 1}{3}$$
$$= \frac{7}{3}$$

Extra Skill Practice

TEACHER NOTES

For each Exploration, the corresponding Extra Skill Practice Exercises are noted.

Exploration 1: 1–6
Exploration 2: 7–21

EXTRA HELP

Teacher's Resource Book
• Practice and Applications
• Study Guide

Technology Resources
• @Home Tutor
• Test Generator

ASSESSMENT

• Section 4 Quick Quiz
• Test Generator

Section 4
Extra Skill Practice

Tell whether each statement is true or false. If a statement is false, explain why.

1.

$\frac{1}{2}$ of the triangle is shaded.
False; The two parts of the triangle are not the same size.

2.

$\frac{2}{6}$ of the trapezoid is shaded. **True**

3.

$\frac{3}{4}$ of the rectangle is shaded. **True**

 represents the whole. Write each part to whole relationship as a fraction and as a mixed number.

4.
$\frac{7}{4}, 1\frac{3}{4}$

5.
$\frac{5}{2}, 2\frac{1}{2}$

6.
$\frac{12}{9}, 1\frac{3}{9}$

Write each fraction as a mixed number.

7. $\frac{10}{3}$ $3\frac{1}{3}$
8. $\frac{14}{9}$ $1\frac{5}{9}$
9. $\frac{17}{4}$ $4\frac{1}{4}$
10. $\frac{5}{3}$ $1\frac{2}{3}$
11. $\frac{21}{2}$ $10\frac{1}{2}$

Write each mixed number as a fraction.

12. $1\frac{1}{2}$ $\frac{3}{2}$
13. $5\frac{4}{9}$ $\frac{49}{9}$
14. $2\frac{1}{8}$ $\frac{17}{8}$
15. $3\frac{3}{7}$ $\frac{24}{7}$
16. $9\frac{4}{5}$ $\frac{49}{5}$

Write each quotient as a mixed number.

17. $11 \div 5$
$2\frac{1}{5}$
18. $35 \div 3$
$11\frac{2}{3}$
19. $18 \div 4$
$4\frac{2}{4}$
20. $19 \div 2$
$9\frac{1}{2}$

21. Jake has $\frac{1}{3}$ of the money he needs to buy a kite. If he has $1.50, how much does the kite cost? **$4.50**

Standardized Testing

1. a.   b.   c.

Standardized Testing ◀▶ Free Response

1. Draw each figure. Then shade the part that represents the given fraction.

   A $\frac{4}{6}$ of a rectangle

   B $\frac{3}{4}$ of a square

   C $\frac{2}{8}$ of a circle

2. Fill in the missing terms of the sequence. Explain your reasoning.

   $\frac{8}{9}$, _?_ , $1\frac{7}{9}$, $2\frac{2}{9}$, _?_ , _?_ , $3\frac{5}{9}$, 4, _?_

   $1\frac{3}{9}, 2\frac{6}{9}, 3\frac{1}{9}, 4\frac{4}{9}$; Sample Response: To get the next term, add 4 to the numerator of the previous term and use the same denominator. Then rewrite any improper fractions to mixed numbers or whole numbers.

Section ⑤ Equivalent Fractions

Setting the Stage

GETTING STARTED

In preparation for finding equivalent fractions, Module 1 Section 5 *Warm-Up* assesses student facility with multiplication and division of whole numbers.

In this section, students will learn that a number may have more than one name. In particular, a fraction can be called by whatever name is appropriate for the context in question. Have students reflect on the fact that it is not only numbers that may be referred to by various names. A person may be known by his given name and also by his nickname. Give the example of actor John Wayne, whose given name was Marion Morrison, and whose nickname was "The Duke".

Setting the Stage

Although you may not notice them, many everyday objects show a variety of designs and patterns.

Designs for floors range from simple squares and rectangles to many-sided polygons.

Think About It

1 Some of the pattern block shapes can be seen in the sidewalk above. Which can you identify? **rhombus, hexagon**

2 Use a fraction to describe a part of the sidewalk design.
   Sample: Each rhombus appears to be $\frac{1}{3}$ of each hexagon.

▶ **Different fractions can name the same part of a whole design. In this section you will find different ways to name parts of floor designs.**

Exploration 1

DEVELOPING MATH CONCEPTS

It is important that students understand the idea of equivalent fractions. For example, the fractions $\frac{6}{12}$ and $\frac{12}{24}$ found in

Questions 3 and 4 are equal even though they are named differently. Students should already understand this concept since they are familiar with its application to whole numbers. For example, they know that 4 + 1 is another name for 5, and that 4 + 1 = 5.

ALTERNATIVE APPROACH

Have students work in groups of four using the pattern blocks to represent as many equivalent fractions as they can find. Have one student from each group display a pair of equivalent fractions on the overhead projector using overhead pattern blocks. Record the equivalent fraction on the board. Continue calling on each group and recording the fractions until all of the representations have been displayed.

LEARN HOW TO...
- recognize equivalent fractions

AS YOU...
- explore arrangements of floor tiles

KEY TERM
- equivalent fractions

3. b. $\frac{1}{12}$

c. $\frac{6}{12}$

d. $\frac{1}{24}$

e. $\frac{12}{24}$

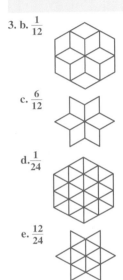

Exploration 1

EQUIVALENT FRACTIONS $\quad \frac{2}{4} \quad \frac{4}{8} \quad \frac{6}{12}$

SET UP *You will need: • Labsheet 5A • pattern blocks*

Use the Hexagon Section on Labsheet 5A for Question 3.

3 a. Estimate the fraction of the hexagon covered by the star. **Accept reasonable estimates; about $\frac{1}{2}$.**

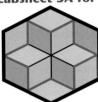

◄ a hexagon-shaped section of a floor design

b. Cover the entire hexagon with **rhombuses** (▰). What fraction of the entire figure does one rhombus represent?

c. Cover just the star portion with **rhombuses** (▰). What fraction of the hexagon do these rhombuses represent?

d. Now cover the entire hexagon with **triangles** (▲). What fraction of the hexagon does one triangle represent?

e. Cover just the star portion with **triangles** (▲). What fraction of the hexagon do these triangles represent?

f. How are your answers to parts (c) and (e) alike? How are they different? **Both fractions represent the part of the hexagon that the star represents. The fractions have different names.**

▶ Fractions that name the same portion of a whole are **equivalent fractions**. Question 3 shows that $\frac{6}{12}$ and $\frac{12}{24}$ are equivalent fractions.

4 **Discussion** Name another fraction that is equivalent to $\frac{6}{12}$ and $\frac{12}{24}$. How do you know it is equivalent?

5 ✔ **CHECKPOINT** Pattern blocks covering part of a hexagon-shaped floor pattern (⬡) are shown below.

A   B   C   D

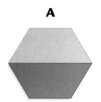 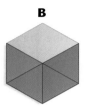 

a. What fraction of each floor pattern is covered?

b. Which of the fractions in part (a) are equivalent?
$\frac{1}{2}$ and $\frac{3}{6}$; $\frac{4}{6}$ and $\frac{2}{3}$

6 The floor designs below are formed within the same outlined shape. Each design has a hexagon of clear tile in the center.

Design A   **Design B**

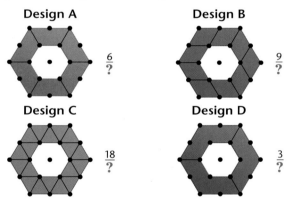

$\frac{6}{?}$ $\frac{9}{?}$

Design C   **Design D**

$\frac{18}{?}$ $\frac{3}{?}$

a. Complete the fractions that represent the part of each floor design that has colored tiles. A: $\frac{6}{8}$ B: $\frac{9}{12}$ C: $\frac{18}{24}$ D: $\frac{3}{4}$

b. Explain why the fractions in part (a) are equivalent.

7 **a.** For designs A–C in Question 6, cover each center with the same type of colored tiles used for the outer part of the design. What fraction of each floor design is covered with colored tiles now?

b. What whole number does each fraction in part (a) represent? 1

HOMEWORK EXERCISES ▶ See Exs. 1–9 on pp. 62–63.

 QUESTION 5

...checks that you can recognize equivalent fractions.

4. Sample: $\frac{1}{2}$; the two figures below represent $\frac{1}{2}$ and $\frac{6}{12}$. Since the shaded regions are congruent, both represent the same fraction.

5. a. A: $\frac{1}{2}$ B: $\frac{4}{6}$
   C: $\frac{2}{3}$ D: $\frac{3}{6}$

6. b. Sample Response: Since all the outlined shapes are congruent and all the shaded regions are congruent, the fractions are equivalent.

7. a. A: $\frac{8}{8}$ B: $\frac{12}{12}$ C: $\frac{24}{24}$

DIFFERENTIATED INSTRUCTION
Provide a copy of **Exercise 6** with the center hexagon divided into the same shape pieces as the colored panes. Ask students to find the number of shaded and unshaded shapes (for designs A–C, name the shape: trapezoid, parallelogram, triangle). Then use these numbers to write the fraction of shaded shapes to the total number of shapes. For Design D, use 2 trapezoid pattern blocks connected together with sticky tack or tape. Allow students to rearrange the pieces to see that the center hexagon is the same as one of the taped pieces.

Exploration 2

DEVELOPING MATH CONCEPTS

Question 9 After students have learned to multiply fractions, they can show that multiplying the numerator and denominator of a fraction by the same number produces an equivalent fraction because multiplying by $\frac{x}{x}$ where $x \neq 0$ is the same as multiplying by 1.

TEACHING NOTES

Students may benefit from another concrete demonstration that the fractions $\frac{4}{6}$ and $\frac{12}{18}$ in **Question 9** are equivalent. You can relate the equations $\frac{4}{6} = \frac{4 \cdot 3}{6 \cdot 3} = \frac{12}{18}$ to cutting each piece of a 6-slice pizza into 3 equal-sized pieces to make 18 total slices. Sketch a circle (pizza) with 6 equal-sized slices. Then explain that you could then cut each of those pieces into 3 equal-sized slices which multiplies the total number of pieces by 3 to equal 18. If you eat 4 of the original-sized 6 slices it is the same as eating 12 of the smaller-sized 18 slices.

GOAL

LEARN HOW TO...
- find equivalent fractions
- write a fraction in lowest terms

AS YOU...
- use pattern blocks to make floor designs

KEY TERM
- lowest terms

Exploration 2

FINDING = EQUIVALENTS

SET UP *You will need pattern blocks.*

▶ **Equivalent fractions can be used to describe the floor designs shown below.**

Original floor design made with 6 trapezoids (◮).

New floor design made by replacing 4 trapezoids (◮) with triangles (▲).

8 a. Use trapezoids (◮) to create the original floor design. *Check students' work.*

b. What fraction of the original floor design will be replaced with triangles (▲) to create the new floor design? $\frac{4}{6}$

c. Without looking at the picture of the new floor design, how can you determine the number of triangles you will need to replace the 4 trapezoids? $4 \cdot 3 = 12$ triangles

d. If you were going to replace all of the trapezoids with triangles, how many triangles would you need? $6 \cdot 3 = 18$ triangles

e. What fraction of the new floor design pictured above is covered with triangles? $\frac{12}{18}$

9 An equivalent fraction for the part of the new floor design that is covered by triangles can be found as follows.

You replaced 4 of the 6 trapezoids with triangles.

4 trapezoids became 12 triangles.

$$\frac{4}{6} = \frac{4 \cdot ?}{6 \cdot ?} = \frac{12}{18}$$

You would need 18 triangles (▲) to replace all 6 trapezoids (◮).

a. What number must replace each question mark to make the equations true? 3

b. How are the products in the middle fraction related to your answers from Questions 8(c) and 8(d)? The numerator is the answer to 8(c); the denominator is the answer to 8(d).

10 Copy and complete the equivalent fractions. Be sure to include all the missing steps.

a. $\frac{1}{2} = \frac{1 \cdot 2}{2 \cdot 2} = \frac{2}{?}$ 4   **b.** $\frac{1}{3} = \frac{1 \cdot 2}{3 \cdot 2} = \frac{2}{?}$ 6   **c.** $\frac{2}{3} = \frac{2 \cdot ?}{3 \cdot ?} = \frac{?}{12}$

d. $\frac{3}{3} = \frac{3 \cdot ?}{3 \cdot ?} = \frac{?}{12}$ **e.** $\frac{3}{4} = \frac{3 \cdot ?}{4 \cdot ?} = \frac{?}{12}$ **f.** $\frac{8}{6} = \frac{? \cdot ?}{? \cdot ?} = \frac{?}{12}$

10. c. $\frac{2 \cdot 4}{3 \cdot 4} = \frac{8}{12}$

d. $\frac{3 \cdot 4}{3 \cdot 4} = \frac{12}{12}$

e. $\frac{3 \cdot 3}{4 \cdot 3} = \frac{9}{12}$

f. $\frac{8 \cdot 2}{6 \cdot 2} = \frac{16}{12}$

11 ✔ **CHECKPOINT** Complete each pair of equivalent fractions.

a. $\frac{3}{7} = \frac{?}{28}$ 12   **b.** $\frac{5}{6} = \frac{45}{?}$ 54   **c.** $\frac{2}{5} = \frac{?}{30}$ 12

✔ **QUESTION 11**

...checks that you can use multiplication to find equivalent fractions.

▶ **Equivalent fractions can also be used to describe these floor designs.**

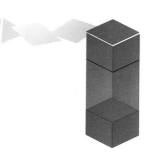

Original floor design has $\frac{12}{18}$ of the design made from **triangles** (▲).

New floor design made by replacing triangles (▲) with rhombuses (▰).

12. d. A single rhombus replaces 2 triangles, so to determine the number of rhombuses you need, divide the number of triangles by 2.

12 **Discussion** The following equation can be used to find an equivalent fraction representing the part of the new floor design that is covered by **rhombuses** (▰).

$$\frac{12}{18} = \frac{12 \div ?}{18 \div ?} = \frac{6}{9}$$

a. Use pattern blocks to create the original floor design. Check students' work.

b. How many **triangles** (▲) can be covered with one **rhombus** (▰)? How can you use this information to find how many rhombuses you need to replace all of the triangles? two triangles; divide the number of triangles by 2.

c. Create the new floor design. Is $\frac{6}{9}$ of the new floor design covered with rhombuses? Explain. Yes; $\frac{12}{18} = \frac{12 \div 2}{18 \div 2} = \frac{6}{9}$

d. Why was division used in the equations?

e. What number must replace each question mark? 2

TEACHING NOTES

Prior to **Checkpoint 11**, you may want to present the following Classroom Example to show how to write an equivalent fraction without the prompts given in **Question 10**.

CLASSROOM EXAMPLE

Complete the pair of equivalent fractions $\frac{3}{10} = \frac{?}{40}$.

Answer: 10 · 4 = 40, so 3 · 4 = 12.

$$\frac{3}{10} = \frac{3 \cdot 4}{10 \cdot 4} = \frac{12}{40}$$

For **Checkpoint Questions 11 and 14**, have students verbalize how they arrived at their solutions. In both cases, they should be able to describe the operation they used with the numerator and denominator.

In the window design before **Question 12**, make sure students see that the two trapezoids that form the middle parts of the windows form a hexagon that is equivalent to 3 rhombuses.

TEACHING NOTES

In **Question 15**, students who have been using other terminology may need to have it explained that *writing a fraction in lowest terms* is the same as *simplifying the fraction* or *reducing the fraction*.

TIPS FROM TEACHERS

If you have fraction calculators, introduce Practice and Applications **Exercises 27–29**. Then have students use the calculator to help them write an Example Box like the one on this page, but using one of the fraction pairs in **Exercise 29**.

13. c. $\frac{8 \div 8}{16 \div 8} = \frac{1}{2}$

d. $\frac{64 \div 8}{72 \div 8} = \frac{8}{9}$

e. $\frac{25 \div 5}{30 \div 5} = \frac{5}{6}$

f. $\frac{30 \div 3}{36 \div 3} = \frac{10}{12}$

✔ QUESTION 14

...checks that you can use division to find equivalent fractions.

15. a. No; 3 and 6 are both divisible by 3.

b. Yes; 1 is the greatest whole number that will divide both the numerator and denominator evenly.

c. Yes; 1 is the greatest whole number that will divide both the numerator and denominator evenly.

d. No; 11 and 66 are both divisible by 11.

16. a. The chosen factor must divide both the numerator and the denominator evenly.

c. Sample Response: $\frac{24}{72} = \frac{24 \div 24}{72 \div 24} = \frac{1}{3}$

---

13 Copy and complete the equivalent fractions.

a. $\frac{9}{12} = \frac{9 \div 3}{12 \div 3} = \frac{3}{?}$ 4 b. $\frac{4}{6} = \frac{4 \div 2}{6 \div 2} = \frac{?}{3}$ 2 c. $\frac{8}{16} = \frac{? \div ?}{16 \div 8} = \frac{?}{?}$

d. $\frac{64}{72} = \frac{64 \div 8}{? \div ?} = \frac{?}{9}$ e. $\frac{25}{30} = \frac{? \div ?}{? \div ?} = \frac{5}{?}$ f. $\frac{30}{36} = \frac{? \div ?}{? \div ?} = \frac{?}{12}$

14 ✔ CHECKPOINT Complete each pair of equivalent fractions.

a. $\frac{40}{64} = \frac{?}{8}$ 5 b. $\frac{36}{108} = \frac{4}{?}$ 12 c. $\frac{21}{33} = \frac{?}{11}$ 7

▶ **Lowest Terms** Fractions like $\frac{2}{3}$ and $\frac{3}{4}$ are said to be in **lowest terms** since 1 is the greatest whole number that will divide both the numerator and denominator of the fraction evenly.

15 Tell whether or not each fraction is in lowest terms. Explain how you know.

a. $\frac{3}{6}$ b. $\frac{21}{29}$ c. $\frac{5}{8}$ d. $\frac{11}{66}$

▶ You can write fractions in lowest terms by dividing the numerator and the denominator by the same whole number.

EXAMPLE

Express $\frac{24}{72}$ in lowest terms.

SAMPLE RESPONSE

Step 1   Step 2   Step 3

$\frac{24}{72} = \frac{24 \div 2}{72 \div 2} = \frac{12 \div 4}{36 \div 4} = \frac{3 \div 3}{9 \div 3} = \frac{1}{3}$

16. b. Sample Response: $\frac{24}{72} = \frac{24 \div 3}{72 \div 3} = \frac{8 \div 4}{24 \div 4} = \frac{2 \div 2}{6 \div 2} = \frac{1}{3}$

16 Discussion

a. Why does the number you divide by have to be a common factor of both the numerator and the denominator?

b. Divide by a different common factor in Step 1 of the Example. Show the steps to find the fraction in lowest terms.

c. How can you write $\frac{24}{72}$ in lowest terms in fewer than three steps?

17 ✔ **CHECKPOINT** For each fraction, write an equivalent fraction in lowest terms.

a. $\frac{7}{14}$ $\frac{1}{2}$ b. $\frac{10}{30}$ $\frac{1}{3}$ c. $\frac{6}{48}$ $\frac{1}{8}$ d. $\frac{25}{125}$ $\frac{1}{5}$

HOMEWORK EXERCISES ▶ See Exs. 10–29 on pp. 63–64.

Exploration 3

Fractions of Whole Numbers

SET UP Work in a group. You will need: • Labsheet 5B
• 25 pattern blocks

▶ Fractions can be used to make predictions from a **sample**, which is part of a whole set of objects being studied. Your group has a sample of all the pattern blocks being used by the class. The whole set of pattern blocks is the **population**.

18 What fraction of your group's pattern blocks are triangles?
Answers may vary.

19 **a. Discussion** Predict what fraction of the pattern blocks in use by the class are triangles. How can you use your answer to Question 18 to help you make your prediction?

b. In a collection of 250 pattern blocks, how many do you think are triangles? How could you use your answer to part (a) to help you find out?

▶ **Use Labsheet 5B.** For Questions 20 and 21 you will use dot paper to find fractions of whole numbers. **20–21. See margin.**

20 Follow the directions for *Dot Grid 1* to find out how many pattern blocks are triangles if $\frac{2}{3}$ of the 36 pattern blocks are triangles.

21 Follow the directions for *Dot Grid 2* to find out how many pattern blocks are squares if $\frac{3}{4}$ of the 24 pattern blocks are squares.

Sidebar (right column of main page)

✔ QUESTION 17
...checks that you can write fractions in lowest terms.

GOAL

LEARN HOW TO...
• find a fraction of a whole number

AS YOU...
• make predictions from a sample of pattern blocks

KEY TERMS
• sample
• population

19. a. Answers may vary; Assume that the sample is representative of the population, so the fraction is the same as the number in Question 18.
b. Answers may vary. Sample: Multiply the number of triangles in your group's set of pattern blocks by 10, or multiply 250 by the fraction in part (a).

Teaching Notes (far right column)

TEACHING NOTES
For **Question 17**, have students discuss what numbers they divided the numerators and denominators by. They should make the connection that dividing by 2 and then 5 in **part (b)** gives the same result as dividing by 10.

Exploration 3

MANAGING THE MATERIALS
Before beginning this exploration, prepare ten sets of 25 pattern blocks. Each set should contain some of each shape pattern block, but the number of each shape in the sets can be different. (The ideal way to do this is to have each group of students randomly select 25 blocks, but this may not be feasible.) Each group should be given one set of blocks. Set aside the remaining sets for use in **Question 26**.

TEACHING NOTES
Begin the activity by discussing polls and how they are used to predict the outcome of elections, etc. Emphasize how only a sample of the whole population is used to make the predictions. Explain that in this activity, students will learn how pollsters use fractions to make their predictions.

As students complete the exploration, they should pay close attention to how their own group results compare to those of groups with which they combine results. They will certainly notice that the more groups that are combined, the closer the results approximate the actual number of triangles in the 250 pattern blocks. Of course, if all 250 pattern blocks were distributed among the groups, the combined results of all the groups must exactly equal the number of triangles.

20.–21. See Additional Answers beginning on page A1.

 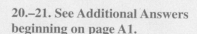

TEACHING NOTES
For **Question 26** be sure to include any sets of pattern blocks that were not given to groups.

▶ You can also use mental math to find a fraction of a whole number.

22 A class predicts that $\frac{3}{8}$ of their 48 pattern blocks are hexagons.

   a. To find $\frac{3}{8}$ of 48 pattern blocks, you can first think about dividing 48 pattern blocks into how many groups of equal size? **8 groups**

   b. How many pattern blocks will be in each group? **6 pattern blocks**

   c. How many groups do you need to make $\frac{3}{8}$? **3 groups**

   d. What is $\frac{3}{8}$ of 48? **18**

   e. How many of the 48 pattern blocks do you predict are hexagons? **18 pattern blocks**

✔ **QUESTION 23**

...checks that you can use mental math to find a fraction of a number.

23 ✔ **CHECKPOINT** Use mental math to find each value.

   a. $\frac{4}{5}$ of 30   **24**   **b.** $\frac{5}{6}$ of 18   **15**   **c.** $\frac{2}{3}$ of 12   **8**

24 **Discussion** Think about the mental math method you used in Questions 22 and 23. Would you use this method to find $\frac{2}{5}$ of 12? Explain why or why not. **No; 12 ÷ 5 is not a whole number. OR 12 is not evenly divisible by 5.**

25 **a.** Combine your pattern blocks with those of another group. What fraction of the combined pattern blocks are triangles? **Answers may vary.**

   b. Use your answer to part (a) to predict what fraction of the pattern blocks being used by the class are triangles. **Answers may vary.**

   c. In a collection of 250 pattern blocks, how many do you think are triangles? **Answers may vary.**

26 **Try This as a Class** Count how many of the pattern blocks being used by the class are triangles.

   a. What fraction of the class's pattern blocks are triangles? **Answers may vary.**

   b. Was your prediction from Question 19(a) close? **Answers may vary.**

27 **Try This as a Class** Suppose you combined your class's pattern blocks with 250 pattern blocks from another class.

   a. Predict how many of the combined pattern blocks are triangles. **Answers may vary.**

   b. Did you use the fraction from Question 18 or from Question 26(a) to make your prediction? Why?

27. b. Sample Response: I used the answer to 26(a) because it was based on a larger sample.

 HOMEWORK EXERCISES ▶ See Exs. 30–49 on pp. 64–66.

Section 5

Key Concepts

Equivalent Fractions (pp. 54–59)

Fractions that name the same portion of a whole are equivalent.

Examples

$\frac{1}{2}$, $\frac{2}{4}$, and $\frac{3}{6}$ are equivalent fractions since

$\frac{1}{2}$ = ▭ ,　　　$\frac{2}{4}$ = ▭ ,　　　and $\frac{3}{6}$ = ▭ .

Given a fraction, you can find an equivalent fraction by multiplying or dividing the numerator and denominator by the same nonzero whole number.

Examples

$\frac{5}{6} = \frac{5 \cdot 3}{6 \cdot 3} = \frac{15}{18}$, so $\frac{5}{6}$ is equivalent to $\frac{15}{18}$.

$\frac{24}{28} = \frac{24 \div 4}{28 \div 4} = \frac{6}{7}$, so $\frac{24}{28}$ is equivalent to $\frac{6}{7}$.

Lowest Terms (pp. 58–59)

In the example above, $\frac{6}{7}$ is in lowest terms because 1 is the only whole number that will divide both 6 and 7 evenly.

Key Concepts Questions

28　**a.** Divide the numerator and denominator of $\frac{18}{30}$ by 2. $\frac{9}{15}$

　　b. Is the result in lowest terms? If not, how can you find an equivalent fraction in lowest terms?

29　Make shaded drawings for the fractions in each pair. Use your drawings to explain whether or not the fractions in each pair are equivalent. **a–c. See margin.**

　　a. $\frac{1}{3}$, $\frac{3}{9}$　　　　**b.** $\frac{3}{8}$, $\frac{1}{4}$　　　　**c.** $\frac{2}{5}$, $\frac{4}{10}$

28. b. No; divide the numerator and denominator of $\frac{9}{15}$ by 3. (You could have divided the numerator and the denominator of $\frac{18}{30}$ by 6.)

Key Concepts

CLOSURE QUESTION

Explain how you can tell if two fractions are equivalent.

Sample Response: Write both fractions in lowest terms. If the new fractions are identical, then the original fractions are equivalent. Otherwise they are not equivalent.

OR

Write both fractions as equivalent fractions with a common denominator. If the new fractions are identical, then the original fractions are equivalent. Otherwise they are not equivalent.

29. a. Yes

　　b. No

　　c. Yes

Key Concepts *continued*

ABSENT STUDENTS

For students who were absent for all or part of this section, the blackline Study Guide for Section 5 may be used to present the ideas, concepts, and skills of Section 5.

Practice & Applications

SUGGESTED ASSIGNMENTS

Core Course

Day 1: Exs. 1–9, 50–59
Day 2: Exs. 10–25, 60–65
Day 3: Exs. 30–46, 48–49

Extended Course

Day 1: Exs. 1–9, 50–59
Day 2: Exs. 13–29, 60–65
Day 3: Exs. 30–49

Note: Extended Course assignments can be used to differentiate within the regular classroom. In classrooms where students are grouped homogeneously, the material might be covered in fewer days. In this case assignments may be combined.

ADDITIONAL PRACTICE

See the *Teacher's Resource Book* for additional practice and application exercises for this section.

Section 5

Key Terms

sample

population

Key Concepts

Finding a Fraction of a Whole Number (pp. 59–60)

Example

A sample of 15 fish is taken from a population of fish. $\frac{2}{3}$ of the sample are tuna. Use mental math to find $\frac{2}{3}$ of 15.

Think: Divide 15 into 3 groups of equal size. There are 5 in each group. There are 10 in two groups, so $\frac{2}{3}$ of 15 = 10.

30 Key Concepts Question Which is greater, $\frac{3}{4}$ of 24 or $\frac{3}{10}$ of 70?
$\frac{3}{10}$ of 70

Section 5

Practice & Application Exercises

YOU WILL NEED

For Ex. 8:
◆ pattern blocks

For Exs. 27–29:
◆ fraction calculator

1. The windows in the photograph below are identical except that the bottom window is partly open.

a. What fraction of the bottom window is open? $\frac{1}{2}$

b. The photograph shows that another fraction is equivalent to the one in part (a). What is the other fraction? $\frac{4}{8}$

Write two equivalent fractions that tell what part of each figure is shaded.

2. $\frac{1}{2}, \frac{2}{4}$

3. $\frac{2}{5}, \frac{4}{10}$

4. $\frac{9}{12}, \frac{3}{4}$

5.  $\frac{2}{3}, \frac{4}{6}$

6. $\frac{1}{4}, \frac{2}{8}$

7. $\frac{1}{3}, \frac{2}{6}$

8. Use your pattern blocks to show how $\frac{2}{5}$ is equivalent to $\frac{4}{10}$. Trace around the blocks you used. **Answers will vary. Check students' work.**

9. When special stamps are printed, several related designs may be arranged on a sheet.

   a. Write three equivalent fractions to represent the portion of the stamps that show the purple flower. **Samples:** $\frac{4}{16}, \frac{2}{8}, \frac{1}{4}$.

   b. What is the value in cents of the two rows of 13¢ stamps? **208¢**

   c. Write a fraction different from the ones in part (a) that compares the value in cents of the stamps showing the purple flower with the total value in cents of the two rows of stamps. $\frac{52}{208}$

   d. How is the fraction in part (c) related to the fractions you found in part (a)? Explain. **It is equivalent because each stamp has the same value.**

Complete each pair of equivalent fractions.

10. $\frac{3}{8} = \frac{?}{16}$ 6

11. $\frac{4}{7} = \frac{12}{?}$ 21

12. $\frac{2}{9} = \frac{?}{27}$ 6

13. $\frac{12}{18} = \frac{?}{3}$ 2

14. $\frac{32}{40} = \frac{?}{5}$ 4

15. $\frac{12}{27} = \frac{4}{?}$ 9

Find the next three terms in each sequence.

16. $\frac{1}{2}, \frac{2}{4}, \frac{3}{6}, \frac{4}{8}, \dots$

17. $\frac{2}{3}, \frac{4}{6}, \frac{6}{9}, \frac{8}{12}, \dots$

18. $\frac{1}{5}, \frac{3}{15}, \frac{9}{45}, \frac{27}{135}, \dots$

16. $\frac{5}{10}, \frac{6}{12}, \frac{7}{14}$

17. $\frac{10}{15}, \frac{12}{18}, \frac{14}{21}$

18. $\frac{81}{405}, \frac{243}{1215}, \frac{729}{3645}$

EXERCISE NOTES

In **Exercises 10–15**, you might want to have students show what number they multiplied by to find the missing part of each equivalent fraction.

In **Exercises 16–18**, students should notice that the terms in each sequence are equivalent fractions. You might ask students to describe the rule for finding the nth terms in **Exercises 16 and 17** to check their understanding of equivalent fractions. Many students will find the next three terms by merely counting by 1s, 2s, or 3s in the numerators and denominators to get to the next term. (*Exercise 16: the nth term is $\frac{1 \cdot n}{2 \cdot n}$ where n is the term number. Exercise 17: the nth term is $\frac{2 \cdot n}{3 \cdot n}$ where n is the term number.*) In **Exercise 18**, it may be a bit more obvious that each succeeding term is the result of multiplying the numerator and denominator of the previous term by 3. Representing the nth term in this sequence is a bit more difficult. It can be represented by $\frac{1 \cdot 3^{n-1}}{5 \cdot 3^{n-1}}$ where n is the term number.

Practice & Applications

EXERCISE NOTES

Exercises 27–29 are written for use with a fraction calculator. The key strokes given may be different for other calculator styles.

27. c. $\frac{3}{4}$; divided the numerator and denominator of $\frac{9}{12}$ by 3.

Choose the fractions in each list that are in lowest terms.

19. $\frac{5}{20}$, $\frac{4}{20}$, $\frac{3}{20}$ $\frac{3}{20}$ **20.** $\frac{8}{6}$, $\frac{9}{12}$, $\frac{5}{8}$ $\frac{5}{8}$ **21.** $\frac{4}{8}$, $\frac{4}{9}$, $\frac{4}{10}$ $\frac{4}{9}$

Write each fraction in lowest terms.

22. $\frac{12}{20}$ $\frac{3}{5}$ **23.** $\frac{24}{36}$ $\frac{2}{3}$ **24.** $\frac{13}{52}$ $\frac{1}{4}$ **25.** $\frac{5}{60}$ $\frac{1}{12}$

26. Challenge Find two pairs of equivalent fractions in the list below. Explain how you know each pair is equivalent.

$$\frac{12}{9} \qquad \frac{5}{4} \qquad 1\frac{3}{4} \qquad 1\frac{2}{6} \qquad \frac{6}{9} \qquad 1\frac{21}{28}$$

Fraction Calculator Use a fraction calculator for Exercises 27–29.

27. Some fraction calculators can be used to find equivalent fractions, in particular equivalent fractions in lowest terms.

  a. Enter the key sequence [1] [8] [/] [2] [4] on your calculator. What number appears on the display? $\frac{18}{24}$

  b. Now press [SIMP] [=]. What number appears on the display? What did the calculator do to get that number? $\frac{9}{12}$; divided both numerator and denominator by 2.

  c. Press [SIMP] [=]. What number appears on the display? What did the calculator do?

  d. What happens if you press [SIMP] [=] again? Why do you think this happens? $\frac{3}{4}$; the fraction is in lowest terms.

28. a. Enter the fraction $\frac{16}{28}$ on your calculator. **Check students' work.**

  b. Press [SIMP] [=] repeatedly to find an equivalent fraction in lowest terms. $\frac{4}{7}$

29. Use your calculator to tell if each pair of fractions is equivalent.

  a. $\frac{27}{45}$, $\frac{5}{7}$ No   b. $\frac{85}{272}$, $\frac{20}{64}$ Yes c. $\frac{14}{49}$, $\frac{2}{7}$ Yes

Mental Math Use mental math to find each value.

30. $\frac{2}{3}$ of 12 8   **31.** $\frac{5}{6}$ of 18 15   **32.** $\frac{2}{5}$ of 20 8   **33.** $\frac{3}{4}$ of 12 9

34. $\frac{2}{9}$ of 27 6   **35.** $\frac{3}{16}$ of 32 6   **36.** $\frac{5}{8}$ of 24 15   **37.** $\frac{5}{10}$ of 30 15

26. $\frac{12}{9}$ and $1\frac{2}{6}$ are equivalent because $\frac{12}{9} = \frac{12 \div 3}{9 \div 3} = \frac{4}{3} = 1\frac{1}{3}$ and $1\frac{2}{6} = 1 + \frac{2 \div 2}{6 \div 2} = 1\frac{1}{3}$. $1\frac{3}{4}$ and $1\frac{21}{28}$ are equivalent because $\frac{21}{28} = \frac{21 \div 7}{28 \div 7} = \frac{3}{4}$.

38. If $\frac{2}{3}$ of 6 pattern blocks are rhombuses, how many are rhombuses?
4 rhombuses

39. If $\frac{4}{5}$ of 10 pattern blocks are triangles, how many are triangles?
8 triangles

40. How many squares are there in a set of 14 pattern blocks that is $\frac{4}{7}$ squares? 8 squares

41. Ten of Group A's pattern blocks were triangles. When they combined their pattern blocks with those of Group B, they had a total of 32 pattern blocks. When combined, $\frac{3}{4}$ of the pattern blocks were triangles. How many of Group B's pattern blocks were triangles? 14 triangles

Plant Pollen A pollen expert counted the pollen grains in a sample of a pollen deposit to make predictions about the deposit. Use the table of results for Exercises 42 and 43.

42. What fraction of the sample is each type of pollen? Write each fraction in lowest terms.

   a. pine $\frac{2}{5}$

   b. grass $\frac{3}{10}$

   c. oak $\frac{1}{4}$

   d. cactus $\frac{1}{20}$

Type of pollen	Number of grains in sample
pine	48
grass	36
oak	30
cactus	6
total	**120**

43. Suppose the pollen expert estimates 540 grains are in the deposit. Use your answers to Exercise 42 to estimate the number of grains of each type of pollen in the deposit. pine: 216 grains; grass: 162 grains; oak: 135 grains; cactus: 27 grains

◄ Scientists study plant pollen that has been preserved in the ground to help learn how plants were used by ancient people.

For Exercises 44–46, use compatible numbers to estimate.

Example: $\frac{5}{6}$ of 31 is close to $\frac{5}{6}$ of 30, or about 25.

44. $\frac{2}{3}$ of 34 about 22   **45.** $\frac{1}{5}$ of 19 about 4   **46.** $\frac{3}{4}$ of 15 about 12

47. Challenge A researcher catches 45 fish, tags them, and puts them back in a pond. Later, a sample is taken from the pond and tags are found on $\frac{3}{5}$ of the fish. Estimate how many fish live in the pond. Explain how you made your estimate.

47. about 75 fish; I assumed that the fraction of tagged fish in the sample is about the same as the fraction of tagged fish in the pond. $\frac{3}{5}$ of the fish is 45 fish and $\frac{1}{5}$ of the fish is 15 fish, so there are about 5 · 15 = 75 fish in the pond.

FOR◄HELP
with *compatible numbers*, see
MODULE 1, p. 11

EXERCISE NOTES

Challenge Exercise 47 asks students to estimate the number of fish in the pond when it is known that the relationship of the 45 tagged fish to the total number of fish is probably in the ratio of 3 to 5. The natural approach to this problem would be to set up a proportion, but students have not yet learned how to work with this method of solving problems. Instead, the problem can be solved by using guess and check. Students might start with 250 fish and see that $\frac{45}{250}$ (or $\frac{9}{50}$) is not close to $\frac{3}{5}\left(\frac{30}{50}\right)$. Others might start with $\frac{3}{5}$ and find equivalent fractions until reaching $\frac{45}{75}$ to find that there are about 75 fish in the pond.

Practice & Applications

EXERCISE NOTES

In **Exercises 48 and 49**, fractions of a dollar are given. On a historical note, students may not know that a quarter was also commonly referred to as "two bits". A simple ditty from early in the 20th century included the line "shave and a haircut, six bits". Ask students how much a barber might have charged for a shave and a haircut in those days. (*75 cents*) What fraction of a dollar is this? $\left(\frac{75}{100}, \text{ or } \frac{3}{4}\right)$

Include in the discussion other currencies from countries other than the United States. Research the unit of currency and the fractional parts. Encourage students who have lived or traveled in other countries to describe the currency system of that country.

Discussion

Exercises 48 and 49 check that you understand equivalent fractions.

51. 14,000, not possible to tell

52. 1600, not possible to tell

Reflecting on the Section

Be prepared to discuss your responses to Exercises 48 and 49 in class.

48. United States coins represent fractions of a dollar. For example, the value of a quarter is 25 cents or $\frac{25}{100}$ of a dollar.

   a. What is $\frac{25}{100}$ in lowest terms? $\frac{1}{4}$

   b. Why do you think our 25 cent coin is called a quarter?
   One quarter is worth $\frac{25}{100}$ or $\frac{1}{4}$ of a dollar

49. Give two equivalent fractions that tell what part a dime is of a dollar. Are any of your answers in lowest terms? Explain.
   Sample: $\frac{10}{100}$ and $\frac{1}{10}$; $\frac{1}{10}$ is in lowest terms because 1 is the only whole number that divides 1 and 10 evenly.

Spiral Review

Estimate each answer. If possible, decide whether your estimate is *greater than* or *less than* the exact answer. (Module 1, p. 10)

50. 256 + 88
   350, greater than

51. 210 • 68

52. 78 • 21

53. 573 − 218
   400, greater than

54. 81 ÷ 19
   4, less than

55. 8632 − 794
   7800, less than

Use compatible numbers to find each answer by mental math. (Module 1, p. 11)

56. 27 + 18 + 13 58

57. 216 + 139 + 41 + 84 480

58. 2 • 35 • 4 280

59. 3 • 8 • 25 • 2 1200

Use the table to answer Exercises 60 and 61. (Module 1, p. 21)

Term Number	1	2	3	4	5
Term	7	14	21	28	35

60. Describe the relationship between the term and the term number. **The term is 7 times the term number.**

61. What is the 60th term of the sequence? 420

62. Is $\frac{1}{4}$ of the circle shaded? Explain why or why not. (Module 1, p. 46) No, the circle is not divided into 4 equal parts.

Subtract without using a calculator. (Toolbox, p. 570)

63.
   291
   − 156
   135

64.
   9431
   − 934
   8,497

65.
   3101
   − 1808
   1,293

Extra Skill Practice

Write two equivalent fractions that tell what part of each figure is shaded.

1. $\frac{2}{10}, \frac{1}{5}$

2. $\frac{2}{6}, \frac{1}{3}$

3. $\frac{4}{8}, \frac{1}{2}$

For each fraction, write three equivalent fractions. **4–13. Sample responses are given.**

4. $\frac{2}{5}$ $\frac{4}{10}, \frac{6}{15}, \frac{8}{20}$

5. $\frac{4}{9}$ $\frac{8}{18}, \frac{12}{27}, \frac{16}{36}$

6. $\frac{4}{16}$ $\frac{1}{4}, \frac{2}{8}, \frac{3}{12}$

7. $\frac{3}{8}$ $\frac{6}{16}, \frac{9}{24}, \frac{12}{32}$

8. $\frac{8}{24}$ $\frac{1}{3}, \frac{2}{6}, \frac{3}{9}$

9. $\frac{1}{6}$ $\frac{2}{12}, \frac{3}{18}, \frac{4}{24}$

10. $\frac{2}{7}$ $\frac{4}{14}, \frac{6}{21}, \frac{8}{28}$

11. $\frac{4}{32}$ $\frac{1}{8}, \frac{2}{16}, \frac{3}{24}$

12. $\frac{2}{18}$ $\frac{1}{9}, \frac{3}{27}, \frac{4}{36}$

13. $\frac{6}{15}$ $\frac{2}{5}, \frac{12}{30}, \frac{18}{45}$

Complete each pair of equivalent fractions.

14. $\frac{6}{9} = \frac{?}{54}$ 36

15. $\frac{3}{7} = \frac{18}{?}$ 42

16. $\frac{6}{8} = \frac{?}{4}$ 3

17. $\frac{3}{12} = \frac{?}{48}$ 12

18. $\frac{18}{27} = \frac{2}{?}$ 3

19. $\frac{17}{51} = \frac{?}{3}$ 1

20. $\frac{72}{99} = \frac{8}{?}$ 11

21. $\frac{100}{?} = \frac{5}{6}$ 120

Write each fraction in lowest terms.

22. $\frac{6}{9}$ $\frac{2}{3}$

23. $\frac{5}{30}$ $\frac{1}{6}$

24. $\frac{12}{20}$ $\frac{3}{5}$

25. $\frac{8}{40}$ $\frac{1}{5}$

26. $\frac{18}{30}$ $\frac{3}{5}$

27. $\frac{21}{48}$ $\frac{7}{16}$

28. $\frac{12}{24}$ $\frac{1}{2}$

29. $\frac{4}{15}$ $\frac{4}{15}$

30. $\frac{30}{100}$ $\frac{3}{10}$

31. $\frac{9}{24}$ $\frac{3}{8}$

Use mental math to find each value.

32. $\frac{1}{2}$ of 16   8

33. $\frac{3}{5}$ of 20   12

34. $\frac{1}{3}$ of 27   9

35. $\frac{2}{7}$ of 21   6

36. $\frac{7}{8}$ of 56   49

37. $\frac{4}{9}$ of 54   24

38. $\frac{3}{4}$ of 124   93

39. $\frac{1}{6}$ of 90   15

Standardized Testing ◀▶ Multiple Choice

1. Which fraction is equivalent to $\frac{28}{36}$?   B

   A $\frac{12}{18}$ B $\frac{70}{90}$ C $\frac{84}{106}$ D $\frac{128}{136}$

2. Which fraction is in lowest terms?   B

   A $\frac{7}{84}$ B $\frac{9}{43}$ C $\frac{27}{72}$ D $\frac{18}{100}$

Module Project

PROJECT NOTES

Since this is the first module project for students, you will want to explain that the project allows students to demonstrate their knowledge in a different way than a test or quiz. Each project is a bit different, but many conclude with an oral or visual presentation. This project presents a problem to solve and steps the students through the 4-step problem solving approach that they learned in this module. Students then work in a group to present their solution.

Labsheet: Each student needs a copy of Project Labsheet A, which is found in the *Teacher's Resource Book*.

Read **Project Labsheet A** with the students. Encourage students to use coins or other objects and to record the results of their work throughout the problem. Some students may prefer to use pictures rather than solid objects.

Projects usually take 2 days to complete. You may want to help students pace themselves by requiring that they complete a certain number of questions in class or at home. You can also check with groups as they work, listening to their discussions and strategies to make sure they understand the problem.

1. b., 2. See Additional Answers beginning on page A1.

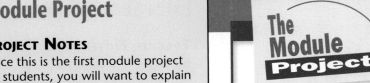

A Puzzling Problem

Throughout this module you have been working with patterns and learning how to solve problems. In this project, you will apply some of the ideas you have learned to solve the *30 Pennies In A Row* problem. You will work as a team to prepare a written report and to share your solution.

SET UP

Work in a group. You will need:
* Project Labsheet A

Understanding the Problem

1 It will help to study the situation before you try to solve the *30 Pennies in a Row* problem.

   a. Read the entire labsheet. Then read *The Situation* again.

   b. Breaking *The Situation* into steps can help you understand it. Suppose that in Step 1 you place 30 pennies in a row. What do you do in Step 2? In Steps 3–5? **See margin.**

2 **Focusing on Patterns** You can use a table to look at the patterns the coins create. **a–d. See margin.**

   a. Copy the table. For Steps 2–5, fill in the pattern using *P, N, D, Q*, and *F* to represent the different coins.

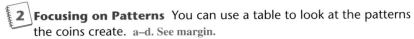

Term number	1	2	3	4	5	6	7	8	9	10
Step 1 Term	P	P	P	P	P	P	P	P	P	P
Step 2 Term	?	?	?	?	?	?	?	?	?	?
Step 3 Term	?	?	?	?	?	?	?	?	?	?
Step 4 Term	?	?	?	?	?	?	?	?	?	?
Step 5 Term	?	?	?	?	?	?	?	?	?	?

   b. Describe the sequence of coins in the row for Step 2.

   c. **Discussion** Discuss any relationships you see between each term in the row for Step 3 and its term number.

   d. Describe any patterns you see in the rows for Steps 4–5.

3 Your answer to the problem will be the value of the coins. Is $30 a reasonable estimate of the answer? Is $15 reasonable? Explain.

Making and Carrying Out Your Plan

4 Read *The Problem* again. Choose a strategy or strategies and solve the problem. **$9.18**

3. No; No;
There are only 30 coins, and they are not all silver dollars. There are 5 silver dollars and 5 fifty-cent pieces. For the sum to be $15, the other 20 coins would have to have an average value of about 38¢. However, they are all pennies, nickels, dimes, and quarters so their average value can't be 38¢.

Looking Back Now you will look back at your answer to the *30 Pennies in a Row* problem. Answers to Questions 5 and 6 will vary.

 5 a. Check that you solved the problem you were given and that your answer is reasonable.

b. Check your work for computational errors.

c. Can you think of any other way to check your answer? If so, explain your method and use it to check your work.

6 a. Is this problem like other problems you have solved? Explain.

b. How can you extend the problem to more than 30 coins?

7 Look at your table from Question 2.

a. Did the coin in position 1 change? in position 2? in position 6? No, Yes, Yes

b. In which positions do the coins seem to change the most? Why?

7. b. Positions 12, 24, 30; These numbers can be divided evenly by 4 of the numbers 2, 3, 4, 5, and 6. The more factors a number has, the more often it changes.

Presenting the Solution

8 Work as a team to prepare a presentation for the *30 Pennies in a Row* problem.

> ### Ideas for Preparing a Team Presentation
> - Everyone should participate in the presentation.
> - Presentation
>   possible types
>   - lecture/demonstration
>   - panel discussion
>   - news show
>   - skit
>   - musical
>   - magic show
>   use visuals (diagrams, pictures, graphs, tables)
> - Written Report
>   - restate the problem
>   - explain your plan
>   - show your work
>   - include visuals
>   - identify strategies used
>   - verify the solution
>   - extend the solution
>   - look for connections

a. Prepare your written report.

b. Plan how your team will present its solution to the class.

c. Practice your presentation a few times to make sure everyone on your team understands what to do.

9 As a team, present your solution to the rest of the class.

TEACHER NOTES

Students should complete the Review and Assessment independently in preparation for the Module Test.

Allow class time to discuss solutions and address any questions students may have. During this time, you may want to allow students to work in groups to share methods for solving the problems and to quiz each other on the concepts covered in this module.

20.

Term No.	5	6	7
Term	9	10	11

$t = n + 4$ where t = term and n = term number
$t = 50 + 4 = 54$

21.

Term No.	5	6	7
Term	20	24	28

$t = 4n$ where t = term and n = term number
$t = 4(50) = 200$

MODULE 1 Review and Assessment

Find the value of each expression. (Sec. 1 Explor. 1)

1. $54 - 63 \div 7$ 45
2. $12 + 7 \cdot 5$ 47
3. $180 \div (5 \cdot 6)$ 6
4. $7 + 45 - 22 - 9$ 21
5. $24 \div 4 \cdot 2$ 12
6. $(33 + 8) - (5 + 17)$ 19

Estimation For Exercises 7–12, show how to estimate each answer. (Sec. 1 Explor. 2)

7. $42 \cdot 66$
   about $40 \cdot 70 = 2,800$
8. $251 - 188$
   about $250 - 190 = 60$
9. $3122 + 890$
   about $3,100 + 900 = 4,000$
10. $257 + 34 + 85$
    about $260 + 30 + 90 = 380$
11. $186 \cdot 12$
    about $200 \cdot 10 = 2,000$
12. $3452 - 2128$
    about $3,500 - 2,100 = 1,400$

13. **Writing** Marco estimated the difference between $47.98 and $22.31 to be $30. Is his estimate *less than* or *greater than* the actual difference? Explain how you can tell without finding the exact difference. (Sec. 1 Explor. 2) greater than; He rounded $47.98 up and $22.31 down, so he increased the difference.

Mental Math For Exercises 14–17, explain how you can use mental math to find each answer. (Sec. 1 Explor. 3)

14. $67 + 19 + 143 + 31$
15. $7 \cdot 4 \cdot 5 \cdot 25$
16. $5 \cdot 46 \cdot 2$
17. $34 + 158 + 66$

14. $67 + 143 = 210$
    $19 + 31 = 50$
    $210 + 50 = 260$

15. $4 \cdot 25 = 100$
    $7 \cdot 5 = 35$
    $100 \cdot 35 = 3,500$

16. $5 \cdot 2 = 10$
    $10 \cdot 46 = 460$

17. $34 + 66 = 100$
    $100 + 158 = 258$

For Exercises 18 and 19, replace each ? with the correct term. Describe the rule you used for each sequence. (Sec. 2 Explor. 1)

18. 188, 185, 182, 179, _?_ , _?_ , _?_ , 167
19. 15, 30, 45, 60, _?_ , _?_ , _?_ , 120

18. 176, 173, 170; Start with 188. Subtract 3 from each term to get the next term, or subtract 3 times the term number from 191 to find the term.

19. 75, 90, 105; The term is 15 times the term number, or start with 15 and add 15 to each term to get the next term.

For each sequence,

- copy and complete the table,
- write an equation for the rule for the sequence, and
- use your rule to find the 50th term. (Sec. 2 Explor. 2)

20–21. See margin.

20.

Term Number	1	2	3	4	?	?	?
Term	5	6	7	8	?	?	?

21.

Term Number	1	2	3	4	?	?	?
Term	4	8	12	16	?	?	?

22. In Linda Tetley's 6th grade class, Gail, Lita, and Ben have been chosen to fill the positions of class president, vice president, and secretary. Make an organized list to find the number of different ways the three positions can be filled. (Sec. 3 Explor. 2) **See margin.**

23. Tom and Sarah are reading the same book. When Tom asked Sarah what page she was on, she replied that the product of the page number and the next page number was 17,030. What page was she reading? (Sec. 3 Explor. 3) **page 130; 130 · 131 = 17,030**

Tell whether each statement is *true* or *false*. If a statement is false, explain why. (Sec. 4 Explor. 1)

24. $\frac{1}{2}$ of the square is shaded.

25. $\frac{1}{3}$ of the circle is shaded.

26. $\frac{3}{8}$ of the rectangle is shaded. **True**

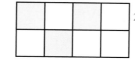

24. False; The square is not divided into two equal-sized parts.

25. False; The circle is divided into 4 equal-sized pieces, so $\frac{1}{4}$ of the circle is shaded.

Find the missing number. (Sec. 4 Explor. 2)

27. $6\frac{3}{5} = \frac{?}{5}$ **33** **28.** $\frac{34}{9} = ?\frac{7}{9}$ **3** **29.** $4\frac{2}{7} = \frac{30}{?}$ **7** **30.** $\frac{31}{8} = 3\frac{?}{8}$ **7**

31. Write three equivalent fractions for the fraction of the window at the right that is colored red. (Sec. 5 Explor. 1) **Answers will vary.** $\frac{1}{5}, \frac{4}{20}, \frac{2}{10}$

32. Which methods below will give a fraction equivalent to $\frac{2}{4}$? Explain. (Sec. 5 Explor. 2)

    a. $\frac{2+2}{4+2}$ b. $\frac{2 \cdot 2}{4 \cdot 2}$ c. $\frac{2 \div 2}{4 \div 2}$ d. $\frac{2-2}{4-2}$

Write each fraction in lowest terms. (Sec. 5 Explor. 2)

33. $\frac{6}{24}$ **$\frac{1}{4}$**   **34.** $\frac{9}{12}$ **$\frac{3}{4}$**   **35.** $\frac{25}{30}$ **$\frac{5}{6}$**   **36.** $\frac{3}{8}$ **$\frac{3}{8}$**   **37.** $\frac{42}{48}$ **$\frac{7}{8}$**

32. b and c. Multiplying or dividing both the numerator and denominator of a fraction by the same number yields an equivalent fraction.

Find each value. (Sec. 5 Explor. 3)

38. $\frac{3}{7}$ of 21 **9**   **39.** $\frac{5}{6}$ of 24 **20**   **40.** $\frac{2}{5}$ of 125 **50** **41.** $\frac{7}{9}$ of 63 **49**

R e f l e c t i n g ◀▶ on the Module

42. Write a letter to an adult member of your family describing the math you learned in this module and what you liked most and least about the module. **Answers will vary.**

Module 1   Review and Assessment   **71**

Assessment Options

TEACHER'S RESOURCE BOOK
• Module 1 Tests A and B
• Module 1 Standardized Test
• Module 1 Performance Assessment

TEST GENERATOR

22.

Pres.	VP	Sec.
G	L	B
G	B	L
L	G	B
L	B	G
B	G	L
B	L	G

G = Gail
B = Ben
L = Lita

Module 2 Overview

The *Assessment Scales* that will be used throughout the year to assess student performance on E²s, module projects, and other assignments are introduced in this module. The *Assessment Scales* are designed to help students improve their problem solving, reasoning, and communication skills. The module begins with a probability investigation, then introduces the *Assessment Scales* using the *World Cup* problem. Finally, playing the game *I Describe, You Draw* helps develop understanding of geometric language including the properties of triangles and other polygons.

Module 2 Planner

Day 1: Section 1	Day 2: Section 1	Day 3: Section 1	Day 4: Section 2	Day 5: Section 2
Setting the Stage, *p. 74* Exploration 1, *pp. 75–76*	Exploration 2 *through Question 17, pp. 77–78*	Exploration 2 *from Example, pp. 78–79* Key Concepts, *p. 80*	Setting the Stage, *p. 85* Exploration 1, *pp. 86–88*	Exploration 2, *pp. 88–89*
Day 6: Section 2	**Day 7: Review and Assessment**	**Day 8: Section 3**	**Day 9: Section 3**	**Day 10: Section 3**
Exploration 3, *pp. 90–91* Key Concepts, *p. 92*	Mid-Module Quiz	Setting the Stage, *p. 97* Exploration 1, *pp. 98–100*	Exploration 2, *pp. 101–102*	Exploration 3 *through Question 20, pp. 103–104*
Day 11: Section 3	**Day 12: Section 4**	**Day 13: Section 4**	**Day 14: Section 4**	**Day 15: Section 4**
Exploration 3 *from Question 21, p. 105* Key Concepts, *pp. 106–107*	Setting the Stage, *p. 112*	Exploration 1 *through Question 8, pp. 113–114*	Exploration 1 *from Question 9, pp. 114–115*	Exploration 2, *pp. 116–117*
Day 16: Section 4	**Day 17: E²**	**Day 18: Module Project**	**Day 19: Review and Assessment**	**Day 20: Review and Assessment**
Exploration 3, *p. 118* Key Concepts, *p. 119*	Work on Extended Exploration, *p. 123*	Assign Module Project, *pp. 124–125*	Assign Review and Assessment, *pp. 126–127*	Finish Module Project, *pp. 124–125* Discuss Review and Assessment, *pp. 126–127*
Day 21: Assessment				
Module 2 Test				

Materials List

Section	Materials
1	• Labsheets 1A–1B, 1 coin per group of 2, 1 number cube per group of 2
2	• Labsheets 2A–2B, students' solutions to World Cup and Handshake problems
3	• Labsheets 3A–3D, unlined paper, ruler, scissors, sticks of different lengths (optional)
4	• Labsheets 4A–4B, index cards or sticky notes, 2 pieces of string (each 3 ft long) per pair of students, scissors, protractor, *String Art Problem* solution, *Handshake Problem* solution, Assessment Scales, Self-assessment Scales
Project	• construction paper, scissors, ruler, glue stick or tape

Module 2 Objectives

Section	Objectives	NCTM Standards 2000*
1	• Find experimental and theoretical probabilities. • Determine if outcomes are equally likely. • Use probabilities to make predictions. • Identify impossible and certain events. • Plot probabilities on a number line.	**1, 4, 5, 6, 7, 8, 9, 10**
2	• Understand and use the Problem Solving Scale. • Apply different problem solving strategies. • Understand and use the Representations Scale. • Extend solutions to the general case. • Understand and use the Connections Scale.	**1, 2, 6, 7, 8, 9, 10**
3	• Name basic geometric figures (point, line, segment, ray, etc.). • Classify triangles by the lengths of their sides and by their angles. • Determine when triangles can be formed. • Identify types of angles. • Understand and use the Mathematical Language Scale.	**1, 3, 6, 7, 8, 9, 10**
4	• Classify polygons by their sides, angles, and pairs of parallel sides. • Sort polygons using a Venn diagram. • Measure an angle using a protractor. • Draw an angle using a protractor. • Understand and use the Presentation Scale.	**1, 3, 4, 6, 7, 8, 9, 10**

* See page T14.

Section 1 Probability

Section 1 Planner

Section Objectives

Exploration 1
- Find experimental probabilities
- Determine if outcomes are equally likely
- Use probabilities to predict

Exploration 2
- Find theoretical probabilities
- Identify impossible and certain events
- Plot probabilities on a number line

Days for Section 1

First Day
Setting the Stage, *p. 74*
Exploration 1, *pp. 75–76*

Second Day
Exploration 2 through Question 17,
pp. 77–78

Third Day
Exploration 2 from Example, *pp. 78–79*
Key Concepts, *p. 80*

Teaching Resources

Teacher's Resource Book
- Warm-Up
- Labsheets 1A and 1B
- Practice and Applications
- Study Guide
See page 73 for additional teaching resources.

Materials List

Exploration 1
- Labsheet 1A
- 1 coin per group of 2

Exploration 2
- Labsheet 1B
- 1 number cube per group of 2

Assessment Options

EMBEDDED ASSESSMENT
- Find experimental probabilities
  Exercises 1, 3
- Determine if outcomes are equally likely
  Exercises 4, 7
- Use probabilities to predict
  Exercise 5(d)
- Find theoretical probabilities
  Exercises 6, 8(b)
- Identify impossible and certain events
  Exercise 10
- Plot probabilities on a number line
  Exercises 8(e)

PERFORMANCE TASK/PORTFOLIO
- Exercise 10 on *p. 83 (open-ended)*
- Exercise 11 on *p. 83 (journal)*
- Exercise 16 on *p. 83 (extension)*

QUIZZES/TESTS
- Section 1 Quick Quiz

TEST GENERATOR

Section 1 Overview

In this section, students will perform coin toss and number cube rolling experiments so they can learn about experimental and theoretical probabilities. The explorations will suggest that over the long run, an experimental probability will approach the theoretical probability of an experiment.

Exploration 1
Students learn to use outcomes to write experimental probabilities and then use these probabilities to make predictions. Some students may anticipate the concept of *theoretical probability*, which is addressed in Exploration 2. Try to keep their attention on the point that, for the moment, they are performing *experiments* in probability. For that reason they should keep an open mind concerning how an experiment turns out.

Exploration 2
Students play the *Never a Six* game and compare the experimental probabilities to the theoretical probabilities of various outcomes on a number cube. Probabilities are represented as points from 0 (impossible) to 1 (certain) on a number line.

Guide for Assigning Homework

REGULAR SCHEDULING (45 MIN CLASS PERIOD)			EXERCISES TO NOTE		
Section/ P&A Pages	Core Assignment	Extended Assignment	Additional Practice/Review	Open-ended Problems	Extended Problems
1 pp. 81–84	**Day 1:** 1–4 **Day 2:** 5, SR 12–15 **Day 3:** 6–10, ROS 11	1–4 5, SR 12–15 6–10, ROS 11, Ext 16	EP, p. 84	PA 10	Ext 16

Key: PA = Practice & Application; ROS = Reflecting on the Section; SR = Spiral Review; TB = Toolbox; EP = Extra Skill Practice; Ext = Extension; ST = Standardized Testing

Math Background and Teaching Strategies

Classroom Notes

Bulletin board display ideas for this section include:

- collected class data for the coin flip experiment with comparisons of experimental and theoretical probabilities

- a probability number line for different events

- game shows and the related probabilities of winning

Interest centers for this section might include:

- experiments students can perform with related questions about the experimental probabilities

Math Strands

Topic Integration and Spiraling

Exploration 1

Exploration 1 focuses on experiments and experimental probability. The key terms *experiment, outcome, probability, experimental probability,* and *equally likely* are defined in the context of a coin flipping simulation. This way students can associate each term with an actual action or calculation made from an activity they have experienced. The simplicity of flipping a coin allows students to focus on the probability concepts without too many different possible outcomes. Students see how fraction concepts from Module 1 can be used to describe the chance of an event occurring and that a probability must be a number from 0 through 1.

Exploration 2

Exploration 2 focuses on theoretical probability. A game allows students to see an experiment that has more than 2 outcomes. Students continue to collect experimental data in order to compare experimental and theoretical probabilities. Students learn to interpret the likelihood of an event by plotting the probabilities of events on a number line and comparing them to certain, equally likely, and impossible events.

Books 2 and 3 build on the basic concepts of probability taught in Book 1. Studies will include probabilities of complementary events, probabilities for multistage experiments, and geometric probabilities based on lengths, areas, and volumes.

Section 2 Assessment Scales

Section 2 Planner

Section Objectives

Exploration 1
- Understand and use the Problem Solving Scale

Exploration 2
- Apply different problem solving strategies
- Understand and use the Representations Scale

Exploration 3
- Understand and use the Connections Scale
- Extend solutions to the general case

Days for Section 2

First Day
Setting the Stage, *p. 85*
Exploration 1, *pp. 86–88*

Second Day
Exploration 2, *pp. 88–89*

Third Day
Exploration 3, *pp. 90–91*
Key Concepts, *p. 92*

Teaching Resources

Teacher's Resource Book
- Warm-Up
- Labsheets 2A and 2B
- Practice and Applications
- Study Guide
See page 73 for additional teaching resources.

Materials List

Exploration 2
- Team solutions to *World Cup Problem*

Exploration 3
- Labsheets 2A–2B
- Team solutions to *World Cup* and *Handshake Problems*

Assessment Options

EMBEDDED ASSESSMENT
- Understand and use the Problem Solving Scale
  Exercises 1, 2
- Apply different problem solving strategies
  Exercises 1, 2, 3
- Understand and use the Representations Scale
  Exercises 6, 8
- Understand and use the Connections Scale
  Exercise 9
- Extend solutions to the general case
  Exercise 8(b)

PERFORMANCE TASK/PORTFOLIO
- Exercise 4 on *p. 93 (challenge)**
- Exercise 6 on *p. 94**
- Exercise 7 on *p. 94 (create your own)*
- Exercise 9 on *p. 94**
- Exercise 10 on *p. 95 (journal)*
- Standardized Testing on *p. 96 (free response)*

* *indicates a problem solving task that can be assessed using the Assessment Scales*

QUIZZES/TESTS
- Section 2 Quick Quiz
- Mid-Module Quiz

TEST GENERATOR

Section 2 Overview

In this section, students will have the opportunity to assess how well they apply the 4-step problem solving approach developed in Module 1.

Exploration 1
Students begin this exploration by working as a team to solve the *World Cup Problem* to determine the number of games played in the first round of the 2006 World Cup finals. The Assessment Scales that students will be using during the year to assess and improve their problem solving, reasoning, and communications skills are introduced. Students use the *Problem Solving Scale* to assess solutions to the *World Cup Problem*.

Exploration 2
Students use the *Representations Scale* to assess a solution to the *World Cup Problem*. They then solve the *Handshake Problem* and use the *Representations Scale* to assess how well they used visual representations such as diagrams, tables, and graphs to solve the problem and to help explain their solution.

Exploration 3
The *Connections Scale* assesses how well students relate problems to other problems, to mathematical ideas, or to applications. It also assesses students' ability to extend and generalize solutions. To illustrate the *Connections Scale*, students analyze connections among the triangular numbers from the *Setting the Stage*, the *World Cup Problem*, and the *Handshake Problem*.

Guide for Assigning Homework

REGULAR SCHEDULING (45 MIN CLASS PERIOD)			EXERCISES TO NOTE		
Section/ P&A Pages	**Core Assignment**	**Extended Assignment**	**Additional Practice/Review**	**Open-ended Problems**	**Extended Problems**
2 pp. 93–96	**Day 1:** 1–3 **Day 2:** 5–8 **Day 3:** 9, ROS 10, SR 11–14	1–4 5–8 9, ROS 10, SR 11–14	EP, p. 96	PA 7	Challenge, PA 4

Key: PA = Practice & Application; ROS = Reflecting on the Section; SR = Spiral Review; TB = Toolbox; EP = Extra Skill Practice; Ext = Extension; ST = Standardized Testing

Math Background and Teaching Strategies

Classroom Notes

Bulletin board displays for this section include:

• enlarged copy of the *Assessment Scales*

Student work displays for this might section include:

• teams' *World Cup* and *Handshake Problem* solutions

• Exercise 7 visuals with student generated word problems

Visitors for this section might include:

• tournament planners

Math Strands

Topic Spiraling and Integration
The purpose of this section is to introduce students to the use of the *Assessment Scales* both in solving a problem and in evaluating solutions.

The problems in each exploration are solved in teams so that students can learn from one another by seeing different ways others might approach a problem. The overall intention of this section is not for students to be correct in answering each problem, but to learn how to analyze their work and use self-assessment to improve their problem solving skills.

Exploration 1
The first exploration builds on students' work in Module 1 where they learned the 4-step problem solving process. Now students look at their work on a problem and relate the four steps to the *Problem Solving Scale* of the *Assessment Rubric*.

Exploration 2
Students learn how using diagrams, tables, graphs, equations and other representations can help solve problems and explain solutions. By viewing the work of a fictitious

student, they learn to look at a solution impartially and to assess the solution on the *Representations Scale*.

Exploration 3
The *Connections Scale* encourages students to look for patterns among similar problems presented in different contexts. Connections help students to extend and generalize solutions and to determine how newly learned mathematics concepts integrate with their existing band of knowledge. Connections are often the most difficult for students because they may have been programmed to solve a problem and then stop as stated at a score of 1 on the rubric. With practice, examples of connections throughout the curriculum, and the opportunity to solve many rich problems that will serve as resources, students should improve in their ability to make connections.

72F

Section ③ Lines, Angles, and Triangles

Section 3 Planner

Section Objectives

Exploration 1
- Name basic geometric figures (point, line, segment, ray, etc.)

Exploration 2
- Classify triangles by the lengths of their sides
- Determine when triangles can be formed

Exploration 3
- Identify types of angles
- Classify triangles by their angles
- Understand and use the Mathematical Language Scale

Days for Section 3

First Day
Setting the Stage, *p. 97*
Exploration 1, *pp. 98–100*

Second Day
Exploration 2, *pp. 101–102*

Third Day
Exploration 3 through Question 20, *pp. 103–104*

Fourth Day
Exploration 3 from Question 21, *p. 105*
Key Concepts, *pp. 106–107*

Teaching Resources

Teacher's Resource Book
- Warm-Up
- Labsheets 3A, 3B, 3C, and 3D
- Practice and Applications
- Study Guide
See page 73 for additional teaching resources.

Materials List

Setting the Stage
- cards from Labsheet 3A
- 2 sheets of unlined paper per two students

Exploration 2
- Labsheets 3B–3C
- scissors or sticks in different lengths
- ruler

Exploration 3
- Labsheet 3D

Practice and Applications
- ruler or straightedge

Assessment Options

EMBEDDED ASSESSMENT
- Name basic geometric figures
  Exercises 1–7
- Classify triangles by side lengths
  Exercises 8–10, 23–28
- Determine when triangles can be formed
  Exercises 11–14, 15
- Identify types of angles
  Exercises 19–22
- Classify triangles by their angles
  Exercises 23–28
- Understand and use the Mathematical Language Scale
  Exercise 29b

PERFORMANCE TASK/PORTFOLIO
- Exercise 30 on *p. 110 (challenge)*
- Exercise 31 on *p. 110 (research)*
- Standardized Testing on *p. 111 (free response)*

QUIZZES/TESTS
- Section 3 Quick Quiz

TEST GENERATOR

Section 3 Overview

In this section, students will learn the importance of language in communicating about geometric figures. The *Mathematical Language Scale* will be introduced to help students assess and improve their use of appropriate vocabulary to communicate ideas.

Exploration 1
After completing the *I Describe, You Draw* activity in the *Setting the Stage*, students learn vocabulary that will help them describe certain figures such as lines, rays, segments, and points. Conventions such as using capital letters to name points and correct symbols for naming figures are discussed. Relationships between lines in a plane are represented using symbols for parallel and perpendicular.

Exploration 2
Students reflect back on the *I Describe, You Draw* activity to see how vocabulary related to triangles could help them better complete the activity. Triangles are classified according to their sides lengths. Students use hands-on materials to discover which lengths will form triangles.

Exploration 3
Students learn how to use symbols to name an angle. Triangles are classified according to their angle measures. Students create their own *I Describe, You Draw* cards and identify how mathematical language can help them better communicate.

Guide for Assigning Homework

REGULAR SCHEDULING (45 MIN CLASS PERIOD)			EXERCISES TO NOTE		
Section/ P&A Pages	Core Assignment	Extended Assignment	Additional Practice/Review	Open-ended Problems	Extended Problems
3 pp. 108–112	**Day 1:** 1–7 **Day 2:** 8–15 **Day 3:** 16–28 **Day 3:** 29, ROS 31, SR 32–41	1–7 8–15 16–28 29–30, ROS 31, SR 32–41	EP, p. 111	PA 29(a), 31	Challenge, PA 30 E² p. 112

Key: PA = Practice & Application; ROS = Reflecting on the Section; SR = Spiral Review; TB = Toolbox; EP = Extra Skill Practice; Ext = Extension; ST = Standardized Testing

Math Background and Teaching Strategies

Classroom Notes

Bulletin board displays for this section include:

• chart of geometric terms, figures and symbols from this section

Student work displays for this section might include:

• student created *I Describe, You Draw* cards from Question 23

• responses to Reflecting Exercise 31

Math Strands

Topic Spiraling and Integration

In the *Setting the Stage* students describe a geometric drawing to a partner using only verbal clues. The partner then uses the clues to try to reproduce the drawing. This activity shows students how difficult it can be to communicate without a common vocabulary. It also provides an opportunity for the teacher to assess students' knowledge of geometry concepts and vocabulary.

Exploration 1
Exploration 1 introduces basic geometry terms and the related symbols for describing and naming points, lines, segments, rays, planes, and parallel and perpendicular lines. Students will use this knowledge in Module 6 when they identify similar and congruent figures and their corresponding parts. Parallel and perpendicular segments form the basis for classifying quadrilaterals in Section 4 of Module 2.

Exploration 2
In Exploration 2, students learn to classify triangles by their side lengths. They also use physical models to discover the *triangle inequality* which is not formally introduced until Module 3 of Book 2. In Module 6, the different classifications of triangles will help students justify why not all triangles are similar or congruent.

Exploration 3
Angle notation and the classification of angles are introduced in Exploration 3. This information is then used to classify triangles by the types of angles they contain. Students explore whether a triangle can have two right angles and how an obtuse angle in a triangle dictates what type of angle the other two angles in the triangle must be. These discoveries will provide important references when students investigate the sum of the measures of the angles in a triangle.

The section concludes with an introduction to the *Mathematical Language Scale*. Now that students have a more robust geometry vocabulary, they are able to better use the scale for assessment.

Section 4   Polygons and Angles

Section 4 Planner

Section Objectives

Exploration 1
- Classify polygons
- Sort using Venn diagrams

Exploration 2
- Measure an angle using a protractor
- Draw an angle using a protractor

Exploration 3
- Understand and use the Presentation Scale

Days for Section 4

First Day
Setting the Stage, *p. 112*

Second Day
Exploration 1 through Question 8, *pp. 113–114*

Third Day
Exploration 1 from Question 9, *pp. 114–115*

Fourth Day
Exploration 2, *pp. 116–117*

Fifth Day
Exploration 3, *p. 118*
Key Concepts, *p. 119*

Teaching Resources

Teacher's Resource Book
- Warm-Up
- Labsheets 4A and 4B
- Practice and Applications
- Study Guide
See page 73 for additional teaching resources.

Materials List

Exploration 1
- Labsheet 4A
- index cards or sticky notes
- 2 pieces of string (each 3 ft long) per pair of students
- scissors

Exploration 2
- Labsheet 4B
- protractor

Exploration 3
- *Handshake Problem* solution
- *String Art Problem* solution

Practice and Applications
- *String Art Problem* solution

Assessment Options

EMBEDDED ASSESSMENT
- Classify polygons
  Exercises 1, 2
- Sort using Venn diagrams
  Exercise 12
- Measure and draw an angle
  Exercises 6, 8
- Understand and use the Presentation Scale
  Exercise 11

PERFORMANCE TASK/PORTFOLIO
- Exercise 11 on *p. 120*
- Exercise 12 on *p. 121 (visual thinking)*
- Extended Exploration on *p. 123*
- Module Project on *pp. 124–125*

* indicates a problem-solving task that can be assessed using the Assessment Scales

QUIZZES/TESTS
- Section 4 Quick Quiz
- Module Tests A and B
- Module Standardized Test
- Module Performance Assessment

TEST GENERATOR

Section 4 Overview

In this section, students will name and classify polygons by the number of sides and other characteristics. They will also learn to measure and draw angles. The section culminates with the application of the *Presentation Scale* to assess their work on the string art problem.

Exploration 1
Students begin this exploration by creating Venn diagrams using loops of string. First they use one circle and show set inclusion/exclusion by sorting different shapes into polygons, regular polygons, octagons, and quadrilaterals. Then, using two circles, students see how different quadrilaterals share certain characteristics.

Exploration 2
Students learn to measure angles with a protractor. The measures of angle in degrees are related to rotations between 0° and 360°.

Exploration 3
Students learn about the *Presentation Scale* and use it to help plan the presentation of their solution of the *Handshake Problem* and to assess their work.

Guide for Assigning Homework

REGULAR SCHEDULING (45 MIN CLASS PERIOD)			EXERCISES TO NOTE		
Section/ P&A Pages	**Core Assignment**	**Extended Assignment**	**Additional Practice/Review**	**Open-ended Problems**	**Extended Problems**
4 pp. 120–122	**Day 1:** SR 13–15 **Day 2:** 1, SR 16–17 **Day 3:** 2–3 **Day 4:** 5–10 **Day 5:** 11, ROS 12	SR 13–15 1, SR 16–17 2–4 5–10 11, ROS 12	EP, p. 122 Review & Assessment, pp. 126–127		Challenge, PA 4 Mod Proj, pp. 124–125

Key: PA = Practice & Application; ROS = Reflecting on the Section; SR = Spiral Review; TB = Toolbox; EP = Extra Skill Practice; Ext = Extension; ST = Standardized Testing

Math Background and Teaching Strategies

Classroom Notes

Bulletin board displays for this section include:

- the word part table from page 114 with pictures of polygons and their names

- steps for measuring and drawing angles with a protractor with examples showing angles and their measures

Student work displays for this section might include:

- E^2 presentations

- pop-up cards from Module Project

Math Strands

Topic Spiraling and Integration

Exploration 1
In this exploration, students use Venn diagrams as a tool for sorting polygons. Students already know from Section 3 that triangles can be sorted and classified according to their side lengths and by the measures of their angles. Now the concept of classifying is applied to quadrilaterals. Students begin by using one circle and showing set inclusion/exclusion by sorting different shapes into polygons, regular polygons, octagons, and quadrilaterals. Next, two loops are used in an overlapping Venn diagram to sort and compare quadrilaterals according to various properties of their angles and sides. Using Venn diagrams to sort geometric figures helps students develop understanding of the definitions and the properties of the objects.

Exploration 2
In Section 3, students classified angles by sight. Now they will learn how to use a protractor to measure angles in degrees. Measuring with a protractor is an important skill that will be used throughout Books 1, 2, and 3 of this series. Students often can measure given angles but not know how to draw an angle with a given measure. Students' knowledge of how to measure an existing angle is used to help develop techniques for using a protractor to draw an angle with a specified measure.

Exploration 3
The introduction of the *Assessment Scales* is completed in this exploration with the introduction of the *Presentation Scale*. Students use the *Presentation Scale* to assess their solutions to the *Handshake Problem*. The *Presentation Scale* helps students develop their ability to present their solutions to problems and to communicate their reasoning in an effective manner.

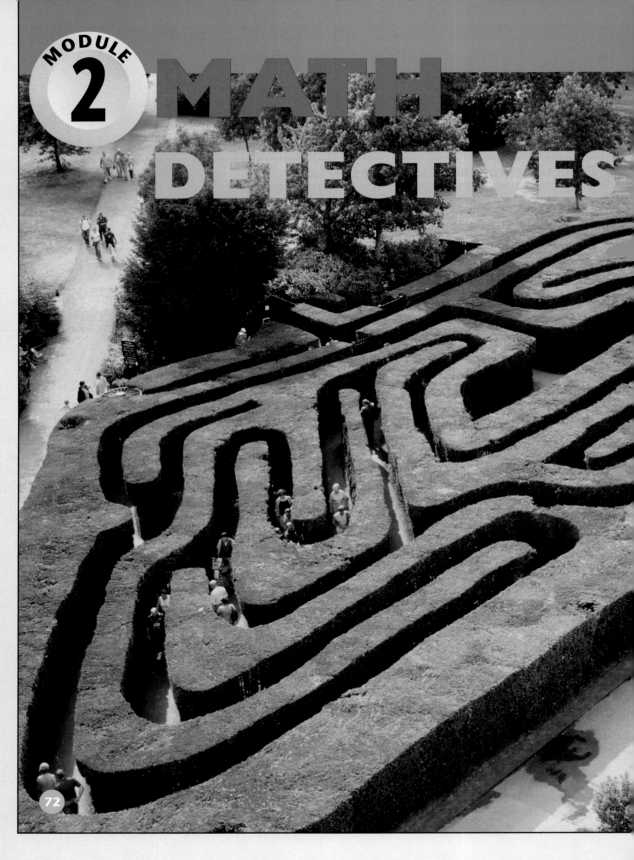

Module 2

OVERVIEW

The *Assessment Scales* that will be used throughout the year to assess student performance on E²s, module projects, and other assignments are introduced in this module. The *Assessment Scales* are designed to help students improve their problem solving, reasoning, and communication skills. The module begins with a probability investigation, then introduces the *Assessment Scales* using the *World Cup* problem. Finally, playing the game *I Describe, You Draw* helps develop understanding of geometric language including the properties of triangles and other polygons.

PREREQUISITE SKILLS

Warm-Up Exercises for each section are provided in the *Teacher's Resource Book*. You can use these exercises to review skills and concepts students will need for each section. In addition, the Spiral Review exercises at the end of each section in the student edition provide practice on prerequisite skills.

MODULE DIAGNOSTIC TEST

The Module Diagnostic Test in the *Teacher's Resource Book* can be used to assess students' prior knowledge of skills and concepts that will be taught in each section of this module. You can use test results to help structure your teaching to meet the diverse needs of your classroom.

MODULE

2 **MATH**
DETECTIVES

72

CONNECTING
MATHEMATICS
The & Theme

MODULE 2 · SECTION OVERVIEW

1 Probability
As you perform coin tosses and play a game with a number cube:
- ◆ Find experimental and theoretical probabilities.

2 Assessment Scales
As you explore problems about the World Cup and about string art:
- ◆ Learn to assess and improve your problem solving skills.

3 Lines, Angles, and Triangles
As you learn to accurately describe and draw geometric figures:
- ◆ Name basic geometric figures.
- ◆ Classify angles and triangles.
- ◆ Decide when a triangle can be formed.

4 Polygons and Angles
As you explore shapes found in puzzles and nature:
- ◆ Classify polygons.
- ◆ Sort polygons using a Venn diagram.
- ◆ Measure and draw angles using a protractor.

The Module Project ▸ Pop-Up Art

Pop-up art is made by cutting and folding paper using geometric shapes and patterns. You will explore some of the techniques and mathematical skills that are used to create pop-ups. Then you will use the mathematics you have learned to design and create a pop-up of your own.

For the Module Project
See pp. 124–125.

INTERNET
Resources and practice at
classzone.com

Module Resources

TEACHER'S RESOURCE BOOK
Resources
- *The Math Gazette* (parent newsletter)
- Warm-Ups
- Labsheets
- Practice and Applications
- Study Guide

Assessment
- Section Quick Quizzes
- Mid-Module Quiz
- Module 2 Diagnostic Test
- Module 2 Tests A and B
- Module 2 Standardized Test
- Module 2 Performance Assessment
- Modules 1 and 2 Cumulative Test

SPANISH RESOURCES
- *The Math Gazette* (parent newsletter)
- Practice and Applications
- Assessment
- Spanish Glossary

STUDENT WORKBOOK

TECHNOLOGY BOOK

TECHNOLOGY RESOURCES
- @Home Tutor
- Test Generator
- Activity Generator
- Professional Development DVD
- Online Activities

Section ① Probability

Detecting Outcomes

Setting the Stage

In this module, you will use clues to solve problems and make decisions just like detectives do when they are solving a mystery. First you will explore *chance* to see how it can help you understand games and make decisions.

Using a coin can solve the mystery of who gets to start a game. In a pick-up basketball game, for example, a coin toss may be used to decide which team gets the ball first.

▲ The Romans used coin flipping to make decisions. The face of the emperor Caesar was on one side of many Roman coins. If Caesar's head came up on a coin toss, it was taken to mean that he approved of the decision.

1. Yes, because a coin has one heads side and one tails side, the chances are equal. However, some students may take the view that teams should earn the choice based on their winning record, not a coin.

Think About It

1 Do you think a coin toss is a fair way to decide which team gets the ball first? Why?

2 Suppose your teacher announced that each day from Monday through Friday a coin would be flipped and you would have a quiz if a head appeared. About how many quizzes do you think you would have each week? Explain your answer. 2 or 3 quizzes. I would expect a quiz about $\frac{1}{2}$ of the time, or on 2–3 days out of the 5 days.

Exploration 1

Experimental Probability

SET UP *Work with a partner. You will need: • a coin • Labsheet 1A*

Sometimes detectives act out the events of a crime to help solve it. You will flip a coin to find the chance of flipping a head or a tail.

▶ A single flip of a coin is an example of an **experiment**. The result of the flip, a *head* or a *tail*, is an **outcome**.

Use Labsheet 1A for Questions 3–12.

3 With your partner, flip a coin 20 times. Tally the outcomes of your 20 flips in the table. **Check students' work.**

4 **a.** Which outcome occurred most often in the 20 flips?
 Answers will vary for partner pairs.
 b. What fraction of the flips were heads? What fraction were tails?
 Answers will vary. Fractions for heads or for tails may be close to $\frac{1}{2}$.

▶ A **probability** is a number that tells how likely something is to happen. The fractions you found in Question 4 are probabilities.

5 **Discussion** How can you use the fraction of the flips that were heads from Question 4(b) to describe the chance of getting a head?

▶ A probability found by repeating an experiment a number of times and observing the outcomes is an **experimental probability**.

$$\frac{\text{experimental probability}}{\text{of an outcome}} = \frac{\text{number of times the outcome occurred}}{\text{number of times the experiment was repeated}}$$

EXAMPLE

Suppose heads occurred on 23 out of 40 flips of a coin. What is the experimental probability of heads?

SAMPLE RESPONSE

$$\frac{\text{experimental}}{\text{probability of heads}} = \frac{\text{number of times heads occurred}}{\text{number of times the coin was flipped}} = \frac{23}{40}$$

6 In the table on Labsheet 1A, record the number of heads and tails flipped by four other pairs of students. **Answers will vary by groups.**

GOAL

LEARN HOW TO...
 ◆ find experimental probabilities
 ◆ determine if outcomes are equally likely
 ◆ use probabilities to make predictions

AS YOU...
 ◆ perform coin toss experiments

KEY TERMS
 ◆ experiment
 ◆ outcome
 ◆ probability
 ◆ experimental probability
 ◆ equally likely

FOR ◀ HELP
with *fractions*, see
MODULE 1, p. 46

5. The denominator describes the number of times you flipped the coin and the numerator expresses how many of those flips were heads, so it tells you out of a certain number of flips how many you expect to be heads.

Exploration 1

TEACHING NOTES
Question 3 Instruct students to let the coins land on their desks or the floor instead of trying to catch them. Some students may find it difficult to flip a coin. Provide a small paper cup that they can use to shake the coin and then dump it out onto their desks.

Question 4 It is not expected that students' tallies be close to 50% heads and 50% tails with only 20 flips. Students will observe the effects of repeated trials in **Questions 8 and 10** when they combine their data with that of four other groups and the class respectively.

The Classroom Example below can be used in addition to the Example in the text before students find the experimental probabilities of four other pairs of students.

CLASSROOM EXAMPLE

Suppose tails occurred on 17 out of 40 tosses of a coin. What is the experimental probability of tails? of heads?

Answers:
Experimental probability of tails
$$= \frac{\text{number of times tails occurred}}{\text{number of times coin was tossed}}$$
$$= \frac{17}{40}$$

Since the outcome of a flip must either be a head or a tail, 40 − 17 = 23 of the flips were heads.

Experimental probability of heads
$$= \frac{\text{number of times heads occurred}}{\text{number of times coin was tossed}}$$
$$= \frac{23}{40}$$

Exploration 1 *continued*

TEACHING NOTES
Checkpoint Question 7 focuses on how well students understand experimental probability. Intuitively, they should see that the probability of tossing a head is approximately equal to $\frac{10}{20}$ or $\frac{1}{2}$. Students should also understand that even though they all were doing the same experiment, there is no reason to be surprised or disappointed by the fact that individual results vary greatly. In fact, it would be surprising if the results of the four groups were to agree exactly.

To predict the class results in **Question 9**, students will need to determine how many total flips were made by multiplying the number of groups by 20. Watch for non-proportional reasoning such as in 100 tosses, 45 or 5 less than half were heads, so in 260 tosses, 5 less than half or 125 will be heads. Instead, encourage use of groups. It would take 2 groups of 100 and 3 groups of 20 to reach 260 trials. For each group of 100 there would be 45 heads, and since $\frac{45}{100} = \frac{9}{20}$, for each group of 20 there would be 9 heads. So the number of heads would be $2 \cdot 45 + 3 \cdot 9 = 117$. The problem could also be solved by finding the numerator of a fraction with denominator 260 that is equivalent to $\frac{45}{100}$. Once students have had fraction multiplication, they will recognize that this is the same as finding $\frac{45}{100}$ of 260 or $\frac{45}{100} \cdot 260$.

9., 11., and 13. c. See Additional Answers beginning on page A1.

✔ **QUESTION 7**

...checks that you can find experimental probabilities.

7. b. Answers will vary. Students may choose the most commonly occurring probability or an average probability for their group.

8. Check students' work. Answers will vary. Probabilities should be closer to 50 out of 100 or $\frac{1}{2}$ heads when data are combined.

13. b. No, the "2" can be obtained on three-fourths of the circle's area, so "2" has a greater chance of occurring.

✔ **QUESTION 12**

...checks that you can use probabilities to predict results.

14. a. Yes, each choice has the same chance of occurring since tossing heads and tails are equally likely.

7 ✔ **CHECKPOINT** Use your table of data from Question 6.

a. Find the experimental probability of heads for each pair of students. Are the probabilities the same for each pair? Answers will vary. Some may have the same probability.

b. Suppose you flip the coin again 20 times. What do you expect the experimental probability of heads to be? Why?

8 The table now has data for 100 flips. What is the experimental probability of heads and of tails for the 100 flips?

9 **Try This as a Class**

a. How can you use the probabilities from Question 8 to predict the number of heads and tails for the whole class? See margin.

b. In the whole class, how many of the flips would you expect to be heads? to be tails? See margin.

10 a. Collect the coin toss data for the whole class. Data will vary.

b. How many times was the outcome heads? tails? Answers will vary. Results should be close to half of the flips.

c. How do the number of heads and of tails compare to your predictions in Question 9(b)? Answers will vary.

d. What is the experimental probability of heads for the whole class? the experimental probability of tails? Answers will vary. Probabilities should be close to $\frac{1}{2}$ for each outcome.

11 **Discussion** Compare the experimental probability for your 20 flips, for the 100 flips recorded on Labsheet 1A, and for the class's total flips. Which gives you the best idea of the chances of getting heads? See margin.

12 ✔ **CHECKPOINT** Suppose you flip a coin 1000 times. About how many times do you expect the result to be heads? tails? about 500; about 500

▶ Outcomes are **equally likely** if they have the same chance of occurring.

13 a. When you flip a coin, are the chances of getting heads and of getting tails equally likely? Yes, they are equally likely.

b. When you spin the spinner at the left, are the chances of the spinner stopping on 1 and stopping on 2 equally likely? Why?

c. Describe an experiment that has equally likely outcomes. See margin.

14 a. Based on what you have learned, do you think the toss of a coin is a fair way to decide between two choices? Explain.

b. Give an example other than a coin flip of a fair way to decide between two choices. Answers will vary.

 HOMEWORK EXERCISES ▶ See Exs. 1–5 on pp. 81–82.

Exploration 2

Theoretical Probability

SET UP | *Work with a partner. You will need:* • *Labsheet 1B*
• *number cube*

Detectives examine evidence before they make decisions. You will play a game in which you have to decide whether to roll the number cube again or to stop based on the results of the previous rolls.

The object of the game *Never a Six* is to be the first player to score a total of 50 or more points.

Never a Six

- Players alternate turns.

- On your turn, roll the number cube. If the result is not a 6, record the number rolled. This is your point score for that roll.

- If you roll a 6, your turn is over. Any points rolled during the turn **cannot** be added to your total score.

- You may continue to roll the number cube and record points until you decide to stop or until you roll a 6.

- If you decide to stop, total the points you rolled during your turn and add them to your total score.

Use Labsheet 1B for Questions 15–16.

15 **a.** With a partner, play one game of *Never a Six*. Record each number you roll and your total points for each turn in the table. **Check students' work on labsheet.**

b. Discussion Explain the strategies you used when you played the game. **Answers will vary.**

16 **a.** List all the possible outcomes for a single roll of a number cube.
1, 2, 3, 4, 5, 6

b. Look at the numbers you rolled during the game of *Never a Six*. Do all the numbers seem to have an equal chance of occurring? Explain. **Yes, each number occurs only once on the number cube.**

TEACHING NOTES
For **Question 10**, ask each pair of students for their data on the number of outcomes that were heads. Record the responses on the board so the entire class can see all the results. Use each pair's data for 20 flips. Do not use the results in their table of 100 flips since some groups' data would then be represented more than once.

In **Question 11**, point out that although the number of heads each pair got in their 20 trials may have varied greatly, the combined data for 5 groups and for the whole class shows that as the number of trials increases, the experimental probability of a head begins to approach $\frac{1}{2}$.

Exploration 2

TEACHING NOTES
Remind students that as in the coin flipping problem in Exploration 1, predictions tend to be more accurate with more data. Thus they should review all of their rolls from *Never a Six*, not just one turn, before answering **Question 16(b)**.

TEACHING NOTES

In **Question 17(e)**, make sure students understand why it is impossible to score six points. By the rules of the game, no points are awarded for a 6, so the probability of getting six points is zero.

It is important to discuss the correct answers to **Question 17** before introducing theoretical probability, since the answers will be used to calculate the theoretical probabilities in **Checkpoint Question 18**. The total number of possible outcomes can be determined from the list of outcomes in **Question 17(c)** and used to calculate the theoretical probabilities in **Question 18**.

Students may benefit from finding additional probabilities for the spinner in the **Example**. Ask students questions such as, "Describe an event that has a probability of $\frac{2}{5}$." (*landing on an even number*) or "What is the probability of landing on a number greater than 2?" $\left(\frac{3}{5}\right)$

18. a. $\frac{3}{6}$ or $\frac{1}{2}$

b. $\frac{3}{6}$ or $\frac{1}{2}$

c. $\frac{6}{6}$ or 1

d. $\frac{1}{6}$

e. $\frac{0}{6}$ or 0

▶ A **set** is any collection of objects. An **event** is a set of outcomes for a particular experiment. For example, in *Never a Six* the outcomes **a roll of 4** and **a roll of 5** make up the event **scoring more than 3 points on a single roll.**

| Event | = | set of outcomes |

Scoring more than 3 points on a roll in *Never a Six*

$\left\{ \boxed{\vdots}, \boxed{\because} \right\}$

You can write a set by enclosing the objects of the set in braces.

17 Suppose you roll a number cube one time. List the outcomes that would result in each of the following events when playing *Never a Six*.

   a. scoring less than 3 points {1, 2, 6}

   b. scoring an odd number of points {1, 3, 5}

   c. scoring 0, 1, 2, 3, 4, or 5 points {6, 1, 2, 3, 4, 5}

   d. scoring 0 points {6}

   e. scoring 6 points {} (no outcomes)

▶ A probability found without doing an experiment is a **theoretical probability**. *When the outcomes of an experiment are equally likely*:

$$\text{theoretical probability of an event} = \frac{\text{number of outcomes in the event}}{\text{total number of possible outcomes}}$$

EXAMPLE

What is the theoretical probability that the spinner stops on an odd number?

The outcomes are equally likely.

SAMPLE RESPONSE

odd outcomes: 1, 3, 5

$$\text{theoretical probability of an odd number} = \frac{\text{number of odd outcomes}}{\text{total number of possible outcomes}} = \frac{3}{5}$$

all possible outcomes: 1, 2, 3, 4, 5

✔ **QUESTION 18**

...checks that you can find the theoretical probability of an event.

You need to count the number of times the outcome was either 4 or 5.

18 ✔ **CHECKPOINT** Determine the theoretical probability of each event in Question 17.

19 **a.** What is the theoretical probability of scoring more than 3 points on the first roll of a turn in *Never a Six*? $\frac{2}{6}$ or $\frac{1}{3}$

   b. **Use Labsheet 1B.** Find the experimental probability of the event *scoring more than 3 points on the first roll of a turn*. Answers will vary.

   c. How do the probabilities in parts (a) and (b) compare? Answers will vary.

20 Did any of the events in Question 17 have a probability of 0? Why? Yes, scoring six points is not possible. If you roll a 6, you get zero points.

21 Did any of the events in Question 17 have a probability of 1? Why?

▶ **Impossible and Certain Events** If an event cannot happen, it is an **impossible event** and has a probability of 0. If an event must happen, it is a **certain event** and has a probability of 1.

22 **Discussion** Could the probability of an event ever be greater than 1 or less than 0? Explain.

You can plot probabilities on a number line by dividing the part of the number line between 0 and 1 into equal parts.

EXAMPLE

Plot the probability that the spinner in the Example on page 78 lands on an odd number.

- Sketch a number line. Label 0 and 1.
- Mark off and label five equal-size parts between 0 and 1.
- Plot the point $\frac{3}{5}$.

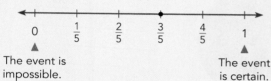

The event is impossible.   The event is certain.

23 **Try This as a Class**

a. Including the 0 and 1 marks, how many equally-spaced marks are needed to plot the probabilities you found in Question 18 on the number line? 7 marks

b. Draw and label a number line. Plot and label each probability from Question 18 on your number line.

$$\xleftarrow{\quad}\overset{0\ \ \frac{1}{6}\ \ \frac{2}{6}\ \ \frac{3}{6}\ \ \frac{4}{6}\ \ \frac{5}{6}\ \ 1}{\mid\ \ \mid\ \ \mid\ \ \mid\ \ \mid\ \ \mid\ \ \mid}\xrightarrow{\quad}$$

24 Look back at Question 2 on page 74.

a. What is the probability you will have a quiz today? $\frac{1}{2}$

b. How many quizzes would you expect to have each week? 2 or 3

HOMEWORK EXERCISES ▶ See Exs. 6–11 on pp. 82–83.

21. Yes, scoring 0, 1, 2, 3, 4, or 5 points, because no matter what number you roll on the number cube, you will earn either 0, 1, 2, 3, 4, or 5 points.

22. No. 0 represents an event never happening and 1 represents it always happening. An event can't happen more than always or less than never.

DEVELOPING MATH CONCEPTS
After students have completed **Question 22**, they should begin to realize that probabilities range from 0 to 1 inclusive. Help students understand that a probability of 1 corresponds to an event that happens 100% of the times a probability experiment is performed. Similarly, a probability of 0 corresponds to an event that happens 0% of the times a probability experiment is performed. All other probabilities fall within the range of 0 to 1.

COMMON ERROR
Because the segment in **Question 23** is being divided into sixths, some students may think that they need to make only six marks rather than seven. Remind them that the number of marks must always be one greater than the number of sections. Point out the simplest case: for *one* section, *two* marks are required to indicate the beginning and end of the segment.

Key Concepts

CLOSURE QUESTION

In a probability written as a fraction, what does the numerator tell you? What does the denominator tell you?

Sample Response: Numerator: the number of outcomes that make up an event; Denominator: the total number of possible outcomes for the experiment.

ABSENT STUDENTS

For students who were absent for all or part of this section, the blackline Study Guide for Section 1 may be used to present the ideas, concepts, and skills of Section 1.

Section 1
Key Concepts

Key Terms

experiment

outcome

equally likely

probability

experimental probability

theoretical probability

set

event

impossible event

certain event

Outcomes of an Experiment (p. 75)

An experiment is an activity whose results can be observed and recorded. The result of an experiment is an outcome. When each outcome has the same chance of occurring, the outcomes are equally likely.

Probability (p. 75)

A probability is a number from 0 through 1 that tells you how likely something is to happen.

Experimental Probability (pp. 75–76)

An experimental probability is found by repeating an experiment and observing the outcomes.

Theoretical Probability (p. 78)

A theoretical probability is found without doing an experiment.

Example The theoretical probability the spinner stops on red is $\frac{1}{3}$ and the experimental probability is $\frac{29}{80}$.

Outcome	Number of spins
red	29
blue	24
green	27
total	80

Event (pp. 78-79)

A set is any collection of objects. An event is a set of outcomes. For the spinner above, landing on yellow is an impossible event and landing on red, blue, or green is a certain event.

---

25 Key Concepts Question For the spinner above, find each probability.

a. experimental probability the spinner stops on blue or green $\frac{51}{80}$

b. theoretical probability the spinner stops on blue or green $\frac{2}{3}$

Section 1

Practice & Application Exercises ▸▸▸▸▸▸▸▸▸

1. What is the experimental probability the spinner stops on B? $\frac{25}{60}$ or $\frac{5}{12}$

Outcome	Total
A	17
B	25
C	18

2. An octahedron has eight identical sides numbered 1–8.

   a. What are the possible outcomes when the octahedron is rolled?
   $\{1, 2, 3, 4, 5, 6, 7, 8\}$

   b. Are the outcomes equally likely? Why or why not?

   c. The octahedron was rolled 16 times. The results were:

   | 6 | 2 | 5 | 1 | 1 | 2 | 7 | 3 |
   | 6 | 4 | 3 | 6 | 8 | 5 | 2 | 4 |

   Based on these results, what is the experimental probability of rolling a number less than 6? $\frac{11}{16}$

3. a. Complete the *Experimental Probability of Heads* column in the table. **See margin.**

John Kerrich's Data for 10,000 Tosses of a Coin		
Number of Tosses	Number of Heads	Experimental Probability of Heads
10	4	?
100	44	?
1,000	502	?
10,000	5,067	?

◂ While a prisoner of war during World War II, mathematician John Kerrich wrote a book about probability and conducted a coin-tossing experiment.

   b. Kerrich got 5,067 heads in 10,000 tosses. How many tails did he get? **4,933 tails**

   c. What was the experimental probability of getting tails? $\frac{4933}{10000}$

4. A bag contains one blue, one green, and one red marble.

   a. What are the possible outcomes when you draw one marble from the bag without looking? Are the outcomes equally likely?
   {blue, green, red}; Yes, the outcomes are equally likely.

   b. What are the possible outcomes when you draw two marbles at once from the bag without looking? Are the outcomes equally likely? {red and green, red and blue, green and blue}; Yes, the outcomes are equally likely.

Section 1 Probability **81**

Practice & Applications

Practice & Applications

Exercise Notes

Exercise 5 provides an opportunity to informally develop ideas about finding the probabilities of complementary events. The events *a five is rolled* and *a five is not rolled* are complementary because one or the other must occur, but they cannot both happen at the same time. In **part (c)**, students see that the sum of the probabilities of these two complementary events is 1. So in **part (b)**, instead of first calculating the number of rolls that were not a 5, students could have calculated the *probability of not rolling a five* by simply subtracting the *probability of rolling a 5* from 1. *Probability of not rolling a 5* $= 1 - \frac{8}{25} = \frac{25}{25} - \frac{8}{25} = \frac{17}{25}$.

In **Exercises 7 and 8**, an ace is not counted as a numbered card. Students should again be aware of the opportunity to use complements in answering **Question 8(c)**.

9. b. No, they only had a 1 in 66 chance of being first.

Answers will vary. Sample response: Yes it is reasonable, because the best team probably has the least need of good new players, while the poorest teams most need to obtain some top players in order to improve their roster.

8. e. See Additional Answers beginning on page A1.

---

5. c. The probabilities have a sum of $\frac{8}{25} + \frac{17}{25} = \frac{25}{25}$, or 1.

d. about 32 $(25 \times 4 = 100$, so $8 \times 4 = 32)$; about 68 $(100 - 32)$

7. Yes, all outcomes have the same chance of occurring because each specific numbered card or face card does not appear more than once.

8. a. {2, 3, 4, 5, 6, 7, 8, 9, 10}

c. $\frac{4}{13}$; Yes, you can count that there are four non-numbered cards or you can subtract the numbered cards (9) from the total number of cards (13).

Rank of Non-Playoff Team	Number of Balls
1st	1
2nd	2
3rd	3
⋮	⋮
11th	11

---

5. a. A number cube was rolled 25 times. On 8 rolls, the outcome was . What is the experimental probability of rolling ? $\frac{8}{25}$

b. On how many rolls was the outcome not ? What is the experimental probability of not rolling ? 17; $\frac{17}{25}$

c. What do you notice about your answers in parts (a) and (b)?

d. Suppose the number cube is thrown 100 times. Based on the experimental probabilities you found, about how many times do you expect to roll a ? to not roll a ?

6. Find the theoretical probability of each event.

a. The spinner stops on A. $\frac{1}{5}$

b. The spinner does not stop on A. $\frac{4}{5}$

c. The spinner stops on a vowel. $\frac{2}{5}$

For Exercises 7 and 8, suppose you pick a card, without looking, from the thirteen heart cards in a standard deck. (An Ace is *not* considered a numbered card.)

Hearts (♥):

7. Are all the outcomes for picking one card equally likely? Explain.

8. a. List the possible outcomes for picking a numbered card.

b. What is the theoretical probability of picking a numbered card? $\frac{9}{13}$

c. What is the theoretical probability of picking a non-numbered card? Is there more than one way to find the probability? Explain.

d. What is the theoretical probability of picking an even-numbered card? an odd-numbered card? $\frac{5}{13}$; $\frac{4}{13}$

e. Plot your answers from parts (b)–(d) on a number line. **See margin.**

9. Basketball Each season the National Basketball Association (NBA) holds a lottery to decide the order in which its teams will pick new players. Until 1993, each of the 11 teams that did not make the playoffs was assigned from 1 to 11 balls marked with the team's logo. As shown in the table, the number of balls assigned to a team depended on the team's rank for the season. The first ball drawn determined the team that would get first pick.

a. What was the theoretical probability that the team assigned 11 balls got the first pick? the team assigned 5 balls? $\frac{11}{66}$ or $\frac{1}{6}$; $\frac{5}{66}$

b. Writing Did the team assigned 1 ball have a good chance of getting one of the top new players for the next season? Does this seem reasonable? Explain your thinking. **See margin.**

10. **Open-ended** Give an example of a certain event and of an impossible event in everyday life.

Reflecting ◀▶on the Section

Write your response to Exercise 11 in your journal.

11. a. Develop a strategy for playing the game *Never a Six*. Explain why your strategy helps. **See margin.**

   b. Play the game again to test your strategy. **Monitor students.**

   c. How does probability relate to your strategy? **Answers will vary.**

Spiral ◀▶Review

12. In how many different ways can you make 35 cents in change using only nickels, dimes, and quarters? (Module 1, p. 33) **See margin.**

Write the next two terms of each sequence. (Module 1, p. 21)

13. 9, 13, 17, 21, ... **25, 29**   14. 2, 5, 9, 14, ... **20, 27**

15. Write a rule for finding the terms of each sequence in Exercises 13 and 14. **See margin.**

Journal

Exercise 11 checks that you can apply probability.

10. Answers will vary. Sample Responses:

Certain events may include the sun will rise, school will start at 9 am tomorrow, my dog will bark when a fire truck drives by.

Impossible events may include my dog will talk, I will get a driver's license this year, It will snow in July.

Extension ▶ ▶

Applying Experimental Probability

16. Have a friend or relative put 10 pennies into a bag—some shiny and the rest dull. Do not look at how many of each are put into the bag!

   a. Take one penny from the bag. Record whether it is shiny or dull in a tally table. Put the coin back in the bag. **Answers will vary.**

   b. Repeat part (a) 29 more times. **Answers will vary.**

   c. Use the data in your table to find the experimental probability of drawing each kind of penny. **Answers will vary.**

   d. Predict how many shiny pennies and how many dull pennies are in the bag. Then check your prediction. **Answers will vary.**

Exercise Notes

Extension Exercise 16 allows for home involvement. Encourage students to explain to a family member what an experimental probability is and to share with him or her how they used mathematics to make their prediction.

11. a. Answers will vary. Sample strategy may be to roll five times or less on each turn, since the probability of rolling a six is $\frac{1}{6}$, thus leaving $\frac{5}{6}$ probability of not rolling a six.

12. six ways

Quarters	Dimes	Nickels
1	1	0
1	0	2
0	3	1
0	2	3
0	1	5
0	0	7

15. Exercise 13: Begin with 9 as the first term. Add 4 to the previous term to get the next term; Exercise 14: Begin with 2 as the first term, then add 3, then 4, then 5, increasing the amount you add to the previous term by one each time.

Extra Skill Practice

TEACHER NOTES
For each Exploration, the corresponding Extra Skill Practice Exercises are noted.

Exploration 1: 1–5
Exploration 2: 6–12

EXTRA HELP
Teacher's Resource Book
• Practice and Applications
• Study Guide

Technology Resources
• @Home Tutor
• Test Generator

ASSESSMENT
• Section 1 Quick Quiz
• Test Generator

Section ① Extra Skill Practice

Suppose a number cube was rolled 80 times with the results shown.

Outcome	Total
⚅	16
⚄	14
⚃	13
⚂	15
⚁	12
⚀	10

1. What is the experimental probability of rolling a 3? $\frac{15}{80}$ or $\frac{3}{16}$

2. What is the experimental probability of rolling an even number? $\frac{41}{80}$

3. What is the experimental probability of rolling a number less than 5? $\frac{50}{80}$ or $\frac{5}{8}$

4. What is the experimental probability of rolling an odd number? $\frac{39}{80}$

5. An experiment consists of spinning the spinner once.

   a. What are the outcomes of the experiment?
   {A, I, E, G, D, C, F, H}

   b. Are the outcomes equally likely? Why or why not?

Find the theoretical probability of each event.

6. The spinner stops on A. $\frac{1}{8}$

7. The spinner stops on B. $\frac{0}{8}$ or 0

8. The spinner stops on C or F. $\frac{2}{8}$ or $\frac{1}{4}$

9. The spinner stops on a vowel. $\frac{3}{8}$

10. If you know that the theoretical probability the spinner stops on G is $\frac{1}{8}$, how can you find the probability that it does not stop on G? Subtract $\frac{1}{8}$ from 1.

11. Were any of the events in Exercises 6–9 impossible? certain? If so, which ones?
   "The spinner stops on B" is impossible since there is no B on the spinner. None are certain.

12. Plot each probability you found in Exercises 6–9 on a number line. Label your number line and each point you plot.

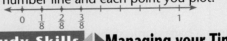

5. b. Yes, each outcome has the same chance of occurring because the circle is divided into equal partitions and each outcome appears on the spinner once.

 Study Skills ◀▶ Managing your Time

The probability of achieving your goals is greater if you learn to manage your time. One way to plan your time is to make a schedule.

1. Beginning with the time you get up in the morning, write a schedule of things you do on a normal school day. **Answers will vary.**

2. a. Suppose that one day you need to spend an hour working on a school project. Neighbors who are away have also asked you to spend 30 minutes cat-sitting and 20 minutes watering their plants. Adjust your schedule to include time for these activities. **Answers will vary.**

   b. Are there any other ways to adjust your schedule to include the activities from part (a)? Explain. **Answers will vary.**

Section ② Assessment Scales

Detecting the Score

Setting the Stage

People have been reading about the adventures of Sherlock Holmes and Dr. Watson since 1887. Holmes was considered the world's greatest detective because he could solve almost any problem. If detectives were rated on a scale of 1-5, Holmes would easily score a 5.

In the stories, Holmes often describes the methods that made him so successful. Here are a few examples.

> "As a rule, when I have heard some slight indication of the course of events, I am able to guide myself by the thousands of other similar cases which occur to my memory." **The Red-headed League**
>
> "...the strangest and most unique things are very often connected not with the larger but with the smaller crimes ..." **The Red-headed League**
>
> "In solving a problem of this sort, the grand thing is to be able to reason backward. That is a very useful accomplishment, and a very easy one, but people do not practice it much." **A Study in Scarlet**

Think About It

1 How would examining similar cases help Holmes solve a problem?

2 Holmes talks about things being connected. What does he mean? See margin.

3 Holmes describes reasoning backward as a valuable problem-solving strategy. What other strategies have you used? See margin.

1. Comparing to similar cases might help Holmes to make conclusions more quickly, to rule out possibilities, and to use similar problem-solving strategies that previously proved effective.

85

Exploration 1

TEACHING NOTES

Question 5 is designed to reinforce the 4-step approach to problem solving and to make sure that students are thoroughly familiar with it. This is important since the *Problem Solving Scale* which is introduced in **Questions 6–8** assesses students' ability to apply the four steps.

Question 5(b) helps students see that there may be a variety of plans for solving a problem. Often students skip the last step, *looking back*. In **Question 5(d)**, emphasize the importance of looking back to check the reasonableness of the answer and to verify the solution.

Question 7 Be sure students understand their solutions cannot be scored unless they show their work. This is true on all the assessment scales, not just the *Problem Solving Scale*. Have the class discuss ways students can be sure they understand the problem well enough to get started. For example, "Restate the problem in your own words and ask for clarification before leaving class," or "Discuss the problem with a classmate or family member."

4., 5., and 8. See Additional Answers beginning on page A1.

LEARN HOW TO...
- use the problem solving scale

AS YOU...
- apply the 4-step approach to solve the *World Cup Problem*
- assess your group's solution

Exploration 1

The Problem Solving SCALE

SET UP   *Work in a group.*

▶ To solve problems, Sherlock Holmes used an approach similar to the 4-step approach you used in Module 1 on page 33.

4 Work as a team and use the 4-step problem-solving approach to solve the *World Cup Problem*. Write up an explanation of your team's solution. See margin.

> **World Cup Problem**
>
> The World Cup is a world championship soccer tournament that is held every 4 years and is played over several rounds. In the first round of the 2006 finals, 32 teams competed against one another. The teams were divided into eight groups of four teams. Within each group, each team played the other three teams once. How many games were played in the first round of the 2006 World Cup finals?

▲ The World Cup draws a huge audience. In 2006, over 3.3 million fans attended the 64 World Cup matches.

6. The scale assesses whether you followed the 4-step problem solving approach to see if you understood the problem, made a plan, used the plan (took action to carry out the plan), and verified the solution (looked back).

5 **Discussion** For each question, explain what your team did when you solved the *World Cup Problem*.

  a. What did you do to make sure you understood the problem? See margin.

  b. What was your plan for solving the problem? See margin.

  c. What steps did you use to carry out your plan? See margin.

  d. What did you do when you looked back at your solution? See margin.

▶ **Assessment Scales** This year you will be using the *Assessment Scales* on page 87 to help improve your problem solving and communication skills.

The first scale is the *Problem Solving Scale*. It is used to assess the application of the 4-step approach to problem solving. You will use the scale to think about your work and how to improve it.

6 How is the problem solving scale related to the 4-step problem-solving approach?

7 If you score a "1" on this scale, you cannot score your work using any of the other assessment scales on page 87. Why?
   There is no work shown to be scored.

8 How can you score a "5" on the problem solving scale? a "4"?
   See margin.

86

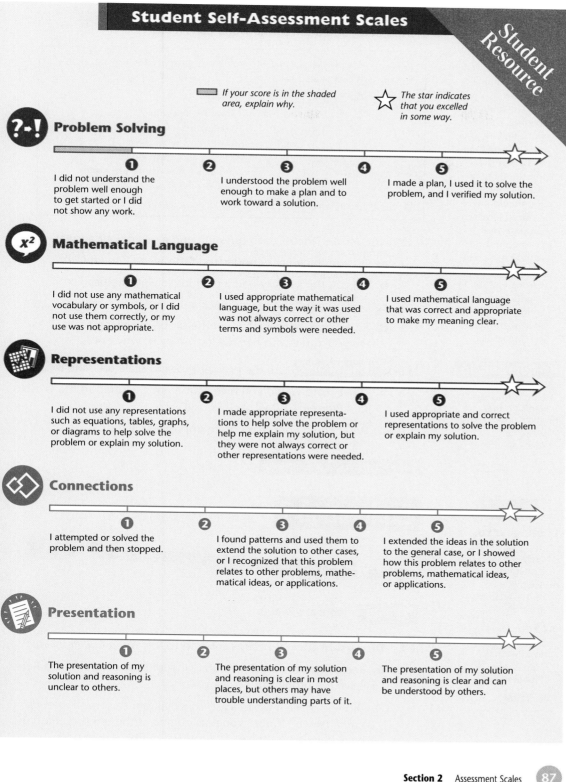

Student Self-Assessment Scales

☐ If your score is in the shaded area, explain why.

☆ The star indicates that you excelled in some way.

Problem Solving

① I did not understand the problem well enough to get started or I did not show any work.

③ I understood the problem well enough to make a plan and to work toward a solution.

⑤ I made a plan, I used it to solve the problem, and I verified my solution.

Mathematical Language

① I did not use any mathematical vocabulary or symbols, or I did not use them correctly, or my use was not appropriate.

③ I used appropriate mathematical language, but the way it was used was not always correct or other terms and symbols were needed.

⑤ I used mathematical language that was correct and appropriate to make my meaning clear.

Representations

① I did not use any representations such as equations, tables, graphs, or diagrams to help solve the problem or explain my solution.

③ I made appropriate representations to help solve the problem or help me explain my solution, but they were not always correct or other representations were needed.

⑤ I used appropriate and correct representations to solve the problem or explain my solution.

Connections

① I attempted or solved the problem and then stopped.

③ I found patterns and used them to extend the solution to other cases, or I recognized that this problem relates to other problems, mathematical ideas, or applications.

⑤ I extended the ideas in the solution to the general case, or I showed how this problem relates to other problems, mathematical ideas, or applications.

Presentation

① The presentation of my solution and reasoning is unclear to others.

③ The presentation of my solution and reasoning is clear in most places, but others may have trouble understanding parts of it.

⑤ The presentation of my solution and reasoning is clear and can be understood by others.

Student Resource

TEACHER NOTES

The *Math Thematics* Assessment Scales are designed to help students answer the question "How can I improve my performance in problem-solving, reasoning, and communication?" They provide a generalized rubric that defines the various dimensions of mathematical investigation. The scales are designed to be applied to open-ended questions, *Module Projects*, *Reflecting on the Section* exercises, and especially *Extended Explorations* (E^2s). For more information about using the *Math Thematics* Assessment Scales, see pages T32–T33 in the *Teacher's Edition*. Also see the *Teacher's Resource Book* for Modules 1 and 2.

Exploration 1 continued

TEACHING NOTES
In **Question 10**, make sure students realistically address how well they have verified their solution. Upon reflection, some students may decide to assign themselves a 4 rather than a 5.

Exploration 2

CLASSROOM MANAGEMENT
Students should work in the same teams as they did in Exploration 1.

Make sure teams have access to their *World Cup Problem* solution before beginning the exploration.

11. a. She represented each game with a line segment joining the two teams that played each other. This way she could count the number of segments and be sure she had covered all the games.
b. Answers will vary; Using one of these representations helps visualize the problem and form a strategy.

88

---

9. c. No; if she did, she did not check to see if her answer was reasonable or accurate.
d. No; she told her method, showed work on how she used her method to answer the question, but on the look back she should have realized fourteen games is not reasonable and caught her error of 6 × 8 = 14 (instead of 48). I would score her solution as a 4 on the problem solving scale.

✔ **QUESTION 10**

... checks that you understand the problem solving scale.

GOAL

LEARN HOW TO...
◆ Apply different problem-solving strategies
◆ use the representations scale

AS YOU...
◆ work as a team to solve the *Handshake Problem*

KEY TERM
◆ representations

▶ **Here is Becky's solution to the *World Cup Problem*.**

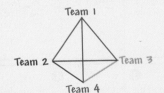

First I used a diagram to find the number of games for one group. Then I used that to find the number of games for all the groups.

Group A
Team 1 – 3 games
Team 2 – 2 other games
Team 3 – 1 other game
Team 4 – 0 other games
3 + 2 + 1 = 6 games per group
6 × 8 = 14 games in all

14 games were played in the first round of the 2006 World Cup.

9 Discussion Discuss each question and explain your answer.
Sample responses are given.
a. Do you think Becky understood the *World Cup Problem*?
Yes; her understanding shows in her work.
b. Do you think Becky had a plan for solving the problem?
Yes; she tried a simpler problem and used a diagram.
c. Do you think she looked back at her solution?

d. Becky gave herself a "5" on the problem solving scale. Do you agree with her scoring? Why or why not?

10 ✔ CHECKPOINT Use the problem solving scale on page 87.

a. What score would you give your team's solution to the *World Cup Problem*? Why? Answers will vary.

b. What could your team do to improve its score?
Answers will vary.

HOMEWORK EXERCISES ▶ See Exs. 1–4 on p. 93.

Exploration 2

The Representations SCALE

SET UP *Work in a group.*

11 Discussion Look at Becky's solution to the *World Cup Problem*.

a. Becky started with a diagram. How did the diagram help her solve the problem? See margin.

b. Did you make a table, a list, or a diagram to solve the *World Cup Problem*? If not, would using one of these representations have helped you solve the problem? Why or why not?
See margin.

▶ Diagrams, tables, and graphs are **representations** that can help you solve problems and explain your solutions. You will use the *Representations Scale* to assess and improve your use of representations.

Representations

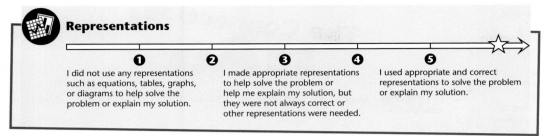

① I did not use any representations such as equations, tables, graphs, or diagrams to help solve the problem or explain my solution.

②

③ I made appropriate representations to help solve the problem or help me explain my solution, but they were not always correct or other representations were needed.

④

⑤ I used appropriate and correct representations to solve the problem or explain my solution.

12 **Discussion** What score would you give Becky's solution of the *World Cup Problem* on the representations scale? Why?

13 **a.** Work as a team. Use appropriate problem-solving strategies and visual representations to solve the *Handshake Problem.*

> **Handshake Problem**
>
> Five people are hired to work together on a fundraising project. As they are introduced, they shake hands with each other exactly one time. How many handshakes take place?

b. Write an explanation that shows how your team solved the problem. See margin.

14 **Discussion**

a. What representations did your team use to solve the problem or to explain your solution? Answers will vary.

b. Were your representations appropriate? Explain. Answers will vary.

c. Were your representations correct? Explain. Answers will vary.

15 ✔ **CHECKPOINT** What score would you give your team on the representations scale? Why? Answers will vary.

HOMEWORK EXERCISES ▶ See Exs. 5–8 on pp. 93–94.

12. Becky should score a 5 on representation because she used a diagram and made a list showing how she concluded that each group plays six games.

✔ **QUESTION 15**

...checks that you understand the representations scale.

TEACHING NOTES

Encourage students to be realistic in their responses to **Checkpoint Question 15**. If the team did not find the correct number of handshakes, then it should examine whether their incorrect response is due to an error with the representation they used or, like Becky's solution to the *World Cup Problem*, an error in computation.

13. a. 10 handshakes took place.
   b. Team explanations will vary. A diagram similar to the one Becky used in the World Cup problem could be used. Students may also have recognized the pattern in Becky's solution and applied it so that the first person makes 4 handshakes, the next person 3 more, the next 2 more, then 1 more and the last 0 since she has already shaken each person's hand. This totals to $4 + 3 + 2 + 1 + 0 = 10$.

Exploration 3

CLASSROOM MANAGEMENT

Students should work in the same teams as they did in Exploration 2.

Make sure teams have access to their *World Cup Problem* and *Handshake Problem* solutions before beginning the exploration.

TEACHING NOTES

Question 18 For students who are inclined to think Becky may give herself a 5, ask, "What did Becky do to show how the problem relates to other problems, mathematical ideas, or applications?"

16. b. With the triangular numbers at first there are no dots, then 1, then 3, then 6; the newest row grows in length by one more than the previous row. In the World Cup and Handshake problems, with one team/person there are 0 matches/handshakes, then with two there is 1 match/handshake, then with three there are 3, with four there are 6. They follow the same pattern of growth.

18. Sample Response: 3; She recognized that the World Cup Problem was like the Handshake Problem, but she did not explain how in her solution.

17. See Additional Answers beginning on page A1.

90

GOAL

LEARN HOW TO...
- extend solutions to the general case
- use the connections scale

AS YOU...
- look for connections among problems you have solved

KEY TERMS
- connection
- general case

16. a. In both problems, each item (either a person or a team) is paired once with another person or team. Once the first person or team is matched with others, the next person or team has one less match, and the following has one less than the previous, etc. until the final person or team cannot make any new matches.

Exploration 3

The Connections SCALE

SET UP   *Work in a group. You will need Labsheets 2A and 2B.*

▶ Here is the final part of Becky's solution of the *World Cup Problem*.

> When I looked at the diagram, I saw that the problem was like the Handshake problem.

16   Try This as a Class Compare Becky's final solution to the *World Cup Problem* with your solution to the Handshake Problem.

    a. How is the *World Cup Problem* like the *Handshake Problem*?

    b. How are the *World Cup* and *Handshake* problems related to the triangular numbers on page 15 in Module 1? See margin.

▶ One type of **connection** is made when you relate a problem to other problems, mathematical ideas, or applications.

17   Is there a pattern in the *World Cup Problem* or the *Handshake Problem* that you can extend? Explain. See margin.

▶ You make another type of **connection** when you identify patterns and extend them to other cases. For example, in Module 1 you predicted the next triangular number and found the lowest safe bid for playing *Card Swappers* with different numbers of cards. The *Connections Scale* is used to assess either type of connection.

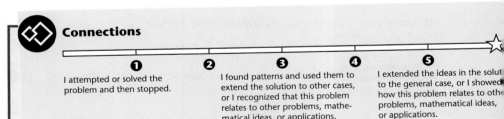

Connections

1 I attempted or solved the problem and then stopped.

2 **3** I found patterns and used them to extend the solution to other cases, or I recognized that this problem relates to other problems, mathematical ideas, or applications.

4 **5** I extended the ideas in the soluti to the general case, or I showed how this problem relates to othe problems, mathematical ideas, or applications.

18   What score do you think Becky should give her final solution on the connections scale? Why? See margin.

▶ As you work on the string art problem in Questions 19–22, think about the connections scale.

19 In the design shown, string links each of the six pegs in every way possible. How many linkups are there altogether? 15

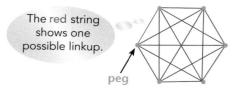

The red string shows one possible linkup.

peg

20 ✔ **CHECKPOINT** Is the string design problem related to any other problems you have solved? Explain.

21 Copy and complete the table to find the number of linkups for different numbers of pegs. See margin.

Number of pegs	1	2	3	4	5	6	7
Number of linkups	?	?	?	?	?	?	?

22 **Try This as a Class**

a. How many linkups can be made in a string design with 9 pegs like the one at the right? 36

b. Explain how you can find the total number of linkups made in a string design with any number of pegs. See margin.

c. Compare your method for solving part (b) with those of other class members. If different methods were used, are they all correct? See margin.

▶ One way to score a "5" on the connections scale is by extending a solution to the **general case**. You did this when you found the number of linkups for any number of pegs. You also did this in Module 1 when you wrote a rule to find any term of a sequence.

23 **a.** Write a complete explanation that shows how you solved the string art problem. Remember to explain the connections.
Explanations will vary.

b. What score would you give yourself on the connections scale? Why? Answers will vary.

HOMEWORK EXERCISES ▶ See Exs. 9–10 on pp. 94–95.

20. Yes; the Handshake Problem. Connecting each peg to every other peg is like having one person shake hands once with every other person.

✔ **QUESTION 20**

…checks that you understand connections.

▲ String art designs can be simple or complicated depending on the pattern and the number of pegs used.

TEACHING NOTES
The concept of extending a solution of a problem to the general case will be unfamiliar to most students. However, its mathematical importance justifies spending considerable time helping students with **Question 22**, which asks them to generalize the string art problem. To guide them in the right direction, ask them how each linkup number is related to both the number of pegs and to an adjacent linkup number. One way to express the generalization is to say, "Add one less than the current peg number to the previous linkup number to get the current linkup number," or "Add the current peg number to the current linkup number to get the next linkup number."

22. b. Sample Response: A rule for the sequence in the bottom row of the table is, "Start with 0. Add 1 to get the second term. Then add the next counting number to each term to get the following term." Use this rule to extend the table to any number of pegs. Sample equation: $\frac{n(n-1)}{2}$, where $n =$ the number of pegs.

c. Methods will vary. Generally, if students still resort to counting for $n = 6, 7, 8 \dots$, there will be greater chances of error.

21. See Additional Answers beginning on page A1.

91

State how to score well on the *Problem Solving Scale,* on the *Representations Scale,* and on the *Connections Scale.*

Answer: Responses should include all aspects that score a 5 on each scale.

ABSENT STUDENTS

For students who were absent for all or part of this section, the blackline Study Guide for Section 2 may be used to present the ideas, concepts, and skills of Section 2.

Section 2
Key Concepts

Key Terms

Problem Solving Scale (pp. 86–88)

This scale can be used to assess how well you use the 4-step problem-solving approach.

- Did I understand the problem?
- Did I make a plan and get started toward a solution?
- Did I carry out my plan and find a solution?
- Did I look back to make sure my work was correct and my answer was reasonable?
- Did I make sure I answered the right questions?
- Did I try a different method to solve the problem?

Representations Scale (pp. 88–89)

representations

This scale can be used to assess how well you use representations such as equations, tables, graphs, and diagrams.

- Were my representations appropriate?
- Were my representations correct?
- Were there any other representations I should have used?

Connections Scale (pp. 90–91)

connection

general case

This scale can be used to assess your ability to show how a problem relates to other problems, mathematical ideas, or applications or to extend the solution to the general case.

- Did I identify a pattern?
- Did I extend the solution to other cases or to the general case?
- Did I relate the problem to another situation, problem, or mathematical idea?
- Did I clearly show the connections I found?

> To extend the solution to the general case, you need to find a rule that will work for any case.

24 Key Concepts Question Use Labsheets 2A and 2B. On the labsheets are explanations of how two teams solved the *Handshake Problem.* Score each team on the **problem solving, representations,** and **connections scales.** See margin.

24. See Additional Answers beginning on page A1.

Section 2

Practice & Application Exercises

For Exercises 1 and 2, solve each problem and score your solution using the problem solving scale on page 87. Student scores for Exercises 1 and 2 will vary.

1. A snail starts at the bottom of a well 10 ft deep and crawls up 3 ft each day. Each night the snail slips back 2 ft. How long will it take the snail to reach the top of the well? 8 days since on the 8th day the snail advances 3 ft and is out of the well before night when he usually slips back.

2. Use the clues below to find the mystery number. 84

   • The number is between 0 and 150.

   • If you start with 7 and keep counting by 7s, the number will be on your list.

   • The sum of the digits in the number is 12.

   • The number can be divided evenly by four.

3. a. Find the digit represented by each letter. A letter stands for the same digit throughout the problem. Every letter has a different value. $C = 2, E = 5, D = 7, G = 1, K = 3$

   ```
       C E D
   ×     G K
     ─────────
       D D 1
     2 5 7
   ─────────
     K K 4 G
   ```

   b. How can you verify your solution? Multiply 257 by 13 and check your solution.

4. **Challenge** A jeweler had four pieces of gold chain. Each piece has three links. The jeweler wants to join the links to form a closed necklace. Explain how to do this by cutting and rejoining the least number of links.

5. **Geometry Connection** Explain why each drawing is or is not an appropriate and correct solution to the problem: Draw a segment that divides a square into two right triangles.

   a.

   b.

   c.

4. Cut each of the three links on one piece and separate them. Use them to join together the ends of the other three pieces.

5. a. Not correct. This line divides the square into one right triangle and one pentagon.

   b. Correct. The square figure is broken into two three sided polygons that each have a right angle, since the line only affected two of the four right angles in the square.

   c. Not correct. Although there are two right triangles, the figure is not a square.

Practice & Applications

SUGGESTED ASSIGNMENTS

Core Course

Day 1: Exs. 1–3

Day 2: Exs. 5–8

Day 3: Exs. 9–14

Extended Course

Day 1: Exs. 1–4

Day 2: Exs. 5–8

Day 3: Exs. 9–14

Note: Extended Course assignments can be used to differentiate within the regular classroom. In classrooms where students are grouped homogeneously, the material might be covered in fewer days. In this case assignments may be combined.

ADDITIONAL PRACTICE

See the *Teacher's Resource Book* for additional practice and application exercises for this section.

TEACHING NOTES

For **Exercises 1 and 2,** have students refer not only to the Problem Solving Scale on page 87, but also to the checklist at the top of Key Concepts page 92.

Practice & Applications

EXERCISE NOTES

Exercise 6 Share with students that in this problem when the end of the line is reached, counting continues on from the beginning of the line until half the crew is left. This is a good problem to demonstrate in class by having the students act it out. Afterwards the effects of different counting methods can be explored such as: Once the end of the line is reached, start over at the beginning of the line with 1. Or, once the end of the line is reached, reverse the direction, counting back toward the front and vice versa, until half the crew is left.

7. Answers vary.
   Sample Response:
   How many ways
   can the lower star
   reach the upper star
   through left and up
   moves only?

9. a. least is 5 games;
   greatest is
   11 games;
   Explanations
   will vary. This
   problem is similar
   to the first round
   of the World Cup
   Problem.

6. a. Half of a boat's crew of 15 men and 15 women could leave to visit a port. The crew lined up. Every ninth person was allowed to leave until half the crew had left. When the last person in line was counted, the counting continued to the front of the line. The crew that remained was all women. In what order did the crew line up? Show how you found your answer. **See margin.**

   b. Use the representations scale on page 87. What score would you give your solution to part (a)? Why? **Scores will vary.**

7. **Create Your Own** Write a word problem that could be solved using one of the visuals shown below.

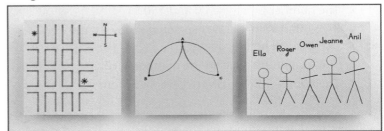

8. Large stained glass windows are made of panels of colored glass held together by an iron frame.

   a. Suppose a glass panel is 4 ft wide and 10 ft long. About how many feet of iron framing are needed to hold two glass panels stacked vertically as shown? to hold three glass panels stacked vertically? **about 52 ft; about 76 ft**

   b. How can you find how many feet of framing are needed to hold any number of glass panels stacked vertically? **Sample: Multiply the number of panels by 24 and add 4.**

   c. Use the representations scale on page 87. What score would you give your solution to part (b)? Why? **Scores will vary.**

   |— 4 ft —|

   10 ft

9. Six teams compete in a contest. In the first round every team plays one game against each of the other teams. The top three teams go on to the second round where every team plays against each of the other teams twice. In the third round, the top two teams from the second round play against each other twice.

   a. Find the least and the greatest number of games a team may play. Explain your solution and how it is related to another problem, mathematical idea, or application.

   b. Use the connections scale on page 87. What score would you give your solution to part (a)? Why? **Scores will vary.**

6. a. See Additional Answers beginning on page A1.

Reflecting ◀▶on the Section

Write your responses to Exercise 10 in your journal.

10. **Language Arts** The detective Sherlock Holmes uses the clues below in "The Case of the Itinerant Yeggman" by June Thomson.

Journal

Exercise 10 checks that you can use problem-solving strategies.

December 27, 1894 – Letter arrives at mansion. Professor from Germany wants to visit to study design of buildings.

January 25, 1895 – Professor visits mansion.

July 21, 1895 – Mansion robbed. Among items stolen: Priceless prayer book passed down in owner's family.

November 26, 1894 – Letter arrives at old estate. Historian from France wants to visit to study woodwork of rooms.

December 28, 1894 – Historian visits estate.

June 22, 1895 – Estate robbed. Among items stolen: jewelled fan passed down by owner's great grandparents

October 28, 1894 – Letter arrives at country home. Professor from Chicago wants to visit to study design of floor tiling.

November 27, 1894 – Professor visits country home.

May 24, 1895 – Country home robbed. Among items stolen: gold cup passed down by owner's great grandfather.

a. Describe any patterns that you see in the clues.

b. Holmes learns that the owner of a fourth home received a letter on January 25, 1895, and a visit from a professor on February 24, 1895. He suspects that another break-in may occur. Choose the most likely date. Explain your thinking. See margin.
- ◆ Apr. 15, 1895
- ◆ July 7, 1895
- ◆ Aug. 20, 1895
- ◆ June 5, 1895

10. a. Sample Response: In each case, a letter arrived, approximately 1 month later, there was a visitor, and approximately 6 months after the visit, the house was robbed. Some of the items stolen in each case were family heirlooms.

Spiral ◀▶Review

Find the value of each expression. (Module 1, p. 10)

11. 6 • 5 + 13 43   12. 54 − 81 ÷ 9 45   13. 144 ÷ (12 − 8) 36

14. Make a table for the sequence 5, 9, 13, 17, … . Extend it to include the next two terms. Then write a rule for the sequence. (Module 1, p. 21) See margin.

EXERCISE NOTES
For **Reflecting Exercise 10**, encourage students to not only look for and describe patterns in the dates of the events, but also of the events themselves. This problem connects back to the module theme of math detectives and shows how strategies learned in mathematics apply to other contexts.

10. b. August 20, 1895; the letter arrived in January of 1895 and the visit occurred approximately one month later. If the pattern is followed, the house will be robbed 7 months after the letter and 6 months following the visit.

14. See Additional Answers beginning on page A1.

Extra Skill Practice

TEACHER NOTES

The six problems are designed to be assigned after students have completed all three explorations. You may choose to assign one or two after each exploration, focusing only on the particular *Assessment Scale* presented in that lesson.

EXTRA HELP

Teacher's Resource Book
• Practice and Applications
• Study Guide

Technology Resources
• @Home Tutor
• Test Generator

ASSESSMENT

• Section 2 Quick Quiz
• Mid-Module Quiz
• Test Generator

4. Lay the 10 in. and 5 in. sticks end to end to form 15 in. total. Then lay the 7 in. stick on top of the 5 in. stick with ends aligned. The remaining part of the 10 in. stick that is not covered will measure 8 in. since $10 + 5 - 7 = 8$.

3., 5., and 6. See Additional Answers beginning on page A1.

Section ② Extra Skill Practice

Show how to use the 4-step approach and a diagram, a table, or a graph to solve each problem. Remember to make connections. In Exercises 1–6, check students' work for 4-step approach and connections.

1. A school bus travels 3 blocks east, 4 blocks north, 10 blocks west, 2 blocks south, and 1 block east. At this point, the bus is how many blocks north or south of its starting point? How many blocks east or west?

1. 2 blocks north; 6 blocks west

2. An elevator in an office building started at ground level. It rose 5 floors, descended 2 floors, rose 9 floors, descended 3 floors, and rose 7 floors. Which floor is the elevator on?

3. John, Sue, Lisa, and Fernando are student council officers. The council has four officers: president, vice president, secretary, and treasurer. Use the clues below to determine which student is the president. See margin.

   ◆ John is neither president nor secretary.
   ◆ A boy holds the office of vice president.
   ◆ Sue is not secretary.
   ◆ The names of the treasurer and the vice president have the same number of letters.

2. 16th floor

4. The lengths of three sticks are 5 in., 7 in., and 10 in. How can you use these sticks to mark off a length of 8 in.? See margin.

5. A restaurant has two types of tables. One type seats two people and the other seats four. If 28 people are in the restaurant, how many full tables of each type can there be? See margin.

6. Tickets to the musical cost $8 for students and $12 for all others. If $520 was earned by the sale of 49 tickets, how many student tickets were sold? See margin.

Standardized Testing ▶ Free Response

Caroline and Juanita are going camping. Their tent weighs 7 pounds. They have two sleeping bags that weigh 3 pounds each, a camp stove that weighs 6 pounds, 14 pounds of food and assorted supplies, 15 pounds of water, 10 pounds of clothing, a 1-pound first-aid kit, and a 3-pound lantern.

Can Caroline and Juanita divide their gear so that each person carries the same amount of weight? Explain. **Yes; Each person can carry 31 lb. There are a number of ways to divide the weight. Sample: Caroline carries clothing 10 lb, food 14 lb, first-aid kit 1 lb, camping stove 6 lb. Juanita carries the tent 7 lb, lantern 3 lb, water 15 lb, two sleeping bags 6 lb.**

Section 3 Lines, Angles, and Triangles

IN THIS SECTION

EXPLORATION 1
◆ Geometric Language

EXPLORATION 2
◆ Sides of a Triangle

EXPLORATION 3
◆ Angles of a Triangle

Language Clues

Setting the Stage ▸▸▸▸▸▸▸▸▸▸▸▸▸▸▸▸▸▸▸▸

SET UP *Work with a partner. You will need: • I Describe, You Draw cards from Labsheet 3A • two sheets of unlined paper*

▶ Detectives depend on crime scene investigators to collect evidence to help solve cases. It is very important that the investigators accurately describe the evidence and provide detailed sketches. In this section you will learn to accurately describe and draw geometric figures.

In the game *I Describe, You Draw,* one person describes the design on a card. The other person tries to draw what is described without asking any questions.

I Describe, You Draw

◆ Decide who will draw and who will describe.

◆ Play the game using the first card.

◆ Switch roles and play the game with the second card.

Be sure your partner does not see your card. Be sure you cannot see the drawing.

Think About It

1 How do the drawings compare with the cards? Answers will vary.

2 Did you use mathematical terms to describe the drawing?

3 If you did use mathematical terms, did it help? Explain. Answers will vary.

2. Answers will vary. Possible terms: square, circle, triangle, line, ray, bisect, diagonal, center, midpoint, diameter, perpendicular

Setting the Stage

GETTING STARTED
In preparation for the drawing activity in the *Setting the Stage*, the Module 2 Section 3 *Warm-Up* has students draw some basic geometric figures such as circles, squares, triangles, and diamonds.

ABOUT THE MATERIALS
The cards for this activity must be prepared ahead of time. Have someone other than the students cut out Cards 1 and 2 on **Labsheet 3A**, since the students should not see the cards.

CLASSROOM MANAGEMENT
Seat students back to back so that neither can see the work of the other. Hand Card 1 to the student that will describe first. Reserve Card 2 for when rolls are reversed. Save Cards 1 and 2 for use with **Question 10**.

You will want to arrange your classroom seating so that none of those drawing can see the describers' cards. One set up may include forming two long rows of chairs back to back. Place all the describers in the two inside rows that face each other since it does not matter if they see each others cards, then place all those drawing on the outside rows so there is also less of a chance that they will see what another person is drawing.

TIPS FROM TEACHERS
Laminate the sets of cards so they can be used year after year without getting torn or marked up.

Exploration 1

TEACHING NOTES

Question 4 Some students may think they cannot answer **Question 4** because they don't know what all of the terms mean. Remind students that the theme of this module is math detectives. Encourage them to use their detective skills to match those that seem most logical or use a process of elimination to match the last few terms to each figure. Assure them that as a class you will make sure they understand the different terms, but that for now you want to see them use their detective reasoning.

Be sure students have the right matches for **Question 4** before beginning the discussion in **Question 5**.

DEVELOPING MATH CONCEPTS

At a beginning level of geometric understanding, students can often recognize figures, such as parallel lines or perpendicular lines, without being able to discuss their characteristics. Since the focus of this section is on developing mathematical vocabulary, when discussing questions, help students by informing them of how to use the proper mathematical language in their descriptions. The key terms will be further explained in this exploration through introduction of the symbols and notation used to describe and name each object.

GOAL

LEARN HOW TO...
- name basic geometric figures

AS YOU...
- describe and draw figures

KEY TERMS
- point
- line
- segment
- ray
- plane
- parallel
- perpendicular

Exploration 1

Geometric Language

To help detectives, the crime scene investigator's written reports must accurately describe the evidence. Using accurate mathematical terms can help you understand and solve problems.

▶ **Terms for Geometric Figures** Special terms and symbols can help you describe geometric figures.

4 Choose the number of the best term for each figure.

a.  5

b.  1

c.  2

d. • 6

e.  4

f.  3

1. line

2. segment

3. perpendicular lines

4. ray

5. parallel lines

6. point

5 **Discussion** Segments and rays are parts of lines.

a. How are lines, rays, and segments alike? All are straight. Each is a set of infinite points.

b. How are they different? Lines have no endpoints and continue forever in opposite directions. Rays have one endpoint and continue forever in a given direction. Segments have two endpoints and do not continue forever since they have a definite length.

▶ **You can use letters and symbols to name geometric figures.**

EXAMPLE

In the diagram:

J means **point** *J*.

$\overline{KL}$ means **segment** *KL*.

$\overleftrightarrow{KL}$ means **line** *KL*.

$\overrightarrow{KL}$ means **ray** *KL*.

> The segment includes endpoints *K* and *L* and all points between *K* and *L*.

> The ray starts at endpoint *K* and passes through *L*.

6 **Discussion** Use the diagram in the Example to help answer the following questions.

a. Why are two points enough to name a line but one point is not? There are many lines that can go through one point, but with two points only one specific line can contain two points.

b. Are all three letters necessary to name line *JLM*? Explain.

7 **Try This as a Class** In each part below, the name of a figure is printed in red followed by two other names. Are the figures whose names are printed in black the same figures as the one whose name is printed in red? Explain.

a. $\overleftrightarrow{EG}$: $\overleftrightarrow{EF}$, $\overleftrightarrow{GE}$

b. $\overrightarrow{EG}$: $\overrightarrow{EF}$, $\overrightarrow{GE}$

c. $\overline{EG}$: $\overline{EF}$, $\overline{GE}$

8 ✔ **CHECKPOINT** Draw and label the following objects. **Sample Responses:**

a. point *P*

b. ray *SQ*

c. segment *MT*

d. line *UV*

e. $\overrightarrow{YX}$

f. $\overleftrightarrow{ND}$

g. $\overline{RG}$

h. $\overrightarrow{XY}$

c.

e.

f.
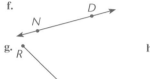

g.

h.

6. b. No, no matter which two points are used, the line continues forever and will pass through all other points on the line.

7. a. Yes, all points lie on the same line and any two of the points can be used to name the line.
   b. No, $\overrightarrow{GE}$ has a different endpoint and continues in the opposite direction of $\overrightarrow{EG}$.
   c. No, $\overline{EF}$ is shorter than $\overline{EG}$ and has a different endpoint.

✔ **QUESTION 8**

...checks that you can identify and name points, lines, segments, and rays.

DEVELOPING MATH CONCEPTS

To develop the ideas in **Question 6**, draw a point on the board and ask a student volunteer to draw a line through the point. Then ask if anyone can draw a different line through the point. Allow volunteers to continue drawing different lines until the idea that "an infinite number of lines could be drawn through the point" is grasped. Next draw two points on the board and ask a volunteer to use a strightedge to draw a line that passes through both points. Then ask for volunteers to draw a different line which passes through the two points. Students will see that there is only one line that passes through the two points.

COMMON ERROR

Questions 7 and 8 When identifying rays, students often think that the symbol notation indicates the direction of the ray. Explain that the standard notation always gives the endpoint first with the arrow headed to the right even if the ray in a diagram heads in a different direction. This can be emphasized in the discussion of **Question 7(b)** and by asking students to share their sketches for **Question 8(e)**. **Questions 7 and 8** also provide an opportunity to explain why there can be more than one way to name a particular line or segment.

Have students perform a scavenger hunt around the classroom, finding examples that could be used to illustrate rays, lines, segments, planes, parallel lines, and perpendicular lines. Have students share the objects they found with the class. For figures that extend indefinitely, suggest students describe how to alter the object to fit the term. For example, if the ceiling continued on forever in each direction, it would represent a plane.

9. a. $\overleftrightarrow{AB}$ and $\overleftrightarrow{CD}$
   b. Possible answers include any pair of lines other than $\overleftrightarrow{AB}$ and $\overleftrightarrow{CD}$.
   c. $\overleftrightarrow{AB}$ and $\overleftrightarrow{EF}$; $\overleftrightarrow{CD}$ and $\overleftrightarrow{EF}$
   d. Possible answers include any pair of lines other than $\overleftrightarrow{AB}$ and $\overleftrightarrow{EF}$, or $\overleftrightarrow{CD}$ and $\overleftrightarrow{EF}$.

10. Answers will vary. Samples Responses: perpendicular, parallel, ray, line, triangle, angle, rectangle.

▶ **Letters and symbols can also be used to describe relationships between geometric figures.**

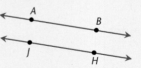

A **plane** can be thought of as a flat surface that goes on forever in all directions. The floor and walls of your classroom are each part of a plane.

Two lines in a plane are **parallel** if they don't *intersect*, or meet.

$\overleftrightarrow{AB} \parallel \overleftrightarrow{JH}$ means
$\overleftrightarrow{AB}$ and $\overleftrightarrow{JH}$ are parallel.

Two lines that intersect at a *right angle* are **perpendicular**. You will learn more about right angles and other types of angles in Exploration 3 on page 103.

$\overleftrightarrow{QV} \perp \overleftrightarrow{UT}$ means
$\overleftrightarrow{QV}$ and $\overleftrightarrow{UT}$ are perpendicular.

The ¬ tells you the angle is a right angle. The measure of a right angle is 90 degrees.

9 Name two lines in the photo below that have the given characteristic.

   a. They are parallel.   **b.** They are not parallel.

   c. They are perpendicular. **d.** They are not perpendicular.

10 Look back at the cards you used for *I Describe, You Draw*. If you described the cards again, what geometric terms could you use to help your partner draw the figures correctly?

| HOMEWORK EXERCISES ▶ See Exs. 1–7 on p. 108.

Exploration 2

Sides of a Triangle

SET UP You will need: • a ruler • Labsheet 3B and scissors, or sticks with different lengths • Labsheet 3C

Jessie described the design on Card 5 as "a square that is inside a triangle and has one side that lies on the bottom side of the triangle." Jessie's partner made two drawings.

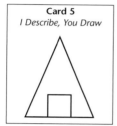

Card 5
I Describe, You Draw

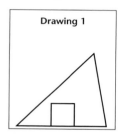

Drawing 1

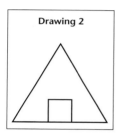

Drawing 2

▶ **Types of Triangles** The design on the card would have been easier to describe if Jessie knew how to classify triangles. One way to classify triangles is by the lengths of the sides.

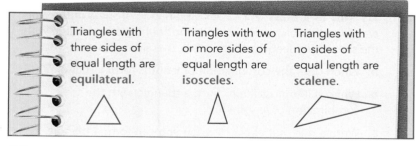

Triangles with three sides of equal length are **equilateral**.

Triangles with two or more sides of equal length are **isosceles**.

Triangles with no sides of equal length are **scalene**.

11 Discussion

a. What type of triangle is on Card 5? How do you know?
Isosceles; Two sides are of equal length.

b. How can you show that the triangle in Drawing 1 is scalene?

c. Identify the type of triangle in Drawing 2. Why did you classify it that way? Equilateral; All three sides are of equal length.

d. Why can the triangle in Drawing 2 be classified in two different ways?

GOAL

LEARN HOW TO...
- classify triangles by the lengths of their sides
- determine when triangles can be formed

AS YOU...
- construct triangles with sides of different lengths

KEY TERMS
- equilateral triangle
- isosceles triangle
- scalene triangle

11. **b.** Measure the side lengths and compare. All sides should be different lengths.

d. If a triangle has 3 sides of equal length, then it has 2 or more sides of equal length. So any equilateral triangle is also an isosceles triangle.

Exploration 2

DEVELOPING MATH CONCEPTS

Question 11 The definition of an isosceles triangle is stated in such a way that an equilateral triangle is included as a type of isosceles triangle. Explain to students that while an equilateral triangle is both equilateral and isosceles, it is not always true that every isosceles triangle is also equilateral. You may want to draw a triangle to illustrate this fact. To identify a triangle with three sides of equal length using its most specific name, we state that it is an equilateral triangle.

Exploration 2 *continued*

TEACHING NOTES

Before students start **Questions 13 and 14**, point out that to form a triangle, the sticks must touch at the vertices with no overlapping and without extending beyond a vertex. The triangles could also be drawn using a geometry utility program on a computer. After drawing a triangle, the information could be entered in a five-column table, labeling the column heads *length of shorter side 1, length of shorter side 2, sum of the lengths of the two shorter sides, length of the longest side,* and *triangle formed? (yes or no)*. This procedure should lead students to discover the rule in **Question 15**.

Question 15 helps insure that all students understand which combinations of side lengths can form a triangle. Students should verify that the rule is correct by using sticks to test several combinations of side lengths.

12. Answers will vary. Sample Response: "Draw an isosceles triangle with a base about $\frac{3}{4}$ the length of each equal side. Draw a small square centered on the base of the triangle, but not touching either of the other two sides of the triangle."

> **✔ QUESTION 13**
>
> ...checks that you can classify triangles based on the lengths of their sides.

15. a. A triangle is formed when the sum of the lengths of the two shortest sides is greater than the length of the longest side.
  b. It is impossible when the sum of the lengths of the two shortest sides is less than or equal to the length of the longest side.
  c. You can form a triangle if the sum of the lengths of the shortest two sides of the triangle is greater than the length of the longest side.

> **✔ QUESTION 16**
>
> ...checks that you understand when a combination of side lengths will form a triangle.

12 Write a description of the design on Card 5 that does not also describe the other two drawings.

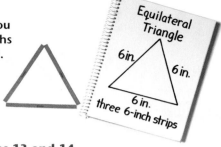

▶ **Constructing Triangles** You can use sticks of different lengths to explore a variety of triangles.

Equilateral Triangle
6 in. 6 in.
6 in.
three 6-inch strips

Use Labsheet 3B for Questions 13 and 14.

13 **✔ CHECKPOINT** Use the *Sticks of Different Sizes* to construct one example of each type of triangle. List the lengths of the sticks you use for each.

  a. an isosceles triangle Answers vary. Sample Responses: 5 in., 5 in., 8 in.; 8 in., 8 in., 6 in.; 6 in., 6 in., 8 in.
  b. a scalene triangle Answers vary. Sample Responses: 5 in., 6 in., 8 in.; 6 in., 5 in., 4 in.; 5 in., 2 in., 6 in.
  c. an equilateral triangle (different from the one shown above)
  Answers vary. Sample Responses: 5 in., 5 in., 5 in.; 4 in., 4 in., 4 in.; 8 in., 8 in., 8 in.

Use Labsheet 3C for Questions 14 and 15.

14 Using your sticks, decide whether you can form a triangle for each combination of lengths listed in the *Sides of a Triangle* table. Sketch each triangle you form and record its type and the lengths of its sides in the table. See margin.

15 **Try This as a Class** For each combination of sticks in the *Sides of a Triangle* table, compare the length of the longest side with the sum of the lengths of the other two sides.

  a. When does the combination of lengths form a triangle?

  b. When is it impossible to form a triangle with the combination of lengths?

  c. Write a rule that explains when you can form a triangle.

16 **✔ CHECKPOINT** Without using sticks, decide which combinations of side lengths can form a triangle. Explain.

  a. 5 in., 12 in., and 6 in.
    No; $5 + 6 < 12$
  b. 9 in., 6 in., and 5 in.
    Yes; $5 + 6 > 9$
  c. 6 in., 8 in., and 10 in.
    Yes; $6 + 8 > 10$
  d. 4 in., 1 in., and 3 in.
    No; $1 + 3 = 4$

HOMEWORK EXERCISES ▶ See Exs. 8–15 on p. 108.

Module 2 Math Detectives

14. See Additional Answers beginning on page A1.

Exploration 3

Angles of a Triangle

SET UP *You will need:* • Labsheet 3D

17. Answers may vary. Sample Response: Corresponding vertex angles are different sizes.

17 Discussion Both red triangles below are isosceles. Besides their side lengths, what makes them look different?

▶ **Naming and Describing Angles** You can use an *angle* measurement to describe how the sides of a roof meet. An **angle** is formed by two rays that have a common endpoint.

EXAMPLE

This angle can be named in any of the following ways:

- angle *B* (written ∠*B*)
- angle *ABC* (written ∠*ABC*)
- angle *CBA* (written ∠*CBA*)

The endpoint of the rays is the **vertex** of the angle.

B

A

C

18 Try This as a Class

a. Explain how the vertex is used in naming an angle.

b. Write all the possible names that identify the angle marked in red.
∠*SRT*, ∠*TRS*

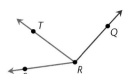

T   *Q*

S   *R*

18. a. The letter of the vertex is always written in the center of the three-letter sequence used to name an angle, or the vertex is used alone to name an angle as long as there are no more than two rays containing the vertex.

▶ The measure of an angle refers to the size of the opening between the two rays of the angle. Angles are measured in units called **degrees**. The symbol for degrees is °. For example, the measure of an 80 degree angle can be written as 80°.

Exploration 3

DEVELOPING MATH CONCEPTS
Question 18 is done as a class to make sure students understand that in this figure, three points must be used to name the angle marked in red. Since the three rays form more than one angle with vertex *R*, the angle marked in red can be named ∠*SRT* or ∠*TRS*, but not simply ∠*R*. This is different from the angle in the **Example** that can be referred to in three ways because it has only two rays extending from point *B*.

Exploration 3 *continued*

TEACHING NOTES

The definitions given for the types of angles use the degree measures of the angles. Although the measures are an important part of the definitions, students should also be able to identify the types of angles by sight. (They are not expected to measure the angles with a protractor at this time.)

The following Classroom Example may be used to provide additional practice classifying angles before students begin classifying triangles by their angles.

CLASSROOM EXAMPLE

Classify each angle as right, acute, obtuse, or straight.

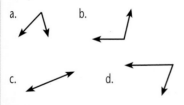

Answer:

a. acute   b. obtuse

c. straight   d. acute

DIFFERENTIATED INSTRUCTION

For students having a difficult time classifying angles, give them an overhead transparency with a right angle drawn on it. Show them how to lay the transparency over angles, aligning the vertices and a side, to judge whether the angle is less than, equal to, or greater than 90°.

20. See Additional Answers beginning on page A1.

CLASSIFYING ANGLES

Right Angle	Acute Angle	Obtuse Angle	Straight Angle
Its measure is 90°.	Its measure is greater than 0° but less than 90°.	Its measure is greater than 90° but less than 180°.	Its measure is 180°.

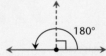

✔ QUESTION 19

...checks that you can classify and name angles.

19 ✔ CHECKPOINT For each of the following, find an angle of that type in the diagrams below and write all the names that identify the angle.

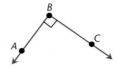 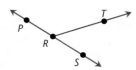

a. right angle ∠ABC, ∠B, ∠CBA   **b.** acute angle ∠TRS, ∠SRT

c. obtuse angle ∠PRT, ∠TRP   **d.** straight angle ∠PRS, ∠SRP

▶ **Classifying Triangles by Angles** In Exploration 2, you learned to use the side lengths to classify triangles. You can also classify triangles by the types of angles they have.

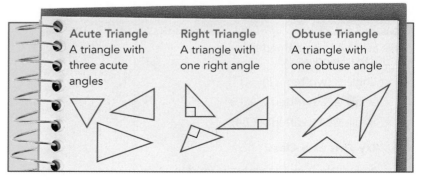

Acute Triangle	Right Triangle	Obtuse Triangle
A triangle with three acute angles	A triangle with one right angle	A triangle with one obtuse angle

Use Labsheet 3D for Questions 20 and 21.

✔ QUESTION 20

...checks that you can classify triangles based on their angles.

20 ✔ CHECKPOINT

a. For each triangle in the *Angles in a Triangle* table, list the names of its angles in the appropriate columns. See margin.

b. Use the definitions above to classify the triangle by the measures of its angles and record the type in the last column. See margin.

 Module 2   Math Detectives

---

21 Use Labsheet 3D to help answer each question. It may also help to try drawing triangles on a piece of scrap paper.

    a. Can a triangle have two right angles? Why or why not?
        No; It doesn't close to make a triangle. (sides don't intersect)
    b. If a triangle has one obtuse angle, what kind of angles will the other two angles be? Why?

22 **Discussion** After examining a triangle, a student decides it is an acute triangle and a right triangle. Is this possible? Explain.

23 Think about how the geometric terms you have learned can help you when playing *I Describe, You Draw.* **a.– d. Answers will vary.**

    a. Make up an *I Describe, You Draw* card that can be described using the mathematical terms you learned in this section.

    b. Play the game with another student using the cards you created.

    c. How do your drawings compare with the cards?

    d. Which were closer to the drawings on the cards, your drawings in part (b) or your drawings for Cards 1 and 2 from the *Setting the Stage?*

21. b. acute; The sides of the triangle won't come together if there are 2 obtuse angles, two right angles, or one obtuse angle and one right angle. So both of the other 2 angles must be acute.

22. No; It is a right triangle by definition, even though it has two acute angles. It takes only one right angle to be a right triangle, but three acute angles to be named an acute triangle, so it cannot be both right and acute.

▶ This year you will use the Mathematical Language Scale to assess and help improve your use of mathematical language.

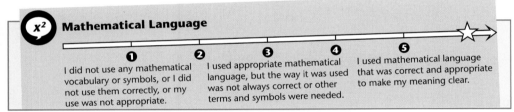

x² **Mathematical Language**

① I did not use any mathematical vocabulary or symbols, or I did not use them correctly, or my use was not appropriate.

②

③ I used appropriate mathematical language, but the way it was used was not always correct or other terms and symbols were needed.

④

⑤ I used mathematical language that was correct and appropriate to make my meaning clear.

This scale is part of the Assessment Scales on page 87.

24 What score would you give this description on the mathematical language scale? Why?

This is a square with two lines inside that meet at the top of the square and start at the two bottom corners of the square.

24. Sample: 2; The student uses the word *lines* incorrectly where it should be *segments. Corners* should be replaced with *vertices.* Student could have included vocabulary such as right and scalene triangles, acute and isosceles triangle to describe the divisions within the square.

HOMEWORK EXERCISES ▶ See Exs. 16–31 on pp. 109–110.

Students may be confused about why a triangle with an acute angle and a right angle is not classified as acute as well as right. When discussing **Question 22**, use the results on **Labsheet 3D** and students' answers to **Question 21** to point out that all triangles have at least two acute angles, thus it is the third angle that distinguishes a triangle as either acute, right, or obtuse.

CLASSROOM MANAGEMENT
For **Question 23(b)**, students will need to be paired with someone whose card they have not seen. Chairs will again need to be arranged back to back, but since each pair of students has a different set of cards it is not imperative that all the drawers be in the same row.

Most students will want to have an opportunity to describe their card, but an alternative is to call a student to the front of the room to describe his or her card while everyone in the class attempts to draw it. This can be repeated with other students as time permits or until the class sees the benefits of using and understanding geometry vocabulary.

TEACHING NOTES
After assessing the description in **Question 24**, you may want students to work in groups to write a description that would score a 5 on the scale. These can then be shared with the class to be sure students understand the *Mathematical Language Scale.*

105

Key Concepts

CLOSURE QUESTION

Why will 3 lengths of equal measure always form a triangle?

Sample Response: In a triangle, the sum of the lengths of the two shorter sides must always be greater than the length of the longest side. The sides are all equal in length. So, when you add any two lengths, their sum is always greater than the length of the third side, no matter what length is used.

ABSENT STUDENTS

For students who were absent for all or part of this section, the blackline Study Guide for Section 3 may be used to present the ideas, concepts, and skills of Section 3.

Section 3
Key Concepts

Key Terms

point
line
ray
segment

plane
parallel
perpendicular

equilateral triangle
isosceles triangle
scalene triangle

Basic Geometric Figures (pp. 98–99)

Figure	Words	Symbol
•A	point A	A
A ←•——•→ B	line AB or line BA	$\overleftrightarrow{AB}$ or $\overleftrightarrow{BA}$
A •——•→ B	ray AB	$\overrightarrow{AB}$
A •——• B	segment AB or segment BA	$\overline{AB}$ or $\overline{BA}$

Line Relationships (p. 100)

A plane is a flat surface that goes on forever in all directions. Two distinct lines in a plane either intersect or are parallel. When lines intersect at a 90° angle, they are perpendicular.

intersecting lines   parallel lines   perpendicular lines

This is a right angle symbol.

Classifying Triangles by Sides (p. 101)

- Equilateral triangles have three sides of equal length.
- Isosceles triangles have two or more sides of equal length.
- Scalene triangles have no sides of equal length.

Triangle Side Lengths (p. 102)

The sum of the lengths of the two shortest sides of a triangle is greater than the length of the longest side.

25 Key Concepts Question A triangle has a 5 in. side and an 11 in. side. The length of the third side is a whole number of inches. What are the possible lengths of the third side? **All whole numbers greater than 6 and less than 16.**

Section 3
Key Concepts

▶▶▶▶▶▶▶▶▶▶▶▶▶▶▶▶▶▶▶▶▶▶▶▶

Key Terms

Naming and Classifying Angles (pp. 103–104)

An angle is formed by two rays that have a common endpoint. The endpoint of the rays is the vertex of the angle. The angle at the right is formed by $\overrightarrow{RQ}$ and $\overrightarrow{RS}$. It can be named $\angle R$, $\angle QRS$, or $\angle SRQ$. Angles are measured in units called degrees. An angle can be classified by its measure.

angle

vertex

Right Angle
Its measure is 90°.

Acute Angle
Its measure is greater than 0° but less than 90°.

Obtuse Angle
Its measure is greater than 90° but less than 180°.

Straight Angle
Its measure is 180°.

degrees

right angle

acute angle

obtuse angle

straight angle

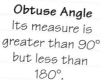 

Classifying Triangles by Angles (pp. 104–105)

- Acute triangles have three acute angles.
- Right triangles have one right angle.
- Obtuse triangles have one obtuse angle.

acute triangle

right triangle

obtuse triangle

Mathematical Language Scale (p. 105)

To assess your use of mathematical language, ask yourself:
- Was my use of terms and symbols correct?
- Was my use of terms and symbols appropriate?
- Are there other mathematical terms or symbols I should have used to make my meaning clearer?

26 Key Concepts Question Sketch an example of each type of triangle. **Sample responses are given.**

a. a triangle that is both right and scalene

b. a triangle that is both acute and isosceles

State how to classify triangles by angles and by sides.

Sample Response:

A triangle can be classified as obtuse or right if it contains one of these angles. It must have 3 acute angles to be classified as acute.

A triangle is equilateral if all of its sides have the same length, isosceles if at least two of its sides have the same length, or scalene if none of its sides have the same length.

SUGGESTED ASSIGNMENTS

Core Course

Day 1: Exs. 1–7
Day 2: Exs. 8–15
Day 3: Exs. 16–28
Day 4: Exs. 29, 31–41

Extended Course

Day 1: Exs. 1–7
Day 2: Exs. 8–15
Day 3: Exs. 16–28
Day 4: Exs. 29–41

Note: Extended Course assignments can be used to differentiate within the regular classroom. In classrooms where students are grouped homogeneously, the material might be covered in fewer days. In this case assignments may be combined.

ADDITIONAL PRACTICE

See the *Teacher's Resource Book* for additional practice and application exercises for this section.

YOU WILL NEED

For Exs. 8–10:
♦ ruler or straightedge

2. Sample Response: $\overrightarrow{XY}$, $\overrightarrow{YZ}$, $\overrightarrow{YX}$, $\overrightarrow{ZY}$; They differ in endpoints and some differ in direction.

8.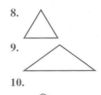

9.

10.

15. The segments won't form a triangle since the sum of the lengths of the two shorter sides is not greater than the length of the third side. There could be no such triangle-shaped piece of land.

Section 3
Practice & Application Exercises

Use the points on the line to write each answer using symbols.

$\overset{\longleftrightarrow}{\underset{X \qquad Y \qquad\qquad Z}{\rule{6cm}{0.4pt}}}$

1. Name three different segments. How are they different?
Sample Response: $\overline{XY}$, $\overline{YZ}$, $\overline{XZ}$; They differ in length and endpoints.

2. Name three different rays. How are they different?

3. Name the line in six ways. $\overleftrightarrow{XY}$, $\overleftrightarrow{XZ}$, $\overleftrightarrow{YZ}$, $\overleftrightarrow{YX}$, $\overleftrightarrow{ZX}$, $\overleftrightarrow{ZY}$

Write *line*, *segment*, *ray*, *parallel*, or *perpendicular* to best describe each object or pair of objects.

4. flagpole segment

5. light from car's headlight ray

6. flagpole and the edge of the road perpendicular

7. light from headlight and the edge of the road parallel

Use a ruler or a straightedge to draw an example of each type of triangle. **Sample responses are given.**

8. equilateral   **9.** isosceles   **10.** scalene

A triangle has sides of lengths 20 ft and 15 ft. Tell whether each length *can* or *cannot* be the length of the third side of the triangle.

11. 29 ft can   **12.** 3 ft cannot   **13.** 5 ft cannot   **14.** 37 ft cannot

15. Read the story. Then explain Smith's answer to the problem.

Jones said to Smith: "I think I'll sell that piece of land at the bottom of my garden, but I can't make up my mind how much to ask for it. What do you suggest?"

"Well," said Smith, "what are its dimensions?"

Jones drew the diagram below and handed it over.

Smith studied the drawing for a second or two, then passed it back. "If your dimensions are right, you don't get so much as a dime for it," he said laughing.

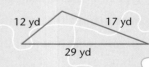

from Puzzles and Brain Twisters, by Fred Walls

Explain what is wrong with each statement.

16. This is $\angle JHI$.

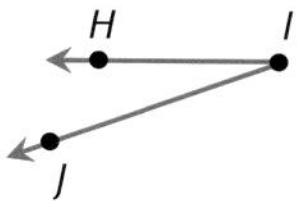

17. This is $\overrightarrow{CB}$.

18. This is $\angle G$.

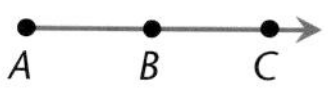

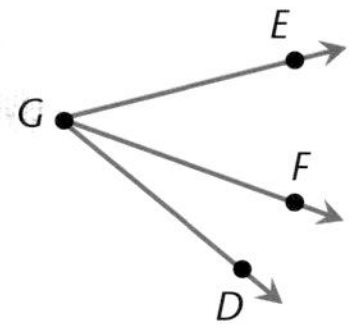

Classify each angle as *right, acute, straight,* or *obtuse.*

19.

20.

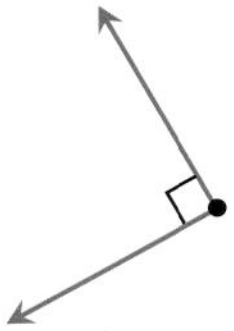

21.

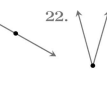

22.

Classify each triangle according to the measures of its angles and according to the lengths of its sides.

23.

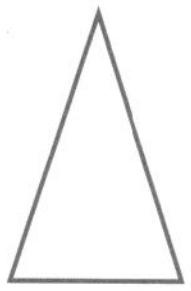

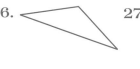

24.

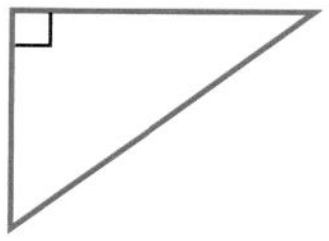

25.

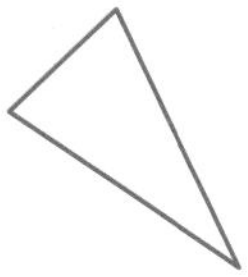

26.

27.

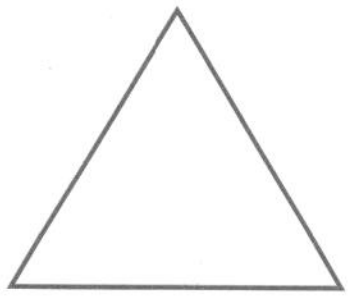

28.

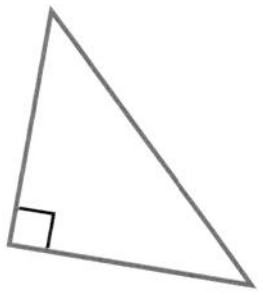

29. a. The shop owner described a missing watch to the detectives. Will the detectives be able to identify the correct watch? If not, how can you improve the description?

The missing watch has a silver band and there are two blue triangles next to the dial.

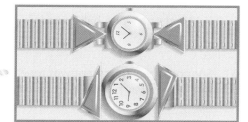

b. What would you score the shop owner's description on the mathematical language scale? Why?

16. The vertex is *I*, not *H*.

17. The ray pictured has *A* as an endpoint and goes in the direction opposite of $\overrightarrow{CB}$.

18. There are three angles pictured that all have *G* as the vertex, so three points are needed to specify a particular angle in the diagram.

19. obtuse

20. right

21. straight

22. acute

23. acute isosceles

24. right scalene

25. acute scalene

26. obtuse isosceles

27. acute equilateral

28. right isosceles

29. a. No; Give the type of triangles and whether the vertex or side of the triangle is touching the watch face. Give the size of the circular face and whether the face has all numbers 1-12 or just 12, 3, 6, and 9.

b. 2 or 3: The owner used triangles to describe the watch, but they were not specific enough to identify the watch.

Exercise Notes

Question 29 Students may think they need to know which watch is the missing one in order to improve the description. Instead encourage them to look at the differences between the two watches and note the details that need to be addressed in the description, such as "the description needs to identify whether the triangles are equilateral or scalene." Alternatively, students might write a description for each watch.

Practice & Applications

EXERCISE NOTES

Exercise 31 In addition to their own thoughts, students may need to do some research to answer **part (a)**. They may want to ask several adults how they use geometry vocabulary. For **part (b)**, ask students to provide the context in which the words are used, such as when looking at a map or taking a hike, "Where's the *point* we are trying to reach?"

Students might enjoy keeping a log book for a week of the math vocabulary they hear used in everyday life (including their own use).

30. Challenge *Acute-isosceles* is an example of a combination name for a triangle. A name describing the angles (*acute*, *right*, or *obtuse*) is joined with a name describing the number of sides of equal length (*equilateral*, *isosceles*, or *scalene*). List all the combination names that can be written. Then explain which names describe triangles that cannot actually be formed.

RESEARCH

Exercise 31 checks that you understand how important mathematical language is in everyday life.

30. acute-isosceles, acute-scalene, acute-equilateral, obtuse-isosceles, obtuse-scalene, obtuse-equilateral, right-isosceles, right-scalene, right-equilateral;

All except right-equilateral and obtuse-equilateral can be formed.

31. a. Answers will vary. Sample Responses: The angle of a shot in a soccer game. People standing in line. A triangular kitchen design for efficiency of the sink, fridge and stove.

Reflecting ◀▶ on the Section

31. a. Describe ways in which people may need to use words like line, angle, or triangle in their everyday life or work.

b. What mathematical terms do you use outside of school besides numbers? Answers will vary.

Spiral ◀▶ Review

Write each fraction in lowest terms. (Module 1, p. 61)

32. $\frac{6}{18}$ $\frac{1}{3}$ **33.** $\frac{24}{30}$ $\frac{4}{5}$ **34.** $\frac{15}{25}$ $\frac{3}{5}$ **35.** $\frac{18}{27}$ $\frac{2}{3}$

Use mental math to find each value. (Module 1, p. 62)

36. $\frac{1}{4}$ of 28 7 **37.** $\frac{5}{6}$ of 48 40 **38.** $\frac{2}{3}$ of 24 16

Use the following information to answer Exercises 39–41. A bag contains 2 red, 3 blue, and 5 white balls. One ball is drawn from the bag. (Module 2, p. 80)

39. What are the outcomes of the experiment? red, blue, and white ball

40. Find the theoretical probability of the given event.

   a. A red ball is drawn. $\frac{2}{10}$ or $\frac{1}{5}$

   b. A green ball is drawn. $\frac{0}{10}$ or 0

   c. A red or a white ball is drawn. $\frac{7}{10}$

   d. The ball drawn is not white. $\frac{5}{10}$ or $\frac{1}{2}$

41. Suppose the experiment was repeated 20 times, and the ball that was drawn was put back in the bag after each trial. About how many times would you think a blue ball was drawn? Explain.
   6 times because the probability the ball is blue is $\frac{3}{10}$. 20 is twice 10, so 6 would be twice 3.

Section ③
Extra Skill Practice

Choose the letter of the symbol that matches each term.

1. segment *AB* C
2. point *A* A
3. line *AB* D
4. ray *AB* B

   A. *A*
   B. $\overrightarrow{AB}$
   C. $\overline{AB}$
   D. $\overleftrightarrow{AB}$

Tell whether each combination of side lengths *can* or *cannot* form a triangle.

5. 20 ft, 12 ft, 10 ft can
6. 8 in., 9 in., 18 in. cannot
7. 15 yd, 6 yd, 6 yd cannot
8. 11 ft, 12 ft, 13 ft can

Tell whether each statement is *true* or *false*.

9. A right triangle has one right angle. true
10. A scalene triangle has two sides of equal length. false
11. An obtuse triangle has one obtuse angle. true

Classify each angle as *right*, *acute*, *obtuse*, or *straight*.

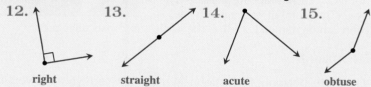

12. right   13. straight   14. acute   15. obtuse

Standardized Testing ◀▶ Free Response

Find an example of each type of triangle that is formed by putting together two or more of the small triangles. List the numbers of the small triangles you used. Sample responses are given.

Ⓐ right 2, 5, 6
Ⓑ equilateral 4, 5
Ⓒ acute 1, 2
Ⓓ isosceles 1, 4
Ⓔ scalene 1, 3, 4
Ⓕ obtuse 2, 5

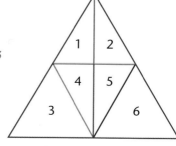

Extra Skill Practice

TEACHER NOTES
For each Exploration, the corresponding Extra Skill Practice Exercises are noted.

Exploration 1: 1–4
Exploration 2: 5–8
Exploration 3: 9–15

EXTRA HELP
Teacher's Resource Book
- Practice and Applications
- Study Guide

Technology Resources
- @Home Tutor
- Test Generator

ASSESSMENT
- Section 3 Quick Quiz
- Test Generator

GETTING STARTED

Module 2 Section 4 *Warm-Up* reviews the classification of triangles in preparation for classifying polygons by various characteristics.

TEACHING NOTES

The star lies to the left and down a bit from the center of the drawing. One of its points is approximately in the center of the drawing. For students having difficulty finding the star, suggest turning the paper to view the design from a different angle, or placing the design on the floor and standing up to look down at it from a distance.

CLASSROOM MANAGEMENT

The *Setting the Stage* is the designated lesson for the first class period. This allows plenty of time for students to try to discover the star within the drawing.

Students can work independently on **Questions 1 and 2** and then compare their total score with a partner's to see if they found the same polygons. Then the class can discuss **Question 2** together. You may choose to introduce the names for 4, 5, and 6-sided polygons using the table on p. 114.

1. See Additional Answers beginning on page A1.

112

Section ④ Polygons and Angles

IN THIS SECTION

EXPLORATION 1
♦ Naming Polygons

EXPLORATION 2
♦ Measuring Angles

EXPLORATION 3
♦ The Presentation Scale

Detecting Shapes

‹‹·‹ Setting the Stage ►►►►►►►►►►►►►►►►►►►►►►►►►►►►►►►►

Sometimes being a detective means examining clues over and over again, hoping to see something you did not see before. For example, examine the drawing at the right. Can you find the five-pointed star**?**

The five-pointed star is an example of a *polygon*. A **polygon** is a closed plane figure made from segments, called sides, that do not cross. Each endpoint of a side is a **vertex**. (The plural of vertex is vertices.) A polygon can be named by listing the vertices in consecutive order.

Think About It

1 List all the polygons in the figure at the left. Record your answers in a table like the one below. (One polygon has been done for you.) Then compute the total score by adding the points described. **See margin.**

- ♦ 1 point for each triangle
- ♦ 2 points for each 4-sided polygon
- ♦ 3 points for each 5-sided polygon
- ♦ 5 points for each 6-sided polygon

Type	Names	Score
Triangle		
4-sided polygon	*HBIG*	
5-sided polygon		
6-sided polygon		
	TOTAL SCORE	

2 Discussion What is the greatest possible score for the figure**?**
83 points possible

Exploration 1

Naming Polygons

SET UP *Work with a partner. You will need:* • *index cards or sticky notes* • *Labsheet 4A* • *2 pieces of string, each 3 feet long* • *scissors*

GOAL

LEARN HOW TO...
♦ classify polygons
♦ sort polygons using a Venn diagram

AS YOU...
♦ explore geometric shapes

KEY TERMS
♦ regular polygon
♦ quadrilateral
♦ Venn diagram
♦ trapezoid
♦ parallelogram
♦ rhombus

▶ **Just as examining the clues over and over again can help detectives solve a mystery, sorting polygons in various ways can help you identify their properties.**

3 **Use Labsheet 4A.** Cut out the *Shape Cards*. Then follow the steps below to sort them.

You may want to tie the ends of the string together.

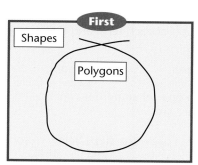

First

Shapes

Polygons

Place a loop of string on your workspace. Write *Polygons* on an index card and place it in the loop. Write *Shapes* on another card and place it outside the loop.

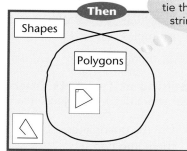

Then

Shapes

Polygons

Place all the cards with a polygon inside the loop. Place the cards with shapes that are not polygons outside the loop.

▶ **The shapes you placed inside the loop in Question 3 are a set of polygons.**

4 A **regular polygon** is a polygon in which all the sides have the same length and all the angles have the same measure.

a. Use a loop of string and an index card labeled *Regular Polygons*. Sort the polygon *Shape Cards* so the regular polygons are inside the loop and the non-regular polygons are outside the loop.

b. What is another name for a regular triangle? **equilateral triangle**

3. Outside the *Polygon* loop: Cards N, W, Y, Q

Inside the *Polygon* loop: All remaining cards A, B, C, D, E, F, G, H, I, J, K, L, M, O, P, R, S, T, U, V, X

4. **a.** Inside the *Regular Polygons* loop: Cards B, J, L, M, O

Outside the *Regular Polygons* loop: all other polygon cards A, C, D, E, F, G, H, I, K, P, R, S, T, U, V, X

Exploration 1

TEACHING NOTES
Question 4 Instruct students to set cards N, Q, W, and Y face down, off to the side, since they were not in the *Polygons* loop.

The Classroom Example below can be used after **Question 4** to emphasize that it takes both congruent sides and congruent angles for a polygon to be regular.

CLASSROOM EXAMPLE

State the polygons below that are shaped like regular polygons.

a.   b.

c.   d.

Answer: Figures (a), (c), and (d). Figure (b) is not regular because the interior angles are not congruent. Some are acute and some measure more than 180°.

Section 4 Polygons and Angles 113

Exploration 1 continued

TEACHING NOTES

Questions 7 and 8 Since the number of angles in a polygon equals the number of sides, an octagon can be described as an 8-sided figure even though the suffix "gon" with the prefix "octa" literally means "eight angles". A polygon is traditionally defined by the number of sides it has. Some students may wish to further explore the origins of the words like triangle, quadrilateral, and quadrangle, that do not use the "gon" suffix.

Students should set all non-quadrilateral cards face down off to the side of their desk for **Question 9**.

▶ Another way to sort polygons is by the number of sides.

✔ **QUESTION 5**

...checks that you can distinguish polygons based on their number of sides.

5 ✔ **CHECKPOINT** Identify the polygons on the *Shape Cards* that have the given number of sides.

    a. eight sides M, P, X   **b.** four sides A, C, D, E, F, G, H, I, L

▶ The word **polygon** comes from the Greek **poly-** meaning "many" and **-gon** meaning "angles." Polygons have many angles and sides. Many of the terms used to classify polygons also come from the Greek word parts shown at the right. For example, *pentagon* means "five angles."

Word part	Meaning
tri-	three
quadri-	four
penta-	five
hexa-	six
octa-	eight
deca-	ten
poly-	many
-gon	angle(s)
-lateral	side(s)

6 What is the name of a polygon with eight angles? octagon

7 **Try This as a Class** With the exception of **quadrilateral**, which means "four sides," the names of polygons refer to the number of angles. How are the number of sides and the number of angles of a polygon related? The number of sides and angles are equal in a polygon.

✔ **QUESTION 8**

...checks that you can name polygons by the number of sides or angles.

9. Region I: D, H
   Region II: C, G
   Region III: F, I, L
   Region IV: A, E

8 ✔ **CHECKPOINT** Write a definition of each term and sketch two examples. Check students' sketches.

    a. triangle   **b.** pentagon   **c.** hexagon
      3-sided polygon   5-sided polygon   6-sided polygon

▶ **Looking at Two Sets** Objects in one set sometimes share characteristics with objects in another set.

9 Use the quadrilateral *Shape Cards*. Follow the steps below to sort them into two sets.

Two sides are parallel if they are parts of parallel lines.

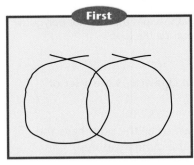

Place two overlapping loops on your workspace.

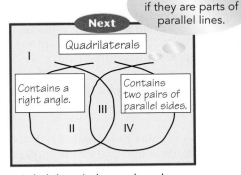

Label three index cards and place them as shown.

Then Place the *Shape Cards* in the correct regions, I, II, III, or IV.

10
  a. Where did you place the cards that belong to both sets?
  Region III
  b. Why were some cards placed in region I?

▶ Diagrams like the ones you have made with loops are **Venn diagrams**. Venn diagrams use a drawing to show how the objects in sets are related.

11 A quadrilateral that has exactly one pair of parallel sides is a **trapezoid**. In what region(s) did you place the trapezoids? **Why?**

12 A quadrilateral that has two pairs of parallel sides is a **parallelogram**.

  a. In what region(s) did you place the parallelograms? **Why?** *Region IV if it did not contain a right angle, Region III if it did*

  b. What is another name for parallelograms that contain a right angle? *rectangle*

13 A parallelogram with all sides the same length is a **rhombus**.

  a. Where did you place the rhombuses? Explain.
  Region IV if it did not contain a right angle, Region III if it did
  b. What is another name for a rhombus that contains a right angle? *square*

14 ✔ **CHECKPOINT**

  a. Sort the parallelogram *Shape Cards* into two sets, a set labeled *Rectangles* and a set labeled *Rhombuses*.
  Rectangles: I, F, L; Rhombuses: A, E, L
  b. Did you have any shapes that belong to both sets? Explain. *Yes, L; The square has four sides of equal length and four right angles.*

15
  a. What kind of polygon is the five-pointed star in the *Setting the Stage*? *decagon*

  b. Is the five-pointed star a regular polygon? Explain.

  c. Sketch a four pointed star. *Check students' work.*

  d. What kind of polygon is a four pointed star? *octagon*

HOMEWORK EXERCISES ▶ See Exs. 1–4 on p. 120.

---

10. b. These cards did not fit any of the descriptors for either loop. Polygons in Region I do not contain a right angle and do not contain two pairs of parallel sides.

11. Regions I and II; Region I for the trapezoid without a right angle, and Region II for the trapezoid with a right angle. Trapezoids do not have two pairs of parallel sides so Regions III and IV are eliminated.

✔ **QUESTION 14**

...checks that you can sort parallelograms using a Venn diagram.

15. b. No, the sides are all the same length, but the interior angles have different measures. Some are acute and others measure greater than 180°.

DEVELOPING MATH CONCEPTS

Questions 11–14 should help students grasp the set/subset relationships that exist among quadrilaterals. For example, all rectangles belong to the set of parallelograms and to the set of quadrilaterals. So, a rectangle is a parallelogram and a quadrilateral, but its most specific name is rectangle. You may want to reinforce these relationships and check for understanding by identifying a shape card in the diagram and asking students to give all its names, identifying the most specific name for the figure. This will also help students understand why a square is both a rectangle and a rhombus in **Checkpoint Question 14**.

In **Question 15(b)**, students should recognize that the sides of the star are equal in length, but the interior angles differ in measure. Some are acute and others are greater than 180°, so the star not regular. Since a concave polygon must have some angles that are less than 180° and at least one angle greater than 180°, no concave polygon can be a regular polygon. The distinction between concave and convex polygons will be addressed in Book 2.

Exploration 2

TEACHING NOTES

In **Question 16**, ∠A appears to be close to a right angle, but students may differ as to whether it is right or acute. This can provide a lead in to the measuring lesson that follows. In **Question 18**, students will measure the sea star angles and at that time you may want to confirm the correct classification of each angle, particularly ∠A.

In the diagram at the bottom of the page, emphasize that the ray from point D can be thought of as two distinct rays, one that is fixed and one that has been rotated 0°. When students measure angles, they will align the 0° mark on one of the scales of their protractor with the fixed ray of an angle and use that scale to read the measure of the angle.

GOAL

LEARN HOW TO...
- measure an angle using a protractor
- draw an angle using a protractor

AS YOU...
- examine angles in geometric figures

KEY TERM
- protractor

16. ∠A acute,
    ∠B acute,
    ∠C obtuse,
    ∠D right,
    ∠E obtuse

FOR ◄ HELP

with *ray and vertex,* see

MODULE 2, pp. 106–107

Exploration 2

MEASURING Angles

SET UP *You will need: • a protractor • Labsheet 4B*

Stars like the one you found in the *Setting the Stage* are also found in nature.

Use Labsheet 4B for Questions 16–18.

16 The angles the sea star in the photo makes with its arms, ∠A, ∠B, ∠C, ∠D, and ∠E, determine its shape. Identify each angle as acute, right, or obtuse. Record your answers in the table on Labsheet 4B.

▶ **Measuring Angles** The shape of a polygon is also determined by the measures of its angles. To measure an angle, imagine one ray of an angle rotating around the vertex while the other ray is fixed in place. The measure of the angle is the amount of rotation measured in degrees.

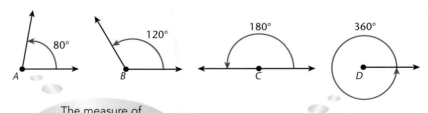

The measure of this angle is 80 degrees. Another way to write this is m∠A = 80°.

There are 360° in a complete rotation, so one degree is $\frac{1}{360}$ of a complete rotation.

---

17 Try this as a Class

a. What is the measure of half a complete rotation? 180°

b. What does an angle with that measure look like? a line

c. Estimate the measure of the angles shown in the sea star photo on Labsheet 4B. Record your estimates in the table on the labsheet. Estimates will vary.

▶ You can use a **protractor** to measure and draw angles.

Using a Protractor

The steps below show how to use a protractor to measure an angle.

First Place the center mark of the protractor on the vertex of the angle.

Next Place the 0° mark on one side of the angle. You may need to extend the sides of the angle.

Then Read the number where the other side of the angle crosses the scale.

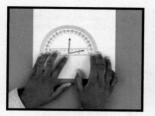  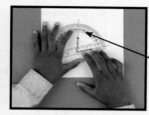

Read the number on the bottom scale since you used its 0° mark.

The measure of ∠ABC is 75°.

---

18 a. Use a protractor to find the exact measure of each angle in the sea star photo on Labsheet 4B. Record the measures in the table on the labsheet. $m\angle A = 88°$, $m\angle B = 75°$ $m\angle C = 102°$ $m\angle D = 90°$ $m\angle E = 100°$

b. How close were your estimates in Question 17(c)? Answers will vary.

19 Discussion How can you use what you have learned about measuring angles with a protractor to draw a 62° angle? See margin.

20 ✔ **CHECKPOINT** Use a protractor to draw an angle with each measure. a–c. Check students' work.

a. 90°   **b.** 38°   **c.** 125°

✔ **QUESTION 20**

...checks that you can use a protractor.

HOMEWORK EXERCISES ▶ See Exs. 5–10 on p. 120.

TEACHING NOTES

In discussing **Question 19** with students, have them look at the steps for measuring an angle. The first step involves only the vertex, or point. Next is one side of the angle, or a ray, then the point where the second ray crosses the scale on the protractor. These steps can translate into "Draw a point with a ray extending from it. Align your protractor so the center is on the point and the ray passes through 0° on one of the scales. Use this scale to mark a point where you would read the angle measure. Use this mark to draw a second ray from the point, which is the vertex of your angle." Students can then try the steps and measure their angle to be sure it is correct.

19. **Sample Response:** Start with a fixed ray representing 0°. Align the protractor on the ray with the endpoint at the center mark and the ray in line with 0°. Follow the scale that begins with 0° up to 62°. Make a mark at 62°. Then use your straightedge to connect this mark to the endpoint of the ray.

Exploration 3

TEACHING NOTES

If students did not do the *Handshake Problem*, they can use their *Geese Galore E²* solution or another solution from previous work to complete **Questions 22 and 23**.

Exploration 3

The **Presentation** Scale

SET UP *You will need • your Handshake Problem solution • your String Art Problem solution*

▶ **Presenting Your Solution** So far in Module 2, you have learned about four different scales that help you assess your work. The last scale you will learn about is the presentation scale. This scale helps you assess how well you present your solutions.

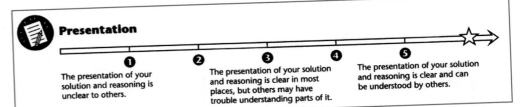

Presentation

① The presentation of your solution and reasoning is unclear to others.

③ The presentation of your solution and reasoning is clear in most places, but others may have trouble understanding parts of it.

⑤ The presentation of your solution and reasoning is clear and can be understood by others.

21 **Try This as a Class** Discuss why the presentation of your solution is important. Sample Response: To present your solution, you must organize your work and make it clear to others so it can be understood.

22 Prepare a team presentation for the *Handshake Problem*. Answers will vary.

> Explain your solution so others can understand your reasoning.
>
> Make certain your presentation:
> - explains the plan you used,
> - uses correct and appropriate mathematical language,
> - includes appropriate and correct representations,
> - extends the solution to a general case or shows how it is related to other problems, and
> - is clear and can be understood by others.

23 Use the presentation scale to score your presentation. Answers will vary.

HOMEWORK EXERCISES ▶ See Exs. 11–12 on pp. 120–121.

Section 4
Key Concepts

Polygons (pp. 112–114)
A polygon is a closed plane figure made from segments, called sides, that do not cross. A regular polygon is a polygon in which all the sides have equal lengths and all the angles have equal measures.

Quadrilaterals (pp. 114–115)
Quadrilaterals can be classified by the number of parallel sides. Sides are parallel if they are parts of parallel lines.

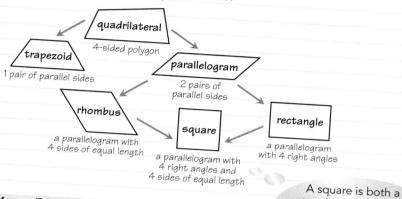

quadrilateral
4-sided polygon

trapezoid
1 pair of parallel sides

parallelogram
2 pairs of parallel sides

rhombus
a parallelogram with 4 sides of equal length

square
a parallelogram with 4 right angles and 4 sides of equal length

rectangle
a parallelogram with 4 right angles

A square is both a rectangle and a rhombus. It is also a parallelogram and a quadrilateral.

Venn Diagram (p. 115)
A Venn diagram uses a drawing to show how sets are related.

Measuring Angles (pp. 116–117)
A complete rotation is 360 degrees, or 360°.

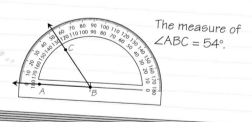

You can use the top scale of the protractor to measure this angle.

The measure of ∠ABC = 54°.

Key Terms

polygon
regular polygon

quadrilateral

parallelogram
trapezoid

rhombus

Venn diagram

protractor

---

24 Key Concepts Question How do you know you should use the top scale to measure ∠ABC? **The fixed ray is aligned as the ray at 0°, and that scale is on the outside, top scale.**

Key Concepts

CLOSURE QUESTION
State at least four ways to classify polygons.

Sample Response: by the number of sides, by the number of angles, by the lengths of the sides, by the measures of the angles, by the number of parallel sides.

ABSENT STUDENTS
For students who were absent for all or part of this section, the blackline Study Guide for Section 4 may be used to present the ideas, concepts, and skills of Section 4.

Practice & Applications

SUGGESTED ASSIGNMENTS

Core Course

Day 1: Exs. 13–15
Day 2: Exs. 1, 16–17
Day 3: Exs. 2–3
Day 4: Exs. 5–10
Day 5: 11–12

Extended Course

Day 1: Exs. 13–15
Day 2: Exs.1, 16–17
Day 3: Exs. 2–4
Day 4: 5–10
Day 5: 11–12

Note: Extended Course assignments can be used to differentiate within the regular classroom. In classrooms where students are grouped homogeneously, the material might be covered in fewer days. In this case assignments may be combined.

ADDITIONAL PRACTICE

See the *Teacher's Resource Book* for additional practice and application exercises for this section.

YOU WILL NEED

For Ex. 11:
- solution to string art problem in Section 2

1. a. Not regular.
   Angles are not of equal measure.
   b. Not regular. Angles are not of equal measure.
   c. Not regular. Side lengths are not equal.
   f. Not regular. Side lengths are not equal; angles are not of equal measure.

Practice & Application Exercises

1. Which figures are regular polygons? If a polygon is not regular, explain why not.

   a.    b.   c.

   d.   Regular   e.   Regular   f.

2. Name each polygon in Exercise 1. Be as specific as possible.
   a. rhombus   b. hexagon   c. rectangle   d. regular pentagon   e. square   f. trapezoid

3. **Probability Connection** Suppose you reached into a bag that contained the shapes from Exercise 1 and pulled one out. What is the probability of getting the given shape?

   a. a pentagon $\frac{1}{6}$

   b. a polygon $\frac{6}{6}$ or 1

   c. a quadrilateral $\frac{4}{6}$ or $\frac{2}{3}$

4. **Challenge** How many triangles are in the figure at the right? **13 triangles; There are 1 large, 3 medium, and 9 small triangles.**

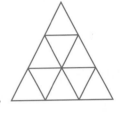

Trace each angle and extend the rays. Then measure each angle.

5. z   6.   7.

   $m\angle Z = 35°$ $m\angle W = 125°$ $m\angle G = 75°$

Use a protractor to draw an angle with each measure.
8–10. Check students' work.

8. 56°   9. 123°   10. 79°

11. Use your solution to the string art problem to answer parts (a)–(c).

    a. Use the presentation scale to score your solution to the string art problem. **Scores will vary.**

    b. Exchange solutions to the string art problem with a partner. Score your partner's solution using the presentation scale. **Scores will vary.**

    c. Compare your self assessment score with your partner's score. Discuss any differences. **See students' work.**

Reflecting ▶ on the Section

12. The Venn diagram shows how several shapes can be sorted according to their common properties.

Exercise 12 checks that you can apply ideas about polygons.

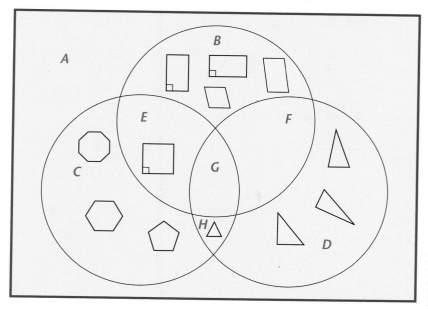

a. What labels could be used for regions *A, B, C,* and *D*?

b. Explain why a square is in region *E*. **The square is both a regular polygon and a quadrilateral.**

Spiral ◀▶ Review

Classify each triangle by its angles. Then classify each triangle by its sides. (Module 2, pp.106–107)

13.

Right; Isosceles

14.

Obtuse; Scalene

15.

Acute; Equilateral

16. A triangle has a perimeter of 12 cm. The length of one side is 5 cm. If the lengths of the sides are whole numbers, what is a possible length for each of the other sides? (Module 2, p. 106)
2 cm, 5 cm or 3 cm, 4 cm

17. The blue box is to the left of the yellow box. The green box is to the right of the red box. The blue box is to the right of the green box. In what order are the boxes? (Module 1, p. 33)
Red, green, blue, yellow

12. a. A: Polygons
B: Quadrilaterals or Parallelograms
C: Regular Polygons
D: Triangles

EXERCISE NOTES

Exercise 12 can be extended to include writing labels for regions F, G, and H. Ask students, "Determine which types of figures would be placed in regions F, G, and H. Draw an example of a figure for each region. If it is not possible explain why. (*Region F would contain figures that are both a triangle and a parallelogram. Region G would require a figure to be regular, a triangle, and a parallelogram. It is impossible for a figure to have exactly three and four sides at the same time; therefore, regions F and G are empty, and Region H contains figures that are equilateral triangles.*)

Extra Skill Practice

TEACHER NOTES

For each Exploration, the corresponding Extra Skill Practice Exercises are noted.

Exploration 1: 1–12
Exploration 2: 13–18

EXTRA HELP

Teacher's Resource Book
- Practice and Applications for Section 4
- Study Guide
- Practice and Applications for Sections 1–4

Technology Resources
- @Home Tutor
- Test Generator

ASSESSMENT
- Section 4 Quick Quiz
- Test Generator

---

2. See Additional Answers beginning on page A1.

122

Section 4

Extra Skill Practice

Is each figure a polygon? If not, explain why not.

1.

Yes

2.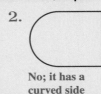

No; it has a curved side

3.

Yes

4.

No; lines cross and it is not a closed figure.

Is each figure a regular polygon? If a figure is not a regular polygon, explain why not.

5.

Yes

6.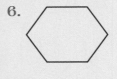

7.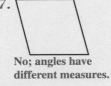

No; angles have different measures.

8.

No; only two angles and two sides are of equal measure.

Name each polygon. Be as specific as possible.

9.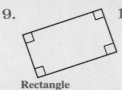

Rectangle

10.

Trapezoid

11.

Regular pentagon

12.

Parallelogram

Use a protractor to draw an angle with each measure. 13–18. Check students' work.

13. 81°   14. 177°   15. 21°

16. 90°   17. 110°   18. 180°

6. No; angles have different measures, sides are not of equal length

---

Study Skills ◀▶ **Taking Notes**

Sometimes it is helpful to include a diagram or another visual representation when you take notes.

1. Look back at the *Key Concepts* on page 119. What does the quadrilateral diagram illustrate?

2. Make a table or a concept map to organize what you know about angles. **See margin.**

1. It illustrates the classifications of quadrilaterals according to the number of pairs of parallel sides, the number of sides of equal length, and the number of right angles.

FOR ASSESSMENT AND PORTFOLIOS

Pattern BLOCK Angles

SET UP *You will need pattern blocks or the Extended Exploration Labsheet.*

The Situation See the *Teacher's Resource Book* for a sample solution for this Extended Exploration.

You know that a square has four right (90°) angles and that a straight angle measures 180°.

The Problem

For each polygon in the table, figure out the sum of the measures of the angles without using a measuring tool. How can you find the sum of the measures of the angles of any polygon?

Polygon	Number of sides	Sum of the measures of its angles
triangle	?	?
quadrilateral	?	?
pentagon	?	?
hexagon	?	?
heptagon	7	?
octagon	?	?
nonagon	9	?
decagon	?	?

Something to Think About

Suppose you start by tracing around each pattern block. How can you find and label the angle measures? Use pattern blocks to create the polygons in the table. Trace around each polygon you create.

Present Your Results

Describe how you found the angle measures for each polygon in the table. What relationship did you find between the number of sides of a polygon and the sum of the measures of its angles?

Extended Exploration

E² NOTES

Labsheet: Each student needs a copy of the Extended Exploration Labsheet, which is found in the *Teacher's Resource Book*.

Using an E²: Suggestions for managing and evaluating an Extended Exploration are available in the *Teacher's Resource Book* for Modules 1 and 2. See also pages T44–T45 in the *Teacher's Edition*.

Alternate E²: See the *Teacher's Resource Book* for an alternate Extended Exploration that can be used after Module 2 Section 4.

It may take students a while to devise a plan for solving the E². You may refer them back to Module 1 where they used pattern blocks to find equivalent fractions. This can be related to using pattern blocks to find equivalent angle measures.

The E² is designed to be completed over a few days to a week, allowing students to experience and understand that not all problems can be solved in one class period.

Module Project

The Module Project

Pop-Up Art

Throughout this module you have been working with various polygons and learning about their characteristics. In this project you will apply some of the ideas you have learned to create pop-up art.

Triangles and Angles The photos below show how to make a pop-up cutout.

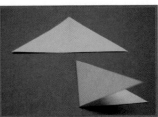 

 1 a. Experiment with isosceles triangles where the sides with the same length form acute, right, or obtuse angles. **Answers will vary.**

 b. What effect do the different angled triangles have on the pop-up? What adjustments did you make in taping down the tabs? **Answers will vary.**

2 Experiment with making a pop-up cutout using equilateral and scalene triangles. **Check students' work.**

Parallel Segments and Polygons Experiment with the double-slit method shown below to create pop-up polygons.

> This hexagon pop-up is composed of two identical parallelograms.

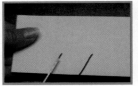  

Step 1	**Step 2**	**Step 3**
Fold a piece of paper in half. Cut two parallel segments across the fold.	Fold the loose section between the cuts backward and forward.	Open the card. Pull the loose section toward you and close the card.

3. b. Check students' work. The cuts must be made the same depth into the paper so that the uncut sides of the loose section between the cuts are parallel.

 3 a. Make two identical trapezoids by using two parallel cuts. **Check students' work. The cuts must be different lengths to form trapezoids. Cuts of the same length will form parallelograms.**
 b. Make two identical trapezoids using two non-parallel cuts.

 c. Explain why you can create trapezoids with either parallel or non-parallel cuts. **A trapezoid has only 1 set of parallel sides; therefore the cut sides can be the parallel or the non-parallel sides.**

 Module 2 Math Detectives

Follow the directions below to make a Pop-Up Staircase.

Step 1 Use the double-slit method to construct a pop-up like the one shown.

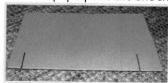

This cut creates two rectangles.

Step 2 Fold the paper back down along its central fold.

 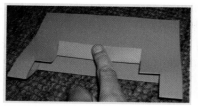 

Make a smaller double slit across one of the two new folds.

Fold back the two loose sections between the cuts.

Open the card. Pull the loose sections toward you and re-crease to create a traditional staircase effect.

Step 3 Repeating the double-slit method on some or all of the new folds creates a pop-up staircase.

4 The cuts above created pop-ups that form rectangles. How should the double-slit be cut to form square steps? The distance between the cuts must be equal to the length of each cut.

Completing the Project To complete the module project, you will create your own pop-up. Your pop-up should include several of the techniques you have learned and can use more than one piece of paper.

5 Plan the design of your pop-up. Make a drawing or sketch if necessary. Be sure your design includes the following features. Check students' work.

- two different types of quadrilaterals
- perpendicular lines

- two different types of triangles
- parallel lines

6 Describe how you used each of the mathematical ideas from Question 5 to create your pop-up. Check students' work.

PROJECT NOTES
Students should start the project in class, but will require time at home to complete their pop-up. Encourage creativity and the use of color. After the pop-ups have been completed, provide a display area where students can view finished projects.

MODULE 2 **Review and Assessment**

TEACHER NOTES

Students should complete the Review and Assessment independently in preparation for the Module Test.

Allow class time to discuss solutions and address any questions students may have. During this time, you may want to allow students to work in groups to share methods for solving the problems and to quiz each other on the concepts covered in this module.

10.

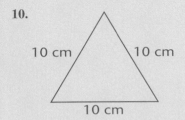

10 cm   10 cm

10 cm

A tetrahedron with sides numbered 1 to 4 was rolled 75 times with the results shown in the table. For Exercises 1-3, find the experimental probability of each event. Write each answer as a fraction. (Sec. 1 Explor. 1)

Outcomes	Total
1	16
2	18
3	22
4	19

1. rolling the number 2 $\frac{18}{75}$ or $\frac{6}{25}$

2. rolling an even number $\frac{37}{75}$

3. rolling a number greater than 4 $\frac{0}{75}$ or 0

4. Find the theoretical probability of each event in Exercises 1-3. Write each probability as a fraction. (Sec. 1 Explor. 2)

5. From home, Leon walked 6 blocks east, 5 blocks north, 3 blocks west, and then 7 blocks south on errands. Draw a diagram to show two ways he can get home by walking the fewest blocks. He cannot cut diagonally across any blocks because of buildings. (Sec. 2 Explor. 2) **See margin.**

6. Vina is putting together 1-cm squares as shown. (Sec. 2 Explor. 3)

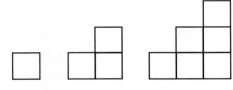

   a. How many squares will she need to build a figure that has a perimeter of 32 cm? **36 squares**

   b. Explain how you can extend your solution in part (a) to the general case. **See margin.**

If possible, sketch each triangle. If it isn't possible, explain why.
(Sec. 3 Explor. 2)

7. a triangle that is obtuse and isosceles **Answers will vary. Sample Response:**

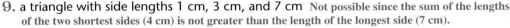

8. a triangle that is both right and equilateral

9. a triangle with side lengths 1 cm, 3 cm, and 7 cm **Not possible since the sum of the lengths of the two shortest sides (4 cm) is not greater than the length of the longest side (7 cm).**

10. a triangle with side lengths 10 cm, 10 cm, and 10 cm **See margin.**

4. probability of rolling a $2 = \frac{1}{4}$
probability of rolling an even number $= \frac{1}{2}$
probability of rolling a number greater than $4 = 0$

8. Not possible; the angles in an equilateral triangle all have the same measure. But if a triangle had two right angles, it would have two parallel sides, which is impossible.

5. and 6. b. See Additional Answers beginning on page A1.

126

For Exercises 11–19, use the diagram at the right. Name an example of each figure.

(Sec. 3 Explor. 1 and Explor. 3) **Sample responses are given.**

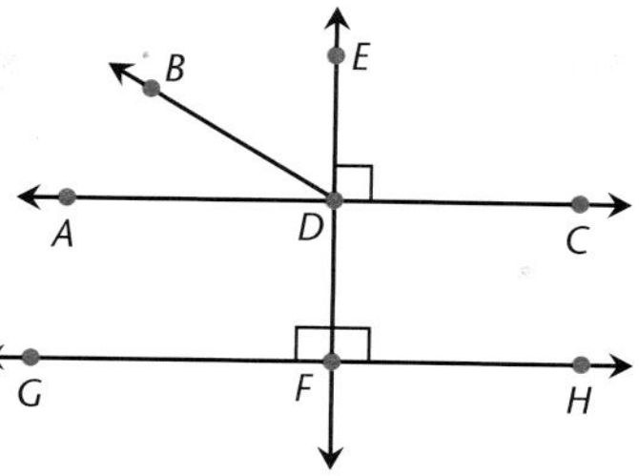

11. an acute angle
$\angle ADB$

12. a segment
$\overline{GF}$

13. a ray
$\overrightarrow{DB}$

14. perpendicular lines
$\overleftrightarrow{GH} \perp \overleftrightarrow{FE}$

15. a right angle
$\angle ADF$

16. an obtuse angle
$\angle CDB$

17. a line
$\overleftrightarrow{GH}$

18. a point
H

19. parallel lines
$\overleftrightarrow{GH} \parallel \overleftrightarrow{AC}$

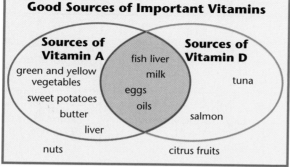

20. Complete the Review and Assessment Labsheet for *Identifying Quadrilaterals*. (Sec. 4 Explor. 1) **See margin.**

Use the Venn diagram for Exercises 21–23. (Sec. 4 Explor. 1)

21. Which foods are good sources of vitamin A? **See margin.**

22. How many foods are good sources of vitamins A and D?
4 (fish liver, milk, eggs, and oils)

23. Why are nuts and citrus fruits outside of the sets?
See margin.

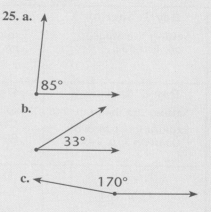

Good Sources of Important Vitamins

Sources of Vitamin A
green and yellow vegetables
sweet potatoes
butter
liver

fish liver
milk
eggs
oils

Sources of Vitamin D
tuna
salmon

nuts

citrus fruits

24. Estimate the measure of each angle below. Then trace each angle and use a protractor to measure it. (Sec. 4 Explor. 2)
Estimates will vary. Accept any reasonable answer.

a.  112°
b. 40° 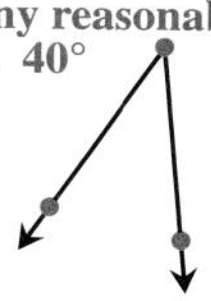
c. 90°

25. Use a protractor to draw an angle with each measure (Sec. 4 Explor. 2)

a. 85° **See margin.**
b. 33° **See margin.**
c. 170° **See margin.**

Reflecting ◀▶ on the Module

26. a. Describe two different mathematical ideas you explored in this module. **Answers will vary.**

b. What discoveries did you make about these ideas? **Answers will vary.**

Assessment Options

TEACHER'S RESOURCE BOOK
• Module 2 Tests A and B
• Module 2 Standardized Test
• Module 2 Performance Assessment
• Modules 1 and 2 Cumulative Test

TEST GENERATOR

21. green and yellow vegetables, sweet potatoes, butter, liver, fish liver, milk, eggs, and oils

23. Nuts and citrus fruits are not sources of either vitamin A or vitamin D, so they are not in either set.

25. a.

85°

b.

33°

c.

170°

20. See Additional Answers beginning on page A1.

Mind Games

Module 3 Overview

Students explore mathematical content by solving puzzles and playing and analyzing strategy games. Winning strategies are developed through the use of tables, Venn diagrams, factor trees, and number sense. Topics studied include number theory, decimal numeration and operations (addition, subtraction, and multiplication), and multiplication of fractions and mixed numbers. Manipulatives and visual models are used to develop an understanding of number concepts.

Module 3 Planner

Day 1: Section 1	Day 2: Section 1	Day 3: Section 1	Day 4: Section 2	Day 5: Section 2
Setting the Stage, *pp. 130–131*	Exploration 1, *pp. 131–132*	Exploration 2, *p. 133* Key Concepts, *p. 134*	Setting the Stage, *p. 138* Exploration 1, *pp. 139–140*	Exploration 2, *pp. 141–142* Key Concepts, *p. 143*
Day 6: Section 3	**Day 7: Section 3**	**Day 8: Section 3**	**Day 9: Section 3**	**Day 10: Section 3**
Setting the Stage, *p. 148* Exploration 1 *through Question 5, p. 149*	Exploration 1 *from Question 6, pp. 150–151*	Exploration 2 *through Question 21, pp. 152–153*	Exploration 2 *from Example, pp. 153–154*	Exploration 3, *pp. 155–157* Key Concepts, *pp. 157–158*
Day 11: E²	**Day 12: Review and Assessment**	**Day 13: Section 4**	**Day 14: Section 4**	**Day 15: Section 5**
Begin E², *p. 164*	Mid-Module Quiz	Setting the Stage, *p. 165* Exploration 1 *through Question 7, p. 166*	Exploration 1 *from Question 8, p. 167* Key Concepts, *p. 168*	Setting the Stage, *p. 172* Exploration 1 *through Question 9, pp. 173–174*
Day 16: Section 5	**Day 17: Section 5**	**Day 18: Section 6**	**Day 19: Section 6**	**Day 20: Section 6**
Exploration 1 *from Question 10, p. 175*	Exploration 2, *pp. 176–178* Key Concepts, *p. 178*	Setting the Stage, *p. 184* Exploration 1 *through Question 6, pp. 185–186*	Exploration 1 from, Question 7, *pp. 186–187*	Exploration 2, *pp. 188–189* Key Concepts, *p. 190*
Day 21: Module Project	**Day 22: Module Project**	**Day 23: Review and Assessment**	**Day 24: Review and Assessment**	**Day 25: Assessment**
Begin Module Project, *pp. 194–195*	Finish Module Project, *pp. 194–195*	Assign Review and Assessment, *pp. 196–197*	Discuss Review and Assessment, *pp. 196–197*	Module 3 Test

Materials List

Section	Materials
1	• Labsheets 1A–1B, base-ten blocks, number cubes
2	• Labsheets 2A–2B, base-ten blocks, scissors, calculators
3	• Labsheets 3A–3C, paper clips, 15 each of 2 different colored chips per student pair, paper for folding, calculators
4	• Labsheet 4A
5	• paper for folding, colored pencils, pattern blocks
6	• Labsheets 6A–6B, calculators

Module 3 Objectives

Section	Objectives	NCTM Standards 2000*
1	• Identify decimal place value. • Read and write decimal numbers. • Compare and order decimals.	**1, 4, 6, 7, 8, 9, 10**
2	• Add decimals. • Subtract decimals.	**1, 4, 6, 7, 8, 9, 10**
3	• Use divisibility tests for 2, 3, 5, 9, and 10. • Find all the factors of a number. • Find the greatest common factor (GCF) of two or more numbers. • Identify prime and composite numbers. • Find the prime factorization of a number. • Identify powers and write numbers using exponents. • Convert between standard and exponential form. • Write the prime factorization of a number using exponents.	**1, 2, 6, 7, 8, 9, 10**
4	• List the multiples of a number. • Find the least common multiple of two or more numbers.	**1, 2, 6, 7, 8, 9, 10**
5	• Model and find fraction products. • Use the distributive property to multiply a mixed number by a whole number. • Multiply with fractions and mixed numbers.	**1, 2, 3, 4, 6, 7, 8, 9, 10**
6	• Find and estimate decimal products.	**1, 2, 3, 4, 6, 7, 8, 9, 10**

* See page T14.

Section 1 Planner

Section Objectives

Exploration 1
• Identify decimal place value
• Read and write decimal numbers

Exploration 2
• Compare and order decimals

Days for Section 1

First Day
Setting the Stage, *pp. 130–131*

Second Day
Exploration 1, *pp. 131–132*

Third Day
Exploration 2, *p. 133*
Key Concepts, *p. 134*

Teaching Resources

Teacher's Resource Book
• Warm-Up
• Labsheets 1A and 1B
• Practice and Applications
• Study Guide
• Labsheets
See page 129 for additional teaching resources.

Materials List

Setting the Stage
• base-ten blocks
• 1 number cube per group

Exploration 1
• base-ten blocks
• Labsheets 1A and 1B

Exploration 2
• base-ten blocks

Assessment Options

EMBEDDED ASSESSMENT
• Identify decimal place value
  Exercises 3, 4, 5
• Read and write decimal numbers
  Exercises 7, 9, 10, 14
• Compare and order decimals
  Exercises 22, 25, 27

PERFORMANCE TASK/PORTFOLIO
• Exercise 17 on *p. 135*
• Exercise 18 on *p. 135*
• Exercise 29 on *p. 136 (journal)*

QUIZZES/TESTS
• Section 1 Quick Quiz

TEST GENERATOR

Section 1 Overview

In this section, students will use manipulatives to review decimal place value and compare decimals.

Exploration 1
In the *Setting Stage*, students played a game with base-ten blocks. Base-ten blocks are used in Exploration 1 to model decimal numerals. Students practice expressing values less than one as fractions, as decimals, and in words. Key terms include *decimal system* and *place value*.

Exploration 2
Students continue to use base-ten blocks to model and compare decimals. Students use base-ten blocks to create models for decimals, such as two tenths and twenty hundredths that represent the same amount. The key term, *equivalent decimal*, is defined.

Guide for Assigning Homework

REGULAR SCHEDULING (45 MIN CLASS PERIOD)			EXERCISES TO NOTE		
Section/ P&A Pages	Core Assignment	Extended Assignment	Additional Practice/Review	Open-ended Problems	Extended Problems
1 pp. 135–137	**Day 1:** SR 30–38 **Day 2:** 1–18 **Day 3:** 19–28, ROS 29	SR 30–38 1–18 19–28, ROS 29	EP, p. 137	PA 29	

Key: PA = Practice & Application; ROS = Reflecting on the Section; SR = Spiral Review; TB = Toolbox; EP = Extra Skill Practice; Ext = Extension; ST = Standardized Testing

Math Background and Teaching Strategies

Classroom Notes

Bulletin board display ideas for this section include:

- decimal place value chart

- evidence of decimal numbers used in real-life situations, like grocery advertisements, winning race times, computer parts, etc.

Math Strands

Topic Integration and Spiraling

Exploration 1
Exploration 1 is a review of the decimal numeration system. Base-ten blocks are used to help students understand the structure of the system. This knowledge is essential for understanding the operations with decimal numbers.

Students familiar with decimal place value should be able to complete Exploration 1 fairly quickly, but will still benefit from using base-ten blocks to conceptualize the relationship between fractions and decimals. Ask those students who have a firm grasp of the decimal system to explain how base-ten blocks can be used to illustrate the relationship between decimals and fractions.

Exploration 2
Students use base-ten blocks to compare decimals and to show equivalence of decimals. Then, students use their understanding of decimal place value to compare decimals without modeling the numbers with base-ten blocks.

Decimal addition, subtraction, and multiplication will be developed in Sections 2 and 6 of Module 3, and division of decimals will be covered in Module 4. Relationships among fractions, decimals, and percents will be developed in Module 6 when students work with ratios, proportions, and percent.

Section 2 · Decimal Addition and Subtraction

Section 2 Planner

Section Objectives

Exploration 1
- Add decimals

Exploration 2
- Subtract decimals

Days for Section 2

First Day
Setting the Stage, *p. 138*
Exploration 1, *pp. 139–140*

Second Day
Exploration 2, *pp. 141–142*
Key Concepts, *p. 143*

Teaching Resources

Teacher's Resource Book
- Warm-Up
- Labsheets 2A and 2B
- Practice and Applications
- Study Guide
See page 129 for additional teaching resources.

Materials List

Setting the Stage
- Labsheets 2A–2B
- scissors

Exploration 1
- *Decimal Puzzle* solution
- base-ten blocks

Exploration 2
- base-ten blocks

Practice and Applications
- calculator

Assessment Options

EMBEDDED ASSESSMENT
- Add decimals
  Exercises 4, 5, 26
- Subtract decimals
  Exercises 22, 23, 27, 31

PERFORMANCE TASK/PORTFOLIO
- Exercise 8 on *p. 144 (estimation)*
- Exercises 26–27 on *p. 145*
- Exercises 46–49 on *p. 146 (extension)*
- Standardized Testing on *p. 147 (performance task)**

* *indicates a problem solving task that can be assessed using the Assessment Scales*

QUIZZES/TESTS
- Section 2 Quick Quiz

TEST GENERATOR

Section 2 Overview

In this section, students will apply the techniques for regrouping base-ten blocks that they learned in Section 1 to adding and subtracting decimals.

Exploration 1
Students make models of decimals using base-ten blocks. The models help them to see that when adding decimals, digits with the same place value are added and any necessary regrouping is done. Students then discuss how they can add decimals without using base-ten blocks. Because students are developing methods from their work with base-ten blocks, no formal algorithm for adding decimals is stated until the *Key Concepts* page for this section.

Exploration 2
Regrouping and renaming are modeled as students learn to exchange base-ten blocks in decimal subtraction. Students discuss the similarity between whole number subtraction and decimal subtraction. Annexing of zeros is done together as a class and estimation is used to check the reasonableness of an answer. Again, no formal algorithm for subtracting decimals is given until the *Key Concepts*.

Guide for Assigning Homework

REGULAR SCHEDULING (45 MIN CLASS PERIOD)			EXERCISES TO NOTE		
Section/ P&A Pages	**Core Assignment**	**Extended Assignment**	**Additional Practice/Review**	**Open-ended Problems**	**Extended Problems**
2 pp. 143–147	**Day 1:** 1–17, SR 38–45 **Day 2:** 18–34, ROS 37	4–17, SR 38–45 21–36, ROS 37, Ext 46–49	EP, p. 147	PA 37	Challenge PA 35, 36 Ext 46–49

Key: PA = Practice & Application; ROS = Reflecting on the Section; SR = Spiral Review; TB = Toolbox; EP = Extra Skill Practice; Ext = Extension; ST = Standardized Testing

Math Background and Teaching Strategies

Classroom Notes

Bulletin board display ideas for this section include:

- addition and subtraction examples with base-ten blocks

- student work display of number puzzles from Exercise 37 on p. 146

Math Strands

Topic Spiraling and Integration

Addition and subtraction of decimals will be embedded in other mathematics throughout Books 1, 2, and 3. Perimeter problems, use of formulas, calculating averages, and solving equations are a few of the contexts in which students will be expected to use addition and subtraction skills with decimals. The approach in Book 1 is to make sure students understand the reasons why "they line up the decimals" when adding and subtracting (but then do not do the same when multiplying). This is accomplished through use of base-ten blocks to model the need for adding digits of like place values and of regrouping when necessary.

Exploration 1

Exploration 1 focuses on use of base-ten blocks to model addition of decimals with regrouping. The effect of annexing zeros is addressed and can then be used as a strategy for students who are more comfortable adding decimal numbers when they all have the same number of decimal places. Students also employ estimation skills to check the reasonableness of their answer.

Exploration 2

Exploration 2 focuses on use of base-ten blocks to model subtraction of decimals with regrouping. The necessity of annexing zeros in the minuend when the subtrahend has more decimal places than the minuend. Addition skills are revisited as a strategy for checking subtraction answers. Estimation is again employed as a means for checking the reasonableness of answers.

Section 3 Factors and Divisibility

Section 3 Planner

Section Objectives

Exploration 1
- Use divisibility tests
- Find all the factors of a number
- Find the greatest common factor (GCF) of two or more numbers

Exploration 2
- Identify prime and composite numbers
- Find the prime factorization of a number

Exploration 3
- Identify powers
- Write a power in standard form and vice versa.
- Write prime factorizations using exponents

Days for Section 3

First Day
Setting the Stage, *p. 148*
Exploration 1 through Question 5, *p. 149*

Second Day
Exploration 1 from Question 6, *pp. 150–151*

Third Day
Exploration 2 through Question 21,
pp. 152–153

Fourth Day
Exploration 2 from Example, *pp. 153–154*

Fifth Day
Exploration 3, *pp. 155–157*
Key Concepts, *pp. 157–158*

Teaching Resources

Teacher's Resource Book
- Warm-Up
- Labsheet 3A
- Practice and Applications
- Study Guide
See page 129 for additional teaching resources.

Materials List

Setting the Stage
- Labsheet 3A
- 2 paper clips per pair of students
- 10 each of two different-colored chips per pair of students

Exploration 1
- Labsheets 3A–3B

Exploration 2
- Labsheet 3C
- paper clips
- 15 each of two different-colored chips per pair of students

Exploration 3
- paper for folding
- calculator

Practice and Applications
- Labsheet 3A

Assessment Options

EMBEDDED ASSESSMENT
- For a list of embedded assessment exercises, see p. 159

PERFORMANCE TASK/PORTFOLIO
- For a list of performance task/portfolio exercises, see *p. 160*

QUIZZES/TESTS
- Section 3 Quick Quiz
- Mid-Module Quiz

TEST GENERATOR

Section 3 Overview

In this section, students will play the *Paper Clips Products* and *Prime Time* games and solve a paper-folding puzzle to prepare them for the study of divisibility tests, factors, and powers of numbers.

Exploration 1
By using Venn diagrams to sort numbers students identify numbers that are divisible by 2, 3, 5, 9, and 10 and develop divisibility rules for each of these numbers. The concept of divisibility is used to list all the factors of a number and extended to find the greatest common factor of two or more numbers. Key terms include *divisible, factors, common factors,* and *greatest common factor.*

Exploration 2
The game *Prime Time* is used to develop the concepts of prime and composite and to introduce prime factorization. Key terms include *prime, composite, prime factorization,* and *factor tree.*

Exploration 3
Students use paper folding to recognize patterns relating to exponents. Key terms include *exponent, power, base,* and *standard form.*

Guide for Assigning Homework

REGULAR SCHEDULING (45 MIN CLASS PERIOD)			EXERCISES TO NOTE		
Section/ P&A Pages	Core Assignment	Extended Assignment	Additional Practice/Review	Open-ended Problems	Extended Problems
3 pp. 159–163	**Day 1:** SR 62–70 **Day 2:** 1–14, 16–28 even **Day 3:** 31–36 **Day 4:** 37–43 **Day 5:** 45–60, ROS 61	SR 62–70 2–28 even, 29–30 31–36 37–44 45–60, ROS 61	EP, p. 163		Challenge PA 30, 44 E² , p. 164

Key: PA = Practice & Application; ROS = Reflecting on the Section; SR = Spiral Review; TB = Toolbox; EP = Extra Skill Practice; Ext = Extension; ST = Standardized Testing

Math Background and Teaching Strategies

Classroom Notes

Bulletin board display ideas for this section include:

- divisibility rules for 2, 3, 5, 6, 9, and 10; each rule displayed as students discover it

- student work display of E² solutions

Math Strands

Topic Spiraling and Integration

Exploration 1

Concepts of factors and divisibility are developed intuitively by playing the game *Paper Clip Products*. After analyzing strategies for playing the game and using a Venn diagram to sort numbers from the game board, formal definitions of divisible and factor are introduced. Divisibility tests for 2, 5, and 10 are covered quickly, since they should be familiar to students from their elementary

level mathematics studies. More exploration time is given to the development of divisibility tests for 3 and 9. Factors and common factors are introduced by discussing strategies used in playing *Paper Clip Products*. Then the idea of greatest common factor (GCF) is introduced and the method of listing factors to find the GCF is explained and practiced.

Exploration 2

A strategy game is used to extend the concept of factor to prime and composite numbers and prime factorization. Numbers on the *Prime Time* game board are identified as composite numbers and those in the factor list as primes. Prime factorization is introduced by observing that every number on the game board can be formed by multiplying two or more numbers from the factor list. It is

important that students see that, since 1 has only one distinct whole number factor, it is neither prime nor composite. It is a common misconception among students of this age that because 1 is not composite, it must be prime. Some may argue that 1 has 1 and itself as its two factors, however, these two factors are not distinct.

Exploration 3

Paper folding provides a hands-on model for the powers of 2. The numbers in the pattern that is developed are written in the form of a power and the key terms *exponent*, *base*, *standard form*, and *power* are defined so that students will be able to communicate the different forms in which an expression might be written. Powers are then applied to prime factorization. In Module 8, powers will be applied to scientific notation.

Section 4 Multiples

Section 4 Planner

Section Objectives

Exploration 1
- List multiples of a number
- Find the least common multiple of two or more numbers

Days for Section 4

First Day
Setting the Stage, *p. 165*
Exploration 1 through Question 7, *p. 166*

Second Day
Exploration 1 from Question 8, *p. 167*
Key Concepts, *p. 168*

Teaching Resources

Teacher's Resource Book
- Warm-Up
- Labsheet 4A
- Practice and Applications
- Study Guide
See page 129 for additional teaching resources.

Materials List

Exploration 1
- Labsheet 4A

Assessment Options

EMBEDDED ASSESSMENT
- List multiples of a number
    Exercises 4, 5, 7
- Find the least common multiple of two or more numbers
    Exercises 14, 15, 17

PERFORMANCE TASK/PORTFOLIO
- Exercises 18–20 on *p. 169 (discussion)*
- Exercise 28 on *p. 170 (career connection)*
- Standardized Testing on *p. 171 (multiple choice)*

QUIZZES/TESTS
- Section 4 Quick Quiz

TEST GENERATOR

Section 4 Overview

In this section, students use a game to learn about multiples and common multiples.

Exploration 1
Students begin by reflecting on the game *Tick-Tock* played in the *Setting the Stage*. They identify that it was important to understand multiples to be able to play the game. Students then see how multiples of a number form a number sequence. Students use variables to describe the general rule for the sequence and then use their expression to find the 100th term. Lists of multiples are used to identify the least common multiple of two numbers.

Guide for Assigning Homework

REGULAR SCHEDULING (45 MIN CLASS PERIOD)			EXERCISES TO NOTE		
Section/ P&A Pages	Core Assignment	Extended Assignment	Additional Practice/Review	Open-ended Problems	Extended Problems
4 pp. 169–171	**Day 1:** 1–7, SR 21–27 **Day 2:** 8–17, ROS 18–20	1–7, SR 21–27 11–17, ROS 18–20, 28	EP, p. 171		PA 18–20 Career Connect, PA 28

Key: PA = Practice & Application; ROS = Reflecting on the Section; SR = Spiral Review; TB = Toolbox; EP = Extra Skill Practice; Ext = Extension; ST = Standardized Testing

Math Background and Teaching Strategies

Classroom Notes

Bulletin board displays for this section include:

• real life applications of multiples (see p. 169 Exercise 17 and p. 170 *Career Connection*)

Math Strands

Topic Spiraling and Integration

Students use their counting skills and their understanding of divisibility developed in Section 3 to play the game *Pattern Tick-Tock*. This mental and verbal game sets the stage for defining multiples and common multiples represented by *Tick* or *Tock* and *Tick-Tock* respectively.

Exploration 1

In Module 1, students explored patterns and sequences and learned to write an equation to find the terms of a sequence and to predict given terms. These same concepts are applied to multiples as students represent multiples in a sequence and write an expression for the general term of the sequence.

The concept of common multiples is related to the game played in the *Setting the Stage*, where both *Tick* and *Tock* are said when the number is a multiple of both given numbers. The least common multiple is then identified by listing multiples and circling common multiples. Since 0 is a multiple of every number, the least common multiple is defined as the least positive number that is a multiple of all the given numbers.

Students use least common multiples in real world contexts in the *Practice and Application Exercises* and in the *Career Connection Exercise*. Students will also apply least common multiples in Module 5 when they add and subtract fractions. Least common multiples will be used to find the least common denominators of fractions when adding or subtracting.

Section 5 · Fraction and Mixed Number Multiplication

Section 5 Planner

Section Objectives

Exploration 1
• Multiply fractions

Exploration 2
• Use the distributive property
• Multiply mixed numbers

Days for Section 5

First Day
Setting the Stage, *p. 172*
Exploration 1 through Question 9,
pp. 173–174

Second Day
Exploration 1 from Question 10, *p. 175*

Third Day
Exploration 2 , *pp. 176–178*
Key Concepts, *p. 178*

Teaching Resources

Teacher's Resource Book
• Warm-Up
• Practice and Applications
• Study Guide
See page 129 for additional teaching
resources.

Materials List

Exploration 1
• paper for folding
• colored pencils

Exploration 2
• pattern blocks

Assessment Options

EMBEDDED ASSESSMENT
• Multiply fractions
  Exercises 1, 2, 7
• Use the distributive property
  Exercises 16, 17, 18
• Multiply mixed numbers
  Exercises 22, 25, 26

PERFORMANCE TASK/PORTFOLIO
• Exercise 13 on *p. 180 (challenge)*
• Exercise 28 on *p. 181*
• Exercise 34 on *p. 182*
• Exercise 35 on *p. 182 (discussion)*
• Exercises 46–47 on *p. 182 (extension)*

QUIZZES/TESTS
• Section 5 Quick Quiz

TEST GENERATOR

Section 5 Overview

In this section, solving a puzzle leads students to develop a rule for finding a fractional part of a part.

Exploration 1
Students fold paper vertically and horizontally to model finding the product of two fractions. The results of several paper foldings are recorded in a table. Students then generalize their results and write a rule for multiplying two fractions.

Exploration 2
Pattern blocks are used to model finding the product of a fraction and a mixed number. The distributive property will be introduced for those exercises requiring multiplication of a whole number by a mixed number. Students will also multiply two mixed numbers by first expressing the mixed numbers as fractions.

Guide for Assigning Homework

REGULAR SCHEDULING (45 MIN CLASS PERIOD)			EXERCISES TO NOTE		
Section/ P&A Pages	**Core Assignment**	**Extended Assignment**	**Additional Practice/Review**	**Open-ended Problems**	**Extended Problems**
5 pp. 179–183	**Day 1:** 1, SR 36–45 **Day 2:** 2–12, 14–15 **Day 3:** 16–34, ROS 35	1, SR 36–45 2–15, Ext 46–47 16–34, ROS 35	EP, p. 183		Challenge PA 13 Ext 46–47

Key: PA = Practice & Application; ROS = Reflecting on the Section; SR = Spiral Review; TB = Toolbox; EP = Extra Skill Practice; Ext = Extension; ST = Standardized Testing

Math Background and Teaching Strategies

Classroom Notes

Bulletin board display ideas for this section include:

- a copy of the doubloons puzzle
- folded-paper models of various fraction multiplication problems
- distributive property and its use with fractions

Math Strands

Topic Spiraling and Integration

Exploration 1
The puzzle in the *Setting the Stage* is used to motivate multiplication of fractions. By the conclusion of this exploration, students will see that by not understanding the concept of a fraction of a fraction, the treasure hunters did not all receive their fair share. Instead of just instructing students to multiply the fractions in the story puzzle, students use paper folding to model what occurred when the second treasure hunter took a part of a part. The modeling reinforces concepts of fractional parts and provides students with a visual of what $\frac{1}{3}$ of $\frac{2}{3}$ means. Students then explore patterns in the products they found with paper folding. Using the patterns, they discover a method for multiplying fractions without using a model.

Exploration 2
Exploration 2 focuses on the multiplication of a whole number and a mixed number and the multiplication of two mixed numbers. Again, a model is used for understanding. This time students use groups of pattern blocks to show the multiplication of a whole number and mixed number. The models are then used to introduce the distributive property of multiplication over addition by rewriting the mixed number as a whole number plus a fraction. The distributive property is an important tool for simplifying algebraic expressions and for mental math computations. This is the intent with fractions—for students to become exposed to the property and to use it in situations where it may make computations easier. Students are also introduced to the option of changing all mixed and whole numbers to fractions and then using skills learned in Exploration 1 to multiply the fractions. This method is then applied to multiplying two mixed numbers since the distributive property is too cumbersome in this situation. Many formulas and equations in Books 1–3 will involve fraction multiplication.

128L

Section 6 | Decimal Multiplication

Section 6 Planner

Section Objectives

Exploration 1
- Multiply decimals
- Recognize when a product is reasonable

Exploration 2
- Estimate decimal products

Days for Section 6

First Day
Setting the Stage, *p. 184*
Exploration 1 through Question 6,
pp. 185–186

Second Day
Exploration 1 from Question 7, *pp. 186–187*

Third Day
Exploration 2, *pp. 188–189*
Key Concepts, *p. 190*

Teaching Resources

Teacher's Resource Book
- Warm-Up
- Labsheets 6A and 6B
- Practice and Applications
- Study Guide
See page 129 for additional teaching resources.

Materials List

Setting the Stage
- Labsheet 6A
- calculators

Exploration 1
- Labsheet 6B

Exploration 2
- calculators

Assessment Options

EMBEDDED ASSESSMENT
- Multiply decimals
  Exercises 7, 8, 10
- Recognize when a product is reasonable
  Exercises 2, 3, 7
- Estimate decimal products
  Exercises 16, 18(a), 22

PERFORMANCE TASK/PORTFOLIO
- Exercise 11 on *p. 191 (writing)*
- Exercise 24 on *p. 192 (challenge)*
- Exercise 25 on *p. 192 (visual thinking)*
- Standardized Testing on *p. 193 (open-ended)*
- Module Project on *pp. 194–195*

QUIZZES/TESTS
- Section 6 Quick Quiz
- Module Tests A and B
- Module Standardized Test
- Module Performance Assessment

TEST GENERATOR

Section 6 Overview

In this section, students play a game in which they must estimate a factor of a given whole number. They will discover that a decimal may give a better approximation of the factor.

Exploration 1
Students continue exploring decimal products and the use of estimation from the game in the *Setting the Stage*. They model decimal products by shading a 10 x 10 grid and relate decimal multiplication to multiplication of fractions. Estimation skills developed in the game are then used to place decimal points in the correct positions of decimal products. This leads students to develop a method for multiplying decimals without shading grids or expressing the decimals as fractions.

Exploration 2
Students play a calculator game involving decimal multiplication to help improve their estimation skills. The follow-up questions focus on developing the estimation skills used in the game and on using mental math to multiply a whole number by 0.1 and 0.01.

Guide for Assigning Homework

REGULAR SCHEDULING (45 MIN CLASS PERIOD)			EXERCISES TO NOTE		
Section/ P&A Pages	Core Assignment	Extended Assignment	Additional Practice/Review	Open-ended Problems	Extended Problems
6 pp. 190–193	**Day 1:** SR 26–33 **Day 2:** 1–12 **Day 3:** 13–23, ROS 25	SR 26–33 1–12 13–24, ROS 25	EP, p. 193 Review & Assessment, pp. 196–197	PA 23 ST, p. 193 Mod Proj, p. 195	PA 19–21 Challenge, PA 24

Key: PA = Practice & Application; ROS = Reflecting on the Section; SR = Spiral Review; TB = Toolbox; EP = Extra Skill Practice; Ext = Extension; ST = Standardized Testing

Math Background and Teaching Strategies

Classroom Notes

Bulletin board display ideas for this section include:

- examples of puzzles and brain teasers

- student work display of Module Project puzzles

Visitors/fieldtrips might include:

- game inventors

Interest Centers might include:

- rules and materials for playing the games in this module

Math Strands

Topic Spiraling and Integration

In this section students multiply decimals and practice estimation skills with decimal products.

Exploration 1

To model decimal multiplication, students use the same technique of shading a grid that they used when they multiplied fractions in Section 5. For decimal multiplication, a 100-grid is used to represent the whole, similar to paper folding where the paper represented the whole. The 100-grid corresponds to the 10×10 flat that students used when they were adding and subtracting decimals in Section 2 of this module. The grid helps students see that, just as in the case of multiplying two fractions that are less than 1, multiplying two decimals that are less than 1 results in a product that is less than either of the factors.

The concept of a zero placeholder is addressed when students begin using the number of decimal places in the factors of a multiplication problem

to place the decimal in the product. Estimation is emphasized as a tool for checking the reasonableness of an answer and as an alternative method for placing the decimal in a product, thus helping to eliminate errors caused by incorrect application of an algorithm.

Exploration 2

Exploration 2 uses a game that requires students to reason and predict to extend students' estimation skills. Multiplication by a factor of 0.1 or 0.01 is used to find products mentally and to emphasize understanding of decimal placement in products.

Module 3

OVERVIEW
Students explore mathematical content by solving puzzles and playing and analyzing strategy games. Winning strategies are developed through the use of tables, Venn diagrams, factor trees, and number sense. Topics studied include number theory, decimal numeration and operations (addition, subtraction, and multiplication), and multiplicaiton of fractions and mixed numbers. Manipulatives and visual models are used to develop an understanding of number concepts.

PREREQUISITE SKILLS
Warm-Up Exercises for each section are provided in the *Teacher's Resource Book*. You can use these exercises to review skills and concepts students will need for each section. In addition, the Spiral Review exercises at the end of each section in the student edition provide practice on prerequisite skills.

MODULE DIAGNOSTIC TEST
The Module Diagnostic Test in the *Teacher's Resource Book* can be used to assess students' prior knowledge of skills and concepts that will be taught in each section of this module. You can use test results to help structure your teaching to meet the diverse needs of your classroom.

MODULE 3 MIND GAMES

CONNECTING
MATHEMATICS
The & Theme

MODULE 3 — SECTION OVERVIEW

① Understanding Decimals
As you play place value games:
- ◆ Read and write decimals.
- ◆ Compare and order decimals.

② Decimal Addition and Subtraction
As you solve a puzzle:
- ◆ Add and subtract decimals.

③ Factors and Divisibility
As you develop game strategies:
- ◆ Use divisibility tests.
- ◆ Find factors and greatest common factors.
- ◆ Find prime factorizations.
- ◆ Explore powers of a number.

④ Multiples
As you explore patterns in a game:
- ◆ Find multiples and least common multiples.

⑤ Fraction and Mixed Number Multiplication
As you solve a story puzzle:
- ◆ Multiply fractions.
- ◆ Use the distributive property.
- ◆ Multiply mixed numbers.

⑥ Decimal Multiplication
As you play target number games:
- ◆ Multiply decimals.
- ◆ Estimate decimal products.

The Module Project
Puzzle Making

Story and logic puzzles can be fun to solve and fun to create. You will explore how to solve several different types of puzzles. Then you will use the mathematics you have learned in this module to create your own puzzle. At the end of the project you will combine your puzzle with those of your classmates in a *Class Puzzle Book*.

For the Module Project
See pp. 194–195.

INTERNET
Resources and practice at
classzone.com

 129

Module Resources

TEACHER'S RESOURCE BOOK
Resources
- *The Math Gazette* (parent newsletter)
- Warm-Ups
- Labsheets
- Practice and Applications
- Study Guide

Assessment
- Pre-Course Test
- Section Quick Quizzes
- Mid-Module Quiz
- Module 3 Diagnostic Test
- Module 3 Tests A and B
- Module 3 Standardized Test
- Module 3 Performance Assessment

SPANISH RESOURCES
- *The Math Gazette* (parent newsletter)
- Practice and Applications
- Assessment
- Spanish Glossary

STUDENT WORKBOOK

TECHNOLOGY BOOK

TECHNOLOGY RESOURCES
- @Home Tutor
- Test Generator
- Activity Generator
- Professional Development DVD
- Online Activities

ABOUT THE THEME

The module theme of *Mind Games* allows students to explore the mathematics of decimals and fractions through games and puzzles. These activities are designed to promote an understanding of the concepts and related algorithms as opposed to just memorizing rules.

GETTING STARTED

Module 3 Section 1 *Warm-Up* assesses students' ability to read numbers in standard form and write them using words. This same skill will be applied to decimals once students become familiar with decimal place value.

CLASSROOM MANAGEMENT

The *Place Value Game* is best played in groups of four. If students have a good understanding of place-value concepts, they may play a shorter version of the game, stopping after a student collects one flat. To complete the game in less time, it can be played in smaller groups or using two number cubes instead of one.

ABOUT THE MATERIALS

The 1 x 1 x 1 cube is referred to as a "small cube" to distinguish it from the 10 x 10 x 10 "large cube" contained in many sets of base-ten blocks. Some kits also contain a 0.1 x 1 x 1 "square chip" that can be used to extend the use of base-ten blocks to include thousandths.

Section 1 **Understanding Decimals**

IN THIS SECTION
EXPLORATION 1
♦ Decimal Place Value
EXPLORATION 2
♦ Comparing Decimals

Quite a Collection

Setting the Stage

SET UP *Work in a group. You will need:* • *base-ten blocks* • *a number cube*

In this module you will discover mathematical ideas as you solve puzzles and develop strategies for playing games. In the *Place Value Game,* you will use base-ten blocks to explore decimal place value.

Follow the steps below to play the *Place Value Game.*

Game Rules Players alternate turns. On each turn follow the steps below. The first person with two flats is the winner.

First
Roll a number cube. Take the number of **small cubes** shown on the number cube.

Next
Trade in small cubes for a **rod** whenever possible.

Then
Trade in rods for a **flat** whenever possible.

Think About It

1 a. One small cube is what fraction of a rod? $\frac{1}{10}$

b. One rod is what fraction of a flat? $\frac{1}{10}$

c. One small cube is what fraction of a flat? $\frac{1}{100}$

2 a. How many small cubes would make $\frac{17}{100}$ of a flat? **17**

   b. After trading the small cubes from part (a) for as many rods as possible, how many full rods would you have? **1**

   c. How many small cubes would be left? **7**

3 How can you represent each of the following fractions of a flat using the least number of small cubes, rods, and flats?

   a. $\frac{3}{10}$
     b. $\frac{28}{100}$
     c. $\frac{1}{2}$
     d. $\frac{299}{100}$

   3 rods
     2 rods, 8 cubes
    5 rods
     2 flats, 9 rods, 9 cubes

Exploration 1

Decimal Place Value

SET UP   *You will need: • base-ten blocks • Labsheets 1A and 1B*

GOAL

LEARN HOW TO...
♦ read and write decimals

AS YOU...
♦ discover patterns using base-ten blocks

KEY TERMS
♦ decimal system
♦ place value

▶ The base-ten blocks used in the *Place Value Game* are based on ones, tens, and hundreds, which makes the small cubes, rods, and flats a good model for our **decimal system**.

4 Copy the place-value chart and fill in the **place values** to the left of the decimal point. **See margin.**

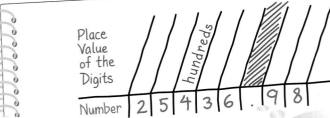

5 Use your place value chart for 25,436.98.

   a. Start in the ones place. Each time you move to the left one place, the place value is multiplied by what number? **10**

   b. Fill in the blanks with the appropriate operation and number.

    Starting in the ten-thousands place, each time you move right one place, the place value is __?__ by __?__. **divided, 10**

Section 1   Understanding Decimals **131**

TEACHING NOTES
Question 3 Make sure students model each fraction using as few base-ten blocks as possible.

Exploration 1

CLASSROOM MANAGEMENT
Students should work individually. However, if there are not enough base-ten blocks available, they can also work in groups. Each student will need copies of the labsheets.

TEACHING NOTES
Questions 5–7 extend the ideas of whole number place value to decimal fractions. Make sure students understand that the value of a digit in a numeral is determined by its place value. Our system of notation is a decimal system because the place values are powers of 10. Consequently, the values of any two adjacent places in a numeral differ by a multiple of 10.

4. See Additional Answers beginning on page A1.

Exploration 1 *continued*

COMMON ERROR

Students sometimes have difficulty keeping track of place value when reading numbers. Ask them to read the number 25,436.98 at the bottom of page 131 as *twenty five thousand four hundred thirty-six and ninety-eight hundredths*. Mention the common error made by radio and TV commentators who often use too many "ands" when reading a number (inserting "and" between the hundreds and tens or thousands and hundreds). The word "and" is used only to separate the whole number portion of a number from the decimal or fractional portion. In particular, "and" is not used at all when reading a whole number, no matter how great it may be.

TEACHING NOTES

Question 9 is best done individually. After students have completed **Labsheet 1B**, have them team up with a partner and compare answers. If some students have difficulty, provide more examples for them. Students who did not have difficulty may begin the assignment.

9. b. These numbers had both whole number and decimal parts. The "and" separates the whole numbers and the decimal fractions in the name of the number. The "and" represents the decimal point in these numbers.

7. a., 8. a–b., 9. a. See Additional Answers beginning on page A1.

132

---

6 **Try This as a Class** The pattern you found in Question 5(b) continues to the right of the decimal point. Think of the flat as one whole or 1.

   a. To find the place value of the digit to the right of the ones place, imagine dividing the flat by 10. Which base-ten block models this place value? **rod**

   b. This block is what fraction of the flat? $\frac{1}{10}$

   c. Which base-ten block would you use to model the place value of the next digit to the right? **cube**

   d. This block is what fraction of the flat? $\frac{1}{100}$

7 **a.** Fill in the place values of the 9 and the 8 in your chart. **See margin.**

   b. What would the place value of the digit to the right of the 8 be?
   thousandths

▶ Place values to the right of the decimal point can be written using **words**, **fractions**, or **decimals**. Knowing the different forms for one tenth and one hundredth can help you write numbers in three ways.

Words	Fractions	Decimals	Models
one tenth	$\frac{1}{10}$	0.1	rod
one hundredth	$\frac{1}{100}$	0.01	small cube

8 **Use Labsheet 1A.** Follow directions on the Labsheet to:
   a–b . See margin.
   a. Complete the *Missing Values Table.*

   b. Shade the *Pattern Block Flat.*

9 ✔ **CHECKPOINT** **Use Labsheet 1B.**

   a. Follow the directions on Labsheet 1B to complete the *Words to Fractions to Decimals* table. **See margin.**

   b. Why was the word "and" used in only three of the word names in the *Words to Fractions to Decimals* table?

✔ QUESTION 9

...checks that you can write numbers using words, fractions, and decimals.

HOMEWORK EXERCISES ▶ See Exs. 1–20 on p. 135.

 Module 3 Mind Games

Exploration 2

Comparing Decimals

SET UP *You will need base-ten blocks.*

GOAL

LEARN HOW TO...
- compare and order decimals

AS YOU...
- work with base-ten blocks

KEY TERM
- equivalent decimals

▶ **You can use decimals to make comparisons.**

10 **Discussion**

    a. Use your base-ten blocks to model 0.6 and 0.36.
       Check students' blocks. 0.6 = 6 rods, 0.36 = 3 rods, 6 cubes
    b. Which is greater, 0.6 or 0.36? How can you tell?
       0.6; It has more rods than 0.36.

11 **a.** Show how you could use base-ten blocks to determine which is greater, 1.12 or 1.21.

    b. Which is greater, 1.12 or 1.21? Why? **1.21; The flats are equal in number, but 1.21 has more rods.**

12 **Try This as a Class**

    a. A small cube can be sliced into 10 square chips. Each chip is what fraction of a flat? $\frac{1}{1000}$

    b. How many thousandths would it take to make a hundredth? **10**

    c. Discuss how, without using base-ten blocks, you could determine which decimal is greater, 1.068 or 1.07.

▶ **Equivalent Decimals** You have compared decimals that represent different amounts. If two decimals represent the same amount, they are **equivalent decimals**.

13 **a.** Write the decimal for each picture below. **0.2, 0.20**

    two tenths   twenty hundredths

    b. Are the decimals in part (a) equivalent? Explain. **yes; All the place values are equal, 20 squares are used to represent both decimals.**

14 ✔ **CHECKPOINT** Compare each pair of decimals. Use <, >, or =.

    a. 0.4 **_>_** 0.39   **b.** 0.31 **_<_** 1.2

    c. 4.06 **_=_** 4.0600   **d.** 1.061 **_>_** 1.008

▶ **HOMEWORK EXERCISES** ▶ See Exs. 21–29 on p. 136.

---

11. a. Represent the numbers with base-ten blocks and then compare first flats, then rods, then cubes. **Check students' representations.**

    1.12 = 1 flat, 1 rod, 2 cubes;
    1.21 = 1 flat, 2 rods, 1 cube

12. c. Compare the place values, beginning at the places of greatest value and working to the right. Compare the numerals in the first decimal place for which the 2 numbers differ, in this case the hundredths place. Since 6 < 7, 1.068 < 1.07.

✔ **QUESTION 14**

...checks that you can compare decimals.

Exploration 2

TEACHING NOTES
To help students answer **Question 10(b)**, suggest that they think about playing the *Place Value Game* and which amount would be closer to obtaining a flat. For **Question 11(b)**, they can think about which amount is closer to obtaining a second flat.

COMMON ERROR
Question 10 Some students may think that 0.36 > 0.6 because 36 > 6. Have these students exchange each rod in their representation of each number for 10 small cubes. Then ask which number is represented by the most cubes. Reinforce this process by writing 0.6 as 0.60 and asking which inequality is true, 0.36 > 0.60 or 0.36 < 0.60. After students complete **Question 11**, you can quickly present more examples using overhead base-ten blocks.

TEACHING NOTES
Question 12 If your set of base-ten blocks contains the 0.1 x 1 x 1 small square (thousandth chip) you may want to demonstrate **part (a)** by stacking 10 of them next to a small cube. In **part (c)**, allow the class to explain ways to determine the greater of two decimals. Make sure students understand that to compare two decimals, they should compare the digits in corresponding places beginning with the greatest place value.

Question 14 Have individual students read their solutions using words such as "tenths", "hundredths", and so on. For **part (c)** students may read 4.0600 either as *four and six hundred ten-thousandths* or as *four and six hundredths*. Students should realize these are equivalent values.

133

Name the first four place values to the right of the decimal point in a decimal number. How are these related to one another?

Sample Response: tenths, hundredths, thousandths, ten-thousandths; As you move right one place, the place value is divided by ten.

ABSENT STUDENTS

For students who were absent for all or part of this section, the blackline Study Guide for Section 1 may be used to present the ideas, concepts, and skills of Section 1.

Section 1

Key Concepts

Key Terms

decimal system

place value

equivalent decimals

Decimal System (pp. 131–132)

In the decimal system, the positions of the digits in a number determine their values.

As you move **left** one place, the place value is **multiplied** by 10.

ten-thousands thousands hundreds tens ones . tenths hundredths thousandths ten-thousandths

$$7\ 5\ 8\ 2\ 1\ .\ 6\ 3\ 9\ 4$$

As you move **right** one place, the place value is **divided** by 10.

A number can be written in different ways.

Example

Words	Fraction	Decimal
Five and three thousandths	$5\frac{3}{1000}$	5.003

Comparing Decimals (p. 133)

To compare decimals, you need to compare their place values. Decimals that represent the same amount are equivalent.

Example

1.43 > 1.428

The **ones** digits are equal and the **tenths** digits are equal. Compare the **hundredths** digits: 3 > 2. So, 1.43 > 1.428.

Since $1.43 = 1\frac{43}{100} = 1\frac{430}{1000} = 1.430$, 1.43 and 1.430 are equivalent.

Key Concepts Questions

15 Write each number as a fraction or mixed number and as a decimal.

a. forty-five and thirty-one hundredths $\quad 45\frac{31}{100} = \frac{4531}{100}, 45.31$

b. six hundred and ten thousandths $\quad 600\frac{10}{1000} = \frac{600010}{1000}, 600.010$

c. seven hundred three thousandths $\quad \frac{703}{1000}, 0.703$

16 Why are there two zeros in the decimal 5.003 in the Example above?
The zeros are place holders and record that there are no tenths or hundredths.

17 Explain why 0.13 < 0.5 even though 13 > 5. Sample Response:
$0.13 = \frac{13}{100}$ and $0.5 = \frac{50}{100}$. Since $\frac{13}{100} < \frac{50}{100}$, $0.13 < 0.5$.

Section 1

Practice & Application Exercises

Science It takes the planet Saturn 29.458 years to revolve around the sun. Give the place value of each digit in the number 29.458.

1. 2 — tens
2. 9 — ones
3. 4 — tenths
4. 5 — hundredths
5. 8 — thousandths

Write each decimal in words and as a fraction or mixed number.

6. 0.62
7. 8.3
8. 345.04
9. 1.002

Write each number as a decimal.

10. $\frac{29}{100}$ 0.29

11. $\frac{3}{100}$ 0.03

12. six and seven tenths 6.7

13. $\frac{205}{10,000}$ 0.0205

14. ninety-nine and nine thousandths 99.009

15. United States money can be used to model our decimal system.

   a. If the one-dollar bill represents one whole, which coin represents one tenth? dime

   b. Which coin represents one hundredth? penny

16. Using only pennies, dimes, and one-dollar bills, how can you represent four and sixteen hundredths? 4 dollars, 1 dime, 6 pennies

17. How could you use United States money to show that 0.40 = 0.4? Show that 40 pennies is equal in value to 4 dimes.

18. Josh says that *two hundred five thousandths* and *two hundred and five thousandths* are the same number. Bonnie claims they are different numbers. Who is correct, Josh or Bonnie, and why?

Arts Many cultures make designs by piecing together sections of fabric. This cloth from Ghana was made by sewing together long, narrow strips.

19. In the photo at the right, what part of the entire cloth does each strip represent? $\frac{1}{10}$

20. Written as a decimal, what part of the cloth is represented by the section outlined in yellow? 0.4

6. sixty-two hundredths, $\frac{62}{100}$

7. eight and three tenths, $\frac{83}{10}$ or $8\frac{3}{10}$

8. three hundred forty-five and four hundredths, $\frac{34504}{100}$ or $345\frac{4}{100}$.

9. one and two thousandths, $\frac{1002}{1000}$ or $1\frac{2}{1000}$

18. Bonnie; "and" indicates the decimal placement to separate the whole numbers from the decimal parts, so two hundred and 5 thousandths is 200.005, while two hundred five thousandths is 0.205

1 strip

SUGGESTED ASSIGNMENTS

Core Course
Day 1: Exs. 30–38
Day 2: Exs. 1–18
Day 3: Exs. 19–29

Extended Course
Day 1: Exs. 30–38
Day 2: Exs. 1–18
Day 3: Exs. 19–29

Note: Extended Course assignments can be used to differentiate within the regular classroom. In classrooms where students are grouped homogeneously, the material might be covered in fewer days. In this case assignments may be combined.

ADDITIONAL PRACTICE
See the *Teacher's Resource Book* for additional practice and application exercises for this section.

EXERCISE NOTES
Exercise 14 Students who do not understand that the "and" separates the whole number and the decimal portions of a number will often write an incorrect answer such as 0.999 instead of 99.009. Also watch for students who write 99.900 because the last digit ends in the thousandths place. You may want to demonstrate with base-ten blocks how a set of 9 rods is different from a set of 9 small squares (thousandth chips).

136

EXERCISE NOTES

Since students have never been asked to order a list of numbers, you may want to do an example like **Exercises 21–23** before assigning them.

For **Exercises 24–27**, encourage students to find the greatest place value for which the two numbers have different digits. In **Exercise 24**, point out that the greatest place value for which the numbers have different digits is the thousandths place, that 16.12 is equivalent to 16.120, and that 0 is less than 5.

For **Exercise 28**, have several students share their solutions with the class. Initiate a discussion about the number of possible solutions and which solution requires the fewest keystrokes.

Order each list of numbers from least to greatest.

21. 0.3, 0.03, 0.51, 0.16   0.03, 0.16, 0.3, 0.51

22. 0.24, 0.4, 0.08, 0.28   0.08, 0.24, 0.28, 0.4

23. 0.717, 0.17, 0.105, 0.008   0.008, 0.105, 0.17, 0.717

Compare each pair of decimals. Use <, >, or =.

24. 16.12 _?_ 16.125   <

25. 98.099 _?_ 98.901   <

26. 2.65 _?_ 2.650   =

27. 11 _?_ 10.989   >

28. Calculator Yvette's calculator is broken. Only these keys work: **0**, **1**, **+**, and **·**. How can Yvette get 27.063 to appear on the screen? Sample Response:
11 + 11 + 1 + 1 + 1 + 1 + 1 + .01 + .01 + .01 + .01 + .01 + .01 + .001 + .001 + .001

Reflecting ▶ on the Section

Journal

Exercise 29 checks that you understand decimal place value.

Write your response to Exercise 29 in your journal.

29. Suppose you are teaching a younger student about decimals and place value. Explain how you can tell which is greater, 0.6 or 0.58.
Sample Response: I would explain that $0.6 = \frac{6}{10} = \frac{60}{100}$ and $0.58 = \frac{58}{100}$. Since $60 > 58$, $\frac{60}{100} > \frac{58}{100}$.

Spiral ▶ Review

Estimate each sum or difference. (Module 1, p. 10)

30. $13.67
    + $5.89
    about $20

31. $158.23
    − $34.67
    about $123

32. $7.39
    + $1.87
    about $9

Identify each geometric figure. Use letters and symbols to name the figure. (Module 2, p. 106)

33.
line, $\overleftrightarrow{AB}$ or $\overleftrightarrow{BA}$

34.
segment, $\overline{CD}$ or $\overline{DC}$

35.
ray, $\overrightarrow{FE}$

Name each polygon. Be as specific as possible. Explain why you chose that name. (Module 2, p. 119)

36. regular pentagon; All angles are equal in measure and the five sides are the same length.

37. parallelogram; Opposite sides are parallel and equal in length.

38. trapezoid; It has exactly one pair of parallel sides.

36.

37.

38.

Section 1

Extra Skill Practice

Write the place value of each underlined digit.

1. 0.00<u>5</u>
   thousandths

2. 3564.2<u>2</u>
   ones

3. 90.<u>2</u>86
   tenths

4. 116.9<u>8</u>
   hundredths

5. 12.<u>3</u>5
   ones

6. 0.0<u>1</u>8
   hundredths

7. 159.<u>5</u>34
   tenths

8. 5.102<u>6</u>
   ten-thousandths

Write each number as a decimal and as a fraction or mixed number.

9. two tenths $0.2, \frac{2}{10}$

10. five hundred thousandths $0.500, \frac{500}{1000}$

11. four thousand and six tenths

12. one and twenty-five hundredths

13. three hundred fifty-six and forty hundredths

11. 4000.6, $\frac{40006}{10}$ or $4000\frac{6}{10}$

12. 1.25, $\frac{125}{100}$ or $1\frac{25}{100}$

13. 356.40, $\frac{35640}{100}$ or $356\frac{40}{100}$

Write each decimal in words. 15–19 and 21. See margin.

14. 4.2
    four and two tenths

15. 0.026

16. 531.08

17. 10.205

18. 3.25

19. 1.004

20. 0.01
    one hundredth

21. 11.100

Compare each pair of decimals. Use <, >, or =.

22. 6.13 _?_ 6.125
    >

23. 75.001 _?_ 75.0009
    >

24. 3.60 _?_ 3.600
    =

25. 1.999 _?_ 1.9009
    >

26. 0.520 _?_ 0.52
    =

27. 73.04 _?_ 73.401
    <

Order each list of numbers from least to greatest.

28. 6, 6.04, 6.008, 66.002
    6, 6.008, 6.04, 66.002

29. 123.1, 124, 12.3, 1.233, 0.123
    0.123, 1.233, 12.3, 123.1, 124

30. 1.9, 1.99, 1.099, 1.909
    1.099, 1.9, 1.909, 1.99

31. 75.24, 7.0652, 7.526, 75.024
    7.0652, 7.526, 75.024, 75.24

Standardized Testing ◀▶ **Multiple Choice**

Choose the decimal that represents each number.

1. Three thousand fifty-nine and one tenth D

   Ⓐ 0.10359   Ⓑ 359.1   Ⓒ 3000.69   Ⓓ 3059.1

2. Four hundred and three thousandths B

   Ⓐ 0.4003   Ⓑ 400.003   Ⓒ 0.403   Ⓓ 403,000

Extra Skill Practice

TEACHER NOTES

For each Exploration, the corresponding Extra Skill Practice Exercises are noted.

Exploration 1: Exs. 1–21
Exploration 2: Exs. 22–31

EXTRA HELP

Teacher's Resource Book
- Practice and Applications
- Study Guide

Technology Resources
- @Home Tutor
- Test Generator

ASSESSMENT
- Section 1 Quick Quiz
- Test Generator

15. twenty-six thousandths

16. five hundred thirty-one and eight hundredths

17. ten and two hundred five thousandths

18. three and twenty-five hundredths

19. one and four thousandths

21. eleven and one hundred thousandths

138

Setting the Stage

GETTING STARTED

In preparation for adding and subtracting decimals, Module 3 Section 3 *Warm-up* assesses student ability with adding and subtracting whole numbers.

The *Decimal Puzzle* pieces will fit together in several ways but will only make the given sum if all the decimal points, and thus place values, are aligned. There is more than one solution, but the solutions only vary by the order in which the numbers appear. The addends are 3, 4.06, 3.8, 1.57, 2.8, and 0.09. Since students will be learning decimal addition in this section, they will have to rely on estimation skills to check their solutions. You may also choose to let students use a calculator to check their puzzle solution. The exact sum will be calculated by students in **Question 6** of Exploration 1.

Section ② Decimal Addition and Subtraction

IN THIS SECTION

EXPLORATION 1
♦ Adding Decimals

EXPLORATION 2
♦ Subtracting Decimals

A Fitting Puzzle

SET UP   *You will need: • Labsheets 2A and 2B • scissors*

Decimal Puzzle

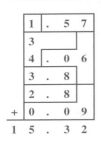

1	.	5	7
3			
4	.	0	6
3	.	8	
2	.	8	
+ 0	.	0	9
1 5	.	3	2

Setting the Stage

Adding decimals can be a bit puzzling, especially when the numbers are not aligned in columns for you to add. Solving the *Decimal Puzzle* will help you recognize some key patterns in adding decimals.

Use Labsheets 2A and 2B. Follow the directions on Labsheet 2A to solve the *Decimal Puzzle*.

Think About It

1 **a.** What is the place value of the 9 in the puzzle piece 0.09?
    hundredths
   b. What do you notice about the place value of all the other digits in the same column as the 9? They are all hundredths.

2 All the cards except two have decimal points in them. What is the place value of the digits without a decimal point? ones

▶ In this section, you will use base-ten blocks to investigate addition and subtraction of decimals.

Exploration 1

Adding .DECIMALS

GOAL

LEARN HOW TO...
- add decimals

AS YOU...
- model with base-ten blocks

SET UP You will need: • Decimal Puzzle solution • base-ten blocks

▶ The example below shows how base-ten blocks can be used to add two of the numbers from the *Decimal Puzzle*.

EXAMPLE

Find the sum 2.8 + 1.57 using base-ten blocks.

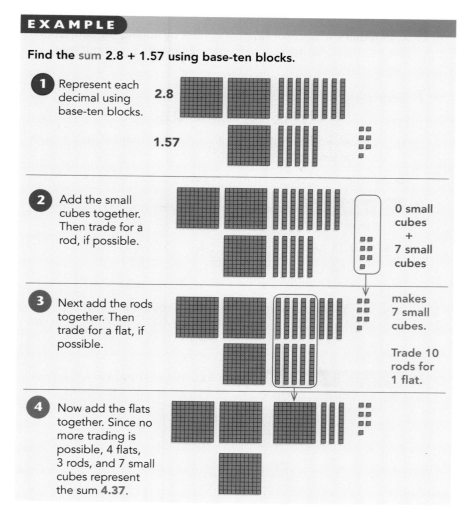

1 Represent each decimal using base-ten blocks. 2.8

1.57

2 Add the small cubes together. Then trade for a rod, if possible.

0 small cubes + 7 small cubes

3 Next add the rods together. Then trade for a flat, if possible.

makes 7 small cubes.

Trade 10 rods for 1 flat.

4 Now add the flats together. Since no more trading is possible, 4 flats, 3 rods, and 7 small cubes represent the sum **4.37**.

Exploration 1

TEACHING NOTES

Go through the **Example** with the class. Use base-ten blocks to demonstrate the trading that occurs and to emphasize how cubes are added with cubes, rods with rods and flats with flats. You may want to ask questions related to the example throughout the demonstration to check for student understanding of how to add with base-ten blocks. The illustration with the blocks reinforces the importance of adding digits with the same place values to avoid the common error of adding 2.8 + 1.57 by aligning the end digits 8 and 7.

ALTERNATIVE APPROACH

For advanced students, you may want to begin by having them find the sum 2.8 + 1.57 followed by **Discussion Question 4.** Discuss page 139 only with students who did not get the correct sum because they did not add digits with the same place values.

TEACHING NOTES

After discussing **Question 4**, you may want to discuss the difference between eliminating the zero on 2.80 versus a number like 2.08, making sure students understand why the zero in the number 2.08 is not optional. (*It is an important place holder since eliminating it would change the value of the succeeding digits to the right.*) Then ask students to complete the sentence, "Writing or deleting a zero in a decimal number is optional if..."

Checkpoint Question 8 You might want students to rewrite **parts (c)–(f)** vertically so that they can check the alignment of their numbers. **Parts (e) and (f)** give students practice in substituting values for variables to evaluate expressions.

---

3. a. 4.15 (4 flats, 1 rod, and 5 small cubes)
   b. 6.8 (6 flats and 8 rods)

4. Sample Response: Yes, both represented 2 and 8 tenths. Jerome recorded that there were no hundredths by writing a zero in the hundredths place, while Rankin left the hundredths place empty since there were no hundredths.

5. Rankin's Jerome's

$$
\begin{array}{r} 3.8 \\ +3 \\ \hline 6.8 \end{array}
\qquad
\begin{array}{r} 3.8 \\ +3.0 \\ \hline 6.8 \end{array}
$$

6.
$$
\begin{array}{r} 4.37 \\ 4.15 \\ +6.80 \\ \hline 15.32 \end{array}
$$

✔ **QUESTION 8**

...checks that you can add decimals.

7. a. Sample Response: Think of money. $1.50 plus ten cents is less than $2.60. So Leigha did not add correctly. Or: 0.11 contains one tenth, so 1.5 + 0.1 = 1.6, not 2.6

---

3 The sums below use the remaining numbers from the *Decimal Puzzle*. Use base-ten blocks to find each sum. **Check students' models.**

a. $4.06 + 0.09$ 　　　　　b. $3.8 + 3$

4 **Discussion** Two students used numbers to record the addition problem modeled in the Example. Did they both represent the problem correctly? Explain.

Rankin wrote:
$$
\begin{array}{r} 2.8 \\ +1.57 \end{array}
$$

Jerome wrote:
$$
\begin{array}{r} 2.80 \\ +1.57 \end{array}
$$

5 Add the numbers in Question 3(b) using either Rankin's or Jerome's representation.

6 Check that the *Decimal Puzzle* is correct by adding the sum from the Example and the two sums from Question 3, without using base-ten blocks.

7 Leigha wrote the number sentence:

$$1.5 + 0.11 = 2.6$$

a. How can you use estimation to determine that Leigha's answer must be wrong?

b. What mistake do you think Leigha made?

8 ✔ **CHECKPOINT** Find each sum. Use estimation to check the reasonableness of your answers.

a. $\begin{array}{r} 0.25 \\ +1.79 \end{array}$ 　2.04 　　　　b. $\begin{array}{r} 52.03 \\ +0.785 \end{array}$ 　52.815

c. $0.009 + 0.999$ 　1.008 　　　d. $1.26 + 0.32$ 　1.58

e. $n + 3.706$ where $n = 0.4$ 　4.106

f. $10.006 + p + q$ where $p = 11$ and $q = 0.07$ 　21.076

| **HOMEWORK EXERCISES** ▶ See Exs. 1–17 on pp. 143–144.

7. b. Sample Response: Leigha aligned the 5 tenths with the 1 hundredth instead of the 1 tenth.　wrong
$$
\begin{array}{r} 1.5 \\ +0.1\,1 \end{array}
$$

Subtracting .DECIMALS

SET UP *You will need base-ten blocks.*

▶ Base-ten blocks can also be used to model decimal subtraction.

EXAMPLE

Find the **difference** 1.43 – 0.58 using base-ten blocks.

1 Represent 1.43 using base-ten blocks.

1.43

Trade 1 rod for 10 small cubes.

2 You need to take away 5 rods and 8 small cubes. Since there are only 3 cubes, you must make a trade before you can take 8 cubes away.

Now, take away 8 small cubes.

3 Next you must take away 5 rods. Since there are only 3 rods, you must make another trade before you take 5 rods away.

Now, take away 5 rods.

4 The **difference** is 8 rods and 5 small cubes, or 0.85.

9 Use base-ten blocks to find each difference.

a. 1.62 – 0.8 *0.82*   **b.** 1.62 – 0.80 *0.82*   **c.** 1.62 – 0.08 *1.54*

10 In Question 9, is subtracting 0.8 the same as subtracting 0.80 or subtracting 0.08? Explain.

10. Subtracting 0.8 is the same as subtracting 0.80, since 80 cubes can be traded in for 8 rods. Both numbers have 8 tenths and no hundredths.

Exploration 2

ALTERNATIVE APPROACH
For advanced students, you may want to begin by having them find the difference 1.43 – 0.58 followed by **Discussion Question 11.** Present the **Example** with base-ten blocks only for students who did not get the correct difference due to an error in regrouping.

TEACHING NOTES
Go through the **Example** with the class, demonstrating each step with base-ten blocks. Involve students by asking, "Why is a rod being traded for cubes?"; "How many cubes is it being traded for? Why?"

For an additional example, use base-ten blocks to model the steps in the Classroom Example below.

CLASSROOM EXAMPLE

Find the difference 1.32 – 0.87 using base-ten blocks.

Answer:

1. Represent 1.32 using base-ten blocks.

2. You need to take away 8 rods and 7 small cubes. Since there are only 2 small cubes you must make a trade. Trade 1 rod for 10 small cubes, then take away 7 small cubes.

3. Next you must take away 8 rods. Since there are only 3 rods, you must make another trade. Trade 1 flat for 10 rods, then take away 8 rods.

4. The difference is 4 rods and 5 small cubes, or 0.45.

141

Exploration 2 *continued*

TEACHING NOTES

Make sure that when students write the problems in **Question 14** vertically, they have the minuend and the subtrahend in the correct positions. Students will need to insert zeros after the minuends in **Questions 14(a)–(d)** in order to perform the subtraction.

15. Answers will vary. In parts a–e, round to the nearest whole number and subtract. For part f, round to the nearest hundredth and subtract.

11. In both you must align numbers with the same place value before subtracting. When subtraction in a column is not possible, both rely on trading to complete the subtraction.

12. a. Step 1: Write 1.063 under 2.85 so place values and decimals are aligned.
Step 2: Add a zero so the two numbers have the same number of places.
Step 3: Subtract.
Step 4: Position the decimal point in the answer.
Step 5: Check by estimating.

✔ **QUESTION 14**

...checks that you can subtract decimals and check the results.

12. b. The zero is needed to apply whole number subtraction methods of regrouping and renaming, since the first number, 2.85, has fewer decimal places than the second number, 1.063.

---

11 **Discussion** How is subtraction of decimals like subtraction of whole numbers?

12 **Try This as a Class** The subtraction 2.85 – 1.063 is shown below.

a. Explain what is being done in each step.

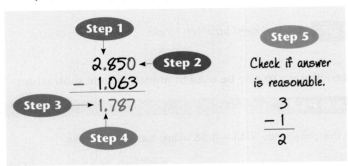

b. Placing zeros so both numbers have an equal number of decimal places is optional when adding decimals. Why is writing a zero in the thousandths place necessary in this subtraction problem?

13 a. To check that the answer was reasonable, 2.850 was rounded to 3. How do you know that 2.850 is closer to 3 than to 2?
   2.5 is half way between 2 and 3. So 2.8 is closer to 3 since 8 > 5.
b. The subtraction 15 – 8 = 7 can be checked by making sure that 8 + 7 = 15. Show how you could use addition to check the subtraction 2.85 – 1.063 = 1.787.
   Check that 1.787 + 1.063 = 2.85.

14 ✔ **CHECKPOINT** Find each difference. Check your answers using addition.

a. 12001.7 – 120.017 11881.683   b. 43 – 16.535 26.465

c. 17.3 – 17.30 0   d. 21.5 – 0.009 21.491

e. n – 0.56 where n = 2.45 1.89   f. x – y where x = 0.82 and y = 0.015 0.805

15 **Discussion** Explain how you could use estimation to check if each difference in Question 14 is reasonable. See margin.

16 Complete this puzzle. Use the digits 0, 1, 2, 3, 4, 5, and 6 to make two decimal numbers that have a difference of 3.866. Each digit can only be used once. 5.206 – 1.34

HOMEWORK EXERCISES ▶ See Exs. 18–37 on pp. 145–146.

Section 2

Key Concepts

Adding and Subtracting Decimals (pp. 139–142)

To find the sum or difference of two decimal numbers:

1 Align the numbers so that the digits with the same place value are in the same column.

2 Write zeros so that both numbers have the same number of decimal places.

3 Add or subtract as with whole numbers.

4 Place the decimal point in the final answer. Place a zero in the ones place when there are no ones.

Example

Addition	Subtraction
4.57 + 3.9	4.57 − 3.9
4.57 + 3.90	4.57 − 3.90
4.57 + 3.90 8 47	4.57 − 3.90 67
4.57 + 3.90 8.47	4.57 − 3.90 0.67

17 Key Concepts Question

a. Explain how you can use estimation to check that the sum and the difference above are reasonable. **4.57 is close to 4.6 and 3.9 is close to 4 for a sum of about 8.6. 4.6 minus 4 is close to 0.6.**

b. Use addition to check the subtraction. **3.90 + 0.67 = 4.57**

Section 2

Practice & Application Exercises

YOU WILL NEED

For Ex. 17:
- calculator

Find each sum without using a calculator.

1. $\begin{array}{r} 3.241 \\ + 10.6 \\ \hline 13.841 \end{array}$

2. $\begin{array}{r} 14.606 \\ 8.217 \\ + 0.888 \\ \hline 23.711 \end{array}$

3. $\begin{array}{r} 6.32 \\ + 72.59 \\ \hline 78.91 \end{array}$

4. $x + 20.005$ where $x = 4.76$
   24.765

5. $4.102 + 5.6 + 10.99$
   20.692

Key Concepts

CLOSURE QUESTION

Compare addition and subtraction of decimals with addition and subtraction of whole numbers. Describe the similarities and differences.

Sample Response: Adding and subtracting decimals is just like adding and subtracting whole numbers, except you have to place the decimal in the final answer. For both, you align the digits with the same place value so they will be added or subtracted. Regrouping can take place in both decimal and whole number subtraction. With decimals you can add zeros to the end of the decimal part to make the numbers you are adding or subtracting the same length. With whole numbers you never add zeros to the end because without the decimal point written in, the value of the number would be changed.

Practice & Applications

SUGGESTED ASSIGNMENTS

Core Course
Day 1: Exs. 1–17, 38–45
Day 2: Exs. 18–34, 37

Extended Course
Day 1: Exs. 4–17, 38–45
Day 2: Exs. 21–37, 46–49*

Note: Extended Course assignments can be used to differentiate within the regular classroom. In classrooms where students are grouped homogeneously, the material might be covered in fewer days. In this case assignments may be combined.

*denotes Extension Exercises

EXERCISE NOTES

Exercises 6 and 7 provide an opportunity to discuss the question of how to handle a situation in which one is short-changed after making a purchase. The following strategy may help resolve an argument over the matter. Before handing a 5-, 10-, or 20-dollar bill to a cashier, memorize the last three digits of the serial number. Ask the cashier to check the 3 digits you have memorized with that of the bill in the drawer. This should convince the cashier of any error. It is also good practice to announce aloud the denomination of the bill when handing it to the cashier. As a cashier, it is a good practice to lay the bill across the drawer until the change is accepted by the customer before placing it in the correct section of the cash drawer.

8. Yes; The sum of the whole dollar amounts is 3 + 13 + 2 = $18. The cents on the first two items combined are less than $1, and the cents on the third item are less than $1. Therefore the total will be under $20.

11. 0.75 + 0.25 = 1
2 + 3 + 1 = 6

12. 0.7 + 0.3 = 1
6 + 13 + 1 = 20

13. 0.35 + 0.65 = 1
1 + 5 + 2 + 1 = 9
9 + 0.8 = 9.8

14. 2 + 3 = 5
0.16 + 0.8 = 0.96
5 + 0.96 = 5.96

15. 3.138 + 0.002
= 3.140
3.140 + 0.045 =
3.185
3.185 − 0.002 =
3.183

16. 77.3 + 10 = 87.3
87.3 − 0.1 = 87.2

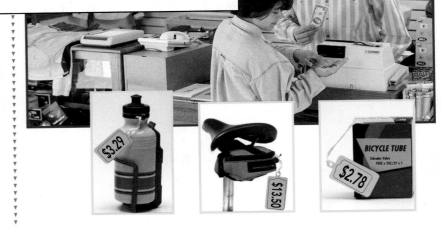

Lucita pays for a $.49 item with a ten-dollar bill. After the numbers are entered, 0.51 shows up on the cash register display. The cashier hands Lucita $.51 in change.

6. Explain the cashier's mistake. **The cashier must have entered $1.00 instead of $10.00.**

7. What is Lucita's correct change? **$9.51**

Bottle label: **$3.29**

Seat label: **$13.50**

Bicycle tube label: **BICYCLE TUBE** Schrader Valve 700C × 19C/27 × 1 **$2.78**

8. **Estimation** Suppose you have exactly $20. Without finding the exact sum, decide whether you have enough money to buy the three items with the prices shown. (There is no tax on these items.) Explain how you know.

Find the missing terms in each sequence.

9. 0.3, 0.41, 0.52, __?__ , __?__ , __?__ , 0.96, ... **0.63, 0.74, 0.85**

10. 6.3, 6.4, 6.6, 6.9, __?__ , __?__ , __?__ , 9.1, ... **7.3, 7.8, 8.4**

Mental Math Explain how to use mental math to find each sum. It may help to think about money.

11. 2.75 + 3.25

12. 6.7 + 13.3

13. 5.35 + 2.8 + 1.65

14. 2.16 + 3.8

15. 0.045 + 3.138

16. 77.3 + 9.9

17. Calculator Use your calculator to find the sum 4.562 + 3.138.

a. What sum does the calculator display? **7.7**

b. How many decimal places are there in the calculator display? Why does this happen? **one decimal place; since 7.700 = 7.7, the calculator does not display the additional zeros.**

Find each difference without using a calculator. Use addition to check your answers.

18. $10 - 4.5$
    5.5

19. $124.4 - 95.13$
    29.27

20. $0.567 - 0.49$
    0.077

21. $3.1 - 0.9$
    2.2

22. $76 - 54.87$
    21.13

23. $0.008 - 0.0034$
    0.0046

Follow the order of operations to evaluate each expression when $x = 2$ and $y = 2.13$.

24. $4.07 + 5 \cdot x$ 14.07

25. $26 \div (y + 10.87)$ 2

Each answer in Exercises 26–29 is wrong. Explain what the error is in each exercise and give the correct answer.

26. $4.6 + 0.42 = 0.88$

27. $10.3 - 6.041 = 4.341$

28. $12.30 - 0.03 = 12$

29. $116.89 - 0.689 = 11.00$

30. James had $126.59 in his bank account. Then he withdrew $27.50 and deposited $48.65. What is his new balance? **$147.74**

Machine Parts Sometimes the actual size of manufactured machine parts is a little bit bigger or smaller than the desired size, but they still work, so they are accepted and used. If parts are too far from the desired size, they won't fit or work right, so they are rejected.

Compute the differences to decide whether each part would be accepted or rejected. Explain your answer.

	Part	Desired Size	Actual Size	Difference	Difference Allowed	Accepted?
	Example	4.5 in.	4.38 in.	4.5 − 4.38 0.12	0.05 in.	No
31.	Part 1	1.355 in.	1.3720 in.		0.005 in.	
32.	Part 2	1.280 in.	1.099 in.		0.025 in.	
33.	Part 3	4.45 in.	4.671 in.		0.205 in.	
34.	Part 4	2.010 in.	2.008 in.		0.010 in.	

0.12 in. > 0.05 in. The error is too great, so the part is rejected.

Challenge Find the missing terms in each sequence.

35. 7.1, 6.9, 7.2, 7.0, ? , ? , ? , 7.2, ... 7.3, 7.1, 7.4

36. 74, 75.1, 77.3, 80.6, 85, ? , ? , ? , 113.6, ... 90.5, 97.1, 104.8

Section 2   Decimal Addition and Subtraction   145

26. The problem solved was $0.46 + 0.42$. The correct answer is 5.02.

27. It appears that the whole numbers were subtracted and the decimal parts were added. The correct answer is 4.259.

28. The problem solved was either $12.30 - 0.30$ or $12.03 - 0.03$. The correct answer is 12.27.

29. The problem solved was $11.689 - 0.689$. The correct answer is 116.201.

31. Difference 0.017; No, $0.017 > 0.005$

32. Difference 0.181; No, $0.181 > 0.025$

33. Difference 0.221; No, $0.221 > 0.205$

34. Difference 0.002; Yes, $0.002 < 0.010$

Practice & Applications

EXERCISE NOTES
Reflecting Exercise 37 Display students' puzzles or allow students to trade puzzles with a partner and try to solve each other's puzzle.

Journal

Exercise 37 checks that you understand the role of place value in adding or subtracting decimals.

38. one and twelve hundredths

39. eight hundred three thousandths

40. three and four tenths

41. fifty and twenty-eight hundredths

43. $8 \cdot 5 = 40$;
$40 \div 8 = 5$;
$40 \div 5 = 8$

44. $6 \cdot 7 = 42$;
$7 \cdot 6 = 42$;
$42 \div 7 = 6$;
$42 \div 6 = 7$

45. $18 \div 9 = 2$;
$18 \div 2 = 9$;
$9 \cdot 2 = 18$;
$2 \cdot 9 = 18$

Reflecting ◀▶ on the Section

Write your response to Exercise 37 in your journal.

37. Design a number puzzle that involves adding or subtracting decimals. Include the solution to your puzzle. **Check students' puzzles.**

Spiral ◀▶ Review

Write each number in words. (Module 3, p. 134)

38. 1.12   **39.** 0.803   **40.** 3.4   **41.** 50.28

42. Find the numbers that fit all three clues. (Module 2, p. 92) **69 or 87**

Clue 1	Clue 2	Clue 3
The number is odd.	The sum of its digits is 15.	The number is less than 100.

Complete each number fact family. (Toolbox, p. 573)

43. $5 \cdot 8 = 40$ $8 \cdot \underline{?} = 40$ $40 \div \underline{?} = 5$ $\underline{?} \div 5 = 8$

44. $6 \cdot \underline{?} = 42$ $\underline{?} \cdot \underline{?} = 42$ $42 \div \underline{?} = 6$ $\underline{?} \div 6 = 7$

45. $18 \div 9 = \underline{?}$ $\underline{?} \div \underline{?} = 9$ $\underline{?} \cdot 2 = 18$ $\underline{?} \cdot \underline{?} = 18$

46. nine hundred-thousandths, eight ten-thousandths, one and two hundred-thousandths, one hundred-thousandth, fifteen hundred-thousandths

Extension ▶ ▶

Extending Decimal Place Value

Use the following list of decimals to answer Exercises 46–49.
0.00009, 0.0008, 1.00002, 0.00001, 0.00015

46. Write each decimal using words. (You may want to first extend your place-value table and fill in the missing place-value names. Then write the decimal in the table.)

47. Write the decimals above in order from least to greatest.
0.00001, 0.00009, 0.00015, 0.0008, 1.00002

48. Which two decimals above have a sum of one ten-thousandth?
0.00009 and 0.00001

49. Find the difference between 1.00002 and 0.00009. **0.99993**

146

Find each sum.

1.
```
  12.06
+  9.4
-------
 21.46
```

2.
```
   1.599
+ 70.6
--------
  72.199
```

3.
```
  41.75
+  9.673
--------
  51.423
```

4.
```
   6.61
  21.85
+  4.3
-------
  32.76
```

5. 14.9 + 231.07 245.97   6. 16.08 + 0.37 + 5.9 22.35   7. 27 + 4.6 + 0.017 31.617

8. 1.25 + 12.75 14   9. 0.049 + 0.026 0.075   10. 98.2 + 4.7 102.9

11. 21.209 + 12.75 33.959   12. 33.55 + 0.55 34.1   13. 0.007 + 0.763 0.77

Find each difference.

14.
```
   4.5
-  1.7
------
   2.8
```

15.
```
  70.42
- 35.7
-------
  34.72
```

16.
```
  28.4
-  5.162
--------
  23.238
```

17.
```
  86.005
- 14.32
--------
  71.685
```

18. 6.4 – 2.367 4.033   19. 147.61 – 5.724 141.886   20. 349 – 51.06 297.94

21. 12 – 3.5 8.5   22. 0.09 – 0.045 0.045   23. 132.42 – 61.34 71.08

24. 1.089 – 0.6 0.489   25. 34.2 – 0.004 34.196   26. 13 – 6.347 6.653

27. Jana had $30.50. She earns $6.75 baby-sitting one morning, but then spends $4.15 on lunch. Now how much money does Jana have? $33.10

Find the next three terms in each sequence.

28. 0.4, 0.54, 0.68, 0.82, ... 0.96, 1.1, 1.24   29. 5.4, 5.5, 5.7, 6.0, ... 6.4, 6.9, 7.5

30. 2.5, 2.7, 3.1, 3.7, ... 4.5, 5.5, 6.7   31. 1.02, 1.12, 1.22, 1.32, ... 1.42, 1.52, 1.62

Standardized Testing ◀▶ Performance Task

Jim receives $0.10 from his father for mowing the lawn. His father promises that next time Jim mows he will get $0.20, then $0.40 for the third time, and so on.

Jim races to his calculator, does a few calculations, and exclaims, "The tenth time I mow I'll get $51.20!" "No, Jim," says Jim's dad, who takes the calculator and does his own calculation, "the tenth time you mow you'll get $4.60. You are $46.60 too high."

Given the promise, how can both Jim and his dad be right? Show your work. See margin.

Extra Skill Practice

TEACHER NOTES
For each Exploration, the corresponding Extra Skill Practice Exercises are noted.

Exploration 1: Exs. 1–13, 28–31
Exploration 2: Exs. 14–27

EXTRA HELP
Teacher's Resource Book
• Practice and Applications
• Study Guide

Technology Resources
• @Home Tutor
• Test Generator

ASSESSMENT
• Section 2 Quick Quiz
• Test Generator

Standardized Testing. See Additional Answers beginning on page A1.

Setting the Stage

GETTING STARTED

In preparation for working with factors of numbers, Module 3 Section 3 *Warm-Up* assesses student facility with listing pairs of numbers whose product is a given number.

Introduce the game by displaying a visual of **Labsheet 3A** on the overhead projector. Use the visual to explain and demonstrate how the game is played. Allow students time to ask questions, making sure they understand the game rules before beginning play.

DEVELOPING MATH CONCEPTS

Playing *Paper Clip Products* and discussing the strategies used in the game develops students' intuitive notions of factors, common factors, and divisibility. This lays the groundwork for the material in Explorations 1 and 2 on divisibility tests, greatest common factors, and prime and composite numbers.

Section ③ Factors and Divisibility

IN THIS SECTION

EXPLORATION 1
◆ Testing for Divisibility

EXPLORATION 2
◆ Prime Factors

EXPLORATION 3
◆ Powers of Numbers

Paper Clip Products

Setting the Stage

SET UP — *Work with a partner. You will need:* • *Labsheet 3A* • *2 paper clips* • *10 each of two different-colored chips*

Paper Clip Products is a strategy game involving multiplication.

1. Sample Response: I chose 2 and 6 to get the product of 12, which would place me at the center of the board.

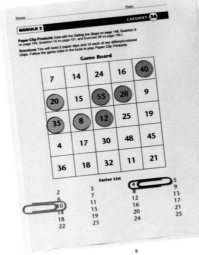

Paper Clip Products

◆ Player 1 starts. Place the paper clips on numbers in the factor list. They may both be on the same factor. Multiply the numbers and place a chip on the product on the game board. (Player 2 will use a different color chip.)

  ◆ Player 1 and Player 2 alternate turns. On a turn, leave one paper clip where it is, and move the other clip to any factor. Cover the new product with a chip.

    ◆ A turn ends when a player covers a product or if a product is not on the game board or is already covered.

      ◆ A player wins by covering three adjacent products horizontally, vertically, or diagonally.

Use Labsheet 3A. Play *Paper Clip Products* twice.

Think About It

1 If you are Player 1, where might you want to place the first two paper clips? Why?

2 What kind of moves did you avoid? Why?
  Avoid moves that would result in a product not on the board or already covered.

Testing for Divisibility

SET UP *You will need Labsheets 3A and 3B.*

GOAL

LEARN HOW TO...
* use divisibility tests
* find factors
* find the greatest common factor

AS YOU...
* develop a strategy for playing *Paper Clip Products*

KEY TERMS
* divisible
* factor
* greatest common factor (GCF)

▶ To develop a strategy for playing *Paper Clip Products*, you can use a Venn diagram to sort the numbers on the game board.

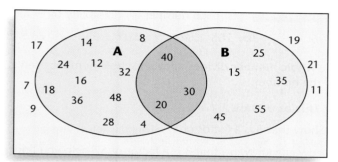

3 **Use Labsheet 3A.**

a. If you put a paper clip on 2, your opponent will be able to cover any number in Set *A*. Explain why. **Every number in set A is even, therefore a multiple of 2.**

b. Putting a paper clip on what factor makes it possible for your opponent to cover any number in Set *B*? **5**

c. 20, 30, and 40 are in both Set *A* and Set *B*. Putting your paper clip on what factors would make it possible for your opponent to cover these numbers? **2, 5, or 10**

▶ When a number can be divided evenly by another number, it is **divisible** by that number.

4 Look back at your answers to Question 3. Just by looking at a number, how can you tell if it is divisible

a. by 2? **b.** by 5? **c.** by 10?
  Its ones digit is even. **Its ones digit is 5 or 0.** **Its ones digit is 0.**

5 **✔ CHECKPOINT** Without dividing, tell whether each number is divisible by 2, by 5, or by 10.

a. 125 **5** **b.** 326 **2** **c.** 270 **2, 5, 10** **d.** 681 **none**

✔ QUESTION 5

... checks that you can determine whether a number is divisible by 2, by 5, or by 10.

Section 3 Factors and Divisibility 149

Exploration 1

CLASSROOM MANAGEMENT
Students should work in pairs for Exploration 1. Each pair of students will need a copy of **Labsheets 3A** and **3B**. **Labsheet 3A** will be used again later in this exploration and also in **Practice and Applications Exercise 28**, so students will need to keep **Labsheet 3A** accessible during class and for homework.

Exploration 1 *continued*

TEACHING NOTES

Since the focus of **Questions 6–9** is for students to discover divisibility tests by recognizing patterns, allow students to use a calculator to check divisibility by 3 and by 9.

Question 10 Make sure students understand that because a factor of a number divides the number evenly, the quotient will also divide the number evenly. Thus the quotient is also a factor of the number. For example, since $57 \div 3 = 19$, 19 also divides 57 ($57 \div 19 = 3$), so 19 is a also a factor of 57.

Multiplication and division fact families can be used to show how factors and divisibility are related to multiplication. If $a \cdot b = c$, then $c \div b = a$ and $c \div a = b$. Thus, if the product of two whole numbers equals a third whole number, the two numbers are factors of the third number.

7. See Additional Answers beginning on page A1.

---

8. A number is divisible by 9 if the sum of its digits is divisible by 9. The numbers in parts (a)–(e) are all divisible by 9.

7. See Additional Answers beginning on page A1.

✔ **QUESTION 9**

... checks that you can determine whether a number is divisible by 3 or by 9.

▶ In Questions 6–8, you will discover divisibility tests for 3 and 9.

6 The number 351 is divisible by 3. Tell whether each rearrangement of the digits of 351 is still divisible by 3.
a–e. All are divisible by 3.
  a. 135   **b.** 153   **c.** 315   **d.** 513   **e.** 531

7 **Use Labsheet 3B.** Follow the directions to discover a *Divisibility Test for 3.* See margin.

8 **Discussion** The test for divisibility by 9 is similar to the one for 3. Find a divisibility test for 9. Try your divisibility test on the following numbers to be sure it works.
  a. 18   **b.** 54   **c.** 117   **d.** 243   **e.** 5409

9 ✔ **CHECKPOINT** Test each number for divisibility by 3 and by 9.
  a. 96 3   **b.** 288 3, 9   **c.** 502 neither **d.** 68,913 3, 9

▶ When one whole number divides another whole number evenly, it is a **factor** of the number.

10 **Try This as a Class**
  a. Show that 3 is a factor of 57. Find the sum of the digits: $5 + 7 = 12$. Since 12 is divisible by 3, so is 57. $57 \div 3 = 19$
  b. How can knowing that 3 is a factor of 57 help you find another factor of 57? Divide 57 by 3 to complete the factor pair.

▶ **Finding Factors** To find a complete list of factors, it is helpful to begin with 1 and check in order for pairs of factors.

EXAMPLE

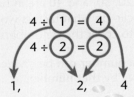

To find the factors of 12:

$12 \div \boxed{1} = \boxed{12}$
$12 \div \boxed{2} = \boxed{6}$
$12 \div \boxed{3} = \boxed{4}$

1, 2,   3,   4, 6, 12
factors of 12

To find the factors of 4:

$4 \div \boxed{1} = \boxed{4}$
$4 \div \boxed{2} = \boxed{2}$

1,   2,   4
factors of 4

Since $4 \div 2 = 2$, the factor 2 pairs with itself.

---

11 How do you know when you have found all the factors? If you begin with 1 and check in order finding pairs of factors, you will know you have found all the factors when a factor pair repeats itself. For example, suppose you just found $10 \cdot 12$ as a factor pair for 120. Try 11; it doesn't work. Try 12; the factor pair is $12 \cdot 10$, which is already listed, so you are finished.

12 ✔ **CHECKPOINT** List all the factors of each number.

    a. 24   **b.** 13 1, 13   **c.** 32   **d.** 18

▶ **Common Factors** Developing a strategy for playing *Paper Clip Products* involves finding factors that numbers have in common.

13 Use your lists of factors from Question 12. Find the common factors of each pair of numbers.

    a. 18 and 32 1, 2   **b.** 18 and 24 1, 2, 3, 6 **c.** 13 and 18 1

14 **Use Labsheet 3A.** Suppose the paper clips are on 2 and 3.

    a. Name two different moves you could use to cover 18.
      Move the clip from 2 to 6 or move the clip from 3 to 9.
    b. Which move from part (a) should you avoid if you do not want your opponent to cover 32 on the next turn?
      Moving 3 to 9, because it leaves 2 as a remaining factor

15 **Discussion** How is each of the following used in *Paper Clip Products*?

    a. finding the factors of a number

    b. finding common factors of two numbers

▶ The **greatest common factor (GCF)** of two or more numbers is the greatest number that is a factor of each number.

EXAMPLE

Find the greatest common factor of 16 and 20.

SAMPLE RESPONSE

List the factors of each number.

      Factors of 16: ①, ②, ④, 8 , 16

      Factors of 20: ①, ②, ④, 5 , 10 , 20

      Common factors: 1, 2, and 4

The GCF of 16 and 20 is 4.

16 ✔ **CHECKPOINT** Use the common factors you listed in Question 13. Find the greatest common factor of each set of numbers.

    a. 18 and 32 2   **b.** 18 and 24 6   **c.** 13 and 18 1

HOMEWORK EXERCISES ▶ See Exs. 1–30 on pp. 159–160.

✔ **QUESTION 12**

… checks that you can find the factors of a number.

12. **a.** 1, 2, 3, 4, 6, 8, 12, 24
   c. 1, 2, 4, 8, 16, 32
   d. 1, 2, 3, 6, 9, 18

15. **a.** Finding the factors of a number can be useful to determine when it is possible to cover a number on the board.
   b. Finding common factors is effective for defensive playing, so that your opponent will not be able to make a desirable move on the next turn.

✔ **QUESTION 16**

… checks that you can find the greatest common factor of a set of numbers.

TEACHING NOTES
Before having students do **Questions 13–16**, have them discuss the meaning of the words *greatest*, *common*, and *factor*. Then ask them to describe and give an example of what they think a *greatest common factor* would be.

The following Classroom Example may be used to provide additional guidance on finding greatest common factors before completing **Checkpoint Question 16**.

CLASSROOM EXAMPLE

Find the greatest common factor of 28 and 42.

Answer:

Factors of 28:

①, ②, 4, ⑦, ⑭, 28

Factors of 42:

①, ②, 3, 6, ⑦, ⑭, 21, 42

Common factors: 1, 2, 7, and 14
The GCF of 28 and 42 is 14.

Exploration 2

TEACHING NOTES

Introduce the game by displaying a visual of **Labsheet 3C** on the overhead projector. Use the visual to explain and demonstrate how the game is played. Allow students time to ask questions, making sure they understand the game rules before beginning play. When demonstrating *Prime Time*, explain that there is no limit to the number of paper clips that may be placed on a factor at any time during the game. Explain also that if a student makes a mistake he or she must redo the problem and not leave an incorrectly placed chip on the board.

Playing *Prime Time* develops students' intuitive notions of prime and composite numbers and prime factorization.

GOAL

LEARN HOW TO...
- recognize prime and composite numbers
- use a factor tree to find prime factors

AS YOU...
- develop a strategy for playing *Prime Time*

KEY TERMS
- prime
- composite
- prime factorization
- factor tree

Exploration 2

Prime Factors

SET UP | *Work with a partner. You will need:* • Labsheet 3C • paper clips • 15 each of two different-colored chips

Prime Time is another strategy game involving factors.

Prime Time

- To begin, the first player places two paper clips on factors below the game board. He or she then covers the product of the factors on the game board with a colored chip.

- Players alternate turns. On a turn, a player has a choice of three ways to cover a new product.

    Move one paper clip to another factor.
  OR Place another paper clip on any factor.
  OR Take a paper clip off any factor.

- A turn ends when a player covers a product. A turn also ends if a product is not on the game board or is already covered.

- A player wins by covering three adjacent numbers horizontally, vertically, or diagonally.

Player 1 began by placing clips on the factors 3 and 5 to cover the product 15.
3 • 5 = 15

17 **Use Labsheet 3C.** With your partner, play three games of *Prime Time*.

Player 2 then placed another clip on 3 to cover 45.
3 • 3 • 5 = 45

Observe students playing Prime Time.

152

▶ All whole numbers greater than 1 are either *prime* or *composite*.
A **prime** number has exactly two factors, 1 and the number itself.
A **composite** number has more than two factors.

18 Explain why 1 is neither prime nor composite.

19 **Use Labsheet 3C.** Tell whether the numbers in each of the following sets are prime or composite. Explain your answers.

    a. the factors below   **b.** the numbers on
       the game board **prime**   the game board **composite**

20 ✔ **CHECKPOINT** Tell whether each number is prime or composite. Explain your reasoning.

    a. 13   **b.** 305   **c.** 71   **d.** 243

21 **a.** **Use Labsheet 3C.** Suppose a player covers 20 on the game board. What factors do the paper clips cover? **2 and 5**

    b. How many paper clips are on each factor in part (a)?
       two on 2, one on 5
    c. Besides the factors covered in part (a), are there any other prime numbers that can be used to get a product of 20? **no**

▶ Every composite number can be written as the product of prime factors. This product is the **prime factorization** of the number. A **factor tree** can be used to find the prime factorization.

EXAMPLE

Use a factor tree to find the prime factorization of 12.

SAMPLE RESPONSE

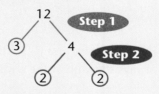

The prime factorization of 12 is 2 · 2 · 3.

---

22 **Try This as a Class** Use the Example above.

    a. What is done in Step 1? Why is the 3 circled but not the 4?

    b. What is done in Step 2? Why does the factor tree end?

    c. What parts of the tree are used to write the prime factorization? **The circled numbers at the end of each branch.**

---

18. 1 has exactly one factor. Primes have exactly two factors. Composites have more than two factors.

✔ **QUESTION 20**

… checks that you can determine whether a number is prime or composite.

20. a. prime; It has exactly two factors, 1 and 13.
   b. composite; It has a factor of 5.
   c. prime; It has exactly two factors, 1 and 71.
   d. composite; It has a factor of 3.

22. a. 12 is rewritten as the product of two factors, 3 and 4. Three is prime, 4 is not prime.
   b. 4 is rewritten as the product of two factors, 2 and 2. The factor tree ends because 2 is a prime factor.

Exploration 2 continued

TEACHING NOTES

Question 27 To illustrate that a number can be factored into primes using various factor trees, have several students with different factor trees put their work on the board. Then show that they all have the same final prime factorization. If students are having difficulty, encourage them to start the prime factorization process by systematically dividing by the least prime number and proceeding through greater and greater primes.

24. a.

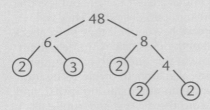

23. a.

b. The prime factorization of a number is unique. It does not matter which factors you begin with, because the result will always be the same prime factors.

c. Neither 1 nor 12 is prime and 1 can't be factored, so to find the prime factorization, you still must rewrite 12 as a product of two factors.

27. b. Yes, the same prime factors appeared, but their order may have been different.; The prime factorization of a number is unique.

---

23 **a.** Sketch a factor tree for 12 using 2 and 6 for factors in the first step.

  b. Why do you think your tree ends with the same circled numbers as the tree in the Example?

  c. Why do you not want to use the factors 1 and 12 for factors in the first step of the tree?

24 **a.** Copy and complete the factor tree for 48 shown below. See margin.

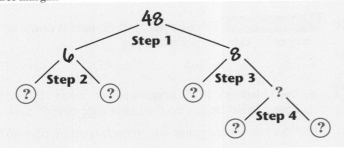

  b. Why are more branches necessary to make this tree than to make the factor tree for 12? 48 has more prime factors than 12.

  c. What is the prime factorization of 48? $2 \cdot 2 \cdot 2 \cdot 2 \cdot 3$

25 **Discussion**

  a. What happens when you try to make a factor tree for 47? It is not possible since 47 is prime and the only two factors are 1 and 47.

  b. Does 47 have a prime factorization? Explain. Yes; The prime factorization of 47 is 47 because it is a prime number.

26 Use a factor tree to find the prime factorization of 36. $2 \cdot 2 \cdot 3 \cdot 3$

27 **Try This as a Class** Compare your factor tree for 36 with those of your classmates.

  a. Did everyone use the same pair of factors in the first branch? Probably not.

  b. Did the same prime factors always show up at the ends of the branches? Why?

28 **Discussion** Explain how prime factorization is used in the game *Prime Time*. The paper clips tell the prime factorization of the number just covered.

29 Think about making another *Prime Time* game board using the factors 2, 3, 5, and 7. What are two composite numbers you can put on your game board that cannot be covered? Sample: 22 and 26

HOMEWORK EXERCISES ▶ See Exs. 31–44 on pp. 160–161.

Exploration 3

Power^s of Numbers

SET UP *You will need: • paper for folding • a calculator*

GOAL

LEARN HOW TO...
- identify powers
- write numbers using exponents

AS YOU...
- investigate a paper folding puzzle

KEY TERMS
- exponent
- base
- power
- standard form

▶ **A paper-folding puzzle can help you learn a special notation for writing numbers with repeated factors.**

30 Fold a piece of paper in half and then unfold it. The fold divides the paper into two sections. Predict how many sections the paper would be divided into if you could fold the paper in half 8 times. Explain your reasoning. **Predictions will vary.**

▶ **One strategy for solving Question 30 is to look for a pattern.**
a–b. See the first two columns in the table in Exercise 34(a).

31 **a.** Make a table like the one below. Record the number of sections formed by one fold.

Number of folds	Number of sections		
1	2		
2	?		
3	?		

b. Continue folding the paper in half as many times as possible. After each fold, record the number of sections.

c. Look at your table. Each time you make a new fold, how does the number of sections change? **It doubles.**

d. Use the pattern to extend the table to 8 folds. **See the first two columns in the table in Exercise 34(a).**

32 How does your prediction in Question 30 compare with the result for 8 folds in Question 31(d)? **Answers will vary.**

Exploration 3

TEACHING NOTES
Make sure students make a prediction in **Question 30** before beginning **Question 31**. List the students' predictions on the board. Students may be surprised to find that when they try to fold the paper in half eight times, they can't do it. Have them fold the paper in half as many times as they can and then use the pattern they observe to complete the table in **Question 31**.

33. See the third column in the table in Exercise 34(a).

33 You can use the pattern you discovered in Question 31(c) to rewrite the number of sections. Label and fill in the third column of your table as shown.

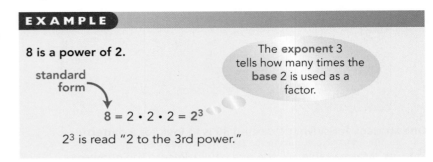

Number of folds	Number of sections	Rewritten form	
1	2	2	
2	4	2 · 2	
3	8	2 · 2 · 2	

▶ **Using Exponents** A short way to write a product like $2 \cdot 2 \cdot 2$ is to use an **exponent** to tell how many times the **base** 2 is used as a factor. A number that can be written using an exponent and a base is a **power** of the base.

EXAMPLE

8 is a power of 2.

standard form

The **exponent** 3 tells how many times the **base** 2 is used as a factor.

$$8 = 2 \cdot 2 \cdot 2 = 2^3$$

2^3 is read "2 to the 3rd power."

---

34 **a.** In your table, label the fourth column *Power of 2*. Fill it in by rewriting each number of sections using an exponent.
See margin.

b. **Discussion** How did you write 2 using exponents? Why?
2^1; There is only one factor of 2.

35 How do you read 3^4? What is its value? three to the fourth power; 81

36 ✔ **CHECKPOINT** Find the value of each expression.

a. 3^5 243   **b.** 5^3 125   **c.** 10^2 100   **d.** 7^1 7

37 Calculator Scientific calculators have a power key .
Follow the steps below to find the value of 2^8. $2^8 = 256$

First	Next	Then
Enter the base.	Press the power key.	Enter the exponent and press the equals key.
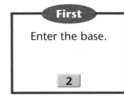	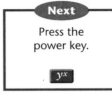	

38 a. How many sections would be formed if you could fold a piece of paper in half 12 times? Use exponents to write your answer. 2^{12}

b. Use a calculator to find the standard form of your answer in part (a). $2^{12} = 4096$

▶ **You can use exponents to write prime factorizations. For example, the prime factorization of 75 is 3 • 5 • 5 = 3 • 5^2 or 3 • 5^2.**

39 Write the prime factorization of each number, using exponents for repeated factors.

a. 40 $2^3 \cdot 5$ **b.** 81 3^4 **c.** 23 23

HOMEWORK EXERCISES ▶ See Exs. 45–61 on pp. 161–162.

Section ③
Key Concepts

Divisibility Rules (pp. 149–150)
When a number can be divided evenly by another number, it is divisible by that number.

You can tell whether a number is divisible by 2, 5, or 10 by looking at the ones digit.

Divisible by	Ones digit
2	0, 2, 4, 6, or 8
5	0 or 5
10	0

A number is divisible by 3 if the sum of its digits is divisible by 3.

A number is divisible by 9 if the sum of its digits is divisible by 9.

Factors and Common Factors (pp. 150–151)
When one whole number divides another whole number evenly, it is a factor of the number.

To find the greatest common factor of a set of numbers, find all the factors the numbers have in common. Then, pick the greatest of these common factors.

Example The common factors of 30 and 45 are 1, 3, 5, and 15. The greatest common factor of 30 and 45 is 15.

Key Terms

divisible

factor

greatest common factor (GCF)

Section 3 Factors and Divisibility 157

ABSENT STUDENTS
For students who were absent for all or part of this section, the blackline Study Guide for Section 3 may be used to present the ideas, concepts, and skills of Section 3.

CLOSURE QUESTION

Explain how you can use divisibility rules, a factor tree, and powers to factor a number and write its prime factorization.

Sample Response: Use divisibility rules to see if the number is divisible by 2, 3, 5, 9, or 10. If it is divisible by one or more of these numbers, begin a factor tree using a possible combination of two factors. If not, check to see if there are any other possible factors of the number or if it is prime. Continue this process for the factors written on the factor tree until all the factors written at the ends of the tree are prime numbers. Write a multiplication expression using all the "prime ends" to write the number in factored form. Then if any of the numbers in the factored form are the same, write them using exponents.

Section 3
Key Concepts

Key Terms

prime

composite

prime factorization

factor tree

exponent

base

power

standard form

Prime and Composite Numbers (pp. 152–154)

All whole numbers greater than 1 are either prime or composite. A prime number has exactly two factors, 1 and the number itself. A composite number has more than two factors.

Every composite number can be written as the product of prime factors. Factor trees can be used to find prime factorizations.

Example Find the prime factorization of 24.

The prime factorization of 24 is $2 \cdot 2 \cdot 2 \cdot 3$.

Powers (pp. 155–157)

When a number can be written using an exponent and a base, the number is a power of the base. The example below shows that 64 is the 3rd power of 4.

Example $64 = 4 \cdot 4 \cdot 4 = 4^3$

standard form

The exponent 3 tells how many times the base 4 is used as a factor.

You can use exponents to write prime factorizations.

Example The prime factorization of 24, shown above, can be written as $2^3 \cdot 3^1$, or $2^3 \cdot 3$.

40. You can use divisibility rules to find one factor of 261 to start a factor tree. In this case, since the sum of the digits is 9, 261 is divisible by 3 and 9. You can begin by dividing by 9.

Key Concepts Questions

40 How can divisibility rules help you find the prime factorization of 261?

41 Write the prime factorization of 261 using exponents. $3^2 \cdot 29$

Section 3

Practice & Application Exercises

YOU WILL NEED

For Ex. 28:
◆ Labsheet 3A

Test each number for divisibility by 2, 3, 5, 9, and 10.

1. 168 2, 3
2. 53 none
3. 499 none
4. 66,780 2, 3, 5, 9, 10
5. 4326 2, 3
6. 75 3, 5
7. 1011 3
8. 50,436 2, 3, 9

9. a. If a number is divisible by 9, is it divisible by 3? Explain.
      Yes, 9 is a multiple of 3.
   b. If a number is divisible by 3, is it divisible by 9? Explain.
      Sometimes, but not all multiples of 3 are a multiple of 9.

List all the factors of each number.

10. 28
11. 51
12. 64
13. 72
14. 80

10. 1, 2, 4, 7, 14, 28
11. 1, 3, 17, 51
12. 1, 2, 4, 8, 16, 32, 64
13. 1, 2, 3, 4, 6, 8, 9, 12, 18, 24, 36, 72
14. 1, 2, 4, 5, 8, 10, 16, 20, 40, 80

Find the greatest common factor of each set of numbers.

15. 14 and 28 14
16. 12 and 17 1
17. 21 and 51 3
18. 43 and 69 1
19. 54, 36, and 72 18
20. 22, 64, and 80 2

Greatest Common Factors can be used to write fractions in lowest terms.

Example: Write $\dfrac{12}{30}$ in lowest terms.

$$\dfrac{12}{30} = \dfrac{2 \cdot 6}{5 \cdot 6}$$ Use the GCF to write the numerator and denominator as products.

$$= \dfrac{2 \cdot \overset{1}{\cancel{6}}}{5 \cdot \cancel{6}}$$ Divide the numerator and denominator by the GCF.

$$= \dfrac{2}{5}$$ lowest terms

FOR ◀ HELP

with *writing fractions in lowest terms,* see
MODULE 1, p. 61

Use the greatest common factor of the numerator and denominator to write each fraction in lowest terms.

21. $\dfrac{12}{32}$ $\dfrac{3}{8}$
22. $\dfrac{25}{35}$ $\dfrac{5}{7}$
23. $\dfrac{36}{54}$ $\dfrac{2}{3}$
24. $\dfrac{27}{63}$ $\dfrac{3}{7}$

Mental Math Show how to find each product using mental math. Use what you know about factors and compatible numbers.

Example: $36 \cdot 25 = 9 \cdot 4 \cdot 25 = 9 \cdot 100 = 900$

25. $25 \cdot 48$
26. $12 \cdot 75$
27. $16 \cdot 125$

25. $25 \cdot 48 = 25 \cdot 4 \cdot 12 = 100 \cdot 12 = 1200$

26. $12 \cdot 75 = 4 \cdot 3 \cdot 25 \cdot 3 = 4 \cdot 25 \cdot 3 \cdot 3 = 100 \cdot 9 = 900$

27. $16 \cdot 125 = 4 \cdot 4 \cdot 5 \cdot 25 = 4 \cdot 5 \cdot 4 \cdot 25 = 20 \cdot 100 = 2000$

28. **Use Labsheet 3A.**

   a. What numbers on the game board cannot be covered?
      7, 11, 17, 19
   b. Find the factors of each number from part (a).
      $1 \cdot 7, 1 \cdot 11, 1 \cdot 17, 1 \cdot 19$
   c. What do you notice about the factors of the numbers that cannot be covered? They all have exactly 2 factors, so they are all prime.

Practice & Applications

SUGGESTED ASSIGNMENTS

Core Course
Day 1: Exs. 62–70
Day 2: Exs. 1–14, 16–28 even
Day 3: Exs. 31–36
Day 4: Exs. 37–43
Day 5: 45–61

Extended Course
Day 1: Exs. 62–70
Day 2: Exs. 2–28 even, 29–30
Day 3: Exs. 31–36
Day 4: Exs. 37–44
Day 5: 45–61

Note: Extended Course assignments can be used to differentiate within the regular classroom. In classrooms where students are grouped homogeneously, the material might be covered in fewer days. In this case assignments may be combined.

EMBEDDED ASSESSMENT

- Use divisibility tests
  Exercises 2, 4, 6
- Find all the factors of a number
  Exercises 10, 12
- Find the greatest common factor (GCF) of two or more numbers
  Exercises 16, 20
- Identify prime and composite numbers
  Exercises 32, 33, 34
- Find the prime factorization of a number
  Exercises 37, 40
- Identify powers
  Exercises 45, 46
- Convert between standard and exponential form
  Exercises 51, 52
- Write prime factorizations using exponents
  Exercise 49

Practice & Applications

PERFORMANCE TASK/ PORTFOLIO

- Exercise 58 on *p. 161 (writing)*
- Exercise 61 on *p. 162 (oral report)*
- Standardized Testing on *p. 163 (performance task)*
- Extended Exploration on *p. 164**

* indicates a problem solving task that can be assessed using the Assessment Scales

ADDITIONAL PRACTICE

See the *Teacher's Resource Book* for additional practice and application exercises for this section.

BACKGROUND INFORMATION

Challenge Exercise 30 Perfect numbers can be traced back over 2,500 years to the Pythagoreans, a Greek society of mathematicians. The Pythagoreans studied not only perfect numbers but also *deficient numbers* and *abundant numbers*, numbers that are, respectively, less than and greater than the sum of all their factors (except the number itself). 25 is a deficient number $(1 + 5 < 25)$, and 12 is an abundant number $(1 + 2 + 3 + 4 + 6 > 12)$. A later development in Pythagorean thought was the concept of *amicable numbers*. Two numbers are *amicable* if the sum of the factors of each number (except the number itself) is equal to the other number. The first such pair of numbers is 220 and 284 since $1 + 2 + 4 + 5 + 10 + 11 + 20 + 22 + 44 + 55 + 110 = 284$ and $1 + 2 + 4 + 71 + 142 = 220$. Students completing the extended assignment might want to explore these types of numbers further after answering **Exercise 30**.

29. b. See Additional Answers beginning on page A1.

Approximately ▶ 60,000 of the world's 90,000 known plant species are endangered. The photo shows a tumboa plant lying on a desert in Namibia, a country of southwest Africa.

FOR ▶ HELP

with *making a pictograph,* see **TOOLBOX, p. 579**

43. a. Prime factorization of each number is in a box with the common factors in the overlapping region.
    b. The GCF is the product of the numbers in the overlapping region. GCF = $2 \cdot 2 = 4$.

c.

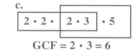

```
2 · 2 ·  2 · 3  · 5
```

GCF = $2 \cdot 3 = 6$

Module 3 Mind Games

---

29. **Displaying Data** You are going to make a pictograph of the data below using the symbol ✿ to represent a number of plant species. You must decide how many plant species each ✿ will represent.

Endangered Plant Species	
Place	Number of plant species
Namibia	18
Portugal	90
Sicily	48

   a. What numbers of plant species can each ✿ stand for so you can make a pictograph using only whole symbols? common factors of 18, 90, and 48 or 1, 2, 3, and 6.
   b. Use your answer from part (a) to make a pictograph that contains as few symbols as possible. Be sure to tell how many species each ✿ represents. See margin.

30. **Challenge** A perfect number equals the sum of all its factors, not including the number itself. The first perfect number is 6 because $6 = 1 + 2 + 3$. Find the next perfect number. 28

Tell whether each number is prime or composite.

31. 25 composite 　　32. 37 prime 　　33. 135 composite

34. 51 composite 　　35. 306 composite 　　36. 91 composite

Write the prime factorization of each number, using exponents for repeated factors.

37. 42 $2 \cdot 3 \cdot 7$ 　　38. 144 $2^4 \cdot 3^2$ 　　39. 53 53

40. 280 $2^3 \cdot 5 \cdot 7$ 　　41. 484 $2^2 \cdot 11^2$ 　　42. 840 $2^3 \cdot 3 \cdot 5 \cdot 7$

43. This diagram organized the prime factors of 20 and 36.

    20　　36

    5 · 2 · 2 · 3 · 3

   a. Describe how the prime factorizations of 20 and 36 were used to make the diagram above.

   b. How are the numbers in the overlapping region in the diagram above related to the GCF of 20 and 36?

   c. Create a similar diagram for the prime factors of 24 and 30 and use it to find the GCF of 24 and 30.

44. **Challenge** The prime factorization of 60 has four prime factors since $60 = 2 \cdot 2 \cdot 3 \cdot 5$. Which two-digit numbers have the most factors in their prime factorizations? **64 and 96 each have six factors in their prime factorizations.**

Find the value of each expression.

45. 7^4 **2401**　　46. 5^2 **25**　　47. 6^3 **216**　　48. 3^5 **243**

49. Write the prime factorization of 1800 using exponents. **$2^3 \cdot 3^2 \cdot 5^2$**

Write each of the following as a single number raised to either the 2nd or 3rd power.

50. 36 **6^2**　　51. 8 **2^3**　　52. 100 **10^2**　　53. 125 **5^3**

54. **Computers** The smallest pieces of information stored in computer memory are called bits. One byte of memory is made up of 2^3 bits. One kilobyte of memory is 2^{10} bytes.

　　a. In standard form, how many bits are in a byte? How many bytes are in a kilobyte? **8 bits; 1024 bytes**

　　b. A computer with 512 kilobytes can store how many bytes of information? How many bits of information? **524,288 bytes; 4,194,304 bits**

 Calculator In Exercises 55–57, predict which number will be greater or if the two numbers are equal. Then check your prediction with a calculator. **Predictions may vary.**

55. 2^{15} or 3^{15} **3^{15}**　　56. 10^3 or 3^{10} **3^{10}**　　57. 4^4 or 16^2 **equal**

58. a. **Writing** Write each power of ten from 10^1 to 10^9 in exponential and standard form. How does the exponent of each power relate to the number of zeros in the standard form?

　　b. A *googol* is 10^{100}. Written in standard form, a *googol* is 1 followed by how many zeros? **100 zeros.**

59. **Visual Thinking** The number 9 is a square number because you can make a square from 9 square tiles.
　　a–b. See margin.
　　a. Use drawings to find three other square numbers.

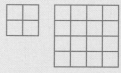

　　b. Rewrite 9 and each square number from part (a) as a number raised to the 2nd power. Can every square number be written this way? Explain.

58. a. $10^1 = 10$,
　　$10^2 = 100$,
　　$10^3 = 1000$,
　　$10^4 = 10000$,
　　$\ldots 10^9 = 1{,}000{,}000{,}000$;
　　The exponent is the same as the number of zeros in the standard form.

The term *googol* was invented by Milton Sirotta, the 9-year old nephew of mathematician Edward Kasner. Kasner asked Milton what he thought such a large number should be called. After thinking briefly, Milton answered that the number could only be called something as silly as… a *googol*!

Practice & Applications

EXERCISE NOTES

Reflecting on the Section
Exercise 61 As a class, discuss the divisibility tests for 6 that students discovered. Let students share their tests and explain why they always work.

$2^5 = 32$

$2^4 = 16$

$2^3 = 8$

$2^2 = 4$

$2^1 = 2$

Oral Report

Exercise 61 checks that you can apply your understanding of divisibility and prime factorization.

61. a. $72 = 2^3 \cdot 3^2$;
$30 = 2 \cdot 3 \cdot 5$;
$114 = 2 \cdot 3 \cdot 19$;
$24 = 2^3 \cdot 3$;

$138 = 2 \cdot 3 \cdot 23$;
$44 = 2^2 \cdot 11$;
$39 = 3 \cdot 13$;
$175 = 5^2 \cdot 7$;

$63 = 3^2 \cdot 7$;
$70 = 2 \cdot 5 \cdot 7$

60. a. What mathematical operation is used to go from 32 to 16? from 16 to 8? Does this pattern continue throughout the sequence 32, 16, 8, 4, 2? **division by 2; division by 2; yes.**

b. Based on the pattern, what is the value of 2^0? $2 \div 2 = 1$

c. How does this compare with the number of sections after 0 folds in the paper-folding pattern in Exploration 3 on page 155? Explain. **It is the same. Before it was folded, the paper had 1 section.**

Reflecting ◀▶ on the Section

Be prepared to discuss your answer to Exercise 61 in class.

61. a. Write the prime factorization of each number in the table.

b. What do you notice about the prime factors of the numbers that are divisible by 6? **They contain both 3 and 2 as factors.**

c. Use your results from part (b) and the divisibility tests you know. Write a divisibility test for 6. **If a number is divisible by both 3 and 2, then it is divisible by 6.**

Divisible by 6	Not Divisible by 6
72	44
30	39
114	175
24	63
138	70

Spiral ◀▶ Review

62. A bag contains 1 red marble, 2 yellow marbles, and 7 blue marbles. What is the theoretical probability of drawing a red marble from the bag? a green marble? (Module 2, p. 80) $\frac{1}{10}$; 0

63. If possible, sketch a triangle that is both obtuse and scalene. (Module 2, pp. 106–107) **Possible. Check students' sketches.**

Decide if the given lengths will form a triangle. (Module 2, p. 106)

64. 3 in., 2 in., 6 in.
No; $3 + 2 = 5 < 6$

65. 4 ft, 22 ft, 25 ft
Yes; $4 + 22 = 26 > 25$

Write an equation for each word sentence in Exercises 66–69. Use t for the term and n for the term number. (Module 1, p. 21)

66. The term is three more than the term number. $t = 3 + n$

67. The term is four times the term number. $t = 4 \cdot n$

68. The term is two more than three times the term number. $t = 3 \cdot n + 2$

69. The term is the term number to the third power. $t = n^3$

70. Use your equations from Exercises 66–69 to find the first 4 terms of each sequence. (66) 4, 5, 6, 7; (67) 4, 8, 12, 16; (68) 5, 8, 11, 14; (69) 1, 8, 27, 64

Section 3

Extra Skill Practice

Test each number for divisibility by 2, 3, 5, 9, and 10.

1. 16 _2_   2. 19 _none_   3. 42 _2, 3_   4. 135 _3, 5, 9_   5. 141 _3_

Find the GCF of each set of numbers.

6. 12 and 24 _12_   7. 8 and 15 _1_   8. 30 and 100 _10_

9. 45 and 63 _9_   10. 14, 49, and 98 _7_   11. 24, 40, and 88 _8_

Use the greatest common factors from Exercises 6–9 to write each fraction in lowest terms.

12. $\frac{12}{24}$ $\frac{1}{2}$ 13. $\frac{8}{15}$ $\frac{8}{15}$ 14. $\frac{30}{100}$ $\frac{3}{10}$ 15. $\frac{45}{63}$ $\frac{5}{7}$

Tell whether each number is prime or composite.

16. 49   17. 57   18. 11   19. 132   20. 79
composite   _composite_   _prime_   _composite_   _prime_

Write the prime factorization of each number, using exponents for repeated factors.

21. 18 $3^2 \cdot 2$ 22. 32 2^5 23. 27 3^3 24. 49 7^2 25. 100 $2^2 \cdot 5^2$

Find the value of each expression.

26. 8^2 _64_   27. 7^3 _343_   28. 2^5 _32_   29. 4^4 _256_   30. 12^2 _144_

Replace each ? with >, <, or =. Explain your choice.

31. 2^3 ? 3^2 32. 2^4 ? $2 \cdot 2 \cdot 2 \cdot 2$ 33. 3^4 ? $4 \cdot 4 \cdot 4$
_<; 8 < 9_   _=; both equal 16_   _>; 81 > 64_

Write the prime factorization of each number, using exponents for repeated factors.

34. 126   35. 300   36. 54   37. 256   38. 98
$2 \cdot 3^2 \cdot 7$ $2^2 \cdot 3 \cdot 5^2$ $2 \cdot 3^3$ 2^8 $2 \cdot 7^2$

Write each of the following as a single number raised to a power of either 2 or 3.

39. 25 5^2 40. 49 7^2 41. 1000 10^3 42. 64 8^2 or 4^3 43. 121 11^2

Standardized Testing ◀▶ Performance Task

1. a. List ten numbers that have 20 as a factor.
   Sample: 20, 40, 60, 80, 100, 120, 140, 160, 180, 200
   b. Look for patterns in your list from part (a). Then write a divisibility test for 20. _Sample: The last digit must be zero, the other digits must represent an even number._

2. a. Use a factor tree to find the prime factorization of each of these powers of ten: 10^1, 10^2, and 10^3. _$2 \cdot 5$; $2^2 \cdot 5^2$; $2^3 \cdot 5^3$_

   b. Use your results from part (a) to find the prime factorization of 10^8 without sketching a factor tree. _$2^8 \cdot 5^8$_

Extended Exploration

E² NOTES

Using an E²: Hints for managing and evaluating an Extended Exploration are available in the *Teacher's Resource Book* for Modules 1 and 2. See also pages T44–T45 in the *Teacher's Edition*.

FOR ASSESSMENT AND PORTFOLIOS

THE CLEANING CREW

The Situation See the *Teacher's Resource Book* for a sample solution for this Extended Exploration.

A group of middle school students decided to spend the summer cleaning parks. In their area, there are 25 city and county parks they can clean. The students were given a choice of payment methods.

payment method A

$100 per park

payment method B

One cent for the first park, two cents for the second park, four cents for the third park, eight cents for the fourth park, and so on.

The Problem

Decide which payment method you would advise the students to choose.

Something to Think About

- Which problem-solving strategies seem helpful for this problem?

- Do you see any connections to other problems you have solved?

Present Your Results

Write a summary that clearly explains why you chose the method of payment you did. Include any drawings, diagrams, charts, or tables you used to solve the problem.

Section 4 Multiples

IN THIS SECTION

EXPLORATION 1
◆ Multiples and Common Multiples

Pattern Play

Setting the Stage

GETTING STARTED
Module 3 Section 4 *Warm-Up* assesses students' ability to complete missing terms in a sequence. In this section, number sequences will be used to express multiples.

CLASSROOM MANAGEMENT
First play the *Pattern Tick-Tock* game as a class. Sit in a circle. When counting starts over, begin with the last student that counted out loud. This will give more students an opportunity to participate. Then play the game in groups with more than six students. For a challenge, pick up the tempo or start with 100 and count to 150. **Questions 1 and 2** can be answered as a class.

Setting the Stage ▸▸▸▸▸▸▸▸▸▸▸▸▸▸▸▸▸▸▸▸▸▸▸▸▸▸▸

SET UP *Work in a group.*

▶ *Pattern Tick-Tock* is a game that tests your ability to see number patterns.

Pattern Tick-Tock

- Sit in a circle. The first person begins the counting with "one." Then the next person says "two," and so on **except** when a number is divisible by:

    4–the person say **tick** instead of the number

    6–the person says **tock** instead of the number

    4 and **6**–the person says **tick-tock** instead of the number

- If a mistake is made, the counting starts over with the next student.

- Continue counting until you reach 50.

Think About It

1 List all the numbers that each word replaced.

  a. tick
  4, 8, 16, 20, 28, 32, 40, 44

  b. tock
  6, 18, 30, 42

  c. tick-tock
  12, 24, 36, 48

2 **a.** Which word was said most often: *tick, tock,* or *tick-tock*? tick

  b. Why was it said most often?

2. b. There are more numbers between 0 and 50 that are divisible by 4 than there are numbers divisible by 6 or by both 4 and 6.

Three   Tick   Five   Tock

Exploration 1

DEVELOPING MATH CONCEPTS

The number of *multiples* of a number is infinite. Also, any pair of numbers has an infinite number of *common multiples*. However, any such pair has only one *least* common multiple. To help those students who confuse *least* and *greatest* with the *common factors* and *multiples,* explain there is no *greatest common multiple* because there are an infinite number of multiples. On the other hand, the *least common factor* is always 1.

7. a–d. See Additional Answers beginning on page A1.

166

GOAL

LEARN HOW TO...
◆ find multiples and least common multiples

AS YOU...
◆ analyze the game *Pattern Tick-Tock*

KEY TERMS
◆ multiple
◆ least common multiple (LCM)

3. a. No; no whole number *n* exists such that
  $n \cdot 6 = 15$
 c. No; no positive whole number *n* exists such that
  $n \cdot 6 = 0$.

 QUESTION 7

...checks that you can write and extend lists of multiples.

Exploration 1

Multiples and Common Multiples

SET UP You will need Labsheet 4A.

▶ In *Pattern Tick-Tock*, it is important to be able to recognize *multiples*. A **multiple** of a whole number is the product of that number and any nonzero whole number.

For example, 12 is a multiple of 6 since $6 \cdot 2 = 12$.

3 Explain whether each of the following numbers is or is not a multiple of 6.

  a. 15   **b.** 42 Yes; $7 \cdot 6 = 42$ **c.** 0

4 When you played *Pattern Tick-Tock*, "tick" replaced the multiples of what number? 4

▶ The multiples of a number form a sequence. Study the sequence for the multiples of 4 shown below.

Term number	1	2	3	4	5	6	...
Term	4	8	12	16	20	24	...

5 **a.** How is each term in the sequence above related to its term number? The term is four times the term number.

  b. Write an expression for the general term of the sequence. Use the variable *n* for the term number. term = $4 \cdot n$

  c. What is the 100th term in the sequence? 400

6 When you played *Pattern Tick-Tock,* what sequence of multiples did "tick-tock" replace? multiples of 12

7 ✔ **CHECKPOINT** Use Labsheet 4A. Follow the directions on the labsheet to complete the *Sequence Tables for Multiples*. For each sequence, you will also write an expression for the general term and use it to extend the sequence. See margin.

▶ You will use what you know about multiples to answer Question 8.

8 Maya met Jim at the mall. They really liked each other but were too shy to say how they felt. Hoping to see Maya, Jim returns to the mall every 5 days. Hoping to see Jim, Maya returns to the mall every 6 days.

   a. List the first seven multiples of 5. What do these multiples represent? 5, 10, 15, 20, 25, 30, 35; days Jim was at the mall

   b. List the first seven multiples of 6. What do these multiples represent? 6, 12, 18, 24, 30, 36, 42; days Maya was at the mall

   c. Look at the two lists of multiples. In how many days will Maya and Jim be at the mall on the same day? 30 days

▶ The answer to Question 8(c) is the least common multiple of 5 and 6. The **least common multiple (LCM)** of two or more whole numbers is the least number that is a multiple of all the numbers.

EXAMPLE

Find the least common multiple of 8 and 6.

SAMPLE RESPONSE

List the multiples of each number.
Then circle the common multiples.

Multiples of 8: 8, 16, (24) 32, 40, (48) ...

Multiples of 6: 6, 12, 18, (24) 30, 36, 42, (48) ...

Common multiples: 24, 48, ...

The LCM of 8 and 6 is 24.

9 ✔ **CHECKPOINT** Find the least common multiple of each pair of numbers.

   a. 3 and 9 9   **b.** 12 and 9 36   **c.** 25 and 15 75

10 Use lists of multiples to find all the numbers that "tick-tock" will replace in a game of *Pattern Tick-Tock* if you count to 100. Use *tick* for 8 and *tock* for 12. 24, 48, 72, 96

HOMEWORK EXERCISES ▶ See Exs. 1–20 on p. 169.

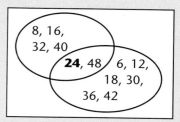

Key Concepts

CLOSURE QUESTION

The LCM of two numbers is 48. When a third number is included, the LCM of all three numbers is still 48. Explain how this can be true. Then give an example of numbers of which this is true.

Sample Response:
One of the original numbers must be a multiple of the third number or vice-versa. Examples include 6, 8, 3, or 6, 8, 12.

Section 4

Key Concepts

Key Terms

multiples

Multiples (p. 166)

A multiple of a whole number is the product of that number and any nonzero whole number.

Example

18 is a multiple of 6 since 6 • 3 = 18.

least common multiple

Least Common Multiple (LCM) (p. 167)

You can find the least common multiple (LCM) of two or more whole numbers by listing the multiples of each number in order. You can stop when you find a multiple that is common to all the numbers.

Example

multiples of 4: 4, 8, 12, 16, 20, 24 ...

multiples of 6: 6, 12, 18, 24 ...

multiples of 8: 8, 16, 24 ...

The least common multiple of 4, 6, and 8 is 24.

Key Concepts Question

11 Corey painted a row of circles numbered 1 through 100. Every ninth circle was painted yellow and every fifteenth circle was painted with red stripes.

   a. Which circles were painted yellow? What do the circles painted yellow represent? 9, 18, 27, 36, 45, 54, 63, 72, 81, 90, 99; multiples of 9 less than 100

   b. Which circles were painted with red stripes? What do these striped circles represent? 15, 30, 45, 60, 75, 90; multiples of 15 less than 100.

   c. Which circles were painted yellow with red stripes? What do these circles represent? 45, 90; multiples of 45 less than 100

Section 4

Practice & Application Exercises

List the first seven multiples of each number.

1. 7
2. 25
3. 99
4. 106
5. 8
6. 32

7. Suppose you can withdraw only multiples of $20 from a bank teller machine. Which amounts can you withdraw? **a, c, d**

   a. $40
   b. $250
   c. $160
   d. $220

Find the least common multiple of each set of numbers.

8. 3 and 7 **21**
9. 14 and 10 **70**
10. 6 and 12 **12**
11. 16 and 20 **80**
12. 6, 9, and 12 **36**
13. 48 and 12 **48**
14. 4 and 8 **8**
15. 15 and 35 **105**
16. 2, 5, and 8 **40**

17. The International Fountain in Seattle, Washington, contains special-effect devices called *shooters*. They shoot arcs of water at different time intervals.

    a. Suppose a fountain has one shooter that shoots water every 8 sec and another that goes off every 12 sec. How long after the fountain is turned on will both shooters go off at the same time? **24 seconds**

    b. A third shooter shoots water every 6 sec. Suppose all three shooters just went off together. How many seconds will pass before all three go off again at the same time?
    24 seconds

Reflecting on the Section

Be prepared to discuss your responses to Exercises 18–20 in class.

18. What is the first multiple of any whole number? **the number itself**

19. The greatest common factor of each of the following pairs of numbers is 1. What is the least common multiple of each pair?

    a. 2 and 3 **6**
    b. 5 and 8 **40**
    c. 4 and 9 **36**

20. If the greatest common factor of two whole numbers is 1, what do you think the least common multiple of the numbers will be?
    the product of the two numbers

Discussion

Exercises 18–20 check your understanding of multiples and common multiples.

---

1. 7, 14, 21, 28, 35, 42, 49

2. 25, 50, 75, 100, 125, 150, 175

3. 99, 198, 297, 396, 495, 594, 693

4. 106, 212, 318, 424, 530, 636, 742

5. 8, 16, 24, 32, 40, 48, 56

6. 32, 64, 96, 128, 160, 192, 224

Practice & Applications

SUGGESTED ASSIGNMENTS

Core Course
Day 1: Exs. 1–7, 21–27
Day 2: Exs. 8–20

Extended Course
Day 1: Exs. 1–7, 21–27
Day 2: Exs. 11–20, 28

Note: Extended Course assignments can be used to differentiate within the regular classroom. In classrooms where students are grouped homogeneously, the material might be covered in fewer days. In this case assignments may be combined.

ADDITIONAL PRACTICE

See the *Teacher's Resource Book* for additional practice and application exercises for this section.

EXERCISE NOTES

Questions 19 and 20 connect the ideas of GCF and LCM. If the GCF of two numbers is 1, then their LCM is the product of the numbers. For example, the GCF of 5 and 6 is 1, so their LCM is 5 · 6, or 30.

Practice & Applications

EXERCISE NOTES
Career Connection Exercise 28 allows students to see how common multiples are applied in real life. You might ask students to bring in other examples of how multiples are used in daily life. Make a display of the different examples students bring in.

27. b. triangle, quadrilateral, trapezoid, rhombus, pentagon, hexagon, heptagon, octagon

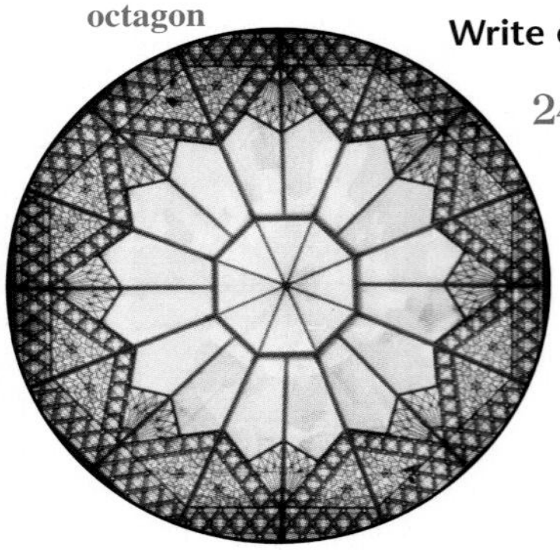

Find the missing numerator or denominator in each pair of equivalent fractions. (Module 1, p. 61)

21. $\frac{25}{100} = \frac{?}{4}$ 1

22. $\frac{3}{8} = \frac{15}{?}$ 40

23. $\frac{?}{3} = \frac{24}{36}$ 2

Write each fraction as a mixed number. (Module 1, p. 46)

24. $\frac{13}{4}$ $3\frac{1}{4}$

25. $\frac{28}{5}$ $5\frac{3}{5}$

26. $\frac{29}{8}$ $3\frac{5}{8}$

27. The picture at the left shows the stained glass dome of the Great Hall on the third floor of the National Portrait Gallery in Washington D.C.

   a. What fractions do you see in the figure? $\frac{1}{2}, \frac{1}{4}, \frac{1}{8}, \frac{1}{16}$
   (Module 1, p. 46)

   b. What polygons do you see in the figure?
   (Module 2, p. 119)

Career ▪ Connection

Choreographer and Dancer: Emiko Tokunaga

Choreographers like Emiko Tokunaga create the steps dancers perform. Emiko designs combinations of dance steps to fit a piece of music. A piece of music can be broken into *measures*, which are groups of beats.

28. Emiko would like two dancers to each perform a different combination of steps, repeating the combination as needed so each reaches the final pose at the end of a piece of music.

   a. One dancer is to perform a combination of steps that is 4 measures long while the other is to perform a combination that is 12 measures long. How many measures long must the piece of music be?
   a multiple of 12; for example, 12,24,36

   b. Suppose Emiko adds a third dancer. This dancer performs a combination of steps that is 8 measures long. Can the same piece of music be used? Explain.

Emiko Tokunaga is the artistic director of Tokunaga Dance Ko (TDK). With her sister Yasuko, she started TDK, which has performed around the world. TDK was the first company selected by the Japan-United States Friendship Commission for their cultural exchange program.

28. b. Yes, the same piece of music can be used if its number of measures is a multiple of 24, since the LCM of 4, 8, and 12 is 24.

List the first seven multiples of each number.

1. 4 4, 8, 12, 16, 20, 24, 28

2. 12 12, 24, 36, 48, 60, 72, 84

3. 33 33, 66, 99, 132, 165, 198, 231

4. 110 110, 220, 330, 440, 550, 660, 770

Find the least common multiple of each set of numbers.

5. 9 and 27 27

6. 2, 4, and 9 36

7. 30 and 50 150

8. 15 and 45 45

9. 20, 40, and 60 120

10. 140 and 210 420

11. Find all the numbers that "tick-tock" will replace in a game of *Pattern Tick-Tock* if you use *tick* for 6, *tock* for 15, and count to 100. 30, 60, 90

12. Jackie spent the same amount of money on used CDs as she did on new CDs. If used CDs cost $12 and new CDs cost $16, what is the least amount she could have spent on each? $48

Standardized Testing ▶ Multiple Choice

For Exercises 1–3, choose the word that makes the statement true.

1. The product of two positive whole numbers is ___?___ a common multiple of the two numbers. B

   A sometimes   B always   C never

2. The least common multiple of two whole numbers is ___?___ one of the numbers. A

   A sometimes   B always   C never

3. The least common multiple of two whole numbers is ___?___ less than both numbers. C

   A sometimes   B always   C never

Extra Skill Practice

TEACHER NOTES

For each Exploration, the corresponding Extra Skill Practice Exercises are noted.

Exploration 1: 1–12

EXTRA HELP

Teacher's Resource Book
• Practice and Applications
• Study Guide

Technology Resources
• @Home Tutor
• Test Generator

ASSESSMENT
• Section 4 Quick Quiz
• Test Generator

Setting the Stage

GETTING STARTED

Module 3 Section 5 *Warm-Up* assesses students' ability to find the GCF of two numbers and to write mixed numbers as fractions. Common factors will be used to simplify fraction products to lowest terms. In multiplying mixed numbers, students will need to be able to change the mixed numbers to fractions.

To get students thinking about fraction concepts, hand each student a card with a fraction or mixed number written on it. Then have them order themselves from least to greatest using the fraction card they were given. This will provide a quick review of fractions, equivalent fractions, ordering fractions, and converting between fractions and mixed numbers.

CLASSROOM MANAGEMENT

Have students work in groups of three or four to answer **Questions 1 and 2** so they will have to discuss the puzzle. Many students will naturally want to solve it. Allow them enough time to answer the questions based on how they solved the problem. If time permits, have different groups share their strategies for solving the puzzle. It is not imperative that groups agree on a solution at this time. The division of coins will be modeled through paper folding and multiplication of fractions in **Exploration 1**.

Section 5 Fraction and Mixed Number Multiplication

IN THIS SECTION

EXPLORATION 1
♦ Fraction Multiplication

EXPLORATION 2
♦ Multiplying Mixed Numbers

A Fair Share

- - - *Setting the Stage*

Since ancient times, mathematics problems have been used as puzzles. The story below is an example of such a puzzle.

Three brave, but not very bright, treasure hunters recovered a small box of priceless Spanish doubloons aboard a sunken ship. They took the coins back to their campsite. Since it was late, they decided to go to sleep and divide the treasure the next day.

One of the treasure hunters, fearing that the others did not understand mathematics well enough to give out fair shares, took $\frac{1}{3}$ of the coins in the middle of the night and fled into the darkness.

Later that night, another treasure hunter awoke and saw that some of the coins were missing. That treasure hunter took $\frac{1}{3}$ of the remaining coins and also fled into the night.

The third treasure hunter awoke and was surprised to see the others gone and many of the coins missing. Trusting that the others left a fair share, the third treasure hunter took the remaining coins and walked away whistling happily.

Which of the treasure hunters ended up with the greatest share of the doubloons?

1. Answers will vary. Sample Response: The third treasure hunter got more than his share. The first got $\frac{1}{3}$, which was each hunter's fair share. The second hunter took only $\frac{1}{3}$ instead of $\frac{1}{2}$ of the remaining doubloons, leaving the third hunter with the greater share.

Think About It

1 Do you think any of the treasure hunters ended up with more than a fair share of doubloons? If so, which one and why?

2 Do you need additional information to solve this puzzle? Explain.
Sample Response: No, the problem can be solved with proportions of the treasure, so total number of coins is not needed.

 Module 3 Mind Games

Exploration 1

Fraction Multiplication

GOAL

LEARN HOW TO...
- multiply fractions

AS YOU...
- use paper folding to solve the treasure puzzle

SET UP You will need: • paper for folding • colored pencils

▶ Amazingly, you don't need to know how many doubloons were in the box to solve the puzzle—all you need is a piece of paper!

3 The first treasure hunter took $\frac{1}{3}$ of the treasure. What fraction of the treasure was left for the others? $\frac{2}{3}$

▶ **Finding a Part of a Part** The second treasure hunter took $\frac{1}{3}$ of the part that was left behind. To find the part of the treasure he took, you must find $\frac{1}{3}$ of $\frac{2}{3}$. When you find a fractional part of a part, you are multiplying fractions.

4 Let a sheet of paper represent the whole treasure. Work through Steps 1–4 to model $\frac{1}{3}$ of $\frac{2}{3}$, or $\frac{1}{3} \cdot \frac{2}{3}$.
Observe students' paper folding.

$\frac{1}{3}$ of $\frac{2}{3}$

Step 1

Fold the paper into thirds with vertical folds. Shade two of the columns to represent the remaining coins.

Step 2

Refold the paper so only the shaded part is showing.

Step 3

Fold the paper into thirds with horizontal folds. Shade one of the rows using a different color.

Step 4 Unfold your paper and examine your results.

Exploration 1 *continued*

COMMON ERROR

Questions 6 and 7 Some students may erroneously conclude that the third treasure hunter walked away with the same amount as the other two treasure hunters, since "all took away a third." One way for students to see that this is not so without doing multiplication or knowing the original number of doublons in the treasure box is to reason as follows:

The first person takes $\frac{1}{3}$ of the whole and the second person takes $\frac{1}{3}$ of *something less than a whole.* Since the second person took less than $\frac{1}{3}$ of the whole, there is more than $\frac{1}{3}$ of the whole left for the third person.

7. b. half; $\frac{1}{2}$ of $\frac{2}{3}$ is $\frac{2}{6}$ or $\frac{1}{3}$, the same as what the first hunter took, leaving $\frac{1}{3}$ for the third hunter.

8. a.

b.

---

5 Use your unfolded paper to answer parts (a)–(d).

The second hunter took $\frac{1}{3}$ of the $\frac{2}{3}$ left behind by the first hunter.

The first hunter took $\frac{1}{3}$ of the whole treasure.

a. How many small regions is the whole paper divided into? 9

b. What fraction of the whole paper is double-shaded? $\frac{2}{9}$

c. What fraction of the whole treasure did the second treasure hunter take? $\frac{2}{9}$

d. Write the fraction multiplication problem that represents the part the second treasure hunter took. $\frac{1}{3} \cdot \frac{2}{3} = \frac{2}{9}$

6 **Try This as a Class**

a. What fraction of your unfolded paper represents the part of the whole treasure that was left for the third treasure hunter? $\frac{4}{9}$

b. Write a fraction multiplication problem that represents the part left for the third treasure hunter. $\frac{2}{3} \cdot \frac{2}{3} = \frac{4}{9}$

7 **Discussion**

a. Which treasure hunter got the greatest share of the treasure? third

b. What fraction of the remaining coins should the second treasure hunter have taken so that everyone got a fair share? Use paper folding to explain.

Remember, this means $\frac{1}{3}$ of $\frac{1}{2}$.

8 Use paper folding to find $\frac{1}{3} \cdot \frac{1}{2}$. Check student work.

a. Use vertical folds and shading to model $\frac{1}{2}$ with paper folding.

b. Use your model from part (a) to find $\frac{1}{3} \cdot \frac{1}{2}$. Remember to use horizontal folds and shade with a different color.

c. What fraction of the whole paper is double-shaded? $\frac{1}{6}$

✔ **QUESTION 9**

...checks that you can multiply fractions using a model.

9 ✔ **CHECKPOINT** A student folded paper as shown to find $\frac{2}{3} \cdot \frac{4}{5}$. Use the sketch to find the product. $\frac{8}{15}$

► **A Pattern for Multiplication** By looking back at the results of your paper folding, you can discover a method for multiplying fractions without using a model.

10 **Try This as a Class** Make a table of the products you found.

Question Number	Multiplication problem	Product
5(c)–(d)	$\frac{1}{3} \cdot \frac{2}{3}$	$\frac{2}{9}$
6	$\frac{2}{3} \cdot \frac{2}{3}$	? $\frac{4}{9}$
8	$\frac{1}{3} \cdot \frac{1}{2}$	? $\frac{1}{6}$
9	$\frac{2}{3} \cdot \frac{4}{5}$	? $\frac{8}{15}$

10. c. Multiply numerators to get the new numerator. Multiply denominators to get the new denominator.

a. How is the numerator of each product related to the numerators in the problem? **The numerator is the product of the numerators in the problem.**

b. How is the denominator of each product related to the denominators in the problem? **The denominator is the product of the denominators in the problem.**

c. Explain how you can multiply two fractions without using paper folding or a sketch.

d. Use your method from part (c) to find $\frac{3}{4} \cdot \frac{4}{5} \cdot \frac{12}{20}$ or $\frac{3}{5}$

11 **✔ CHECKPOINT** Find each product without using a model. Write each product in lowest terms.

a. $\frac{3}{7} \cdot \frac{1}{2}$ $\frac{3}{14}$ **b.** $\frac{2}{3} \cdot \frac{3}{5}$ $\frac{6}{15} = \frac{2}{5}$ **c.** $\frac{2}{5} \cdot \frac{10}{12}$ $\frac{20}{60} = \frac{1}{3}$ **d.** $\frac{3}{4} \cdot \frac{4}{9}$ $\frac{12}{36} = \frac{1}{3}$

12 In the story, each treasure hunter took a whole number of coins.

a. Give two possibilities for the number of coins that could have been in the treasure box. **Sample Responses: 9, 18, 27, 36, …**

b. What do you know about the original number of coins in the treasure box? **The original number of coins must be a multiple of 9.**

HOMEWORK EXERCISES ➤ See Exs. 1–15 on pp. 179–180.

FOR ◄ HELP

with *writing fractions in lowest terms,* see

MODULE 1, p. 61

✔ QUESTION 11

...checks that you can multiply fractions and write the product in lowest terms.

TEACHING NOTES
Question 10 Students should notice that the product can be found by multiplying the numerators of the fractions to find the numerator of the product and multiplying the denominators of the fractions to find the denominator of the product. They should also be making the connection between their paper folding and the paper-and-pencil computation.

The example below can be used to summarize and reinforce how to use the method developed in **Question 10**.

CLASSROOM EXAMPLE
Find the product $\frac{5}{6} \cdot \frac{9}{20}$. Write the answer in lowest terms.

Answer:
$$\frac{5}{6} \cdot \frac{9}{20} = \frac{45}{120}$$
$$= \frac{45 \div 5}{120 \div 5}$$
$$= \frac{9}{24}$$
$$= \frac{9 \div 3}{24 \div 3}$$
$$= \frac{3}{8}$$

TEACHING NOTES
Dividing out common factors before finding the product of two fractions is presented as an **Extension** on page 182. You might direct students who demonstrate understanding of the material to complete the **Extension** and then complete **Checkpoint 11** using this method.

Exploration 2

CLASSROOM MANAGEMENT
For **Questions 13 and 14**, groups of 2 to 4 students will each need a set of pattern blocks that contain at least 9 hexagons, 4 trapezoids, and 4 rhombuses.

DEVELOPING MATH CONCEPTS
Students may need to use pattern blocks to understand the **Example** illustrating use of the distributive property. **Question 15** on the following page provides an opportunity to make certain all students understand how to use the distributive property. A discussion of the word *distribute* as meaning "to spread out or over" may be helpful. In addition to using the distributive property, students will also learn to multiply a whole number by a mixed number by rewriting each of the numbers as a fraction. However, understanding the distributive property is necessary for work with algebraic expressions and is a useful tool for mental math computation.

GOAL

LEARN HOW TO...
- use the distributive property
- multiply mixed numbers

AS YOU...
- find the weight of the coins in a treasure

KEY TERM
- distributive property

1 lb of coins

$\frac{1}{3}$ lb of coins

Exploration 2

Multiplying Mixed Numbers

SET UP Work in a group. You will need pattern blocks.

▶ Four treasure hunters found a chest containing gold coins. When they divided the treasure, each treasure hunter received $1\frac{1}{3}$ lb of coins. Pattern blocks can be used to find how many pounds of coins were in the chest.

13 If one treasure hunter receives $1\frac{1}{3}$ lb of coins, then the whole treasure contains 4 times that many pounds of coins.

    a. Use pattern blocks to show $4 \cdot 1\frac{1}{3}$. **See margin.**

    b. Group together any rhombuses that can form hexagons, and trade them for hexagons. Record the total number of hexagons and rhombuses you have after the trade.
    5 hexagons, 1 rhombus
    c. How many pounds of coins were in the chest? $5\frac{1}{3}$

14 Use pattern blocks to find the number of pounds of coins in the chest if the four treasure hunters each received the given amount.

    a. $1\frac{1}{2}$ lb of coins 6 lb   **b.** $2\frac{1}{3}$ lb of coins $9\frac{1}{3}$ lb

▶ To multiply an amount by 4, you can add the same amount four times. You can also use the **distributive property** as shown in the Example.

EXAMPLE

Find $4 \cdot \left(1\frac{1}{3}\right)$.

SAMPLE RESPONSE

multiply the **1** by 4

multiply the $\frac{1}{3}$ by 4

$$4 \cdot \left(1 + \frac{1}{3}\right) = (4 \cdot 1) + \left(4 \cdot \frac{1}{3}\right)$$

$$= 4 + \frac{4}{3}$$

$$= 4 + 1\frac{1}{3}$$

$$= 5\frac{1}{3}$$

$1\frac{1}{3} = 1 + \frac{1}{3}$

$4 \cdot \frac{1}{3} = \frac{4}{1} \cdot \frac{1}{3} = \frac{4}{3}$

13. a. See Additional Answers beginning on page A1.

176

15 **Discussion** Explain how to find $2\frac{1}{2} \cdot 3$ using the distributive property. $2\frac{1}{2} \cdot 3 = \left(2 + \frac{1}{2}\right) \cdot 3 = (2 \cdot 3) + \left(\frac{1}{2} \cdot 3\right) = 6 + \frac{3}{2} = 6 + 1\frac{1}{2} = 7\frac{1}{2}$

16 ✔ **CHECKPOINT** Find each product. Show your steps.

a. $6 \cdot 4\frac{1}{2}$ 27

b. $2 \cdot 2\frac{1}{6}$ $4\frac{1}{3}$

c. $3\frac{1}{4} \cdot 3$ $9\frac{3}{4}$

Karina

Number of pounds of coins if 4 hunters each received $2\frac{1}{3}$ lb of coins:

$4 \cdot 2\frac{1}{3} = \frac{4}{1} \cdot \frac{7}{3}$ Step 1

$= \frac{28}{3}$ Step 2

$= 9\frac{1}{3}$ Step 3

$9\frac{1}{3}$ lb of coins

17 **Try This as a Class** Explain each step of Karina's method for finding $4 \cdot 2\frac{1}{3}$.

18 Use Karina's method to find each product.

a. $3 \cdot \frac{2}{5}$ $1\frac{1}{5}$

b. $6 \cdot 1\frac{5}{8}$ $9\frac{3}{4}$

c. $4 \cdot 6\frac{1}{2}$ 26

✔ **QUESTION 16**

...checks that you can use the distributive property to multiply a whole number and a mixed number.

17. Step 1: Rewrite all mixed and whole numbers as fractions.
Step 2: Multiply the fractions.
Step 3: Rewrite the product as a mixed number.

▶ **Multiplying Mixed Numbers** You have learned to multiply fractions and to write a mixed number as a fraction. You can combine these two skills to multiply mixed numbers.

EXAMPLE

Multiply $2\frac{2}{3} \cdot 1\frac{1}{5}$.

SAMPLE RESPONSE

$2 \cdot 3 + 2 = 8$

$1 \cdot 5 + 1 = 6$

$2\frac{2}{3} \cdot 1\frac{1}{5} = \frac{8}{3} \cdot \frac{6}{5}$

$= \frac{8 \cdot 6}{3 \cdot 5}$

$= \frac{48}{15}$ $48 \div 15$

$= 3\frac{3}{15}$

$= 3\frac{1}{5}$

19 Find the product $5\frac{1}{2} \cdot 3\frac{1}{2}$ by first writing the mixed numbers as fractions. Write your answer as a mixed number in lowest terms.
$19\frac{1}{4}$

COMMON ERRORS

Question 16 Some students may simply multiply the whole numbers and write the fraction beside the result. To correct this error, encourage students to think about their work in **Questions 13 and 14**.

TEACHING NOTES

Question 17 Make certain students notice how Karina's method insures that *both* the whole number and the fraction part of the mixed number are multiplied by the whole number.

Once students understand Karina's method and are able to use it, they may question why they should bother to use the distributive property. Pose a problem such as $4 \cdot 16\frac{1}{2}$. Show how in this case $4 \cdot 16 + 4 \cdot \frac{1}{2}$ can be done mentally to produce $64 + 2$ or 66, whereas $4 \cdot \frac{33}{2} = \frac{132}{2} = 66$ is harder to compute mentally. Explain that students now have 2 methods that both produce the product, so each time they multiply a whole number and a fraction, they have a choice as to which method they use.

The distributive property is rarely used with two mixed numbers since in the **Example** this would require distributing the 2 to the 1 and to the $\frac{1}{5}$ AND distributing the $\frac{2}{3}$ to the 1 and to the $\frac{1}{5}$, resulting in a variety of fractions with denominators that require common denominators to combine. In this case, Karina's method of changing the mixed numbers to fractions is easier. Once the mixed numbers are rewritten as fractions, students can also apply the method of simplifying before multiplying shown in the **Extension** on page 182.

Exploration 2 *continued*

TEACHING NOTES

Checkpoint Question 20
Have students estimate each product in **Question 20** before finding the exact product. This will encourage them to continue the habit of estimating to check the reasonableness of answers. Sharing responses to **part (b)** may help students become better at determining when it might be best to use each method of multiplying fractions.

Key Concepts

CLOSURE QUESTION
Describe how to multiply fractions and check that the answer is in lowest terms.

Sample Response: Multiply the numerators of the fractions to find the numerator of the product, and multiply the denominators of the fractions to find the denominator of the product. If the numerator and denominator of the product have any factors in common, the product is not in lowest terms.

ABSENT STUDENTS
For students who were absent for all or part of this section, the blackline Study Guide for Section 5 may be used to present the ideas, concepts, and skills of Section 5.

✔ **QUESTION 20**

...checks that you can multiply mixed numbers.

Key Term

distributive property

---

20 ✔ **CHECKPOINT** Below are three multiplication expressions.

A. $6 \cdot 3\frac{1}{2}$ **B.** $\frac{3}{4} \cdot 1\frac{3}{8}$ **C.** $2\frac{1}{6} \cdot 12\frac{1}{2}$

a. Find each product in lowest terms. $A = 21, B = 1\frac{1}{32}, C = 27\frac{1}{12}$

b. Did you use the same method to find each product? Explain.
Answers will vary. Distributive property can be used with A.

HOMEWORK EXERCISES ▶ See Exs. 16–35 on pp. 180–182.

Section ⑤

Key Concepts

Multiplying Fractions (pp. 173–175)

Step 1 Multiply the numerators of the fractions to find the numerator of the product.

Step 2 Multiply the denominators of the fractions to find the denominator of the product.

Example $\frac{3}{4} \cdot \frac{8}{15} = \frac{3 \cdot 8}{4 \cdot 15} = \frac{24}{60} = \frac{2}{5}$

Multiplying Mixed Numbers (pp. 176–178)

One way to multiply a mixed number by a whole number is to use the distributive property.

Example $3 \cdot 2\frac{1}{4} = 3 \cdot \left(2 + \frac{1}{4}\right) = (3 \cdot 2) + \left(3 \cdot \frac{1}{4}\right) = 6 + \frac{3}{4} = 6\frac{3}{4}$

You can always write mixed numbers as fractions to multiply.

Example $1\frac{1}{2} \cdot 3\frac{2}{5} = \frac{3}{2} \cdot \frac{17}{5} = \frac{3 \cdot 17}{2 \cdot 5} = \frac{51}{10}$, or $5\frac{1}{10}$

21 **Key Concepts Question** When you multiply two whole numbers other than 0, the product is always greater than or equal to either number. Is this true when you multiply two fractions? Give an example. No; Sample: $5 \cdot 3 = 15$, but $\frac{1}{5} \cdot \frac{1}{3} = \frac{1}{15}$ which is less than $\frac{1}{5}$ and $\frac{1}{3}$.

Section 5

Practice & Application Exercises

1. **a.** Find $\frac{1}{3}$ of $\frac{5}{8}$. $\frac{5}{24}$

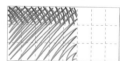

   b. Find $\frac{5}{8}$ of $\frac{1}{3}$. $\frac{5}{24}$

   c. How do the products in parts (a) and (b) compare?
   They are the same.

Find each product. Write your answer in lowest terms.

2. $\frac{3}{5} \cdot \frac{1}{2}$ $\frac{3}{10}$
3. $\frac{4}{9} \cdot \frac{5}{6}$ $\frac{10}{27}$
4. $\frac{7}{10} \cdot \frac{2}{3}$ $\frac{7}{15}$
5. $\frac{1}{12} \cdot \frac{1}{12}$ $\frac{1}{144}$

6. $\frac{1}{2} \cdot \frac{4}{5}$ $\frac{2}{5}$
7. $\frac{9}{16} \cdot \frac{2}{3}$ $\frac{3}{8}$
8. $\frac{10}{20} \cdot \frac{14}{30}$ $\frac{7}{30}$
9. $\frac{16}{21} \cdot \frac{3}{4}$ $\frac{4}{7}$

10. **Visual Thinking**

   a. The model at the right was used to multiply two fractions. The double shaded part shows the product. What are the fractions, and what is their product? $\frac{2}{3}$ and $\frac{5}{8}$; $\frac{10}{24}$

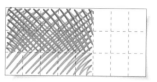

   b. Use your method for multiplying fractions to check your answer to part (a). $\frac{2}{3} \cdot \frac{5}{8} = \frac{2 \cdot 5}{3 \cdot 8} = \frac{10}{24}$

   c. Express the product of the fractions in lowest terms. $\frac{5}{12}$

11. One fifth of a farmer's corn crop is destroyed by hail. Later that summer, $\frac{1}{3}$ of the remaining crop is eaten by insects. To file an insurance claim, the farmer needs to find what part of the total original crop was eaten by insects. The farmer says it is $\frac{1}{15}$. Is this correct? Explain.

12. Three fifths of a group of students surveyed said they would like to visit the National Zoo. If $\frac{5}{6}$ of those $\frac{3}{5}$ also said they would like to visit the Air and Space Museum, what fraction of the students surveyed said they would like to visit both attractions? $\frac{1}{2}$

11. No, the farmer multiplied $\frac{1}{3} \cdot \frac{1}{5}$, but it is really $\frac{1}{3} \cdot \frac{4}{5}$ since $\frac{1}{3}$ of the remaining $\frac{4}{5}$ was eaten by insects. So, $\frac{4}{15}$ of the entire crop was eaten by insects.

Practice & Applications

SUGGESTED ASSIGNMENTS

Core Course
Day 1: Exs. 1, 36–45
Day 2: Exs. 2–12, 14–15
Day 3: Exs. 16–35

Extended Course
Day 1: Exs. 1, 36–45
Day 2: Exs. 2–15, 46–47*
Day 3: Exs. 16–35

Note: Extended Course assignments can be used to differentiate within the regular classroom. In classrooms where students are grouped homogeneously, the material might be covered in fewer days. In this case assignments may be combined.

* denotes Extension Exercises

ADDITIONAL PRACTICE
See the *Teacher's Resource Book* for additional practice and application exercises for this section.

EXERCISE NOTES
Exercise 1 illustrates that the commutative property of multiplication applies to fractions as well as to whole numbers. In symbols, if a and b are fractions then $a \cdot b = b \cdot a$.

Exercise 10 checks to see if students connect the visual representations of paper folding they have been using in this section to the paper-and-pencil algorithms for multiplying fractions.

Exercise Notes

For each of the **Exercises 16–21**, students should be able to find the product in lowest terms by using mental math. If not, encourage students to do as much as possible mentally, writing down interim steps when necessary. For some students it may take practice before they are able to comfortably do the products in their head.

13. **Challenge** Read the story puzzle below. How many brownies did the original recipe make? 360

▲ Don decided to make $\frac{1}{2}$ the number of brownies from a recipe. He changed the recipe by cutting the amount of each ingredient in half.

▲ Later he gave his reduced recipe to his sister Sylvie. She changed it to make only $\frac{1}{4}$ of Don's recipe.

▲ Sylvie gave her recipe to Julio, who made $\frac{2}{3}$ of the amount in Sylvie's recipe. Julio made 30 brownies.

Science Rocks contain small amounts of radioactive elements that decrease over time. Scientists measure the age of rocks using *half lives*, the time it takes for a rock to lose half of its radioactive material.

Example: A rock that has $\frac{1}{4}$ of its radioactive elements is **2 half lives** old since $\frac{1}{4} = \frac{1}{2} \cdot \frac{1}{2}$.

14. How many half lives old is a rock that has $\frac{1}{16}$ of its original radioactive elements?
4 half lives

15. What fraction of its original radioactive elements does a rock have that is 6 half lives old? $\frac{1}{64}$

Amount of radioactive elements remaining	Number of half lives
1	0
$\frac{1}{2}$	1
$\frac{1}{4}$	2

Mental Math Use the distributive property and mental math to find each product. Write each answer in lowest terms.

16. $3 \cdot 5\frac{1}{4}$ $15\frac{3}{4}$

17. $2\frac{1}{3} \cdot 3$ 7

18. $10 \cdot 3\frac{1}{5}$ 32

19. $4 \cdot 2\frac{1}{2}$ 10

20. $5\frac{1}{6} \cdot 5$ $25\frac{5}{6}$

21. $6\frac{1}{8} \cdot 8$ 49

Find each product. Write each answer in lowest terms.

22. $2\frac{1}{3} \cdot 3\frac{1}{5}$ $7\frac{7}{15}$

23. $6\frac{1}{2} \cdot \frac{2}{3}$ $4\frac{1}{3}$

24. $\frac{3}{5} \cdot 2\frac{1}{4}$ $1\frac{7}{20}$

25. $1\frac{1}{3} \cdot 2\frac{1}{5}$ $2\frac{14}{15}$

26. $7\frac{1}{6} \cdot 1\frac{1}{2}$ $10\frac{3}{4}$

27. $1\frac{5}{8} \cdot \frac{3}{13}$ $\frac{3}{8}$

28. Show two methods for finding $3\frac{2}{3} \cdot 5$.

$\frac{11}{3} \cdot \frac{5}{1} = \frac{55}{3} = 18\frac{1}{3};$

$3\frac{2}{3} \cdot 5 = \left(3 + \frac{2}{3}\right)5 = 15 + 3\frac{1}{3} = 18\frac{1}{3}$

29. **Language Arts** In Mildred Pitts Walter's novel *Justin and the Best Biscuits in the World*, ten-year-old Justin Ward learns about much more than biscuits on a visit to his grandfather's ranch. Justin learns that past generations of Wards were among the many African-American cowhands who helped build the American West.

As he prepares a lunch of homemade biscuits, stewed raisins, and smoked pork, Justin's grandfather remembers:

"When I was a boy about your age, I used to go with my father on short runs with cattle. We'd bring them down from the high country onto the plains."

"Did you stay out all night?" [Justin asks.]

"Sometimes. That was the time I liked most. The cook often made for supper what I am going to make for lunch."

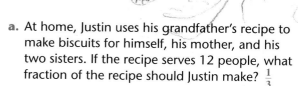

a. At home, Justin uses his grandfather's recipe to make biscuits for himself, his mother, and his two sisters. If the recipe serves 12 people, what fraction of the recipe should Justin make? $\frac{1}{3}$

b. If the biscuit recipe calls for $1\frac{3}{4}$ cups of all-purpose flour, how much flour should Justin use? $\frac{7}{12}$ cup

c. How much flour is needed if the original recipe is increased to serve 30 people? $4\frac{3}{8}$ cups

Predict whether each product will be *greater than* or *less than* $4\frac{4}{5}$.

30. $\frac{2}{3} \cdot 4\frac{4}{5}$

less than

31. $1\frac{1}{12} \cdot 4\frac{4}{5}$

greater than

32. $\frac{9}{8} \cdot 4\frac{4}{5}$

greater than

33. $4\frac{4}{5} \cdot \frac{2}{5}$

less than

EXERCISE NOTES
Exercises 30–33 Check students' understanding that multiplying the mixed number $4\frac{4}{5}$ by a fraction less than 1 results in a product less than $4\frac{4}{5}$ because you are finding a part of $4\frac{4}{5}$. Students should not work the problems, but rather try to use reasoning to make their predictions.

Practice & Applications

EXERCISE NOTES

For **Exercises 46 and 47**, make sure students understand the mathematics of what may appear to just be a *shortcut*. Students who do not understand the mathematics often use the method incorrectly. An example would be dividing the GCF from the numerator and denominator of two different fractions in an addition or subtraction problem $\left(\frac{\overset{1}{\cancel{3}}}{5} + \frac{1}{\cancel{6}_2} = \frac{1}{5} + \frac{1}{2}\right)$.

In a multiplication problem, dividing the numerator of one of the factors and the denominator of the other factor by the same number is the same as dividing the numerator and the denominator of the product by the same number, which results in a fraction equivalent to the product

$$\left(\frac{\overset{1}{\cancel{3}}}{5} \cdot \frac{1}{\cancel{6}_2} = \frac{3 \div 3}{5} \cdot \frac{1}{6 \div 3}\right.$$
$$= \frac{3 \div 3}{5 \cdot 6 \div 3}$$
$$= \frac{3 \div 3}{30 \div 3}$$
$$= \left.\frac{1}{10}\right).$$

34. Suppose you multiply two fractions that are between 0 and 1. Is the product between 0 and 1 or greater than 1? Give some examples to support your answer. **Between 0 and 1. Sample:** $\frac{1}{2} \cdot \frac{3}{4} = \frac{3}{8}$

Reflecting ◀▶ on the Section

Be prepared to discuss your response to Exercise 35 in class.

35. Choose a different method to find each product. Show your work and explain why you chose each method.

   a. $6\frac{1}{8} \cdot 3$ **b.** $10\frac{2}{5} \cdot \frac{1}{3}$

Discussion

Exercise 35 checks that you can choose a method to multiply mixed numbers.

35. a. $18\frac{3}{8}$; Use the distributive property.

   b. $3\frac{7}{15}$; Convert the mixed number to a fraction.

Spiral ◀▶ Review

Write the prime factorization of each number using exponents. (Module 3, p. 158)

36. 44 $2^2 \cdot 11$ 37. 125 5^3 38. 56 $2^3 \cdot 7$ 39. 117 $13 \cdot 3^2$

Estimate each answer. (Module 1, p. 10)

40. $82 \cdot $51   41. $178 - $59   42. $34.69 + $17.14
   about $4000   about $120   about $52

Find each sum or difference. (Module 3, p. 143)

43. 5.002 − 1.243   44. 12.4 − 9.75   45. 1.73 + 15.6 + 0.015
   3.759   2.65   17.345

Extension ▶ ▶

Products in Lowest Terms

46. Find $\frac{3}{20} \cdot \frac{4}{5}$. Write the answer in lowest terms. $\frac{3}{25}$

   Here is another way to find a product like $\frac{3}{20} \cdot \frac{4}{5}$ in lowest terms. Divide a numerator and a denominator by the common factor 4 *before* you multiply.

   Divide by 4, the GCF of 4 and 20.

$$\frac{3}{20} \cdot \frac{4}{5} = \frac{3 \cdot \overset{1}{\cancel{4}}}{\underset{5}{\cancel{20}} \cdot 5} = \frac{3 \cdot 1}{5 \cdot 5} = \frac{3}{25}$$

   Divide by 4.

47. $3 \frac{\overset{1}{\cancel{5}} \cdot \overset{1}{\cancel{4}}}{\cancel{12} \cdot \cancel{15}_3} = \frac{1}{9}$, Sample: Dividing by a common factor before multiplying is easier because you don't have to multiply larger factors such as 12 · 15, or reduce the answer to lowest terms after multiplying.

47. Find $\frac{5}{12} \cdot \frac{4}{15}$ in lowest terms by dividing by the common factor after you multiply and then before you multiply. Which method is easier for you? Why?

Extra Skill Practice

Find each product. Write each answer in lowest terms.

1. $\frac{1}{2} \cdot \frac{2}{3}$ $\frac{1}{3}$

2. $\frac{3}{16} \cdot \frac{4}{9}$ $\frac{1}{12}$

3. $\frac{5}{12} \cdot \frac{6}{25}$ $\frac{1}{10}$

4. $\frac{27}{32} \cdot \frac{2}{9}$ $\frac{3}{16}$

5. $\frac{7}{9} \cdot \frac{12}{20}$ $\frac{7}{15}$

6. $\frac{10}{39} \cdot \frac{13}{20}$ $\frac{1}{6}$

7. $\frac{14}{24} \cdot \frac{2}{3}$ $\frac{7}{18}$

8. $\frac{18}{45} \cdot \frac{15}{36}$ $\frac{1}{6}$

9. The string section makes up about $\frac{2}{3}$ of a symphony orchestra. Cellos make up about $\frac{1}{5}$ of the string section, and about $\frac{3}{5}$ of the string section are violins.

   a. About what part of a symphony orchestra are cellos? $\frac{2}{15}$

   b. About what part of a symphony orchestra are violins? $\frac{6}{15}$ or $\frac{2}{5}$

Find each product. Write each answer in lowest terms.

10. $5 \cdot 4\frac{1}{8}$ $20\frac{5}{8}$

11. $2 \cdot 6\frac{2}{5}$ $12\frac{4}{5}$

12. $1\frac{1}{8} \cdot 6\frac{1}{4}$ $7\frac{1}{32}$

13. $2\frac{1}{2} \cdot \frac{3}{8}$ $\frac{15}{16}$

14. $3\frac{1}{5} \cdot 1\frac{3}{4}$ $5\frac{3}{5}$

15. $2\frac{2}{9} \cdot 5\frac{1}{3}$ $11\frac{23}{27}$

16. Skirts for a school play each require $1\frac{2}{3}$ yd of fabric. How much material should be ordered so that 5 skirts can be made? $8\frac{1}{3}$ yards

Standardized Testing ◀▶ Free Response

How many cups of apple juice do you need to make $2\frac{1}{2}$ times the recipe?

$8\frac{1}{3}$ cups of apple juice

Beverages

Fruit Smoothie

Blend together:

$\frac{1}{3}$ c frozen strawberry puree

$\frac{1}{4}$ c frozen banana puree

1 c white grape fruit juice

$3\frac{1}{3}$ c apple juice

Extra Skill Practice

TEACHER NOTES

For each Exploration, the corresponding Extra Skill Practice Exercises are noted.

Exploration 1: Exs. 1–9
Exploration 2: Exs. 10–16

EXTRA HELP

Teacher's Resource Book
• Practice and Applications
• Study Guide

Technology Resources
• @Home Tutor
• Test Generator

ASSESSMENT

• Section 5 Quick Quiz
• Test Generator

Setting the Stage

GETTING STARTED

In preparation for finding decimal products, Module 3 Section 6 *Warm-Up* assesses students' ability to multiply one and two digit numbers.

An overhead transparency copy of **Labsheet 6A** can be displayed on an overhead projector instead of providing each group with its own copy. When playing *Target Number*, each group will need paper and pencil to record answers and to keep score.

Section 6 · Decimal Multiplication

IN THIS SECTION

EXPLORATION 1
♦ Multiplying Decimals

EXPLORATION 2
♦ Estimating Decimal Products

Target Games

Setting the Stage

SET UP Work with a partner. You will need: • Labsheet 6A • calculator

Games like darts test your ability to hit a target. The goal of *Target Number* is to find a product close to the target number.

Use mental math and estimation.

Target Number

♦ Player 1 chooses a number to multiply by the constant factor, trying to come as close to the target number as possible. The player then uses a calculator to find the product.

♦ Players take turns challenging each other's product. A player can win a game in two ways–if his or her product is not challenged, or if it is closer to the target number than the challenger's product.

Sample Game 1 Target Number = 226	Constant Factor = 13
Perry multiplies the constant factor by 15.	13 • 15 = 195
Mary challenges by multiplying by 18.	13 • 18 = 234
Perry challenges by multiplying by 16.	13 • 16 = 208 Mary wins!

Mary wins since 234 is closer to the target number than Perry's 208.

Use Labsheet 6A. Play at least three games of *Target Number*.

Think About It

1 In *Sample Game 1*, is there a way that Perry could have successfully challenged Mary? Explain. **Yes, multiplying by 17 or any number between 17 and 18 could have successfully challenged Mary.**

Multiplying Decimals

SET UP *You will need Labsheet 6B.*

Mary and Perry played *Sample Game 2* of *Target Number* as shown.

2 Think about using a decimal to challenge Perry in Game 2. Should the decimal be greater than or less than 58.5? Why?

Sample Game 2 Target Number = 408	Constant Factor = 7
Mary multiplies the constant factor by 59.	7 · 59 = 413
Perry challenges by multiplying by 58.	7 · 58 = 406
Mary decides not to challenge Perry.	Perry wins!

▶ To successfully challenge another player in *Target Number*, it may be necessary to multiply by a decimal. Decimal products, like fraction products, can be modeled by shading a part of a part.

EXAMPLE

Model the product 0.2 · 0.6 using a 10 · 10 grid to represent 1 whole.

The 12 double-shaded squares represent the product 0.2 · 0.6.

Step 1
Represent 0.6 by lightly shading six tenths of the grid.

Step 2
Double-shade two tenths or 0.2 of the part shaded in Step 1.

3 **Discussion**

a. What part of the whole grid is each small square? Write your answer as a fraction and as a decimal. $\frac{1}{100}$, 0.01

b. What part of the whole grid is double-shaded? Write your answer as a decimal. 0.12

c. What does 0.2 · 0.6 equal? 0.12

GOAL

LEARN HOW TO...
- multiply decimals
- estimate decimal products

AS YOU...
- model decimal products on grids

2. Less than. Perry is within 2 of the target number. Multiplying by greater than 58.5 would produce a number more than half way between 406 and 413.

Exploration 1

TEACHING NOTES
Go through the **Example** thoroughly with students before discussing **Question 3**. Students should be familiar with shading and double shading from fraction multiplication in Section 5. **Questions 3 and 4** will help make the connection between fraction multiplication and decimal multiplication.

After completing **Questions 3 and 4**, students may need to see another decimal product modeled before completing **Labsheet 6B** on their own. Use the example below and ask students to participate by explaining the steps. An overhead transparency of a 10 × 10 grid is helpful for demonstration.

CLASSROOM EXAMPLE

Model the product 0.3 · 0.7 using a 10 × 10 grid to represent 1 whole.

Answer:
Step 1:

Lightly shade 0.7.

Step 2:

Double-shade 0.3 of the part shaded in Step 1.

The 21 double-shaded squares represent the product 0.3 · 0.7, so 0.3 · 0.7 = 0.21.

185

CLASSROOM MANAGEMENT

For most classes, this exploration will need to be split into two class periods. For those students who do not finish **Questions 5 and 6** on the first day, have them complete them for homework so they will be prepared for the next lesson.

TEACHING NOTES

Students may want to check their response to **Question 9(c)** by using fractions to find the product 0.25 · 0.3 and making sure the fraction product is equivalent to the decimal they chose. To further emphasize the location of the placeholder in **Question 9(c)**, ask students how the problem would have to be changed in order to obtain a product equivalent to 0.750. (*Sample response: 2.5 · 0.3*)

4. c. $\frac{2}{10}$ = 0.2 and $\frac{6}{10}$ = 0.6; You are multiplying decimal equivalents of the fractions multiplied.

7. c. First multiply 52 · 4 = 208. Then count the total number of decimal places in the factors, which is 3. Finally, position the decimal point in the product so it has three decimal places: 0.208.

4 **a.** Find $\frac{2}{10} \cdot \frac{6}{10}$ in fraction form. $\frac{12}{100}$

   b. Write your answer from part (a) as a decimal. 0.12

   c. Compare your answers from part (b) and Question 3(c). Why is $\frac{2}{10} \cdot \frac{6}{10}$ the same as 0.2 · 0.6?

Use Labsheet 6B for Question 5–7.

5 Use the *Decimal Multiplication Grids* to model the decimal products 0.5 · 0.4 and 0.3 · 0.3. See margin.

6 Follow the directions for *Decimal and Fraction Products* to compute decimal products using fraction multiplication. See margin.

7 **Try This as a Class** Look back at your completed *Decimal and Fraction Products* table.

   a. How are the digits in the decimal factors in the first column used to find the digits in the decimal product? The digits are multiplied like whole numbers.

   b. How is the number of decimal places in the decimal product related to the number of decimal places in the factors? The number of places in the product is the sum of the number of decimal places in the factors.

   c. Explain how to multiply 5.2 · 0.04 without finding equivalent fraction products or using a grid. Then find the product.

8 Find 0.5 · 0.4 and 0.3 · 0.3 without using grids or fractions. Then compare the products with those in Question 5. 0.20, 0.09; The products are equal to those found by the grid model.

9 **Discussion**

   a. How many decimal places will there be in the product 0.3 · 0.2? two

   b. **Use Labsheet 6B.** Why was a zero needed in the tenths place in the decimal product 0.3 · 0.2 in the *Decimal and Fraction Products* table? The zero was needed as a place holder to be able to write 6 hundredths instead of 6 tenths.

   c. To find the product 0.25 · 0.3, you need to write a zero as a placeholder after you multiply the digits. Which is correct, 0.075 or 0.750? Explain. 0.075 is correct; $\frac{25}{100} \cdot \frac{3}{10} = \frac{75}{1000} = 0.075$. 0.750 is $\frac{750}{1000}$ or $\frac{75}{100}$.

10 ✔ **CHECKPOINT** Find each decimal product.

   a. 0.8 · 0.09 0.072

   b. 0.3 · 1.5 0.45

   c. 2.5 · 4 10.0

   d. 0.02 · r, where $r = 0.003$ 0.00006

   e. r · 3.1, where $r = 22.6$ 70.06

   f. s · t, where $s = 2.004$ and $t = 0.5$ 1.0020

▶ **Estimating Products** Games like *Target Number* require decimal estimation skills. The example shows how estimating can be used to help place the decimal point in a product and to check that the product is reasonable.

EXAMPLE

Find the product of 789 and 4.8.

SAMPLE RESPONSE

> **Estimate:**
> The product is about 800 · 5, or 4,000.

> Place the decimal point here since 3787.2 is about 4000.

$$789 · 4.8 = 3787.2$$

11 **Try This as a Class** Use estimation to place the decimal point in the correct position in each product. Explain your reasoning.

   a. 0.9 · 0.7 = 63 0.63; The product is about 1 · 0.7, or 0.7.

   b. 416 · 0.23 = 9568 95.68; The product is about 400 · 0.25. One-fourth of 400 is 100.

   c. 0.35 · 0.6 = 21 0.21; The product is about 0.4 · 0.5. One-half of 0.4 is 0.2.

   d. 3.05 · 0.13 = 3965 0.3965; The product is about 3 · 0.1, or 0.3.

HOMEWORK EXERCISES ▶ See Exs. 1–12 on pp. 190–191.

✔ **QUESTION 10**

...checks that you can find decimal products.

TEACHING NOTES

Question 11 Some students may be tempted to forego estimation and resort to counting the number of decimal places of the factors.

Part (c) should catch those students since the trailing zero has been eliminated; thus counting decimal places would given an incorrect estimate. You may want to clarify this by performing the multiplication to show the zero.

The Classroom Example below provides additional instruction on estimating decimal products.

CLASSROOM EXAMPLE

Use estimation to help place the decimal point in the product when finding 412 · 9.08.

Answer:
Estimate: the product is about 400 · 9, or 3600.

   412 · 9.08 = 3740.96

Place the decimal point between the "0" and the "9" since 3740.96 is about 3600.

Exploration 2

Before beginning the new game, go through the flowchart with the whole class. Make sure students understand how to follow the chart.

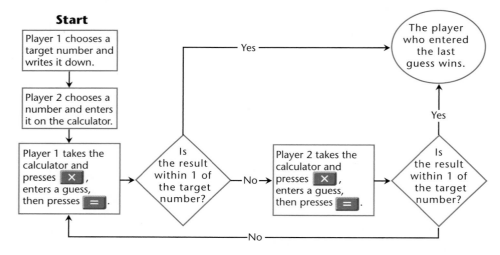

GOAL

LEARN HOW TO...
- improve your estimating skills

AS YOU...
- play *Target Number Plus or Minus 1*

Exploration 2

Estimating Decimal Products

SET UP *Work with a partner. You will need one calculator per pair of students.*

In a new game, *Target Number Plus or Minus 1*, the goal is to find a product that is within 1 of the target number. To play the game, follow the flowchart below. You must use estimation and mental math to decide what numbers to enter in the calculator.

Sample Game

Player 1 chose 196 for the target number.
Player 2 chose the number 7.

Player	Keys pressed	Display
2	7	7.
1	× 2 5 =	175.
2	× 1 . 1 =	192.5
1	× 1 . 0 2 =	196.35

Since 196.35 is within 1 of 196, Player 1 wins!

12 Play *Target Number Plus or Minus 1* at least 5 times. Each time you play, record the following: Answers will vary.

- the target number
- the keys pressed during each player's turn
- the products that are displayed

13 Lian and Elena are playing *Target Number Plus or Minus 1*. The target number is 54. After Lian completes her turn, the calculator display shows 55.05. "I've won!," Lian shouts. "55 is within one of 54!" Elena disagrees. She says the game is not over yet. Who is right? Why? Elena is correct; 55.05 − 54 = 1.05, which is greater than 1.

14 You and a friend are playing *Target Number Plus or Minus 1*. It is your turn and the number on the calculator display is greater than the target number. Should you multiply by a number that is *greater than 1* or *less than 1*? Why? Less than 1; If you multiply by a number greater than one the product will be even greater, and therefore farther from the target.

15 **Mental Math** Use mental math to find each product.

a. 545 • 0.1 54.5   **b.** 72 • 0.01 0.72   **c.** 23.8 • 0.01 0.238

16 **Try This as a Class** In parts (a)–(d), use your estimation skills to choose the decimal that will give a product within 1 of the target number when multiplied by the number on the calculator. Explain each choice.

a. Target Number = 50   Calculator displays ⎡ 7. ⎤

  Choices   7.1   7.5   7.7   7.9

b. Target Number = 75   Calculator displays ⎡ 11. ⎤

  Choices   7.05   6.17   6.45   6.82

c. Target Number = 88   Calculator displays ⎡ 160. ⎤

  Choices   1.90   1.82   0.75   0.55

d. Target Number = 50   Calculator displays ⎡ 545. ⎤

  Choices   0.09   0.2   2.00   10.9
  0.09; 545 • 0.1 = 54.5, so 0.09 will produce a product close to but less than 54.5.

| HOMEWORK EXERCISES | ▶ See Exs. 13–25 on pp. 191–192.

16. a. 7.1; 7 • 7 = 49 and 7 • 8 = 56, so 7 • 7.5 or higher will be too great, since 50 is less than halfway between 49 and 56.

b. 6.82; 6 • 11 = 66 and 7 • 11 = 77, 75 is more than half way between 66 and 77, so choices 6.17 and 6.45 are eliminated. Choice 7.05 will be greater than 77 so it is also eliminated.

c. 0.55; A factor less than one is needed and 0.55 is close to half. Half of 160 is 80, so 0.55 will produce a number just greater than 80.

TEACHING NOTES

In **Question 16**, have students justify why certain choices were eliminated. This will provide additional estimation practice and reinforce elimination as an effective method that can be used on multiple choice standardized tests.

The Classroom Example below can be used to reinforce the concepts being developed in **Question 16**.

CLASSROOM EXAMPLE

Use estimation to find a decimal that will give a product within 1 of 45 when it is multiplied by 7.

Answer:

Begin by thinking of the nearest whole numbers to multiply by 7.

6 • 7 = 42 (too low), and 7 • 7 = 49 (too high), thus narrowing it down to a decimal between 6 and 7.

Since 45 is a little less than half way between 42 and 49, numbers 6.5 or slightly less should work.

Possible Answers: 6.3, 6.4, or 6.5

Key Concepts

CLOSURE QUESTIONS

How are multiplication of decimals and multiplication of whole numbers alike? How are they different?

Sample Response: Decimal multiplication begins by multiplying the numbers as whole numbers, but for decimal multiplication only, the sum of the number of decimal places in the factors is used to place the decimal point in the product.

Practice & Applications

SUGGESTED ASSIGNMENTS

Core Course
Day 1: Exs. 26–33
Day 2: Exs. 1–12
Day 3: Exs. 13–23, 25

Extended Course
Day 1: Exs. 26–33
Day 2: Exs. 1–12
Day 3: Exs. 13–25

Note: Extended Course assignments can be used to differentiate within the regular classroom. In classrooms where students are grouped homogeneously, the material might be covered in fewer days. In this case assignments may be combined.

ADDITIONAL PRACTICE

See the *Teacher's Resource Book* for additional practice and application exercises for this section.

Section 6

Key Concepts

Decimal Multiplication and Estimation (pp. 185–189)

Example Find 6.17 • 5.3.

Step 1 Multiply the numbers as whole numbers.

$617 • 53 = 32701$

2 decimal places   1 decimal place

$6.17 • 5.3 = 32.701$

Step 2 Use the sum of the numbers of decimal places in the factors to place the decimal point in their product.

$2 + 1 = 3$
3 decimal places

Step 3 Use estimation to check that your answer is reasonable.

6.17 • 5.3 is about 6 • 5 or 30. The answer of 32.701 is reasonable.

17. Answers will vary. Sample: 9 • 10 = 90, so the number must be greater than 10, but less than 11, since 9 • 11 = 99. Also, 93 is close to, but less than halfway between 90 and 99, so the decimal should be close to but less than 0.5. I would choose 10.3 or 10.4. Check: 10.3 • 9 = 92.7; 10.4 • 9 = 93.6.

17 **Key Concepts Question** Your goal is to multiply 9 by a decimal to get a product within 1 of 93. Use estimation to find such a decimal. Explain your thinking. Multiply to check your estimate.

Section 6

Practice & Application Exercises

The digits in each product are correct, but the decimal point is missing. Copy each problem. Then, without using a calculator, place the decimal point in the correct place in each product.

1. 255 • 0.21 = 5355   **53.55**

2. 3.2 • 8.8 = 2816   **28.16**

3. 0.98 • 1.05 = 1029   **1.029**

4. 0.05 • 9.8 = 49   **0.49**

Find each product without using a calculator. Then use estimation to check that your answer is reasonable.

5. 0.3 • 0.12
   0.036; 0.3 • 0.1 = 0.03

6. 4.8 • 5.9
   28.32; 5 • 6 = 30

7. 7.8 • 0.6
   4.68; 8 • 0.6 = 4.8

190

Find each product where *n* = 0.36 **and** *m* = 0.09.

8. 0.01 · *m* 0.0009   9. 24.8 · *n* 8.928   10. *m* · *n* 0.0324

11. **Writing** Without multiplying, would you expect 2.8 · 0.52 to be *greater than or less than* 1.4? Why? Greater than; 2.8 · 0.5 = 1.4, and 0.52 > 0.5

12. A recycling company recycles aluminum for a manufacturer for $1.13 per pound. If the recycling company has 329.7 pounds to recycle, how much money will the recycling company receive? $372.56 (Actual product = 372.561 is rounded to 372.56 since it is money)

Mental Math Use mental math to find each product.

13. 67 · 0.01 0.67   14. 0.01 · 84.7 0.847   15. 263.5 · 0.01 2.635

16. **Energy** A color TV uses 0.23 kilowatts of power. Suppose the electric company charges $0.14 per kilowatt for every hour of use. Choose the best estimate of the cost to watch one hour of TV. b

   A. $0.32   B. $0.03   C. $3.22

WELCOME TO PAY TELEVISION

Charge is 14¢ per kilowatt/hour

Please insert money in box at right

INSERT COINS ABOVE THEN PUSH BUTTON

17. By age 18, a child in the United States will have watched an average of about 17,000 hours of television. Use your answer from Exercise 16 to estimate the cost of watching 17,000 hours of television. about $510

18. This week, Julie Elliot worked her regular 40 hours plus 5.75 hours overtime. For every hour she works overtime, she is paid for 1.5 hours. Her hourly wage is $6.34.

   a. Estimate Julie's total wages this week. Estimates will vary. About $300

   b. Find the exact amount Julie earned this week. $308.28

N **is a decimal number greater than 0. Decide whether each product will be** *greater than, less than*, **or** *equal to N*. **Explain how you know.**

19. 0.87 · *N*   20. 1 · *N*   21. 1.5 · *N*

19. Less than; *N* is multiplied by a number less than 1.

20. Equal to; 1 times any number is that number.

21. Greater than; *N* is multiplied by a number greater than 1.

22. Tamika has a certificate of deposit that earns 4% interest annually. At the end of one year the bank will pay her 4% of the $235.73 she deposited. Estimate 0.04 · $235.73 to choose the correct amount she will receive after one year. b

   A. $.94   B. $9.43   C. $94.29   D. $942.92

23. **Open-ended** Use estimation to find a decimal that will give a product within 1 of 164 when multiplied by 80.
   Accept any estimate from 2.0375 to 2.0625.

Practice & Applications

TEACHING NOTES

In **Exercise 25**, a grid of 1000 squares is used instead of 100. If a 100 grid was used, 21 squares could be shaded (to represent 0.21), but then 3 tenths of the 21 squares could not be represented using full squares. All grids up to this point have been 10 × 10 because the factors were decimals with only tenths. Now, one of the factors has *hundredths*, requiring a 10 × *100* grid. Students should note that 210 squares are shaded (not 21), because this grid is out of thousandths, so 0.21 is equal to 0.210 or 210 thousandths.

24. Challenge Find the least and the greatest possible products for each expression using any of the digits 1–9. A digit may be used only once to find each product.

a. $\boxed{?}.\boxed{?} \times \boxed{?}$
least: $2.3 \cdot 1 = 2.3$,
greatest: $8.7 \cdot 9 = 78.3$

b. $\boxed{?}.\boxed{?} \times \boxed{?}.\boxed{?}$
least: $1.3 \cdot 2.4 = 3.12$,
greatest: $8.7 \cdot 9.6 = 83.52$

Reflecting ◀▶ **on the Section**

25. a. Explain how you can use the product $3 \cdot 21$ to find $0.3 \cdot 0.21$.

b. Part of a 10 x 100 grid used to model $0.3 \cdot 0.21$ is shown. If the whole grid were shown, how many small squares would there be? **1000**

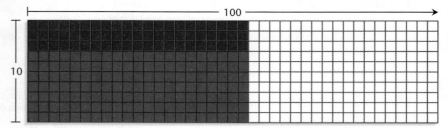

c. Does the shading on the grid show the same result as you found in part (a)? Explain. **Yes, the 63 double-shaded squares represent 63 out of 1000, or 0.063.**

Visual THINKING

Exercise 25 checks that you understand decimal multiplication.

25. a. Multiply the digits of the product. Count the decimal places in the factors of $0.3 \cdot 0.21$. Position the decimal point in the product so it has 3 decimal places. The product is 0.063.

Spiral ◀▶ **Review**

Write each product in lowest terms. (Module 3, p. 178)

26. $\frac{1}{4} \cdot \frac{3}{8}$ $\frac{3}{32}$

27. $\frac{2}{9} \cdot \frac{3}{5}$ $\frac{2}{15}$

28. $\frac{4}{9} \cdot \frac{3}{4}$ $\frac{1}{3}$

Sketch a polygon that fits the description. Then give the name of the polygon. (Module 2, p. 119)

29. A quadrilateral with four sides of equal length and no right angles **Check student sketches. A rhombus that is not a square.**

30. A quadrilateral with at least one right angle and exactly one pair of parallel sides **Check student sketches. a trapezoid**

Evaluate each expression. (Module 1, p. 10)

31. $34 - 6 \cdot 3$ 16

32. $(7 + 16) \cdot 4$ 92

33. $35 - 12 + 9$ 32

Section 6

Extra Skill Practice

The digits in each product are correct, but the decimal point is missing. Copy each problem. Then, without using a calculator, place the decimal point in the correct place in each product.

1. 5.23 • 38 = 19874 **198.74**
2. 652 • 0.24 = 15648 **156.48**
3. 0.002 • 46 = 92 **0.092**
4. 0.4 • 9.01 = 3604 **3.604**

Mental Math Use mental math to find each product.

5. 0.1 • 27.6 **2.76**
6. 3.05 • 0.01 **0.0305**
7. 534 • 0.01 **5.34**

Find each product without using a calculator. Then use estimation to check that your answer is reasonable.

8. 0.6 • 0.42 **0.252**
9. 2.7 • 3.1 **8.37**
10. 9.4 • 0.8 **7.52**
11. 4.35 • 0.54 **2.349**
12. 216 • 1.49 **321.84**
13. 5.6 • 0.009 **0.0504**
14. 0.24 • 16.2 **3.888**
15. 37.5 • 0.02 **0.75**
16. 9.8 • 2.08 **20.384**

Use estimation to choose the decimal that will give a product within 1 of each target number when multiplied by the constant factor. Explain your choice.

17. Target Number = 35   Constant Factor = 101

    Choices: 0.25   0.35   2.9 **0.35; 100 • 0.35 = 35**

18. Target Number = 80   Constant Factor = 55

    Choices: 0.75   1.45   1.65 **1.45; 55 + 25 = 80, and 25 is less than half of 55, so it takes less than 1.5 times 55.**

19. Target Number = 176   Constant Factor = 28

    Choices: 5.89   6.31   7.17 **6.31; 28 • 6 = 168 and 28 • 7 = 196**

Standardized Testing ▷ Open-ended

1. Write a word problem that can be solved using the number sentence 8.99 • 2.5 = __?__. **Sample: Sam bought 2.5 lb of fish at $8.99 per pound. How much did Sam pay for the fish?**

2. Find a number you can multiply 7.6 by to get a product which is greater than 3.8, but less than 7.6. **Sample: 0.75 (Any number between 0.5 and 1 is an acceptable answer.)**

3. Write an example to show that the product of two numbers can sometimes be less than either of the factors. **Sample: 0.5 • 0.1 = 0.05**

Extra Skill Practice

TEACHER NOTES

For each Exploration, the corresponding Extra Skill Practice Exercises are noted.

Exploration 1: Exs. 1–4
Exploration 2: Exs. 5–19

Note that Exercises 8–16 could be completed following Exploration 1. However, students may be able to better estimate the products to check for reasonableness after having completed the additional estimation activities in Exploration 2.

EXTRA HELP

Teacher's Resource Book

• Practice and Applications for Section 6
• Study Guide
• Practice and Applications for Sections 1–6

Technology Resources

• @Home Tutor
• Test Generator

ASSESSMENT

• Section 6 Quick Quiz
• Test Generator

Module Project

PROJECT NOTES

The Module Project follows the module theme of *Mind Games* by introducing students to the process of creating a number puzzle using some of the concepts taught in this module. It culminates with students creating their own unique puzzle for a class book of puzzles. As students create their own puzzles, encourage them to be imaginative in choosing their puzzle theme. Make sure students realize they should not spend time decorating/illustrating their first draft, as there may be revisions to make following **Question 9**. For accessibility for all students, you might encourage some to perfect their puzzles created in **Questions 4 and 7. Questions 4 and 7** might also be done as a class to provide additional discussion of how to create a puzzle.

Puzzle Making

Story and number puzzles can be fun to solve and fun to create. You will explore how to solve several different types of puzzles. Then you will use the mathematics you have learned in this module to create your own puzzle. At the end of the project you will combine your puzzle with those of your classmates in a *Class Puzzle Book*.

Divisibility The puzzle on the notebook includes clues that involve divisibility.

> **What's the number?**
> - It has two digits.
> - It is divisible by 5.
> - It is divisible by 3.
> - It is an odd number.
> - It is greater than 70.

1 Solve the puzzle. Is there more than one possible answer?
75; No, the next odd multiple of 15 is 105 which has 3 digits.

2 How can you combine the two divisibility clues?
The number is divisible by 15.

3 Suppose the fourth clue had been, "It is an even number." What would the solution be? 90

4 **Create Your Own** Write a number puzzle that has 5 clues. At least one clue must involve divisibility.
Answers will vary. Check students' puzzles.

Cross Number Puzzles Cross Number Puzzles can be created by writing problems so that answers in overlapping squares of the puzzle have the same digits. Unused squares are filled in gray.

5 Use the clues to answer *3 down* and *7 across*.
3 down: 50.2
7 across: 125

Across	Down
1. 11.4 · 0.4	**1.** 12.8 – 7.9
5. one and four thousandths	**2.** 0.05 · 0.03
6. numerator of $32\frac{2}{9}$ when written as a fraction.	**3.** 22 + 28.2
	4. 8^2
7. a multiple of 25	**5.**
9.	**8.** a prime between 50 and 60
10. GCF of 27 and 18	

Parts of this puzzle were created by working backwards, first filling in answers on the cross number grid and then writing the clues.

6 Clues for *9 across* and *5 down* have not yet been written. Write a clue for each that will produce the answers shown in the corresponding numbered boxes of the cross number puzzle.
Answers will vary. Sample Response: 9 across: 1.7 · 5; 5 down: $(1.6)^2 \div 0.2$

Using Fractions Here is a way to create a story puzzle.

Puzzle answer = 120   **Puzzle clues**

Step 1: Start with a number that has many factors. Choose some operations to carry out.

$\frac{1}{2}$ of 120 = 60 $\longrightarrow$
120 − 60 = 60 $\longrightarrow$
$\frac{1}{3}$ of 60 = 20
60 − 20 = 40 $\longrightarrow$
40 − 40 = 0

• Person A took $\frac{1}{2}$.
• Person B took $\frac{1}{3}$ of what was left.
• Person C took the 40 that were left.

Step 2: Use the numbers from Step 1 to write the clues.

Step 3: Think of a theme. Then create a story using the clues.

Camp Cookies Puzzle When Janell went to camp, her mom sent along a box of cookies. Janell gave half of the cookies to her roommate. She then gave one third of the remaining cookies to her camp counselor. Janell hid the 40 cookies that were left. How many cookies did Janell's mom send?

7 **Create Your Own** Follow Steps 1-3 to write your own fraction story puzzle that has an answer of 270. Answers will vary. Check students' puzzles.

Choosing a Puzzle You have learned to create different kinds of puzzles. Now you will decide on a puzzle to include in a class puzzle book.
8–12. Check students' completed puzzles and answer keys.

8 Choose the best puzzle you have created, or write a new one. Your puzzle should include at least one idea from this module:

- ◆ Factors and multiples
- ◆ Fraction multiplication
- ◆ Primes and composites
- ◆ Decimal multiplication

- ◆ Powers of a number
- ◆ Mixed numbers as fractions
- ◆ Divisibility
- ◆ Decimal addition/subtraction

9 Look back over your puzzle. Are the directions and the information clear? Try your puzzle on a friend or a family member. Then make any necessary revisions.

10 Write your puzzle neatly on a sheet of paper that can be three-hole punched to fit in a class notebook. You can attach an envelope to include any clue cards or other materials needed to solve the puzzle.

11 Label your puzzle sheet with the title of the puzzle and your name as the puzzle maker. You may decorate or illustrate your puzzle sheet if you wish.

12 On a separate sheet of paper write the answer to your puzzle and show how it can be solved. Label your answer sheet the same way as your puzzle sheet.

Review and Assessment

Write each decimal in words. (Sec. 1, Explor. 1)

1. 6.56
six and fifty-six hundredths
2. 0.0007
seven ten-thousandths
3. 1208.3

4. 35.1
thirty-five and one tenth
5. 0.123
6. 25,001.05

7. 521.63
8. 1.022
9. 600.07

3. one thousand two hundred eight and three tenths

5. one hundred twenty-three thousandths

6. twenty-five thousand one and five hundredths

7. five hundred twenty-one and sixty-three hundredths

8. one and twenty-two thousandths

9. six hundred and seven hundredths

Replace each ? with <, >, or =. (Sec. 1, Explor. 2)

10. 3.1456 ? 3.1465 <
11. 0.17 ? 0.1701 <
12. 475.12 ? 475.120 =
13. 28.883 ? 28.8829 >
14. sixteen hundredths ? four tenths <
15. fourteen and seven hundredths ? fourteen and seventy thousandths =

Find each sum or difference without using a calculator. (Sec. 2, Explors. 1 and 2)

16. 500 + 0.92 500.92
17. 9.253 + 1.747 11
18. 0.453 + 2.6 + 3.05 6.103
19. 18.25 − 3.08 15.17
20. 4.93 − 2.718 2.212
21. 7.147 − 0.9 − 1.03 5.217

22. Max spent $3.85 on materials to make a birthday card. Rachel spent $2.34 less than Max. Alisha spent $1.47 more than Rachel. (Sec. 2, Explors. 1 and 2)

   a. Find how much each student spent. Max $3.85, Rachel $1.51, Alisha $2.98

   b. What was the total amount spent by the three students? $8.34

The ones digit in the number below is missing. For Exercises 23–26, list every digit from 0 through 9 that will complete the number to make each statement true. (Sec. 3, Explor. 1)

721,638,51__

23. The number is divisible by 2. 0, 2, 4, 6, 8
24. The number is divisible by 5. 0, 5
25. The number is divisible by 3. 0, 3, 6, 9
26. The number is divisible by 9. 3
27. **Writing** Jim listed 1, 2, 3, 4, 9, 12, 27, 36, 54, and 108 as the factors of 108. Is his list complete? How did you check?
(Sec. 3, Explor. 1) No; he missed 6 × 18; Sample Response: I tried all the factors from 1 to 11 and checked for each matching factor so that the pairs produce a product of 108.

Find the GCF of each set of numbers. (Sec. 3, Explor. 1)

28. 36 and 48 12   **29.** 15, 20, and 32 1 **30.** 26 and 52 26

Tell whether each number is prime or composite. (Sec. 3, Explor. 2)

31. 22 composite **32.** 51 composite **33.** 47 prime   **34.** 111,111 composite

Replace each ? with >, <, or =. Explain your choice. (Sec. 3, Explor. 3) 36. =; $4 \cdot 4 \cdot 4 =$

35. 2^5 ? 5^2 **36.** 4^3 ? 2^6 **37.** 3^3 ? $3 \cdot 3 \cdot 3 \cdot 3$ $(2 \cdot 2) \cdot (2 \cdot 2) \cdot (2 \cdot 2) = 64$
>; $32 > 25$ <; $3^3 < 3^4$

Write the prime factorization of each number, using exponents for repeated factors. (Sec. 3, Explor. 3)

38. 32   **39.** 97   **40.** 300   **41.** 231
2^5 97 $2^2 \cdot 3 \cdot 5^2$ $3 \cdot 7 \cdot 11$

42. Mark has swim practice every other day. His brother swims every third day. If they both practice on Monday, what is the next day both Mark and his brother will have practice? (Sec. 4, Explor. 1) Sunday

Find each product. Write each answer in lowest terms.
(Sec. 5, Explors. 1 and 2)

43. $\frac{3}{8} \cdot \frac{4}{15}$ $\frac{1}{10}$ **44.** $\frac{5}{7} \cdot \frac{2}{3}$ $\frac{10}{21}$ **45.** $\frac{5}{16} \cdot \frac{8}{9}$ $\frac{5}{18}$ **46.** $\frac{3}{5} \cdot \frac{15}{24}$ $\frac{3}{8}$

47. $6\frac{3}{4} \cdot 1\frac{2}{3}$ **48.** $3\frac{1}{3} \cdot 2\frac{1}{2}$ **49.** $1\frac{5}{8} \cdot \frac{1}{3}$ $\frac{13}{24}$ **50.** $\frac{3}{5} \cdot 4\frac{5}{6}$
$\frac{45}{4}$ or $11\frac{1}{4}$ $\frac{50}{6}$ or $8\frac{1}{3}$ $\frac{29}{10}$ or $2\frac{9}{10}$

Use the distributive property and mental math to find each product. Write each answer in lowest terms. (Sec. 5, Explor. 2)

51. $4 \cdot 1\frac{3}{4}$ 7   **52.** $2\frac{5}{6} \cdot 12$ 34 **53.** $5 \cdot 3\frac{1}{5}$ 16   **54.** $2\frac{3}{5} \cdot 10$ 26

Find each product without using a calculator. Then use estimation to check that your answer is reasonable. (Sec. 6, Explor. 1)

55. $0.4 \cdot 0.32$ 0.128   **56.** $36.3 \cdot 51$ 1851.3   **57.** $4.7 \cdot 0.006$ 0.0282

Reflecting ◀▶ on the Module

58. Write a letter to an adult member of your family describing the math you learned in this module and what you liked most and least about the module. Answers will vary.

Statistical Safari

Module 4 Overview

Data about animals are used to explore techniques for displaying information visually and analyzing it numerically. There are opportunities to apply written computation skills, develop mental math and estimation strategies, and use a calculator, as well as to apply algebraic concepts and work with metric measurement. Students focus on such themes as mammals of Yellowstone Park, threatened and endangered species, dinosaurs, and the mathematics in the book *Phantom Toolbooth*.

Module 4 Planner

Day 1: Section 1	Day 2: Section 1	Day 3: Section 1	Day 4: Section 1	Day 5: Section 2
Setting the Stage, p. 200 Exploration 1, pp. 201–202	Exploration 2 *through* Question 8, p. 203	Exploration 2 *from* Question 9, pp. 203–205	Exploration 3 pp. 205–207 Key Concepts, p. 208	Setting the Stage, p. 214 Exploration 1, pp. 215–217
Day 6: Section 2	**Day 7: Section 2**	**Day 8: Section 2**	**Day 9: Section 3**	**Day 10: Section 3**
Exploration 2 *through* Question 15, pp. 218–219	Exploration 2 *from* Question 16, pp. 219–220	Exploration 3, pp. 221–224 Key Concepts, pp. 224–225	Setting the Stage, p. 231 Exploration 1, pp. 232–233	Exploration 2, pp. 234–237
Day 11: Section 3	**Day 12: E²**	**Day 13: Review and Assessment**	**Day 14: Section 4**	**Day 15: Section 4**
Exploration 3, pp. 237–239 Key Concepts, p. 240	Begin E², p. 247	**Mid-Module Quiz**	Setting the Stage, p. 248 Exploration 1, pp. 249–250	Exploration 2, pp. 251–252
Day 16: Section 4	**Day 17: Section 4**	**Day 18: Module Project**	**Day 19: Section 5**	**Day 20: Section 5**
Exploration 3 through Question 19, pp. 253–254	Exploration 3 *from* Labsheet, pp. 254–255 Key Concepts, p. 256	Begin Module Project pp. 276–277	Setting the Stage, pp. 264–265 Exploration 1 *through* Question 6, p. 265	Exploration 1 *from* Question 7, p. 266
Day 21: Section 5	**Day 22: Module Project**	**Day 23: Review and Assessment**	**Day 24: Review and Assessment**	**Day 25: Assessment**
Exploration 2, pp. 267–269 Key Concepts, p. 270	Work on Module Project, pp. 276–277	Assign Review and Assessment, pp. 278–279	Discuss Review and Assessment, pp. 278–279	Module Test

Materials List

Section	Materials
1	• Labsheets 1A–1F, scissors, tape, metric ruler
2	• 30 chips per group, calculator
3	• Labsheets 3A–3B, algebra tiles
4	• Labsheets 4A–4D, graph paper
5	• Labsheets 5A–5D, graph paper, calculator
Project	• Project Labsheet A, access to newspapers, magazines, or internet articles

Module 4 Objectives

Section	Objectives	NCTM Standards 2000*
1	• Sort sets of data. • Use benchmarks to estimate metric length and metric mass. • Use appropriate metric units to measure length and mass. • Multiply decimals mentally by special multipliers like 0.001 and 1000. • Convert between metric units of length and between metric units of mass.	1, 4, 5, 6, 7, 8, 9, 10
2	• Draw and interpret line plots. • Use averages to describe data. • Write a fraction as a decimal using a calculator. • Choose appropriate averages. • Round decimal quotients.	1, 4, 5, 6, 7, 8, 9, 10
3	• Divide a decimal by a whole number. • Write addition and subtraction equations. • Solve addition equations using models. • Use inverse operations to solve addition and subtraction equations.	1, 2, 4, 6, 7, 8, 9, 10
4	• Make and interpret a stem-and-leaf plot. • Divide by a decimal. • Graph pairs of values on a coordinate grid.	1, 2, 4, 5, 6, 7, 8, 9, 10
5	• Make a line graph. • Understand how changing a graph scale can create different impressions of the data • Choose an appropriate average.	1, 4, 5, 6, 7, 8, 9, 10

* See page T14.

Section 1 Sets and Metric Measurement

Section 1 Planner

Section Objectives

Exploration 1
• Sort sets of data

Exploration 2
• Use benchmarks to estimate metric length and metric mass
• Use appropriate metric units to measure length and mass

Exploration 3
• Multiply decimals mentally by special multipliers like 0.001 or 1000
• Convert between metric units of length and between metric units of mass

Days for Section 1

First Day
Setting the Stage, *p. 200*
Exploration 1, *pp. 201–202*

Second Day
Exploration 2 through Question 8, *pp. 203*

Third Day
Exploration 2 from Question 9, *pp. 203–205*

Fourth Day
Exploration 3, *pp. 205–207*
Key Concepts, *p. 208*

Teaching Resources

Teacher's Resource Book
• Warm-Up
• Labsheets 1A–1F
• Practice and Applications
• Study Guide
See page 199 for additional teaching resources.

Materials List

Exploration 1
• Labsheets 1A–1C
• scissors

Exploration 2
• Labsheet 1D
• scissors
• tape

Exploration 3
• Labsheets 1E–1F

Practice and Applications
• metric ruler

Assessment Options

EMBEDDED ASSESSMENT
• Sort sets of data
  Exercises 1, 3, 4, 5
• Use benchmarks to estimate metric length and metric mass
  Exercises 13, 15, 19, 21, 24, 26
• Use appropriate metric units to measure length and mass
  Exercises 16, 18, 23
• Multiply decimals mentally by special multipliers like 0.001 or 1000
  Exercises 30, 32, 33
• Convert between metric units of length and between metric units of mass
  Exercises 36, 38, 42, 44

PERFORMANCE TASK/PORTFOLIO
• Exercises 13–21 on *p. 210*
• Exercise 46 on *p. 211 (journal)*

QUIZZES/TESTS
• Section 1 Quick Quiz

TEST GENERATOR

Section 1 Overview

In this section, students begin a study of statistics that will continue throughout Module 4. They will learn to use graphs, averages, equations, and metric measurements to describe and compare animals.

Exploration 1
Students use a sorting grid to sort mammal cards into various sets by characteristics such as mass, body length, and life span. The concept of empty set is introduced and defined.

Exploration 2
Exploration 2 focuses on estimating metric lengths. Students develop their own benchmarks for metric lengths and use them to estimate other metric lengths. Once students are able to associate a millimeter, a centimeter, and a meter with the lengths of physical objects, they learn to convert between metric units.

Exploration 3
In Exploration 3, the metric prefixes *kilo, hecto, deka, deci, centi,* and *milli* are introduced as a tool for determining the relationships between metric units of both length and mass.

Guide for Assigning Homework

Section/ P&A Pages	Core Assignment	Extended Assignment	Additional Practice/Review	Open-ended Problems	Extended Problems
1 pp. 209–213	**Day 1:** 1–7 **Day 2:** 8–12, SR 47–51 **Day 3:** 13–27 **Day 3:** 28–45, ROS 46	1–7 8–12, SR 47–51 13–27 28–45, ROS 46	EP, p. 213		

Key: PA = Practice & Application; ROS = Reflecting on the Section; SR = Spiral Review; TB = Toolbox; EP = Extra Skill Practice; Ext = Extension; ST = Standardized Testing

Math Background and Teaching Strategies

Classroom Notes

Bulletin board display ideas for this section include:

- pictures and information to match animal cards
- information on Yellowstone Park
- chart of metric prefixes and their meanings

Visitors for this section might include:

- wildlife biologist or a veterinarian

Math Strands

Topic Integration and Spiraling

Exploration 1

A set of animal statistics cards are used to introduce the metric measures for length and mass. By sorting the animals into various sets according to a given characteristic such as mass, students begin to develop a sense of how different measures such as kilograms and grams compare. After simple sorting into 2 columns, students create a diagram with cells that correspond to two characteristics such as mass *and* length. Sorting the cards in this new diagram opens up the opportunity for discussion of an empty set. In this exploration students are exposed to a method of sorting that can be used in place of or in addition to the Venn diagrams used in Module 2 Section 4.

Exploration 2

In Exploration 2 students develop benchmarks for metric measures of length in order to improve their estimation skills and their ability to visualize and compare measures in the metric system. Actual lengths are measured to the nearest millimeter and centimeter, helping to develop the relationship between the two. Metric benchmarks for mass are given and choosing an appropriate metric unit for measuring the masses of different items is practiced.

Exploration 3

Students apply the decimal multiplication skills learned in Section 6 of Module 3 as they learn to convert between metric units of length and between metric units of mass. The relationships between metric measures are expressed in conjunction with the prefix meanings. Understanding the meanings of the prefixes enables students to apply conversion methods to units of either length or mass, and eventually to units of capacity in Module 8.

In Modules 5–8, students will apply metric measurement to proportions, perimeter, area, volume, and capacity. The development of metric capacity will occur in Module 8.

Section ② Line Plots and Averages

Section 2 Planner

Section Objectives

Exploration 1
• Draw and interpret line plots

Exploration 2
• Use averages to describe data

Exploration 3
• Write a fraction as a decimal using a calculator
• Choose appropriate averages
• Round decimal quotients

Days for Section 2

First Day
Setting the Stage, *p. 214*
Exploration 1, *pp. 215–217*

Second Day
Exploration 2 through Question 15, *pp. 218–219*

Third Day
Exploration 2 from Question 16, *pp. 219–220*

Fourth Day
Exploration 3, *pp. 221–224*
Key Concepts, *pp. 224–225*

Teaching Resources

Teacher's Resource Book
• Warm-Up
• Practice and Applications
• Study Guide
See page 199 for additional teaching resources.

Materials List

Exploration 2
• 30 chips per group

Exploration 3
• 11 chips per group
• calculator

Assessment Options

EMBEDDED ASSESSMENT
• Draw line plots
  Exercises 5, 6
• Interpret line plots
  Exercises 7–9
• Use averages to describe data
  Exercises 12, 14, 16
• Write a fraction as a decimal using a calculator
  Exercises 21, 22, 26
• Choose appropriate averages
  Exercises 18, 19
• Round decimals
  Exercises 31, 35

PERFORMANCE TASK/PORTFOLIO
• Exercise 16 on *p. 227 (open-ended)*
• Exercise 17 on *p. 227 (challenge)*
• Exercise 28 on *p. 228*
• Exercise 37 on *p. 229 (discussion)*
• Standardized Testing on *p. 230 (free response)*

QUIZZES/TESTS
• Section 2 Quick Quiz

TEST GENERATOR

Section 2 Overview

In this section, students continue to study statistics by organizing their data in visual displays for easier interpretation. They will also use the plots to determine types of averages that can be reported.

Exploration 1
Students use a table and a line plot to gather information about the average number of children in a family. By comparing the data in the table to the line plot, students learn how a line plot is constructed. The key term *range* is defined through a discussion of the scale of the line plot. Students then create their own line plot from a table showing the hours various animals sleep each day.

Exploration 2
Exploration 2 explores data about animals to discuss the meaning of average. Students learn how either the mean, the median, or the mode can describe the average number in a data set. They begin their study of averages by physically modeling the average of a set of data with chips on a line plot.

Exploration 3
Students use chips to try to find the mean of a data set and realize that sometimes this average may include decimals or fractions. Students use a calculator to express a fraction as a decimal when calculating means and medians, rounding to the nearest hundredth or thousandth when necessary.

Guide for Assigning Homework

REGULAR SCHEDULING (45 MIN CLASS PERIOD)			EXERCISES TO NOTE		
Section/ P&A Pages	Core Assignment	Extended Assignment	Additional Practice/Review	Open-ended Problems	Extended Problems
2 pp. 226–230	**Day 1:** 1–9 **Day 2:** SR 38–47 **Day 3:** 10–16 **Day 4:** 18–36, ROS 37	1–9 SR 38–47 10–17 18–29, 36, ROS 37	EP, p. 230	PA 16 ST, p. 230	Challenge PA 17

Key: PA = Practice & Application; ROS = Reflecting on the Section; SR = Spiral Review; TB = Toolbox; EP = Extra Skill Practice; Ext = Extension; ST = Standardized Testing

Math Background and Teaching Strategies

Classroom Notes

Bulletin board display ideas for this section include:

• Yellowstone mammal cards

• Information on Yellowstone Park and its wolf packs

Interest centers for this section might include:

• copies of *The Phantom Tollbooth* by Norton Juster

• computer station with access to a data analysis program for creating line plots

Math Strands

Topic Spiraling and Integration

In this section students explore different averages that are commonly used to describe sets of data.

Exploration 1

Line plots are simple visual data displays that show the range, the modes, and any clusters or gaps in a set of data. A line plot makes it easy to find the median of a set of data since the data values are ordered and each value is represented by marking a symbol, such as an X or O, above the corresponding number on a number line. If students have worked with bar graphs and pictographs, they should be able to easily read and interpret line plots. It is important to note that line plots differ from pictographs and bar graphs in that line plots are only used to display numerical data, not categorical data.

Exploration 2

In statistics, an average is a way to describe a "typical" value in a data set. The word average is often erroneously used as a synonym for the mean, an average found by summing the data and dividing by the number of data values. The median and mode are also averages frequently used in the media to report such things as the "average" house price or the "average" number of household pets.

Exploration 3

By learning to convert fractions to decimals, students become aware that an average like 2.58 is probably referring to the mean of the data. When working with whole number data it is not possible for the mode to be anything but one of the whole number data values, and the median must either equal one of the data values or be halfway between two values, perhaps producing 2.5, but not 2.58. As students encounter fractions in percents, proportions, and equations, they will be able to convert the fractions to decimals when necessary.

Section 3 Planner

Section Objectives

Exploration 1
• Divide a decimal by a whole number

Exploration 2
• Write addition and subtraction equations
• Solve addition equations using models

Exploration 3
• Use inverse operations to solve addition and subtraction equations

Days for Section 3

First Day
Setting the Stage, *p. 231*
Exploration 1, *pp. 232–233*

Second Day
Exploration 2, *pp. 234–237*

Third Day
Exploration 3, *pp. 237–239*
Key Concepts, *p. 240*

Teaching Resources

Teacher's Resource Book
• Warm-Up
• Labsheets 3A and 3B
• Practice and Applications
• Study Guide
See page 199 for additional teaching resources.

Materials List

Exploration 1
• Labsheets 3A–3B

Exploration 2
• algebra tiles

Practice and Applications
• algebra tiles

Assessment Options

EMBEDDED ASSESSMENT
• Divide a decimal by a whole number
  Exercises 6, 9, 11
• Write addition and subtraction equations
  Exercises 18, 29, 32
• Solve addition equations using models
  Exercises 22, 23
• Use inverse operations to solve addition and subtraction equations
  Exercises 34, 36, 40

PERFORMANCE TASK/PORTFOLIO
• Exercise 23 on *p. 242*
• Exercises 19–20 on *p. 242 (open-ended)*
• Exercise 46 on *p. 243 (challenge)*
• Exercise 50 on *p. 243 (writing)*
• Extended Exploration on *p. 247**

* *indicates a problem-solving task that can be assessed using the Assessment Scales*

QUIZZES/TESTS
• Section 3 Quick Quiz
• Mid-Module Quiz

TEST GENERATOR

Section 3 Overview

In this section, students will divide decimals and learn to write, model, and solve addition and subtraction equations.

Exploration 1
Students begin by investigating the mean masses of small mammals living in Yellowstone National Park. This activity introduces them to division of a decimal by a whole number. Students use a 10×10 grid to perform the divisions. Then they use compatible numbers to check the reasonableness of a quotient. Students also explore division problems that have remainders.

Exploration 2
Students use the masses of foods eaten by various animals to model addition and subtraction equations. Algebra tiles are introduced and used to model and solve these equations.

Exploration 3
Solving addition and subtraction equations is extended to using inverse operations. Students are exposed to solving equations containing whole numbers and/or decimals.

Guide for Assigning Homework

REGULAR SCHEDULING (45 MIN CLASS PERIOD)			EXERCISES TO NOTE		
Section/ P&A Pages	**Core Assignment**	**Extended Assignment**	**Additional Practice/Review**	**Open-ended Problems**	**Extended Problems**
3 pp. 241–246	**Day 1:** 1–16, SR 58–68 **Day 2:** 17–32, SR 69–78 **Day 3:** 33–56, ROS 57	1–16, SR 58–68 17–32, SR 69–78 34–46 even, 51–56, ROS 57, Ext 79–84	EP, p. 246	PA 19, 20 E², p. 247	Challenge PA 46 Ext 79–84

Key: PA = Practice & Application; ROS = Reflecting on the Section; SR = Spiral Review; TB = Toolbox; EP = Extra Skill Practice; Ext = Extension; ST = Standardized Testing

Math Background and Teaching Strategies

Classroom Notes

Bulletin board displays for this section include:

- pictures and information to match animal cards

- information on Yellowstone National Park

- a display showing an equation solved using tiles and solved algebraically.

- student generated situations to P&A Exercises 19 and 20

Math Strands

Topic Spiraling and Integration

Exploration 1

Students continue their work with decimals, learning to divide a decimal by a whole number. The concept is developed in the context of finding the mean of a set of data. To understand the placement of the decimal, the divisions are modeled with 10×10 grids. The use of the grids reviews and reinforces decimal place value and the modeling of decimals with base ten blocks from Module 3. Students continue to practice mental math strategies, using compatible numbers and estimation to check the reasonableness of their quotients. Division of decimals with decimal divisors will be introduced in Section 4 of Module 4.

Exploration 2

Exploration 2 focuses on writing and modeling equations. Students have used pattern blocks and base ten blocks to model fractions and decimals respectively. Now students learn how to use algebra tiles to model equations. Representing quantities that can change or are unknown with variables is revisited

from Module 1.

Exploration 3

Algebra tile models are used to introduce the use of inverse operations for solving equations. The solution of an equation using algebra tiles and its solution using inverse operations are modeled side by side, helping students make the transition from the concrete to the abstract. The need for solving equations with inverse operations is introduced via equations containing decimals.

At this point, the equations students are solving involve only addition and subtraction. Solving equations involving multiplication and division is introduced in Module 5 when one of the dimensions needed for calculating the area of a figure is missing. Equations with more than one operation involving decimals, fractions, or integers are covered in Books 2 and 3.

Section 4 Stem-and-Leaf Plots, Decimal Division, and Graphing

Section 4 Planner

Section Objectives

Exploration 1
• Make and interpret a stem-and-leaf plot

Exploration 2
• Divide by a decimal

Exploration 3
• Graph pairs of values on a coordinate grid

Days for Section 4

First Day
Setting the Stage, *p. 248*
Exploration 1, *pp. 249–250*

Second Day
Exploration 2, *pp. 251–252*

Third Day
Exploration 3 through Question 19, *pp. 253–254*

Fourth Day
Exploration 3 from Labsheet, *pp. 254–255*
Key Concepts, *p. 256*

Teaching Resources

Teacher's Resource Book
• Warm-Up
• Labsheets 4A, 4B, 4C, and 4D
• Practice and Applications
• Study Guide
See page 199 for additional teaching resources.

Materials List

Exploration 1
• Labsheet 4A

Exploration 2
• Labsheet 4B

Exploration 3
• Labsheets 4C–4D

Practice and Applications
• graph paper

Assessment Options

EMBEDDED ASSESSMENT
• Make and interpret a stem-and-leaf plot
  Exercises 1, 2, 7, 8
• Divide by a decimal
  Exercises 15, 19, 21, 28
• Graph pairs of values on a coordinate grid
  Exercises 39, 41, 43(a)

PERFORMANCE TASK/PORTFOLIO
• Exercise 26 on *p. 259*
• Exercise 46 on *p. 260 (challenge)*
• Exercises 50–51 on *p. 261 (journal)*
• Standardized Testing on *p. 263 (performance task)*

QUIZZES/TESTS
• Section 4 Quick Quiz

TEST GENERATOR

Section 4 Overview

In this section, students will study the characteristics and habits of different dinosaurs. They will use stem-and-leaf plots, decimal division, and graphing on a coordinate grid to represent data about the dinosaurs.

Exploration 1
Students use a stem-and-leaf plot to gather information about the lengths of various dinosaurs. They learn how a stem-and-leaf plot shows the spread of data. Students analyze the plot to determine the range, the mode, and the median of the plotted data. The exploration concludes with students making their own stem-and-leaf plot from a table of data.

Exploration 2
Using the mass of food dinosaurs need to eat each day, students are introduced to division of a decimal by a decimal. They use division grids, patterns, and multiplication by powers of 10 to find the quotients.

Exploration 3
Students play the game *Guess My Rule*, in which they use input and output values to try to guess the rule or expression that creates the given output. Values are recorded in a table and then as ordered pairs that are plotted in the first quadrant of a coordinate grid.

Guide for Assigning Homework

Section/ P&A Pages	Core Assignment	Extended Assignment	Additional Practice/Review	Open-ended Problems	Extended Problems
REGULAR SCHEDULING (45 MIN CLASS PERIOD)			**EXERCISES TO NOTE**		
4 pp. 257–263	**Day 1:** 1–14 **Day 2:** 15–29 **Day 3:** 47–49, SR 52–57 **Day 4:** 31–45, ROS 50–51	1–14, Ext 58–61 15–23 odd, 24–30 47–49, SR 52–57 31–46, ROS 50–51	EP, p. 263		Challenge PA 30, 46 Ext 58–61

Key: PA = Practice & Application; ROS = Reflecting on the Section; SR = Spiral Review; TB = Toolbox; EP = Extra Skill Practice; Ext = Extension; ST = Standardized Testing

Math Background and Teaching Strategies

Classroom Notes

Bulletin board display ideas for this section include:

• information about dinosaurs

Visitors/field trips might include:

• paleontologists

• museum exhibits on dinosaurs

Interest centers might include:

• books on dinosaurs

• more "Guess My Rule" activities

• coordinate graphing activities that form pictures when points are connected in order

Math Strands

Topic Spiraling and Integration

In this section, the theme of dinosaurs connects graphical representations and decimal division.

Exploration 1

Exploration 1 introduces the use of stem-and-leaf plots for organizing and interpreting sets of data. Students learned to create and interpret line plots in Section 2. The addition of stem-and-leaf plots expands their repertoire of different types of data displays. Measures of central tendency are revisited from Section 2 of this module as students use stem-and-leaf plots to find the mean, median, mode, and range of sets of data.

Exploration 2

The study of decimal division is continued from Section 3 of this module by introducing division containing a decimal divisor. The topic is approached by using division grids and by looking for patterns. The trick of "moving the decimals to the right in the divisor and dividend" is demystified by relating the equivalence of various division problems to equivalent fractions in which the numerator and the denominator have been multiplied by the same factor.

Exploration 3

Exploration 3 begins an informal study of functions and graphing through a game in which students "guess the rule" based on input and output values. Using the algebra skills learned in Section 2 of Module 1, students look for a pattern and write an equation to represent the pattern observed. The study of how input and output values relate to coordinate graphing begins building a foundation for writing, reading, and graphing equations. Graphing at this point is limited to the first quadrant. Extension to the other three quadrants will be made in Module 7 and Books 2 and 3 where coordinate graphing is used extensively.

Section 5 Planner

Section Objectives

Exploration 1
- Construct a line graph
- Understand how changing a graph scale can create different impressions of the data

Exploration 2
- Choose an appropriate average

Days for Section 5

First Day
Setting the Stage, *pp. 264–265*
Exploration 1 through Question 6, *p. 265*

Second Day
Exploration 1 from Question 7, *p. 266*

Third Day
Exploration 2, *pp. 267–269*
Key Concepts, *p. 270*

Teaching Resources

Teacher's Resource Book
- Warm-Up
- Labsheets 5A, 5B, 5C, and 5D
- Practice and Applications
- Study Guide
See page 199 for additional teaching resources.

Materials List

Exploration 1
- Labsheets 5A–5B

Exploration 2
- Labsheet 5C
- calculator

Practice and Applications
- graph paper
- Labsheet 5D

Assessment Options

EMBEDDED ASSESSMENT
- Construct a line graph
  Exercise 1
- Understand how changing a graph scale can create different impressions of the data
  Exercises 5, 6
- Choose an appropriate average
  Exercises 10(b), 12

PERFORMANCE TASK/PORTFOLIO
- Exercise 14 on *p. 273 (open-ended)*
- Exercises 15–17 on *p. 274 (challenge)*
- Exercise 18 on *p. 274 (research)*
- Standardized Testing on *p. 275 (open-ended)*
- Module Project on *pp. 276–277*

QUIZZES/TESTS
- Section 5 Quick Quiz
- Module Tests A and B
- Module Standardized Test
- Module Performance Assessment

TEST GENERATOR

Section 5 Overview

In this section, students will study ways in which graphs displaying data can be misleading, and how an average of a set of data can give a false impression of the typical data value.

Exploration 1
Students construct two line graphs using population data for the California condor. The two line graphs display the same data but have different vertical scales, thus helping students see how the choice of the scale can affect the appearance of a line graph and the interpretation of the data it displays.

Exploration 2
Students analyze a wildlife article to predict which average (mean, median, or mode) a reporter used. They confirm or reject their predictions by calculating all three averages for the data upon which the article was based. Then students discuss why they think the reporter used the average he or she did. Students study populations that are endangered or extinct to determine when a particular average is more appropriate to use.

Guide for Assigning Homework

REGULAR SCHEDULING (45 MIN CLASS PERIOD)			EXERCISES TO NOTE		
Section/ P&A Pages	Core Assignment	Extended Assignment	Additional Practice/Review	Open-ended Problems	Extended Problems
5 pp. 271–275	**Day 1:** 2–5, SR 19–23 **Day 2:** 1, 6–9 **Day 3:** 10–14, ROS 18	2–5, SR 19–23 1, 6–9 10–17, ROS 18	EP, p. 275 Review & Assessment, pp. 278–279	PA 14 ST, p. 275 Mod Proj, pp. 276–277	Challenge PA 15–17 Mod Proj, pp. 276–277

Key: PA = Practice & Application; ROS = Reflecting on the Section; SR = Spiral Review; TB = Toolbox; EP = Extra Skill Practice; Ext = Extension; ST = Standardized Testing

Math Background and Teaching Strategies

Classroom Notes

Bulletin board display ideas for this section include:

- chart showing local population density and growth rate

- information on the endangered species act with a list of species currently listed

- misleading graphs from newspapers and magazines

- Module Project information and schedule (see p. 276 notes)

Student work displays might include:

- graphs from Question 11(c)

- responses to Reflecting Exercise 18

- Module Project articles

Math Strands

Topic Spiraling and Integration

Line graphs and choosing an appropriate average for a set of data are introduced in this section.

Exploration 1

Line graphs are typically used to show change over time. Since time is the independent variable, it is usually graphed along the horizontal axis and the variable being measured is graphed along the vertical axis. The graph is completed by connecting successive data points with segments. Students explore how the steepness of the segments reflects change, thus providing an informal introduction to slope. Students use graphing skills from Section 4 to plot points and create line graphs. Line graphs with different scales are compared to see how the choice of scales can alter the impression and interpretation of the data displayed in the graphs.

Exploration 2

The topic of central tendency is revisited from Section 2 with a new emphasis on *when* to use each type of average. Students will examine the effects of extreme data values on each average (the mean, the median, and the mode) and discover that when there are extreme values, the mean is often the most affected. The module project provides an open-ended situation where students must choose which average to use to communicate their data accurately and effectively.

Module 4

OVERVIEW

Data about animals are used to explore techniques for displaying information visually and analyzing it numerically. There are opportunities to apply written communication skills, developmental math and estimation strategies, and use a calculator, as well as to apply algebraic concepts and work with metric measurement. Students focus on such themes as mammals of Yellowstone Park, threatened and endangered species, dinosaurs, and the mathematics in the book *The Phantom Tollbooth*.

PREREQUISITE SKILLS

Warm-Up Exercises for each section are provided in the *Teacher's Resource Book*. You can use these exercises to review skills and concepts students will need for each section. In addition, the Spiral Review exercises at the end of each section in the student edition provide practice on prerequisite skills.

MODULE DIAGNOSTIC TEST

The Module Diagnostic Test in the *Teacher's Resource Book* can be used to assess students' prior knowledge of skills and concepts that will be taught in each section of this module. You can use test results to help structure your teaching to meet the diverse needs of your classroom.

MODULE **4** STATISTICAL SAFARI

198

MATHEMATICS
The & Theme

MODULE 4 · **SECTION OVERVIEW**

① Sets and Metric Measurement

As you study the mammals of Yellowstone Park:

◆ Sort data using a sorting grid.
◆ Estimate metric length and mass.
◆ Convert between metric units.

② Line Plots and Averages

As you think about the average number of children for families:

◆ Create and interpret line plots.
◆ Calculate mean, median, and mode.
◆ Use a calculator to change a fraction to a decimal.
◆ Round decimals.

③ Dividing Decimals and Solving Equations

As you study animals in the wild and in zoos:

◆ Divide a decimal by a whole number.
◆ Write, model, and solve addition and subtraction equations.

④ Stem-and-Leaf Plots, Decimal Division, and Graphing

As you study dinosaurs:

◆ Make and interpret stem-and-leaf plots.
◆ Divide by a decimal.
◆ Graph ordered pairs on a coordinate grid.

⑤ Line Graphs and Choosing an Average

As you study population growth:

◆ Make and interpret line graphs.
◆ Choose an appropriate average.

The Module Project

Be a Reporter

Extra, Extra! Read all about it!

"Study shows that there are over a million pet snakes in the United States."

As a reporter you will collect data about pets or another topic that interests you. The mathematics you learn in this module will help you organize, interpret, and present your results in a newspaper article.

For the Module Project
See pp. 276–277.

INTERNET
Resources and practice at
classzone.com

 199

Module Resources

TEACHER'S RESOURCE BOOK
Resources
• *The Math Gazette* (parent newsletter)
• Warm-Ups
• Labsheets
• Practice and Applications
• Study Guide
Assessment
• Section Quick Quizzes
• Mid-Module Quiz
• Module 4 Diagnostic Test
• Module 4 Tests A and B
• Module 4 Standardized Test
• Module 4 Performance Assessment
• Modules 3 and 4 Cumulative Test
• Mid-Year Test

SPANISH RESOURCES
• *The Math Gazette* (parent newsletter)
• Practice and Applications
• Assessment
• Spanish Glossary

STUDENT WORKBOOK

TECHNOLOGY BOOK

TECHNOLOGY RESOURCES
• @Home Tutor
• Test Generator
• Activity Generator
• Professional Development DVD
• Online Activities

Section ① **Sets and Metric Measurement**

The Mammals of Yellowstone

··Setting the Stage

Yellowstone National Park contains one of the most abundant concentrations of mammals in the lower 48 states. Eighteen kinds of carnivores roam the area. Over 40 other kinds of mammals also live within the park.

An adult bull bison may weigh up to 900 kilograms and stand more than 2 meters high at the shoulder.

An adult red squirrel can have a total length of 38.5 centimeters, including the tail.

An adult grizzly bear may be 2.6 meters long and 1.3 meters tall at the shoulder.

1. No; A bison is much heavier than a red squirrel. It would take too many small units for a bison. A red squirrel is too small to measure with a large unit.

Think About It

1 Would you expect to use the same unit of measure when finding the masses of a bison and a red squirrel? Why?

2 The ear of a red squirrel can be about 31 millimeters long. The claws of an adult grizzly are about 7 centimeters long. What everyday object has a length approximately equal to each of the following measures? Sample Responses: a. thickness of a coin; b. fingernail on smallest finger; c. leg from hip to heel

  a. a millimeter   **b.** a centimeter   **c.** a meter

▶ In this module you will learn about the measurements and habits of different mammals. You will also describe and compare animal data using graphs and averages.

 200 **Module 4** Statistical Safari

S·o·r·t·i·n·g Data

GOAL

LEARN HOW TO...
- sort data using a rectangular diagram

AS YOU...
- explore the characteristics of Yellowstone Park mammals

KEY TERM
- empty set

SET UP Work in a group. You will need: • a set of Yellowstone Mammal Cards from Labsheets 1A and 1B • Labsheet 1C

3 Follow the steps below to sort the *Mammal Cards* into two sets by the unit of mass.

a. Divide a piece of notebook paper into two columns and label the columns as shown below. **Observe students.**

Mass Measured in Kilograms	Mass Measured in Grams
Set A	Set B

b. Place the cards for the animals whose mass is measured in grams in the right column, and place the cards for those whose mass is measured in kilograms in the left column. The animal cards in the left column are in Set *A*, and those in the right column are in Set *B*. **See margin.**

4 **Discussion**

a. What characteristics do the animals on the cards in Set *A* have in common? the animals on the cards in Set *B*? Set A has "larger, longer, taller" animals. Set B has "smaller, shorter" animals.

b. How would you describe the size of an animal whose mass is measured in kilograms? in grams? Set A has animals generally larger than a house cat. Set B has animals generally smaller than a house cat.

▶ **Looking at Two Sets** The animals on the cards you placed in the left column in Question 3 belong to the set of mammals whose mass is measured in kilograms. Objects in one set sometimes share characteristics with objects in another set.

FOR ◄HELP
with *sets*, see
MODULE 2, p. 80

Exploration 1

ABOUT THE MATERIALS
Each group will need a set of *Yellowstone Mammal Cards* that need to be cut from **Labsheets 1A and 1B**. Having the cards cut and in sets prior to starting Exploration 1 will facilitate completion of the lesson in one class period. Add scissors to the materials list and allow more time if cards are not cut apart ahead of time.

TIPS FROM TEACHERS
For use year after year, laminate the mammal cards and store them in zip lock baggies for easy distribution to groups. Parents or other volunteers may be enlisted to laminate and cut apart cards the first year.

3. b. See Additional Answers beginning on page A1.

TEACHING NOTES
In **Question 5**, students use a sorting grid to place each card in its correct location according to the *two* characteristics listed for each section. Emphasize that to be placed in a section of the grid, the card must have *both* characteristics listed, not just one.

5   **Use Labsheet 1C.** Sort the *Mammal Cards* into separate piles by placing the cards inside the correct rectangles.

   a. Look at the mammals on the cards in Sets *C–F*. Which sets have the large mammals? C and E

   b. What is the largest mammal on the cards? Bison

   c. Which set has the small animals? F

   d. What is the smallest animal on the cards? Dwarf Shrew

   e. List the mammals in Set *E*. porcupine, marten, striped skunk, bobcat, coyote

   f. How many mammals are in Set *C*? Set *D*? Set *E*? Set *F*? 5; 0; 5; 8

   g. A set with no objects in it is an **empty set**. Are any of the Sets *C–F* empty sets? yes, set D

✔ **QUESTION 6**

...checks that you can sort data using a rectangular diagram and list a set of objects.

6. a. Set *G*: porcupine, marten, striped skunk;

   Set *H*: gray wolf, bighorn sheep, bison, black bear, bobcat, grizzly bear, coyote;

   Set *I*: water vole, red squirrel, dwarf shrew, northern flying squirrel, pika, least chipmunk;

   Set *J*: little brown bat

6   ✔ **CHECKPOINT** Use your *Mammal Cards* and a sorting grid like the one below to sort the mammals by life span and mass. (Draw the diagram large enough to contain the cards.)

	Life span ≤ 10 years	Life span > 10 years
Mass measured in kilograms	Set G	Set H
Mass measured in grams	Set I	Set J

   a. List the mammals in Sets *G–J*.

   b. Of the mammals that live less than or equal to 10 years, how many have a mass measured in kilograms? in grams? 3;7

   c. Of the mammals that live more than 10 years, how many have a mass measured in kilograms? in grams? 7;1

   d. Do larger mammals or smaller mammals appear to live longer, or does there seem to be little difference? Larger animals appear to live longer.

 HOMEWORK EXERCISES ▶ See Exs. 1–7 on pp. 209–210.

Exploration 2

Metric Length and Mass

SET UP *Work in pairs. You will need: • Labsheet 1D • scissors • tape*

GOAL

LEARN HOW TO...
- estimate length and mass in metric units

AS YOU...
- build rulers and measure everyday objects

KEY TERMS
- meter (m)
- millimeter (mm)
- centimeter (cm)
- kilometer (km)
- benchmark
- gram (g)
- milligram (mg)
- kilogram (kg)
- metric ton (t)

7 Think back to the *Mammal Cards.*

a. Was the length of small mammals measured in meters or centimeters? centimeters

b. Was the mass of large mammals measured in kilograms or grams? kilograms

▶ **Metric Length** The metric system is used in most countries today. Metric units of length are based on the **meter (m).**

The distance between short tick marks is a **millimeter (mm).**　　The distance between long tick marks is a **centimeter (cm).**

If you continue the ruler up to 100 centimeters, you get a meter. ⟶

A **kilometer (km)** is a metric unit used to measure longer distances such as highway distances. It is also based on the meter.

$$1 \text{ km} = 1000 \text{ m}$$

8 **Use Labsheet 1D.** Cut out the ruler and use it to answer the questions on the labsheet. See margin.

▶ **You can use the length of an object you know as a benchmark to estimate lengths. For example, if you know the height of a table in centimeters, you can use it as a benchmark to estimate other heights.**

9 If the table in the picture is about 75 cm high, about how high is the tip of the umbrella? About 250–300 cm

---

Exploration 2

TEACHING NOTES
Question 8 Students will measure in millimeters and centimeters and then combine four rulers together to form a meter. Even though students will build their own meter tape you may want to show them a meter stick when introducing the measures of meter, millimeter, and centimeter prior to **Question 8**.

8. 1. 50
　2. 8
　3. 250
　4.–8. Answers will vary.
　　　Approximations are given:
　4. length: 8.7 cm　width: 6.3 cm
　5. length: 87 mm　width: 63 mm
　6. length: 27 mm　width: 16 mm
　7. 6 cm　60 mm
　8. 2.4 cm　24 mm
　9. Check students' sketches. Yes, the sketch will fit the page.
　10. a. Observe students' work.
　　　b. 100 cm
　　　c. 1000 mm
　　　d. Answers will vary.
　　　　Sample: 70 cm

Exploration 2 *continued*

TEACHING NOTES

You may want to make a list of the benchmarks students share in **Question 11** and post it in the classroom so students can use it as a reference, adding new benchmarks as they are discovered.

For **Checkpoint Question 13**, choose a few students to measure the classroom height and share the results. Meantime the rest of the class can check their shoe and thumbnail size. A standard running track measures 400 m, thus four times around is 1600 m or 1.6 km.

10. Answers will vary.
Sample Responses:

1 mm = thickness of quarter;
1 cm = fingernail on smallest finger;
1 meter = leg from hip to heel;
1 km = 2 laps around a standard running track

10 Copy and complete the table. Use your meter tape from Labsheet 1D to find a benchmark for each unit of length.

Length	Benchmark
1 millimeter (mm)	Length of _?_
1 centimeter (cm)	Length of _?_
1 meter (m)	Length of _?_
1 kilometer (km)	Length of _?_

11 **Discussion** Share the benchmarks you chose in Question 10 with the class. *Monitor students' discussion.*

12 Use benchmarks to estimate the following: *Answers will vary.*
Sample Responses:

a. the height of your classroom in meters **2.5 m**

b. the length of your shoe in centimeters **25 cm**

c. the width of your thumbnail in millimeters **10–15 mm**

d. the length of four laps around a running track in kilometers **1.5–2 km**

✔ QUESTION 13

...checks that you can use a ruler to measure length in metric units.

13 ✔ **CHECKPOINT** Check your estimates in parts (a)–(c) of Question 12 by measuring each distance. *Answers will vary. Check students' work.*

▶ When you measure to find actual lengths, it can be helpful to use decimals to record your measurements.

EXAMPLE

Find the length of the white-footed mouse's body in centimeters.

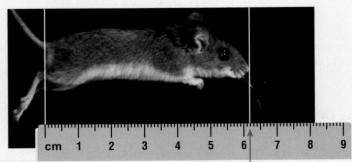

SAMPLE RESPONSE

The body of the white-footed mouse measures 6 cm 2 mm. There are ten divisions in 1 cm, so 2 of these are $\frac{2}{10}$ of a centimeter, or 0.2 cm.

This means that 6 cm 2 mm = 6.2 cm.

 Module 4 *Statistical Safari*

204

14 **Discussion** a–c. See margin.

    a. Why can 5 m 35 cm be written as 5.35 m?

    b. Why can 4.2 cm be written as 4 cm 2 mm?

    c. Why can 65 cm be written as 0.65 m?

▶ **Metric Mass** Metric units of mass are based on the **gram**. Sample benchmarks for some common units of mass are shown below.

A Grain of Sugar
1 milligram (mg)

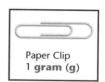

Paper Clip
1 gram (g)

1-Liter Bottle
of Water
1 kilogram (kg)

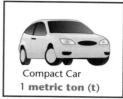

Compact Car
1 metric ton (t)

15 Choose the appropriate metric unit (*metric ton, kilogram, gram,* or *milligram*) for measuring the mass of each animal.

    a. a wolf   **b.** a whale   **c.** a flea   **d.** a chipmunk
    kilogram   metric ton   milligram   gram

16 ✔ **CHECKPOINT** Estimate the mass of each object using the given unit. **Answers will vary. Sample responses:**

    a. a pencil (g)   **b.** a chair (kg)   **c.** your math book (kg)
      6 g   5 kg   1 kg

HOMEWORK EXERCISES ▶ See Exs. 8–27 on pp. 210–211.

Exploration 3

Converting Metric Units

SET UP *You will need Labsheets 1E and 1F.*

Use the Student Resource at the top of page 206 to answer Questions 17–19.

17 **a.** What does the prefix *kilo-* mean? thousand

    b. A kilogram is how many times as large as a gram? 1000 times

    c. Name an animal whose mass would be measured in kilograms.
    Answers will vary. Sample Response: Bison

TIPS FROM TEACHERS
For **Questions 15–16**, bring a balance scale and metric weights into the classroom. Then students can check their estimates against the objects in **Question 16** by trying to balance an item against the mass they estimated.

14. a. 100 cm = 1 m, so 1 cm = $\frac{1}{100}$ m and 35 cm = $\frac{35}{100}$ m or 0.35 m

    b. 1 cm = 10 mm, so $\frac{1}{10}$ cm = 1 mm and 0.2 cm = $\frac{2}{10}$ cm = 2 mm

    c. 100 cm = 1 m, so 1 cm = $\frac{1}{100}$ m and 65 cm = $\frac{65}{100}$ m or 0.65 m

✔ **QUESTION 16**

...checks that you can estimate mass in metric units.

GOAL

LEARN HOW TO...
◆ convert between metric units

AS YOU...
◆ relate metric prefixes to place values

Metric Prefixes

Student Resource

You can look at the prefixes of metric units of measure to see the relationships between the units. The most commonly used prefixes are in the shaded areas.

The prefixes are like place values, becoming ten times as great each time you move to the left in the table.

Centi- means "hundredth," so 1 centimeter is $\frac{1}{100}$ of a meter, and 100 centimeters is 1 meter.

Prefix	kilo-	hecto-	deka-	basic unit meter gram	deci-	centi-	milli-
Meaning	1000	100	10	1	0.1 or $\frac{1}{10}$	0.01 or $\frac{1}{100}$	0.001 or $\frac{1}{1000}$

A decimeter is 10 times as long as a centimeter. A centimeter is 10 times as long as a millimeter.

So a decimeter is 10 • 10, or 100 times as long as a millimeter.

---

19. 10 mm; Sample Response:

$10 • 1$ mm =

$10 • \frac{1}{1000}$ m =

$\frac{10}{1000}$ m = $\frac{1}{100}$ m =

1 cm, so 10 mm = 1 cm

According to the *Student Resource*, a centimeter is 10 times as long as a millimeter, so there are ten millimeters in a centimeter.

18 a. What does the prefix *milli*- mean? thousandth

b. A millimeter is what fractional part of a meter? $\frac{1}{1000}$ or 0.001

c. Name an animal whose length would be measured in millimeters. Answers will vary: Sample Response: ant

19 A centimeter is one hundredth of a meter and a millimeter is one thousandth of a meter. How many millimeters are in one centimeter? How do you know?

▶ **Metric Conversions** You may need to convert from one unit to another to compare measurements. Use the photos of the red fox and the badger below for Questions 20 and 21 on the following page.

Red fox

← 0.8 m →

Badger

← 75 cm →

20 To compare the lengths of the fox and the badger, you can convert 0.8 m to centimeters.

$$1 \text{ m} = 100 \text{ cm}$$
$$0.8 \cdot 1 \text{ m} = 0.8 \cdot 100 \text{ cm}$$
$$0.8 \text{ m} = 80 \text{ cm}$$

Which mammal is longer, the fox or the badger? By how many centimeters? The fox is longer by 5 cm.

21 You can also compare the lengths of the fox and the badger in meters.

$$1 \text{ cm} = 0.01 \text{ m}$$
$$75 \text{ cm} = 75 \cdot 0.01 \text{ m}$$

a. Find $75 \cdot 0.01$. 0.75

b. The fox is how many meters longer than the badger? The fox is longer by 0.05 m.

▶ To convert between metric units, it is helpful to know how to multiply by the special multipliers 0.001, 0.01, 0.1, 1, 10, 100, and 1000.

22 **Use Labsheet 1E.** Use your calculator to complete the *Special Multipliers Multiplication Table*. See margin.

23 **Use Labsheet 1F.** Use the table of prefix meanings to fill in the missing information for the *Metric Conversions*. See margin.

EXAMPLE

Convert 453 mm to meters.

SAMPLE RESPONSE

$$1 \text{ mm} = 0.001 \text{ m}$$
$$453 \text{ mm} = 453 \cdot 0.001 \text{ m} = 0.453 \text{ m}$$

24 **Discussion** How can you check that the answer, 0.453 m, in the Example is reasonable? Sample Response: Estimate 453 mm is about 500 mm; 0.453 m is about 0.5 m, so 0.453 m is a reasonable answer.

25 ✔ **CHECKPOINT** Replace each _?_ with the number that makes the statement true.

a. 1 g = _?_ mg **b.** 1 m = _?_ km **c.** 1 metric ton = _?_ kg
   5 g = _?_ mg   37 m = _?_ km   4.2 metric tons = _?_ kg
   1000; 5000   0.001; 0.037   1000; 4200

✔ **QUESTION 25**

...checks that you can convert between metric units.

HOMEWORK EXERCISES ▶ See Exs. 28–46 on p. 211.

For **Questions 20–21**, it may be helpful to go over the steps that were used in converting the metric lengths. Be sure students understand that the first step comes from the relationship between the two units of conversion.

Question 22 Remind students that they mentally multiplied decimals by 0.01 and 0.1 in Section 6 of Module 3. Once they recognize the patterns in the *Special Multipliers Multiplication Table* on **Labsheet 1E**, they can apply the same techniques of mental math to converting between metric units.

Question 23 As students use **Labsheet 1F**, they may notice that some of the headings are in light face while others are in bold. This would be a good time to mention that some metric unit measures are encountered less frequently than others. Those used more often are printed on the labsheet in bold face.

After discussing **Question 24**, you may want to go through another example with the class before they do **Checkpoint Question 25**.

CLASSROOM EXAMPLES

Convert 25 km to meters.

Answer: 1 km = 1000 m
       25 km = 25 · 1000 m
       25 km = 25,000 m

Convert 32 mg to grams.

Answer: 1 mg = 0.001 g
       32 mg = 32 · 0.001 g
       32 mg = 0.032 g

22–23. See Additional Answers beginning on page A1.

207

Key Concepts

CLOSURE QUESTION
How can benchmarks help you estimate metric mass and length?

Sample Response: Benchmarks give you a basis for your judgement. For example, if a known benchmark is 5 meters in length, then you can compare the new object to the benchmark to see if it is longer or shorter than 5 meters.

ABSENT STUDENTS
For students who were absent for all or part of this section, the blackline Study Guide for Section 1 may be used to present the ideas, concepts, and skills of Section 1.

Key Terms

empty set

benchmark

kilometer (km)

meter (m)

centimeter (cm)

millimeter (mm)

metric ton (t)

kilogram (kg)

gram (g)

milligram (mg)

Section 1
Key Concepts

Empty Set (p. 202)
The empty set is a set with no objects in it.

Metric System (pp. 203–207)
The tables below show the relationships among some commonly used metric units.

Units of length are based on the meter. A benchmark for 1 m is the length of an outstretched arm.

kilometer (km)	meter (m)	centimeter (cm)	millimeter (mm)
1 km = 1,000,000 mm	1 m = 1000 mm	1 cm = 10 mm	
1 km = 100,000 cm	1 m = 100 cm		1 mm = 0.1 cm
1 km = 1000 m		1 cm = 0.01 m	1 mm = 0.001 m
	1 m = 0.001 km	1 cm = 0.00001 km	1 mm = 0.000001 km

Units of mass are based on the gram. A benchmark for 1 g is the mass of a paper clip.

metric ton (t)	kilogram (kg)	gram (g)	milligram (mg)
1 t = 1,000,000,000 mg	1 kg = 1,000,000 mg	1 g = 1000 mg	
1 t = 1,000,000 g	1 kg = 1000 g		1 mg = 0.001 g
1 t = 1000 kg		1 g = 0.001 kg	1 mg = 0.000001 kg
	1 kg = 0.001 t	1 g = 0.000001 t	1 mg = 0.000000001 t

26 Key Concepts Question The mass of a large horse is about 0.8 metric ton, and the mass of a four-eyed opossum is about 800 g. The mass of the horse is about how many times as great as the mass of the four-eyed opossum? **1000 times**

Section 1

Practice & Application Exercises

YOU WILL NEED

For Exs. 22–27:
◆ a metric ruler

1. **Connection** Animals can be sorted into sets according to what they eat. *Carnivores* eat meat and *herbivores* eat plants.

Carnivores	Omnivores	Herbivores
Wolf		Bison
Cougar	Bear	Elk
Brown Bat		Rabbit

Sorting Grid

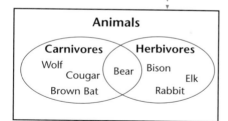

Animals

Carnivores: Wolf, Cougar, Brown Bat
Bear
Herbivores: Bison, Elk, Rabbit

Venn Diagram

a. What does the sorting grid tell you about the bear?
   The bear is an omnivore.
b. What does the Venn diagram tell you about the bear?
   The bear eats both meat and plants.
c. What is an omnivore? How can you tell from the diagrams?

1. c. If a bear is an omnivore and eats both meat and plants, then an omnivore eats both meat and plants.

Several mammals were sorted by their diets and maximum speeds. The results are shown on the sorting grid below. Use the grid for Exercises 2–7.

	Carnivores ⬇	Omnivores ⬇	Herbivores ⬇
Speed < 60 km/hr ➡	**Set A** Tiger Domestic Cat	**Set B** Grizzly Bear Patas Monkey Red Fox Raccoon Mouse Squirrel	**Set C** Rabbit Giraffe Donkey Hippopotamus Rhinocerous Elephant Manatee
Speed ≥ 60 km/hr ➡	**Set D** Cheetah Lion Gray Wolf Coyote Jaguar	**Set E**	**Set F** Horse Pronghorn Antelope

2. List the mammals in Set *A*. tiger, domestic cat

3. List the herbivores that have a maximum speed greater than or equal to 60 km/hr. To which set do they belong? Horse and pronghorn antelope; Set F

Practice & Applications

SUGGESTED ASSIGNMENTS

Core Course

Day 1: Exs. 1–7
Day 2: Exs. 8–12, 47–51
Day 3: Exs. 13–27
Day 4: Exs. 28–46

Extended Course

Day 1: Exs. 1–7
Day 2: Exs. 8–12, 47–51
Day 3: Exs. 13–27
Day 4: Exs. 28–46

Note: Extended Course assignments can be used to differentiate within the regular classroom. In classrooms where students are grouped homogeneously, the material might be covered in fewer days. In this case assignments may be combined.

EXERCISE NOTES

You may want to review how to read a Venn diagram before assigning **Exercise 1**.

ADDITIONAL PRACTICE

See the *Teacher's Resource Book* for additional practice and application exercises for this section.

Practice & Applications

EXERCISE NOTES

For **Exercises 10–21**, discuss as a class how students decided on the units or made their estimates. Did they use their benchmarks? Did they actually use the items listed, or did they compare in their mind the items to an item they had discussed in class?

8. Nearest centimeter; measuring to the smaller unit provides a more exact measurement.

9. Nearest millimeter; measuring to the smaller unit provides a more exact measurement.

4. Fill in the blanks to complete the description of Set *B*.

   Set *B* is the set of __?__ that have a maximum speed __?__ 60 km/hr.
   omnivores; less than

5. a. List the animals in Set *D*. Cheetah, Lion, Gray wolf, Coyote, Jaguar

   b. Describe Set *D* in words. The animals in Set D are carnivores that have a maximum speed greater than or equal to 60 km/hr.

6. Are any of the sets an empty set? What does this mean?
   Set E is empty. There are no omnivores able to run 60 km/hr or faster.

7. a. In general, what seems to be the diet of the fastest mammals?
      meat
   b. Is this what you would have expected? Explain. Answers will vary.
      Sample Response: Yes. Carnivores use speed to catch other animals.

8. Suppose a table needs to be moved into a classroom. You want to know whether the table will fit through the doorway. Should you measure to the nearest *meter* or *centimeter*? Explain your answer.

9. Suppose you are cutting a board for a shelf in a cabinet. Should you measure to the nearest *centimeter* or *millimeter*? Explain.

Decide which metric unit (*millimeter, centimeter,* or *meter*) to use for the length of each object.

10. an automobile
    meter

11. a pencil eraser
    millimeter

12. a dollar bill
    centimeter

Choose the best estimate for each measurement.

13. the width of your classroom   *1 m*   *7 m*   *30 m* 7 m

14. the height of a soda can   *1.2 m*   *3.5 cm*   *120 mm* 120 mm

15. the thickness of a quarter   *8 mm*   *1 cm*   *1 mm* 1 mm

Decide which metric unit (*milligram, gram, kilogram,* or *metric ton*) to use for the mass of each object.

16. a vitamin pill
    milligram

17. a baseball bat
    gram or kilogram

18. an airplane
    metric ton

Choose the best estimate for the mass of each object.

19. a bicycle   *15 kg*   *150 g*   *0.5 t* 15 kg

20. a loaf of bread   *5 g*   *500 g*   *5 kg* 500 g

21. a piece of paper   *0.5 kg*   *0.5 g*   *5 kg* 0.5 g

22. Measure the length of this page in centimeters. 25.6 cm

23. Measure the thickness of your book in the given metric unit.

    a. millimeters 25–30 mm   b. centimeters 2.5–3.0 cm

Use benchmarks and estimation to draw a segment with each length.
Then check your estimates with a metric ruler. **24–27. Check students' work.**

24. 9 cm   25. 25 cm   26. 24 mm   27. 68 mm

Find each product.

28. 2 • 0.01 0.02   29. 3.4 • 0.001 0.0034   30. 0.4 • 0.01 0.004

31. 0.007 • 10 0.07   32. 0.35 • 100 35   33. 0.001 • 0.1 0.0001

Replace each _?_ with the number that makes the statement true.

34. 5 km = _?_ m
    5000

35. 6.5 m = _?_ cm
    650

36. 584 g = _?_ kg
    0.584

37. 2540 mg = _?_ g
    2.54 or 2.540

38. 0.6 m = _?_ mm
    600

39. 72 cm = _?_ mm
    720

Use the table to answer Exercises 40 and 41.

40. List the animals in order from least to greatest mass at birth.

41. **Research** A kilogram is a little more than 2 pounds. Which animals in the table have a mass similar to that of a human baby at birth?

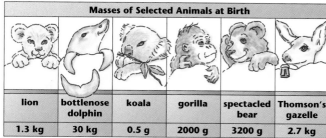

Masses of Selected Animals at Birth					
lion	bottlenose dolphin	koala	gorilla	spectacled bear	Thomson's gazelle
1.3 kg	30 kg	0.5 g	2000 g	3200 g	2.7 kg

Spectacled Bear; Thomson's Gazelle (It is possible for human infants to survive at birth weights as low as those of an infant lion or gorilla.)

40. Koala
    Lion
    Gorilla
    Thomson's Gazelle
    Spectacled Bear
    Bottlenose Dolphin

Replace each _?_ with <, >, or =.

42. 75 mg _?_ 7.5 g
    <

43. 6 t _?_ 600 kg
    >

44. 5.3 km _?_ 5380 m
    <

45. 1500 kg _?_ 0.75 t
    >

R e f l e c t i n g ◀▶on the Section

Write your response to Exercise 46 in your journal.

46. Danny had the following six animal cards: octopus, kangaroo, lobster, sea otter, cheetah, and giant clam. He correctly placed his cards in the set *Animals with a Mass Greater than 20 kg* and in the set *Animals that Live in Water.* He found that he had four animals in each set. How can this be, since he had only six cards?
Two animals, probably the sea otter and giant clam, belong to both sets.

Journal

Exercise 46 checks that you understand set relationships.

Practice & Applications

EXERCISE NOTES
The **Spiral Review**
Exercises 47–51 continue the
concept of sorting through the
review of Venn diagrams.

Dinosaurs Found in North America

Dinosaurs Found in Alberta: Euoplocephalus, Hadrosaurus, Parasaurolophus, Pentaceratops, Stegoceras

Dinosaurs Found in Colorado: Brontosaurus, Allosaurus, Diplodocus, Omitholestes, Tocosaurus, Stegosaurus

Triceratops, Torosaurus

Coelophysis, Tyrannosaurus, Dilophasaurus, Corythosaurus, Nodosaurus, Segisaurus, Anchisaurus

Spiral ◀▶ Review

Use the Venn diagram below for Exercises 47–50. (Module 2, p. 119)

47. Find the number of types of dinosaurs that were found in the given area.

a. Colorado 8   b. Alberta 7   c. North America 20

48. How many types of dinosaurs were found in North America but not in Alberta or Colorado? 7

49. How many types of dinosaurs found in North America have been found outside of Colorado? 12

50. What does the Venn diagram tell you about *Triceratops* and *Torosaurus*? They were found in both Alberta and Colorado.

51. a. inside rectangles, but outside rhombuses
b. inside rhombuses, but outside rectangles
c. inside the overlap area of rectangles and rhombuses
d. outside of rectangles and rhombuses, but inside quadrilaterals

51. Tell where each shape should be placed in the Venn diagram.
(Module 2, p. 119)

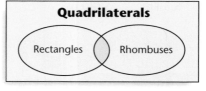

Quadrilaterals — Rectangles, Rhombuses

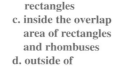

a.   4 cm, 2 cm

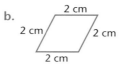

b.   2 cm, 2 cm, 2 cm

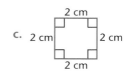

c.   2 cm, 2 cm, 2 cm

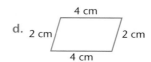

d.   4 cm, 2 cm, 2 cm, 4 cm

212

Section ① Extra Skill Practice

Several mammals were sorted by habitat and whether or not the animals have tails. The results are shown on a sorting grid below.

1. List the mammals that live on land and do not have tails. To which set do they belong?

2. Describe Set *A* in words.

3. How many mammals are in Set *B*? **3**

4. Are any of the sets an empty set? What does this mean?

5. In which set would you place a chimpanzee? Why?
Set C; chimpanzees live on land and do not have tails

	Live on land	Live in water
	Set *A*	Set *B*
Have tails	Grizzly Bear Armadillo Zebra Tiger Fox Rabbit Bison	Bottlenose Dolphin Killer Whale Manatee
	Set *C*	Set *D*
Do not have tails	Vampire Bat Pika Koala Gorilla Guinea Pig Orangutan	

Find each product.

6. 3 · 0.01 **0.03**   7. 2.5 · 0.001 **0.0025**   8. 0.2 · 0.1 **0.02**   9. 3.48 · 100 **348**

Replace each __?__ with the number that makes the statement true.

10. 350 cm = __?__ m
    3.5

11. 2930 mg = __?__ g
    2.93 or 2.930

12. 280 kg = __?__ g
    280,000

13. 0.4 t = __?__ kg
    400

1. **Vampire Bat, Pika, Koala, Gorilla, Guinea Pig, Orangutan; Set C**

2. **animals that live on land and have tails**

4. **Yes, Set D; no animal lives in the water and does not have a tail**

Study Skills ▷ Preparing to do Homework

Looking back at examples and reviewing the key terms can help you prepare to do your homework.

1. Look at an Example in Section 1. What does it show you how to do? **The example on page 204 shows how to use decimals to record measurements. The example on page 207 shows how to convert a measurement from millimeters to meters.**

2. a. What are the key terms in Section 1? **empty set, benchmark, kilometer, meter, centimeter, millimeter, metric ton, kilogram, gram, milligram**
   b. Use one of the key terms in a sentence that shows you understand the meaning of the term. **Answers will vary. Sample Response: A set with no objects is an empty set.**

Extra Skill Practice

TEACHER NOTES

For each Exploration, the corresponding Extra Skill Practice Exercises are noted.

Exploration 1: Exs. 1–5
Exploration 3: Exs. 6–13

EXTRA HELP

Teacher's Resource Book
• Practice and Applications
• Study Guide

Technology Resources
• @Home Tutor
• Test Generator

ASSESSMENT

• Section 1 Quick Quiz
• Test Generator

Setting the Stage

GETTING STARTED

Module 4 Section 2 *Warm-Up* assesses student facility with identifying decimal place values. In calculating means, students will need to be able to round to an appropriate decimal place.

TEACHING NOTES

Read the *Setting the Stage* as a whole class and then discuss **Questions 1 and 2** with the students. Instead of reading it yourself, you may wish to have two students read the excerpt with one student playing Milo and another student playing the child. Students may need help answering **Questions 1 and 2**, especially **Question 1(b)**, since it requires familiarity with the definition of *mean*, which is introduced in Exploration 1.

TECHNOLOGY

For a related technology activity, see the *Technology Book*.

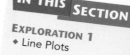

Section 2 — Line Plots and Averages

IN THIS SECTION

EXPLORATION 1
♦ Line Plots

EXPLORATION 2
♦ Finding Averages

EXPLORATION 3
♦ Appropriate Averages

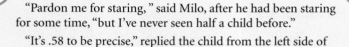

Animal Averages

·· Setting the Stage

The Phantom Tollbooth, by Norton Juster, is a story about a boy named Milo who visits a strange land where he has many adventures. One day while resting on the stairs to the land of infinity, Milo is surprised to see what seems to be half of a child.

1. b. **Sample: Find the total number of children and divide by the number of families.**

> "Pardon me for staring," said Milo, after he had been staring for some time, "but I've never seen half a child before."
>
> "It's .58 to be precise," replied the child from the left side of his mouth (which happened to be the only side of his mouth).
>
> "I beg your pardon?" said Milo.
>
> "It's .58," he repeated; "it's a little bit *more* than half."
>
> "Have you always been that way?" asked Milo impatiently, for he felt that that was a needlessly fine distinction.
>
> "My goodness, no," the child assured him. "A few years ago I was just .42 and believe me, that was terribly inconvenient."
>
> "What is the rest of your family like?" said Milo, this time a bit more sympathetically.
>
> "Oh, we're just the average family," he said thoughtfully; "mother, father, and 2.58 children—and, as I explained, I'm the .58."

Think About It

1 **a.** What do you think the word average means?
Answers vary. Sample Response: Average is the middle or the typical.
b. How do you think the average 2.58 was found?

2 Do you think the average number of children for families in your class is 2.58? Why or why not? Answers vary.

Line Plots

GOAL

LEARN HOW TO...
◆ draw and interpret line plots

AS YOU...
◆ work with data

KEY TERMS
◆ line plot (dot plot)
◆ range
◆ cluster
◆ gap

Exploration 1

TEACHING NOTES
Questions 3 and 4 are designed to help students make connections between the table and the line plot. By comparing the two displays, students should begin to understand how a line plot can be constructed from data given in a table. Students will be expected to construct a line plot from a data table in **Checkpoint Question 7**.

▶ To investigate the average number of children in a family, sixth grade students at Anderson School collected data about themselves. The number of children in each student's family is displayed below in a table and in a *line plot*. The line plot, sometimes called a *dot plot*, was created with a data analysis program.

Table

Student	Number of Children in Family	Student	Number of Children in Family
Amanda	4	John	2
Bill	1	Karen	2
Ramon	2	Micki	4
Ladonna	3	Tammy	3
Noreen	5	Massimo	3
Amos	7	Gerald	4
Neil	4	Miya	3
Obed	3		

▲ Anderson school is a rural Montana school located north of Yellowstone Park.

Line Plot

Number of Children in 15 Families

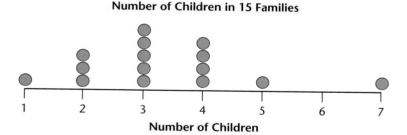

Number of Children

3 **Discussion**

a. How do you think the data in the table were used to draw the line plot?

b. At what numbers does the scale on the line plot start and end?

3. a. Sample Response: A dot was used to represent the number of children in the family of each child at Anderson School.
b. 1 and 7, the least and greatest number of children in a family.

TEACHING NOTES

Question 6 A line plot does not necessarily have to start and end with the least and greatest data values, but it needs to encompass these values.

5. a. Sample Response: Large, because 6 is only one less than the greatest number of children on the line plot.

4 a. What is the greatest number of children in any of the families? the least number? 7; 1

b. Did you use the table or the line plot to find the greatest and the least numbers of children? Why? Sample Response: The line plot, since the data were ordered and easier to see.

c. Based on the line plot, what would you report as the average number of students in a family? Why? Sample Response: The average number is 3 because that is where most of the data are.

5 Discussion Samantha and Ron were absent the day the data were collected.

a. Samantha's family has 6 children. In comparison to the families on the line plot, is the number of children in Samantha's family small, average, or large? Explain.

b. Ron's family has 2 children. Is the number of children in Ron's family small, average, or large in comparison to the other families? Explain. Sample Response: Small, because 2 is near the least number of children per family

▶ A **line plot** or **dot plot** displays data using a line marked with a scale. The scale must include the greatest and least values of the data. If you make a line plot before having all your data, you may want to include some extra numbers to the left and right in case the set of data includes surprisingly small or large values.

▶ The **range** of a set of numerical data is the difference between the greatest and least values.

> **EXAMPLE**

Find the range of the numbers 120, 180, 61, 57, and 100.

SAMPLE RESPONSE

$$\text{Range} = \text{greatest value} - \text{least value}$$
$$= \quad 180 \quad - \quad 57$$
$$= \quad 123$$

6 a. What is the range of the numbers of children in the fifteen families? Range = 7 − 1 = 6 children

b. How can the range of the data help you decide what numbers to use on the numerical scale of a line plot? The range helps you decide what intervals to use for the scale and where to start and end the line plot.

▶ You have seen how a line plot can be used to display the numbers of children in families. A line plot can also be used to investigate how long animals sleep each day.

7 ✔ **CHECKPOINT** Use the table below.

  a. Find the range of the data. Range = 19 − 2 = 17 hr

  b. Make a line plot for the data. (You may use either **X**'s or **0**'s when constructing your line plot.) See margin.

...checks that you can draw a line plot.

Sleeping Habits of Selected Animals	
Animal	Hours spent sleeping each day
Asian elephant	4
chimpanzee	10
giraffe	2
gray wolf	13
horse	3
hyena	18
jaguar	11
koala	19
lion	16
mouse	12
okapi	5
rabbit	11
raccoon	13
three-toed sloth	19

8 **Discussion** What do you notice about how the data are distributed in the line plot? Look for *clusters* of data and *gaps* in the data. A **cluster** is a place where the data items are bunched closely together, and a **gap** is a large space where there are no data items. There are clusters from 2 to 5, from 10 to 13, and from 18 to 19. There is a gap between 5 and 10.

9 **Try This as a Class** Use the table above and your line plot to help estimate how many hours a day each animal below sleeps. (*Hint:* Look at the clusters of animals in your line plot. Think about what the animals in each cluster have in common.)
Answers will vary. Sample Responses:
  a. donkey
    2 to 5 hours
  b. cheetah
    16 to 19 hours
  c. beaver
    10 to 13 hours

HOMEWORK EXERCISES ▶ See Exs. 1–9 on p. 226.

DEVELOPING MATH CONCEPTS

The *mean*, *median*, and *mode* are all *measures of central tendency*, that is, they are all "averages" of a set of data. The median is easier to calculate than the mean and is often more reliable than the mean as an indicator of what most people would expect of an "average." If the family incomes of five neighboring houses are $32,000, $28,000, $37,000, $30,000, and $280,000, then the median income, $32,000, probably provides a better idea of the financial condition of the neighborhood than does the mean, which is $81,400. In this example, there is no mode.

10. a. See Additional Answers beginning on page A1.

GOAL

LEARN HOW TO...
- use averages to describe data

AS YOU...
- explore data about animals

KEY TERMS
- average
- mode
- median
- mean

Exploration 2

FINDING Averages

SET UP   Work in a group. You will need 30 chips.

Like humans, many animals live together in groups. For example, wolves live in packs. Wolf packs once roamed from the Arctic tundra to Mexico. However, they were considered dangerous predators and were driven out of most areas. By 1926 there were no wolf packs left in Yellowstone Park. In 1995, fourteen wolves were captured in Alberta, Canada, and released in the park. By 2002, at least 148 wolves in 14 packs were living in Yellowstone Park.

2002 Yellowstone National Park Wolf Population													
Pack Name	Agate Creek	Bechler Group	Geode Creek	Buffalo Fork	Tower	Chief Joseph	Leopold	Mollie's	Nez Perce	Rose Creek II	Cougar Creek	Swan Lake	Druid Peak	Yellowstone Delta
Estimated Pack Size	10	4	9	4	2	10	16	12	20	10	10	16	11	14

11. Answers will vary. Sample Response: The typical number might indicate the best size for a pack to find enough to eat and to stay healthy and survive. If this is true, the biologist may want to equalize the sizes of the packs by relocating wolves from the larger packs to the smaller ones.

10 a. Make a line plot of the pack sizes. See margin.

b. What is the range of the pack sizes?
Range = 20 – 2 = 18 wolves

11 Discussion Why might a wildlife biologist monitoring the Yellowstone wolf population want to know the typical, or most common, number of wolves in a pack?

▶ One way to describe the typical, or **average**, number of wolves in a pack is to find the pack size that occurs most often. The item that occurs most often in a set of data is the **mode**. A set of data may have more than one mode or no mode.

12 a. According to the table on page 218, what pack size occurs most often? **10 wolves**

b. Using your line plot, how can you determine the pack size that occurs most often? **It is the number with the most data points above it.**

c. What is the mode of the pack sizes? **10 wolves**

d. Discussion Suppose two more wolf packs were found, both containing 4 wolves. What would the mode(s) of the 16 packs be? **4 and 10**

▶ Another way to describe the average number of wolves in a pack is to find the *middle* pack size.

13 a. List the number of wolves in each of the first five packs (starting with the Agate Creek pack) from least to greatest.
2 4 4 9 10

b. Using your list from part (a), cross out data items two at a time so that each time you cross out the least and greatest remaining items. The first step is shown below.

~~2~~ 4 4 9 ~~10~~ **Check students' work.**

c. What is the middle pack size for the five wolf packs? **4 wolves**

14 a. Now list the number of wolves in the next 6 packs (starting with the Chief Joseph pack) from least to greatest.
10 10 10 12 16 20

b. Using your list from part (a), cross out data items two at a time so that each time you cross out the least and greatest remaining items. **Check students' work.**

c. Try This as a Class Is there a middle pack size for these six wolf packs? If so, what is it? If not, what other number can you think of as being "in the middle"?
No; 11 could be the middle because it is halfway between 10 and 12.

▶ **The middle item in a set of data listed in numerical order is the median. If there is no single middle item, the median is the number halfway between the two data items closest to the middle.**

15 What is the median number of wolves in the 14 Yellowstone Park wolf packs? **10 wolves**

▶ Suppose the 14 Yellowstone Park wolf packs all had the same number of wolves in them. Then the average pack size would be the number of wolves in any pack. Since the packs don't all have the same number of wolves, we must level off or balance the number of wolves in the packs to find the common size.

TEACHING NOTES
After students have completed **Question 12**, point out that a set of data can have no mode. Also, a set of data can have more than one mode. If there are two data points occurring most often, the data is bimodal; three points is tri-modal.

To summarize Exploration 1 thus far you may want to use the Classroom Example below after **Question 15**.

CLASSROOM EXAMPLE

Find the median and the mode for the following data: 11, 18, 12, 14, 12, 17.

Answer:
Median: 11, 12, 12, 14, 17, 18
13 is halfway between 12 and 14. The median is 13.

Mode:
11, **12**, **12**, 14, 17, 18
The mode is 12.

You may also want to present a set of data that has no mode or multiples modes. {10, 13, 13, 15, 21, 21, 26} is an example of a set of data that has two modes and one of the data values as the median. (*median: 15, modes: 13 and 21*)

CLASSROOM MANAGEMENT
The last transition statement on this page should be read in conjunction with the start of the second day of lessons on Exploration 2 just prior to beginning **Question 16**.

TEACHING NOTES

Some prompts for **Question 17(a)** may be needed to get students to the *sum and divide* rule for finding the mean. Ask, "Did the total number of wolves change or remain the same?" (*remained the same*) "What was your goal when moving the chips to different wolf packs?" (*to divide them equally among the 5 packs*)

Question 19 If some students believe 2.58 can be the median, explain that it would have to be between 2 children and 3 children. Have them find the number in the middle of 2 and 3 to see that 2.58 is impossible for this situation.

FOR ▶ HELP

with *pictographs*, see
TOOLBOX, p. 579

19. a. Mean, yes;
Median, No
because the
median of 2
whole numbers
must be either a
whole number
or end with
0.5.; Mode,
no because
the number
of children in
a family must
always be a
whole number.
b. Mean, yes;
Median, yes;
Mode, no
because the
number of
children in a
family must
always be a
whole number.

✔ QUESTION 18

...checks that you can find the mean, the median, and the mode of a set of data.

16 **a.** Follow the steps below to balance the pack size in the first five wolf packs in the table on page 218.
Observe students following the steps.

Step 1: Use chips on a piece of paper to make a pictograph of the number of wolves in each of the first five wolf packs. Let each chip represent one wolf.

Step 2: Move the chips so that each of the packs has as close to the same number of wolves as possible.

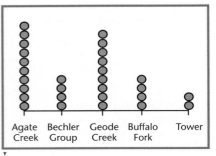

Agate Creek   Bechler Group   Geode Creek   Buffalo Fork   Tower

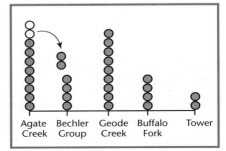

Agate Creek   Bechler Group   Geode Creek   Buffalo Fork   Tower

b. How many wolves are in each pack after the moves?
Four packs would have 6 wolves and one pack would have 5 wolves.

▶ **The common or average pack size you found in Question 16(b) is an approximation of the mean.** In this case, the mean tells you how many wolves would be in each pack if all five packs had the same number of wolves.

17 **Try This as a Class**

a. How can you find the mean of the number of wolves in the 14 Yellowstone Park packs without using chips?
Find the total number of wolves and divide the sum by 14.

b. What is the mean of the number of wolves in the 14 wolf packs?
About 10.57 wolves

18 **✔ CHECKPOINT** Most elephants live in herds that consist of many adults and their young. The number of young elephants in eight different herds is listed below. Find the mean, the median, and the mode.

27, 16, 31, 27, 11, 51, 40, 93
Mean = 37; Median = 29; Mode = 27

▲
A herd of African elephants can have anywhere from 10 to 200 members.

19 **Discussion**

a. If the average number of children in a family is 2.58, could this average be the mean? the median? the mode? Explain.

b. Repeat part (a) if the average number of children is 2.5.

HOMEWORK EXERCISES ▶ See Exs. 10–17 on p. 227.

Appropriate Averages

SET UP *Work in a group. You will need:* • *11 chips* • *calculator*

GOAL

LEARN HOW TO...
- ◆ write a fraction as a decimal using a calculator
- ◆ choose appropriate averages
- ◆ round decimal quotients

AS YOU...
- ◆ find the average number of children for different families

▶ Average family size has fallen in most areas of the world over the past 30 years. In the United States, the mean number of children per family decreased to 2.1 in 2002. Since families have whole numbers of children, it may seem strange for the mean number of children to be a decimal. To see how this can happen, you will explore the mean number of children for four families.

Family A	Family B	Family C	Family D
2 children	0 children	1 child	0 children

20 **a.** Find the median and the mode for the data in the table.

   b. What operations would you have to perform to find the mean? **Divide the sum 2 + 0 + 1 + 0 = 3 by 4**

21 **a.** Use chips to make a pictograph showing the number of children for each family. Let each chip stand for 1 child. **See margin.**

   b. Can you move the chips so that each family has the same number of chips? Explain. **No; There are three chips to be divided among four families; 3 ÷ 4 is not a whole number.**

22 **a.** Suppose you can divide each of the three chips into four equal-sized parts. If you move the parts so that each family has the same number of parts, how many parts does each family get? **three parts**

   b. What fraction of a whole chip does each family get? $\frac{3}{4}$

20. a. Median = $\frac{1}{2}$ or 0.5; Mode = 0

Exploration 3

CLASSROOM MANAGEMENT
Question 21 relates back to the chip activity used to equalize the wolf pack sizes in Exploration 2. Since it is impossible to move 3 chips so that each of 4 families has the same number of chips without cutting (dividing) the chips into pieces, students see the need for the *sum and divide* method of finding the mean.

The point of **Questions 20–23** is to show that sometimes the mean is a fraction or decimal value. This point should be made in a timely manner so there will be time to complete the rest of the lesson on writing fractions as decimals, rounding the quotients, and choosing an appropriate average.

Students will be adding chips to the pictograph made in **Question 21**, so be sure students leave it assembled until after they complete **Question 24**.

TIPS FROM TEACHERS
Question 22 Use cutouts or fraction circles with fourths on the overhead projector to provide a visual of how the three circles can be divided equally into four groups.

21. a.

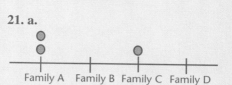

TEACHING NOTES

Some calculators are outfitted with a fraction to decimal key. Although the fraction to decimal key is handy, the division key is used in order to emphasize the fraction bar as a division symbol and also to relate to the concept of calculating a mean by dividing the sum by the total number of data items.

The example below can be used in addition to the one given in the student text.

CLASSROOM EXAMPLE

Use division to write $\frac{5}{16}$ as a decimal.

Answer:

$\frac{5}{16} = 5 \div 16$

0.3125

24. a. See Additional Answers beginning on page A1.

---

23. c. $\frac{3}{4}$ or 0.75

24. g. Sample Response: the median; The mean is affected too much by the one large family, and the mode might suggest none of the families have any children. Four of the 5 data values are clustered around the median.

23 **Discussion** Look at your answers to Question 20(b) and Question 22(b).

   a. What fraction does 3 ÷ 4 equal? $\frac{3}{4}$

   b. What decimal does 3 ÷ 4 equal? 0.75

   c. What is the mean number of children in the four families?

   d. Do you think the mean, the median, or the mode best describes the number of children for the four families? Explain. Sample Response: I would choose the mean or median. The mode might suggest none of the families has any children.

▶ A fraction represents a division. In Question 22 you found that 3 chips divided by 4 equals $\frac{3}{4}$ of a chip. You can use division to write any fraction as a decimal.

EXAMPLE

Use division to write $\frac{3}{8}$ as a decimal.

SAMPLE RESPONSE

$\frac{3}{8} = 3 \div 8$ Use a calculator: 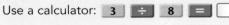 0.375

---

24 **a.** Add a Family E with 8 children to the pictograph you made in Question 21. See margin.

   b. If you move the chips so that each family has as close to the same number of chips as possible, how many chips are left over? 1 chip is left over.

   c. Calculator What fraction of a chip should each family get? Use division to write this as a decimal. $\frac{1}{5}$; 0.2

   d. Find the mean, the median, and the mode for the five families. Mean = 2.2; Median = 1; Mode = 0

   e. Compare the averages you found in part (d) with the averages you found in Question 20(a) and Question 23(c). Which average changed the least? the mode - no change

   f. Which average changed the most? the mean

   g. Which average do you think best describes the number of children in the five families? Why?

25 Calculator Use division to write $\frac{4}{7}$ as a decimal. 0.571428...

▶ **Rounding** Some quotients, like the one you found in Question 25, have many decimal places. You can round a decimal to a specific place value to make it easier to work with.

26 a.  Calculator Use a calculator to find the mean of the number of offspring for the three baboon troops in the table. Mean = 29.6666667

Baboon troop	Number of adults	Number of offspring
A	30	34
B	14	16
C	35	39

b. Is the mean closer to 29.6 or 29.7? Explain.
29.7; 29.65 is halfway between 29.6 and 26.7 and 29.6666667 > 29.65.

c. In part (b), to what place value was your chosen answer rounded? tenths

Baboons live in groups called troops.

EXAMPLE

To the nearest hundredth, find the mean number of adults in the three troops of baboons from Question 26.

SAMPLE RESPONSE

Find the mean of 30, 14, and 35.

$(30 + 14 + 35) \div 3 = 79 \div 3$

[7] [9] [÷] [3] [=]

You can round decimals in the same way you round whole numbers.

26.333333

hundredths place

Look at the digit to the right of the hundredths place.

The 3 in the thousandths place is less than 5, so 26.333333 is closer to 26.33 than to 26.34.

27 **Discussion** Use the Example above.

a. Why is the 3 in the thousandths place compared with 5?

b. Explain how to round 26.333333 to the nearest thousandth.

28 ✔ **CHECKPOINT** Calculator Write each fraction as a decimal. Round your answers to the nearest hundredth.

a. $\frac{2}{3}$ 0.67   b. $\frac{5}{9}$ 0.56   c. $\frac{1}{7}$ 0.14   d. $\frac{8}{5}$ 1.60

27. a. To round to a given place, consider the digit one place to the right. If the digit is 5 or more, round up. If it is less than 5, round down.

b. Look at the digit in the ten-thousandths place. Since it is less than 5, round down. To the nearest thousandth, 26.333333 ≈ 26.333.

✔ QUESTION 28

...checks that you can write fractions as decimals and round decimals.

ALTERNATIVE APPROACH
Using a number line can help students build number sense in **Question 27**, since they can visualize why a 5 to the right of a place value makes a difference when rounding. Ask students to plot 26.3 on a number line to determine if it is closer to 26 or 27. Then have them find a digit for x in the number 26.x so that the number would be closer to 27. Use the responses to demonstrate that digits 5 through 9 in the tenths place will round up to 27. This idea can then be extended to rounding to the nearest tenth and hundredth.

ABSENT STUDENTS

For students who were absent for all or part of this section, the blackline Study Guide for Section 2 may be used to present the ideas, concepts, and skills of Section 2.

29. a. for 1900: Mean = 4.17; Mode = 5; Median = 4.5; for 2000: Mean = 3; Mode = 3; Median = 3
b. Sample Response: For the 1900's, the mean or the median; The numbers are nearly equal and both give a better description than the mode. For the 2000's, all three averages are the same.

29 **a.** 📟 Calculator For each table below, find the mean, the median, and the mode of the data. If necessary, round to the nearest hundredth.

TV Family 1900's	Number of Children
Brady Bunch	6
Dr. Quinn, Medicine Woman	4
Partridge Family	5
Full House	3
Family Matters	2
Cosby Show	5

TV Family 2000's	Number of Children
The George Lopez Show	2
Malcolm in the Middle	4
Reba	3
According to Jim	3
Family Affair	3
My Wife and Kids	3
Like Family	3

b. Which average or averages (mean, median, or mode) do you think best describe the number of children in the TV families of the 1900s? the TV families of the 2000s? Explain.

30 In the *Phantom Tollbooth*, Milo is told that the average number of children in a family is 2.58. How does this compare to the average number of children in the TV families in Question 29?
Sample Response: The average 2.58 is close to the averages for 2000. If you round 2.58 up to 3, you get the average for the families in 2000.

HOMEWORK EXERCISES ▶ See Exs. 18–37 on pp. 227–229.

Section ② Key Concepts

Key Terms

line plot

range

cluster

gap

Line Plot (Dot Plot) (pp. 215–217)

A line plot (also called a dot plot) displays data using a line marked with a scale. The scale must include the greatest and least values of the data. The range is the difference between the greatest and least values.

Heights of 16 Anderson School Sixth Graders

Section 2
Key Concepts

Averages (pp. 218–220)
An average is a number used to describe a typical item in a set of data. The mean, the median, and the mode are types of averages.

Example Data: 6, 3, 2, 4, 6, 3

Sum of data = 24
Number of items = 6
mean = 24 ÷ 6 = 4

Ordered data: 2, 3, 3, 4, 6, 6
modes: 3 and 6
2, 3, **3, 4**, 6, 6
median = (3 + 4) ÷ 2 = 3.5

For some situations, and depending on the data, some averages may be more appropriate to use than others.

Writing a Fraction as a Decimal (pp. 221–224)
You can use division to write any fraction as a decimal.

Example $\frac{3}{7} = 3 \div 7 \approx 0.4285714286$

Rounding Decimals (pp. 223–224)
It is often helpful to round a decimal to a particular place.

Example Round 0.4285714286 to the nearest thousandth.

5 ≥ 5

0.429 ← Round the 8 up to 9.

Key Terms

average

mean

median

mode

Key Concepts Questions

Use the line plot on page 224 for Questions 31–33.

31 What are the range, the mean, the median, and the mode of the heights of the 16 Anderson School sixth graders? If necessary, round to the nearest hundredth. **Range = 178 – 134 = 44; Mean = 148.63; Median = (147 + 148) ÷ 2 = 147.5; Mode = 134.**

32 Which average, the mean, the median, or the mode, do you think best describes the typical height of the 16 Anderson School sixth graders?

33 Ramon, a 136 cm tall sixth grader, was absent the day the heights were measured. In comparison to the 16 students on the line plot, is he short, tall, or of average height? Explain.

Section 2 Line Plots and Averages

225

SUGGESTED ASSIGNMENTS

Core Course
Day 1: Exs. 1–9
Day 2: Exs. 38–47
Day 3: Exs. 10–16
Day 4: Exs. 18–37

Extended Course
Day 1: Exs. 1–9
Day 2: Exs. 38–47
Day 3: Exs. 10–17
Day 4: Exs. 18–29, 36–37

Note: Extended Course assignments can be used to differentiate within the regular classroom. In classrooms where students are grouped homogeneously, the material might be covered in fewer days. In this case assignments may be combined.

EXERCISE NOTES
You may want to suggest that students use graph paper to construct their line plots in **Exercises 5 and 6**.

ADDITIONAL PRACTICE
See the *Teacher's Resource Book* for additional practice and application exercises for this section.

5. b.
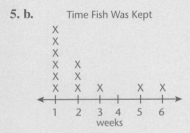
Time Fish Was Kept

6. See Additional Answers beginning on page A1.

Section ②
Practice & Application Exercises
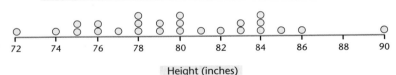

Use the line plot for Exercises 1–4.

National Basketball Association All Star Basketball Players, 2006

Height (inches)

1. What is the range of the heights of the players?
   Range: 90 − 72 = 18

2. How many players are over 82 inches?
   7 players

3. What are the two middle heights?
   79 in. and 80 in.

4. What heights occur most often?
   78 in., 80 in., and 84 in.

▲ Tim Duncan, one of the 2006 NBA All Stars.

5. A pet store owner kept track of how long it took to sell a shipment of tropical fish. She recorded how many weeks each fish was kept before it was sold. The results are shown in the list below.

   1, 2, 3, 1, 5, 1, 1, 2, 1, 1, 2, 6

   a. Find the range of the data. **Range = 5**

   b. Make a line plot for the data. **See margin.**

Use the table below for Exercises 6–9.

Average Life Spans of Some Yellowstone Park Mammals

Animal	pika	porcupine	dwarf shrew	gray wolf	grizzly bear	bison	bobcat	little brown bat	striped skunk
Life span (years)	6	6	2	16	25	20	12	30	3

6. Make a line plot for the data using X's for the symbols. **See margin.**

7. Is there a life span on your line plot that occurs more frequently than the others? If yes, what is it?
   Yes; 6 years

8. Is there a life span on your line plot that has the same number of X's to the right of it as there are to the left of it? Explain.
   Yes; 12 has 4 X's before it and 4 X's after it.

9. What can you conclude about the life spans of the animals?
   Answers vary. Sample Response: They are spread out over a wide range.

Find the mean, the median, and the mode(s) of each data set.

10. masses of 8 butterflies (mg): 12, 18, 15, 8, 11, 17, 18, 13
    Mean = 14; Median = 14; Mode = 18

11. weights of 7 kittens (ounces): 5, 8, 12, 4, 12, 3, 5
    Mean = 7; Median = 5; Modes = 5 and 12

12. litter sizes of 10 coyotes: 4, 6, 4, 8, 7, 6, 7, 9, 5, 4
    Mean = 6; Median = 6; Mode = 4

13. lengths of 5 babies (in.): 19, 22, 21, 20, 18
    Mean =20; Median = 20; No mode

14. the heights of the NBA All Star players in the line plot on
    page 226. Mean = 79.71; Median = 79.5; Modes = 78, 80, and 84

15. **Writing** The average depth of a local lake is reported to be 2 ft.
    Do you think you can wade across the lake? What information
    might be hidden when reporting this average?

16. **Open-ended** Find a set of six whole numbers that have a mean,
    a median, and a mode of 50. The numbers cannot all be the
    same. Answers will vary. Sample Response: 20, 40, 50, 50, 60, 80

17. **Challenge** The mean of nine test scores is 61.

    a. What is the sum of the scores? 549

    b. If a score of 100 is added to the group of scores, what is the
       new mean? 64.9

18. The masses (in kilograms) of six animals in a zoo are listed as 5, 8,
    24, 30, 32, and 1020. The zookeeper reported the average mass
    to be 186.5 kg. Which average did the zookeeper use? Is this
    average appropriate? Explain.

19. The grade book below shows Thom's scores on his quizzes. He
    told his mom he had an average of 92 for his quiz scores.

    a. Which average is he using? The mode

    b. Is this an appropriate average in this case? Why?

Subject ... STEM 6	Assignment	Quiz 1	Quiz 2		Quiz 3	Quiz 4		Quiz 5	Quiz 6		Quiz 7	Quiz 8	
Section ... 3		1st week			2nd week			3rd week OCT→			4th week		
Month / Date ...	Sept.	14 15 16 17 18			21 22 23 24 25			28 29 30 1 2			5 6 7 8 9		
Students ...		M T W T F			M T W T F			M T W T F			M T W T F		
Thom Wilson		92	85		78	92		71	77		80		
Kamala Pramar		98	79		84	90		90	89		75		
Sarah Adams		82	84		91	92		80	80		83		

15. Sample Response:
    You can't tell. It is
    possible that much
    of the lake is about
    2 ft deep with one
    or two very deep
    spots.

18. The mean; No; It
    is much greater
    than five of the
    six weights. The
    median (27 kg)
    would give a much
    better description.

19. b. No; The mode
    implies Thom
    will probably
    get an A. The
    mean (about 82)
    and the median
    (80) are better
    descriptions of
    his scores. The
    teacher will
    probably use the
    mean.

EXERCISE NOTES
Exercise 15 provides an
opportunity to discuss that an
average may not provide all the
information a person needs to know
about a situation. Ask students what
other statistical measure studied in
this section might help them decide
whether they can wade across the
lake safely. (*If a person knew that
the range of the lake depths were,
say 1.2 ft, he or she might be able to
wade across safely.*)

Have students discuss what
strategies other than guess and
check could be used to solve
Exercise 16. Possible strategies
might have included beginning
with six values of 50 and then
increasing and decreasing some of
the 50s to keep the same sum for
the mean.

Practice & Applications

29.

28. Compare the numerator and denominator. If the numerator is greater than the denominator, the fraction is greater than 1.

 **Calculator** Write each fraction in Exercises 20–27 as a decimal rounded to the nearest hundredth.

20. $\frac{5}{8}$ 0.63   21. $\frac{8}{11}$ 0.73   22. $\frac{1}{8}$ 0.13   23. $\frac{5}{6}$ 0.83

24. $\frac{4}{3}$ 1.33   25. $\frac{9}{8}$ 1.13   26. $\frac{2}{5}$ 0.40   27. $\frac{7}{4}$ 1.75

28. Look at Exercises 20–27. How can you tell whether a fraction is greater than 1 or less than 1 without doing any calculations?

29. Copy the number line and mark a point for each fraction from Exercises 20–27. **See margin.**

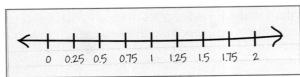

Round each decimal to the given place.

30. 0.3962 (tenths) 0.4

31. 0.3962 (thousandths) 0.396

32. 13.695 (hundredths) 13.70

33. 4.346 (tenths) 4.3

34. 56.6 (ones) 57

35. 102.342 (hundredths) 102.34

36. **Gymnastics** Six judges each score a gymnast from 1 through 10 points. The highest and lowest scores are not used. The mean of the remaining four scores is the final score. The table shows the top women's scores for the balance beam in the 2004 Olympic Games in Athens, Greece.

36. a. Sample: To prevent a judge's favorable or unfavorable attitude toward a particular nation or gymnast from affecting the outcome.

GYMNAST	JUDGES' SCORES					
Carly Patterson, USA	9.80	9.75	9.80	9.75	9.75	9.80
Alexandra Eremia, ROM	9.70	9.70	9.70	9.65	9.70	9.70
Catalina Ponor, ROM	9.80	9.80	9.80	9.75	9.75	9.80

a. Why do you think the highest and lowest scores are not used in finding the mean?

b. **Calculator** Use a calculator to find the posted score for each gymnast. Round to the nearest thousandth.
Patterson: 9.775; Eremia: 9.700; Ponor: 9.788

c. Who won the gold medal in the balance beam? Ponor

Reflecting ◀▶ on the Section

Be prepared to discuss your response to Exercise 37 in class.

37. Look back at the table and line plot of the *Number of Children in 15 Families* on page 215.

a. What are the mean, median, and mode of the data set? If necessary, round to the nearest hundredth.
Mean = 3.33; Mode = 3; Median = 3

b. Which average, the mean, median, or mode, do you think best decribes the average number of children in the families? Explain. **See margin.**

c. What type of information shows up clearly in the table? What type of information is difficult to see?

d. What type of information shows up clearly in the line plot?

e. What do you see as the advantages of the table? of the line plot? **Sample Response: The table gives more specific information, the name of the student and how many children are in each family. The line plot gives a clear picture of how the data are distributed. So it is easier to find averages on the line plot.**

> *Discussion*
>
> Exercise 37 checks that you understand the meaning of mean, median, and mode and can choose an appropriate average.

Spiral ◀▶ Review

For Exercises 38–40, use the bar graph below. (Toolbox, p. 578)

38. Which bird has the widest wingspan? the narrowest? **Royal Albatross; arctic tern**

39. Estimate the greatest difference between the wingspans of the seabirds. **about 225 cm**

40. Estimate the difference between the wingspans of the gulls. **about 20 cm**

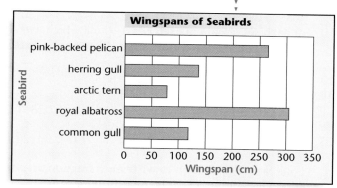

Wingspans of Seabirds

Seabird: pink-backed pelican, herring gull, arctic tern, royal albatross, common gull

Wingspan (cm): 0 50 100 150 200 250 300 350

Write each decimal as a fraction in lowest terms. (Module 3, p. 134)

41. 0.5 $\frac{1}{2}$ 42. 1.9 $\frac{19}{10}$ 43. 0.75 $\frac{3}{4}$ 44. 0.04 $\frac{1}{25}$

Find the value of each expression. (Module 1, p. 10)

45. $2 + \frac{6}{2}$ 5   46. $5 \cdot 12 - 7$ 53   47. $77 - 10 \cdot 2$ 57

37. d. **Sample Response: It is easy to see the range, mode, clusters and gaps in the data.**

37. c. **Sample Response: It is easy to see the data for each individual family on the table. It is difficult to see the median and the clusters or gaps.**

EXERCISE NOTES

Exercise 37 allows students to reflect back on the first line plot introduced in this section and apply what they have learned in all three explorations to one situation. Although this is a discussion question, you may want students to copy the line plot from page 215 into their math journals and write a summary based on the class discussion responses.

37. b. Sample Response: The median since it is in the center of the cluster of data. The mode is also in the center of the cluster, but 3 only occurs one more time than 4 which isn't a significant difference. 7 is much greater than the other data values and pulls the mean higher.

Extra Skill Practice

5. Sample Response: Median, because that is about the center of where the data are clustered and the mean is affected by the extreme (20).

10. Samples Responses:

(6) all three; They are nearly identical.

(7) all three; They are identical.

(8) The mean or the median; The mode 9 occurs only one more time than 12 and is the least of the seven data items.

(9) the median; The mean is affected by the extreme value (601) and there is no mode.

1. See Additional Answers beginning on page A1.

230

Section ② Extra Skill Practice

Use the table for Exercises 1–5.

Average Life Spans									
Animal	cat	dog	goat	guinea pig	horse	pig	rabbit	sheep	white mouse
Life span (years)	12	12	8	4	20	10	5	12	3

1. Make a line plot of the data.
   See margin.

2. What is the range of the data?
   Range = 17

3. How many of the animals have a life span greater than 8 years? 5

4. What are the mean, the median, and the mode of the life spans of the animals? If necessary, round to the nearest hundredth.
   Mean = 9.56; Median = 10; Mode = 12

5. Which average, the mean, the median, or the mode, do you think best describes the life span of the animals? Explain.
   See margin.

For Exercises 6–9, find the mean, the median, and the mode(s) for each set of data.

6. 10, 12, 9, 8, 15, 12
   Mean=11; Median = 11; Mode = 12

7. 4, 4, 2, 3, 4, 6, 5
   Mean = 4; Median = 4; Mode = 4

8. 16, 9, 13, 9, 12, 16, 9
   Mean = 12; Median = 12; Mode = 9

9. 245, 601, 322, 212
   Mean = 345; Median = 283.5; no mode

10. For each set of data in Exercises 6–9, tell which average or averages you think are most appropriate to use. Explain your choices. See margin.

Round each decimal to the given place.

11. 12.457 (hundredths) 12.46

12. 5.02841 (tenths) 5.0

13. 367.125 (hundredths) 367.13

14. 0.9912 (thousandths) 0.991

Calculator Use division to write each fraction as a decimal. Round your answers to the nearest hundredth.

15. $\frac{9}{48}$ 0.19 16. $\frac{8}{15}$ 0.53 17. $\frac{4}{3}$ 1.33 18. $\frac{14}{9}$ 1.56 19. $\frac{17}{21}$ 0.81

Standardized Testing ◀▶ Free Response

Find five whole numbers that have a mean of 4, a median of 3, and a mode of 2. Answers will vary. Sample Response: 2 2 3 6 7

Section ③ Dividing Decimals and Solving Equations

IN THIS SECTION

EXPLORATION 1
◆ Dividing Decimals

EXPLORATION 2
◆ Writing and Modeling Equations

EXPLORATION 3
◆ Using Inverse Operations

LITTLE CRITTERS

Setting the Stage ▸▸▸▸▸▸▸▸▸▸▸▸▸▸▸▸▸▸▸▸▸▸▸▸▸▸▸▸▸▸▸

Numerous small mammals, including martens, squirrels, and pikas, live in Yellowstone National Park. A pika is a stocky tailless animal about the size of a hamster. Pikas live between the tree line and the mountain peaks. Scientists believe pikas would be one of the first mammals to fall victim to global warming, so they are very carefully monitored.

Pika
body length: 185 mm
mass: 145 g
▼

◀ Marten
body length: 400 mm
mass 1.1 kg

▲
Squirrel
body length: 20 cm
mass: 220 g

Think About It

1 a. Which animal is shorter, the pika or the squirrel? by how many centimeters? **The pika; 1.5 cm**

b. Estimation The mass of the squirrel is about how many times the mass of the pika? **about 1.5 times**

2 a. The marten is how many times as long as the squirrel? **2 times**

b. The mass of the squirrel is what fraction of the mass of the marten? $\frac{220}{1100} = \frac{1}{5}$

▶ **The body length and mass given for each animal are averages. In Exploration 1, you will look more closely at how averages may have been calculated.**

Section 3 Dividing Decimals and Solving Equations

Setting the Stage

GETTING STARTED
Module 4 Section 3 *Warm-Up* assesses students' ability to find quotients of whole numbers mentally. Students will use division of whole numbers to estimate decimal quotients and check the reasonableness of their answers. When appropriate, mental math will be used to divide decimal numbers.

TEACHING NOTES
For **Questions 1 and 2**, it may be helpful to remind students that in order to add, subtract, or compare measurements, they must be in the same units.

Exploration 1

TEACHING NOTES

In **Questions 4–6**, students divide decimals by whole number divisors by shading and partitioning hundred grids. The grids should be familiar from their use with multiplication in Module 3. Students have also been dividing whole numbers and producing decimal quotients when calculating means in Section 2 of this module. Now they will extend their division skills to include decimal dividends.

DEVELOPING MATH CONCEPTS

The skill for estimating a quotient may take a good deal of practice but the time that students spend on it is worthwhile. Students who acquire good estimation skills develop "number sense" and consequently tend to make fewer errors. As a result, they gain a feeling of confidence that is based on accomplishment.

The Classroom Example below provides extra support for developing estimation skills before students complete **Checkpoint Question 8**.

CLASSROOM EXAMPLE

Six books on a scale weigh 11.4 lb. Could the mean weight of the books be 1.9 lb? Why or why not?

Answer:
Estimate 11.4 ÷ 6 to check whether 1.9 is a reasonable answer.

11.4 ÷ 6 is a little less than 12 ÷ 6.

12 ÷ 6 = 2, so the answer of 1.9 is reasonable.

4. b–c., 5. a–b., and 6. See
Additional Answers beginning on
page A1.

232

GOAL

LEARN HOW TO...
- divide a decimal by a whole number

AS YOU...
- work with 10 x 10 grids

4. a. 0.01
   d. 0.15
   e. 0.15 kg

5. c. 0.4
   d. 0.4
   e. 0.4 m

✔ QUESTION 6

...checks that you can use grids to divide a decimal by a whole number.

Exploration 1

Dividing).Decimals

SET UP *You will need Labsheets 3A and 3B.*

3 The masses of four pikas are 0.14 kg, 0.15 kg, 0.18 kg and 0.13 kg.

    a. Find the sum of the masses. **0.60 kg**

    b. What do you need to do next to find the mean of the masses of the pikas? **divide the sum of the masses by 4**

▶ **Using a Grid to Divide** To find the mean of the masses of the pikas you need to divide a decimal by a whole number. You can model the division on a 10 x 10 grid.

4 **Use Labsheet 3A.** Follow the directions on the labsheet to find the *Mean Mass of Four Pikas* using a 10 x 10 grid.
See margin for parts (b) and (c).

5 **Use Labsheet 3A.** The total body length of 6 martens is 2.40 m. Follow the directions and use the grids on the labsheet to find the *Mean Body Length of Six Martens*. **See margin for parts (a) and (b).**

6 ✔ **CHECKPOINT** **Use Labsheet 3B.** Use the *Decimal Division Grids* to find the quotients 0.06 ÷ 3, 0.36 ÷ 9, and 2)1.30. **See margin.**

▶ **Estimating a Quotient** You can use compatible numbers to quickly check that a quotient seems reasonable.

EXAMPLE

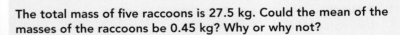

The total mass of five raccoons is 27.5 kg. Could the mean of the masses of the raccoons be 0.45 kg? Why or why not?

SAMPLE RESPONSE

Estimate 27.5 ÷ 5 to check whether 0.45 is a reasonable answer.

    27.5 ÷ 5 is slightly greater than 25 ÷ 5.

25 ÷ 5 = 5, so the answer of 0.45 is *not* reasonable.

7 Try This as a Class Copy each division at the right.

a. Use estimation to place the decimal point in each quotient. Explain your reasoning.

b. How do you think the numbers in each quotient in part (a) were determined? **by dividing as though the dividend were a whole number**

c. Look at the position of the decimal points in each quotient and dividend you wrote in part (a). How can you place the decimal point without estimating?

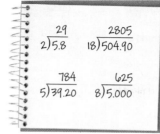

$$
\begin{array}{r} 29 \\ 2\overline{)5.8} \end{array}
\qquad
\begin{array}{r} 2805 \\ 18\overline{)504.90} \end{array}
$$

$$
\begin{array}{r} 784 \\ 5\overline{)39.20} \end{array}
\qquad
\begin{array}{r} 625 \\ 8\overline{)5.000} \end{array}
$$

8 ✔ **CHECKPOINT** Find each quotient. Estimate to check that each answer seems reasonable.

a. $3\overline{)106.23}$
35.41; 105 ÷ 3 = 35

b. 3.78 ÷ 14
0.27; 4 ÷ 16 = 0.25

c. $5\overline{)258.65}$
51.73; 250 ÷ 5 = 50

▶ **Remainders** Sometimes a division has a remainder. For these divisions, you have to write zeros to the right of the dividend to continue to divide.

EXAMPLE

$$
\begin{array}{r}
2.5 \\
8\overline{)20.2} \\
\underline{-16} \\
4\,2 \\
\underline{-4\,0} \\
2
\end{array}
$$
remainder

$$
\begin{array}{r}
2.52 \\
8\overline{)20.20} \\
\underline{-16} \\
4\,2 \\
\underline{-4\,0} \downarrow \\
20 \\
\underline{-16} \\
4
\end{array}
$$
Write a zero.

$$
\begin{array}{r}
2.525 \\
8\overline{)20.200} \\
\underline{-16} \\
4\,2 \\
\underline{-4\,0} \\
20 \\
\underline{-16} \downarrow \\
40 \\
\underline{-40} \\
0
\end{array}
$$
Write another zero.

9 Try This as a Class

a. Divide 15 by 4. **3.75**

b. How is 15 related to 15.0 and 15.00? **They are all equal.**

c. In part (a), how did you know when to write another zero and when to stop?

10 Find each quotient. Use estimation to check that each quotient seems reasonable.

a. 29.2 ÷ 8
3.65;
32 ÷ 8 = 4

b. $6\overline{)7.05}$
1.175;
6 ÷ 6 = 1

c. $4\overline{)21.25}$
5.3125;
20 ÷ 4 = 5

d. $\dfrac{12}{5}$
2.4;
10 ÷ 5 = 2

HOMEWORK EXERCISES ▶ See Exs. 1–16 on p. 241.

✔ **QUESTION 8**

...checks that you can divide a decimal by a whole number.

7. a. 2.9 (5.8 ÷ 2 ≈ 6 ÷ 2 = 3); 28.05 (504.90 ÷ 18 ≈ 500 ÷ 20 = 25); 7.84 (39.20 ÷ 5 ≈ 40 ÷ 5 = 8); 0.625 (5.000 ÷ 8 ≈ 5 ÷ 10 = 0.5)

c. Sample response: Bring the decimal straight up into the quotient, directly above the decimal point in the dividend. (Or: count the decimal places in the dividend. Position the decimal point in the quotient so it has the same number of places.)

9. c. I knew when I multiplied 5 times 4 and got 20 that there would be no remainder and I did not have to write another zero.

TIPS FROM TEACHERS
For some students, using graph paper for division problems helps them keep the digits aligned. Have students write one digit in each box of the graph paper.

TEACHING NOTES
After completing **Question 7**, you may want to select one or two of the division problems from the notebook page in **Question 7** and show the steps students would have to carry out to complete the division if the quotient had not been given. Students will need to be sure they can complete the steps in dividing in order to answer **Checkpoint Question 8**.

Questions 8 and 10 both make a point of having students verify that the results of their calculations are reasonable. One way to do this is to estimate the quotient and then check whether the actual quotient and the estimate are approximately equal. Quotients can be estimated by using compatible numbers or by rounding the divisor and/or dividend before dividing. Another approach is to round the divisor and the *quotient* and multiply them to see how close the result is to the dividend. For example, the answer to **Question 8(a)**, 35.41, may be checked by rounding 35.41 to 35 and multiplying it by 3 to get 105, which is close to the dividend 106.23.

Students may need help making the distinction between the decimal and a remainder. Using the **Example**, point out to students that the format for writing a remainder, 2.5 R 2, does not apply with decimals. The format, R #, indicates the amount left over from whole number division. In the case of decimals, division continues until the quotient ends, repeats a pattern, or is rounded to a specific place value.

233

Exploration 2

TEACHING NOTES

For students who have not seen a balance scale, borrow one from a science classroom or create a simple one by attaching small paper plates at the ends of a ruler. The eraser end of a pencil held under the center of the ruler can serve as the fulcrum.

Exploration 2

Writing and Modeling Equations

SET UP *You will need algebra tiles.*

▶ **Modeling Equations** Animals living in captivity may not have access to the foods they would eat when living in the wild. To keep the animals healthy, zoo nutritionists prepare special diets for each animal based on its natural diet and nutritional needs. For example, each prairie dog is fed 125 g of food per day. The daily feeding consists of fruits and vegetables plus 50 g of grains, seeds, and nuts. Here are three ways to model the amount of food each prairie dog is fed, where x represents the mass of the fruits and vegetables.

Verbal statement:	Mass of fruits and vegetables	plus	Mass of grains, seeds, and nuts	equals	Total mass of food
Equation:	x g	+	50 g	=	125 g

Balance model:

x g (fruits, vegetables)
+
50 g (grains, seeds, nuts) = 125 g (total)

11 **Try This as a Class** Examine the diagram above.

   a. Why does the balance scale work as a model for an equation?

   b. What is the value of x, the mass of the fruits and vegetables?
     75 g

   c. Explain how you found the value of x in part (b).
     Sample Response: I subtracted 50 g from 125 g, or
     I counted up from 50 g to 125 g.

11. a. The two sides of the equation are joined by an equal sign, so they are the same and therefore, "balanced."

▶ Balance models can help you visualize an equation and remember that both sides represent the same amount. Equations can be used to describe a variety of situations.

EXAMPLE

Suppose 19 prairie dogs, including 11 juveniles, live in the "prairie dog town" at a zoo. Write an equation to model the total number of prairie dogs in the "town."

SAMPLE RESPONSE

Let a = the number of adult prairie dogs.

Number of adult prairie dogs	plus	number of juvenile prairie dogs	equals	total number of prairie dogs
a	+	11	=	19

12 a. Why is 10 not a reasonable value for a in the Example?
$10 + 11 = 21$, not 19
b. How many adult prairie dogs live in the "town" in the Example? 8

13 One day at a zoo, a 170 kg male spectacled bear was fed 11.3 kg of food. Its meal included 3.3 kg of a nutritionally complete meatloaf, 4.0 kg of fruits and vegetables, plus other foods. Choose a variable to represent the number of kilograms of other foods. Then write an equation to model the amount the bear was fed. f = kilograms of other foods; $3.3 + 4.0 + f = 11.3$

▶ Sometimes equations that model situations involve subtraction.

▲
Spectacled bears are the only bears native to South America. They are small bears whose mass is usually less than 200 kg.

EXAMPLE

After spending $7.00 for a poster of a prairie dog, Maria had $16.00. How much money did she have before purchasing the poster?

SAMPLE RESPONSE

Amount before purchase	minus	cost of poster	equals	amount remaining
x	–	$7.00	=	$16.00

14 How much money did Maria have before buying the poster?
$23.00

TEACHING NOTES
Students may wonder why the equation in the **Example** is not written as $19 - 11 = a$. Explain that this is an equivalent equation (one with the same solution for a), however, the **Example** asked for an equation that models the total number of prairie dogs in the colony, so each side of the equation was written to represent the total number of prairie dogs. In $19 - 11 = a$, each side of the equation represents the number of adult prairie dogs.

Exploration 2 continued

USING MANIPULATIVES
Questions 17–20 If commercial algebra tiles are not available, a blackline master that can be copied and cut out to create sets of tiles is included in the *Activity Generator*. Pattern blocks or two-colored chips may also be used.

It is important that students understand how to use the manipulatives to solve equations before moving into Exploration 3, where solving an equation using algebra tiles is paralleled with solving it using inverse operations.

✔ QUESTION 15

...checks that you can use equations to model situations.

15. Sample Response: Joline sold 163 CDs at her concert. Afterwards she counted and found she had 127 CDs remaining. How many CDs did she bring to sell at the concert?; c = number of CDs she brought to the concert; $c - 163 = 127$

16. a. Sample Response: Michen received three new action figures today. Now he has eight figures altogether. J = number of action figures Michen already owned.
   b. Sample Response: Taylor had fifteen T-shirts in her closet. She decided to throw away any T-shirts that had holes or rips. When she finished cleaning out her closet only 4 T-shirts remained. c = number of shirts removed.

17. c. 3; Sample: I removed 5 tiles from each side of the balance scale.

18. c. Remove 2 tiles from each side.

---

15 ✔ CHECKPOINT Describe a situation that can be represented using a subtraction equation. Write an equation to represent the situation. Use one variable and be sure to tell what it represents.

16 Give a situation that each equation could model.

   a. $j + 3 = 8$ **b.** $15 - c = 4$

▶ **Algebra Tiles** You can use algebra tiles to model equations. The [+] tile represents the variable. The + tile represents 1.

EXAMPLE

You can model the equation $x + 5 = 8$ with algebra tiles as follows:

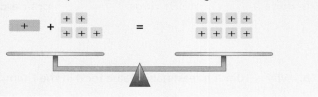

17 a. Use algebra tiles to model the Example above.
   Check students' models.
   b. Remove two + tiles from the side of the equation with the [+]. What must you do to the other side to keep the equation balanced? Remove two tiles.
   c. How many + tiles must [+] represent in the Example for the equation to be balanced? How did you get your answer?
   d. Use your answer from part (c) to complete the equation $x = \underline{?}$. $x = 3$

▶ The value of a variable that makes an equation true is a **solution** of the equation. The process of finding solutions is **solving an equation**.

18 a. Write an equation represented by the algebra tile model.

   + + + + = [+] + + +
   $4 = x + 2$
   b. Use algebra tiles to model the equation in part (a).
   Check students' models.
   c. How can you get the [+] tile alone on one side of the equation while keeping the two sides balanced?
   d. Solve the equation you wrote in part (a). $2 = x$ or $x = 2$

19 ✔ **CHECKPOINT** Repeat Question 18 for this algebra tile model.

$+$ $+$ $+$ $+$ $+$ = $+$ $+$ $+$ $+$ $+$ $+$

20 During the spring and summer, nine prairie dogs living in the wild consume about 8 kg of food per week. Their weekly diet consists of 6 kg of grass plus other vegetation.

a. Choose a variable to represent the number of kilograms of other vegetation. Then write an equation to model the amount the nine prairie dogs eat in a week. *v = kilograms of other vegetation; 6 + v = 8*

b. Use algebra tiles to model and to solve your equation from part (a). **Check students' models; v = 2 kg**

21 Challenge How does the number of grams of food a prairie dog in the wild eats each day compare with the 125 g of food a prairie dog living in a zoo is fed each day? **See margin.**

HOMEWORK EXERCISES ▸ See Exs. 17–32 on pp. 241–243.

See Exs. 17–32 on pp. 241–243.

Exploration 3

Using Inverse Operations

22 Each day, a 1200 kg female giraffe living in a zoo is fed 8.6 kg of hay in addition to other foods. Altogether, she eats 12.7 kg of food. Let x = the number of kilograms of other foods.

a. Write an addition equation that describes the amount of food the giraffe eats each day. **$8.6 + x = 12.7$**

b. What can you do to both sides of the equation to get x alone? **subtract 8.6**

c. Why is it difficult to represent this situation with algebra tiles? **The tiles cannot be broken into 6 tenths and 7 tenths to represent 8.6 and 12.7.**

✔ **QUESTION 19**

...checks that you can use a model to solve an addition equation.

19. a. $x + 3 = 6$
    b. Check students' models.
    c. Remove 3 $+$ tiles from each side.
    d. $x = 3$

GOAL

LEARN HOW TO...
◆ use inverse operations to solve addition and subtraction equations

AS YOU...
◆ examine the diets of zoo animals

KEY TERM
◆ inverse operations

Exploration 3

TEACHING NOTES
Question 22 introduces a problem with extra information (1200 kg female giraffe). Since it involves decimal numbers, it also creates a need for an alternative method to using algebra tiles for solving an equation. For **part (b)**, if students respond with "remove 8.6," lead them to use math vocabulary that states the operation necessary to remove 8.6 (*subtract 8.6*).

21. Answers will vary. Sample Responses:

A prairie dog living in a zoo eats 125 g of food per day or 875 g per week. So 9 prairie dogs living in a zoo would eat 875 g · 9 = 7875 g of food in a week. This is almost 8000 g or 8 kg, the same amount 9 prairie dogs eat per week in the wild.

In the wild, each prairie dog consumes about 0.89 kg of food per week (8 kg/9 prairie dogs). This is about 0.127 kg per day (0.89 kg/7 days) or 127 g per day. In the zoo, each prairie dog is fed 125 g per day. These two amounts of food are very nearly the same, with the wild prairie dog consuming about 2 g more of food per day.

DIFFERENTIATED INSTRUCTION
For students having difficulty making the transition from algebra tiles to inverse operations, let them sketch their algebra tile models next to the equations in **Checkpoint Question 25**, and then guide them in how to record their steps algebraically next to the pictures.

23. b. First, copy the equation. Next, substitute the solution for the variable in the equation and write a question mark over the equal sign to show that it is not yet known whether the two sides of the equation are equal. Finally, simplify each side of the equation by performing the arithmetic operations. If the results of simplifying are the same, the solution is correct. Show this by writing the results of simplifying in an equation followed by a check mark.

c. Checking the solution confirms that it is correct and helps you know if you made any errors in solving the equation.

▶ Addition and subtraction are **inverse operations**. They "undo" each other. Inverse operations are helpful in solving equations.

Here are keys to solving an equation:

- ◆ Use inverse operations to get the variable alone on one side.
- ◆ Keep the equation in balance by keeping both sides equal.

▶ When you use symbols and variables to solve an equation, you are solving the equation *algebraically*.

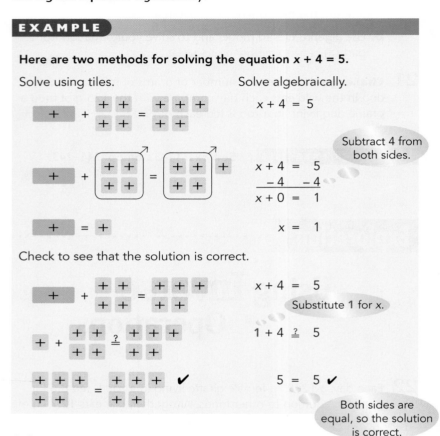

EXAMPLE

Here are two methods for solving the equation $x + 4 = 5$.

Solve using tiles.   Solve algebraically.

$$x + 4 = 5$$

Subtract 4 from both sides.

$$x + 4 = 5$$
$$\underline{-4 \quad -4}$$
$$x + 0 = 1$$

$$x = 1$$

Check to see that the solution is correct.

Substitute 1 for x.

$$1 + 4 \overset{?}{=} 5$$

$$5 = 5 \checkmark$$

Both sides are equal, so the solution is correct.

23 Try This as a Class

a. In the Example, what was done to the equation to get x alone? 4 was subtracted from each side.

b. Describe the steps in checking the solution. Why is the question mark included in the check process?

c. Why is it important to check the solution?

24 Tim solved the equation $x + 47 = 65$ as shown at the right. Check to see whether Tim's solution is correct.
$18 + 47 \overset{?}{=} 65$; $65 = 65$; yes

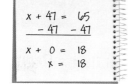

$$x + 47 = 65$$
$$-47 \quad -47$$
$$x + 0 = 18$$
$$x = 18$$

25 ✔ **CHECKPOINT** Solve each equation. Check each solution.

a. $n + 18 = 102$
$n = 84$

b. $12 = a + 5$
$a = 7$

c. $n + 5.6 = 14.3$
$n = 8.7$

✔ **QUESTION 25**

...checks that you understand how inverse operations can help you solve equations.

▶ Inverse operations can also be used to solve equations where a number is subtracted from a variable.

EXAMPLE

Solve the equation $x - 4.8 = 13.5$.

SAMPLE RESPONSE

$$x - 4.8 = 13.5$$
$$+4.8 \quad +4.8$$
$$x + 0 = 18.3$$
$$x = 18.3$$

Add 4.8 to both sides.

26 a. What was done to the equation in the Example to get x alone? **4.8 was added to both sides of the equation.**

b. Why was this operation chosen?
Addition is the inverse of subtraction.

c. Check the solution by substituting 18.3 for x. Is the solution correct? $18.3 - 4.8 \overset{?}{=} 13.5$; $13.5 = 13.5$; yes

27 Solve your equation from Question 22(a) to find the number of kilograms of other foods the giraffe was fed. $x = 4.1$ kg

28 Solve each equation. Check each solution.

a. $n - 3.7 = 6$
$n = 9.7$

b. $16 = k - 7$
$k = 23$

c. $27 = 12 + p$
$15 = p$

d. $z - 5.8 = 14.7$
$z = 20.5$

29 ✔ **CHECKPOINT** A student's solution of the equation $n - 1.3 = 1.5$ is $n = 2$. A check of this solution is shown.

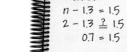

Check
$n - 1.3 = 1.5$
$2 - 1.3 \overset{?}{=} 1.5$
$0.7 = 1.5$ ✗

a. What does the check tell you?
The value for n is incorrect.

b. What is the solution of the equation? $n = 2.8$

✔ **QUESTION 29**

...checks that you understand how to verify a solution.

HOMEWORK EXERCISES ▶ See Exs. 33–57 on pp. 243–244.

DIFFERENTIATED INSTRUCTION
For students still needing the assistance of algebra tiles for solving equations, the ➕ tiles may be replaced with base ten blocks to represent decimal numbers. Students should be familiar with base ten blocks from Module 3 where they were used to represent, add, and subtract decimal numbers.

Key Concepts

CLOSURE QUESTIONS

In working with decimals, explain how inverse operations are used to
(a) check a division answer, and
(b) to solve an addition equation.

Sample Response: (a) In a division problem, you can multiply the answer (quotient) by the number you divided by (divisor) to check if it equals the dividend. If it does, the answer is correct. (b) In solving an equation which has a decimal added to the variable, you can use subtraction (which is the inverse of addition) to get the variable alone on one side of the equation and therefore solve the equation.

ABSENT STUDENTS

For students who were absent for all or part of this section, the blackline Study Guide for Section 3 may be used to present the ideas, concepts, and skills of Section 3.

Key Terms

solving an equation

inverse operations

solution of an equation

31. Sample Response: In the Example you are adding the same amount to two expressions that are already equal, so they remain equal, or "balanced."

Section ③
Key Concepts

Dividing a Decimal by a Whole Number (pp. 232–233)

Divide as though both numbers were whole numbers.

$$\begin{array}{r} 0.15 \\ 4\overline{)0.60} \\ \underline{4} \\ 20 \\ \underline{20} \\ 0 \end{array}$$

← Write a zero to the right of the dividend when the division does not come out evenly.

Write the decimal point in the quotient directly above the decimal point in the dividend.

Modeling Equations (pp. 234–237)

Balance models can help you visualize an equation and remember that the expressions on either side of an equation must be equal. Algebra tile models can help you solve (find a solution of) an equation.

Using Inverse Operations (pp. 237–239)

The goal when you solve an equation is to get the variable alone on one side of the equation. One method that can help you reach the goal is to use inverse operations. Inverse operations "undo" one another. Addition and subtraction are inverse operations. Remember that any operation done on one side of the equation must also be done on the other side to keep the equation balanced.

Example Addition "undoes" the subtraction when you solve an equation.

Solve $n - 6.3 = 4.5$.

$$\begin{array}{rcr} n - 6.3 & = & 4.5 \\ + 6.3 & & + 6.3 \\ \hline n + 0 & = & 10.8 \\ n & = & 10.8 \end{array}$$

Add 6.3 to both sides.

Check that $n = 10.8$.

$$n - 6.3 = 4.5$$
$$10.8 - 6.3 \overset{?}{=} 4.5$$
$$4.5 = 4.5 \ ✔$$

Substitute your solution in the equation.

10.8 is the solution of the equation $n - 6.3 = 4.5$.

Key Concepts Questions

30 Find the quotient $1.6 \div 5$. Use estimation to check that the quotient seems reasonable. **0.32; $1.5 \div 5 = 0.3$**

31 Explain how the steps in the Example above keep the equation "balanced" and help to solve the equation.

Section 3

Practice & Application Exercises

YOU WILL NEED

For Exs. 21–23, 46:
♦ algebra tiles

Estimation Use compatible numbers to check the position of the decimal point on each quotient. If a quotient is incorrect, give the correct quotient.

1. $4\overline{)783.2}$ → 19.58 incorrect;
   $800 \div 4 = 200$; 195.8

2. $20\overline{)41}$ → 2.05 correct;
   $40 \div 20 = 2$

3. $7\overline{)21.14}$ → 30.2 incorrect;
   $21 \div 7 = 3$; 3.02

4. At the beginning of a trip, the trip odometer in Brianna's car read 0 miles. After 4 days of travel, the odometer read 994.8 miles. What is the mean of the distances she drove each day? **248.7 mi**

Find each quotient. Use estimation to check that each quotient seems reasonable.

5. $6\overline{)0.48}$
   0.08; $0.6 \div 6 = 0.1$

6. $8\overline{)4.976}$
   0.622; $4 \div 8 = 0.5$

7. $13.08 \div 12$
   1.09; $12 \div 12 = 1$

8. $124.5 \div 6$
   20.75; $120 \div 6 = 20$

9. $37.3 \div 4$
   9.325; $36 \div 4 = 9$

10. $11\overline{)215.6}$
   19.6; $220 \div 11 = 20$

11. **Geometry Connection** The perimeter of a square is 5.23 cm. Find the length of one side. **1.3075 cm**

12. The Pentagon Building is one of the largest office buildings in the world. Its outermost wall is in the shape of a regular pentagon with a perimeter of about 1.6 km. How many *meters* long is one side of the Pentagon? **320 m**

◄ The Pentagon Building, in Arlington, Virginia, is the headquarters for the Department of Defense of the United States government.

Choosing a Method Use pencil and paper or mental math to write each fraction as a decimal.

13. $\frac{7}{8}$ 0.875

14. $\frac{12}{200}$ 0.06

15. $\frac{9}{5}$ 1.8

16. $\frac{756}{1000}$ 0.756

Write an equation that each model represents.

17. $x + 4 = 8$

18. $x + 3 = 4$

SUGGESTED ASSIGNMENTS

Core Course
Day 1: Exs. 1–16, 58–68
Day 2: Exs. 17–32, 69–78
Day 3: Exs. 33–57

Extended Course
Day 1: Exs. 1–16, 58–68
Day 2: Exs. 17–32, 69–78
Day 3: Exs. 34–46 even, 51–57, 79–84*

Note: Extended Course assignments can be used to differentiate within the regular classroom. In classrooms where students are grouped homogeneously, the material might be covered in fewer days. In this case assignments may be combined.

*denotes Extension Exercises

EXERCISE NOTES
Exercises 13–16 Ask students to be prepared to share in class which method they used and why. You might suggest they note *pp* (pencil and paper) or *mm* (mental math) next to each problem on their paper so they remember which method they used.

ADDITIONAL PRACTICE
See the *Teacher's Resource Book* for additional practice and application exercises for this section.

Practice & Applications

EXERCISE NOTES

Exercises 19 and 20 For students unsure of how to "describe a situation," refer them to the examples on page 235. They might feel more comfortable using the example box format to write a situation in words that gives the desired equation as the solution to the example.

19. Sample: Maxwell had 4 fish in his aquarium. He went to the mall this weekend and purchased more fish. His aquarium now has 6 fish in it. n = number of fish Maxwell purchased at the mall this weekend

20. Sample: Kerry's mom baked her 36 cookies to take back to college. Each day Kerry eats only one cookie. If she has 17 cookies left, how many has she eaten?; $36 - e = 17$; e = number of cookies eaten

21–23. See Additional Answers beginning on page A1.

19. **Open-ended** Describe a situation that can be modeled by the equation $n + 4 = 6$. Be sure to tell what the variable represents.
    See margin.

20. **Open-ended** Describe a situation that can be represented using a subtraction equation. Write an equation to model the situation. Use one variable and tell what it represents.
    See margin.

Make an algebra tile model that represents each equation. Then use the model to find the solution.

21. $6 = x + 4$
    See margin.

22. $x + 3 = 11$
    See margin.

23. $7 + x = 13$
    See margin.

Social Studies In 1933, the 20th Amendment to the Constitution set January 20 as the inauguration date for the President and January 3 as the inauguration date for members of Congress. Write an addition equation to model each situation. Let y = the number of years served.

24. Dwight D. Eisenhower, the first President limited to two terms by a later amendment to the Constitution, served from 1953 to 1961. $1953 + y = 1961$

25. Barbara Jordan, the first African-American woman from a Southern state elected to the House of Representatives, served from 1973 to 1979. $1973 + y = 1979$

26. Dalip Singh Saund, the first Asian-American elected to the House of Representatives, served from 1957 to 1963. $1957 + y = 1963$

Write an addition equation to model each situation. Use one variable and tell what it represents.

27. The track team gets 2 new members, raising the membership to 20. $m + 2 = 20$; m = number of existing members

28. Of the 12 people in the 200 m dash, 5 of them set a new "personal best." $12 = 5 + p$; p = number of runners who did not set personal bests

29. Alice won 3 medals. She now has 17 medals. $m + 3 = 17$; m = number of medals Alice had before

Write a subtraction equation to model each situation. Use one variable and tell what it represents.

30. Anna sold 70 prints. She has 8 left over.
$p - 70 = 8$; p = number of prints Anna had originally

31. After paying $5.75 for lunch, John received $4.25 in change.
$B - 5.75 = 4.25$; B = amount of money John had originally

32. The number of customers on a paper route drops to 28 after 4 people cancel their subscriptions to the newspaper.
$c - 4 = 28$; c = original number of customers

Solve each equation. Check each solution.

33. $a + 19 = 47$
$a = 28$

34. $8 + w = 110$
$w = 102$

35. $q - 26 = 37$
$q = 63$

36. $53 = v - 19$
$v = 72$

37. $b - 27 = 16$
$b = 43$

38. $10 = 8 + n$
$n = 2$

39. $0.66 + x = 2.4$
$x = 1.74$

40. $p - 5.6 = 2.74$
$p = 8.34$

41. $1.5 = n - 3$
$n = 4.5$

42. $y - 1.8 = 2.7$
$y = 4.5$

43. $n + 0.06 = 4$
$n = 3.94$

44. $1.69 = x - 17.4$
$x = 19.09$

45. Is 6 a solution of the equation $0.2 + n = 8$? Explain.
no, $0.2 + 6 = 6.2$, not 8

46. Challenge Write an equation that the model below represents. Then use algebra tiles to solve the equation. $2n + 3 = 9$; $n = 3$

Banking For Exercises 47–49, write an equation to model each banking situation. Identify the variable you use. Solve each equation and check your solution.

47. Shellie withdrew money from her bank account to buy a used mountain bike. What was the balance in her account before the withdrawal?

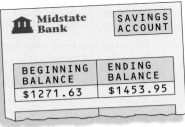

48. Darius is saving money for a trip with the Spanish club. What was the increase in his savings this month?

49. Darius expected his ending balance to be $1450.24. What was the amount of interest he forgot to include?

50. Writing Describe how you would solve the equation $n - 49.75 = 682.94$ using a calculator.

47. $B - 165 = 357.49$;
B = balance before the withdrawal; $522.49

48. $1271.63 + I = 1453.95$; I = increase; $182.32

49. $1450.24 + I = 1453.95$; I = interest; $3.71

50. Evaluate $682.94 + 49.75$ on the calculator

EXERCISE NOTES
You may want to discuss the banking terms in **Exercises 47–49** with students to ensure they understand the meanings of balance, savings, interest, and withdrawal.

Practice & Applications

EXERCISE NOTES

Students may need additional time to complete the research for **Reflecting Exercise 57**. Alternatively you might print out and post a list for students to reference.

Choosing a Method Tell whether you would use mental math or paper and pencil to solve each equation. Then solve.

51. $17.3 + a = 62.1$
$a = 44.8$; paper and pencil

52. $b - 11 = 4$
$b = 15$; mental math

53. $y - 237 = 54$
$y = 291$; paper and pencil

54. $t - 8 = 20.5$
$t = 28.5$; mental math

55. $11 = 6 + s$
$s = 5$; mental math

56. $c + 35 = 88$
$c = 53$; mental math

RESEARCH

Exercise 57 checks that you understand how to write and solve equations.

Reflecting ◀▶ on the Section

57. Research the terms of three former members of Congress from your state who were elected after 1933 and who served full terms. Let y = the number of years served. Write and solve both an addition equation and a subtraction equation to model each situation. Check each solution.
Answers will vary; check students' equations

Spiral ◀▶ Review

Round each decimal to the given place. (Module 4, p. 225)

58. 64.37 (ones) 64

59. 13.403 (hundredths) 13.40

60. 2.97 (tenths) 3.0

61. 0.3611 (thousandths) 0.361

Tell whether each combination of side lengths can form a triangle. Explain your reasoning. (Module 2, p. 106)

62. 2 in., 6 in., 7 in.
$2 + 6 > 7$; yes

63. 5 cm, 8 cm, 3 cm
$5 + 3 = 8$; no

64. 2 ft, 35 ft, 13 ft
$2 + 13 < 35$; no

65. 1 m, 0.7 m, 0.4 m
$0.4 + 0.7 > 1$; yes

Find each value. (Module 1, p. 62)

66. $\frac{3}{5}$ of 35 21

67. $\frac{9}{10}$ of 80 72

68. $\frac{7}{8}$ of 24 21

Find each product. (Module 3, p. 178)

69. $\frac{3}{5} \cdot \frac{7}{9}$ $\frac{21}{45} = \frac{7}{15}$

70. $\frac{9}{10} \cdot 1\frac{2}{3}$ $\frac{3}{2} = 1\frac{1}{2}$

71. $2\frac{3}{4} \cdot 1\frac{1}{8}$ $\frac{99}{32} = 3\frac{3}{32}$

Tell whether each number is divisible by 2, 3, 5, 9, and 10. (Module 3, p. 157)

72. 75 3, 5

73. 630 2, 3, 5, 9, 10

74. 253 none

Evaluate each expression when $a = 32$, $b = 4$, and $c = 6.3$.
(Module 1, p. 21)

75. $2b - 3$ 5

76. $a - 4b$ 16

77. $1.3b + c$ 11.5

78. Susan and Claire worked a total of 20 hours. Susan earned $8.00 per hour. Claire earned $7.00 per hour. Together they earned $148.00 over the weekend. (Module 1, p. 33)

    a. How many hours did Claire work? 12 hours

    b. What problem solving strategies did you use to solve the problem? Answers will vary; Sample Response: make a table, guess and check

83. $n = 1$,
    check $1 + 1 \stackrel{?}{=}$
    $2 \cdot 1$, $2 = 2$
    $n = 4$,
    check $4 + 6 \stackrel{?}{=}$
    $2 + 2 \cdot 4$, $10 = 10$
    $n = 3$,
    check $2 \cdot 3 + 3 \stackrel{?}{=}$
    $3 \cdot 3$, $9 = 9$
    $n = 2$,
    check $2 + 5 \stackrel{?}{=}$
    $3 + 2 \cdot 2$, $7 = 7$

Extension ▶ ▶

Equations with Variables on Both Sides

In this section, the equations you solved had a variable on only one side of the equation. You can apply the ideas you learned to solve equations that have variables on both sides of the equation.

Describe how you would solve each equation modeled below.

79. $n + 1 = 2n$

80. $n + 6 = 2 + 2n$

81. $2n + 3 = 3n$

82. $n + 5 = 3 + 2n$

83. Solve each equation in Exercises 79–82 algebraically. Check each solution.

84. a. Does the equation $x + 35 = x + 13$ have a solution? Explain.

    b. Does the equation $x + 4 = 4 + x$ have a solution? Explain.

84. a. No, there is no number that you can add different amounts to and have the sums remain equal.
b. Yes, every number is a solution. If you take two equal numbers and add the same amount to both of them, the two sums will be equal.

79. Remove one ⊞ tile from each side of the equation.

80. Remove one ⊞ tile and two ⊞ tiles from each side of the equation.

81. Remove two ⊞ tiles from each side of the equation.

82. Remove one ⊞ and three ⊞ tiles from each side of the equation.

TEACHER NOTES
For each Exploration, the corresponding Extra Skill Practice Exercises are noted.

Exploration 1: Exs. 1–9
Exploration 2: Exs. 10–13
Exploration 3: Exs. 14–16

EXTRA HELP
Teacher's Resource Book
• Practice and Applications
• Study Guide

Technology Resources
• @Home Tutor
• Test Generator

ASSESSMENT
• Section 3 Quick Quiz
• Mid-Module Quiz
• Test Generator

Section 3
Extra Skill Practice

Find each quotient. Use estimation to check that each quotient seems reasonable.

1. $5\overline{)0.45}$
   0.09; 0.5 ÷ 5 = 0.1

2. $8\overline{)97.64}$
   12.205; 100 ÷ 10 = 10

3. 12.46 ÷ 4
   3.115; 12 ÷ 4 = 3

4. 110.4 ÷ 6
   18.4; 120 ÷ 6 = 20

5. $9\overline{)31.086}$
   3.454; 27 ÷ 9 = 3

6. $12\overline{)64.8}$
   5.4; 60 ÷ 12 = 5

Tell whether the quotient is correct in each division. If the quotient is not correct, give the correct quotient.

7. $3\overline{)21.66}$ 72.2 no, 7.22

8. $8\overline{)458}$ 57.25 correct

9. $14\overline{)825.44}$ 58.96 correct

Write an equation that each model represents.

10. ☐ + + + + = + + + + + $n + 2 = 5$

11. + + + + + + = + + ☐ + $6 = 1 + n$

Write an addition or subtraction equation to model each situation. Use one variable and tell what it represents.

12. Alexis blew out 11 candles on a cake, but 2 remained lit.
    $n - 11 = 2$; n = number of candles on the cake

13. Jill picked 53 apples. She and her brother together picked 85 apples. $53 + b = 85$; b = number of apples Jill's brother picked

Solve each equation. Check each solution.

14. $a + 14 = 32$ $a = 18$

15. $q - 21 = 29$ $q = 50$

16. $13.6 + f = 31.2$ $f = 17.6$

Standardized Testing ◀▶ **Multiple Choice**

1. Raymond buys 5 quarts of punch for his party for a total of $7.25. Including Raymond, there are 8 people at the party. How many quarts of punch are there for each person? B

   A 1.45 qt   B 0.625 qt   C 0.906 qt   D 1.6 qt

2. Which quotient is not correct? D

   A 1.79
      $3\overline{)5.37}$

   B 1.4
      $4\overline{)5.6}$

   C 20.25
      $4\overline{)81}$

   D 321.25
      $8\overline{)257}$

FOR ASSESSMENT AND PORTFOLIOS

Extended Exploration

E² NOTES

Using an E²: Suggestions for managing and evaluating an Extended Exploration are available in the *Teacher's Resource Book* for Modules 1 and 2. See also pages T44–T45 in the *Teacher's Edition*.

Alternate E²: See the *Teacher's Resource Book* for an alternate Extended Exploration that can be used after Module 4 Section 3.

The Situation   See the *Teacher's Resource Book* for a sample solution for this Extended Exploration.

It is time to order toy animals to sell in the souvenir shop at the zoo. You have been asked to help decide what toy animals to buy and how many of each to order. The table below summarizes the data on sales last year.

Animal	Number ordered	Number sold
lion	60	51
iguana	15	1
panda bear	80	62
tiger	15	15
seal	30	19
total	**200**	**148**

The shop can also order toy monkeys, parrots, and giraffes from the supplier. Each unsold animal costs the souvenir shop $1.00 to return to the supplier.

The Problem

Decide which toy animals the shop should sell and how many of each to order.

Something to Think About

◆ Based on last year's sales, are there any toy animals you should order more of? less of?

◆ Are there questions you would like to ask those who run the zoo that would affect what toy animals you would order?

Present Your Results

Prepare a report for the souvenir shop manager that clearly states your recommendations. Be sure to explain the mathematics and the reasoning that helped you decide.

GETTING STARTED

Module 4 Section 4 *Warm-Up* assesses students' ability to find the range, median, and mode of a set of data. In Section 4, students will be finding these values from a stem-and-leaf plot.

Help students with the pronunciation of *Euoplocephalus* (You-plo-SEPH-ah-lus) and *Tyrannosaurus rex* (Tie-RAN-uh-sore-us rex).

Section 4 — Stem-and-Leaf Plots, Decimal Division, and Graphing

DIN SAURS

Setting the Stage

Tyrannosaurus rex
predator (meat-eater)

A *Tyrannosaurus rex* could eat a lot at once and then not eat for days. An 8-ton *Tyrannosaurus rex* needed to eat an average of 186 lb of meat per day and could eat about 2 tons of meat at a sitting!

length: 40 feet   **weight:** 4-8 tons

Euoplocephalus
(you-plo-**SEPH**-ah-lus)
plant-eater

A *Euoplocephalus* was one of the slowest dinosaurs. Its defense against predators was the bony armor along its back, head, and neck. It also had a huge club at the end of its tail.

length: 18 feet **weight:** 3 tons

Think About It

1 a. What animal living today do you think might be as long as a *Euoplocephalus*? **Sample Response: African elephant**

b. What animal might be as heavy? **Sample Response: rhinoceros**

2 Estimation If an 8-ton *Tyrannosaurus rex* ate 2 tons of meat, in about how many days would it need to eat again? (1 ton = 2000 lb) **Accept reasonable estimates; about 20 days.**

Exploration 1

Stem-and-Leaf Plots

SET UP *You will need Labsheet 4A.*

GOAL

LEARN HOW TO...
- make and interpret a stem-and-leaf plot

AS YOU...
- compare dinosaur data

KEY TERM
- stem-and-leaf plot

▶ A *Euoplocephalus* seems large compared with animals alive today, but how did it compare with other plant-eating dinosaurs? Because the sizes of dinosaurs varied so much, an average size may not tell you much. Instead, it may be more useful to make a **stem-and-leaf plot**.

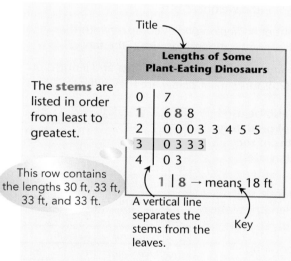

Title

Lengths of Some Plant-Eating Dinosaurs

The **stems** are listed in order from least to greatest.

```
0 | 7
1 | 6 8 8
2 | 0 0 0 3 3 4 5 5
3 | 0 3 3 3
4 | 0 3
```

The **leaf** of each data value is written to the right of its stem.

1 | 8 → means 18 ft

This row contains the lengths 30 ft, 33 ft, 33 ft, and 33 ft.

A vertical line separates the stems from the leaves.

Key

Some Plant-Eating Dinosaurs

Dinosaur	Length (feet)
Anatosaurus	40
Ankylosaurus	25
Centrosaurus	20
Chasmosaurus	16
Corythosaurus	33
Edmontonia	23
Edmontosaurus	43
Euoplocephalus	18
Hadrosaurus	33
Pachyrhinosaurus	20
Panoplosaurus	23
Parasaurolophus	33
Parksosaurus	7
Sauropelta	25
Styracosaurus	18
Tenontosaurus	24
Torosaurus	20
Triceratops	30

3 Discussion Use the stem-and-leaf plot above.

a. Explain what "4 | 0 3" means.
4 | 03 indicates two dinosaur lengths, 40 ft and 43 ft

b. How many of the plant-eating dinosaurs were 18 ft long?
two dinosaurs

c. Why do you think the numbers 0 through 4 were used as the stems in the stem-and-leaf plot? See margin.

d. Was the *Euoplocephalus* long or short compared with the other plant-eating dinosaurs in the table? Explain.
It was fairly short; 14 of the 17 other dinosaurs listed were longer than the *Euoplocephalus*.

Section 4 Stem-and-Leaf Plots, Decimal Division, and Graphing

---

Exploration 1

CLASSROOM MANAGEMENT

Since students are probably not familiar with stem-and-leaf plots, this exploration is best performed with the entire class. Each student should have his or her own copy of Labsheet 4A.

TEACHING NOTES

After discussing **Question 3** with the students, have them practice reading the plot. Ask questions such as "What does the zero after the 2-stem mean?" *(a length of 20 ft)* Then show how easily the modes *(20 ft and 30 ft)* and median *(23.5 ft)* of the dinosaur lengths can be found from the plot.

The Classroom Example below can be used to provide additional practice with finding the median, mode, and range of a set of data displayed in a stem-and-leaf plot.

CLASSROOM EXAMPLE

Use the stem-and-leaf plot below to answer the questions.

Number of Miles Driven on Vacation

```
44 | 1 4
45 |
46 | 2 3 5
47 | 1 1 1 2 7 9
48 | 3 3
49 | 0
50 | 1 2 6
```

44 | 1 means 441 miles

a. Find the median and the mode of the set of data.

b. What is the range of the data?

Answer:
a. 472; 471   b. 65

3. c. See Additional Answers beginning on page A1.

Exploration 1 *continued*

TEACHING NOTES

Question 4(c) Having seen only one stem-and-leaf plot, students may not realize that 2|1 could mean 21 or 2.1 or 0.21, thus a key is necessary for clarification.

COMMON ERROR

Question 6(a) Some students may be bothered by the fact that there are no weights that have a stem of 1. They may want to incorrectly "fill the gap" with a stem of 1 followed by a leaf of 0 to show that there is nothing there. Point out that doing so would actually introduce the data item 1.0, which does not exist in this data set. Mention that there is no need to fill the gap of leaves between the stems 0 and 2.

TEACHING NOTES

Before students begin **Checkpoint Question 7**, remind them that the leaf values should be written in order from least to greatest. However, when recording the leaves from the original data set, it may be easier for students first to write the leaves for each stem in the order they occur in the data instead of in numerical order. Then they can go back and order the leaves. Have students space the leaves equally. If using grid paper, students should write one digit per box with a blank box left in between data values.

7.   **Lengths of Some
          Predatory Dinosaurs**

```
0 | 4  6  7  7  8
1 | 1  3  3  3  7
2 | 6
3 | 0  5
4 | 0
```
          4 | 0 means 40 ft

5., 6. b–c. See Additional Answers
beginning on page A1.

---

4. a. The answers are easier to determine from the stem-and-leaf plot. To answer from the table, you would have to read the entire table, then compare all the lengths. To answer part (b) from the stem-and-leaf plot, you only have to count digits. To answer part (d), you only have to glance at the plot.

c. A key is necessary to clarify what the stem and the leaf represent. 1 | 8 means 18 feet not 1.8 feet or 0.18 foot.

7. a. It was relatively long, longer than 10 of the 14 predatory dinosaurs listed.

QUESTION 7

...checks that you can make and interpret a stem-and-leaf plot.

7. b. Sample Response: Overall, the plant-eating dinosaurs seemed to be longer than the predatory dinosaurs. For example, 10 of the 14 predatory dinosaurs were shorter than the median length for the plant eaters.

---

4 a. Are the answers to parts (b) and (d) of Question 3 easier to determine from the table or from the stem-and-leaf plot? Explain.

b. What information from the table do you lose by showing the data in a stem-and-leaf plot? *what dinosaur has each length*

c. Why does a stem-and-leaf plot require a key?

Use Labsheet 4A for Questions 5 and 6.

5 Try This as a Class Follow the directions on the labsheet to complete the stem-and-leaf plot for the *Weights of Plant-Eating Dinosaurs*. See margin.

6 Look at your stem-and-leaf plot from Question 5.

a. Why is there no leaf for the stem 1? See margin.

b. What are the modes of the plant-eating dinosaur weights?
2.7, 3.0, 3.5, 3.9, 4.0, and 5.0

c. What is the median of the weights? 3.5

d. How did the weight of a *Euoplocephalus* compare with the weights of the other plant-eating dinosaurs in the table?
See margin.

e. How are the stem-and-leaf plots for the weights and lengths of the plant-eating dinosaurs similar? How are they different?
See margin.

▶ Stem-and-leaf plots can also be used to compare the lengths of predatory dinosaurs with the lengths of the plant-eating dinosaurs they ate.

7 ✔ **CHECKPOINT** Make a stem-and-leaf plot for the lengths of the predatory dinosaurs in the table.
See margin.

a. How did an 18-foot-long *Euoplocephalus* compare in length with the predatory dinosaurs?

b. Use your stem-and-leaf plot and the one on page 249. How did the lengths of the plant-eating dinosaurs compare with the lengths of the predatory dinosaurs?

Some Predatory Dinosaurs	
Dinosaur	**Length (feet)**
Albertosaurus	26
Allosaurus	35
Chirostenotes	7
Daspletosaurus	30
Deinonychus	13
Dromaeosaurus	6
Dromiceiomimus	11
Microvenator	4
Nanotyrannous	17
Ornithomimus	13
Struthiomimus	13
Troodon	8
Tyrannosaurus rex	40
Velociraptor	7

 HOMEWORK EXERCISES ▶ See Exs. 1–14 on pp. 257–258.

Exploration 2

Dividing.by a)Decimal

LEARN HOW TO...
♦ divide by a decimal

AS YOU...
♦ explore the feeding habits of predatory dinosaurs

SET UP *You will need Labsheet 4B.*

Some scientists believe that dinosaurs ate, slept, and moved more like birds than like lizards. Assuming that is true, scientists can calculate how much and how often dinosaurs ate.

▶ **A 6-kilogram *Microvenator* needed to eat about 0.4 kg of meat a day. Suppose the animals it hunted had a mass of about 0.05 kg each.**

8 What would you do to find out how many animals a *Microvenator* needed to catch each day? **Divide 0.4 by 0.05**

Use Labsheet 4B for Questions 9 and 10.

9 One way to find how many animals a *Microvenator* needed to catch each day is to divide 0.4 by 0.05. Follow the directions on the labsheet to model the division 0.4 ÷ 0.05 on the *Animal Division Grid.* **See margin.**

10 ✔ **CHECKPOINT** Use the *Division Grids* to find 0.60 ÷ 0.15, 0.28 ÷ 0.04, and 0.45)‾0.9‾. **See margin.**

11 **Discussion** Look for patterns in the divisions.

dividend

6)‾12‾	18)‾36‾	60)‾120‾	600)‾1200‾

divisor

a. How is the divisor of 6 in the first division related to each of the other divisors? **18 = 3 · 6, 60 = 10 · 6, 600 = 100 · 6**

b. How is the dividend of 12 related to each of the other dividends?

c. Write another division problem that has the same divisor and dividend relationship with the first division.
Answers will vary. Sample Response: 30)‾60‾

d. Find all five quotients. What do you notice about them?
2, 2, 2, 2, 2; The quotients are all the same.

e. What happens to a quotient when you multiply the dividend and the divisor by the same number? **It stays the same.**

✔ **QUESTION 10**

...checks that you can use a grid to divide by a decimal.

11. b. 36 = 3 · 12, 120 = 10 · 12, 1200 = 100 · 12. In each division problem, the original divisor and dividend are multiplied by the same number.

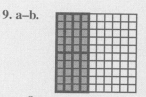

Section 4 Stem-and-Leaf Plots, Decimal Division, and Graphing

---

Exploration 2

TEACHING NOTES
Monitor students' work closely on **Question 9**. Students should be familiar with use of 100 grids from earlier division and place value explorations. However, for those who need it, provide guidance to help them understand that 0.4 = 0.40 or forty hundredths, so 0.4 of the grid is 40 grid squares. Likewise, be sure they represent 0.05 as 5 grid squares.

As you discuss **Question 11** with the students, you may want to bring out the point of the discussion by rewriting the division problems as fractions and then showing why they are equivalent.

$$\frac{12}{6} = \frac{12 \cdot 3}{6 \cdot 3} = \frac{12 \cdot 10}{6 \cdot 10} = \frac{12 \cdot 100}{6 \cdot 100}$$

This shows that to maintain the value of the quotient (or fraction), the dividend and divisor must be multiplied by the same number, just as the numerator and denominator of a fraction must be multiplied by the same number. To check students' understanding of this concept, ask them to give another division problem that will have the same quotient as those listed in **Question 11**.

9. a–b.

c. 8 groups
d. 8
e. 8 animals

10. See Additional Answers beginning on page A1.

251

CLASSROOM EXAMPLE

Find $0.04\overline{)2.62}$.

Answer:
Multiply the divisor and dividend by 100 to get $4\overline{)262.0}$.

$$4\overline{)262.0}^{\,65.5}$$

▶ In Section 3, you divided a decimal by a whole number. You can use this skill and the pattern you found in Question 11 to divide a decimal or a whole number by a decimal.

FOR ◀HELP
with *multiplying by powers of ten,* see
MODULE 4, p. 208

13. No; Since Roland multiplied the divisor by 100, he must multiply the dividend by 100. The correct problem is $25\overline{)2800}$.

✔ QUESTION 14

...checks that you can divide by a decimal.

12 Try This as a Class A 68-kilogram *Deinonychus* needed to eat a mean of about 2.6 kg of meat per day. Suppose a *Deinonychus* ate 12.48 kg of a *Hadrosaurus* all at once. To find out in how many days it needed to eat again, you can do this division:

$$2.6\overline{)12.48}$$

a. What is the least power of ten that 2.6 can be multiplied by to make it a whole number? 10^1

b. If you multiply the divisor by the number you found in part (a), what must you do to the dividend to keep the quotient from changing? Multiply it by 10.

c. Rewrite the division by performing the operations described in parts (a) and (b). Then find the quotient. In how many days did the *Deinonychus* need to eat again?
$26\overline{)124.8}$; 4.8; about 4.8 days

13 Discussion To find the quotient $0.25\overline{)28}$, Roland rewrote the division as $25\overline{)280}$. Is this correct? Explain.

14 ✔ CHECKPOINT Find each quotient.

a. $0.9\overline{)0.072}$ **b.** $0.426 \div 0.12$ **c.** $2.4\overline{)9}$
   0.08   3.55   3.75

15 A *Velociraptor* had a mass of about 70 kg and ate about one fourth of its own body weight in meat at one sitting.

a. How much would a *Velociraptor* eat at one sitting?
about 17.5 kg

b. Suppose a pack of *Velociraptors* ate a 448-kilogram *Tenontosaur*. For about how many *Velociraptors* did the *Tenontosaur* provide a full meal?
about 26 Velociraptors

HOMEWORK EXERCISES ▶ See Exs. 15–30 on pp. 258–259.

Exploration 3

Guess My Rule

SET UP *You will need Labsheets 4C and 4D.*

▶ In Exploration 2, you learned that a *Microvenator* needed to eat about 0.4 kg of meat a day.

16 a. Copy and complete the following table.

Number of days	1	2	6	14
Kilograms of meat needed	0.4	0.8	?	?

b. How would you find the kilograms of meat needed for *d* days? **Multiply *d* days by 0.4.**

▶ In Module 1, you learned that relationships like the one between the number of days and the kilograms of meat a *Microvenator* needed to eat can be written as equations.

First Choose a variable to represent each of the quantities that are unknown or may change.

Let *d* = the number of days.   Let *m* = the kilograms of meat.

Next Represent the word relationship with symbols and variables.

The kilograms of meat are equal to 0.4 times the number of days.

$$m = 0.4 \cdot d$$

17 Discussion

a. What operation is used in the expression 0.4*d*?
Multiplication

b. Why do you think the symbol for the operation was omitted?

c. Give an example of an expression in which the multiplication symbol could not be omitted.

17. b. Sample: Often the symbol · can be confused with a decimal. It is not necessary to show the symbol because 0.4*d* would mean you need *d* 0.4 times.
c. Sample: 4 · 7 because if you omit the symbol it is 47.

16. a.

Number of days	1	2	6	14
Kilograms of meat needed	0.4	0.8	2.4	5.6

Exploration 3

TEACHING NOTES
Question 16 can be related to students' previous experience with *term* and *term number*. The number of days can be related to the term number and the number of kilograms to the term. Some students may feel more comfortable continuing the table between 2 and 6 days to be sure they understand the pattern so they can find the kilograms of meat for 14 days without extending the table.

COMMON ERROR
In eliminating the multiplication symbol between a number and a variable, students often forget to multiply when substituting values in for the variable. Make sure students understand that if an expression says 5*p*, it means 5 times *p* and that if *p* = 7, then 5*p* is 5 · 7, not 57.

TEACHING NOTES

If during the game there are students having difficulty using equations to state their guesses, first encourage them to state the rule in words such as "multiply the input by 8," and then translate that into "input times 8 equals output" and then finally transition to $I \cdot 8 = O$. You may alternatively choose to practice stating the equation from a verbal rule with the entire class before beginning the game.

▶ As you play *Guess My Rule,* you will practice writing equations to represent word relationships.

Guess My Rule

Players alternate turns. On your turn:

◆ Your partner takes a rule card without showing it to you.

◆ You try to guess the hidden rule by giving input values (numbers) one at a time. Your partner will apply the rule on the card to the input and tell you the result, or the output.

◆ You can give at most ten input values, and you can try guessing the rule after any of them. Your turn ends when you correctly guess the rule, or when you have made three incorrect guesses.

The player who correctly guesses the most rules wins.

Sample Turn

Input I	Output O	Guess	Response
2	4	$O = I + 2$	Incorrect
0	0	(no guess made)	
3	6	$O = 2 \cdot I$	Correct

18 **Use Labsheet 4C.** Play *Guess My Rule* using the eight rule cards. Give the rules as equations in which the variable I represents the input and O represents the output.

Observe students playing Guess My Rule.

19 Did you use a special strategy for choosing the input values when you were guessing a rule? If so, describe your strategy.

Answers vary.

▶ Each input and output value in *Guess My Rule* can be written as an ordered pair. An example is shown in the table below.

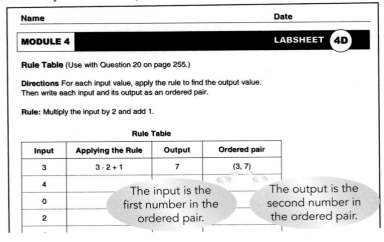

Name		Date	

MODULE 4   **LABSHEET 4D**

Rule Table (Use with Question 20 on page 255.)

Directions For each input value, apply the rule to find the output value. Then write each input and its output as an ordered pair.

Rule: Multiply the input by 2 and add 1.

Rule Table

Input	Applying the Rule	Output	Ordered pair
3	$3 \cdot 2 + 1$	7	(3, 7)
4			
0			
2			

The input is the first number in the ordered pair.

The output is the second number in the ordered pair.

20 Use **Labsheet 4D.** For each input value, apply the rule to find the output value. Then write each input and its output as an ordered pair. Record your results in the *Rule Table*.
See margin.

Graphing on a Coordinate Grid

Ordered pairs can be graphed as points on a **coordinate grid.** The grid is formed using two number lines as *axes.* The **axes** intersect at the point (0, 0), called the **origin.**

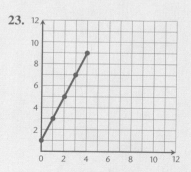

To graph the ordered pair (2, 3) on a coordinate grid, follow these steps.

Step 1 Number a scale on each axis.

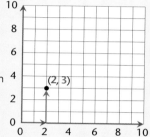

Step 2 Start at the origin. The first coordinate, **2,** tells you how far to move horizontally.

Step 3 The second coordinate, 3, tells you how far to move vertically.

Step 4 Plot the point. This is the graph of (2, 3).

---

21 Read the *Student Resource* above. Describe the steps you need to take to graph each ordered pair.

a. (1, 4)

b. $\left(2\frac{1}{2}, 3\right)$

Use Labsheet 4D for Questions 22–25.

22 Write the ordered pair for each point *A–D* on the *Coordinate Grid* on your labsheet. *A* (0, 8); *B* (3, 3); *C* $\left(6, 2\frac{1}{2}\right)$; *D* $\left(8, 7\frac{1}{2}\right)$

23 ✔ **CHECKPOINT** On the *Empty Coordinate Grid,* graph the ordered pairs you listed in the *Rule Table.* See margin.

24 a. Draw segments connecting the points you plotted on the *Empty Coordinate Grid* in order from left to right.
See graph for Question 23.
b. What do you notice about the points on the graph?
They appear to lie on a line.

25 Use your graph from Question 24 to produce the missing value.

a. input 3.5, output = _?_ 8   **b.** output 11, input = _?_ 5

HOMEWORK EXERCISES ▶ See Exs. 31–51 on pp. 259–261.

Section 4 Stem-and-Leaf Plots, Decimal Division, and Graphing **255**

DEVELOPING MATH CONCEPTS

In the introduction to graphing on a coordinate plane, the axes are referred to as the horizontal and the vertical axes. Since students are already trying to make a connection between a point on the grid and an input and output value, no mention is made of labeling the axes or the coordinates of points as *x* or *y.* You may want to use the *Student Resource* as a guide to show students how to graph some additional points such as (6, 8) and (5, 1).

COMMON ERROR

Question 20 Students may confuse the order of the input number and output number of an ordered pair. Point out that since they have to begin with an input number in order to obtain an output number, it is reasonable to write the input number first and the output number second.

TEACHING NOTES

After finishing **Checkpoint 23**, ask students to plot a few more points such as (0, 3) and (3, 0). Then have students explain the difference between the graphs of points (*n*, 0) and (0, *n*) by asking which is on the horizontal axis and which is on the vertical axis.

21. a. Start at the origin. Move one unit to the right and four units up.
b. Start at the origin. Move two and a half units to the right and three units up.

✔ **QUESTION 23**

...checks that you can graph ordered pairs.

23.

20. See Additional Answers beginning on page A1.

255

Key Concepts

CLOSURE QUESTIONS

Compare reading a stem-and-leaf plot with reading a line plot, and compare dividing by a decimal with dividing by a whole number. How are they alike? How are they different?

Sample Response: Both stem-and-leaf plots and line plots display data so the range, median, and mode are relatively easy to find. A stem-and-leaf plot is usually more useful with a wider range of data values. In both plots, the category in which each data value belongs is lost.

When dividing by a decimal, the first step is to multiply the dividend and the divisor by a number that makes the divisor a whole number. After that, the two processes are the same.

ABSENT STUDENTS

For students who were absent for all or part of this section, the blackline Study Guide for Section 4 may be used to present the ideas, concepts, and skills of Section 4.

Key Terms

stem-and-leaf plot

Stem-and-Leaf Plots (pp. 249–250)

One way to compare data is to make a stem-and-leaf plot.

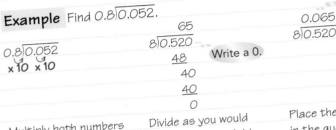

Total Points Scored in a Girls' Basketball Championship Game

stems →
```
0 | 1 1 3 5 5 5 8
1 | 0 3 4 7
2 | 0 2 9
```
← title

leaves

key → 1|4 → means 14 points scored by a player

Dividing by a Decimal (pp. 251–252)

Example Find 0.8)0.052.

Write a 0 in the tenths place.

```
0.8)0.052
 ×10  ×10
```

```
      65
  8)0.520
    48
    40
    40
     0
```
Write a 0.

```
   0.065
8)0.520
```

Multiply both numbers by a number that makes the divisor a whole number.

Divide as you would whole numbers. Add zeros if necessary.

Place the decimal point in the quotient directly above the decimal point in the dividend.

Coordinate Grid (pp. 254–255)

ordered pair
coordinate grid
axes
origin

The numbers in an ordered pair give the location of a point on a coordinate grid.

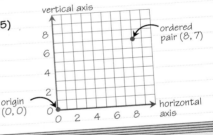

vertical axis

ordered pair (8, 7)

origin (0, 0)

horizontal axis

27. **a.** If you have a remainder that is not a 0, you add a zero in the dividend and continue to divide. You write a zero as a placeholder in the quotient if needed, so that every digit is aligned with a digit in the dividend.

Key Concepts Questions

26 Use the stem-and-leaf plot above showing the points scored in a basketball game. Find the range, median, and mode of the data.
Range = 28 points; Median = 9; Mode = 5

27 **a.** When dividing by a decimal, how do you know when to add a zero in the dividend? in the quotient?

b. How do you know when the division is complete?
The division is complete when the remainder is 0.

Section 4
Practice & Application Exercises

YOU WILL NEED

For Exs. 35–43, 45–46, and 49:
♦ graph paper

For Exercises 1–3, use the stem-and-leaf plot showing the scores on a math test.

1. What was the low score in the class? the high score? **62; 100**

2. How many students scored in the 70s? **4 students**

3. Find the mean, the median, and the mode of the scores. **Mean = 84, Median = 86, Mode = 86**

Math Test Scores

```
 6 | 2
 7 | 2  3  5  8
 8 | 2  6  6  6  8
 9 | 5  5  8
10 | 0
```

8 | 2 represents a score of 82

Use the table and the partially completed stem-and-leaf plot to answer Exercises 4-8.

Small and Medium-Sized Predatory Dinosaurs

Dinosaur	Mass (kg)	Meat Consumption (kg per day)
Chirostenotes	50	2.1
Deinonychus	68	2.6
Dromaeosaurus	45	1.9
Dromiceiomimus	144	4.6
Microvenator	6	0.4
Ornithomimus	153	4.8
Struthiomimus	150	4.7
Troodon	50	2.1
Velociraptor	73	2.7

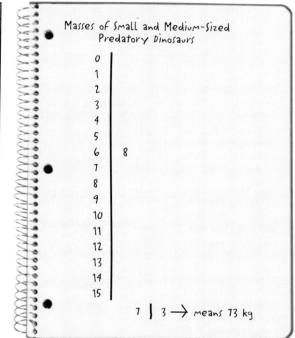

Masses of Small and Medium-Sized Predatory Dinosaurs

```
 0
 1
 2
 3
 4
 5
 6 | 8
 7
 8
 9
10
11
12
13
14
15
```

7 | 3 → means 73 kg

4. Which dinosaur's mass is shown in the stem-and-leaf plot? **Deinonychus**

5. Why were the numbers 0 through 15 used for the stems? **See margin.**

6. Copy and complete the stem-and-leaf plot. **See margin.**

7. Make a stem-and-leaf plot for the meat consumption of the dinosaurs. **See margin.**

8. **Writing** Compare your stem-and-leaf plots from Exercises 6 and 7. Do they have the same gaps or clusters of data? Explain why you think the plots are alike or different. **See margin.**

Practice & Applications

SUGGESTED ASSIGNMENTS

Core Course
Day 1: Exs. 1–14
Day 2: Exs. 15–29
Day 3: Exs. 47–49, 52–57
Day 4: Exs. 31–45, 50–51

Extended Course
Day 1: Exs. 1–14, 58–61*
Day 2: Exs. 15–23 odd, 24–30
Day 3: Exs. 47–49, 52–57
Day 4: Exs. 31–46, 50–51

Note: Extended Course assignments can be used to differentiate within the regular classroom. In classrooms where students are grouped homogeneously, the material might be covered in fewer days. In this case assignments may be combined.

*denotes Extension Exercises

ADDITIONAL PRACTICE

See the *Teacher's Resource Book* for additional practice and application exercises for this section.

5. They represent the integers in the tens place between the least value and the greatest value in the table. The 0 is included to represent the digit in the tens place of a one-digit number.

6–8. See Additional Answers beginning on page A1.

257

Practice & Applications

EXERCISE NOTES

As a follow-up to **Exercises 9–14**, have students discuss the advantages of each type of graph. (*The bar graph gives the types of mammals and visually shows how their lifespans compare. The stem-and-leaf plot does not give the types of mammals, but it makes reading the actual lifespans easy whereas for some values on the bar graph you may have to estimate the number of years.*)

The goal in **Exercise 24** is for students to determine, without doing the actual division, which division problems have equivalent quotients. You may want to have students justify how they can tell the two problems are going to have the same quotients.

13. 15.9 years; Sample Response: The stem-and-leaf plot because the numbers would have to be estimated from the bar graph

14. 13 years and 20 years; Sample Response: The stem-and-leaf plot because the data are easily visible as repeated numbers on the plot

10. 3 years; Answers may vary. Sample Response: The stem-and-leaf plot because the data are ordered from least to greatest

11. Gray Wolf; Sample Response: The bar graph because the stem-and-leaf plot doesn't identify individual animals

12. 15 years; Sample Response: The stem-and-leaf plot because the bar graph doesn't organize the data from least to greatest

Choosing a Data Display Use the bar graph or the stem-and-leaf plot to answer Exercises 9–14. For each question, tell which display you used and why.

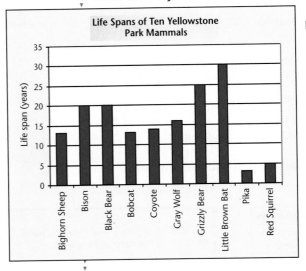

Life Spans of Ten Yellowstone Park Mammals

```
0 | 3  5
1 | 3  3  4  6
2 | 0  0  5
3 | 0
```
1 | 4 means 14 years

9. What is the longest life span? 30 years; Answers may vary. Sample Response: The bar graph because it is easy to see the tallest bar

10. What is the shortest life span?

11. What animal has a life span of 16 years?

12. What is the median of the life spans?

13. What is the mean of the life spans? See margin.

14. What are the modes of the life spans? See margin.

Find each quotient. Show your work.

15. $0.07\overline{)4.2}$
60

16. $3\overline{)0.06}$
0.02

17. $0.3\overline{)0.84}$
2.8

18. $0.5\overline{)0.365}$
0.73

19. $2.4\overline{)45}$
18.75

20. $0.8\overline{)4.9}$
6.125

21. $0.002\overline{)0.571}$
285.5

22. $7.5\overline{)16.2}$
2.16

23. $6.25\overline{)5.6375}$
0.902

24. Which of the following division problems have the same quotient?
1.8 ÷ 0.9 and 0.09)0.18

$1.8 ÷ 0.9$ $0.09\overline{)18}$ $0.09\overline{)0.18}$ $9\overline{)0.18}$

25. Use multiplication to check each division problem.

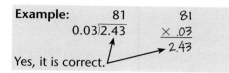

Example:
$$\begin{array}{r} 81 \\ 0.03\overline{)2.43} \end{array} \qquad \begin{array}{r} 81 \\ \times\ .03 \\ \hline 2.43 \end{array}$$
Yes, it is correct.

a. $0.12\overline{)4.32}$ 36

b. $0.05\overline{)6.0}$ 1.2

c. $0.003\overline{)150}$ 50

26. a. Divide: $0.3\overline{)6}$ $0.03\overline{)6}$ $0.003\overline{)6}$
   20, 200, 2000

b. Use your results from part (a) to predict the quotient for $6 \div 0.0003$. Then check your prediction by finding $6 \div 0.0003$. 20,000; 20,000

c. Without dividing, determine $6 \div 0.0000003$. 20,000,000

27. Apples are on sale for $0.48 per pound. How many pounds of apples can you buy for $3? 6.25 lb

28. The height of a tree is 542.85 cm. In a photograph of the tree, the height is only 0.7 cm. The tree's actual height is how many times as great as its height in the photo? 775.5 times

29. Running Over 35,000 runners started the 2003 New York Marathon (26.2 mi). Margaret Okayo of Kenya won the women's race in a record time of 142.5 min. Find her mean time for a mile. Round your answer to the nearest tenth. 5.4 min

30. Challenge A carpenter is cutting a board that is 3.75 m long into pieces that are 0.3 m long. How many pieces can the carpenter cut from the board? How long is the leftover piece of board?
12 pieces; 0.15 m

Apply the rule "multiply by 3 and then add 2" to each input. Write each input and output as an ordered pair.

31. 1   (1, 5)

32. 5   (5, 17)

33. 8   (8, 26)

34. 22   (22, 68)

Copy the coordinate grid on graph paper. Graph each ordered pair on your coordinate grid. Label each point.

35. (4, 1)

36. (2, 6)

37. (0, 5)

38. (1, 3)

39. (2, 0)

40. $\left(\dfrac{1}{2}, \dfrac{1}{2}\right)$

41. (6, 4)

42. (0, 0)

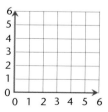

25. a. $36 \times 0.12 = 4.32$; yes it is correct
b. $1.2 \times 0.05 = 0.06$; it is incorrect
c. $50 \times 0.003 = 0.15$; it is incorrect

▲ Margaret Okayo crossing the finish line in the 2003 New York Marathon.

35–42.

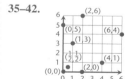

EXERCISE NOTES

Exercise 26 Students should notice in **part (a)** that the three division problems are not equivalent, therefore they need to complete the division to find each quotient.

Exercise 40 Since the axes on the graph are numbered in increments of 1, students may be confused as to how to plot $\left(\dfrac{1}{2}, \dfrac{1}{2}\right)$. Assure them that it is acceptable to mark points that do not lie directly on a grid line. They will also have to estimate the location of the fractions. When graphing several points with fractions, they may want to change the increments on the axes so that the points are easier to determine. For this particular set of points, a line could be skipped between whole numbers so that the axes are numbered by halves.

Practice & Applications

EXERCISE NOTES

Exercise 44 Even though the table is arranged in descending order of quarters, students should still be able look for a pattern and write a rule. If there are any students who find it difficult, suggest they rewrite the table in ascending order of quarters.

Exercise 47 You may have to clarify for students that a set of twins consists of 2 people, a set of triplets 3 people, and a set of quadruplets 4 people.

43. a–b.
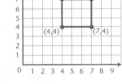

d. (2, 2), (5, 8), (7, 12), (8, 14);
Sample Response: For every

increase of 1 in the input, the

output increases by 2. To find

the output for $4\frac{1}{2}$, **notice that**

$4\frac{1}{2} - 2 = 2\frac{1}{2}$ **and** $2\frac{1}{2} \cdot 2 = 5$;

$2 + 5 = 7.$

45. a–b.
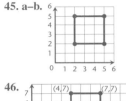

46.
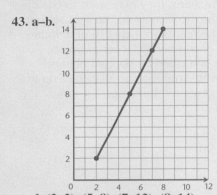

The Twins Days Festival attracts people from every state in the United States and many other countries.
▼

43. a. Graph the ordered pairs in the table on a coordinate grid.

Input	2	7	5	8
Output	2	12	8	14

See margin.

b. Draw segments to connect the points you graphed in order from left to right. **See margin.**

c. Use your graph to predict the missing values.

Input $4\frac{1}{2}$, output = _?_ 7   Output 10, input = _?_ 6

d. List the ordered pairs from the table so that the inputs are in increasing order. How can you use patterns to check your answers in part (c)? **See margin.**

44. The table shows how many minutes of parking time (output) drivers get when they put quarters (input) into a parking meter.

Number of quarters	8	7	6	5	4	3	2	1
Minutes of parking time	120	105	90	?	60	45	?	?

a. Write a rule for the output based on the input. **Let** $q =$ **the number of quarters and** $m =$ **the number of minutes;** $m = 15 \cdot q.$

b. Use your rule to find the missing values in the table.
    75, 30, 15

45. Geometry Connection Use a coordinate grid.

a. Graph the ordered pairs (2, 2), (5, 2), (5, 5), and (2, 5).

b. Draw segments to connect the points in the order listed in part (a). Then connect the last point to the first point.

c. Name the polygon you formed in part (b). Be as specific as possible. **square**

46. Challenge Transform the polygon you graphed in Exercise 45 by sliding it 2 units to the right and 2 units up. What are the new coordinates of the vertices of the polygon?

47. The *Twins Days Festival* in Twinsburg, Ohio, is the largest annual gathering of twins, triplets, and quadruplets in the world. Write an expression for each number in parts (a)–(d). Use *t* for the number of sets of twins, *p* for the number of sets of triplets, and *q* for the number of sets of quadruplets.

a. the number of people at the festival who are twins $2 \cdot t$

b. the number of people at the festival who are triplets $3 \cdot p$

c. the number of people at the festival who are quadruplets $4 \cdot q$

d. the total number of people who are twins, triplets, or quadruplets at the festival $2 \cdot t + 3 \cdot p + 4 \cdot q$

48. At the 1995 Twins Days Festival there were 2798 registered sets of twins, 26 sets of triplets, and 2 sets of quadruplets. Evaluate each expression you wrote in Exercise 47. **a. 5596 b. 78 c. 8 d. 5682**

49. a. Draw four squares of different sizes on graph paper. Record the side length, area, and perimeter of each square in a table.
See margin.

b. Write an equation for finding the area of a square if you know the length of its sides.
Let s = the length of a side and A = the area. $A = s^2$

c. Write an equation for finding the perimeter of a square.
Let s = the length of a side and P = the perimeter. $P = 4 \cdot s$

Reflecting ◀▶ on the Section

Write your responses to Exercises 50 and 51 in your journal.

Weights of Wolf Pups when One Month Old
4 | 3 5
5 | 1 1 7
6 | 0 3
7 | 1

7 | 1   means 7.1 lb

Weights of Wolf Pups when One Year Old
2 | 7 8
3 | 4 5 5
6 | 1 8

6 | 1   means 61 lb

Journal

Exercises 50 and 51 check that you can interpret a stem-and-leaf plot, divide by a decimal, and connect an equation with a graph.

50. Use the stem-and-leaf plots above.

a. Find the mean weight for 1-month-old wolves and for 1-year-old wolves. **5.5 lb; 41.1 lb**

b. A 1-year-old is about how many times as heavy as a 1-month-old? Use the mean weights from part (a).
about 7.5 times

c. Can you estimate what the 1-year-old weight will be for a 6.3 lb 1-month-old wolf? Explain.

50. c. No; Even if the plots give weights for the same wolves, you can't assume the heaviest newborn will be the heaviest 1-year-old.

51. The rule on a *Guess My Rule* card was applied to the input values 0.5, 1.5, and 2. The pairs of input and output values are shown on the graph.

a. Use the graph to predict the output if the input is 1. **4**

b. Guess the rule.
The output is 4 times the input.

c. Let x represent an input value and let y represent an output value. Write your rule in the form of an equation: $y = \underline{\ ?\ }$.
$y = 4 \cdot x$

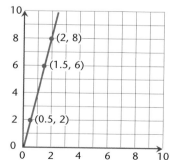

EXERCISE NOTES

For students completing **Exercise 49**, briefly review the concept of area and perimeter or refer them to the glossary in the back of their book if they feel unsure about either term.

49. a. See Additional Answers beginning on page A1.

261

Practice & Applications

EXERCISE NOTES

Extension Exercises 58–61 Some types of data displays make it easy to compare two or more sets of data with one graph. Double bar graphs are one such data display that students may be more familiar with. Instead of recording the data values from each set right next to each other as is done in a double bar graph, a back-to-back stem-and-leaf plot records data values that share the same stems, but with the leaves written in opposite directions from the center out so the two sets are not confused. Ask students how a double bar graph keeps the data sets identified separately. (*Usually the side by side bars are in two different colors, one color used for each data set.*) In Books 2 and 3 students will see how box-and-whisker plots graphed under the same number line can be used to compare more than one data set.

57. range: 145

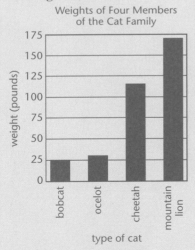

Weights of Four Members of the Cat Family

weight (pounds): 175, 150, 125, 100, 75, 50, 25, 0

type of cat: bobcat, ocelot, cheetah, mountain lion

Find each product. (Module 3, p. 190)

52. $1.5 \cdot 0.06$
0.09

53. $5.23 \cdot 1.008$
5.27184

54. $0.9 \cdot 10.47$
9.423

55. Margo has $1.15 in coins. She wants to buy a note pad that costs $1.00. She does not have exact change. What coins can Margo have? (Module 1, p. 33)
3 quarters and 4 dimes

56. One rectangle represents a whole. Write a fraction and a mixed number to describe the entire shaded amount. (Module 1, p. 46) $\frac{13}{8}$; $1\frac{5}{8}$

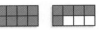

57. Find the range of the weights shown in the table below. Then draw a bar graph to display the weight data. (Module 4, p. 224; Toolbox, p. 578)

Weights of Four Members of the Cat Family				
Type of cat	bobcat	ocelot	cheetah	mountain lion
Weight (pounds)	25	30	115	170

See margin.

Extension

Back-to-Back Stem-and-Leaf Plots

You can use a back-to-back stem-and-leaf plot to compare two related sets of data.

Olympic 100-Meter Dash Winning Times 1956–2004 (to the nearest tenth of a second)

Men		Women
9 9 9 8	9	
6 3 3 1 1 1 0 0 0	10	5 8 8 9 9
	11	0 1 1 1 1 2 5 8

means 10.0 seconds ← 0 |10| 5 → means 10.5 seconds
for a man   for a woman

58. What is the fastest time for a man? for a woman? 9.8 sec; 10.5 sec

59. Find the mean, the median, and the mode(s) for each set of data.

60. Was there a winning time that both a man and a woman got?
No

61. Why does a back-to-back stem-and-leaf plot make it easy to compare data sets?

59. men: mean: 10.1; median: 10.0; modes: 9.9, 10.0, and 10.1; women: mean: 11.1, median: 11.1; mode: 11.1

61. Sample Response: Because the plots line up according to stems, you can easily compare the data. For example, it is clear that the median for the men's winning times is lower than the median for the women's winning times and that more men than women had winning times between 10 sec and 11 sec.

Section 4

Extra Skill Practice

Use the stem-and-leaf plot for Exercises 1–4.

1. What is Mark's lowest score? 77

2. What is his highest score? 100

3. On how many tests did Mark score an 80?
2 tests

4. Find the mean, the median, and the mode of Mark's scores.
about 86.5, 87, 83

Mark's Science Test Scores	
7	7 9 9
8	0 0 3 3 3 7 7 8 9
9	2 4 4 6
10	0

9 | 2   means a score of 92

Find each quotient.

5. $0.08\overline{)5.6}$
70

6. $0.5\overline{)1.28}$
2.56

7. $1.8\overline{)6.12}$
3.4

8. $0.009\overline{)0.108}$
12

9. $0.04\overline{)1.174}$
29.35

10. $7.5\overline{)70.125}$
9.35

11. $6.12\overline{)34.884}$
5.7

12. $0.021\overline{)0.1953}$
9.3

Name the point that is the graph of each ordered pair.

13. (7, 3) *G*

14. $\left(4, 3\frac{1}{2}\right)$ *C*

15. (0, 5) *A*

Write the coordinates of each point.

16. *B* (1, 1)

17. *D* (5, 0)

18. *F* $(6\frac{1}{2}, 6)$

19. The table shows how many hours a machine runs (input) and how many T-shirts it produces (output).

Hours	1	2	3	4	5	20
T-shirts	18	36	54	?	90	?

a. Write a rule for the output based on the input.
$t = 18 \cdot x$ where t = number of T-shirts made and x = hours a machine runs

b. Use your rule to find the missing values in the table.
4 hr: 72 T-shirts
20 hr: 360 T-shirts

Standardized Testing ◀▶ Performance Task

Explain why the quotient is always greater than the dividend when the divisor is between 0 and 1. Include at least one example in your explanation.

Quotient is greater than dividend.

Divisor is between 0 and 1. Dividend is positive.

Sample Response: The product of the divisor and the quotient equals the dividend. Because the divisor is between 0 and 1, the product of the divisor and the quotient is less than the quotient, and therefore the quotient is greater than the dividend. For example, 12 ÷ 0.5 = 24, and you can see that the quotient, 24, is greater than the dividend, 12.

Section 4   Stem-and-Leaf Plots, Decimal Division, and Graphing   263

Extra Skill Practice

TEACHER NOTES
For each Exploration, the corresponding Extra Skill Practice Exercises are noted.

Exploration 1: Exs. 1–4
Exploration 2: Exs. 5–12
Exploration 3: Exs. 13–19

EXTRA HELP
Teacher's Resource Book
• Practice and Applications
• Study Guide

Technology Resources
• @Home Tutor
• Test Generator

ASSESSMENT
• Section 4 Quick Quiz
• Test Generator

Setting the Stage

GETTING STARTED

Module 4 Section 5 *Warm-Up* assesses students' facility with finding the range, mean, median, and mode of a set of data. Students are expected to know how to find these measures so that in this section, they can focus on determining which averages are appropriate for certain sets of data.

Before students open their books to Section 5 *Setting the Stage*, ask them about how many babies they think are born in the world each day. Then have them open their books and read the paragraph superimposed on the graph.

TEACHING NOTES

You may wish to ask students which average should be used to answer **Question 3(b)** and how they would calculate it. (*"Average population increase per year" refers to the mean. Since it is the sum of the changes for each year divided by the number of years, it can be found by using the answers from part (a) to find the total population change from 1950 to 2000 and dividing the total change by 50, the number of years from 1950 to 2000.*)

TECHNOLOGY

For a related technology activity, see the *Technology Book*.

Population Growth

Setting the Stage

The graph below shows how the world population has increased from the year 1000 to 2003.

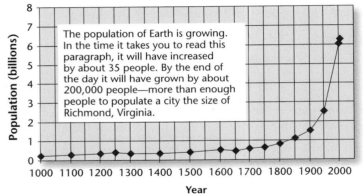

World Population Growth

The population of Earth is growing. In the time it takes you to read this paragraph, it will have increased by about 35 people. By the end of the day it will have grown by about 200,000 people—more than enough people to populate a city the size of Richmond, Virginia.

Think About It

1 About what year did the world's population reach 1 billion? **about 1825**

2 Was the population increasing faster during the period from 1500 to 1600 or during the period from 1800 to 1900? How can you tell just by looking at the graph? **1800 to 1900; The graph rises more steeply over that section.**

3 **a.** What was the approximate population of the world in 1950? in 2000? **2.5 billion; 6 billion**

   b. What was the average population increase per year from 1950 to 2000? **0.07 billion (or 70,000,000, which is needed to answer Question 4.)**

4 Suppose the world's population is increasing at the rate you found in Question 3(b).

   a. How much will the population grow today? **about 192,000 people**

   b. How much will it increase in the time it takes you to read the paragraph on the graph? **Sample answer: about 33 people (based on 15 seconds)**

   c. How do your answers compare to the claims made in the paragraph on the graph? **fairly close to the number of people in 15 seconds, but off by about 8,000 per year**

Exploration 1

Representing Population Data

SET UP   *You will need Labsheets 5A and 5B.*

▶ A **line graph** shows changes that take place over time. The line graph in the *Setting the Stage* shows how the world population has changed over the past thousand years. You can also use a line graph to see how an animal population has changed.

5 **Use Labsheet 5A.** Follow the directions on the labsheet to make two line graphs of the *California Condor Population* close to the time the condor was placed on the endangered species list. **See margin.**

6 Look at your line graphs from Question 5.

   a. In what year was the condor population the least? **1983**

   b. Which graph did you use to answer part (a)? Why did you use that graph? **Graph A is easier to read.**

   c. How are the scales for the two graphs different? **See margin.**

   d. If you were writing an article claiming that the condor population did not change much from 1953 to 1984, which graph would you choose? Why? **See margin.**

   e. What does the other graph seem to show? **See margin.**

GOAL

LEARN HOW TO...
♦ make a line graph

AS YOU...
♦ investigate changes in animal populations

KEY TERM
♦ line graph

▲ The California condor is the largest bird in North America. It has been on the endangered species list since 1967. An "endangered species" is one that is in danger of becoming extinct throughout all or a significant portion of its range.

DEVELOPING MATH CONCEPTS
Question 6 Students should understand that two graphs can display the same data, yet present two very different pictures. Emphasize that using different intervals can cause the graph to present vastly different pictures of the same data. You may want to point out that if the range of the data is very small (such as 35 for the condor populations), a large interval (30 in Graph B) makes it look like there is little or no change, while a small interval (5 in Graph A) makes the difference in data more apparent.

6. c. Graph A has a vertical scale that starts at 20 and has increments of 5, whereas the vertical scale in Graph B starts at 0 and has increments of 30.
   d. Graph B; The lines connecting points are flatter and the line graph stays within the first three horizontal grid lines.
   e. Graph A starts at the top of the grid lines and falls to the second grid line, so changes appear to be much more severe. It appears that the condor population dropped drastically from 1967 to 1979.

5. See Additional Answers beginning on page A1.

265

Exploration 1 *continued*

TEACHING NOTES
Question 7(a) If students simply respond with "increasing," ask them "Is it increasing quickly, slowly, steadily?" and "Between which two years is the increase the greatest?" This gets students to informally use the slopes of the line segments to describe the changes in the graph.

7. a. The condor population is increasing slowly, but rather steadily, except in the year 2000, when the increase was less than in other years.

8. c. Sample Response: The condor population increased at a rate of about 13 birds per year from 1997 to 1999. It continued to increase from 1999 to 2000, but by about one third the rate. The population increased at a rate of about 20 birds per year from 2000 to 2003. If this trend continues, there will be about 285 condors in 2006 and 365 in 2010.

✔ **QUESTION 8**

...checks that you can make a line graph.

▶ In Question 6, you saw how the scale on a line graph affected how the California condor population appeared to change from 1953 to 1984. Now let's look at the condor population from 1997 to 2003.

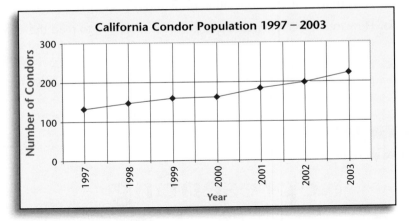

California Condor Population 1997 – 2003

7 Discussion

a. Describe the changes in condor population from 1997–2003.

b. How could you alter the scale on the vertical axis to make it look like the condor population increased rapidly from 1997 to 2003? Sample Response: Start the scale at 120 and number by increments of 40 up to 240.

c. How could you alter the scale on the horizontal axis to make it look like the condor population increased rapidly from 1997 to 2003? Sample Response: change the years to every vertical line, not every other.

8 ✔ CHECKPOINT

a. Choose a different scale for at least one of the axes in the *California Condor Population* graph above. See margin.

b. **Use Labsheet 5B.** Follow the directions on the labsheet to create your own line graph of the *California Condor Population* from 1997 to 2003. See margin.

c. Write a brief paragraph about the change in the condor population shown by your graph. Include predictions for years beyond 2003.

HOMEWORK EXERCISES ▶ See Exs. 1–9 on pp. 271–272.

8. a–b. See Additional Answers beginning on page A1.

Choosing an AVERAGE

GOAL

LEARN HOW TO...
♦ choose an appropriate average

AS YOU...
♦ compare statistics of endangered and threatened animals

SET UP *You will need: • Labsheet 5C • calculator*

▶ When the population of a species reaches low enough numbers, the species may be placed on the threatened or endangered list. Each year since 1980, the U.S. Fish and Wildlife Service has recorded how many mammal, bird, reptile, fish, amphibian, and insect species are listed as endangered or threatened.

The timber wolf has been listed ▶ as a "threatened species" in all or part of 30 states. A threatened species is one that is likely to become endangered in the foreseeable future.

9 **Try This as a Class** Suppose after examining the U.S. Fish and Wildlife data a reporter began an article as follows:

> **Number of Endangered and Threatened Mammals Off the Charts in 2002!**
>
> Prior to 2002, an average of 57 mammal species appeared on the threatened and endangered lists. Yet in 2002, the U.S. Fish and Wildlife Service reported a whopping 74 mammal species as threatened or endangered. In 2002 close to twenty more species, nearly 35% more, are in danger of disappearing. Why has the number of mammal species listed risen by more than a third in 2002? Scientists say it is a result of the change in...

a. Do you think the average of 57 mammals is the *mean*, the *median*, or the *mode*? Why? Answers will vary.

b. Does the average of 57 mammal species mean that in 2001, fifty-seven mammals were listed as endangered or threatened? No, this is an average for years up through 2001.

FOR◀HELP
with *mean, median,* and *mode* see
MODULE 4, p. 225

Exploration 2

TEACHING NOTES
Question 9(a) Allow students to express their opinions and reasoning for **part (a)**, but do not spend excessive time trying to determine from the report the average used. In **Question 10**, students will use the U.S. Fish and Wildlife data to find the mean, median, and mode and determine which average was used.

Exploration 2 *continued*

TEACHING NOTES

Encourage students to use any of the three representations of the data on **Labsheet 5C** to answer the parts of **Question 10**, alternating between the representations as necessary.

Question 11(c) Students may be under the impression they must use line graphs since they were studied in Exploration 1. Assure students that they may choose to represent the information in any type of graph they feel is appropriate.

TIPS FROM TEACHERS

Have students complete **Question 11(c)** on a separate piece of paper that can then be displayed on a bulletin board or classroom wall, so that students can compare the different graphs and scales used to represent data.

---

10. c. It was the least of the three averages and made the jump to 74 in 2002 seem more drastic.

10. d. The reporter is comparing one data value to the average of twenty-two values. Instead, had the reporter

✔ QUESTION 11

...checks that you can choose an appropriate average and make an appropriate graph for a set of data.

compared the 2002 numbers to 2001 or 2000, he would have seen that the numbers had only increased by one mammal species.

e. The line graph shows changes and trends over time. It also shows the individual years and approximate number of species for each year.

---

10 Use Labsheet 5C.

a. Find the mean, the median, and the mode of the data in the *Endangered or Threatened Mammal Species Graphs.*
mean: 57; median: 62.5; mode: 66

b. Did the reporter use the mean, the median, or the mode in Question 9?
mean

c. Why do you think the average in part (b) was used?

d. Why is it not appropriate for the reporter to compare the number of species listed as endangered or threatened in 2002 to the average for 1980–2001 used in the article?

e. What information can you get from the line graph that is not represented by the mean, median, or mode?

11 ✔ CHECKPOINT Data for the number of species of insects listed as endangered or threatened are shown below.

Year	Number	Year	Number	Year	Number
1980	14	1988	18	1996	29
1981	13	1989	19	1997	37
1982	13	1990	21	1998	37
1983	13	1991	23	1999	37
1984	13	1992	25	2000	42
1985	13	1993	26	2001	44
1986	15	1994	28	2002	44
1987	15	1995	29		

a. Find the mean, the median, and the mode of the data.
mean: about 24.7; median: 23; mode: 13

b. What average from part (a) would you report as the typical yearly number of insect species listed as endangered or threatened? mean or median

c. Make a graph to display the numbers of endangered or threatened insect species. Explain why you think the graph you chose is an appropriate way to display the data.

▶ When an animal population no longer exists, it is said to be "extinct." The table on the following page contains information about ten dinosaurs that lived in North America from 65 million to 80 million years ago.

11. c. Check student graphs. A line graph gives the most information, but a stem-and-leaf plot or line plot could also be used.

Name	Length (m)	Mass (metric tons)	Usually walked on	Diet
Albertosaurus	11	2.7	2 legs	carnivore
Centrosaurus	6	13.6	4 legs	herbivore
Chasmosaurus	5.2	1.4	4 legs	herbivore
Edmontosaurus	13.1	3.4	2 legs	herbivore
Euoplocephalus	6.1	2.5	4 legs	herbivore
Pachycephalosaurus	5.5	1.8	2 legs	herbivore
Parasaurolophus	10.1	3.5	2 legs	herbivore
Tanius	10.7	2.7	2 legs	herbivore
Triceratops	7.99	6.4	4 legs	herbivore
Tyrannosaurus	15.2	7.3	2 legs	carnivore

12. c. 2 legs; The mode, because the mean is 2.8 and the median is 3. It is not reasonable to give an average of 2.8 or 3 since dinosaurs walked on either 2 legs or 4 legs.

13. d. The median since it was affected only slightly by the extreme data value, while the mean was affected by the same value.

12 Discussion

a. How would you describe the average diet of the dinosaurs? The average diet is herbivore.

b. Which average, the mean, the median, or the mode, did you use to answer part (a)? Explain. mode; You could not find the mean or median of the diets since they are not numbers.

c. What is the average number of legs walked on by the dinosaurs in the table? Explain which average you chose to use.

d. When is the mode the most appropriate average to use? When the data are categorical, like diet.

13

a. Find the mean, the median, and the mode of the masses of the dinosaurs. mean: 4.53; median: 3.05; mode: 2.7

b. The mass of the *Centrosaurus* is quite a bit greater than the masses of the other nine dinosaurs. Find the mean, median, and mode of the masses of the other nine dinosaurs. mean: about 3.52; median: 2.7; mode: 2.7

c. Compare your answers to parts (a) and (b). Which average, the mean, the median, or the mode, was most affected by the large mass? the mean

d. Discussion Which average in part (a) best describes the average mass of the ten dinosaurs in the table?

14

Try This as a Class Without actually finding the mean, median, and mode, decide which average will best describe the average length of the ten dinosaurs. Explain your choice. Answers will vary. Sample Response: The mean or the median because the data appear to be spread out rather evenly, so either should be appropriate.

HOMEWORK EXERCISES ▶ See Exs. 10–18 on pp. 273–274.

TEACHING NOTES

When selecting the type of average to use, as in **Discussion Question 12**, it is important to note that categorical data can only be described with the mode. This is easily seen with the diets, but students may not realize this with the "Usually walked on" data. Since the data are reported as numbers of legs, a mean and median number of legs could be found, but for reporting the average number of legs walked on, 3 legs does not make much sense. Remind students to look at the type of data, not just the numbers reported, when choosing an average.

The following Classroom Example can be used after **Question 12** to show the reasoning for choosing certain averages to represent data.

CLASSROOM EXAMPLE

Calculate the mean, the median, and the mode for the data. Which average is most representative of the data?

Gasoline Mileage City Driving	
Auto	Miles per gallon
A	17
B	11
C	19
D	19
E	18
F	18
G	18
H	18

Answer:

mean = 17.25; median = 18; mode = 18

The median and the mode are both representative of the data. Six of the eight data values are greater than the mean. The mean is not as representative of the data because it is affected by the extreme value of 11, while the median and mode are not.

269

Key Concepts

CLOSURE QUESTION

How can you tell if a graph is misleading?

Sample Response: A bar graph or line graph may be misleading if the numerical scale does not begin at zero and only shows part of the scale; if the intervals on a numerical scale are not of uniform width or are too large or small; if the scale extends too far beyond the greatest data value.

ABSENT STUDENTS

For students who were absent for all or part of this section, the blackline Study Guide for Section 5 may be used to present the ideas, concepts, and skills of Section 5.

Section 5

Key Concepts

Key Term

line graph

Line Graphs (pp. 264–266)

A line graph is often used to show change over time. This line graph shows the population density (number of people per square mile) of the United States during the period 1790–1890.

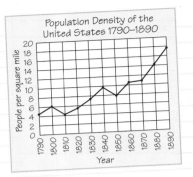

Misleading Graphs (pp. 265–266)

Changing the scales on a line graph can give a different impression of the data.

Choosing an Average (pp. 267–269)

The mean is the most commonly used average. The mean is affected by extreme data.

The median is rarely affected by extreme data values, but if the data are clustered around two different numbers with a large gap in between, the median may give you a false impression of the typical data value.

The mode is best used with categorical data. Movie titles and favorite colors are examples of categorical data.

Key Concepts Questions

16. a. Sample Response: Start the vertical scale at 60 and number it in increments of 4 up to 200.
    b. No; The mode is too low. It is the least value. In all other days more than $80 were raised. The mode is usually only used with categorical data.

15 Use the line graph above. During which 10-year intervals did the number of people per square mile in the United States decrease?
1800–1810 and 1840–1850

16 a. How could you change the numerical scale on the bar graph to make it look like a lot more money was made on the weekend than on weekdays?

b. Do you think the mode would be an appropriate average to use to describe the fundraiser data? Explain.

Section 5
Practice & Application Exercises

YOU WILL NEED

For Ex. 1:
♦ graph paper

For Exs. 3–5:
♦ Labsheet 5D

1. As part of the wolf recovery program in Yellowstone National Park, wildlife biologists track the number of pups that are born and survive until the end of each year.

Year	Number of wolf pups born
1995	9
1996	11
1997	49
1998	37
1999	38
2000	73

   a. Use the data in the table to create a line graph. **See margin.**

   b. Using your graph, write a brief summary about the number of wolf pups born from 1995 to 2000.

2. The *2000 Living Planet Report* shows the following graphs for two animal populations. Study the graphs.

Lesser White-Fronted Goose

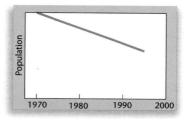

Silvery Gibbon Monkey

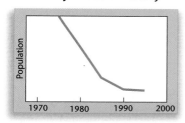

   a. What information do the graphs give about the population of the Lesser White-Fronted Goose? the Silvery Gibbon?

   b. What do you notice about these graphs that may make the information misleading? **There are no numbers on the population scale.**

Use Labsheet 5D for Exercises 3–5.

3. Look at Graph 1 on Labsheet 5D.

   a. Which state has the greatest percent of people that drive to work alone? **Florida**

   b. For each state, estimate the difference between the percent of people who carpool or use public transit and the percent of people who drive alone. Which state has the greatest difference?

4. Complete Part II of Labsheet 5D to create a new double bar graph of the ways people get to work.

1 b. Sample Response: The number of pups born increased slightly from 1995 to 1996 and then made a big jump from 1996 to 1997. From 1997 to 1998, the number of pups born decreased by about 12 pups and then increased slightly the next year. The number increased rapidly from 1999 to 2000.

2. a. The population of Lesser White-Fronted geese decreased steadily from 1970 to 1995; The population of Silvery Gibbon monkeys decreased rapidly from 1975 to 1990 and then began to level off.

3. b. Estimates will vary. Sample Responses are given. Alaska: about 26, California: about 45, Florida: about 47, Kentucky: about 40, Vermont: about 30; Florida

SUGGESTED ASSIGNMENTS

Core Course
Day 1: Exs. 2–5, 19–23
Day 2: Exs. 1, 6–9
Day 3: Exs. 10–14, 18

Extended Course
Day 1: Exs. 2–5, 19–23
Day 2: Exs. 1, 6–9
Day 3: Exs. 10–18

Note: Extended Course assignments can be used to differentiate within the regular classroom. In classrooms where students are grouped homogeneously, the material might be covered in fewer days. In this case assignments may be combined.

ADDITIONAL PRACTICE
See the *Teacher's Resource Book* for additional practice and application exercises for this section.

1. a., 4. See Additional Answers beginning on page A1.

271

Practice & Applications

EXERCISE NOTES

EXERCISE NOTES

Some students may have difficulty deciding which graph to use for **Exercises 7–9**, or they may just choose based on personal preference for a type of graph. You might make a set of data for each situation and assign different groups one of the situations. Have them try to create each type of graph and then report any difficulties they encountered with representing the information with a certain type of graph or any advantages one type had over another in representing the information requested.

6. a. Sample Response: Number the vertical scale by ones and write the groups of years on every line instead of every other line.

b. Sample Response: Number the vertical scale by 15s or 20s and write the groups of years on every fourth line of the horizontal scale.

c. The scale for years are in groups of years, but the groups do not all include the same number of years. For example, 1931–1959 covers 29 years and 1970–1972 only covers 3 years.

d. No; Since the data are grouped in intervals a bar graph or histogram should be used, but the year groupings should be consistent.

---

5. Sample Responses are given.
   a. No, graph 1 appears to show this relationship, but in graph 2 the bar for public transit and carpoolers is about one-fifth of the bar for those that drive alone.
   c. Graph 1; The bars for commuters who carpool or use public transit are longer than the corresponding bars in graph 2

and in comparison to the bars for commuters who drive alone.
   d. On graph 1, the vertical scale goes from 0 to 100 in increments of 10. On graph 2, the vertical scale goes from 20 to 70 in increments of 5.

7. Stem-and-leaf plot (A bar graph would get too crowded for more than 10 contestants)

---

5. a. In Vermont, the percent of commuters who carpool or use public transit to get to work is about one half the percent of commuters who drive alone. Do Graph 1 and Graph 2 both show this relationship? Explain.

   b. Which graph seems to show that very few people carpool or use public transit? How does it show this? **Graph 2; Because the scale starts at 20, the bars are very short.**

   c. Which graph would you use if you wanted to show that a large percent of workers in these five states carpool or use public transit? Why?

   d. How are the scales different for each graph?

6. In 1972, Yellowstone Park began a *Do Not Feed The Bears* campaign to minimize contact between bears and humans. Bear-proof trash cans and dumpsters were installed at campgrounds and picnic areas. The effect of the campaign can be seen in the graph.

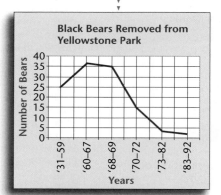

Black Bears Removed from Yellowstone Park

   a. Explain how you could alter either the horizontal or the vertical scale of the graph to make it appear that the number of black bears that had to be removed from the park for unfavorable contact with humans has decreased even more rapidly since the 1972 *Do Not Feed the Bears* campaign. **See margin.**

   b. Explain how you could alter either the horizontal or the vertical scale to make the 1972 *Do Not Feed the Bears* campaign appear less effective. **See margin.**

   c. What do you notice about the scale for the years? **See margin.**

   d. Do you think this is an appropriate way to display the data? Explain. **See margin.**

Tell whether you would use a *line graph*, a *bar graph*, or a *stem-and-leaf plot* for each situation.

7. After a bench press contest, the local gym wants to display the heaviest weights that different contestants were able to press.

8. Your principal wants to see how the number of students has changed over the past six years. **Line graph, as it can show the change over time.**

9. The Humane Society wants to compare the number of female and male dogs, female and male cats, and female and male birds it has placed in homes this year. **Bar graph; a double bar graph can show the difference between male and female numbers.**

10. **Science** The chart lists the number of moons for each planet in our solar system.

   a. Find the mean, the median, and the mode of the data.

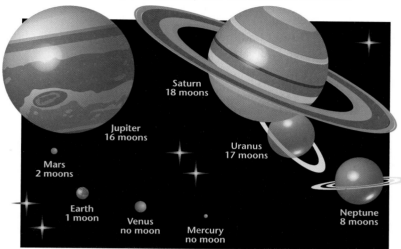

Saturn
18 moons

Jupiter
16 moons

Uranus
17 moons

Mars
2 moons

Earth
1 moon

Venus
no moon

Mercury
no moon

Neptune
8 moons

   b. Which, if any, of the averages would you use to describe the typical number of moons for a planet in our solar system? Why?

Tell whether the *mean*, the *median*, or the *mode* best describes each set of data. Explain your choice.

11. Number of bees in eight hives

293	355	25	92	470	600	71	50

12. Number of ants in five colonies

8200	7004	5216	60,000	8991

13. Number of students in nine college classes

18	14	52	15	20	61	21	22	22

14. **Open-ended**

   a. List the ages of five people in your family. Explain which type of average you think is most appropriate to use to describe the data. **a–c. Answers will vary. Check students' work.**

   b. List the ages of five of your friends. Which average best describes these ages?

   c. Combine your lists from parts (a) and (b). Which average would you use to describe these ages?

10. a. mean: 7.75;
      median: 5;
      mode: 0
   b. Sample Response:
      None; The mode makes it seem like most planets have no moons. The mean and median make it seem as if most planets have 5 to 8 moons, but only Neptune is close to this.

11. Sample Response:
    The median; There is no mode and the mean will be affected by extreme data values.

12. Sample Response:
    The median; There is no mode and the mean will be affected by the one extreme data value.

13. Sample Response:
    The median; The mean is affected by the extreme values 52 and 61. The mode could be used, but the mode usually is only used with categorical data.

EXERCISE NOTES
Provide time for students to discuss and justify their choices for **Exercises 11–14** either in small groups or as a class. This way the teacher can listen to students' justifications, assessing whether students are understanding the different measures of central tendency and aspects such as the effects of extreme data values on the mean. Students will benefit from hearing different justifications and having to defend their choices.

Practice & Applications

Exercise Notes

Exercise 18 For **part (a)** make it clear that students should cut out or provide a photocopy of the graph they choose. You may want to provide a collection of old newspapers and magazines in the classroom. (Ask the librarian or other teachers to donate old papers and magazines.) Students with access to the internet and a printer may be able to find a website with a graph related to an advertisement or article.

16. median; The baby's height would probably make the mean much lower than 5'6'' and the parents are probably not the same height.

RESEARCH

Exercise 18 checks that you understand how graphs and averages can be misleading.

Challenge Tell which type of average you think was used to make each statement. Explain your reasoning.

15. More students at Glenmore Middle School chose swimming as their favorite sport than chose any other sport.
    mode; The data are categorical.

16. The Swansons just had their first child. The average height of the mother, father, and baby is 5 ft 6 in.

17. A group of students took a survey and found that the average person uses a toothbrush 2.8 times a day. mean; The mode has to be a whole number. The median has to be a whole number or the mean of two whole numbers, which would have a 5 in the tenths place.

Reflecting ◀▶ on the Section

18. a. Find a line graph or bar graph in a magazine or newpaper.
       a–d. Answers will vary. Check students' work.
    b. What is the graph trying to show about the data?

    c. How could you change the scale on the graph so that it gives a different message?

    d. Was an average used with the graph? If so, does the average give the same message as the graph?

Spiral ◀▶ Review

Give two ways to name each figure. If two ways are not possible, explain why. (Module 2, pp. 106–107)

19.
    W ● ——————— ● T

    $\overline{WT}, \overline{TW}$

20.
    C ● —— ● A →

    $\overrightarrow{CA}$, A ray must be named with its endpoint first.

21.
    A ● — ● Y
      P ↘

    ∠PAY, ∠YAP, or ∠A

22. You place 2 blue, 1 red, and 3 green marbles in a bag. You choose a marble without looking. What is the probability of choosing the marble described? (Module 2, p. 80)

    a. blue marble $\frac{2}{6}$ or $\frac{1}{3}$ b. yellow marble $\frac{0}{6}$ or 0

    c. green or red marble $\frac{4}{6}$ or $\frac{2}{3}$ d. marble that is not red $\frac{5}{6}$

23. Find the prime factorization of 84. (Module 3, p. 158)
    $2 \cdot 2 \cdot 3 \cdot 7$

Section 5

Extra Skill Practice

In Exercises 1–6, use the graph below showing the number of grizzly bears removed from Yellowstone Park before and after the 1972 *Do Not Feed the Bears* campaign was put into effect.

1. What impression does the line graph give you about the number of grizzlies removed before and after the 1972 campaign? **See margin.**

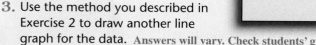

Grizzlies Removed from Yellowstone Park

2. Describe a way you could change the vertical scale to create a different impression of the data. **See margin.**

3. Use the method you described in Exercise 2 to draw another line graph for the data. **Answers will vary. Check students' graphs.**

4. Would a bar graph be an appropriate way to display the data? a circle graph? a line plot? a stem-and-leaf plot? Explain why or why not. **See margin.**

5. What would you report as the average number of grizzlies removed for the 4 time intervals before the campaign in 1972? for the 2 time intervals after the campaign? Tell which type of average you would report and why. **Answers will vary. Before 1972: mean = 6.25, mode = 3, and median = 5.5; After 1972 the mean, mode and median are all 2.**

6. How do your averages compare to the numbers of black bears removed during the same time? See Exercise 6, p. 272. **More black bears were removed before 1972, and then after the campaign was put in place the numbers were almost the same. (There are more black bears than grizzlies in Yellowstone Park.)**

Standardized Testing ▷ Open-ended

1. Explain which type of average, mean, median, or mode, best represents the Asian elephant population in the countries listed. **See margin.**

Estimated Populations of Asian Elephants in 2000				
Country	Bangladesh	Cambodia	China	Laos	Vietnam
Number	195	200	250	950	109

2. Which of the averages could be misleading? **mean; The extreme data value for Laos gives a mean of about 341 elephants. Without that data value the mean for the four countries is about 189.**

Module Project

Be a Reporter

Extra! Extra! Read all about it!

> *"Study shows that there are over a million pet snakes in the United States."*

How do reporters find answers to questions like "How many pet snakes are in the United States?" Using mathematics, of course! Your project is to collect data about a topic that interests you and to write a newpaper article about the topic. The mathematics you have learned in this module will help you organize, interpret, and present your results in the article.

SET UP

You will need:
- *Project Labsheet A*

Choosing a Topic

1 With your group, decide on a topic to investigate and what you want to find out about that topic. You may choose one of the topics below or come up with your own idea.

- ◆ Junk food
- ◆ Computers
- ◆ TV viewing
- ◆ Shopping
- ◆ Phone use
- ◆ Reading
- ◆ Sports
- ◆ Music
- ◆ Pets

Designing a Survey Over the next few days, you will design a *survey* to collect information about your topic. A survey is a set of questions that you ask a group of people.

2 Decide what population, or group of people, you are interested in (for example, just sixth graders or just teachers).

3 **Use Project Labsheet A.** Follow the steps on the *Survey Worksheet* to write the questions for your survey. See margin.

Collecting Your Data Over the next week, you will probably only be able to survey a sample of your population. Usually, the larger the sample, the more accurate your results will be.

4 What do you think your sample size should be in order for your results to be accurate?

5 Now collect your data.

Displaying Your Data After you collect your data, you need to show how people answered your survey questions. Visual displays can quickly help readers understand your results.

6 For each of your survey questions, decide whether a bar graph, a double bar graph, a line plot, a stem-and-leaf plot, or a line graph will best represent the data you are collecting. Consider whether one type of display provides information that another does not.

7 Create your displays. Make sure that anyone looking at them can understand the results of your survey.

Choosing an Average Sometimes a single number can give readers a good idea of what a set of data is like. Now you will look closely at the information you have collected and choose one or more averages to summarize and describe your data.

8 If possible, find the mean, the median, and the mode for the results of each of your survey questions.

9 Think about which average best represents your data for each of your survey questions. Write a paragraph describing your survey results. Be sure you include each of the averages you chose.

Summarizing Your Results Besides gathering data, a newspaper reporter must also present data to readers. Newspaper articles often have visual displays as well as a written summary of the results of a survey.

10 Write your own newspaper article summarizing your group's survey results. Include information on whom you surveyed and why you picked your topic.

11 Include one or more visual displays of your data in your article. These should be described either in the text of the article or in a caption below the display.

12 Write a headline for your article. It should catch your readers' interest and describe what the article is about.

13 Read your entire newspaper article. Make sure it is clear and accurately represents the data you collected.

PROJECT NOTES
Questions 8 and 9 need only be completed for the numerical data collected in the survey.

Labsheet: Each student needs a copy of Project Labsheet A, which is found in the *Teacher's Resource Book*.

Module Project Answers

3. Sample answers:
   a. 1. two pets
      2. one cat and 1 dog
      3. my dog
   b. 1. total number of pets owned
      2. total number of each type of pet owned
      3. favorite pets
   c. Do you own any cats? If so, how many?
   d–e. Check students' work.

MODULE 4

Review and Assessment

TEACHER NOTES

Students should complete the Review and Assessment independently in preparation for the Module Test.

Allow class time to discuss solutions and address any questions students may have. During this time, you may want to allow students to work in groups to share methods for solving the problems and to quiz each other on the concepts covered in this module.

10. yes, clusters appear from 6 to 15 mi/hr, 30 to 35 mi/hr, and 42 to 48 mi/hr. There is a large gap from 16 to 29.

13. Answers will vary. Sample Response: The median since the data are grouped in three clusters and the median falls in the middle of the middle cluster. There is a large gap between the lower cluster and the rest of the data, and this affects the mean. Since there are two modes, the mode is not an appropriate average to use for the data.

You will need: • *graph paper* (Ex. 30)

Replace each ? with the value that makes the statement true. (Sec. 1, Explor. 3)

1. 8 km = ? m
   8000

2. 2.3 cm = ? mm
   23

3. 1300 mg = ? g
   1.3

4. 2.3 kg = ? g
   2300

5. 5 m = ? cm
   500

6. 4 metric tons = ? kg
   4000

Use the table to answer Exercises 7–13. (Sec. 2, Explors. 1–3)

7. What is the range of the speeds? 42

8. Make a line plot of the data. See margin.

9. How many animals have a maximum speed less than 20 mi/hr? 4 animals

10. Are there any clusters or gaps in the data? Explain. See margin.

11. Use the table and your line plot to help estimate the maximum speed of each animal below.

   a. Bison approximately 30–35 mi/hr

   b. Pika approximately 6–15 mi/hr

12. Find the mean, the median, and the mode(s) of the data. If necessary, round your answers to the nearest tenth. modes = 30 and 35, median = 32.5, mean ≈ 29.1

13. Which average, the mean, the median, or the mode, do you think best describes the maximum speed of the animals? Explain. See margin.

| Maximum Speed of Some Yellowstone Park Mammals ||
Animal	Speed (mi/hr)
Beaver	6
Coyote	43
Elk	45
Gray Wolf	42
Grizzly Bear	30
Ground Squirrel	8
Mule Deer	35
Rabbit	35
Raccoon	15
Red Fox	48
Red Squirrel	12
White-tailed Deer	30

Find each quotient. (Sec. 3, Explor. 1)

14. $6\overline{)21.03}$ 3.505

15. $18\overline{)354.69}$ 19.705

16. $\frac{7}{10}$ 0.7

17. Jon bought 45 baseball cards. He now has 315. Write an equation to model the situation. Identify the variable you use. (Sec. 3, Explor. 2)
   Sample: $b + 45 = 315$; b = number of baseball cards Jon had before the purchase.

Solve each equation. Check each solution. (Sec. 3, Explors. 2 and 3)

18. $d - 33 = 18$
    $d = 51$

19. $25 + f = 47$
    $f = 22$

20. $2.6 + k = 7.3$
    $k = 4.7$

21. $s - 1.75 = 3.8$
    $s = 5.55$

22. $0.1 + x = 8$
    $x = 7.9$

23. $15 = w - 6$
    $w = 21$

Find each quotient. (Sec. 4, Explor. 2)

24. $1.4\overline{)1653.54}$
    1181.1

25. $50\overline{)48.944}$
    0.97888

26. $2.5\overline{)3.06}$
    1.224

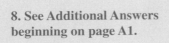

8. See Additional Answers beginning on page A1.

Use the stem-and-leaf plot below to answer Exercises 27–29. (Sec. 4, Explor. 1)

Copperhead Snake Lengths

6	1 5 5
7	2 7 7 7 9
8	0 1 6 6 6
9	0 0 1

7 | 2 means 72 cm

27. What is the length of the longest snake in the stem-and-leaf plot? **91 cm**

28. What is the range of the snake lengths? **30 cm**

29. Find the median and the mode(s) of the snake lengths. **median: 79.5 cm; modes: 77 cm and 86 cm**

30. a. Graph the ordered pairs in the table on a coordinate grid. (Sec. 4, Explor. 3)

Input	3	7	4	8
Output	7	15	9	17

b. Draw segments to connect the points in order from left to right. **a.–b.**

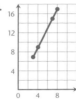

c. Use your graph to predict the missing values.

input $5\frac{1}{2}$, output = **?** **12**   output 10, input = **?** **$4\frac{1}{2}$**

Use the graphs to answer Exercises 31–33. (Sec. 5, Explor. 1)

Graph 1

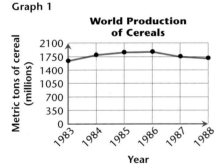

World Production of Cereals

Graph 2

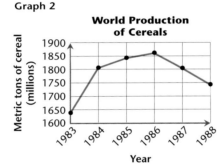

World Production of Cereals

31. The median annual cereal production in the world was 1.8 billion metric tons in the years 1983 through 1988. Which graph do you think shows this fact the best? Why? **See margin.**

32. Which graph would you use to try to show that cereal production in the world did not change much in the years 1983 through 1988? Why? **Graph 1; The line appears almost flat, indicating very little change.**

33. What changes were made to the graph on the left to create the different view of the data shown by the graph on the right? **The scale on the vertical axis was changed so it started at 1600 (instead of 0) and was divided into increments of 50 (instead of 350).**

Reflecting ◀▶ on the Module

34. **Writing** Mathematics can be a powerful tool. Explain how you think people use mathematics to discover and to show how the population and the environment change. **See margin.**

Assessment Options

TEACHER'S RESOURCE BOOK
- Module 4 Tests A and B
- Module 4 Standardized Test
- Module 4 Performance Assessment
- Modules 3 and 4 Cumulative Test
- Mid-Year Test

TEST GENERATOR

31. Graph 2 is easier to read. It clearly shows that there were two years (1983 and 1988) when cereal production was less than 1.8 billion metric tons and two years (1985 and 1986) when production was greater than 1.8 billion metric tons. So the median is the mean of the production in 1984 and 1987 which appears to be about 1.8 billion metric tons.

34. Sample Response: People collect data on population and environment changes and display the data in graphs that display information appropriately. They calculate different averages and choose ones that best describe changes or statistics.

Creating Things

Module 5 Overview

Themes such as mask design, origami, amazing structures, and tile patterns are used to develop fraction operations. Students use models, measurement, mental math, estimation, calculators, and algorithms. They also measure length and area in both customary and metric units, convert among measurements within a system, develop area formulas, and solve algebraic equations.

Module 5 Planner

Day 1: Section 1	Day 2: Section 1	Day 3: Section 1	Day 4: Section 2	Day 5: Section 2
Setting the Stage, pp. 282–283 Exploration 1 *through* Question 5, p. 284	Exploration 1 *from* Question 6, pp. 285–286	Exploration 2, pp. 287–289 Key Concepts, p. 290	Setting the Stage, p. 295 Exploration 1, pp. 296–298	Exploration 2 *through* Question 15, pp. 298–299
Day 6: Section 2	**Day 7: Section 3**	**Day 8: Section 3**	**Day 9: E²**	**Day 10: Review and Assessment**
Exploration 2, pp. 300–301 Key Concepts, pp. 301–302	Setting the Stage, p. 307 Exploration 1 *through* Question 9, pp. 308–310	Exploration 1 *from* Question 10, pp. 310–311 Key Concepts, p. 312	Begin E², p. 317	Mid-Module Quiz
Day 11: Section 4	**Day 12: Section 4**	**Day 13: Section 4**	**Day 14: Section 4**	**Day 15: Section 5**
Setting the Stage, p. 318 Exploration 1 *through* Question 5, pp. 319–320	Exploration 1 *from* Example, pp. 320–321	Exploration 2 *through* Question 18, pp. 321–322	Exploration 2 *from* Question 19, p. 323 Key Concepts, p. 324	Setting the Stage, p. 330 Exploration 1, pp. 331–332
Day 16: Section 5	**Day 17: Section 5**	**Day 18: Section 5**	**Day 19: Section 6**	**Day 20: Section 6**
Exploration 2, pp. 333–335	Exploration 3 *through* Question 27, pp. 335–336	Exploration 3 *from* Question 28, pp. 337–338 Key Concepts, pp. 339–340	Setting the Stage, p. 345 Exploration 1 *through* Question 11, pp. 346–348	Exploration 1 *from* Example, pp. 348–349
Day 21: Section 6	**Day 22: Module Project**	**Day 23: Review and Assessment**	**Day 24: Review and Assessment**	**Day 25: Assessment**
Exploration 2, pp. 350–351 Key Concepts, p. 352	Assign Module Project, pp. 357–359	Assign Review and Assessment, pp. 360–361	Discuss Review and Assessment, pp. 360–361	Module 5 Test

Materials List

Section	Materials
1	• Labsheets 1A–1B, scissors, tape, calculator
2	• Labsheet 2A, customary ruler, yardstick
3	• Labsheet 3A, scissors, tape, fraction strips from Section 1
E²	• Extended Exploration Labsheet, scissors
4	• Labsheet 4A, customary ruler, fraction calculator
5	• Labsheets 5A–5B, customary ruler, yardstick, scissors, newspapers or other large papers, metric ruler, centimeter graph paper, colored pencils, tracing paper
6	• Labsheet 6A, customary ruler, 8.5 in. x 11 in. piece of unlined paper, scissors
Project	• 8.5 in. x 8.5 in. square piece of paper, customary ruler
Rev & Assess	• Review and Assessment Labsheet, metric ruler

Module 5 Objectives

Section	Objectives	NCTM Standards 2000*
1	• Use number sense to compare fractions. • Compare fractions by writing equivalent fractions with a common denominator. • Compare fractions by rewriting as decimals.	1, 3, 4, 6, 7, 8, 9, 10
2	• Use benchmarks to estimate customary length. • Use a ruler to measure in fractions of an inch. • Choose an appropriate unit to measure a length. • Convert between customary units of length. • Add and subtract lengths measured in customary units.	1, 4, 6, 7, 8, 9, 10
3	• Add and subtract fractions with the same or different denominators.	1, 4, 6, 7, 8, 9, 10
4	• Add and subtract mixed numbers. • Estimate mixed number sums. • Use mental math to subtract a mixed number from a whole number.	1, 4, 6, 7, 8, 9, 10
5	• Use customary units to estimate and measure area. • Convert between units of area in the same measurement system. • Develop and use formulas to find the area of a parallelogram and a triangle. • Use an equation to find a missing dimension.	1, 2, 3, 4, 6, 7, 8, 9, 10
6	• Find the reciprocal of a number. • Divide a whole number or mixed number by a fraction. • Divide a fraction by a fraction. • Divide by fractions and mixed numbers.	1, 3, 4, 6, 7, 8, 9, 10

* See page T14.

Section 1 Comparing Fractions

Section 1 Planner

Section Objectives

Exploration 1
- Use number sense to compare fractions

Exploration 2
- Compare fractions by writing equivalent fractions with a common denominator
- Compare fractions by rewriting as decimals

Days for Section 1

First Day
Setting the Stage, *pp. 282–283*
Exploration 1 through Question 5, *p. 284*

Second Day
Exploration 1 from Question 6, *pp. 285–286*

Third Day
Exploration 2, *pp. 287–289*
Key Concepts, *p. 290*

Teaching Resources

Teacher's Resource Book
- Warm-Up
- Labsheets 1A and 1B
- Practice and Applications
- Study Guide
See page 281 for additional teaching resources.

Materials List

Setting the Stage
- Labsheet 1A
- scissors
- tape

Exploration 1
- Labsheet 1B
- scissors

Exploration 2
- calculator

Assessment Options

EMBEDDED ASSESSMENT
- Use number sense to compare fractions
  Exercises 1, 10, 12
- Compare fractions by writing equivalent fractions with a common denominator
  Exercises 18, 20, 30
- Compare fractions by rewriting as decimals
  Exercises 22, 23

PERFORMANCE TASK/PORTFOLIO
- Exercise 15 on *p. 291 (writing)*
- Exercise 31 on *p. 292 (challenge)*
- Exercise 32 on *p. 293 (journal)*

QUIZZES/TESTS
- Section 1 Quick Quiz

TEST GENERATOR

Section 1 Overview

In this section, students make fraction strips to model and compare fractions.

Exploration 1
Students make fraction strips and use them to compare fractions. They also use mental math to compare fractions to $\frac{1}{2}$. The inequality symbols for "greater than" and "less than" are introduced.

Exploration 2
Students learn to compare fractions with different denominators by converting them to equivalent fractions with a common denominator. They also explore the use of decimals to compare fractions. This technique is applied when it may be difficult to find a common denominator.

Guide for Assigning Homework

REGULAR SCHEDULING (45 MIN CLASS PERIOD)			EXERCISES TO NOTE		
Section/ P&A Pages	Core Assignment	Extended Assignment	Additional Practice/Review	Open-ended Problems	Extended Problems
1 pp. 291–294	**Day 1:** SR 33–37 **Day 2:** 1–15 **Day 3:** 16–30, ROS 32	SR 33–37 1–15 18–31, ROS 32, Ext 38–41	EP, p. 294	PA 32	Challenge PA 31 Ext 38–41

Key: PA = Practice & Application; ROS = Reflecting on the Section; SR = Spiral Review; TB = Toolbox; EP = Extra Skill Practice; Ext = Extension; ST = Standardized Testing

Math Background and Teaching Strategies

Classroom Notes

Interest centers for this section might include:

- origami books and paper
- the book *Sadako and the Thousand Paper Cranes*
- information and other patterns for folding flexagons

Visitors for this section might include:

- an artist that uses paper folding

Math Strands

Topic Integration and Spiraling

In Section 1, students apply and extend skills from Modules 1–4 as they develop and choose between different methods of comparing fractions. Students use number sense, common denominators, and decimals to compare fractions. Fractions are also compared in Module 6 as students work with ratios.

Exploration 1

The use of fraction strips provides a hands-on model for comparing fractions. The model helps students visualize fractions and begin building number sense techniques for comparing fractions. It is important to note that all the fraction strips are the same length and width, thus each strip represents the same whole, just divided into a different number of equal-sized parts. Number sense ideas are introduced by comparing fractions to $\frac{1}{2}$. This skill is then applied to compare two fractions by comparing each of them to $\frac{1}{2}$. The fraction strip model is also used to develop the concept that as the denominator of a fraction increases, the part of the whole it represents decreases. This idea is used to compare fractions that have the same numerators but different denominators and to compare fractions in which the numerators are 1 less than the denominators.

Exploration 2

Equivalent fractions were introduced in Module 1. In this exploration, equivalent fractions are used to compare fractions. Writing fractions using the least common denominator is introduced as one way to make comparisons. It also sets the stage for addition and subtraction of fractions in Sections 3 and 4 of this module. As an alternative to the equivalent fractions method of comparing fractions, students learn to use their calculators to write fractions as decimals. They are then able to compare the decimals as learned in Module 3.

Section 2 Planner

Section Objectives

Exploration 1
- Use benchmarks to estimate customary length
- Use a ruler to measure in fractions of an inch
- Choose an appropriate customary unit to measure a length

Exploration 2
- Convert between customary units of length
- Add and subtract lengths measured in customary units

Days for Section 2

First Day
Setting the Stage, p. 295
Exploration 1, pp. 296–298

Second Day
Exploration 2 through Question 15, pp. 298–299

Third Day
Exploration 2, pp. 300–301
Key Concepts, pp. 301–302

Teaching Resources

Teacher's Resource Book
- Warm-Up
- Labsheet 2A
- Practice and Applications
- Study Guide
See page 281 for additional teaching resources.

Materials List

Exploration 1
- customary ruler
- yardstick

Exploration 2
- Labsheet 2A

Practice and Applications
- customary ruler or tape measure

Assessment Options

EMBEDDED ASSESSMENT
- Use benchmarks to estimate customary length
  Exercises 2, 4, 6, 8
- Use a ruler to measure in fractions of an inch
  Exercises 12, 13
- Choose an appropriate customary unit to measure a length
  Exercises 9, 10, 11
- Convert between customary units of length
  Exercises 16, 17, 22, 24
- Add and subtract lengths measured in customary units
  Exercises 25, 26, 29

PERFORMANCE TASK/PORTFOLIO
- Exercises 5–8 on p. 303
- Exercise 24 on p. 304 *(writing)*
- Exercise 33 on p. 304 *(research)*
- Standardized Testing on p. 306 *(performance task)*

QUIZZES/TESTS
- Section 2 Quick Quiz

TEST GENERATOR

Section 2 Overview

In this section, the design of the Great Wall of China is used to introduce customary units of length.

Exploration 1
Students begin this exploration by developing their own benchmarks for customary measures of length. They then use their benchmarks to help estimate various lengths. In order to get more accurate measurements than their benchmarks allow, students measure with a ruler. They learn to read the markings for inches, half-inches, quarter-inches, and eighth-inches. Student also discuss the merits of writing measurements using combinations of units such as feet and inches.

Exploration 2
Students learn to convert from one customary unit of length to another. Then they look at finding the height of the Statue of Liberty by adding the heights of individual parts of the statue. This introduces the need for "simplifying" or regrouping measurements within the sum by converting groups of 12 inches to feet. Converting feet to inches is used in a subtraction example and then applied in situations with miles, yards, feet, and inches.

Guide for Assigning Homework

Section/ P&A Pages	REGULAR SCHEDULING (45 MIN CLASS PERIOD)		EXERCISES TO NOTE		
	Core Assignment	Extended Assignment	Additional Practice/Review	Open-ended Problems	Extended Problems
2 pp. 302–306	**Day 1:** 1–13 **Day 2:** 14–23, SR 34–37 **Day 3:** 24–31, ROS 33	1–13 14–23, SR 34–37 24–32, ROS 33, Ext 38	EP, p. 306	PA 5–8	Challenge PA 32 Ext 38

Key: PA = Practice & Application; ROS = Reflecting on the Section; SR = Spiral Review; TB = Toolbox; EP = Extra Skill Practice; Ext = Extension; ST = Standardized Testing

Math Background and Teaching Strategies

Classroom Notes

Bulletin board displays for this section include:

- Information and pictures of the Great Wall of China

- students' benchmarks for customary length

- a ruler with different fractions of an inch identified

- a completed conversion fact chart from Labsheet 2A

Math Strands

Topic Spiraling and Integration
This section focuses on measurement using customary units of length. It is assumed that students are familiar with the vocabulary and concepts of an inch, foot, yard, and mile from their occurrence in daily situations. The explorations will develop the use of the customary system for measuring, computing, and converting lengths. Customary units of weight and capacity will be introduced in Modules 7 and 8 respectively.

Exploration 1
Benchmarks for the metric units of length were developed in Module 4, so the concept of a benchmark should be familiar. Benchmarks for the customary units of inch, foot, and yard are introduced by having students find everyday objects that can be used as benchmarks. The benchmarks are then used to estimate lengths prior to introducing measuring with a ruler. Reading parts of an inch on a ruler revisits concepts of equivalent fractions from Module 1. In Section 6 students will use customary rulers to model division of fractions.

Exploration 2
Students complete a conversion fact chart that defines the relationships between different customary units of length. This chart is used to determine what factor a measure should be multiplied by to convert it to another given unit of measure. The exclusive use of multiplication (no division is used) to convert between measures requires that students be able to multiply by fractions. Multiplication of fractions was covered in Module 3. Converting units of measure is practiced through adding and subtracting measures and simplifying the results. Regrouping measures provides practice in using groupings other than 10, which is also done when regrouping is required to subtract mixed numbers.

Section 3 — Addition and Subtraction of Fractions

Section 3 Planner

Section Objectives

Exploration 1
- Add fractions with same or different denominators
- Subtract fractions with same or different denominators

Days for Section 3

First Day
Setting the Stage, *p. 307*
Exploration 1 through Question 9, *pp. 308–310*

Second Day
Exploration 1 from Question 10, *pp. 310–311*
Key Concepts, *p. 312*

Teaching Resources

Teacher's Resource Book
- Warm-Up
- Labsheet 3A
- Practice and Applications
- Study Guide
See page 281 for additional teaching resources.

Materials List

Setting the Stage
- Labsheet 3A
- scissors
- tape

Exploration 1
- fraction strips from Section 1

Assessment Options

EMBEDDED ASSESSMENT
- Add fractions with same or different denominators
  Exercises 4, 5, 6
- Subtract fractions with same or different denominators
  Exercises 7, 9, 11

PERFORMANCE TASK/PORTFOLIO
- Exercise 17 on *p. 314 (challenge)*
- Exercise 18 on *p. 314 (writing)*
- Exercise 19 on *p. 314 (oral report)*
- Standardized Testing on *p. 316 (open-ended)*
- Extended Exploration on *p. 317**

* *indicates a problem-solving task that can be assessed using the Assessment Scales*

QUIZZES/TESTS
- Section 3 Quick Quiz
- Mid-Module Quiz

TEST GENERATOR

Section 3 Overview

In this section, addition and subtraction of fractions is used to alter the design of a flexagon by creating different sized rows.

Exploration 1
Students begin this exploration by using their fraction strips from Section 1 to find the sums of fractions with like denominators and unlike denominators. Students will formulate methods for using common denominators to add fractions. The same approach is then applied to subtraction. Students first use fraction strips to find the difference of fractions with like and unlike denominators and then develop algorithms for subtracting fractions without the use of fraction strips.

Guide for Assigning Homework

REGULAR SCHEDULING (45 MIN CLASS PERIOD)			EXERCISES TO NOTE		
Section/ P&A Pages	Core Assignment	Extended Assignment	Additional Practice/Review	Open-ended Problems	Extended Problems
3 pp. 313–316	**Day 1:** 1–6, SR 20–26 **Day 2:** 7–16, 18, ROS 19, SR 27–36	1–6, SR 20–26 7–13 odd, 14–18, ROS 19, SR 27–36	EP, p. 316	ST, p. 316 E², p. 317	Challenge PA 17 E², p. 317

Key: PA = Practice & Application; ROS = Reflecting on the Section; SR = Spiral Review; TB = Toolbox; EP = Extra Skill Practice; Ext = Extension; ST = Standardized Testing

Math Background and Teaching Strategies

Classroom Notes

Bulletin board displays for this section include:

- information on flexagons and the meanings of the different names such as tetra-tetra or tri-hexa flexagons.

- examples showing how to add and how to subtract fractions using fraction strips

- student work display of E² solutions

Math Strands

Topic Spiraling and Integration

Exploration 1

Flexagons and fraction strips are revisited from Section 1 and combined with customary length measurement from Section 2 to introduce addition and subtraction of fractions. Familiarity with the fraction strips allows students to efficiently model fraction addition and subtraction without the additional time needed to experiment with new manipulative materials.

After modeling sums and differences with fraction strips, students develop algorithms for adding and subtracting fractions without the aid of a manipulative. The algorithms involve using common denominators to write equivalent fractions, two concepts that should be familiar from Module 1 and more recently from Section 1 of Module 5 where they were used to compare fractions.

Section 4 · Addition and Subtraction of Mixed Numbers

Section 4 Planner

Section Objectives

Exploration 1
- Add mixed numbers
- Estimate mixed number sums

Exploration 2
- Subtract mixed numbers

Days for Section 4

First Day
Setting the Stage, *p. 318*
Exploration 1 through Question 5,
  pp. 319–320

Second Day
Exploration 1 from Example, *pp. 320–321*

Third Day
Exploration 2 through Question 18,
pp. 321–322

Fourth Day
Exploration 2, *p. 323*
Key Concepts, *p. 324*

Teaching Resources

Teacher's Resource Book
- Warm-Up
- Labsheet 4A
- Practice and Applications
- Study Guide
See page 281 for additional teaching
resources.

Materials List

Setting the Stage
- Labsheet 4A

Exploration 1
- Labsheet 4A
- customary ruler

Exploration 2
- customary ruler

Practice and Applications
- fraction calculator

Assessment Options

EMBEDDED ASSESSMENT
- Add mixed numbers
  Exercises 7, 11, 12
- Estimate mixed number sums
  Exercises 1, 2, 13
- Subtract mixed numbers
  Exercises 17, 20, 21, 27

PERFORMANCE TASK/PORTFOLIO
- Exercise 13 on *p. 325 (estimation)*
- Exercise 31 on *p. 327 (journal)*

QUIZZES/TESTS
- Section 4 Quick Quiz

TEST GENERATOR

Section 4 Overview

In this section, students look at the design of relief masks to motivate the addition and subtraction of mixed numbers.

Exploration 1
Students look at the materials needed for making a relief mask. First they estimate the sum of the mixed number measurements for the string needed. Then they use a ruler to find the actual sum. In a third activity, students see that when adding mixed numbers it is easier to find the sum if the whole numbers are added first. Next, the students use paper and pencil to find the sum of the mixed numbers. Two paper and pencil techniques are introduced.

Exploration 2
Students are introduced to subtraction of mixed numbers as they examine the design of a Native American blanket and use it to make a raised design for a pin. Initially, a ruler is used to model subtraction of mixed numbers. Then students develop paper-and-pencil algorithms and mental math techniques. Students explore two algorithms for subtraction; they can either rename (regroup) fractions where necessary, or they can rewrite the mixed numbers as fractions and then subtract.

Guide for Assigning Homework

REGULAR SCHEDULING (45 MIN CLASS PERIOD)			EXERCISES TO NOTE		
Section/ P&A Pages	Core Assignment	Extended Assignment	Additional Practice/Review	Open-ended Problems	Extended Problems
4 pp. 325–329	**Day 1:** 1–3, SR 32–37 **Day 2:** 4–14 **Day 3:** 15–17, SR 38–46 **Day 4:** 18–30, ROS 31	1–3, SR 32–37 4–14 15–17, SR 38–46 18–30, ROS 31, Ext 47–49	EP, p. 329		Ext 47–49

Key: PA = Practice & Application; ROS = Reflecting on the Section; SR = Spiral Review; TB = Toolbox; EP = Extra Skill Practice; Ext = Extension; ST = Standardized Testing

Math Background and Teaching Strategies

Classroom Notes

Bulletin board display ideas for this section include:

- pictures of masks and other relief art

- information on Dia de Muertos

Visitors might include:

- artists

- speaker on cultural artwork, especially masks

Math Strands

Topic Spiraling and Integration

In this section students are introduced to a variety of methods for adding and subtracting mixed numbers.

Exploration 1

Measurement concepts from earlier sections of Module 5 are reinforced as students use a ruler to add mixed number lengths. Estimation, equivalent fractions, common denominators, adding fractions, and simplifying to lowest terms are reviewed and reinforced as students add mixed numbers.

Exploration 2

In this exploration, previously learned fraction concepts are used to develop algorithms for subtracting mixed numbers. Special emphasis is given to renaming fractions and regrouping in order to subtract and to converting mixed numbers to fractions so that regrouping is not necessary. Mental math techniques are employed for subtracting a whole number and

a mixed number. It is important that students begin to understand that there are different methods for subtracting and that they may apply whichever method best fits the current situation.

Mixed number addition and subtraction are continued in Book 2. In Book 3, the addition and subtraction is extended to negative mixed numbers. In these cases, methods such as changing the mixed numbers to fractions will be employed quite often.

Section 5 Area

Section 5 Planner

Section Objectives

Exploration 1
- Use customary units to estimate and measure area
- Convert between units of area in the same measurement system

Exploration 2
- Develop and use a formula to find the area of a parallelogram

Exploration 3
- Develop and use a formula to find the area of a triangle
- Use equations to find missing dimensions

Days for Section 5

First Day
Setting the Stage, *p. 330*
Exploration 1, *pp. 331–332*

Second Day
Exploration 2, *pp. 333–335*

Third Day
Exploration 3 through Question 27, *pp. 335–336*

Fourth Day
Exploration 3 from Question 28, *pp. 337–338*
Key Concepts, *pp. 339–340*

Materials List

Exploration 1
- customary ruler and scissors
- yard stick or measuring tape
- newspaper or other large paper

Exploration 2
- Labsheet 5A
- scissors and metric ruler
- centimeter graph paper

Exploration 3
- Labsheet 5B
- scissors, metric ruler, colored pencils

Practice and Applications
- Labsheets 5A–5B
- centimeter graph paper, tracing paper
- metric ruler

Teaching Resources

Teacher's Resource Book
- Warm-Up
- Labsheets 5A–5B
- Practice and Applications
- Study Guide
See page 281 for additional teaching resources.

Assessment Options

EMBEDDED ASSESSMENT
- Use customary units to estimate and measure area
  Exercises 1, 2
- Convert between units of area in the same measurement system
  Exercises 4, 5
- Use a formula to find the area of a parallelogram
  Exercises 8, 9, 13
- Use a formula to find the area of a triangle
  Exercise 16
- Use equations to find missing dimensions
  Exercises 19, 20

PERFORMANCE TASK/PORTFOLIO
- Exercise 27 on *p. 342 (create your own)*
- Exercise 29 on *p. 342 (discussion)*
- Exercise 37 on *p. 343 (extension)*
- Study Skills on *p. 344 (graphic organizers)*

QUIZZES/TESTS
- Section 5 Quick Quiz

TEST GENERATOR

Section 5 Overview

In this section, students study some of the architectural features of the Taj Mahal as they learn about the areas of triangles and parallelograms.

Exploration 1
Choosing an appropriate unit of measure for an area is discussed first, then students use geometric models to explore methods for converting an area measurement given in one customary unit to another customary unit, such as converting square feet to square yards.

Exploration 2
Conversions between units of area in the metric system are addressed as students develop a formula for the area of a parallelogram. To discover formulas for the area of a parallelogram and the area of a triangle, students manipulate geometric models so they can express the area of a parallelogram in terms of the area of a rectangle, and the area of a triangle in terms of the area of a parallelogram. In doing so, they study the meanings of *intersect*, *perpendicular*, *height*, and *base*.

Exploration 3
Students write equations based on the formulas for the area of a parallelogram and the area of a triangle, solving equations to find a missing dimension of the respective figure.

280K

Guide for Assigning Homework

REGULAR SCHEDULING (45 MIN CLASS PERIOD)			EXERCISES TO NOTE		
Section/ P&A Pages	Core Assignment	Extended Assignment	Additional Practice/Review	Open-ended Problems	Extended Problems
5 pp. 340–344	**Day 1:** 1–6 **Day 2:** 7–15 **Day 3:** 16–18, SR 30–36 **Day 4:** 19–27, ROS 29	1–6 7–15 16–18, SR 30–33, Ext 37 19–28, ROS 29	EP, p. 344	PA 14, 27	Challenge PA 28 Ext 37

Key: PA = Practice & Application; ROS = Reflecting on the Section; SR = Spiral Review; TB = Toolbox; EP = Extra Skill Practice; Ext = Extension; ST = Standardized Testing

Math Background and Teaching Strategies

Classroom Notes

Bulletin board display ideas for this section include:

- photos and information on the Taj Mahal

- models of 1 in.^{2}, 1 ft^2, 1 yd^2, 1 mm^2, 1 cm^2, 1 m^2

Visitors might include:

- an architect

Math Strands

Topic Spiraling and Integration

Exploration 1
Exploration 1 revisits customary units of measure for length from Section 2 and expands the concept of measurement from one dimension (length) to two dimensions (area). Students use models of a square inch, a square foot, and a square yard to estimate areas and to develop a sense of how square units differ from linear units. Conversions between units of area are addressed using the models and the area formula for a rectangle. A square with sides 1 yd long has an area of 1 yd^2. However, since 1 yd = 3 ft, the sides of the square are 3 ft long and its area is 3 ft • 3 ft or 9 ft^2. Thus, 1 yd^2 = 9 ft^2, so to convert an area from square yards to square feet the area must be multiplied by 9, not 3.

Exploration 2
This exploration begins by using models to review conversions between units of area, but this time with metric units such as square centimeter and square meter. The idea that converting between units of area requires multiplying by the square of the linear conversion factor is reinforced.

Then students use models to explore the relationship between the area of a parallelogram and the area of a rectangle. They discover that the area of a parallelogram is equal to the area of a rectangle with the same base and height. This reinforces that a rectangle is a parallelogram. This idea was developed when classifying polygons in Module 2.

Exploration 3
A formula for finding the area of a triangle is developed by using models to show that the area of a triangle is half the area of a parallelogram with the same height and base.

Areas of polygons will be applied when finding volumes of prisms in Module 7 and in calculating geometric probabilities in Module 8.

Section 6 — Division with Fractions

Section 6 Planner

Section Objectives

Exploration 1
- Find the reciprocal of a number
- Divide a whole number or mixed number by a fraction

Exploration 2
- Divide a fraction by a fraction
- Divide by fractions and mixed numbers

Days for Section 6

First Day
Setting the Stage, *p. 345*
Exploration 1 through Question 11,
pp. 346–348

Second Day
Exploration 1 from Example, *pp. 348–349*

Third Day
Exploration 2, *pp. 350–351*
Key Concepts, *p. 352*

Teaching Resources

Teacher's Resource Book
- Warm-Up
- Labsheet 6A
- Practice and Applications
- Study Guide
See page 281 for additional teaching resources.

Materials List

Exploration 1
- customary ruler
- Labsheet 6A

Exploration 2
- customary ruler
- $8\frac{1}{2}$ in. x 11 in. piece of unlined paper
- scissors

Assessment Options

EMBEDDED ASSESSMENT
- Find the reciprocal of a number
  Exercises 1, 2, 3
- Divide a whole number or mixed number by a fraction
  Exercises 10, 11, 13, 14, 23, 28
- Divide a fraction by a fraction
  Exercises 17, 21, 24, 25
- Divide by fractions and mixed numbers
  Exercises 13, 18, 26, 29

PERFORMANCE TASK/PORTFOLIO
- Exercise 15 on *p. 353*
- Exercise 30 on *p. 355 (challenge)*
- Module Project on *pp. 357– 359*

QUIZZES/TESTS
- Section 6 Quick Quiz
- Module Tests A and B
- Module Standardized Test
- Module Performance Assessment

TEST GENERATOR

Section 6 Overview

In this section, students continue exploring designs similar to the ones in the Taj Mahal by studying the inlaid tile borders. They will use measurements of borders and individual tiles to develop procedures for dividing fractions and mixed numbers.

Exploration 1
As they find the number of tiles needed to make a border for the top edge of the cover of their math books, students explore reciprocals and how they can be used to divide a fraction or mixed number by another fraction. Ruler models are used to explore division by a fraction and to interpret remainders.

Exploration 2
Students use a ruler to model division by mixed numbers. They also use number sense to compare quotients to 1, given the relative values of the divisor and dividend. This will help them determine the reasonableness of the quotient when two mixed numbers are divided.

All exercises in Section 6 require students to write their quotients in lowest terms.

Guide for Assigning Homework

REGULAR SCHEDULING (45 MIN CLASS PERIOD)			EXERCISES TO NOTE		
Section/ P&A Pages	Core Assignment	Extended Assignment	Additional Practice/Review	Open-ended Problems	Extended Problems
6 pp. 353–356	**Day 1:** 1–6, SR 32–40 **Day 2:** 7–16 **Day 3:** 17–29, ROS 31	1–6, SR 32–40 7–16 17–30, ROS 31	EP, p. 356 Review & Assessment, pp. 360–361		Challenge PA 30 Mod Proj, pp. 357–359

Key: PA = Practice & Application; ROS = Reflecting on the Section; SR = Spiral Review; TB = Toolbox; EP = Extra Skill Practice; Ext = Extension; ST = Standardized Testing

Math Background and Teaching Strategies

Classroom Notes

Bulletin board displays for this section include:

- tile borders found in architecture

- examples of division problems modeled with a ruler and the corresponding division problems solved using reciprocals

- student created borders from Question 23

Math Strands

Topic Spiraling and Integration

Exploration 1

This exploration uses a hands-on model to develop an algorithm for dividing a whole number or a mixed number by a fraction. Students used customary rulers to measure in Section 2 of Module 5 and also used them as a tool for adding and subtracting mixed numbers in Section 4. Their ability to read a ruler is reinforced in this exploration as they use rulers to determine how many measures of a fixed length fit into a given length.

Exploration 2

This exploration extends the concepts in Exploration 1 to division of a fraction, whole number, or mixed number by a mixed number. The use of a manipulative is de-emphasized and students rely on use of reciprocals and multiplication to perform the calculations. Reasonableness of results is emphasized by estimating quotients and using the relative sizes of the dividend and divisor to determine whether the quotient will be less than, greater than, or equal to 1.

Students will continue to work with fraction and mixed number division in Books 2 and 3, and as they solve equations requiring division of fractions. Fraction number sense developed in Book 1 will give students tools for checking the reasonableness of their answers in future situations involving fractions.

Module 5

OVERVIEW

Themes such as mask design, origami, amazing structures, and tile patterns are used to develop fraction operations. Students use models, measurement, mental math, estimation, calculators, and algorithms. They also measure length and area in both customary and metric units, convert among measurements within a system, develop area formulas, and solve algebraic equations.

PREREQUISITE SKILLS

Warm-Up Exercises for each section are provided in the *Teacher's Resource Book*. You can use these exercises to review skills and concepts students will need for each section. In addition, the Spiral Review exercises at the end of each section in the student edition provide practice on prerequisite skills.

MODULE DIAGNOSTIC TEST

The Module Diagnostic Test in the *Teacher's Resource Book* can be used to assess students' prior knowledge of skills and concepts that will be taught in each section of this module. You can use test results to help structure your teaching to meet the diverse needs of your classroom.

MODULE 5 CREATING THINGS

The Module Project — **Creating Cubes**

Origami is an ancient Japanese art of paper-folding. It can be used to create animals and other shapes. No scissors or glue are needed. With your knowledge of fractions and measurement learned in this module, you will follow steps to create a cube by paper folding.

More on the Module Project
See pp. 357–359.

280

CONNECTING
MATH&EMATICS
The & Theme

MODULE 5 **SECTION OVERVIEW**

① Comparing Fractions

As you use paper folding:
- ◆ Use number sense to compare fractions
- ◆ Use common denominators to write equivalent fractions
- ◆ Use decimals to compare fractions

② Customary Units of Length

As you investigate the Great Wall of China:
- ◆ Estimate and measure lengths
- ◆ Measure in fractions of an inch
- ◆ Convert, add, and subtract customary units of length

③ Addition and Subtraction of Fractions

As you make a tetra-tetraflexagon:
- ◆ Add and subtract fractions

④ Addition and Subtraction of Mixed Numbers

As you look at masks and relief art from different cultures:
- ◆ Add mixed numbers
- ◆ Subtract mixed numbers

⑤ Area

As you explore the Taj Mahal:
- ◆ Measure and convert customary units of area
- ◆ Find areas of parallelograms
- ◆ Find areas of triangles
- ◆ Find a missing dimension

⑥ Division with Fractions

As you design a decorative border:
- ◆ Divide by fractions and mixed numbers

INTERNET
Resources and practice at
classzone.com

Module Resources

TEACHER'S RESOURCE BOOK
Resources
- *The Math Gazette* (parent newsletter)
- Warm-Ups
- Labsheets
- Practice and Applications
- Study Guide

Assessment
- Section Quick Quizzes
- Mid-Module Quiz
- Module 5 Diagnostic Test
- Module 5 Tests A and B
- Module 5 Standardized Test
- Module 5 Performance Assessment

SPANISH RESOURCES
- *The Math Gazette* (parent newsletter)
- Practice and Applications
- Assessment
- Spanish Glossary

STUDENT WORKBOOK

TECHNOLOGY BOOK

TECHNOLOGY RESOURCES
- @Home Tutor
- Test Generator
- Activity Generator
- Professional Development DVD
- Online Activities

Section ① Comparing Fractions

Paper Folding

Setting the Stage

SET UP *You will need: • Labsheet 1A • scissors • tape*

SADAKO AND THE THOUSAND PAPER CRANES

by Eleanor Coerr with paintings by Ronald Himler

This story takes place in Japan. In the excerpt below, Chizuko visits her friend, Sadako, who is very ill and in the hospital.

Chizuko was pleased with herself. "I've figured out a way for you to get well," she said proudly. "Watch!" She cut a piece of gold paper into a large square. In a short time she had folded it over and over into a beautiful crane.

Sadako was puzzled. "But how can that paper bird make me well?"

"Don't you remember that old story about the crane?" Chizuko asked. "It's supposed to live for a thousand years. If a sick person folds one thousand paper cranes, the gods will grant her wish and make her healthy again." She handed the crane to Sadako. "Here's your first one."

Think About It

1 As the story continues, Sadako folds 644 paper cranes and her classmates fold the rest. Together they fold 1000 cranes.

   a. What fraction of the cranes does Sadako fold? $\frac{644}{1000}$ or $\frac{161}{250}$

   b. Write the fraction from part (a) as a decimal. 0.644

   c. Write the fraction of the cranes Sadako's classmates fold as a decimal. 0.356

2 **Use Labsheet 1A.** Paper folding can be fun, but cranes are challenging to make. Instead follow the directions in parts (a)–(d) to fold a strip of paper into a trihexaflexagon.

   a. Complete Steps 1 and 2 on the labsheet. Check students' work.

   b. What fraction of the strip is marked with a 1? Be sure to count both the front and the back of the strip. $\frac{6}{18}$ or $\frac{1}{3}$

   c. Complete Steps 3–6 on the labsheet. Check students' work.

   d. Complete Steps 1–4 below. Check students' work.

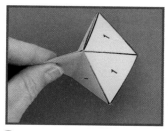

1 Pinch two adjacent triangles together with your thumb and index finger.

2 Push on the line segment directly across from the two pinched triangles.

3 Using both thumbs pull open the flexagon from the top center point.

4 A different number will appear on all the triangles.

Note: If your flexagon did not open, pinch two different adjacent triangles and try again.

▶ When you think of using mathematics to create things, you may imagine spaceships, skyscrapers, robots, and other examples of modern technology. But even the designs of simple things involve mathematics. In this module you will see how mathematics is used to create things.

Question 2 Students will be creating one type of flexagon. Another type will be created in Section 3. Make sure students retain the bottom half of **Labsheet 1A** after cutting out the flexagon pattern. The bottom half includes the directions for folding. You may want to demonstrate the folding process and have students complete their flexagon by folding along with you.

Make students aware that they need to stop after Steps 1 and 2 to answer **part (b)**. Otherwise they will have to unfold their flexagons to be able to answer **part (b)**. Students should count the 1s labeled on the front of the strip as well as the 1s they marked on the back.

Exploration 1

USING MANIPULATIVES

Questions 3 and 4 Students will be cutting and folding their own fraction strips. You may want to cut some extra strips (Labsheet 1B) ahead of time to use as replacements.

TEACHER NOTES

NOTE: Do not throw the fraction strips away at the end of this exploration. They will be used again in Section 3 of this module. After completing this exploration, have students paper clip their strips together. To avoid problems with lost sets, collect the sets and store them. Storing the strips for each group in a small manila envelope works well for quick redistribution of the strips for use in Section 3.

TIPS FROM TEACHERS

Question 4 It is helpful to refold fraction strips for fourths and eighths so each fold faces under. This will help the strips lay flat. If students have trouble seeing the fold lines, have them use a ruler and a pencil to mark the fold lines.

GOAL

LEARN HOW TO...
- use number sense to compare fractions

AS YOU...
- fold fractions strips

KEY TERM
- inequality

Exploration 1

Fraction Number Sense

SET UP You will need: • Labsheet 1B • scissors

▶ The Japanese art of creating things by folding paper is called *origami*. In this exploration, you will fold paper to make fraction strips. An example of a completed strip is shown below.

The dashed segments show where the paper is folded to form three equal-sized pieces.

Each piece is labeled as $\frac{1}{3}$ of a strip.

| $\frac{1}{3}$ | $\frac{1}{3}$ | $\frac{1}{3}$ |

Use Labsheet 1B for Questions 3 and 4.

3 Cut out the *Fraction Strips* for thirds, sixths, and twelfths. Fold each strip along the dashed segments, and label each part with the fraction name. (The strip for thirds is already labeled.) **Check students' work.**

4 Cut out the blank strips and fold them so that one strip is folded into halves, one is folded into fourths, and one is folded into eighths. Label each part with the fraction name. **Check students' work.**

5 Explain how you folded a strip into eighths. **I folded one strip into halves, then into halves again, and finally into halves a third time.**

▶ You can use your strips to compare fractions and to develop your number sense about fractions.

EXAMPLE

Use fraction strips to compare $\frac{2}{3}$ and $\frac{10}{12}$.

SAMPLE RESPONSE

The original strips are the same length, so you are comparing parts of the same whole.

| $\frac{1}{12}$ | $\frac{1}{12}$ | $\frac{1}{12}$ | $\frac{1}{12}$ | $\frac{1}{12}$ | $\frac{1}{12}$ | $\frac{1}{12}$ | $\frac{1}{12}$ | $\frac{1}{12}$ | $\frac{1}{12}$ | $\frac{1}{12}$ | $\frac{1}{12}$ |

| $\frac{1}{3}$ | $\frac{1}{3}$ | $\frac{1}{3}$ |

First Fold the strip for thirds to show $\frac{2}{3}$.

Then Fold the strip for twelfths to show $\frac{10}{12}$ and place it directly above the $\frac{2}{3}$ strip.

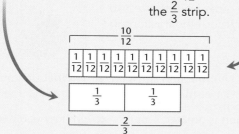

You can see that $\frac{10}{12}$ of a strip is longer than $\frac{2}{3}$ of a strip, so $\frac{10}{12} > \frac{2}{3}$.

▶ A statement such as $\frac{10}{12} > \frac{2}{3}$ that uses the symbol > or < to compare two numbers is an **inequality**.

6 Use your fraction strips to compare each fraction with $\frac{1}{2}$. Replace each __?__ with >, <, or =.

a. $\frac{4}{8}$ _?_ $\frac{1}{2}$ =

b. $\frac{4}{12}$ _?_ $\frac{1}{2}$ <

c. $\frac{7}{8}$ _?_ $\frac{1}{2}$ >

d. $\frac{2}{3}$ _?_ $\frac{1}{2}$ >

e. $\frac{1}{4}$ _?_ $\frac{1}{2}$ <

f. $\frac{2}{6}$ _?_ $\frac{1}{2}$ <

7 **Discussion** Look at your results in Question 6. Just by looking at its numerator and denominator, how can you tell whether a fraction is equal to $\frac{1}{2}$? greater than $\frac{1}{2}$? less than $\frac{1}{2}$?

8 **a.** Explain how you can use your answers to Question 6, parts (c) and (f), to compare $\frac{7}{8}$ and $\frac{2}{6}$.

   b. Write an inequality that compares $\frac{7}{8}$ and $\frac{2}{6}$. $\frac{7}{8} > \frac{2}{6}$

7. Sample Response: If the denominator is twice the numerator, the fraction is equal to $\frac{1}{2}$.

If the denominator is less than twice the numerator, the fraction is greater than $\frac{1}{2}$.

If the denominator is greater than twice the numerator, the fraction is less than $\frac{1}{2}$.

8. a. Sample Response: $\frac{7}{8}$ is greater than $\frac{1}{2}$ and $\frac{2}{6}$ is less than $\frac{1}{2}$, so $\frac{7}{8}$ has to be greater than $\frac{2}{6}$.

Exploration 1 *continued*

TEACHING NOTES

Question 9 Remind students to mentally compare the two fractions in each problem to $\frac{1}{2}$ first, and then to compare them to each other. If they have difficulty, they should refer back to **Question 8**.

Question 10(d) Students should use their fraction number sense to put the fractions in order. If they are unsure, they can check their answer using fraction strips.

Question 12 You may want to call on students to explain the thinking and method used to compare each pair of fractions.

ALTERNATIVE APPROACH

Exploration 1 can also be completed using commercially produced fraction bars. The fractional parts on these bars are shaded so that instead of folding the bars, students would simply compare the shaded sections.

✔ **QUESTION 9**

...checks that you can compare fractions with $\frac{1}{2}$.

10. c. $\frac{1}{4}$, I used the pattern I saw in parts a and b. The numerator of both fractions is 1 and 4 < 9. So $\frac{1}{4} > \frac{1}{9}$.

d. Because the numerators are all the same, write the fractions in order from greatest denominator to least denominator.

11. b. The numerator is 1 less than the denominator.

c. $\frac{1}{2}, \frac{2}{3}, \frac{3}{4}, \frac{5}{6}, \frac{7}{8}, \frac{11}{12}$

d. $\frac{10}{11}$; I used the pattern I noticed in parts b and c. The numerator of both fractions is 1 less than the denominator, and 11 > 7, so $\frac{10}{11} > \frac{6}{7}$.

e. $\frac{50}{51}, \frac{100}{101}, \frac{150}{151}, \frac{1000}{1001}$

✔ **QUESTION 12**

...checks that you can use number sense to compare fractions.

---

9 ✔ **CHECKPOINT** Use mental math to compare each fraction with $\frac{1}{2}$. Then replace each _?_ with >, <, or =.

a. $\frac{2}{9}$ _?_ $\frac{13}{15}$ <

b. $\frac{5}{10}$ _?_ $\frac{1}{12}$ >

c. $\frac{5}{12}$ _?_ $\frac{8}{14}$ <

▶ **Other Patterns** There are other relationships between numerators and denominators that will help you compare fractions.

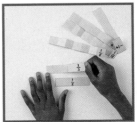

10 a. On each of your fraction strips, fold one part over so the rest of the parts are face down. Arrange the parts facing up in order from shortest to longest and record the fractions in that order. $\frac{1}{12}, \frac{1}{8}, \frac{1}{6}, \frac{1}{4}, \frac{1}{3}, \frac{1}{2}$

b. The numerators of the fractions showing on your fraction strips are all 1. What do you notice about the order of the denominators? *The denominators decrease from left to right.*

c. Which fraction is greater, $\frac{1}{9}$ or $\frac{1}{4}$? Explain how you decided.

d. Explain how to order $\frac{2}{6}, \frac{2}{4}, \frac{2}{3}, \frac{2}{2}$, and $\frac{2}{8}$ from least to greatest.

11 a. Turn each fraction strip over so the one section you folded is underneath. For each strip, write the fraction that names the part of the strip you can see. $\frac{2}{3}, \frac{5}{6}, \frac{11}{12}, \frac{1}{2}, \frac{3}{4}, \frac{7}{8}$

b. What relationship do you notice between the numerator and the denominator of each fraction?

c. Arrange the folded strips so the parts you see are in order from shortest to longest and record the fractions in that order.

d. Which fraction is greater, $\frac{6}{7}$ or $\frac{10}{11}$? Explain how you decided.

e. Order $\frac{100}{101}, \frac{150}{151}, \frac{1000}{1001}$, and $\frac{50}{51}$ from least to greatest.

12 ✔ **CHECKPOINT** Replace each _?_ with >, <, or =.

a. $\frac{3}{15}$ _?_ $\frac{3}{10}$ <

b. $\frac{1}{9}$ _?_ $\frac{1}{11}$ >

c. $\frac{8}{9}$ _?_ $\frac{10}{11}$ <

HOMEWORK EXERCISES ▶ See Exs. 1–15 on p. 291.

 Module 5 Creating Things

Common Denominators

GOAL

LEARN HOW TO...
- use common denominators to write equivalent fractions
- use decimals to compare fractions

AS YOU...
- choose a method to compare fractions

KEY TERMS
- common denominator
- least common denominator

SET UP *You will need a calculator.*

▶ Thelma wants to fold a one-inch strip into thirds. Her ruler does not show thirds of an inch. She thinks $\frac{1}{3}$ is a little less than $\frac{3}{8}$.

13 **Discussion** Use one of the number sense methods you learned in Exploration 1 to compare $\frac{1}{3}$ and $\frac{3}{8}$.

▶ **Using Equivalent Fractions to Compare** One way to compare fractions with different denominators is to find equivalent fractions that are easy to compare.

14 a. Copy and complete each list of equivalent fractions.

$$\frac{1}{3} = \frac{?}{6} = \frac{?}{9} = \frac{?}{12} = \frac{?}{15} = \frac{?}{18} = \frac{?}{21} = \frac{?}{24} = \frac{?}{27}$$

$$\frac{3}{8} = \frac{?}{16} = \frac{?}{24} = \frac{?}{32} = \frac{?}{40}$$

2, 3, 4, 5, 6, 7, 8, 9; 6, 9, 12, 15

b. Use the fractions with 24 as the denominator to compare $\frac{1}{3}$ and $\frac{3}{8}$. Was Thelma correct?

c. Suppose you continue to list equivalent fractions for $\frac{1}{3}$ and $\frac{3}{8}$. What is the next denominator common to both lists? 48

▶ A **common denominator** of two or more fractions is a common multiple of their denominators. The **least common denominator** of two or more fractions is the least common multiple (LCM) of their denominators. The least common denominator of $\frac{1}{3}$ and $\frac{3}{8}$ is 24, which is the LCM of 3 and 8.

13. $\frac{1}{3} = \frac{3}{9}$; The numerators of $\frac{3}{8}$ and $\frac{3}{9}$ are equal, so the fraction with the lesser denominator is greater; $\frac{3}{8} > \frac{3}{9}$. That is, $\frac{3}{8} > \frac{1}{3}$.

14. b. yes; $\frac{1}{3} = \frac{8}{24}$ and $\frac{3}{8} = \frac{9}{24}$ so $\frac{1}{3}$ is a little less than $\frac{3}{8}$.

FOR ◀ HELP
with *least common multiples*, see
MODULE 3, p. 168

COMMON ERRORS

Question 15 Students may incorrectly think the least common denominator can always be found by multiplying the two denominators. Point out that multiplying the two denominators will result in a common denominator that only sometimes is the *least* common denominator.

DEVELOPING MATH CONCEPTS

Question 16 Students should understand that using any common denominator to compare fractions will yield the same results as using the least common denominator.

If needed, the following Classroom Example can be used to provide additional guidance on comparing fractions before students attempt **Checkpoint Question 17**.

CLASSROOM EXAMPLE

Use a common denominator to compare $\frac{5}{9}$ and $\frac{8}{15}$.

Answer:
First: Find a common multiple for the denominators.

multiples of 9: 9, 18, 27, 36, 45,...
multiples of 15: 15, 30, 45, 60,...

The least common multiple of 9 and 15 is 45.

Then: Write equivalent fractions using a common denominator.

$\frac{5}{9} = \frac{25}{45}$ $\frac{8}{15} = \frac{24}{45}$

$\frac{25}{45} > \frac{24}{45}$, so $\frac{5}{9} > \frac{8}{15}$.

---

15 **Try This as a Class** Complete the following to compare $\frac{5}{8}$ and $\frac{7}{10}$.

a. Find the least common denominator of $\frac{5}{8}$ and $\frac{7}{10}$. **40**

b. What else must you do to compare the two fractions in part (a)? **Rewrite the fractions with a common denominator and compare the numerators.**

c. Is $\frac{5}{8}$ *greater than, less than,* or *equal to* $\frac{7}{10}$? **less than**

EXAMPLE

Use a common denominator to compare $\frac{5}{6}$ and $\frac{7}{9}$.

SAMPLE RESPONSE

First Find a common multiple of the denominators.

multiples of 6: 6, 12, **18**, ...

multiples of 9: 9, **18**, ...

18 is the least common multiple of 6 and 9, so **18** is also a common denominator of $\frac{5}{6}$ and $\frac{7}{9}$.

Then Write equivalent fractions using a common denominator.

$\frac{5}{6} = \frac{15}{18}$ $\frac{7}{9} = \frac{14}{18}$

$\frac{15}{18} > \frac{14}{18}$, so $\frac{5}{6} > \frac{7}{9}$.

---

16 **Discussion** Suppose you use 54 as the common denominator to write equivalent fractions in the Example.

a. What will the new numerators be? **45 and 42**

b. Will the final answer be the same? Explain. **Yes; $\frac{45}{54} > \frac{42}{54}$, so $\frac{5}{6} > \frac{7}{9}$.**

✔ **QUESTION 17**

...checks that you can compare fractions using a common denominator.

17 ✔ **CHECKPOINT** Replace each _?_ with >, <, or =.

a. $\frac{5}{7}$ _?_ $\frac{3}{4}$ **<**

b. $\frac{13}{15}$ _?_ $\frac{4}{5}$ **>**

c. $\frac{17}{20}$ _?_ $\frac{21}{25}$ **>**

▶ **Using Decimals to Compare** When the common denominator is difficult to find, you may choose to compare fractions by changing the fractions to decimals.

18 Write $\frac{22}{100}$ and $\frac{3}{8}$ as decimals. Use the decimals to compare the fractions. **0.22 and 0.375; $\frac{22}{100} < \frac{3}{8}$**

19 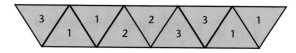 **Calculator** Complete the following to compare $\frac{9}{44}$ and $\frac{8}{31}$.

   a. Enter [9] [÷] [4] [4] [=] to change $\frac{9}{44}$ to a decimal. Explain why these are the correct keys to press.

   b. Use your calculator to change $\frac{8}{31}$ to a decimal. 0.258...

   c. Use the decimals from parts (a) and (b) to compare $\frac{9}{44}$ and $\frac{8}{31}$.

20 Write each fraction as a decimal rounded to the nearest hundredth. Then replace each __?__ with >, <, or =.

   a. $\frac{5}{13}$ __?__ $\frac{4}{11}$ 0.38, 0.36; >

   b. $\frac{17}{26}$ __?__ $\frac{55}{100}$ 0.65, 0.55; >

   c. $\frac{22}{250}$ __?__ $\frac{16}{189}$ 0.09, 0.08; >

21 Would you use *number sense, mental math, paper and pencil,* or a *calculator* to compare $\frac{10}{11}$ and $\frac{120}{121}$? Explain.

22 Thelma wants to fold a one-inch strip into fifths. She thinks $\frac{1}{5}$ is less than the $\frac{1}{4}$ mark on her ruler. Is she correct? Explain.

23 In the *Setting the Stage*, $\frac{4}{9}$ of one side of the strip used to make the trihexaflexagon was labeled with a 1, and $\frac{1}{3}$ of the same side was labeled with a 3.

   a. What fraction of this side of the strip was labeled with a 2? $\frac{2}{9}$

   b. Use the side of the strip in part (a). Compare the fraction of the strip labeled with a 2 to the fraction of the strip labeled with a 3. $\frac{2}{9} < \frac{1}{3}$ because $\frac{1}{3} = \frac{3}{9}$ and $\frac{2}{9} < \frac{3}{9}$.

HOMEWORK EXERCISES ▶ See Exs. 16–32 on pp. 291–293.

Section 1   Comparing Fractions   289

---

19. a. 0.204...; Sample Response: A fraction can be converted to an equivalent decimal by dividing the numerator by the denominator.

c. $\frac{9}{44}$ is about 0.20 and $\frac{8}{31}$ is about 0.26, so $\frac{9}{44} < \frac{8}{31}$.

21. Number sense; The numerators of both fractions are 1 less than the denominator, and 11 < 121, so $\frac{10}{11} < \frac{120}{121}$.

22. Yes; The numerator of both fractions is 1 and 5 > 4 so $\frac{1}{5} < \frac{1}{4}$. If you change the fractions to decimals $\frac{1}{5} = 0.20$ and $\frac{1}{4} = 0.25$, so $\frac{1}{5} < \frac{1}{4}$.

ALTERNATIVE APPROACH

Question 19 If students are using a fraction calculator, have them enter $\frac{9}{44}$ using the fraction keys. Then press the [F↔D] key and ask students what they think the [F↔D] key does. Have them press the [F↔D] key again and ask what they think is happening. Make certain students understand a fraction as division and what is happening when any calculator is being used.

TEACHING NOTES

Question 20 Remind students they may need to round their decimal answers before comparing.

Question 23 can be answered without their trihexaflexagon. Students should change $\frac{1}{3}$ to $\frac{3}{9}$ so they are working with fractions that have a common denominator. It is easy to add $\frac{4}{9}$ and $\frac{3}{9}$ to get $\frac{7}{9}$ and then subtract $\frac{7}{9}$ from 1 to get the $\frac{2}{9}$ for **part (a)**. Then they have $\frac{2}{9}$ and $\frac{3}{9}$ to compare for **part (b)**.

Key Concepts

CLOSURE QUESTION

Describe how to compare fractions by using a common denominator and by using decimals.

Sample Response: When using common denominators to compare fractions, write the fractions as equivalent fractions with the same denominator and compare the numerators. The fraction with the greater numerator is the greater fraction. When using decimals to compare fractions, convert each fraction to a decimal by dividing its numerator by its denominator. The fraction with the greater decimal value is the greater fraction.

ABSENT STUDENTS

For students who were absent for all or part of this section, the blackline Study Guide for Section 1 may be used to present the ideas, concepts, and skills of Section 1.

Key Terms

inequality

common denominator

least common denominator

24. Sample Responses:
   a. Use a common denominator; 15 is a multiple of 5, so I only have to rewrite one fraction.
   b. Use number sense; The denominators are the same, so the fraction with the greater numerator is greater.
   c. Use number sense; I would compare both fractions to $\frac{1}{2}$.

Section 1
Key Concepts

Inequality (pp. 284–285)
A statement that uses the symbol > or < to compare two numbers is an inequality.

Using Number Sense to Compare Fractions (pp. 285–286)
* See if the numerators or the denominators are the same.

Examples $\frac{1}{2} > \frac{1}{3}$, since the numerators are equal and 2 < 3.

$\frac{2}{5} < \frac{3}{5}$, since the denominators are equal and 2 < 3.

* See if one fraction is greater than $\frac{1}{2}$ and the other is less than $\frac{1}{2}$.

Example $\frac{3}{4} > \frac{1}{2}$ and $\frac{2}{9} < \frac{1}{2}$, so $\frac{3}{4} > \frac{2}{9}$.

* See if both fractions are one part less than a whole.

Example $\frac{7}{8} > \frac{6}{7}$, since $\frac{7}{8}$ is closer to a whole.

Using a Common Denominator to Compare Fractions (pp. 287–288)
You can write equivalent fractions to compare any two fractions.

Example $\frac{2}{3} > \frac{5}{8}$, since $\frac{16}{24} > \frac{15}{24}$.

> **24** is the least common denominator.

Using Decimals to Compare Fractions (pp. 288–289)
You can use decimals to compare any two fractions.

Example $\frac{3}{10} = 0.3$ and 4 ÷ 11 results in $\boxed{0.3636364}$,

so $\frac{3}{10} < \frac{4}{11}$.

---

24 **Key Concepts Question** What method would you use to compare each pair of fractions? Explain.

  a. $\frac{7}{15}$ and $\frac{3}{5}$ **b.** $\frac{6}{9}$ and $\frac{8}{9}$ **c.** $\frac{5}{13}$ and $\frac{12}{19}$

Section 1

Practice & Application Exercises

1. **Visual Thinking** Is the fraction strip folded into fifths? Explain.

No; The sections of the strip are not equal in length.

Write an inequality or equation that compares each fraction with $\frac{1}{2}$.

2. $\frac{5}{8}$ $\frac{5}{8} > \frac{1}{2}$

3. $\frac{2}{4}$ $\frac{2}{4} = \frac{1}{2}$

4. $\frac{2}{3}$ $\frac{2}{3} > \frac{1}{2}$

5. $\frac{5}{12}$ $\frac{5}{12} < \frac{1}{2}$

Write the fractions in order from least to greatest.

6. $\frac{5}{7}, \frac{5}{10}, \frac{5}{6}, \frac{5}{100}, \frac{5}{3}$ $\frac{5}{100}, \frac{5}{10}, \frac{5}{7}, \frac{5}{6}, \frac{5}{3}$

7. $\frac{9}{10}, \frac{99}{100}, \frac{2}{3}, \frac{49}{50}$ $\frac{2}{3}, \frac{9}{10}, \frac{49}{50}, \frac{99}{100}$

Mental Math Use number sense to compare the fractions. Replace each ? with >, <, or =.

8. $\frac{7}{15}$? $\frac{7}{12}$ $<$

9. $\frac{59}{60}$? $\frac{58}{59}$ $>$

10. $\frac{47}{100}$? $\frac{24}{36}$ $<$

11. $\frac{19}{20}$? $\frac{5}{6}$ $>$

12. $\frac{15}{22}$? $\frac{15}{23}$ $>$

13. $\frac{11}{18}$? $\frac{9}{20}$ $>$

14. **Algebra Connection** The inequality $x < \frac{3}{4}$ means that x represents any number less than $\frac{3}{4}$. Give two values for x that are fractions and that make the inequality a true statement. Sample Responses: $\frac{3}{5}, \frac{1}{2}$

15. **Writing** Kyra and Chloe each bought a pizza and ate half of it. Explain how it is possible that Kyra ate more pizza than Chloe did. Kyra's pizza was larger.

Use a common denominator to compare the fractions. Replace each ? with >, < or =.

16. $\frac{7}{12}$? $\frac{3}{4}$ $<$

17. $\frac{3}{5}$? $\frac{5}{8}$ $<$

18. $\frac{7}{20}$? $\frac{3}{8}$ $<$

19. $\frac{5}{6}$? $\frac{4}{7}$ $>$

20. $\frac{17}{30}$? $\frac{8}{15}$ $>$

21. $\frac{6}{12}$? $\frac{15}{30}$ $=$

Practice & Applications

SUGGESTED ASSIGNMENTS

Core Course
Day 1: Exs. 33–37
Day 2: Exs. 1–15
Day 3: Exs. 16–30, 32

Extended Course
Day 1: Exs. 33–37
Day 2: Exs. 1–15
Day 3: Exs. 18–32, 38–41*

Note: Extended Course assignments can be used to differentiate within the regular classroom. In classrooms where students are grouped homogeneously, the material might be covered in fewer days. In this case assignments may be combined.

*denotes Extension Exercises

ADDITIONAL PRACTICE
See the *Teacher's Resource Book* for additional practice and application exercises for this section.

EXERCISE NOTES
Exercise 15 Suggest that students think about comparing parts of the same whole. Remind students that the fractions strips they made were all the same length, so in comparing them they were comparing parts of the same whole. This may help students come up with the idea that the pizzas are different sizes.

EXERCISE NOTES

Exercise 30 You may want to point out that socket wrenches come in a range of sizes and that being able to use number sense to estimate which size you will need is a valuable and time-saving advantage. Many industrial mechanics have a highly developed number sense that they use frequently in their work.

28. Exercise 25; Both fractions are greater than $\frac{1}{2}$ and the denominators and numerators are messy, so a calculator would be better to compare. Exercise 26 can be done easily by comparing both fractions to $\frac{1}{2}$. Exercise 27 can be done by using a common denominator.

Use decimals to compare. Replace each ? with >, <, or =.

22. $\frac{93}{126}$? $\frac{321}{400}$ 23. $\frac{65}{121}$? $\frac{15}{29}$ 24. $\frac{225}{276}$? $\frac{24}{25}$
         <   >   <

Choosing a Method Use mental math, paper and pencil, or a calculator to compare the fractions. Replace each ? with >, <, or =.

25. $\frac{11}{17}$? $\frac{51}{82}$ 26. $\frac{45}{160}$? $\frac{101}{200}$ 27. $\frac{22}{25}$? $\frac{4}{5}$
       >   <   >

28. If you could use the calculator for only one comparison in Exercises 25–27, which one would it be? Why?

29. **Probability Connection** Trinja bought 50 of the 540 raffle tickets sold by a sports booster club. Nathan bought 42 of the 490 raffle tickets sold by another booster club. Who is more likely to win a prize? **Trinja**

30. **Industrial Technology** A mechanic needs a socket wrench to remove a bolt. A $\frac{1}{4}$-inch socket is too small. A $\frac{3}{8}$-inch socket is too large. Choose the letter of the size the mechanic should try next. Explain your choice. **C; $\frac{5}{16}$ is between $\frac{1}{4}$ and $\frac{3}{8}$.**

 A. $\frac{7}{32}$ in.   B. $\frac{13}{32}$ in.   C. $\frac{5}{16}$ in.   D. $\frac{3}{16}$ in.

31. **Challenge** The seven colored shapes shown are used in the Chinese tangram puzzle. Copies of the red triangle can be put together to form each of the other pieces.

a. Write a fraction that describes what part of the whole square each group of pieces represents. **Group A: $\frac{4}{16}$ or $\frac{1}{4}$; Group B: $\frac{5}{16}$; Group C: $\frac{7}{16}$**

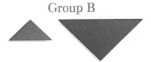

Group A   Group B

Group C

b. Which group represents the greatest fraction? **Group C**

c. Which group represents the least fraction? **Group A**

Reflecting ◀▶ on the Section

Write your response to Exercise 32 in your journal.

32. What types of fractions would you compare using each method? Give an example for each method. **See margin.**

- ◆ number sense
- ◆ a calculator
- ◆ a common denominator

Journal

Exercise 32 checks that you can choose an appropriate method to compare fractions.

Spiral ◀▶ Review

Write each fraction as a mixed number (Module 1, p. 47)

33. $\frac{11}{2}$ $5\frac{1}{2}$ 34. $\frac{27}{12}$ $2\frac{3}{12}$ 35. $\frac{31}{7}$ $4\frac{3}{7}$ 36. $\frac{13}{3}$ $4\frac{1}{3}$

37. Make a stem-and-leaf plot of these daily high temperatures in degrees Fahrenheit for a city in the Midwest during July. (Module 4, p. 256) **See margin.**

July Temperatures:

78, 82, 64, 61, 69, 56, 59, 77, 72, 78, 89, 87, 85, 91, 90, 84, 82, 68, 72, 78, 77, 98, 85, 87, 101, 80, 78, 82, 69, 71, 91

Extension ▶▶

Combining Inequalities

Two inequalities can be combined in one math statement. For example, $\frac{1}{25} < \frac{1}{20}$ and $\frac{1}{20} < \frac{1}{10}$ can be written as $\frac{1}{25} < \frac{1}{20} < \frac{1}{10}$. Find a fraction that can be used to replace each **?**.

Read as "$\frac{1}{25}$ is less than $\frac{1}{20}$ and $\frac{1}{20}$ is less than $\frac{1}{10}$."

38. $\frac{1}{4} < \underline{?} < \frac{1}{2}$ $\frac{3}{8}$

39. $\frac{3}{8} < \underline{?} < \frac{5}{8}$ $\frac{1}{2}$

40. $\frac{4}{7} < \underline{?} < \frac{3}{4}$ $\frac{2}{3}$

41. $\frac{3}{7} < \underline{?} < \frac{5}{6}$ $\frac{1}{2}$

EXERCISE NOTES

In **Extension Exercises 38–41** students may get the false impression that combined inequalities must be stated in terms of less than. The example can also be written as $\frac{1}{10} > \frac{1}{20} > \frac{1}{25}$ and read as "$\frac{1}{10}$ is greater than $\frac{1}{20}$ and $\frac{1}{20}$ is greater than $\frac{1}{25}$." The statement also implies that $\frac{1}{20}$ lies between $\frac{1}{10}$ and $\frac{1}{25}$ on a number line, therefore, the inequalities are never written with one greater than and one less than sign. Writing $\frac{1}{2} < \frac{3}{4} > \frac{1}{4}$ is incorrect since $\frac{3}{4}$ does not lie between $\frac{1}{2}$ and $\frac{1}{4}$ on a number line. In finding a fraction to complete each combined inequality, students should notice that they are finding a fraction that lies between the other two.

32. Sample Responses:

- **Number sense: fractions with the same numerator or denominator $\left(\frac{17}{53}\text{ and }\frac{13}{53}\right)$, fractions with numerators 1 less than the denominators $\left(\frac{97}{98}\text{ and }\frac{110}{111}\right)$, or fractions that can both be easily compared to $\frac{1}{2}\left(\frac{7}{18}\text{ and }\frac{16}{25}\right)$**

- **A calculator: fractions that don't fit into any of the number sense patterns and cannot be easily rewritten with a common denominator or as decimals $\left(\frac{78}{113}\text{ and }\frac{21}{35}\right)$**

- **A common denominator: fractions for which calculations involving common denominators are simple $\left(\frac{7}{12}\text{ and }\frac{13}{18}\right)$**

37. See Additional Answers beginning on page A1.

TEACHER NOTES
For each Exploration, the corresponding Extra Skill Practice Exercises are noted.

Exploration 1: Exs. 1–4
Exploration 2: Exs. 5–22

EXTRA HELP
Teacher's Resource Book
• Practice and Applications
• Study Guide

Technology Resources
• @Home Tutor
• Test Generator

ASSESSMENT
• Section 1 Quick Quiz
• Test Generator

Section 1

Extra Skill Practice

Compare the fractions. Replace each ? with >, <, or =.

1. $\dfrac{5}{6}$? $\dfrac{5}{8}$ >

2. $\dfrac{15}{16}$? $\dfrac{30}{32}$ =

3. $\dfrac{7}{12}$? $\dfrac{1}{4}$ >

4. $\dfrac{3}{8}$? $\dfrac{3}{14}$ >

Use a common denominator to compare the fractions. Replace each ? with >, <, or =.

5. $\dfrac{5}{8}$? $\dfrac{3}{10}$ >

6. $\dfrac{11}{8}$? $\dfrac{4}{9}$ >

7. $\dfrac{3}{5}$? $\dfrac{1}{3}$ >

8. $\dfrac{6}{7}$? $\dfrac{10}{11}$ <

Use decimals to compare the fractions. Replace each ? with >, <, or =.

9. $\dfrac{13}{51}$? $\dfrac{19}{40}$ <

10. $\dfrac{67}{92}$? $\dfrac{17}{23}$ <

11. $\dfrac{32}{73}$? $\dfrac{27}{65}$ >

12. $\dfrac{89}{117}$? $\dfrac{107}{205}$ >

13. $\dfrac{12}{133}$? $\dfrac{23}{197}$ <

14. $\dfrac{6}{35}$? $\dfrac{9}{75}$ >

Use mental math, paper and pencil, or a calculator to compare the fractions. Replace each ? with >, <, or =.

15. $\dfrac{5}{12}$? $\dfrac{1}{6}$ >

16. $\dfrac{19}{101}$? $\dfrac{71}{111}$ <

17. $\dfrac{19}{30}$? $\dfrac{3}{4}$ <

18. $\dfrac{1}{12}$? $\dfrac{1}{14}$ >

19. $\dfrac{25}{26}$? $\dfrac{33}{34}$ <

20. $\dfrac{2}{111}$? $\dfrac{4}{222}$ =

21. $\dfrac{1}{8}$? $\dfrac{2}{9}$ <

22. $\dfrac{3}{14}$? $\dfrac{1}{16}$ >

Study Skills ◀▶ **Reviewing for Assessment**

One way to review for assessment is to read or make a summary of what you have learned. The important ideas are summarized on the *Key Concepts* page at the end of the section.

1. Find the *Key Concepts* page for this section. If you want to know more about using a common denominator to compare fractions, what other pages can you turn to? Pages 287–288

Another way to review is to pair-share by sharing ideas with a partner before and after exploring a new topic.

2. Before you begin the next section, read the *Exploration* titles. Pair up and share with your partner everything you already know about the listed topics. Plan to get together with your partner to share what you have learned after you have completed the section. Check students' work.

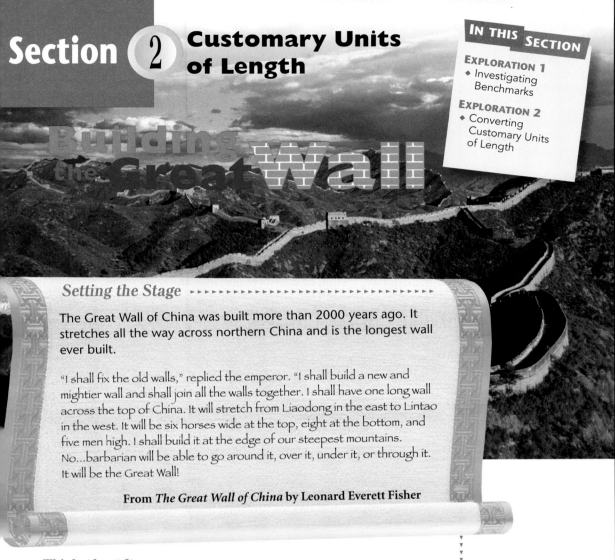

Section ② Customary Units of Length

Building the Great Wall

IN THIS SECTION

EXPLORATION 1
◆ Investigating Benchmarks

EXPLORATION 2
◆ Converting Customary Units of Length

Setting the Stage ▶▶▶▶▶▶▶▶▶▶▶▶▶▶▶▶▶▶▶▶▶▶▶▶▶

The Great Wall of China was built more than 2000 years ago. It stretches all the way across northern China and is the longest wall ever built.

"I shall fix the old walls," replied the emperor. "I shall build a new and mightier wall and shall join all the walls together. I shall have one long wall across the top of China. It will stretch from Liaodong in the east to Lintao in the west. It will be six horses wide at the top, eight at the bottom, and five men high. I shall build it at the edge of our steepest mountains. No...barbarian will be able to go around it, over it, under it, or through it. It will be the Great Wall!

From *The Great Wall of China* by Leonard Everett Fisher

Think About It

1 a. What unit of measure did the emperor use for the height of the Great Wall? Why do you think he chose this unit?

b. Estimate the height of the Great Wall in feet. Explain your reasoning. **Accept reasonable estimates; about 30 ft; I used a height of 6 ft for a man and multiplied by 5.**

2 a. The emperor used "horses" to describe the width of the Great Wall. In most places the Great Wall is about 24 ft wide at the bottom. Use this fact to find the measure of one "horse" in feet. **3 ft**

b. Do you think the emperor was using the length, the width, or the height of one horse as a unit of measure? Explain. **Sample Response: width; I think the length and height of most horses are more than 3 ft.**

Setting the Stage

GETTING STARTED

Module 5 Section 2 *Warm-Up* assesses whether students can determine which customary unit of length (inches, feet, yards, or miles) to use for estimating the lengths of various objects. This will get students thinking about the customary system of linear measurement and provide the teacher with feedback about students' familiarity with the units of measure before developing benchmarks and measuring with a ruler.

Before discussing **Questions 1 and 2**, students should read the excerpt either individually or in groups. Following the questions you may want to share with students that the Great Wall of China was first built for protection and to mark a northern boundary. The wall as we know it today is not a single wall, but a series of walls that have been rebuilt over the years.

1. a. men; Sample Response: I think he pictured the difficulty of men trying to climb over the wall, even climbing on each other's shoulders.

Exploration 1

CLASSROOM MANAGEMENT

Question 4(a) You may want to tell students ahead of time to bring in a box of their own items to use, or plan to have available a box of items from which they may choose. Suggested items include pencils, markers, crayons, notebook paper, chalk, erasers, milk or juice containers, coins, paper clips, a baseball bat, and a towel.

TEACHING NOTES

Question 3 Observing student discussion of this question may help you gain insight as to whether students have an understanding of the approximate lengths of an inch, a foot, and a yard. For a mile, you may want to state a distance from school that represents a mile. Make sure students have access to a ruler and yardstick when determining their benchmarks in **Question 4**.

Question 4(c) Students are not being asked to measure, but rather to use their benchmarks to estimate. Be sure students write down each estimate, since in **Question 9**, they will compare their estimates to the actual measures. You will want to measure and record the length of each object named in **Question 4(c)** in advance to help you quickly identify any students who measure incorrectly.

TIPS FROM TEACHERS

Display benchmark items on a table with the objects divided into three groups for 1-inch, 1-foot, and 1-yard benchmarks. Challenge students to add objects to each group of benchmarks as they work through this section.

GOAL

LEARN HOW TO...
- develop benchmarks for an inch, a foot, and a yard
- find fractional measures on a ruler

AS YOU...
- find the lengths of everyday objects

KEY TERMS
- inch (in.)
- foot (ft)
- yard (yd)
- mile (mi)

FOR HELP

with *benchmarks*, see

MODULE 4, p. 208

3. Sample Response:
   a. is a reasonable benchmark based on my measurements but b. and c. are both too short. However, I think that these measurements are probably reasonable benchmarks for many adults.

4. a. Sample responses are given. inch: a quarter; foot: a piece of uncooked spaghetti; yard: a full-size umbrella

   b. Sample responses are given. inches: a pencil; feet: width of a room; yards: a football field

---

Exploration 1

Investigating Benchmarks

SET UP You will need: • customary ruler • yardstick

▶ The Chinese emperor who built the Great Wall used a person's height to describe the height of the wall.

Our customary system of measurement uses the units **inch (in.)**, **foot (ft)**, **yard (yd)**, and **mile (mi)** to measure lengths. Some of these units were based on the lengths of parts of the body.

3 Which body lengths below make good benchmarks for the units listed? Which do not? Why?

  a. inch: distance from the tip of your thumb to your thumb's first joint

  b. foot: distance from your heel to the tip of your big toe

  c. yard: distance from your nose to your middle fingertip with your arm stretched out straight to the side

4 **a.** Find everyday objects that can be used as benchmarks for an inch, a foot, and a yard.

  b. Name an object that you would measure in each unit.

    ◆ inches   ◆ feet   ◆ yards

  c. Use your benchmarks to estimate each measurement. Answers will vary.

    ◆ the length of your textbook in inches

    ◆ the height of the classroom doorway in feet

    ◆ the length of your classroom in yards

▶ **Reading a Ruler** To get more accurate measurements of the objects in Question 4(c), you can use a ruler. It is important to understand the markings on a ruler so you can read it correctly.

5 **Try This as a Class** Use your ruler.

   a. Find the markings for inches, half-inches, quarter-inches, and eighth-inches. Explain how you found them.

   b. Find the marking for each measurement and give another name for it.

   ◆ $\frac{2}{8}$ in. $\frac{1}{4}$ in.   ◆ $\frac{2}{4}$ in. $\frac{1}{2}$ in.   ◆ $\frac{4}{8}$ in. $\frac{1}{2}$ in.   ◆ $\frac{4}{4}$ in. 1 in.

   c. Draw a segment that is $1\frac{7}{8}$ in. long. Is this segment closer to 2 in. or $1\frac{1}{2}$ in.? Check students' drawings; 2 inches

6 Find the length of the pencil shown on page 296 to the nearest given measure.

   a. $\frac{1}{2}$ in. $3\frac{1}{2}$ in.   b. $\frac{1}{4}$ in. $3\frac{2}{4}$ in.   c. $\frac{1}{8}$ in. $3\frac{5}{8}$ in.

7 **Discussion** Think about your answers to Question 6.
   Sample responses are given.

   a. When is measuring to the nearest $\frac{1}{8}$ in. better than measuring to the nearest $\frac{1}{4}$ in.? Why? when exactness is important, for example, when two things have to fit together

   b. No measurement, no matter how good, is ever exact. Why is this true? See margin.

▶ Sometimes it is helpful to write a measurement using a combination of units, such as feet and inches.

Unit Relationships
1 ft = 12 in.
1 yd = 3 ft = 36 in.
1 mi = 1760 yd = 5280 ft

8 A person who is 4 ft 10 in. tall is between 4 ft tall and 5 ft tall. Is the person's height closer to 4 ft or to 5 ft? 5 ft

9 ✔ **CHECKPOINT** Use a ruler or a yardstick.

   a. Measure each object: Answers will vary. length of textbook = $10\frac{1}{2}$ in.

   ◆ length of your textbook (to the nearest $\frac{1}{8}$ in.)

   ◆ height of the classroom doorway (in feet and inches)

   ◆ length of your classroom (in yards, feet, and inches)

   b. Are the estimates you gave in Question 4(c) close to the actual measurements you just found? Answers will vary.

5. a. Sample Response: The inch markings are indicated by whole numbers. All the markings are indicated by segments. The longest ones indicate inches. The next shorter ones indicate half inches and each divides an inch into two equal sections. The next shorter ones indicate quarter inches and each divides an inch into four equal sections. The next shorter ones indicate eighth inches and each divides an inch into eight equal sections.

✔ **QUESTION 9**

...checks that you can measure length in customary units.

TEACHING NOTES
Students may need some guidance about how to decide which is the nearest half, fourth, or eighth inch before beginning **Question 6**. Using the markings found in **Question 5(a)**, instruct students that if an object's length measures halfway or more to the next mark, then we round up to the next measure. If not, we round down to the closest measure. Point out that if an object being measured in half-inches is closer to 4 in. than $3\frac{1}{2}$ in., then 4 in. is the closest half inch measure. (Even though it is a whole number, 4 can be written as $\frac{8}{2}$.)

ALTERNATIVE APPROACH
For students having difficulty with reading a ruler, relate the inch mark to the fraction strips from Section 1. Explain that the divisions of an inch show different ways to divide the whole (in this case 1 whole inch). The marks are like the fold lines of the fraction strips. You may want to demonstrate by aligning the fraction strips for halves, fourths, and eighths underneath each other. You can then show that if there was only 1 mark at the fold on the halves strip, this would relate to a $\frac{1}{2}$ in. mark on a ruler. Repeat with fourths, showing that when the strip is divided into 4 sections, the marks at the folds relate to the $\frac{1}{4}, \frac{2}{4}, \frac{3}{4}$ and $\frac{4}{4}$ (or 1) inch marks on a ruler. Looking at the halves strip, they can see that the $\frac{2}{4}$ mark is the same as the $\frac{1}{2}$ mark. Repeat for eighths. Seeing this connection may also help students understand why the $\frac{1}{2}$ in. mark on a ruler is longer than $\frac{1}{4}$ in. mark and so on.

7. b. See Additional Answers beginning on page A1.

Students who finish the exploration early may enjoy estimating and then measuring other objects in the classroom. Suggestions include measuring the height of their desk, the length and width of a bulletin board, the width of the doorway, or the dimensions of a classroom window. Working in pairs, students might each write down an estimated length and then measure together to see whose estimate is closest to the actual length.

10 If you could measure the length of the Great Wall of China, what customary unit of length would you use? Why? **miles; Sample Response: The Great Wall stretches all the way across Northern China, so I would want to use the largest possible unit.**

HOMEWORK EXERCISES ▶ See Exs. 1–13 on pp. 302–303.

Exploration 2

GOAL

LEARN HOW TO...
♦ convert between customary units of length
♦ add and subtract lengths

AS YOU...
♦ explore the dimensions of various landmarks

Converting Customary UNITS of Length

SET UP *You will need Labsheet 2A.*

▶ The Chinese refer to the Great Wall as "The Wall of 10,000 *Li*." The *Li* is part of the Chinese measurement system. How long is 10,000 *Li*? To convert 10,000 *Li* to miles, you must first know that one *Li* is approximately one third of a mile.

11 **Try This as a Class**

    a. Do you expect the length of the Great Wall of China to be greater than or less than 10,000 miles? Explain.
       Sample: I expect it to be less since 1 *Li* is less than 1 mile.
    b. The steps below show one way to convert 10,000 *Li* to miles. Find the approximate length of The Wall of 10,000 *Li* in miles by completing the fraction multiplication from Step 2. $3{,}333\frac{1}{3}$ mi

      Step 1: $1\ Li = \frac{1}{3}$ mile

      Step 2: $10{,}000\ Li = 10{,}000 \cdot \frac{1}{3}$ miles

      Step 3: $10{,}000\ Li = ?$ miles

    c. Over the ages, the Great Wall of China was extended by new construction and by incorporating other walls. If stretched out, the eastern end is estimated to be about 27,000 *Li* in length. How many miles is this? **9,000 mi**

► Converting *Li* to our customary miles made it easier to understand the length of the Great Wall.

Sometimes customary units of measurement can be easier to understand if they are converted to a familiar unit of measurement.

Use Labsheet 2A with Questions 12–14.

12 a. Complete Part I of the labsheet.

  b. Why is 1 in. written as a fraction of a foot and a fraction of a yard?

13 a. The Great Wall of China is about 8 yd thick at the bottom. Which fact from the labsheet should you use to see how the thickness of the Great Wall of China compares to your height in feet? 1 yd = 3 ft

  b. Complete Part II of the labsheet to convert 8 yd to feet.
  1 yd = 3 ft; 8 · 1 yd = 8 · 3 ft; 8 yd = 24 ft
  c. The thickness of the Great Wall of China is about how many times your height?
  Answers will vary. Probably between 4 and 6 times

14 Ur was an ancient walled city in Southwest Asia. Its walls were over 1044 in. thick.

  a. 1044 in. may be hard to imagine. Which conversion fact could you use to convert inches to feet?

  b. Complete Part III of the labsheet to convert 1044 in. to feet.

  c. Suppose you and your classmates stand shoulder to shoulder across the top of one of the walls at Ur. About how many students are needed to reach from one side of the wall to the other?
  Sample Response: about 60 students
  d. How many yards thick were the city walls at Ur? How does this compare to the length of your classroom? 29 yd; Answers will vary.

15 ✔ **CHECKPOINT** Replace each ? with the number that makes the statement true.

  a. 3 yd = ? in.   **b.** 90 in. = ? yd   **c.** 3 mi = ? ft
       108                   $2\frac{1}{2}$ 15,840
  d. $\frac{1}{2}$ mi = ? yd   **e.** 16 ft = ? yd   **f.** 2 ft = ? in.
       880                   $5\frac{1}{3}$ 24

---

12. a. 1 ft = 12 in. and
    1 in. = $\frac{1}{12}$ ft
    1 yd = 3 ft and
    1 ft = $\frac{1}{3}$ yd
    1 yd = 36 in. and
    1 in. = $\frac{1}{36}$ yd
    1 mi = 1760 yd and
    1 yd = $\frac{1}{1760}$ mi
    1 mi = 5280 ft and
    1 ft = $\frac{1}{5280}$ mi

  b. Since an inch is shorter than a foot or a yard it can be written as a fraction of either of them. 12 in. make 1 ft and 36 in. make 1 yd.

The walls of Ur were destroyed by attackers in 2006 B.C. Shown here is a stairway on a stone tower, part of an ancient wall still standing in the city of Ninevah.

14. a. 1 in. = $\frac{1}{12}$ ft.

  b. 1 in. = $\frac{1}{12}$ ft;
    1044 · 1 in. =
    1044 · $\frac{1}{12}$ ft;
    1044 in. = 87 ft

✔ **QUESTION 15**

...checks that you can convert between customary units of measure.

Exploration 2

TEACHING NOTES
The following example can be presented to illustrate the process students should use to convert between measures in **Checkpoint Question 15**.

CLASSROOM EXAMPLES

a. Convert 4 ft to inches.

b. Convert 44 in. to feet.

Answer:

a. Write the conversion fact for changing 1 foot to inches:

   1 ft = 12 in.

   Multiply by 4, since you are converting 4 ft to inches.

   4 · 1 ft = 4 · 12 in.
   4 ft = 48 in.

b. Write the conversion fact for changing 1 inch to feet:

   1 in. = $\frac{1}{12}$ ft.

   Multiply by 44, since you are converting 44 in. to feet.

   44 · 1 in. = 44 · $\frac{1}{12}$ ft

   44 in. = $\frac{44}{12}$ ft

   = $3\frac{8}{12}$ ft

   = $3\frac{2}{3}$ ft

TEACHING NOTES
Suggest that students refer to the conversion facts on **Labsheet 2A** while working **Checkpoint Question 15**. You might also request that students show the three steps of converting each measure using Parts II and III of the labsheet as a guide on how to show their work.

TEACHING NOTES
Go through the **Example** with the class, asking questions throughout to check for understanding. Before students individually complete **Checkpoint Question 18**, you may wish to pose an additional problem such as

5 yd 1 ft
– 3 yd 2 ft

and have the class work together to solve it, explaining the steps and reasons. (*1 yd 2 ft*)

9 ft 8 in.

42 ft

99 ft 5 in.

▶ **Adding and Subtracting Measurements** You may need to convert between units when you add or subtract measurements.

16 **Discussion** To find the height of the Statue of Liberty from the base to the tip of the torch, a student added the measurements of its parts.

a. Is the height of the Statue of Liberty closer to 150 ft or 151 ft? Explain. **151 ft; 13 in. is longer than a foot, so the total height is over 151 ft.**

b. To simplify the measurement, the student wrote 150 ft 13 in. as 151 ft 1 in. What do you think *simplify* means in this case?

```
    9 ft  8 in.
    42 ft
+   99 ft  5 in.
   150 ft 13 in.
```

c. In other calculations the student wrote 10 yd 7 ft as 11 yd 4 ft. Why is this not simplified? **Only 3 ft are needed to make one yard, so 4 ft can be converted to 1 yd 1 ft, which makes it 12 yd 1 ft in simplified form.**

▶ When you subtract measurements, you may need to regroup first.

EXAMPLE

In order to subtract 9 in. from 5 in., you must regroup.

There are 12 in. in a foot.
5 in. + 12 in. = 17 in.

```
  3 ft 5 in.
– 2 ft 9 in.
```

Do not forget to decrease the number of feet!

```
   2  17
  3 ft 5 in.
– 2 ft 9 in.
       8 in.
```

16. b. Sample Response: to write the measurement so that all possible conversions from smaller units to larger units have been made

17 In a subtraction problem, a student correctly converted 4 yd 1 ft to 3 yd 4 ft. Why are these measurements equal? **4 yd 1 ft = 13 ft and 3 yd 4 ft = 13 ft**

18 ✔ **CHECKPOINT** Add or subtract. Simplify answers when possible.

a.
```
    8 in.
+  10 in.
  1 ft 6 in.
```

b.
```
   7 ft 8 in.
–  5 ft 9 in.
   1 ft 11 in.
```

c.
```
   6 mi 1280 yd
+  2 mi  927 yd
   9 mi  447 yd
```

d.
```
   4 yd 2 ft
+  2 yd 1 ft
   7 yd
```

e.
```
   6 yd
–  2 yd 2 ft
   3 yd 1 ft
```

f.
```
   5 mi  963 yd
–  2 mi 1258 yd
   2 mi 1465 yd
```

19 Suppose a wall similar to the Great Wall of China is to be built along highways from California to New York through the cities listed in the table.

  a. Find the total distance. Simplify if possible.
  2945 mi 1743 yd

  b. How does this distance compare with the number of miles in 10,000 *Li*?
  It is about 400 miles less.

From	To	Distance
San Francisco, CA	Salt Lake City, UT	735 mi 1672 yd
Salt Lake City, UT	Lincoln, NE	881 mi 475 yd
Lincoln, NE	Chicago, IL	524 mi 528 yd
Chicago, IL	Cleveland, OH	343 mi 546 yd
Cleveland, OH	New York City, NY	461 mi 282 yd

HOMEWORK EXERCISES ▶ See Exs. 14–33 on pp. 303–304.

Section 2

Key Concepts

Key Terms

Measuring Length in Customary Units (pp. 296–298)

Length can be measured in inches, feet, yards, or miles. You can use benchmarks to estimate lengths. To find more accurate measurements, you can use a ruler.

Example Measure the length of a paper clip.

To the nearest inch:

2 in.

To the nearest $\frac{1}{2}$ in.

$\frac{4}{2}$ in. or 2 in.

To the nearest $\frac{1}{4}$ in.

$1\frac{3}{4}$ in.

You can use combinations of units to write a measurement. For example, NBA All-Star basketball player Shaquille O'Neal is 7 ft 1 in. tall.

inches (in.)

feet (ft)

yards (yd)

miles (mi)

20 Key Concepts Question An object is $5\frac{3}{8}$ in. long. What is its length to the nearest inch? $\frac{1}{2}$ in.? $\frac{1}{4}$ in.? **5 in., $5\frac{1}{2}$ in., $5\frac{2}{4}$ in.**

TEACHING NOTES

To help students conceptualize the distances, you may want to display a map of the United States along with **Question 19**. Discuss the scale on the map and then highlight the identified cities along the route from San Francisco to New York City. For **part (b)** show a world map comparing the United States to China so students can get an idea of the enormity of the Great Wall. (The two countries have close to the same area, approximately 9.6 million square kilometers.) Remind students that the Great Wall curves and bends to follow certain contours of the geography of the land not represented by a flat non-contour map.

Key Concepts

ABSENT STUDENTS

For students who were absent for all or part of this section, the blackline Study Guide for Section 2 may be used to present the ideas, concepts, and skills of Section 2.

CLOSURE QUESTION

How is the conversion of customary units of length used in adding and subtracting lengths that are measured in different units?

Sample Response: When adding and subtracting lengths measured in one or more customary units, you may need to regroup, or convert from one measurement to another.

Practice & Applications

SUGGESTED ASSIGNMENTS

Core Course
Day 1: Exs. 1–13
Day 2: Exs. 14–23, 34–37
Day 3: Exs. 24–31, 33

Extended Course
Day 1: Exs. 1–13
Day 2: Exs. 14–23, 34–37
Day 3: Exs. 24–33, 38*

Note: Extended Course assignments can be used to differentiate within the regular classroom. In classrooms where students are grouped homogeneously, the material might be covered in fewer days. In this case assignments may be combined.

*denotes Extension Exercises

ADDITIONAL PRACTICE

See the *Teacher's Resource Book* for additional practice and application exercises for this section.

302

Section 2
Key Concepts

Converting Customary Units of Length (pp. 298–299)

To convert between customary units of length you first need to choose an appropriate relationship.

$$1 \text{ ft} = 12 \text{ in.} = \frac{1}{3} \text{ yd} = \frac{1}{5280} \text{ mi} \qquad 1 \text{ in.} = \frac{1}{12} \text{ ft} = \frac{1}{36} \text{ yd}$$

$$1 \text{ yd} = 3 \text{ ft} = 36 \text{ in.} = \frac{1}{1760} \text{ mi} \qquad 1 \text{ mi} = 1760 \text{ yd} = 5280 \text{ ft}$$

Then you can multiply by the conversion fact to convert one customary unit to another.

Adding and Subtracting Lengths in Customary Units (pp. 300–301)

You may need to convert between units when adding or subtracting measurements. You may need to regroup first when subtracting measurements.

Example

$$\begin{array}{r} 2 \text{ ft } 10 \text{ in.} \\ - 1 \text{ ft } 11 \text{ in.} \\ \hline \end{array} \qquad \begin{array}{r} \overset{1}{\cancel{2}} \text{ ft } \overset{22}{\cancel{10}} \text{ in.} \\ - 1 \text{ ft } 11 \text{ in.} \\ \hline 11 \text{ in.} \end{array}$$

21 **Key Concepts Question** Your windows are 72 in. long. To make curtains, you need fabric the length of the window plus 9 in. How many yards of fabric do you need? $2\frac{1}{4}$ yd

Section 2
Practice & Application Exercises

YOU WILL NEED

For Exs. 4, 33:
◆ customary ruler or tape measure

In Exercises 1–3 use a benchmark to estimate the measurement.
Sample responses are given for Exercises 1–3 and 5–8.

1. length of your pencil, to the nearest inch about 6 in.

2. height of the room you sleep in, to the nearest yard about 3 yd

3. distance from your shoulder to the tip of your middle finger with your arm outstretched, to the nearest foot about 2 ft

4. Use a ruler or a tape measure to find the actual measurement in Exercises 1–3. Were your estimates close to the actual measurements? Answers will vary.

Name an object that has a length close to each measurement.

5. 8 in.   **6.** 4 ft   **7.** 15 ft   **8.** 25 yd

For each situation in Exercises 9–11, name an appropriate customary unit for measuring.

9. checking that the height of a basketball hoop meets NBA regulations feet

10. finding the length of a route when planning a car trip miles

11. deciding on the right size paper for a loose leaf binder inches

12. Social Studies The cubit was a unit of length used in ancient Egypt. Answers will vary.

   a. Use inches to measure your cubit.

   b. The standard Egyptian cubit was about 18 in. long. Is this *longer* or *shorter* than your cubit?

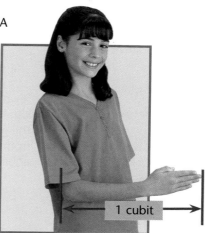

1 cubit

13. What is the length of the bandage to the nearest measure?

  a. $\frac{1}{2}$ in. $1\frac{1}{2}$ in.   **b.** $\frac{1}{4}$ in. $1\frac{2}{4}$ in.   **c.** $\frac{1}{8}$ in. $1\frac{3}{8}$ in.

Replace each _?_ with the number that makes the statement true.

14. 6 yd = _?_ ft   **15.** $5\frac{1}{2}$ yd = _?_ in.   **16.** 12,320 yd = _?_ mi

17. 54 in. = _?_ ft   **18.** 11 ft = _?_ yd   **19.** $8\frac{1}{4}$ ft = _?_ in.

Write each measurement as a fraction of a yard.

20. 15 in.   **21.** 2 ft   **22.** 5 ft   **23.** 1 ft 6 in.
$\frac{15}{36}$ or $\frac{5}{12}$ yd $\frac{2}{3}$ yd $\frac{5}{3}$ yd or $1\frac{2}{3}$ yd $\frac{18}{36}$ yd or $\frac{1}{2}$ yd

---

5. an unsharpened pencil

6. the length of my dog

7. the length of my living room

8. the height of my apartment building

14. 18

15. 198

16. 7

17. $4\frac{1}{2}$

18. $3\frac{2}{3}$

19. 99

EXERCISE NOTES
Exercises 5–8 Have students share and compare objects chosen for each measurement. If they feel an object chosen is not reasonable for a given measurement, have them explain why.

Practice & Applications

EXERCISE NOTES

Exercise 33 Help students make accurate measurements. Students should take several steps in order to establish a natural stride.

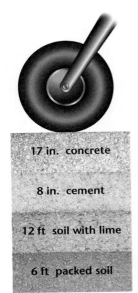

17 in.	concrete
8 in.	cement
12 ft	soil with lime
6 ft	packed soil

(not drawn to scale)

24. **Writing** Four students' measurements of a table's length are 66 in., $5\frac{1}{2}$ ft, 5 ft 6 in., and 1 yd 2 ft 6 in. Explain how they can all be correct.
   The four measurements are all equivalent. They are all equal to 66 in.

25. **Airport Runways** The diagram at the left shows the runway layers at the Denver International Airport. Find the total thickness of the runway in a combination of yards, feet, and inches.
   6 yd 2 ft 1 in.

Find each sum or difference. Simplify answers when possible.

26.   3 yd 2 ft
       + 7 yd 1 ft
         11 yd

27.   1382 yd
       + 1576 yd
       1 mi 1198 yd

28.   3 yd 1 ft
       − 2 yd 2 ft
         2 ft

29.   8 ft   9 in.
      − 3 ft 11 in.
     1 yd 1 ft 10 in.

30.   6 ft 9 in.
      + 3 ft 5 in.
     3 yd 1 ft 2 in.

31.   9 yd
     − 1 yd 2 ft
      7 yd 1 ft

32. **Challenge** For the ship shown to pass through the locks safely, the gate between Locks 1 and 2 must be opened so water flows from Lock 1 to Lock 2. When the water levels in the two locks are equal, how much has the water level in Lock 1 dropped? $5\frac{1}{2}$ ft

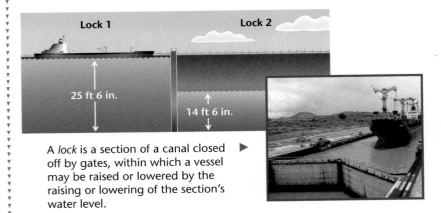

A *lock* is a section of a canal closed off by gates, within which a vessel may be raised or lowered by the raising or lowering of the section's water level.

RESEARCH

Exercise 33 checks that you understand how to use benchmarks.

Reflecting ◀▶ on the Section

33. a. Measure the length of your stride in inches. Measure from the heel of one foot to the heel of the other foot.
   Answers will vary. Check students' work.
   b. Use your stride length from part (a) as a benchmark. Estimate the number of steps it would take you to walk 3,784,000 yd (one estimate of the length of the Great Wall of China).
   Answers will vary. Check students' work.

Replace each _?_ with >, <, or =. (Module 5, p. 290)

34. $\dfrac{2}{5}$ _?_ $\dfrac{7}{15}$ <u><</u>

35. $\dfrac{1}{6}$ _?_ $\dfrac{3}{8}$ <u><</u>

36. $\dfrac{5}{7}$ _?_ $\dfrac{9}{13}$ <u>></u>

37. In how many different ways can you make change for a half-dollar coin using only nickels, dimes, and quarters? (Module 1, p. 33)

37. 10 ways. (2 quarters; 1 quarter 2 dimes 1 nickel; 1 quarter 1 dime 3 nickels; 1 quarter 5 nickels; 5 dimes; 4 dimes 2 nickels; 3 dimes 4 nickels; 2 dimes 6 nickels; 1 dime 8 nickels; 10 nickels)

Extension ▶ ▶

Writing Measurements in Mixed Units

Sometimes when measuring it is helpful to have a measurement such as $1\dfrac{3}{4}$ yd in a combination of yards, feet, and inches.

Example:

Convert $1\dfrac{3}{4}$ yd to yards, feet, and inches.

First, convert $\dfrac{3}{4}$ yd to feet:

$$1 \text{ yd} = 3 \text{ ft}$$

$$\dfrac{3}{4} \cdot 1 \text{ yd} = \dfrac{3}{4} \cdot 3 \text{ ft}$$

$$\dfrac{3}{4} \text{ yd} = \dfrac{9}{4} \text{ or } 2\dfrac{1}{4} \text{ ft}$$

Next, convert any fraction of a foot to inches:

$$1 \text{ ft} = 12 \text{ in.}$$

$$\dfrac{1}{4} \cdot 1 \text{ ft} = \dfrac{1}{4} \cdot 12 \text{ in.}$$

$$\dfrac{1}{4} \text{ ft} = 3 \text{ in.}$$

So, $1\dfrac{3}{4}$ yd = **1 yd 2 ft 3 in.**

38. Convert each of the following lengths into the mixed units given.

a. $2\dfrac{1}{3}$ yd = _?_ yd _?_ ft 2 yd 1 ft

b. $1\dfrac{2}{3}$ ft = _?_ ft _?_ in. 1 ft 8 in.

c. 14 ft = _?_ yd _?_ ft 4 yd 2 ft

Section ② Extra Skill Practice

You will need: • *customary ruler* (Exs. 1–4)

Measure the length of the needle as directed.

1. to the nearest inch 2 in.

2. to the nearest $\frac{1}{2}$ in. $1\frac{1}{2}$ in.

3. to the nearest $\frac{1}{4}$ in. $1\frac{3}{4}$ in.

4. to the nearest $\frac{1}{8}$ in. $1\frac{5}{8}$ in.

Replace each ? with the number that makes the statement true.

5. $2\frac{1}{4}$ ft = _?_ in. 27

6. $3\frac{1}{10}$ mi = _?_ yd 5456

7. $12\frac{1}{2}$ ft = _?_ yd $4\frac{1}{6}$

8. 3900 ft = _?_ mi $\frac{65}{88}$

9. 18 in. = _?_ yd $\frac{1}{2}$

10. 42 in. = _?_ ft $3\frac{1}{2}$

11. $3\frac{3}{4}$ yd = _?_ ft $11\frac{1}{4}$

12. 3080 yd = _?_ mi $1\frac{3}{4}$

13. 5 yd = _?_ in. 180

14. 4 mi = _?_ ft 21,120

15. 8 in. = _?_ ft $\frac{2}{3}$

16. 46 in. = _?_ yd $1\frac{5}{18}$

Find each sum or difference. Simplify answers when possible.

17.   6 ft 3 in.
  + 10 ft 4 in.
   5 yd 1 ft 7 in.

18.   3 yd 4 ft
  +   12 ft
   8 yd 1 ft

19.   8 yd 1 ft
  – 7 yd 2 ft
   2 ft

20.   9 ft 8 in.
  + 2 ft 4 in.
   4 yd

21.   13 yd 2 ft
  –   6 ft
   11 yd 2 ft

22.   11 yd
  – 1 yd 2 ft
   9 yd 1 ft

23.   1122 yd
  + 709 yd
   1 mi 71 yd

24.   6 ft 1 in.
  – 5 ft 9 in.
   4 in.

25.   4 ft 9 in.
  +   16 in.
   2 yd 1 in.

Standardized Testing ◀▶Performance Task

You are given three strips of paper. One is 2 ft 9 in. long, the second is 3 ft 4 in. long, and the third is 3 ft 2 in. long. Without cutting the strips, describe how to attach the three strips of paper together to create a single strip exactly 3 yd long.

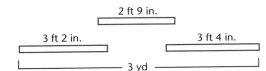

2 ft 9 in.

3 ft 2 in.   3 ft 4 in.

3 yd

Sample Response: To measure 1 in., place the longest strip on top of the midsize strip with the left ends meeting. Mark the right end of the midsize strip on the longest strip. The mark will be 2 in. from the end. Fold the 2 in. strip in half. You now have a 1 in. measure. You can use it to mark off a 3 in. piece or any combination that adds to 3 in. to overlap the strips. The total length will be 3 ft 2 in. + 2 ft 9 in. + 3 ft 4 in. – 3 in. = 3 yd.

Section ③ Addition and Subtraction of Fractions

IN THIS SECTION

EXPLORATION 1
♦ Adding and Subtracting Fractions

Flex This!

Setting the Stage ▷▷▷▷▷▷▷▷▷▷▷▷▷▷▷▷▷▷▷▷▷▷▷▷▷▷▷▷

SET UP *You will need: • Labsheet 3A • scissors • tape*

Have you ever played around with a scrap of paper or a gum wrapper, folding it into different shapes before throwing it away? Well that's exactly what Arthur H. Stone did in 1939 with the strips he cut from American-size paper that was too big for his British-size folder. But not all of Arthur's folded strips ended up in the trash. The ones he kept became known as *flexagons*. In fact, the hexagon you folded in Section 1 was Arthur's first flexagon.

After showing his creations to some friends, Arthur soon had others making and discovering new flexagons. The pictures below show how to work a flexagon called a *tetra-tetraflexagon*.

> A *flexagon* is a polygon made from paper, which when folded can reveal hidden surfaces.

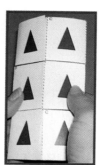

Follow the directions on Labsheet 3A to make a tetra-tetraflexagon.

Think About It

1 The tetra-tetraflexagon you made has 24 shapes on it. When the flexagon is open flat, what fraction of the shapes appear

a. facing you?
$\frac{6}{24}$ or $\frac{1}{4}$

b. on the back side?
$\frac{6}{24}$ or $\frac{1}{4}$

c. hidden inside?
$\frac{12}{24}$ or $\frac{1}{2}$

Setting the Stage

GETTING STARTED
Module 5 Section 3 *Warm-Up* assesses students' ability to find the least common denominator (LCD) of a set of fractions. The LCD was used in Section 1 for comparing fractions and will be used in this section as part of the algorithm for adding and subtracting fractions with unlike denominators.

TEACHING NOTES
When the flexagon is folded as shown in the diagram, students will see the circles, triangles, and hexagons before having to reverse folding directions. The rectangles do not appear facing up, but are on the opposing side when the hexagons are face up.

Exploration 1

TEACHING NOTES

Question 3 should be completed as a class so students can discuss the procedure for adding fractions with the same denominator before moving on to problems where denominators are different. Be sure students understand why in addition of fractions, the denominators are not added together like the numerators. *(Since the denominator of a fraction tells how many equal-sized pieces the whole is divided into and the numerator tells how many of these pieces there are, the denominator is a unit of measure, and when you add measurements, you do not add the unit of measure. For example, when adding 2¢ and 3¢, the unit of measure is cents and 2¢ + 3¢ = 5¢.*

Similarly, $2¢ + 3¢ = \frac{2}{100} + \frac{3}{100}$ where the unit of measure is $\frac{1}{100}$ of a whole (a dollar) and $\frac{2}{100} + \frac{3}{100} = \frac{5}{100}$, not $\frac{5}{200}$.

Once students have learned to multiply fractions, this can also be demonstrated using the distributive property:

$$\frac{2}{100} + \frac{3}{100} = 2 \cdot \frac{1}{100} + 3 \cdot \frac{1}{100}$$
$$= (2 + 3) \cdot \frac{1}{100}$$
$$= 5 \cdot \frac{1}{100}$$
$$= \frac{5}{100}.)$$

Exploration 1

Adding and Subtracting Fractions

SET UP *You will need your fraction strips from Section 1.*

▶ Arthur Stone's first flexagon designs were made from tiny strips of paper. Variations of the flexagon you made in the *Setting the Stage* are shown here. You can find the widths of these flexagons by adding the widths of the columns.

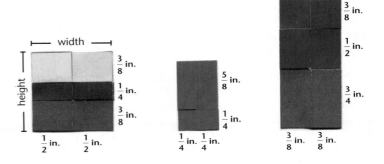

2 Use your fraction strips to find the sum. Each sum represents the width of one of the flexagons above.

a. $\frac{1}{2} + \frac{1}{2}$ 1

b. $\frac{1}{4} + \frac{1}{4}$ $\frac{2}{4}$ or $\frac{1}{2}$

c. $\frac{3}{8} + \frac{3}{8}$ $\frac{6}{8}$ or $\frac{3}{4}$

3 Discussion

a. How can you add fractions with the same denominator without using fraction strips?
Add the numerators and write the sum over the common denominator.

b. Show that you get the same answer for $\frac{5}{12} + \frac{2}{12}$ using your method from part (a) or using strips.
$\frac{7}{12}$

▶ To find the height of each flexagon, you need to add fractions with different denominators.

EXAMPLE

Find the sum $\frac{5}{8} + \frac{1}{4}$ using fraction strips.

First Fold an eighths strip to show $\frac{5}{8}$ and a fourths strip to show $\frac{1}{4}$. Place the folded strips end to end.

$\frac{5}{8}$					$\frac{1}{4}$
$\frac{1}{8}$	$\frac{1}{8}$	$\frac{1}{8}$	$\frac{1}{8}$	$\frac{1}{8}$	$\frac{1}{4}$

Then Fold another eighths strip to match the length of the sum.

$\frac{1}{8}$	$\frac{1}{8}$	$\frac{1}{8}$	$\frac{1}{8}$	$\frac{1}{8}$	$\frac{1}{8}$	$\frac{1}{8}$

$\frac{7}{8}$

$$\frac{5}{8} + \frac{1}{4} = \frac{7}{8}$$

4 Try This as a Class

a. In the Example, to find the sum of $\frac{5}{8}$ and $\frac{1}{4}$, a strip of eighths was used. How many eighths matched the length of $\frac{1}{4}$?

b. If you had a sixteenths strip, could you use it to find $\frac{5}{8} + \frac{1}{4}$? Explain your answer.

c. Could you use a twelfths strip to find $\frac{5}{8} + \frac{1}{4}$? Explain.

5 Which fraction strip(s) can you use to find each sum?

a. $\frac{1}{2} + \frac{3}{4}$ fourths or eighths

b. $\frac{1}{12} + \frac{5}{6}$ twelfths

c. $\frac{2}{6} + \frac{1}{4}$ twelfths

d. $\frac{2}{3} + \frac{1}{4}$ twelfths

6 a. Rewrite each expression in Question 5 so that the fractions have common denominators.

b. Now find each sum. Write each answer in lowest terms.

7 Joan needs to rename two fractions to find their sum. She organized her work like this. Copy and complete her work. $\frac{3}{5} = \frac{18}{30}$; The sum is $\frac{23}{30}$.

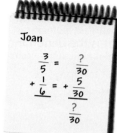

Joan

$$\frac{3}{5} = \frac{?}{30}$$
$$+ \frac{1}{6} = + \frac{5}{30}$$
$$\frac{?}{30}$$

---

4. a. 2 eighths

   b. Yes, 16 is a multiple of 8 and 4. $\frac{5}{8} = \frac{10}{16}$; $\frac{1}{4} = \frac{4}{16}$, so each fraction can be written in equivalent sixteenths.

   c. No, 12 is not a common multiple of 8 and 4.

6. a. $\frac{2}{4} + \frac{3}{4}$; $\frac{1}{12} + \frac{10}{12}$; $\frac{4}{12} + \frac{3}{12}$; $\frac{8}{12} + \frac{3}{12}$

   b. $\frac{5}{4}$ or $1\frac{1}{4}$; $\frac{11}{12}$; $\frac{7}{12}$; $\frac{11}{12}$

DIFFERENTIATED INSTRUCTION

Writing equivalent fractions with common denominators was one of the techniques used to compare fractions in Section 1. However, there may still be students whose conceptual understanding and comfort level supports the continued use of fraction strips to find the denominators in **Question 6**. Students should be comfortable with the use of fraction strips to add fractions before moving on to paper-and-pencil algorithms.

TEACHING NOTES

The following Classroom Example provides another illustration of how fraction strips can be used to add fractions with unlike denominators.

CLASSROOM EXAMPLE

Find the sum $\frac{2}{3} + \frac{1}{9}$ using fraction strips.

Answer: First: Fold a thirds strip to show $\frac{2}{3}$ and a ninths strip to show $\frac{1}{9}$. Place the folded strips end to end.

Then: Fold another ninths strip to match the length of the sum.

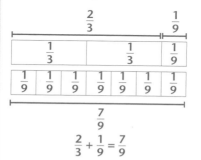

$$\frac{2}{3} + \frac{1}{9} = \frac{7}{9}$$

Exploration 1 *continued*

TEACHING NOTES

To answer **Question 10**, students should use the example under **Subtracting Fractions** that shows the result of subtracting $\frac{1}{4}$ from $\frac{3}{4}$.

You may decide to offer a few other subtraction problems (with common denominators) for students to study. They should make the connection that the same principles applied to adding fractions can be used in subtracting fractions.

✔ **QUESTION 8**

...checks that you can add fractions.

8 ✔ **CHECKPOINT** Find each sum. Write each answer in lowest terms.

a. $\frac{1}{10} + \frac{7}{10}$ $\frac{4}{5}$

b. $\frac{2}{9} + \frac{2}{3}$ $\frac{8}{9}$

c. $\frac{2}{3} + \frac{6}{7}$ $\frac{32}{21}$ or $1\frac{11}{21}$

d. $\frac{5}{8} + \frac{1}{12}$ $\frac{17}{24}$

9 To find the width of each flexagon on page 308, you added the column widths. Look back to page 308 for the measurements of each flexagon. Find the height of each flexagon by adding the heights of the rows.   1 in.; $\frac{7}{8}$ in.; $1\frac{5}{8}$ in.

▶ **Subtracting Fractions** To create a variation of the tetra-tetraflexagon, you can trim the top or bottom rows. Suppose the bottom row's height is $\frac{3}{4}$ in.

You trim $\frac{1}{4}$ in. from the bottom. To find the height of the row after cutting off $\frac{1}{4}$ in., you can subtract:

$$\frac{3}{4} - \frac{1}{4} = \frac{2}{4}.$$

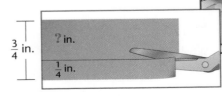

$\frac{3}{4}$ in.   ? in. $\frac{1}{4}$ in.

10 **Discussion** You subtract two fractions that have the same denominator.

    a. How do you find the numerator of the difference?
       subtract the numerators of the two fractions
    b. What is the denominator of the difference?
       the common denominator of the fractions

▶ Suppose a flexagon has a row $\frac{5}{6}$ in. high, and you trim $\frac{1}{4}$ in. from it. You can find the new height of the row by subtracting. Fraction strips can help you think about how to subtract fractions with different denominators.

EXAMPLE

Find the difference $\frac{5}{6} - \frac{1}{4}$ using fraction strips.

First Fold sixths and fourths strips to show $\frac{5}{6}$ and $\frac{1}{4}$. Place the shorter strip over the longer one. Align the strips on the right.

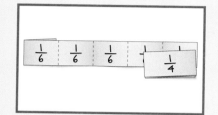

Then Fold another strip to match the length of the part of the $\frac{5}{6}$ strip that is not covered. This part is the difference between $\frac{5}{6}$ and $\frac{1}{4}$.

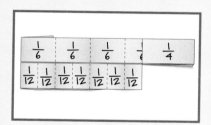

$$\frac{5}{6} - \frac{1}{4} = \frac{7}{12}$$

11 How can you subtract $\frac{1}{4}$ from $\frac{5}{6}$ without using fraction strips?

12 ✔ **CHECKPOINT** Use a common denominator to find each difference. Write each answer in lowest terms.

a. $\frac{5}{6} - \frac{7}{10}$ $\frac{2}{15}$

b. $\frac{2}{3} - \frac{1}{2}$ $\frac{1}{6}$

c. $\frac{4}{7} - \frac{3}{14}$ $\frac{5}{14}$

HOMEWORK EXERCISES ▶ See Exs. 1–19 on pp. 313–314.

11. Rewrite the fractions as equivalent fractions with a common denominator. Then subtract the numerators and write the difference over the common denominator.

✔ **QUESTION 12**

...checks that you can subtract fractions.

TEACHING NOTES
When discussing the **Example**, you may want to have students experiment with their fraction strips to determine why a twelfths strip was used.

If needed, the following Classroom Example illustrating the use of fraction strips to subtract fractions with unlike denominators can be presented before students attempt **Question 11**.

CLASSROOM EXAMPLE

Find the difference $\frac{3}{5} - \frac{1}{2}$ using fraction strips.

Answer: First: Fold a fifths strip to show $\frac{3}{5}$ and a halves strip to show $\frac{1}{2}$. Place the shorter strip over the longer one. Align the strips on the right.

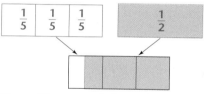

Then: The part of the strip modeling $\frac{3}{5}$ that is not covered represents the difference between $\frac{3}{5}$ and $\frac{1}{2}$. Since the least common denominator of the fractions is 10, fold a tenths strip to match the length of this uncovered portion.

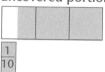

$$\frac{3}{5} - \frac{1}{2} = \frac{1}{10}$$

Key Concepts

CLOSURE QUESTION

Describe the steps involved in adding and subtracting fractions.

Sample Response: To add fractions, first write them with a common denominator, then add the numerators and write the sum over the common denominator. Rewrite the fraction in lowest terms if necessary. To subtract fractions, follow the same steps you use for adding fractions except subtract the numerators and write the difference over the common denominator.

ABSENT STUDENTS

For students who were absent for all or part of this section, the blackline Study Guide for Section 3 may be used to present the ideas, concepts, and skills of Section 3.

Section 3
Key Concepts

Adding Fractions (pp. 308–310)

To add fractions
- first write the fractions with a common denominator,
- next add the numerators,
- then write the sum of the numerators over the common denominator.

Example

Find $\frac{3}{8} + \frac{1}{3}$.

$\frac{9}{24} + \frac{8}{24} = \frac{9+8}{24} = \frac{17}{24}$

Add the numerators. $9 + 8 = 17$

You can use **24** as a common denominator.

Subtracting Fractions (pp. 310–311)

To subtract fractions
- first write the fractions with a common denominator,
- next subtract the numerators,
- then write the difference of the numerators over the common denominator.

Example

Find $\frac{2}{3} - \frac{1}{2}$.

$\frac{4}{6} - \frac{3}{6} = \frac{4-3}{6} = \frac{1}{6}$

Subtract the numerators $4 - 3 = 1$

You can use 6 as a common denominator.

Key Concepts Questions

14. a. Rewrite $\frac{3}{7}$ as $\frac{9}{21}$ and $\frac{1}{3}$ as $\frac{7}{21}$.

Then subtract 7 from 9 and write the difference over 21.

13 Find each sum. Write each answer in lowest terms.

a. $\frac{3}{20} + \frac{7}{10}$ $\frac{17}{20}$ b. $\frac{6}{11} + \frac{5}{44}$ $\frac{29}{44}$ c. $\frac{1}{15} + \frac{6}{20}$ $\frac{11}{30}$ d. $\frac{3}{4} + \frac{4}{7}$ $\frac{37}{28}$ or $1\frac{9}{28}$

14 a. Explain the steps you would take to subtract $\frac{1}{3}$ from $\frac{3}{7}$.

b. Use your steps from part (a) to find $\frac{3}{7} - \frac{1}{3}$. $\frac{2}{21}$

Practice & Application Exercises

Find each sum. Write each answer in lowest terms.

1. $\frac{1}{3}+\frac{4}{9}$ $\frac{7}{9}$

2. $\frac{3}{10}+\frac{3}{5}$ $\frac{9}{10}$

3. $\frac{1}{4}+\frac{4}{5}$ $\frac{21}{20}=1\frac{1}{20}$

4. $\frac{5}{6}+\frac{3}{10}$ $\frac{17}{15}=1\frac{2}{15}$

5. $\frac{4}{9}+\frac{2}{9}+\frac{1}{9}$ $\frac{7}{9}$

6. $\frac{1}{2}+\frac{1}{4}+\frac{3}{8}$ $\frac{9}{8}=1\frac{1}{8}$

Find each difference. Write each answer in lowest terms.

7. $\frac{6}{7}-\frac{2}{7}$ $\frac{4}{7}$

8. $\frac{5}{6}-\frac{1}{6}$ $\frac{2}{3}$

9. $\frac{3}{4}-\frac{5}{8}$ $\frac{1}{8}$

10. $\frac{2}{3}-\frac{1}{6}$ $\frac{1}{2}$

11. $\frac{5}{9}-\frac{2}{5}$ $\frac{7}{45}$

12. $\frac{7}{12}-\frac{1}{10}$ $\frac{29}{60}$

13. **Algebra Connection** Evaluate each expression when $n=\frac{5}{8}$. Write each answer in lowest terms.

   a. $n+\frac{7}{8}$ $\frac{3}{2}$ or $1\frac{1}{2}$

   b. $\frac{15}{16}-n$ $\frac{5}{16}$

   c. $\frac{1}{2}+n-\frac{2}{3}$ $\frac{11}{24}$

Displaying Data The circle graph shows the approximate results of a survey about the ages of Internet users.

14. a. About what fraction of Internet users were over 17 years old? about $\frac{4}{5}$

   b. A circle graph shows the division of a whole into parts. Write a fraction for the part that is labeled 3–17. about $\frac{1}{5}$

   c. What does the fraction you wrote in part (b) tell you about the Internet users surveyed?

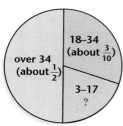

Ages of Internet Users (October 2003)

18–34 (about $\frac{3}{10}$)

over 34 (about $\frac{1}{2}$)

3–17 ?

15. **Solving Equations** In Module 4 you learned to solve one-step equations with whole numbers and decimals. These same steps can be used in solving one-step equations with fractions.

   a. Explain the steps you should use to solve the equation $n+\frac{1}{3}=\frac{5}{7}$.

   b. Solve the equation in part (a). $\frac{8}{21}$

14. c. In October 2003 only about a fifth of the users of the Internet were between the ages of 3 and 17.

15. a. Subtract $\frac{1}{3}$ from each side of the equation. To do this you would need to rewrite $\frac{1}{3}$ as $\frac{7}{21}$ and $\frac{5}{7}$ as $\frac{15}{21}$.

Practice & Applications

SUGGESTED ASSIGNMENTS

Core Course
Day 1: Exs. 1–6, 20–26
Day 2: Exs. 7–16, 18–19, 27–36

Extended Course
Day 1: Exs. 1–6, 20–26
Day 2: Exs. 7–13 odd, 14–19, 27–36

Note: Extended Course assignments can be used to differentiate within the regular classroom. In classrooms where students are grouped homogeneously, the material might be covered in fewer days. In this case assignments may be combined.

ADDITIONAL PRACTICE
See the *Teacher's Resource Book* for additional practice and application exercises for this section.

EXERCISE NOTES
Exercises 5 and 6 You may want to point out that the rules for adding more than two fractions are the same as the rules for adding exactly two fractions.

EXERCISE NOTES
The music teacher might be able to use a musical instrument to demonstrate the differences between a whole note and the fractional notes in **Exercise 16**.

16. **Music** In written music, the shape of a note shows how long the note should be held. A dot to the right of a note tells you to add on half the value of the note to make it last longer. Use the chart to help you find the value of each note or combination of notes.

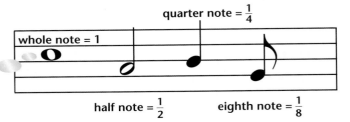

A whole note is held four times as long as a quarter note.

whole note = 1   quarter note = $\frac{1}{4}$

half note = $\frac{1}{2}$ eighth note = $\frac{1}{8}$

a. $\frac{3}{4}$ b. $\frac{3}{8}$ c. $\frac{3}{16}$

d. $\frac{3}{8}$ e. $1\frac{1}{4}$ f. $1\frac{7}{16}$

17. **Challenge** On the map, $\frac{1}{4}$ in. represents about 100 mi. A student measures $\frac{3}{8}$ in. between Medellín and Bogotá, $\frac{1}{2}$ in. between Bogotá and Cali, and $\frac{1}{2}$ in. between Cali and Medellín. What is the total mileage of a trip beginning and ending in Medellín with stops in Bogotá and Cali as shown?
550 mi

Medellín

Bogotá

Cali   COLOMBIA

18. **Writing** Ito and Uri were doing their homework together. Ito said that $\frac{1}{3} + \frac{5}{12} = \frac{6}{15}$. Uri disagreed with Ito, but neither could get the other to change his mind. Convince one of the boys that he is wrong. Be specific in your explanation. Use a model if necessary.
Answers will vary. Check students' work.

19. Answers will vary.
Sample Response:
Food preparation;
Eric's recipe for salad dressing calls for $\frac{1}{4}$ cup of vinegar and $\frac{1}{2}$ cup of salad oil. How much dressing does one recipe make?

Oral Report

Exercise 19 checks that you understand addition and subtraction of fractions.

Reflecting ◀▶ **on the Section**

Be prepared to report on the following topic in class.

19. Find a situation where addition or subtraction of fractions is used to create something. Give an example of how mathematics is used in the situation.

Replace each ? with the number that makes the statement true.
(Module 5, p. 302)

20. 21 in. = ? ft
$1\frac{3}{4}$

21. 2 mi = ? yd
3520

22. 16 ft = ? yd
$5\frac{1}{3}$

Add or subtract. Simplify answers when possible. (Module 5, p. 302)

23.   4 ft   8 in.
     + 2 ft 10 in.
      2 yd 1 ft 6 in.

24.   6 mi
      – 2 mi 1318 ft
      3 mi 1320 yd 2 ft

25.   5 yd 18 in.
      – 2 yd 23 in.
      2 yd 2 ft 7 in.

Use the Venn diagram. (Module 2, p. 119)

26. Find the number of cities listed in the given section of the diagram.

   a. capitals 4

   b. seaports 8

   c. capitals and seaports 3

   d. capitals or seaports 9

   e. neither a capital nor a seaport 1

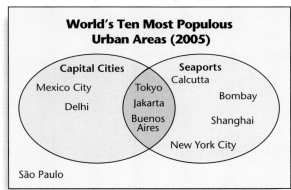

World's Ten Most Populous Urban Areas (2005)

Capital Cities: Mexico City, Delhi
Seaports: Calcutta, Bombay, Shanghai, New York City
Capitals and Seaports: Tokyo, Jakarta, Buenos Aires
São Paulo

Use compatible numbers to find each sum by mental math.
(Module 1, p. 11)

27. 12 + 15 + 8 35

28. 45 + 7 + 33 85

29. 16 + 10 + 14 + 9 49

30. 43 + 7 + 33 83

Find each missing number. (Toolbox, p. 573)

31. 45 ÷ ? = 5 9

32. ? · 8 = 96 12

33. ? – 12 = 25 37

34. ? ÷ 9 = 17 153

35. 12 · ? = 180 15

36. 7 + ? = 30 23

Section 3

Extra Skill Practice

Find each sum. Write each answer in lowest terms.

1. $\frac{1}{6} + \frac{3}{10}$ $\frac{7}{15}$

2. $\frac{1}{8} + \frac{3}{8}$ $\frac{1}{2}$

3. $\frac{2}{3} + \frac{5}{18}$ $\frac{17}{18}$

4. $\frac{7}{12} + \frac{5}{18}$ $\frac{31}{36}$

5. $\frac{8}{11} + \frac{1}{3}$ $\frac{35}{33} = 1\frac{2}{33}$

6. $\frac{7}{15} + \frac{7}{15}$ $\frac{14}{15}$

Find each difference. Write each answer in lowest terms.

7. $\frac{12}{13} - \frac{1}{13}$ $\frac{11}{13}$

8. $\frac{7}{8} - \frac{11}{20}$ $\frac{13}{40}$

9. $\frac{9}{10} - \frac{1}{2}$ $\frac{2}{5}$

10. $\frac{7}{8} - \frac{2}{16}$ $\frac{3}{4}$

11. $\frac{3}{4} - \frac{3}{7}$ $\frac{9}{28}$

12. $\frac{11}{12} - \frac{1}{10}$ $\frac{49}{60}$

Find each sum or difference. Write each answer in lowest terms.

13. $\frac{1}{3} + \frac{9}{10}$ $\frac{37}{30} = 1\frac{7}{30}$

14. $\frac{4}{7} + \frac{3}{14}$ $\frac{11}{14}$

15. $\frac{3}{4} + \frac{1}{6}$ $\frac{11}{12}$

16. $\frac{2}{3} - \frac{9}{16}$ $\frac{5}{48}$

17. $\frac{7}{24} + \frac{7}{8}$ $\frac{7}{6} = 1\frac{1}{6}$

18. $\frac{4}{5} - \frac{1}{2}$ $\frac{3}{10}$

Find the value of each expression. Write each answer in lowest terms.

19. $\frac{7}{10} - \frac{3}{20} + \frac{4}{5}$ $\frac{27}{20} = 1\frac{7}{20}$

20. $\frac{5}{8} + \frac{5}{36} - \frac{1}{4}$ $\frac{37}{72}$

21. $\frac{8}{9} - \frac{2}{7} + \frac{1}{2}$ $\frac{139}{126} = 1\frac{13}{126}$

22. $\frac{5}{7} - \frac{1}{28} + \frac{3}{4}$ $\frac{10}{7} = 1\frac{3}{7}$

23. $\frac{2}{9} + \frac{1}{5} + \frac{7}{30}$ $\frac{59}{90}$

24. $\frac{5}{6} + \frac{1}{8} - \frac{1}{12}$ $\frac{7}{8}$

Evaluate each expression when $n = \frac{3}{4}$. Write each answer in lowest terms.

25. $n + \frac{7}{8}$ $\frac{13}{8} = 1\frac{5}{8}$

26. $\frac{5}{6} - n$ $\frac{1}{12}$

27. $\frac{1}{2} + n - \frac{2}{3}$ $\frac{7}{12}$

Standardized Testing ◀▶ **Open-ended**

1. For each problem, find two fractions with different denominators that have the number shown below as their common denominator. Then write an example showing how to add or subtract the two fractions you chose. **Answers will vary. Check students' work.**

   a. common denominator: 16
   b. common denominator: 24
   c. common denominator: 10
   d. common denominator: 15

2. Pick one of your examples from Question 1. Write a word problem that can be solved using the addition or subtraction you showed.
   Answers will vary. Check students' work.

FOR ASSESSMENT AND PORTFOLIOS

ADD a Square

Extended Exploration

SET UP *You will need:* • *the Extended Exploration Labsheet* • *scissors*

The Situation See the *Teacher's Resource Book* for a sample solution for this Extended Exploration.

Changing the area of a figure may have a surprising effect on its perimeter. In this activity you will explore how the perimeter changes when you add squares to a polygon made up of five squares. Begin by forming a polygon with five 1 in. by 1 in. squares from the labsheet. Add squares to the original polygon until the perimeter reaches 18 in. (*Note:* Added squares must share at least one complete side with another square and they should not overlap.)

The Problem

What is the least number of squares you can add to get a perimeter of 18 in.? What is the greatest number of squares you can add to get a perimeter of 18 in.? Sketch the shapes that give the least and greatest areas for a polygon with a perimeter of 18 in.

Something to Think About

◆ Try several different polygons made with five 1 in. by 1 in. squares. You might want to try these shapes.

◆ Can you predict how the perimeter will change when you add a square in a certain position?

◆ It may be helpful to organize your work in a table which includes sketches and area and perimeter measurements.

Present Your Results

Explain what approaches you tried. Then describe your solutions. Include any tables and sketches you made. Will you get the same results if you start with any polygon made up of five 1 in. by 1 in. squares? Explain.

E² NOTES

Labsheet: Each student needs a copy of the Extended Exploration Labsheet, which is found in the *Teacher's Resource Book.*

Using an E²: Suggestions for managing and evaluating an Extended Exploration are available in the *Teacher's Resource Book* for Modules 1 and 2. See also pages T44–T45 in the *Teacher's Edition.*

OTHER NOTES

Students use squares cut from the E² Labsheet. Alternatively students could use 1-inch square tiles. Graph paper is recommended for sketching the various arrangements students want to show with their solutions.

Section 4

Addition and Subtraction of Mixed Numbers

Masks

Setting the Stage

SET UP *You will need Labsheet 4A.*

Throughout history, masks have been used in many different cultural celebrations. On November 1st and 2nd, many Mexican-Americans celebrate *Día de Muertos*, the Day of the Dead. This holiday honors relatives and friends who have died during the year. It is traditional to make and display papier-mâché masks like the one shown.

Special masks, called ▶ *calaveras*, are made by the entire family.

Think About It

1 About how long and wide would a mask have to be to cover your face? Answers will vary.

2 **Use Labsheet 4A.** List the measurements on the mask that have the given characteristic.

a. less than 1 in. $\frac{1}{4}$ in., $\frac{1}{2}$ in., $\frac{5}{8}$ in., $\frac{3}{4}$ in.

b. greater than 1 in. $1\frac{1}{2}$ in., $1\frac{3}{4}$ in., $1\frac{5}{8}$ in.

Adding MiXed Numbers

SET UP Work with a partner. You will need: • Labsheet 4A
• customary ruler

A relief mask has a design that is raised from a flat background. You can glue string, yarn, cotton balls, or even seashells on a cardboard mask to create a raised design.

▶ **To estimate how much material is needed for a mask, you may need to estimate a sum of mixed numbers.**

3 **Use Labsheet 4A.** The length of string, in inches, needed to outline the jaw on the mask is $1\frac{5}{8} + 1\frac{3}{4} + 1\frac{5}{8}$.

a. Round each measurement to the nearest whole number and find the sum to estimate the length of string. about 6 in.

b. Is your estimate *less than*, *equal to*, or *greater than* the sum? Explain.
greater than; All three numbers were rounded up.

▶ **Using a Ruler** **To find the actual amount of string needed to outline the jaw, you can use a ruler to add the measurements.**

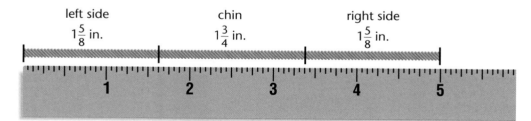

left side
$1\frac{5}{8}$ in.

chin
$1\frac{3}{4}$ in.

right side
$1\frac{5}{8}$ in.

4 **a.** Use the ruler to find $1\frac{5}{8} + 1\frac{3}{4} + 1\frac{5}{8}$. Compare your answer with your estimate in Question 3. 5 in.; It is less than the estimate.

b. Another way to find the sum is to measure off 3 in. and then measure off lengths for $\frac{5}{8}$ in., $\frac{3}{4}$ in., and $\frac{5}{8}$ in. Why does this method work? This method simply involves measuring the whole inches first, then the fractions of an inch.

Section 4 Addition and Subtraction of Mixed Numbers **319**

COMMON ERROR

When finding a common denominator, students may fail to write the whole number beside the equivalent fraction, causing them to forget to add the whole number part when finding the sum. Remind students that to write equivalent mixed numbers, the whole number part must be written along side the fraction.

TEACHING NOTES

Question 6 Ask students to explain how adding mixed numbers is similar to adding fractions.

Be certain students can apply the skills of finding a common denominator and simplifying fractions to the new skill of adding mixed numbers.

Question 9(b) Students should be able to explain both methods and why each one works. The Classroom Example below shows an addition problem solved using each method.

CLASSROOM EXAMPLE

Show two ways to find $1\frac{4}{5} + 2\frac{5}{6}$.

Answer:
Use mixed numbers:

$$1\frac{4}{5} = 1\frac{24}{30}$$
$$+ 2\frac{5}{6} = + 2\frac{25}{30}$$
$$\overline{\qquad\qquad 3\frac{49}{30} = 4\frac{19}{30}}$$

Use fractions:

$$1\frac{4}{5} + 2\frac{5}{6} = \frac{9}{5} + \frac{17}{6}$$
$$= \frac{54}{30} + \frac{85}{30}$$
$$= \frac{139}{30} \text{ or } 4\frac{19}{30}$$

320

---

5 **a.** Estimate $2\frac{2}{3} + 3\frac{3}{4}$ by rounding each number to the nearest whole number. **About 7 in.**

   b. Why is it difficult to find the actual sum $2\frac{2}{3} + 3\frac{3}{4}$ using a ruler?
   The ruler is not divided into thirds of an inch.

▶ **Using Paper and Pencil** You can find the sum of mixed numbers by adding the whole numbers and the fractions separately.

EXAMPLE

Find $2\frac{2}{3} + 3\frac{3}{4}$.

SAMPLE RESPONSE

Add the whole numbers.

Add the fractions.

$$2\frac{2}{3} = 2\frac{8}{12}$$
$$+ 3\frac{3}{4} = + 3\frac{9}{12}$$
$$\overline{\qquad\qquad 5\frac{17}{12} = 6\frac{5}{12}}$$

6 **Try This As a Class**

   a. In the Example, why were $\frac{2}{3}$ and $\frac{3}{4}$ written as $\frac{8}{12}$ and $\frac{9}{12}$?
   So the fractions could be added.

   b. Why was $5\frac{17}{12}$ written as $6\frac{5}{12}$?
   So the fractional part would be less than 1.

7 Find $4\frac{3}{4} + 1\frac{5}{8}$ without a ruler. Then check your answer using a ruler.

8 **Discussion** Explain the steps Paulo used to find $2\frac{2}{3} + 3\frac{3}{4}$.

9 **a.** Use Paulo's method to find $1\frac{4}{5} + 6\frac{2}{3}$.

   b. Do you prefer Paulo's method or the one in the Example? Why?

Paulo

$$2\frac{2}{3} = \frac{8}{3} = \frac{32}{12}$$
$$+ 3\frac{3}{4} = + \frac{15}{4} = + \frac{45}{12}$$
$$= \frac{77}{12} = 6\frac{}{1}$$

7. $6\frac{3}{8}$

8. He rewrote the mixed numbers as fractions. Then he added the fractions. Finally, he wrote the answer as a mixed number.

9. a. $8\frac{7}{15}$

   b. Answers will vary.

10 ✔ **CHECKPOINT** Find each sum. Then write each sum in lowest terms.

a. $10\frac{1}{4} + 2\frac{5}{6}$ $13\frac{1}{12}$ **b.** $\frac{3}{5} + 4\frac{3}{8}$ $4\frac{39}{40}$ **c.** $6\frac{1}{4} + 5\frac{3}{8} + 3\frac{3}{4}$ $15\frac{3}{8}$

11 a. Use Labsheet 4A. Is 20 in. of string enough to outline the jaw, the mouth, and each pair of rectangles that make the eyes on the *Mask*? Yes

b. Did you use *paper and pencil* or *estimation* to find your answer? Explain.

■ **HOMEWORK EXERCISES** ▶ See Exs. 1–14 on p. 325.

See Exs. 1–14 on p. 325.

Exploration 2 ▸▸▸▸▸▸▸▸▸▸▸▸▸▸▸▸▸▸▸▸▸▸▸▸▸▸▸

Subtracting **Mixed Numbers**

SET UP Work with a partner. You will need a customary ruler.

Artists are often inspired by patterns found in nature or in the arts and crafts of other cultures. Suppose you use the pattern on this Native American blanket to make a raised design for a pin.

12 Describe how to use mental math to determine that 5 in. of string is needed to outline this rectangular pin.

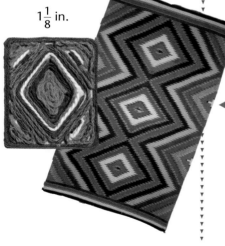

$1\frac{1}{8}$ in.

$1\frac{3}{8}$ in.

◀ Traditional blanket design made by Navajo weavers of the Southwest.

✔ QUESTION 10

...checks that you can add mixed numbers.

11. b. Sample Response: I used paper and pencil. I used estimation first and decided I was rounding up so much my estimate wouldn't really give me a good answer.

GOAL

LEARN HOW TO...
♦ subtract mixed numbers

AS YOU...
♦ design a pin

12. Sample Response: The sum of the whole number parts of the mixed numbers is 4. There are two pairs of fractions, each with a sum $\frac{1}{2}$, so the perimeter of the pin is $4 + \frac{1}{2} + \frac{1}{2} = 5$ in.

COMMON ERROR

Question 11 Students may fail to consider *both* lengths and widths of the rectangles forming the mouth and eyes since only one length and one width are recorded on the labsheet.

Exploration 2

DEVELOPING MATH CONCEPTS

It may be helpful to review equivalencies such as $4\frac{2}{2} = 5$, as this is the conceptual knowledge students will need to understand the regrouping process for mixed number subtraction.

Before starting **Question 17** make certain students are comfortable subtracting mixed numbers where regrouping is not necessary.

If students have trouble with **Question 17(c)**, have them think back to their work on simplifying mixed number sums in Exploration 1. Give them $2\frac{11}{8}$ and ask them how they would simplify the mixed number. This strategy of *working backward* to the value of $3\frac{3}{8}$ may help them better understand the relationship between the two values.

▶ **Using a Ruler** Suppose you have $6\frac{3}{4}$ in. of string. You can use a ruler to see how much string is left after the pin is outlined.

1 Start with $6\frac{3}{4}$ in. of string.

2 Take away 5 in. of string.   **3** This much is left.

15. c. $1\frac{1}{4}$; I subtracted the fractions first and then I subtracted the whole numbers.

17. a. So the fractions would have a common denominator.

   b. No; $\frac{4}{8} > \frac{3}{8}$

   c. $3\frac{3}{8} = 3 + \frac{3}{8} =$

   $2 + 1 + \frac{3}{8} =$

   $2 + \frac{8}{8} + \frac{3}{8} =$

   $2 + \frac{11}{8} = 2\frac{11}{8}$

   d. $1\frac{7}{8}$

18. $2\frac{5}{6}$; check:

   $2\frac{5}{6} + 3\frac{2}{3} =$

   $2\frac{5}{6} + 3\frac{4}{6} = 5\frac{9}{6} =$

   $6\frac{3}{6} = 6\frac{1}{2}$

13 a. Write a subtraction problem to represent the subtraction shown in the ruler diagram. $6\frac{3}{4} - 5$

   b. Find the answer. How can you do this without the ruler?
   $1\frac{3}{4}$; Sample Response: $6 - 5 = 1$, so $6\frac{3}{4} - 5 = 1\frac{3}{4}$.

14 Use a ruler to find $4\frac{1}{2} - 3\frac{1}{4}$. $1\frac{1}{4}$

▶ **Using Pencil and Paper** To subtract mixed numbers without a ruler, you can find a common denominator as you did to add mixed numbers.

15 a. Copy the subtraction problem in Question 14. $4\frac{1}{2} - 3\frac{1}{4}$

   b. Rewrite the problem using equivalent fractions with a common denominator. $4\frac{2}{4} - 3\frac{1}{4}$

   c. Find the difference. Explain how you subtracted.

   d. Compare your answer with the answer from Question 14.
   They are the same.

16 Gwen has $14\frac{3}{4}$ in. of string and uses $5\frac{3}{8}$ in. to outline a feature on a mask. How much string does she have left? $9\frac{3}{8}$ in.

17 **Try this as a Class** Use the problem shown.

   a. Why was $1\frac{1}{2}$ rewritten as $1\frac{4}{8}$?

   b. Can you subtract $\frac{4}{8}$ from $\frac{3}{8}$? Explain.

   $$\begin{array}{rcccc} 3\frac{3}{8} & = & 3\frac{3}{8} & = & 2\frac{11}{8} \\ -1\frac{1}{2} & = & -1\frac{4}{8} & = & -1\frac{4}{8} \\ \hline \end{array}$$

   c. Show that $3\frac{3}{8} = 2\frac{11}{8}$.

   d. Find the difference of $2\frac{11}{8}$ and $1\frac{4}{8}$.

18 Find $6\frac{1}{2} - 3\frac{2}{3}$. Check your answer using addition.

19 Paulo used the same method to subtract mixed numbers as he did to add them. Explain the steps Paulo used to find $2\frac{1}{5} - 1\frac{7}{10}$.

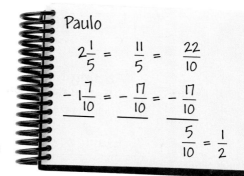

Paulo

$$2\frac{1}{5} = \frac{11}{5} = \frac{22}{10}$$

$$- 1\frac{7}{10} = -\frac{17}{10} = -\frac{17}{10}$$

$$\frac{5}{10} = \frac{1}{2}$$

20 Use Paulo's method to find $4\frac{1}{3} - 2\frac{2}{9}$. $2\frac{1}{9}$

21 **Try This as a Class** Consider the problem $6 - 2\frac{1}{4}$.

  a. Explain why you can write 6 as $5\frac{4}{4}$. $6 = 5 + 1 = 5 + \frac{4}{4} = 5\frac{4}{4}$

  b. Why would you want to write 6 as $5\frac{4}{4}$ to find the difference?
  To subtract the fractional part of the mixed number.

  c. Find the difference.
  $3\frac{3}{4}$

22 If you have 9 yards of yarn and use $3\frac{3}{4}$ yards in a craft project, how much is left for your next craft project? $5\frac{1}{4}$ yd

▶ **Using Mental Math** Addition and mental math can be used to solve subtraction problems when one number is a mixed number and the other is a whole number.

23 **Discussion** Explain how you can find the difference $4 - 2\frac{1}{3}$ by finding the number to add to $2\frac{1}{3}$ to get 4: $2\frac{1}{3} + \underline{?} = 4$.

24 Use mental math to find each difference.

  a. $10 - 7\frac{3}{8}$ $2\frac{5}{8}$ **b.** $8\frac{3}{4} - 5$ $3\frac{3}{4}$ **c.** $11 - 6\frac{2}{3}$ $4\frac{1}{3}$

25 ✔ **CHECKPOINT** Find each difference. Write each answer in lowest terms. Check your answers using addition.

  a. $5\frac{3}{7} - 2\frac{1}{2}$ $2\frac{13}{14}$ **b.** $4\frac{3}{8} - 2$ $2\frac{3}{8}$ **c.** $10\frac{2}{3} - 3\frac{3}{5}$ $7\frac{4}{15}$

  d. $6 - 3\frac{1}{9}$ $2\frac{8}{9}$ **e.** $3\frac{5}{8} - 1\frac{3}{4}$ $1\frac{7}{8}$ **f.** $5\frac{1}{4} - 4\frac{5}{6}$ $\frac{5}{12}$

26 **a.** Sketch your own design for a pin the size of a rectangle that is $1\frac{7}{16}$ in. by $\frac{7}{8}$ in. Check students' work

  b. Suppose you have 6 in. of red yarn. Calculate how much will be left after you use it to outline your pin. $1\frac{3}{8}$ in.

HOMEWORK EXERCISES ▶ See Exs. 15–31 on pp. 326–327.

---

19. Sample Response: Paulo rewrote the mixed numbers as fractions:

$$2\frac{1}{5} = \left(2 \cdot \frac{5}{5}\right) + \frac{1}{5} =$$

$$\frac{10}{5} + \frac{1}{5} = \frac{11}{5} \text{ and}$$

$$1 = \frac{10}{10} \text{ so } \frac{10}{10} + \frac{7}{10}$$

$$= \frac{17}{10}. \text{ Then he}$$

changed $\frac{11}{5}$ to a fraction with a common denominator:

$$\frac{2}{2} \cdot \frac{11}{5} = \frac{22}{10};$$

He subtracted and finally he

simplified: $\frac{5}{10} = \frac{1}{2}$.

✔ **QUESTION 25**

...checks that you can subtract mixed numbers.

23. If you add $\frac{2}{3}$, you get 3. If you add $1\frac{2}{3}$, you get 4.

TEACHING NOTES
Question 25 Ask students to think about the methods they have learned in this exploration and to decide which methods are appropriate for each problem. After they complete the problems, have students check with a partner to compare methods used for each one.

Key Concepts

CLOSURE QUESTION

How are adding and subtracting mixed numbers similar to adding and subtracting fractions? How are they different?

Sample Response: When adding or subtracting both types of numbers, you need to find a common denominator for the fractions, add or subtract the fractions, and write your answer in lowest terms. When adding or subtracting mixed numbers you may also need to regroup to solve, and the whole number parts of the mixed numbers must also be added or subtracted.

ABSENT STUDENTS

For students who were absent for all or part of this section, the blackline Study Guide for Section 4 may be used to present the ideas, concepts, and skills of Section 4.

Section 4
Key Concepts

Adding Mixed Numbers (pp. 319–321)

• **Estimating** One way to estimate a sum or difference of mixed numbers is to round to the nearest whole number.

Example $2\frac{1}{2} + 3\frac{2}{3} \approx 3 + 4 = 7$

• **Using paper and pencil** Add the whole numbers and the fractions separately.

> Write fractions with a **common** denominator.

Example
$$2\frac{1}{2} = 2\frac{3}{6}$$
$$+3\frac{2}{3} = +3\frac{4}{6}$$
$$5\frac{7}{6} = 6\frac{1}{6}$$

> Simplify so that the fraction is less than 1 and in lowest terms.

Subtracting Mixed Numbers (pp. 321–323)

• **Using paper and pencil** First subtract the fractions. Then subtract the whole numbers. You may need to regroup a whole.

> Regroup 4 as $3\frac{6}{6}$.

Example
$$4\frac{1}{3} = 4\frac{2}{6} = 3\frac{8}{6}$$
$$-1\frac{5}{6} = -1\frac{5}{6} = -1\frac{5}{6}$$
$$2\frac{3}{6} = 2\frac{1}{2}$$

> Write in lowest terms.

• **Using mental math** Think of a related addition sentence when subtracting from a whole number.

Example To find $8 - 3\frac{5}{6}$, think $3\frac{5}{6} + \underline{\ ?\ } = 8$.

If you add $\frac{1}{6}$, you get 4. So you need to add $4\frac{1}{6}$ to get 8.

27 Key Concepts Question Find each sum or difference. Use estimation to check that each answer is reasonable.

a. $7\frac{5}{6} + 2\frac{3}{4}$ $10\frac{7}{12}$ **b.** $7 - 1\frac{4}{5}$ $5\frac{1}{5}$ **c.** $10\frac{1}{4} - 6\frac{5}{8}$ $3\frac{5}{8}$

Section 4

Practice & Application Exercises

YOU WILL NEED

For Ex. 26:
♦ fraction calculator

Estimate each sum by first rounding each mixed number to the nearest whole number and then adding.

1. $5\frac{3}{5} + 4\frac{1}{8}$ about 10   2. $7\frac{2}{7} + 2\frac{6}{7}$ about 10   3. $2\frac{1}{3} + 3\frac{1}{8}$ about 5

Find each sum. Write each answer in lowest terms.

4. $2\frac{1}{8} + 1\frac{3}{4}$ $3\frac{7}{8}$ 5. $4\frac{2}{3} + 5\frac{1}{2}$ $10\frac{1}{6}$ 6. $1\frac{2}{3} + 4\frac{4}{5}$ $6\frac{7}{15}$

7. $2\frac{1}{3} + 6\frac{5}{8}$ $8\frac{23}{24}$ 8. $\frac{5}{7} + 1\frac{5}{14}$ $2\frac{1}{14}$ 9. $1\frac{8}{9} + 3\frac{5}{6}$ $5\frac{13}{18}$

Mental Math Show how to use compatible numbers to find each sum. (*Hint:* To add three or more mixed numbers, see if any have fractional parts with a sum of 1.)

10. $4\frac{1}{3} + 18\frac{1}{2} + 5\frac{2}{3}$ 11. $8\frac{4}{5} + 6\frac{1}{3} + 4\frac{3}{8} + 1\frac{1}{5} + 2\frac{5}{8}$

10. $4\frac{1}{3} + 5\frac{2}{3} = 10$;
    $10 + 18\frac{1}{2} = 28\frac{1}{2}$

11. $8\frac{4}{5} + 1\frac{1}{5} = 10$ and
    $4\frac{3}{8} + 2\frac{5}{8} = 7$;
    $10 + 7 + 6\frac{1}{3} = 23\frac{1}{3}$

FOR ◄ HELP

with *compatible numbers,* see

MODULE 1, p. 11

12. Sonya is making costumes for a play. She needs $1\frac{1}{2}$ yd of ribbon for one costume, $3\frac{2}{3}$ yd of ribbon for another costume, and $2\frac{1}{4}$ yd of ribbon for a third costume. What is the total amount of ribbon she needs? $7\frac{5}{12}$ yd

13. **Estimation** Another way to estimate is to first round to the nearest half.

    a. Explain why $3\frac{3}{8}$ was rounded to $3\frac{1}{2}$ instead of 3.

    b. Do you think $8\frac{1}{2}$ is a low or a high estimate? Explain.

    c. Find the exact sum and compare it with the estimate.

$$4\frac{4}{5} \quad \text{about 5}$$
$$+ 3\frac{3}{8} \quad \text{about } 3\frac{1}{2}$$
$$\overline{\text{about } 8\frac{1}{2}}$$

13. a. $3\frac{3}{8}$ is closer to $3\frac{1}{2}$ than to 3.

    b. high; Both numbers were rounded up.

    c. $8\frac{7}{40}$; The sum is lower than the estimate.

14. Estimate $11\frac{2}{7} + 4\frac{3}{5}$ by first rounding to the nearest half.
    $11\frac{1}{2} + 4\frac{1}{2}$; about 16

Practice & Applications

SUGGESTED ASSIGNMENTS

Core Course
Day 1: Exs. 1–3, 32–37
Day 2: Exs. 4–14
Day 3: Exs. 15–17, 38–46
Day 4: Exs. 18–31

Extended Course
Day 1: Exs. 1–3, 32–37
Day 2: Exs. 4–14
Day 3: Exs. 15–17, 38–46
Day 4: Exs. 18–31, 47–49*

Note: Extended Course assignments can be used to differentiate within the regular classroom. In classrooms where students are grouped homogeneously, the material might be covered in fewer days. In this case assignments may be combined.

*denotes Extension Exercises

EXERCISE NOTES

Exercise 12 Cloth and ribbon are usually sold by the yard. People who make clothing, or people who sell materials to make clothing, frequently need to add or subtract mixed numbers.

Exercise 13 presents another way of estimating mixed number sums by rounding to the nearest $\frac{1}{2}$. You could use fraction strips to show why $3\frac{3}{8}$ rounds to $3\frac{1}{2}$ instead of 3 or 4. You may also want to have students brainstorm real life situations where rounding to the nearest half would be better than rounding to the nearest whole number.

ADDITIONAL PRACTICE
See the *Teacher's Resource Book* for additional practice and application exercises for this section.

EXERCISE NOTES
Exercise 25 can be "acted out" in class with four students each holding a sign with the name of one of the characters in the problem and the rest of the class telling them where each should stand in a line up and why.

21. $3\frac{2}{3}$; $3\frac{1}{3} + \frac{2}{3} = 4$, so
$$3\frac{1}{3} + 3\frac{2}{3} = 7$$

22. $3\frac{3}{5}$; $5 - 2 = 3$, so
$$5\frac{3}{5} - 2 = 3\frac{3}{5}$$

23. $1\frac{3}{4}$; $1\frac{1}{4} + \frac{3}{4} = 2$, so
$$1\frac{1}{4} + 1\frac{3}{4} = 3$$

Find each difference. Write each answer in lowest terms. Use addition to check your answers.

15. $3\frac{2}{5} - 2\frac{1}{4}$ $1\frac{3}{20}$

16. $4\frac{2}{3} - 2\frac{8}{9}$ $1\frac{7}{9}$

17. $2\frac{1}{8} - 1\frac{3}{4}$ $\frac{3}{8}$

18. $23\frac{1}{2} - 5\frac{6}{7}$ $17\frac{9}{14}$

19. $17 - 9\frac{5}{11}$ $7\frac{6}{11}$

20. $4\frac{5}{12} - 3\frac{13}{36}$ $1\frac{1}{18}$

Use mental math to find each difference. Explain your steps.

21. $7 - 3\frac{1}{3}$

22. $5\frac{3}{5} - 2$

23. $3 - 1\frac{1}{4}$

24. **Photography** The image on an instant photograph is $3\frac{5}{8}$ in. long and $2\frac{7}{8}$ in. wide. What are the dimensions of a piece of cardboard you would need to make a mat with a $\frac{3}{4}$ in. border around the top and sides and 1 in. along the bottom?
$5\frac{1}{8}$ in. by $4\frac{5}{8}$ in.

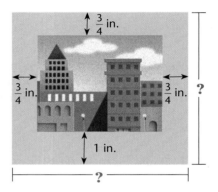

25. Kele is $2\frac{7}{8}$ in. taller than Sharon. Rosa is $2\frac{1}{2}$ in. shorter than Kele but $\frac{5}{8}$ in. taller than Gary.

a. Who is taller, Sharon or Gary? by how much? Sharon; $\frac{1}{4}$ in.

b. Find the difference between Kele's height and Gary's height. $3\frac{1}{8}$ in.

26. **Fraction Calculator** Another way to add and subtract mixed numbers is by using a calculator.

a. To find the sum $3\frac{7}{8} + 1\frac{3}{4}$, enter these keystrokes: $4\frac{13}{8}$

b. Press [Ab/c]. What did this do? changed $4\frac{13}{8}$ to the simplified form $5\frac{5}{8}$

c. Estimate $3\frac{7}{8} + 1\frac{3}{4}$ to check that the answer displayed is reasonable. about 6; reasonable

d. Use a calculator to find $6\frac{1}{2} - 1\frac{4}{5}$. Estimate to check that the answer displayed is reasonable. $4\frac{7}{10}$; about $4\frac{1}{2}$

27. A plumber needs to replace the middle pipe in the diagram. Find the length of the middle pipe. $2\frac{1}{4}$ ft

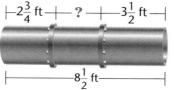

28. Woodworking Nails are sometimes referred to in units called "pennies." A 2-penny nail is 1 in. long. Each increase of a penny means an increase of $\frac{1}{4}$ in. in length up to 3 in.

    a. What is the length of a 4-penny nail? $1\frac{1}{2}$ in.

    b. A carpenter hammers a 4-penny nail through a board that is $\frac{3}{4}$ in. thick. If the nail is hammered in straight, how far will the nail stick out of the board? $\frac{3}{4}$ in.

Interpreting Data Use the table to answer Exercises 29 and 30.

Gold Medal Results for Olympic High Jump 1996–2004			
Winner	**Country**	**Height**	**Year**
Charles Austin	United States	7 ft 10 in.	1996
Sergey Klyugin	Russia	7 ft $8\frac{1}{2}$ in.	2000
Stefan Holm	Sweden	7 ft $8\frac{3}{4}$ in.	2004

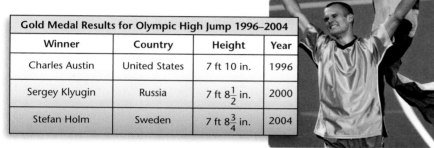

◄ Stefan Holm was the 2004 Olympic gold medalist in the high jump.

29. How much higher did Austin jump than Stefan Holm? $1\frac{1}{4}$ in.

30. How much higher did Holm jump than Sergey Klyugin? $\frac{1}{4}$ in.

Reflecting ◄▶on the Section

Write your response to Exercise 31 in your journal.

31. Mary and Russ each tried to find $4\frac{3}{15} - 1\frac{10}{15}$. Explain what is wrong with each student's work.

EXERCISE NOTES

Journal Exercise 31 One strategy for solving the problem is to have students work the problem themselves and then compare their work to that of Mary and Russ to determine where their steps differ. Then have students explain why Russ's and Mary's work did not lead to the correct result.

Journal

Exercise 31 checks that you understand mixed number subtraction.

31. Instead of regrouping, Mary subtracted the smaller fraction from the greater fraction. Russ regrouped incorrectly:

$$4\frac{3}{15} = 3\frac{18}{15}.$$

327

Find each sum or difference in lowest terms. (Module 5, p. 312)

32. $\frac{1}{5} + \frac{4}{25}$ $\frac{9}{25}$ **33.** $\frac{5}{6} - \frac{3}{4}$ $\frac{1}{12}$ **34.** $\frac{7}{10} + \frac{2}{3}$ $\frac{41}{30}$ or $1\frac{11}{30}$

Write each fraction as a decimal rounded to the nearest hundredth. (Module 4, p. 225)

35. $\frac{13}{25}$ 0.52   **36.** $\frac{4}{7}$ 0.57   **37.** $\frac{5}{8}$ 0.63

Find the prime factorization of each number. (Module 3, p. 158)

38. 126 $2 \times 3^2 \times 7$ **39.** 98 2×7^2 **40.** 153 $3^2 \times 17$

Tell whether each event is *certain*, *impossible*, or *neither* when you roll a single number cube. (Module 2, p. 80)

41. odd number   **42.** multiple of 8   **43.** number less than 7
neither   impossible   certain

Use mental math to find each value. (Module 1, p. 62)

44. $\frac{1}{3}$ of 27 9   **45.** $\frac{2}{5}$ of 15 6   **46.** $\frac{5}{6}$ of 48 40

Extension ▶ ▶

Making Connections about Regrouping

47. a. A flight leaves at 1:37 P.M. and arrives at 4:16 P.M. Show how to use subtraction with regrouping to find the elapsed time. $4:16 - 1:37 = 3:76 - 1:37 = 2:39$; 2 hr 39 min

b. How is the regrouping you use when you add and subtract time measurements like the regrouping you use when you add and subtract mixed numbers? How is it different?

48. Make a list of different types of numbers or measurements that you know how to add and subtract. Describe similarities and differences in how regrouping is used for the items on your list. Check students' work.

49. Make up a money or measurement system of your own. It can be totally imaginary (for example, using zings and zangs) or it can use real objects as units. Explain how the units in your system are related. Then show how to use regrouping to add and subtract with your system. Check students' work.

> **FOR ▶ HELP**
>
> with *elapsed time*, see
> **TOOLBOX, p. 577**

47. b. Sample Response: The regrouping is the same because I had to change a whole (1 hour) into parts (60 minutes). The regrouping is different because the parts (minutes) can be represented by whole numbers.

Extra Skill Practice

Find each sum. Write each answer in lowest terms.

1. $1\frac{1}{2} + 6\frac{3}{4}$ $8\frac{1}{4}$

2. $5\frac{5}{16} + 3\frac{7}{8}$ $9\frac{3}{16}$

3. $2\frac{3}{5} + 7\frac{1}{2}$ $10\frac{1}{10}$

4. $4\frac{3}{4} + 3\frac{1}{6}$ $7\frac{11}{12}$

5. $2\frac{7}{12} + 1\frac{8}{15}$ $4\frac{7}{60}$

6. $6\frac{2}{3} + 5\frac{4}{7}$ $12\frac{5}{21}$

Find each difference. Write each answer in lowest terms. Use addition to check your answers.

7. $4\frac{5}{9} - 2\frac{1}{2}$ $2\frac{1}{18}$

8. $36\frac{2}{3} - 4\frac{1}{6}$ $32\frac{1}{2}$

9. $18\frac{3}{4} - 14\frac{1}{7}$ $4\frac{17}{28}$

10. $12\frac{7}{8} - 10\frac{3}{4}$ $2\frac{1}{8}$

11. $16\frac{4}{9} - 7\frac{5}{6}$ $8\frac{11}{18}$

12. $7\frac{2}{7} - 3\frac{5}{14}$ $3\frac{13}{14}$

Use mental math to find each difference.

13. $8\frac{3}{4} - 5\frac{1}{2}$ $3\frac{1}{4}$

14. $6\frac{5}{8} - 2$ $4\frac{5}{8}$

15. $12 - 9\frac{11}{16}$ $2\frac{5}{16}$

16. $21 - 6\frac{7}{10}$ $14\frac{3}{10}$

17. $32\frac{1}{2} - 14$ $18\frac{1}{2}$

18. $7\frac{1}{3} - 4\frac{2}{3}$ $2\frac{2}{3}$

Find each sum or difference. Write each answer in lowest terms.

19. $33\frac{1}{3} - 16\frac{1}{2}$ $16\frac{5}{6}$

20. $2\frac{1}{3} + 3\frac{8}{9}$ $6\frac{2}{9}$

21. $7\frac{3}{5} - 6\frac{3}{4}$ $\frac{17}{20}$

22. $1\frac{7}{32} + 2\frac{3}{8}$ $3\frac{19}{32}$

23. $4\frac{5}{9} - 1\frac{3}{5}$ $2\frac{43}{45}$

24. $11\frac{3}{4} + 16\frac{5}{6}$ $28\frac{7}{12}$

Standardized Testing ◆ Multiple Choice

1. Mrs. Quant bought a beef roast that weighed $5\frac{1}{4}$ lb and a ham that weighed $8\frac{1}{2}$ lb. How many pounds of meat did she buy?   **D**

   Ⓐ $3\frac{1}{4}$ lb   Ⓑ $13\frac{1}{3}$ lb   Ⓒ $13\frac{3}{8}$ lb   Ⓓ $13\frac{3}{4}$ lb   Ⓔ none of these

2. After being cooked, the $8\frac{1}{2}$-lb ham loses $\frac{5}{8}$ of a pound. Mrs. Quant slices $4\frac{1}{3}$ lb for sandwiches and serves the rest for dinner. How much ham is served for dinner?   **E**

   Ⓐ $3\frac{1}{2}$ lb   Ⓑ $3\frac{7}{12}$ lb   Ⓒ $3\frac{11}{24}$ lb   Ⓓ $12\frac{5}{24}$ lb   Ⓔ none of these

---

Extra Skill Practice

TEACHER NOTES

For each Exploration, the corresponding Extra Skill Practice Exercises are noted.

Exploration 1: Exs. 1–6, 20, 22, 24
Exploration 2: Exs. 7–18, 19, 21, 23

EXTRA HELP

Teacher's Resource Book
• Practice and Applications
• Study Guide

Technology Resources
• @Home Tutor
• Test Generator

ASSESSMENT
• Section 4 Quick Quiz
• Test Generator

Students will be using fraction and decimal multiplication to find areas of parallelograms and triangles. Module 5 Section 5 *Warm-Up* assesses student facility with multiplication of fractions and decimals as well as finding the area of a rectangle.

ALTERNATIVE APPROACH
To help students answer **Question 1**, you may want to have them sketch a layout of the garden to determine that there were 6400 flowers. You could then ask students to think about how much space it would take for a garden of 6400 flowers. This will get them thinking about the concept of area.

Section 5 Area

The Taj Mahal

Setting the Stage

The Taj Mahal, a gigantic domed structure, is the most visited attraction in India. It was created in the 17th century by Emperor Shah Jahan to honor the memory of his beloved wife Mumtaz Mahal. The design of the Taj Mahal is based on the number four and its multiples.

Think About It

1 The garden at the Taj Mahal was laid out in four squares of the same size. Each square was divided into four flower beds, with 400 flowers in each bed. How many flowers were in the garden?
6400 flowers

2 The central chamber of the Taj Mahal was built in the shape of an octagon. How is an octagon related to the number 4?
Sample Responses: An octagon has 4 pairs of sides and 4 pairs of angles. The vertices for an octagon can be formed by placing two congruent squares on top of each other and rotating one square 90 degrees.

Customary
U·N·I·T·S for AREA

SET UP *Work with a partner. You will need: • customary ruler • yardstick or measuring tape • newspaper or other large paper • scissors*

When describing a building, architects often refer to the area of its surfaces. The **area** of a surface is the number of square units that cover it. The area of the floor of the main building of the Taj Mahal is 34,596 ft². To find out whether the size of this floor makes the Taj Mahal "gigantic," you will explore area.

3 Draw two squares, one with sides 1 in. long and the other with sides 1 ft long. Cut out your squares. Check student work.

▶ The area of the small square is **1 square inch (1 in.²)**. The large square is 1 ft x 1 ft and has an area of **1 square foot (1 ft²)**.

4 a. Use your model of a square foot to estimate the area of the top of your desk. Check estimates for reasonableness

b. Do you think that using your squares is a good way to find area? Explain. Sample Response: No; It is difficult to measure the parts of squares that hang over the desk.

5 Discussion The area of a rectangle can be found by multiplying its length by its width.

a. How can you use this relationship to estimate area?
Estimate the length and width and then multiply.
b. How can you use this relationship to find the actual area?
Multiply the actual length and width.

6 a. Copy the table.

b. For each item, choose an appropriate unit of measure for its area.

c. Estimate each area in the units you chose.

d. Measure the length and width of each item in the units you chose. Then calculate the actual area.

GOAL

LEARN HOW TO...
• measure area using customary units
• convert between customary units of area

AS YOU...
• explore the size of the Taj Mahal

KEY TERMS
• area
• square inch (in.²)
• square foot (ft²)
• square yard (yd²)

1 in.

1 in.

The area of the square is 1 in. x 1 in. = 1 in.²

6. a–d. Answers will vary. The areas of the page and the desktop should be measured in square inches, the chalkboard in square feet.

Item	Unit (in.² or ft²)	Estimated area	Actual area
this page	?	?	?
top of your desk	?	?	?
chalkboard	?	?	?

TEACHING NOTES
As students estimate the area of the tops of their desks in **Question 4**, help them understand how to approximate any fractional pieces that are "left over." For instance, when measuring with their square foot model, a student might observe: "I can fit two complete square feet, but there is some leftover space yet to be measured." Tell students to mentally put the "leftover" pieces together to make another square foot, or to make a "nice" fraction of a square foot.

Students should also use their squares to help estimate the area of each item in **Question 6.**

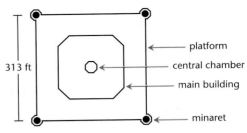

platform
central chamber
main building
313 ft
313 ft
minaret

Exploration 1 continued

CLASSROOM MANAGEMENT

It may be helpful to select a few students to do the actual measuring of the classroom in **Question 8(b)** and then share their information with the class. Meanwhile, the remaining students can be involved in recording their estimates of the classroom area on the board. Then the class can view all the estimates and discuss whether as a whole, estimates were too low or too high in regards to the actual area.

ALTERNATIVE APPROACH

As students answer **Question 9(a)**, you could have them use their square foot models to create a model of a square yard. Call students up one at a time and have them place their square foot model on the floor. Students should decide on their own how many are needed to complete the square yard model. You could extend **Question 9(b)** by asking: "How can you convert an area measurement given in square yards to square feet?" (*Multiply by 9.*)

TEACHING NOTES

The following Classroom Example can be used as a follow-up to **Question 11(b)**.

7 a. The Taj Mahal stands on a square platform that is 313 ft on each side. What is the area of this square in square feet? 97,969 ft²

b. The floor area of the main building is 34,596 ft². What is the area of the part of the platform that is not covered by the main building? 63,373 ft²

8 a. Estimation Estimate the area of your classroom in square feet. Explain your method. a–c. Answers will vary.

b. Check your estimate by measuring the length and the width and finding the area.

c. About how many of your classroom areas does it take to cover the area of the main building of the Taj Mahal?

d. Would you describe the Taj Mahal as "gigantic"? Explain. Sample Response: Yes. The main platform is about as big as two football fields.

▶ **Converting Units of Area** To express the area covered by a large building like the Taj Mahal, you may want to convert square feet to a larger unit.

9 Try This As a Class Use your model of a square foot.

a. There are 3 ft in 1 yd. How many square feet form **1 square yard** (**1 yd²**)? Make a sketch showing how to arrange square feet to form a square yard.

9. a. 9 ft²  }1 ft

b. How can you convert an area measurement given in square feet to square yards? Divide by 9.

10 Use your models of a square inch and a square foot.

a. How many square inches form one square foot? 144 in.²

b. How can you convert an area measurement given in square inches to square feet? Divide by 144.

CLASSROOM EXAMPLE

The area of a floor is 25,920 in.² What is its area in square feet?

Answer:
To convert to square feet, divide by 144. Since 25,920 ÷ 144 = 180, the area is 180 ft².

✔ **QUESTION 11**

...checks that you can convert between customary units of area.

11 ✔ **CHECKPOINT** The floor of the main building of the Taj Mahal has an area of 34,596 ft². What is its area in square yards? 3844 yd²

HOMEWORK EXERCISES ▶ See Exs. 1–6 on p. 340.

Area of a Parallelogram

SET UP *You will need:* • *Labsheet 5A* • *scissors* • *metric ruler*
• *centimeter graph paper*

Thirty-seven specialists including artists, stone cutters, engineers, architects, calligraphers, and inlayers designed the Taj Mahal and supervised the 20,000 workers who built it.

This section of flooring from a terrace at the Taj Mahal is inlaid with white marble and red sandstone tiles.

12 What geometric shapes do you see in the pattern in the floor?
parallelogram, octagon

▶ **The design and construction of the terrace must have involved measuring lengths and finding areas. You can use centimeter graph paper to investigate the dimensions and areas of geometric shapes.**

Square units are also used to measure area in the metric system. Since each small square is 1 cm by 1 cm, it has an area of **1 square centimeter (1 cm²).**

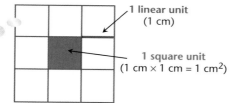

1 linear unit (1 cm)

1 square unit (1 cm × 1 cm = 1 cm²)

13 **Try This as a Class**

a. How are linear units and square units different? **Sample Response: Linear units measure length. Square units measure area.**

b. How many centimeters are in 1 m? **100 cm**

c. How many square centimeters are there in **1 square meter (1 m²)?** Explain.
10,000 cm²; 1 m = 100 cm so 1 m × 1 m = 100 cm × 100 cm = 10,000 cm²

333

Exploration 2 continued

TEACHING NOTES

In the discussion of **Question 14**, encourage students to find several ways to justify that Chen's calculation of the area is correct. This way students will see various ways of finding the area of the parallelogram. The method of regrouping the two half squares to form one will be important, as the idea of cutting and rearranging parts is used in **Question 16** to develop the formula for area of a parallelogram.

Be sure students have correctly drawn their parallelograms in **Question 15** since they will use their parallelograms to answer **Questions 16 and 17**. After discussing **Question 17(a)**, you may want to reinforce the concept that the areas are the same by asking, "If a figure is cut apart and rearranged, is the area of the figure affected?" (*No it is not, as long as the figures are not overlapped at all.*)

16. e. The lengths of the bases are the same; The width of the rectangle is the height of the parallelogram.

   f. Sample Response: 8 cm²; The areas of the parallelogram and the rectangle are the same.

18. Sample responses are given.

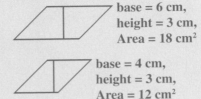

base = 6 cm, height = 3 cm, Area = 18 cm²

base = 4 cm, height = 3 cm, Area = 12 cm²

---

14. yes; The figure consists of two squares, each having an area of 1 cm² and two triangles that together form a square with an area of 1 cm².

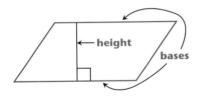

16. Sample responses are given.

   a.

   b. height = 2 cm, length of base = 4 cm

   c–d. length = 4 cm, width = 2 cm, area = 8 cm²

---

14 Discussion Chen drew this parallelogram on graph paper. He says that it has an area of 3 cm². Is he correct? Explain.

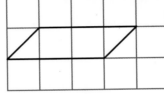

15 On graph paper, draw a different parallelogram that is not a rectangle. Estimate the area of the parallelogram.
Answers will vary. Check student drawings and estimates.

16 a. Lines or segments that meet at a point **intersect**. Recall that if they meet at a right angle they are also perpendicular. Inside the parallelogram you drew in Question 15, draw a segment that extends from one side to the opposite side and is perpendicular to those sides.

   b. The length of the segment you drew in part (a) is the **height** of the parallelogram. The sides that are perpendicular to the height are the **bases** of the parallelogram. Find the height and the length of a base of your parallelogram.

   c. Cut out your parallelogram. Then cut it into two pieces along the segment you drew.

   d. Form a rectangle using the two pieces of your parallelogram. Record the length, width, and area of this rectangle.

   e. How do the length and the width of your rectangle compare with the length of the base and the height of your original parallelogram? See margin.

   f. What is the area of your parallelogram? Explain. See margin.

17 Try This as a Class Use your results from Question 16.

   a. How do the areas of the parallelograms and the rectangles constructed in Question 16 compare? They are the same.

   b. Use the length of the base and the height to write a formula for finding the area of a parallelogram.
   Area = length of base · height

   c. What are the two different formulas that can be used to find the area of a rectangle?
   Area = length of base · height, Area = length · width

18 Draw two parallelograms that are not rectangles on graph paper, one with an area of 12 cm² and the other with an area of 18 cm². What are the length of the base and the height of each parallelogram you drew? See margin.

19 ✓ **CHECKPOINT** **Use Labsheet 5A.** Follow the directions on the labsheet to find the areas of *Parallelograms A–D.*
Answers will vary. Accept reasonable answers.

20 Suppose each parallelogram-shaped marble tile in the photo on page 333 has a base length of 8 in. and a height of 4 in. What is the area of each parallelogram-shaped tile? **32 in.²**

HOMEWORK EXERCISES ▶ **See Exs. 7–15 on pp. 340–341.**

✓ **QUESTION 19**

...checks that you can find the area of a parallelogram.

19. A: 8.2 cm²
   B: 9 cm²
   C: 12.6 cm²
   D: 10.2 cm²

Exploration 3

Area *of a* TRIANGLE

SET UP Work with a partner. You will need: • *Labsheet 5B* • *scissors* • *colored pencil* • *metric ruler*

GOAL

LEARN HOW TO...
◆ find the area of a triangle
◆ find a missing dimension

AS YOU...
◆ explore geometric designs found in wall panels at the Taj Mahal

KEY TERMS
◆ base (of a triangle)
◆ height (of a triangle)

▶ Some of the designs created on this wall of the Taj Mahal can be made using rectangles and triangles. You can use what you know about the area of parallelograms to find the area of triangles.

Any side of a triangle can be the **base**. The diagrams below show the length of the base *(b)* and the **height** *(h)* of several triangles.

  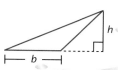

h represents the height.

b represents the length of the base.

21 **Discussion** How is the segment that shows the height of a triangle related to the base?
The height is the length of a segment that is drawn perpendicular to the base of a triangle or its extension from the vertex opposite the base.

Exploration 3

COMMON ERROR
Students often have the misconception that all triangles always "sit" on their base and that the height is always vertical. The sketches prior to **Question 21** are purposely drawn so as to dispel this myth. **Discussion Question 21** focuses on the relationship between a triangle's base and height in contrast to the location of the base and height in a triangle.

TEACHING NOTES
You may want to read through the steps for **Question 22** aloud, so students are aware that they will be cutting out their triangles, thus the importance of recording the measures *inside* the triangles and coloring the base dark enough and thick enough to be seen when cut out.

Students may benefit from discussing their findings to **Questions 23(d) and 23(f)** before formalizing the formula for area of a triangle in **Question 24**.

Question 26 Point out to students that the height of a triangle can be one of its sides. This will occur if either of the legs of a right triangle are used as the base of the triangle.

22. a–d. Sample
Response:

3 cm

height = 1.5 cm, length of base = 3 cm

25. Check students' calculations for their triangles. For sample in Question 22, A = 2.25 cm²

22 Follow these steps to create two triangles.

a. Draw a triangle.

b. Start at any vertex and draw a segment perpendicular to the opposite side or the opposite side extended.

c. Color the base.

d. Measure the length of the base and the height to the nearest tenth of a centimeter. Record your measurements inside the triangle.

23. a.

e. Cut out your triangle. Check students' work.

f. Trace around the triangle to make another one that is identical to it. Cut out the second triangle. Check students' work.

23 a. Arrange the triangles from Question 22 to form a parallelogram that has the colored side of the first triangle as a base. For parts (a)–(c) and (e), sample responses are given.

b. Find the length of a base and the height of this parallelogram to the nearest centimeter.
height = 1.5 cm, length of base = 3 cm

c. Calculate the area of your parallelogram.
Area = 4.5 cm²

d. How is the area of one of the triangles related to the area of the parallelogram? It is half the area of the parallelogram.

e. What is the area of one triangle? 2.25 cm²

f. How are the length of the base and the height of the parallelogram you formed related to the length of the base and the height of your original triangle?
The lengths of the bases are the same and the heights are the same.

24 **Try This as a Class** Use your results from Question 23 to write a formula for finding the area (*A*) of a triangle.
$A = \frac{1}{2} \cdot$ length of base $\cdot$ height

25 Use your formula to find the area of your original triangle using each of the other two sides as the bases.

✔ **QUESTION 26**

...checks that you can find the area of a triangle.

26. A: 6 cm²
B: 7.595 cm²
C: 4.275 cm²
D: 4.68 cm²

26 ✔ **CHECKPOINT** **Use Labsheet 5B** Follow the directions on the labsheet to find the areas of *Triangles A–D*.
Answers will vary. Accept reasonable answers.

27 **Discussion** Suppose you know that the area of a parallelogram is 28 cm² and the height is 4 cm. Explain how you can find the length of the base.
⊢—*b* = ?—⊣
4 cm
Divide the area by the height to find out the length of the base is 7 cm.

▶ **Find Unknown Values** When you want to find a missing dimension, you can use an equation to organize your thinking and find the unknown value by solving the equation. In Module 4, you solved addition and subtraction equations. Now you will learn to solve multiplication and division equations.

EXAMPLE

Find the length of the base of the triangle.

6 cm
├─ b = ? ─┤
$A = 42 \text{ cm}^2$

SAMPLE RESPONSE

$A = \frac{1}{2} \cdot b \cdot h$	Use the formula for area.
$42 = \frac{1}{2} \cdot b \cdot 6$	Substitute the values you know.
$42 = 3 \cdot b$	$\frac{1}{2} \cdot 6$ equals 3.
$42 \div 3 = b$	To find the missing factor, you can divide.
$14 = b$	

The length of the base is 14 cm.

28 **Discussion**

a. In the Example, why can you solve for b by dividing by 3?

b. Explain how inverse operations can be used to solve each equation.

   ♦ $r + 5 = 11.2$

   ♦ $7y = 154$

   ♦ $\frac{w}{4} = 17$

29 A parallelogram has an area of 5.4 cm².

a. The base is 0.9 cm long. Use the formula for the area of a parallelogram to write an equation. Let h represent the height. 5.4 = 0.9 · h

b. How can you use division to solve your equation for h?
divide 5.4 by 0.9

28. a. Division is the inverse operation for multiplication, so division can be used to find the missing factor.
b. subtract 5 from 11.2; divide 154 by 7; multiply 17 by 4

TEACHING NOTES
When reviewing the **Example** with students, point out that calculating $\frac{1}{2} \cdot 6$ makes the equation simpler and thus easier to solve. Otherwise, you would have to divide 42 by $\frac{1}{2}$ and then divide the result by 6 (or vice-versa). Have students check the solution in the **Example** by substituting 14 for the base length to see if the area equals 42 sq cm. You may want to have students check their answers in **Questions 30 and 31** as well.

If needed, the following Classroom Example may be used after **Question 28** to provide additional guidance on using an area formula to set up and solve an equation to find a missing dimension.

CLASSROOM EXAMPLE

Find the height of the triangle.

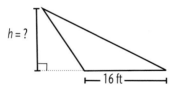
$h = ?$
├── 16 ft ──┤

Area = 116 sq ft

Answer:

$$A = \frac{1}{2} bh$$
$$116 = \frac{1}{2} \cdot 16 \cdot h$$
$$116 = 8 \cdot h$$
$$116 \div 8 = h$$
$$14.5 = h$$

The height is 14.5 ft.

337

In **Question 30,** students learn that when a fraction $\frac{a}{b}$ is multiplied by $\frac{b}{a}$, the product is 1. This prepares them for working with reciprocals, which is covered in the next section.

30 **Try This as a Class** Braedy started to find the height of a triangle with a base $\frac{5}{8}$ in. long and an area of 10 in.², but he stopped before he finished the problem. His work is shown below.

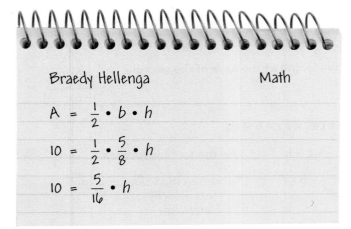

Braedy Hellenga   Math

$$A = \frac{1}{2} \cdot b \cdot h$$

$$10 = \frac{1}{2} \cdot \frac{5}{8} \cdot h$$

$$10 = \frac{5}{16} \cdot h$$

a. What is the next step in solving the equation? divide 10 by $\frac{5}{16}$

b. Finish Braedy's work to find the height of the triangle in inches. 32 in.

c. When Braedy asked his older sister for help, she told him to multiply both sides of the equation by $\frac{16}{5}$. How is $\frac{16}{5}$ related to the $\frac{5}{16}$ in the last step on his paper? The product of $\frac{16}{5}$ and $\frac{5}{16}$ is 1.

d. Finish the problem using his sister's suggestion. Compare the answer with your answer in part (b). 32 in.; They are the same.

30. e. Multiply both sides of the equation by $\frac{4}{3}$.

e. Describe how you could use the method suggested by Braedy's sister to solve the equation $\frac{3}{4} \cdot x = 12$.

 QUESTION 31

...checks that you can use an equation to find a missing dimension.

31  **CHECKPOINT** For each of the following, write and solve an equation to find the missing length.

a. A parallelogram has a base 4 cm long and an area of 20.4 cm². Find the height of the parallelogram.
$4 \cdot h = 20.4; h = 5.1$ cm

b. A triangle has a height of 10 in. and an area of $8\frac{3}{4}$ in.² Find the length of its base.
$\frac{1}{2} \cdot b \cdot 10 = 8\frac{3}{4}; b \cdot 5 = 8\frac{3}{4}; b = 1\frac{3}{4}$ in.

HOMEWORK EXERCISES ▶ See Exs. 16–29 on pp. 341–342.

Section 5
Key Concepts

Units of Area (pp. 331–332)

Area (A) is measured in square units.

You can use the relationships between units in the customary system to convert between square inches, square feet, and square yards.

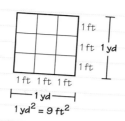

1 ft
1 ft   1 yd
1 ft

1 ft 1 ft 1 ft

├— 1 yd —┤
1 yd² = 9 ft²

Relationships between units in the metric system can be used to convert between square centimeters and square meters.

100 cm 1 m

100 cm
├— 1 m —┤
1 m² = 10,000 cm²

Formulas for Area

Parallelograms (pp. 333–335)

Example

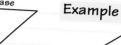

base

3 cm

├— base —┤
6 cm

The **height** is the perpendicular distance between the bases.

Area = length of base • height

$A = b • h = 6 \text{ cm} • 3 \text{ cm}$

The area is 18 cm².

Triangles (pp. 335–336)

Example

6 in.

├ base ┤
$4\frac{1}{2}$ in.

You may have to extend the base.

Area = $\frac{1}{2}$ • length of base • height

$A = \frac{1}{2} • b • h = \frac{1}{2} • 4\frac{1}{2} \text{ in.} • 6 \text{ in.}$

The area is $13\frac{1}{2}$ in.²

area

square inch (in.²)

square foot (ft²)

square yard (yd²)

square centimeter (cm²)

square meter (m²)

intersect

base

height

32 Key Concepts Question Figure *GCEF* is a parallelogram, and figure *CDE* is a triangle. Find the area of the entire figure in square yards. **about 0.97 yd²**

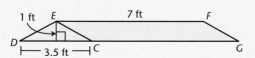

1 ft   E   7 ft   F

D   C   G
├— 3.5 ft —┤

Section 5   Area   **339**

Key Concepts

ABSENT STUDENTS

For students who were absent for all or part of this section, the blackline Study Guide for Section 5 may be used to present the ideas, concepts, and skills of Section 5.

Key Concepts *continued*

CLOSURE QUESTION

State the formulas for finding the area of a parallelogram and for finding the area of a triangle using both words and symbols.

Sample Response:

Parallelogram: $A = b \cdot h$, or area equals the length of the base times the height.

Triangle: $A = 0.5 \cdot b \cdot h$, or area equals one-half times the length of the base times the height.

Practice & Applications

SUGGESTED ASSIGNMENTS

Core Course
Day 1: Exs. 1–6
Day 2: Exs. 7–15
Day 3: Exs. 16–18, 30–36
Day 4: Exs. 19–27, 29

Extended Course
Day 1: Exs. 1–6
Day 2: Exs. 7–15
Day 3: Exs. 16–18, 30–33, 37*
Day 4: Exs. 19–29

Note: Extended Course assignments can be used to differentiate within the regular classroom. In classrooms where students are grouped homogeneously, the material might be covered in fewer days. In this case assignments may be combined.

*denotes Extension Exercises

Section 5
Key Concepts

Finding Unknown Values (pp. 337–338)

You can write and solve an equation to find a missing dimension or other unknown value.

Example Fran bought 3.5 lb of coffee beans for $23.80. What is the cost of one pound?

Let c = cost per pound.

$$3.5c = 23.80$$
$$3.5c \div 3.5 = 23.80 \div 3.5$$
$$1c = 23.80 \div 3.5$$
$$c = \$6.80$$

33 Key Concepts Question Find the unknown value in the equation $6x = 39$. $x = 6.5$

Section 5
Practice & Application Exercises

YOU WILL NEED

For Ex. 13:
- metric ruler
- Labsheet 5A

For Ex. 15:
- graph paper
- a ruler

For Ex. 16:
- metric ruler
- Labsheet 5B

For Ex. 28:
- graph paper

For Ex. 37:
- centimeter graph paper
- tracing paper

Estimation Estimate the area of each object in customary units and explain your method. Then measure the length and width and use an area formula to check your estimates. How did you do?

1. seat of a chair
2. a window

   1–2. Answers will vary. Accept reasonable estimates.

Replace each _?_ with the missing measurement.

3. 81 ft² = _?_ yd² 9

4. 36 in.² = _?_ ft² $\frac{1}{4}$

5. 266 yd² = _?_ ft² 2394

6. 18 ft² = _?_ in.² 2592

7. How many square meters are in a square kilometer? Explain.

   1,000,000; 1 km = 1000 m, so 1 km² = 1 km · 1 km = 1000 m · 1000 m = 1,000,000 m

Find the area of a parallelogram with the given dimensions.

8. $b = 3.5$ mm
   $h = 2.7$ mm
   9.45 mm²

9. $b = 4$ cm
   $h = 5$ cm
   20 cm²

10. $b = 4\frac{1}{2}$ ft
    $h = 3$ ft
    $13\frac{1}{2}$ ft²

11. The groundskeeper at a high school is in charge of mowing the soccer and football fields. How many more square yards of grass does the groundskeeper have to mow on the soccer field than on the football field? **2600 yd²**

12. Shane wants to carpet his bedroom. The dimensions of his rectangular room are 12 ft x 15 ft. The carpet he has chosen costs $11.95 a square yard. How much will the carpet for Shane's room cost? **$239**

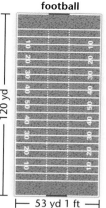
football

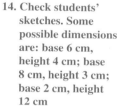
soccer

120 yd

⊢ 53 yd 1 ft ⊣

120 yd

⊢ 75 yd ⊣

13. **Use Labsheet 5A.** Find the areas of *Parallelograms E–H.* **Answers will vary. Accept reasonable answers.**
   E: 12.5 cm²   F: 3.38 cm²   G: 5.2 cm²   H: 5.46 cm²

14. **Open-ended** Sketch two different parallelograms that each have an area of 24 cm² and are not rectangles. Be sure to label the length of the base and the height.

15. a. Draw a parallelogram on graph paper.
      a–c. Check students' sketches and areas.
   b. Find the height by measuring the distance between a pair of parallel sides. Use this measurement and the length of the corresponding base to find the area of the parallelogram.

   c. Repeat part (b) using the other pair of parallel sides.

   d. Are the areas in parts (b) and (c) the same? Why or why not?
      Yes; They represent the area of the same figure.

16. **Use Labsheet 5B.** Find the areas of *Triangles E–H.*
    Answers will vary. Accept reasonable answers.

Find the area of each figure.

17.

4 cm ⊢10 cm⊣
7.5 cm
⊢10 cm⊣8 cm⊣
120 cm²

18.
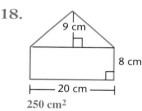
9 cm
8 cm
⊢ 20 cm ⊣
250 cm²

Write and solve an equation to find the missing dimension for each figure.

19.
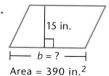
h = ?
⊢ 8 ft ⊣
Area = 24 ft²
$24 = \frac{1}{2} \cdot 8 \cdot h$; **6 ft**

20.
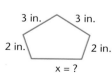
15 in.
⊢ b = ? ⊣
Area = 390 in.²
$390 = b \cdot 15$; **26 in.**

21.
3 in. 3 in.
2 in.   2 in.
x = ?
Perimeter = 14 in.

14. Check students' sketches. Some possible dimensions are: base 6 cm, height 4 cm; base 8 cm, height 3 cm; base 2 cm, height 12 cm

16. E: 4.65 cm²
    F: 3.78 cm²
    G: 6.1 cm²
    H: 7.15 cm²

21. 14 = 2 + 3 + 3 + 2 + x; **4 in.**

Section 5 Area **341**

ADDITIONAL PRACTICE
See the *Teacher's Resource Book* for additional practice and application exercises for this section.

EXERCISE NOTES
Exercise 12 You may want to point out the need for a conversion from square feet to square yards.

Exercise 15 Students should conclude that the areas are the same; however, they may have to account for error in measuring with a ruler. For better precision, it may help to have students measure in tenths of a centimeter as opposed to fractions of an inch.

Practice & Applications

EXERCISE NOTES

There are several approaches students might use to solve **Exercise 27**. They may first decide how to split up the area among the three polygons and draw each one. By cutting the three out, they could then arrange them to form a polygon. The pieces can be traced or glued to a piece of paper. Some students may work backwards, drawing a polygon of area 50 cm² and then trying to draw line segments inside it to divide it into the 3 shapes.

27. Sample Response:

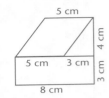

5 cm

5 cm   3 cm

3 cm   4 cm

8 cm

29. a. Any area calculations using this measure will be incorrect since the segment is longer than the height of the parallelogram or triangle.

b. A rectangle or a square; For a rectangle or a square, the sides adjacent to a base are perpendicular to the base.

Discussion

Exercise 29 checks that you understand the relationship between the height and the base of a parallelogram and of a triangle.

22. The multipurpose room of a school building has a rectangular floor with an area of 5828 ft². The length of the floor is 94 ft. What is the width of the floor? 62 ft

Find the unknown value in each equation.

23. $2 \cdot 9x = 72$ 4

24. $5y = 125$ 25

25. $\frac{3}{8}m = 12$ 32

26. $\frac{x}{12} = 7$ 84

27. Create Your Own The area of a polygon can be found by dividing it into polygons whose areas you know how to find.

  a. Using one triangle, one rectangle, and one parallelogram that is not a rectangle, draw a polygon that has an area of 50 cm².

  b. Label the base length and height of each polygon used.

28. Challenge Copy the polygon onto graph paper. Then find its area in square units.
  4.5 square units

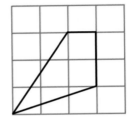

Reflecting ◀▶ on the Section

Be prepared to discuss your response to Exercise 29 in class.

29. a. What happens if you use a segment that is not perpendicular to a base as the height of a parallelogram or a triangle? Explain.

  b. For what type of parallelogram does the height equal the length of a side? Explain.

  c. For what type of triangle does the height equal the length of a side? Explain.
  A right triangle; The legs of a right triangle are perpendicular.

Spiral ◀▶ Review

Use inverse operations to solve each equation. (Module 4, p. 240)

30. $16.3 + w = 34$

31. $\frac{2}{3} + r = \frac{7}{8}$

32. $p - 0.7 = 3.5$

  17.7

  $\frac{5}{24}$

  4.2

33. a. For each input value, apply the rule to find the output value. Record the results in a table like the one below. (Module 4, p. 256)

Rule: Output = 2 • input − 3

Input	2	5	6	10
Output	?	?	?	?

Input	2	5	6	10
Output	1	7	9	17

b. Write each input and its output from part (a) as an ordered pair. (2, 1), (5, 7), (6, 9), (10, 17)

c. On a coordinate grid, graph the ordered pairs you listed in part (b). Draw segments connecting the points in order from left to right.

33. c.

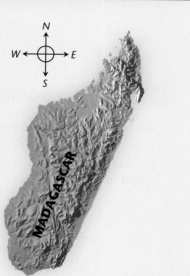

d. Use your graph to predict the input for an output of 2. 2.5

Draw an example of each polygon. (Module 2, p. 119)

34. hexagon   **35.** pentagon   **36.** trapezoid

34–36. Check students' drawings.

Extension ▶ ▶

Area of an Irregularly Shaped Figure

You can estimate areas using grid squares.

First   Trace the outline of the figure.

Next   Place the tracing on a piece of centimeter graph paper.

Then   Count the complete grid squares. Add on the area from the partially filled grid squares. You can use a fraction to estimate a part of a grid square or combine parts to form whole squares.

37. a. On the map, the area of Madagascar is about how many square centimeters? Explain how you made your estimate.

b. An area on the map that is 1 cm by 1 cm represents how many square kilometers? 40,000 km²

c. Estimate the actual area of Madagascar. about 640,000 km²

37. a. 16 cm²; Sample Response: I estimated the average width at about 2 cm and the length at about 8 cm and multiplied.

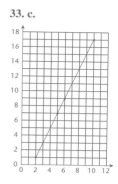

1 cm is about 200 km.

EXERCISE NOTES

Extension Exercise 37 Students might also use centimeter squares (particularly transparent ones) or a base-10 overhead flat (since it is transparent and consists of centimeter squares) to lay over the outline of Madagascar in the book.

Section 5

Extra Skill Practice

Replace each ___?___ with the number that makes the statement true.

1. $168 \text{ ft}^2 = $ ___?___ in.^2 24,192
2. $5 \text{ ft}^2 = $ ___?___ in.^2 720
3. $96 \text{ in.}^2 = $ ___?___ ft^2 $\frac{2}{3}$
4. $117 \text{ ft}^2 = $ ___?___ yd^2 13
5. $4\frac{1}{2} \text{ yd}^2 = $ ___?___ ft^2 $40\frac{1}{2}$
6. $1 \text{ yd}^2 = $ ___?___ in.^2 1296

Find the area of each parallelogram.

7. $b = 38.2$ mm
$h = 24$ mm
916.8 mm²

8. 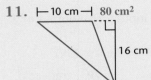 36 ft²

9. $b = 3\frac{1}{4}$ cm $22\frac{3}{4}$ cm²
$h = 7$ cm

Find the area of each figure.

10. 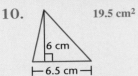 19.5 cm²

11. 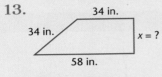 80 cm²

12. 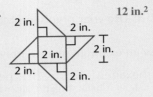 12 in.²

Write and solve an equation to find the missing dimension.

13.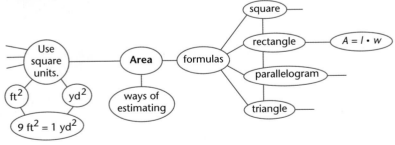

Perimeter = 148 in.
$148 = 34 + 34 + 58 + x;$
$x = 22$ in.

14.
$h = 8$ cm
$b = ?$
Area = 36 cm²
$36 = 0.5 \cdot b \cdot 8;$
$b = 9$ cm

15.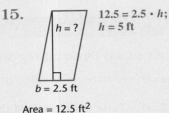
$h = ?$
$b = 2.5$ ft
Area = 12.5 ft²
$12.5 = 2.5 \cdot h;$
$h = 5$ ft

Study Skills ◀▶ **Graphic Organizers**

Visual displays can help you relate ideas and organize information.

Copy and extend the concept map to connect ideas you have learned about area. Add on units of measure, formulas, and notes about relationships. **See margin.**

Use square units.
ft² yd²
$9 \text{ ft}^2 = 1 \text{ yd}^2$
Area
ways of estimating
formulas
square
rectangle — $A = l \cdot w$
parallelogram
triangle

Section ⑥ Division with Fractions

IN THIS SECTION

EXPLORATION 1
- Dividing by a Fraction

EXPLORATION 2
- Dividing Fractions and Mixed Numbers

Designing a Border

Setting the Stage

Glazed ornamental tiles were used to create inlaid borders in the Taj Mahal. In this section you will design a tile and use it to create a border similar to the ones found in the Taj Mahal.

An Islamic ornamental tile ▶

Think About It

▶ Tiles are often used to create borders around doors and windows. The tile above is $2\frac{1}{2}$ in. long along the bottom edge. Three tiles laid end-to-end will create a $7\frac{1}{2}$ in. border.

1 What length border would 5 tiles laid end-to-end cover? Explain.

2 How many tiles are needed for a 10 in. long border?
4 tiles

3 There are times you may need only part of a tile to finish a border. If only $\frac{2}{5}$ of a tile is needed to complete a border, how much of the $2\frac{1}{2}$ in. tile would you need? Explain.
1 in. $\frac{2}{5}$ of $2\frac{1}{2} = \frac{2}{5} \cdot 2\frac{1}{2} = \frac{2}{5} \cdot \frac{5}{2} = 1$

1. $12\frac{1}{2}$ in. You need 5 tiles that are $2\frac{1}{2}$ in. So $5 \cdot 2\frac{1}{2} = 12\frac{1}{2}$ or $5 \cdot 2 + 5 \cdot \frac{1}{2}$ is easy to do in your head.

Setting the Stage

GETTING STARTED
Module 5 Section 6 *Warm-Up* assesses student facility with multiplying fractions. To divide fractions, students will need to able to multiply by the reciprocal of a fraction or mixed number.

TEACHING NOTES
Students may use number sense or multiplication to solve **Questions 1 and 2**. Refer students who may need to review multiplication of fractions to Module 3, Section 5.

Question 3 sets up the use of reciprocals. Reciprocals are defined and explored in Exploration 1.

Section 6   Division with Fractions   **345**

345

Exploration 1

DEVELOPING MATH CONCEPTS

Students often are taught that switching a fraction's numerator and denominator will produce its reciprocal. Although this shortcut works with fractions, it often leads to problems when students are working with mixed numbers since the reciprocal of a mixed number cannot be found by simply interchanging the numerator and denominator in the fractional part. To avoid this problem, the topic of reciprocals is approached here by finding numbers whose product is 1, not just by switching their numerators and denominators. The discussion of **Question 7** provides an opportunity for students to explain that the products of reciprocals must equal 1. Through the discussion have students determine how to find the reciprocal of $2\frac{3}{4}$. (To check to see if $2\frac{3}{4}$ and $2\frac{4}{3}$ are reciprocals, students must multiply the numbers. However, $2\frac{3}{4} \cdot 2\frac{4}{3} = \frac{11}{4} \cdot \frac{10}{3} = \frac{55}{6}$, not 1, so $2\frac{3}{4}$ and $2\frac{4}{3}$ are not reciprocals. Have students look at the product of the fractions and ask them what they must multiply $\frac{11}{4}$ by to get 1. The answer, $\frac{4}{11}$, is the reciprocal of $2\frac{3}{4}$.)

GOAL

LEARN HOW TO...
- divide whole numbers and mixed numbers by fractions

AS YOU...
- design a border for the cover of your math book

KEY TERM
- reciprocals

5. $2 = \frac{2}{1}$, $2\frac{1}{4} = \frac{9}{4}$; The numerator of the first fraction is the denominator of the second fraction, and the denominator of the first fraction is the numerator of the second fraction.

6. a. $\frac{7}{4}$ or any number equivalent, like $1\frac{3}{4}$

✔ QUESTION 8

...checks that you can find the reciprocal of a number.

7. No: Sample Response: $2\frac{3}{4} = \frac{11}{4}$ and its reciprocal is $\frac{4}{11}$, while $2\frac{4}{3} = \frac{10}{3}$ and its reciprocal is $\frac{3}{10}$.

Exploration 1

Dividing $\frac{by}{a}$ Fraction

SET UP You will need: • customary ruler • Labsheet 6A

▶ The numbers you multiplied in Question 3 had a product of 1. Now you will explore other pairs of numbers whose products are 1. Such pairs of numbers are **reciprocals**.

4 Find each product. Write each answer in lowest terms.

a. $\frac{11}{8} \cdot \frac{8}{11}$ 1   **b.** $2 \cdot \frac{1}{2}$ 1   **c.** $\frac{4}{9} \cdot 2\frac{1}{4}$ 1

5 Write 2 and $2\frac{1}{4}$ as fractions greater than one. How are the numerators and denominators of the two numbers in each part of Question 4 related?

6 a. By what number can you multiply $\frac{4}{7}$ to get a product of 1?

b. What is the reciprocal of $\frac{4}{7}$? $\frac{7}{4}$

7 Discussion Are $2\frac{3}{4}$ and $2\frac{4}{3}$ reciprocals? Explain.

8 ✔ CHECKPOINT Write the reciprocal of each number.

a. $\frac{8}{9}$ $\frac{9}{8}$ **b.** 3 $\frac{1}{3}$ **c.** $\frac{1}{5}$ 5   **d.** $1\frac{4}{5}$ $\frac{5}{9}$

▶ Suppose you use $\frac{1}{2}$ in. x $\frac{1}{2}$ in. square tiles to create a border for the cover of your math book as shown at the top of the next page.

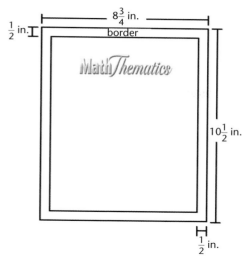

8¾ in.

½ in. border

Math*Thematics*

10½ in.

½ in.

9 Complete the following to find the number of tiles needed to make the $10\frac{1}{2}$ in. border on the right side of the cover.

a. The tiles are $\frac{1}{2}$ in. long, so you must find out how many $\frac{1}{2}$ in. lengths are in $10\frac{1}{2}$ in. This is the same as finding $10\frac{1}{2} \div \frac{1}{2}$. One way to do this is with a ruler. How many times does $\frac{1}{2}$ in. fit into $10\frac{1}{2}$ in.? 21

Continue marking off $\frac{1}{2}$'s to $10\frac{1}{2}$.

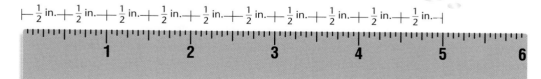

├ $\frac{1}{2}$ in.┼ $\frac{1}{2}$ in.┼ $\frac{1}{2}$ in.┼ $\frac{1}{2}$ in.┼ $\frac{1}{2}$ in.┼ $\frac{1}{2}$ in.┼ $\frac{1}{2}$ in.┼ $\frac{1}{2}$ in.┼ $\frac{1}{2}$ in.┼ $\frac{1}{2}$ in.┤

1   2   3   4   5   6

b. What is $10\frac{1}{2} \div \frac{1}{2}$? 21

c. Instead of marking off each $\frac{1}{2}$ in., think about the number of halves in 1. How many are there? 2

d. Discussion How can your answer to part (c) help you find the number of halves in $10\frac{1}{2}$?

Sample Response: If there are 2 halves in one then there are 20 halves in 10 (2 · 10 = 20) and one more half makes 21 halves.

Exploration 1 continued

Use Labsheet 6A for Questions 10 and 11.

TEACHING NOTES

Question 10 As students work through **Labsheet 6A**, they should discover that division by a fraction is the same as multiplication by the reciprocal and be able to answer **Question 11**.

The Classroom Example below shows how reciprocals can be used to divide fractions. It is best presented after the text example.

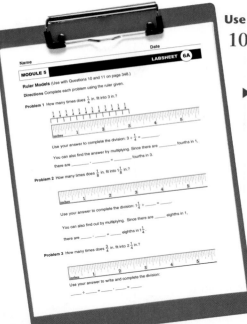

10 The *Ruler Models* and questions will help you explore division by a fraction. Complete the labsheet.

▶ In Question 9(d) you could have multiplied $10\frac{1}{2}$ by 2 to find $10\frac{1}{2} \div \frac{1}{2}$. Notice that $\frac{1}{2}$ and 2 (also written $\frac{2}{1}$) are reciprocals.

11 a. Explain how reciprocals and multiplication were used in Problems 1 and 2 on Labsheet 6A. **See margin.**

b. Use your method from part (a) to find $2\frac{1}{4} \div \frac{3}{4}$. Compare your answer to the one you gave for Problem 3 on Labsheet 6A.

$2\frac{1}{4} \div \frac{3}{4} = 2\frac{1}{4} \cdot \frac{4}{3} = \frac{9}{4} \cdot \frac{4}{3} = 3$; it is the same.

CLASSROOM EXAMPLE

Find $8 \div \frac{4}{5}$. Write the quotient in lowest terms.

Answer: To divide by $\frac{4}{5}$, multiply by its reciprocal $\frac{5}{4}$.

$$8 \div \frac{4}{5} = 8 \cdot \frac{5}{4}$$
$$= \frac{8}{1} \cdot \frac{5}{4}$$
$$= \frac{40}{4}$$
$$= 10$$

---

10. Problem 1: 12 times; $3 \div \frac{1}{4} = 12$; Since there are 4 fourths in 1, there are $4 \cdot 3 = 12$ fourths in 3.

Problem 2: 10 times; $1\frac{1}{4} \div \frac{1}{8} = 10$; Since there are 8 eighths in 1, there are $8 \cdot 1\frac{1}{4} = 10$ eighths in $1\frac{1}{4}$.

Problem 3: 3 times; $2\frac{1}{4} \div \frac{3}{4} = 2\frac{1}{4} \cdot \frac{4}{3} = 3$

11. a. Problem 1 shows that dividing 3 by $\frac{1}{4}$ is the same as multiplying 3 by the reciprocal of $\frac{1}{4}$, or 4. Problem 2 shows that dividing $1\frac{1}{4}$ by $\frac{1}{8}$ is the same as multiplying $1\frac{1}{4}$ by the reciprocal of $\frac{1}{8}$, or 8.

▶ You can use a reciprocal and multiplication to divide by a fraction.

EXAMPLE

Find $5\frac{1}{3} \div \frac{2}{3}$. Write the quotient in lowest terms.

SAMPLE RESPONSE

$$5\frac{1}{3} \div \frac{2}{3} = 5\frac{1}{3} \cdot \frac{3}{2} = \frac{16}{3} \cdot \frac{3}{2} = \frac{16 \cdot 3}{3 \cdot 2} = \frac{48}{6} = 8$$

To divide by $\frac{2}{3}$, multiply by the reciprocal, $\frac{3}{2}$.

✔ **QUESTION 12**

...checks that you can divide a whole number or a mixed number by a fraction.

12 ✔ **CHECKPOINT** Find each quotient. Write the answer in lowest terms.

a. $7 \div \frac{1}{7}$ 49 **b.** $10 \div \frac{2}{5}$ 25 **c.** $1\frac{3}{5} \div \frac{2}{5}$ 4 **d.** $3\frac{3}{4} \div \frac{3}{8}$ 10

▶ **Looking at Remainders** Suppose you use trapezoids to make a border like the one below.

$\vdash \frac{3}{4}$ in. $\dashv$

13 **Try This as a Class** Complete the following to find the number of $\frac{3}{4}$ in. trapezoid-tiles needed to make an 8 in. border.

    a. How does the expression $8 \div \frac{3}{4}$ represent the number of trapezoids needed to make an 8 in. border?

    b. When you use $8 \cdot \frac{4}{3}$ to find $8 \div \frac{3}{4}$, you get the answer $10\frac{2}{3}$. What does the 10 represent?
    The number of complete trapezoids needed to make the border.

    c. What does the fraction part $\frac{2}{3}$ mean?
    The part of the border you have left after fitting in 10 tiles is $\frac{2}{3}$ of a trapezoid.

14 **a.** **Discussion** Describe a situation represented by $5 \div \frac{7}{8}$.

    b. Use multiplication by a reciprocal to find $5 \div \frac{7}{8}$.
    $5 \cdot \frac{8}{7} = 5\frac{5}{7}$

    c. What does the whole number represent in your situation?
    5 complete tiles are needed to fill in the border.
    d. What does the fraction part mean?
    The part of the border left after fitting in 5 tiles is $\frac{5}{7}$ of a complete tile.

15 ✔ **CHECKPOINT** Find each quotient. Write the answer in lowest terms.

    a. $8 \div \frac{7}{10}$ $11\frac{3}{7}$ **b.** $5\frac{2}{3} \div \frac{5}{6}$ $6\frac{4}{5}$ **c.** $1\frac{4}{5} \div \frac{3}{8}$ $4\frac{4}{5}$

16 Find the number of $\frac{1}{2}$ in. x $\frac{1}{2}$ in. square tiles needed to make a border along the top of your math book cover. $17\frac{1}{2}$ tiles

HOMEWORK EXERCISES ▶ See Exs. 1–16 on p. 353.

---

13. a. The length of the border is 8 in., and the length of each tile is $\frac{3}{4}$ in., so the number of tiles that fit in the border is $8 \div \frac{3}{4}$.

14. a. Sample Response: You want to find the number of $\frac{7}{8}$ in. tiles needed to make a 5 in. border.

✔ **QUESTION 15**

...checks that you can divide by a fraction.

TEACHING NOTES

Question 14 can be discussed in small groups or as a class. The purpose is to ensure that students are able to use the division algorithm. It also further ties together their work from **Questions 12 and 13**. By this time in the exploration, students should be able to make the transition from manipulatives to paper-and-pencil computations for fraction division.

Question 15 You may want to have students explain the meaning of each division before they complete the problems. For example, 8 divided by $\frac{7}{10}$ means how many times $\frac{7}{10}$ *fits into* 8 or how many $\frac{7}{10}$ s *are in* 8. This will reinforce their work from the beginning of the exploration and help strengthen their conceptual understanding of division.

Questions 17 and 18 Students should have no difficulty applying the method of reciprocals to dividing a fraction by a fraction. If desired, you can use a ruler to quickly demonstrate how many times $\frac{3}{8}$ in. fits into $\frac{3}{4}$ in.

DEVELOPING MATH CONCEPTS
Division of mixed numbers is approached through the continued use of reciprocals along with renaming the mixed numbers as fractions. Students should be encouraged to use estimation to check the reasonableness of their answers. You may also need to remind them that in Exploration 1 they discovered that to write the reciprocal of a mixed number they cannot just interchange the numerator and denominator of the fractional part of the mixed number. It is easiest to find the reciprocal if the mixed number is written as a fraction first.

GOAL

LEARN HOW TO...
◆ divide by fractions and mixed numbers

AS YOU...
◆ design a border for the cover of your math book

19. a. First, she rewrote the mixed numbers as fractions. Then she wrote a related multiplication expression using reciprocals. She multiplied and finally she simplified the answer.

✔ **QUESTION 18**

...checks that you can divide a fraction by a fraction.

19. b. Sample Response: about $5 \div 2 = 2\frac{1}{2}$

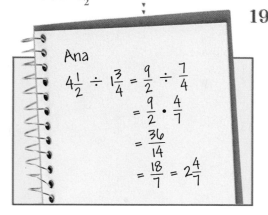

Ana

$4\frac{1}{2} \div 1\frac{3}{4} = \frac{9}{2} \div \frac{7}{4}$

$= \frac{9}{2} \cdot \frac{4}{7}$

$= \frac{36}{14}$

$= \frac{18}{7} = 2\frac{4}{7}$

Exploration 2

DIVIDING
Fractions and Mixed Numbers

SET UP You will need: • customary ruler • $8\frac{1}{2}$ in. x 11 in. piece of unlined paper • scissors

▶ **Using Reciprocals** In Exploration 1, you used reciprocals to divide whole numbers and mixed numbers by fractions. You can use the same method to divide a fraction by a fraction.

17 a. Use the reciprocal of $\frac{3}{8}$ to rewrite $\frac{3}{4} \div \frac{3}{8}$ as a related multiplication expression. $\frac{3}{4} \cdot \frac{8}{3}$

b. Find the product and write your answer in lowest terms. 2

18 ✔ **CHECKPOINT** Find each quotient. Write the answer in lowest terms.

a. $\frac{1}{4} \div \frac{1}{9}$ $2\frac{1}{4}$ b. $\frac{7}{16} \div \frac{3}{4}$ $\frac{7}{12}$ c. $\frac{11}{12} \div \frac{6}{7}$ $1\frac{5}{72}$

▶ **Dividing with Mixed Numbers** Sometimes, to find the number of tiles that are needed for a border, you must divide mixed numbers.

19 **Try This as a Class** Ana is tiling a $4\frac{1}{2}$ in. border with tiles that are $1\frac{3}{4}$ in. long.

a. Explain the steps Ana used to find out how many tiles will fit in the border.

b. Estimate the quotient $4\frac{1}{2} \div 1\frac{3}{4}$.

c. Is Ana's answer reasonable? Explain.
Sample Response: Yes, because her answer is close to $2\frac{1}{2}$.

d. Use Ana's method to find $7\frac{1}{2} \div 2\frac{1}{4}$.

$7\frac{1}{2} \div 2\frac{1}{4} = \frac{15}{2} \div \frac{9}{4} = \frac{15}{2} \cdot \frac{4}{9} = \frac{60}{18} = \frac{10}{3} = 3\frac{1}{3}$

20 ✔ **CHECKPOINT** Find each quotient. Write each answer in lowest terms.

a. $2\frac{1}{3} \div 5$ $\frac{7}{15}$　　b. $4\frac{1}{2} \div 1\frac{3}{4}$ $2\frac{4}{7}$　　c. $2\frac{5}{6} \div \frac{1}{2}$ $5\frac{2}{3}$

d. $3\frac{3}{4} \div 7\frac{1}{2}$ $\frac{1}{2}$　　e. $\frac{7}{12} \div 1\frac{17}{24}$ $\frac{14}{41}$　　f. $13 \div 4\frac{5}{13}$ $2\frac{55}{57}$

21 Discussion

a. Which fraction is greater, $\frac{3}{4}$ or $\frac{7}{8}$? $\frac{7}{8}$

b. Do you think $\frac{3}{4} \div \frac{7}{8}$ is a *whole number*, a *fraction less than 1*, or a *mixed number*? Why?

22 Try This as a Class

a. When you divide a number by a greater number, is the quotient *less than 1*, *equal to 1*, or *greater than 1*?
less than 1

b. When you divide a number by a lesser number, is the quotient *less than 1*, *equal to 1*, or *greater than 1*?
greater than 1

c. When you divide a number by an equal number, is the quotient *less than 1*, *equal to 1*, or *greater than 1*?
equal to 1

23 a. Look back at Question 16. How much must the width of the cover of your math book be decreased so that the border along the top can be made with a whole number of $\frac{1}{2}$ in. x $\frac{1}{2}$ in. square tiles? $\frac{1}{4}$ in.

b. What would the width of the cover be if it was decreased by the amount you found in part (a)? $8\frac{1}{2}$ in.

c. Cut out a rectangular piece of paper with the width you found in part (b) and a length of $10\frac{1}{2}$ in.
Check students' work.

d. How many $\frac{1}{2}$ in. x $\frac{1}{2}$ in. square tiles are needed to make a border around the piece of paper? 72 tiles

e. Create a $\frac{1}{2}$ in. x $\frac{1}{2}$ in. square tile design that can be drawn several times. Check students' work.

f. Use your tile to make a border around the paper.
Check students' work.

HOMEWORK EXERCISES ▶ See Exs. 17–31 on pp. 353–355.

 ✔ **QUESTION 20**

...checks that you can divide by fractions and mixed numbers.

21. b. Less than 1 because $\frac{7}{8} > \frac{3}{4}$ and when you divide a number by a greater number the quotient is less than 1.

Section 6　Division with Fractions　**351**

TEACHING NOTES

Question 21 Allow students to discuss **Question 21** in small groups, defending their response to **part (b)** before sharing their responses with the whole class. Encourage students to discuss **part (b)** without actually doing the division. After the group discussion they may want to calculate the quotient to determine whether their reasoning was correct or incorrect. The discussion of **Question 21** can serve as a motivator for exploring each of the situations in **Question 22**. Ask students, "Can you always tell prior to dividing whether the quotient of two fractions will be less than, equal to, or greater than 1? If so, how?" (*Yes, if the divisor is greater than the dividend, the quotient is less than 1; if it is less than the dividend the quotient is greater than 1. If the divisor and dividend are equal, the quotient is 1.*)

Have students give several examples for each situation in **Question 22**, and then have them determine the quotients. Ask students to explain how they know (other than just based on the few examples) that the quotient in the given situation will be either less than, greater than, or equal to 1. Using number sense to estimate quotients is important for students to determine the reasonableness of their answers as they continue to divide fractions and mixed numbers.

Question 23 Be sure to give students enough time to work through all parts of this question. For students creating more complicated designs, allow them extra time at home or in class to complete their borders. Students' decorated borders can be displayed on a bulletin board.

Key Concepts

CLOSURE QUESTION

Describe the steps involved in the division of fractions and mixed numbers.

Sample Response: To divide fractions, multiply the dividend by the reciprocal of the divisor. Then, if necessary, write the answer in lowest terms. If the division involves mixed numbers, first write each mixed number as a fraction and then follow the above steps to divide the fractions.

ABSENT STUDENTS

For students who were absent for all or part of this section, the blackline Study Guide for Section 6 may be used to present the ideas, concepts, and skills of Section 6.

Key Term

reciprocals

Section 6
Key Concepts

Reciprocals (p. 346)

Two numbers whose product is 1 are reciprocals.

$$4\frac{1}{2} = \frac{9}{2}$$

Example $4\frac{1}{2}$ and $\frac{2}{9}$ are reciprocals, since $\frac{9}{2} \cdot \frac{2}{9} = 1$.

Dividing by a Fraction (pp. 347–350)

To divide by a fraction, you can multiply by its reciprocal.

Example Find $\frac{3}{10} \div \frac{3}{4}$. Write the answer in lowest terms.

Multiply by the reciprocal of the divisor.

$$\frac{3}{10} \div \frac{3}{4} = \frac{3}{10} \cdot \frac{4}{3} = \frac{3 \cdot 4}{10 \cdot 3} = \frac{12}{30} = \frac{2}{5}$$

Using Number Sense in Division (p. 351)

When you divide a number by a lesser number, the quotient is greater than 1. When you divide a number by a greater number, the quotient is less than 1.

The quotient in the Example above is less than 1 since $\frac{3}{4} > \frac{3}{10}$.

Dividing by a Mixed Number (pp. 350–351)

To divide mixed numbers, you can write the mixed numbers as fractions and then multiply by the reciprocal of the divisor.

Example Find $1\frac{1}{2} \div 4\frac{3}{8}$. Write the answer in lowest terms.

Write the mixed numbers as fractions.

$$1\frac{1}{2} \div 4\frac{3}{8} = \frac{3}{2} \div \frac{35}{8}$$

$$= \frac{3}{2} \cdot \frac{8}{35} = \frac{3 \cdot 8}{2 \cdot 35} = \frac{24}{70} = \frac{12}{35}$$

24 Key Concepts Question Suppose a package of strawberry dessert mix makes $5\frac{1}{2}$ cups. How many $\frac{2}{3}$ cup servings does the package make? $8\frac{1}{4}$

Section 6

Practice & Application Exercises

Write the reciprocal of each number.

1. 10 $\frac{1}{10}$

2. $7\frac{1}{2}$ $\frac{2}{15}$

3. $\frac{2}{3}$ $\frac{3}{2}$

4. $\frac{8}{5}$ $\frac{5}{8}$

Mental Math Use mental math to find each product by first multiplying pairs of reciprocals.

5. $3 \cdot \frac{5}{8} \cdot \frac{8}{5}$ 3

6. $2 \cdot \frac{5}{9} \cdot \frac{1}{2} \cdot \frac{8}{11} \cdot \frac{9}{5}$ $\frac{8}{11}$

Find each quotient. Write each answer in lowest terms.

7. $1 \div \frac{1}{2}$ 2

8. $3 \div \frac{1}{3}$ 9

9. $8 \div \frac{3}{5}$ $13\frac{1}{3}$

10. $6 \div \frac{3}{4}$ 8

11. $1\frac{1}{5} \div \frac{2}{5}$ 3

12. $2\frac{5}{6} \div \frac{4}{9}$ $6\frac{3}{8}$

13. $1\frac{1}{2} \div \frac{4}{3}$ $1\frac{1}{8}$

14. $10\frac{1}{8} \div \frac{3}{5}$ $16\frac{7}{8}$

15. Noreen needs to cut a 10-ft long piece of lumber into $\frac{3}{4}$-ft long pieces for a class project.

   a. How many $\frac{3}{4}$-ft pieces will she get?   **13 pieces**

   b. Will there be wood left over? If so, how much?   Yes, $\frac{1}{3}$ of a piece

16. a. Why are $8 \div 5$ and $8 \cdot \frac{1}{5}$ equal?

   b. Are $2.5 \div 10$ and $2.5 \cdot 0.1$ equal? Explain.

   c. Based on part (b), describe a shortcut for finding a quotient when a decimal is divided by 10, 100, 1000, and so on.

Find each quotient. Write each answer in lowest terms.

17. $\frac{2}{9} \div \frac{1}{10}$ $2\frac{2}{9}$

18. $3\frac{3}{4} \div 2\frac{1}{3}$ $1\frac{17}{28}$

19. $4\frac{1}{3} \div 2$ $2\frac{1}{6}$

20. $2\frac{3}{4} \div 6$ $\frac{11}{24}$

21. $\frac{5}{6} \div \frac{2}{3}$ $1\frac{1}{4}$

22. $2\frac{4}{5} \div \frac{8}{9}$ $3\frac{3}{20}$

Find each quotient where $n = \frac{2}{3}$.

23. $6 \div n$ 9

24. $n \div \frac{3}{4}$ $\frac{8}{9}$

25. $n \div n$ 1

26. $5\frac{1}{5} \div n$ $7\frac{4}{5}$

16. a. The first indicates 8 divided by 5 and the second indicates 8 multiplied by the reciprocal of 5, or $\frac{1}{5}$.

   b. Yes; $0.1 = \frac{1}{10}$, the reciprocal of 10. The relationship is the same.

   c. Move the decimal point to the left as many places as there are zeros in the divisor.

SUGGESTED ASSIGNMENTS

Core Course
Day 1: Exs. 1–6, 32–40
Day 2: Exs. 7–16
Day 3: Exs. 17–29, 31

Extended Course
Day 1: Exs. 1–6, 32–40
Day 2: Exs. 7–16
Day 3: Exs. 17–31

Note: Extended Course assignments can be used to differentiate within the regular classroom. In classrooms where students are grouped homogeneously, the material might be covered in fewer days. In this case assignments may be combined.

ADDITIONAL PRACTICE
See the *Teacher's Resource Book* for additional practice and application exercises for this section.

Practice & Applications

EXERCISE NOTES

Exercises 27–29 give real life applications of fraction and mixed number division. You might encourage students to write their own real life application problems using fractions or mixed numbers they come across in their daily lives.

27. **Stock Market** Jodi found an old newspaper that reported stock values by listing the cost per share (in dollars) for each company and the daily change in the cost per share (in dollars) using fractions.

    a. What was the net change in the closing price for a share of MathCo on Tuesday? $-\frac{15}{16}$

    b. How many whole shares of MathCo's stock could an investor have bought with $1000 at the closing price on Monday? on Tuesday? **Monday - 96; Tuesday - 105**

What the price for one share of stock is at the end of the day. ⟶

Change in closing price from the previous day. ⟶

Monday	Hi	Lo	Close	Net Chg
MapLtd	15¾	15¹⁄₁₆	15³⁄₁₆	+⅛
MathCo	10⅝	10¼	10⅜	+¹⁄₁₆
MiniMkt	33⅞	33½	33½	−³⁄₁₆

$+\frac{1}{16}$ means that today's closing price is $\frac{1}{16}$ of a dollar higher than the previous closing price.

Tuesday	Hi	Lo	Close	Net Chg
MapLtd	15½	14¹⁵⁄₁₆	15⅛	−¹⁄₁₆
MathCo	10⅜	9⁵⁄₁₆	9⁷⁄₁₆	
MiniMkt	34³⁄₁₆	33⅛	33⅞	

28. Ali has $12\frac{1}{2}$ gal of paint. He needs about $3\frac{1}{2}$ gal of paint for each room in his house. He plans to paint as many rooms as he can.

    a. How many rooms can he paint? **3 rooms**

    b. About how much paint will he use? **about $10\frac{1}{2}$ gal**

    c. About how much paint will be left over? **about 2 gal**

29. a. less than; Sample Response: $2 \cdot 6 = 12$ and $\frac{3}{4} > \frac{1}{2}$, so $2 \cdot 6\frac{3}{4} > 13$

Upland sandpiper
▼

29. **Bird-watching** Sandpipers are long-legged wading birds. One of the smallest is the semipalmated sandpiper, which is usually no longer than $6\frac{3}{4}$ in. One of the largest is the upland sandpiper, which can be as long as $12\frac{1}{2}$ in.

▲
Semipalmated sandpiper

    a. **Estimation** Without dividing, tell whether the upland sandpiper is *more than* or *less than* twice as long as the semipalmated sandpiper. Explain your thinking.

    b. Find $12\frac{1}{2} \div 6\frac{3}{4}$ to check your answer in part (a). $1\frac{23}{27}$

30. Challenge You learned to use the distributive property and mental math to find the product $6 \cdot 2\frac{1}{3}$.

$$6 \cdot \left(2 + \frac{1}{3}\right) = (6 \cdot 2) + \left(6 \cdot \frac{1}{3}\right)$$

Do you think there is a distributive property for division? Explain your thinking. (*Hint:* Does $6 \div 2\frac{1}{3}$ equal $(6 \div 2) + \left(6 \div \frac{1}{3}\right)$?)

No; $6 \div 2\frac{1}{3} = 6 \div \frac{7}{3} = 6 \cdot \frac{3}{7} = 2\frac{4}{7}$, while $(6 \div 2) + (6 \div \frac{1}{3}) = 3 + 18 = 21$.

Reflecting ◀▶ on the Section

31. The five puzzle pieces below fit together to form a square.

Visual THINKING

Exercise 31 checks that you can apply mixed number skills.

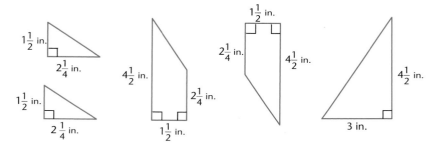

a. How many copies of the puzzle can be cut from a strip of tagboard that measures $4\frac{1}{2}$ in. by 17 in.? **3**

b. What is the area of the strip that will be left over? $15\frac{3}{4}$ in.²

Spiral ◀▶ Review

Use the distributive property to find each product. Write each answer in lowest terms. (Module 3, p. 178)

32. $9 \cdot 2\frac{1}{3}$ **21**   33. $7\frac{1}{5} \cdot 2\frac{5}{6}$ **$20\frac{2}{5}$**   34. $\frac{2}{3} \cdot 1\frac{3}{4}$ **$1\frac{1}{6}$**

Write the ordered pair for each point on the coordinate grid. (Module 4, p. 256)

35. A **(4, 6)**   36. B **(1, 3)**   37. C **(6, 0)**

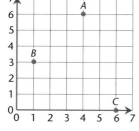

Complete each pair of equivalent fractions. (Module 1, p. 61)

38. $\frac{7}{8} = \frac{?}{16}$ 39. $\frac{4}{5} = \frac{12}{?}$ 40. $\frac{9}{45} = \frac{1}{?}$
    14   **15**   **5**

COMMON ERROR
Some students may think that since there is a distributive property for multiplication, there must be one for division as well. Doing **Exercise 30** should clear up this erroneous reasoning.

Section 6 Division with Fractions **355**

Section 6
Extra Skill Practice

Write the reciprocal of each number.

1. $\frac{1}{6}$ 6

2. $3\frac{7}{8}$ $\frac{8}{31}$

3. 32 $\frac{1}{32}$

4. $\frac{4}{3}$ $\frac{3}{4}$

Use mental math to find each product by first multiplying pairs of reciprocals.

5. $4 \cdot \frac{3}{5} \cdot \frac{1}{2} \cdot \frac{5}{3} \cdot 3$ 6

6. $5 \cdot \frac{9}{7} \cdot \frac{1}{2} \cdot \frac{2}{3} \cdot \frac{3}{2} \cdot \frac{7}{9} \cdot \frac{1}{5}$ $\frac{1}{2}$

Find each quotient. Write each answer in lowest terms.

7. $6 \div \frac{2}{3}$ 9

8. $1 \div \frac{3}{4}$ $1\frac{1}{3}$

9. $2\frac{1}{2} \div \frac{5}{9}$ $4\frac{1}{2}$

10. $7 \div \frac{2}{3}$ $10\frac{1}{2}$

11. $1\frac{5}{7} \div \frac{6}{11}$ $3\frac{1}{7}$

12. $6 \div \frac{5}{4}$ $4\frac{4}{5}$

13. $2\frac{3}{8} \div \frac{4}{7}$ $4\frac{5}{32}$

14. $1\frac{1}{4} \div \frac{5}{3}$ $\frac{3}{4}$

Find each quotient. Write each answer in lowest terms.

15. $\frac{3}{5} \div \frac{1}{6}$ $3\frac{3}{5}$

16. $\frac{1}{6} \div \frac{2}{5}$ $\frac{5}{12}$

17. $\frac{9}{16} \div \frac{3}{8}$ $1\frac{1}{2}$

18. $3\frac{1}{8} \div \frac{1}{8}$ 25

19. $4\frac{2}{3} \div \frac{1}{2}$ $9\frac{1}{3}$

20. $4\frac{2}{5} \div 2\frac{1}{4}$ $1\frac{43}{45}$

21. $6\frac{3}{4} \div 3$ $2\frac{1}{4}$

22. $2\frac{1}{2} \div 1\frac{3}{4}$ $1\frac{3}{7}$

23. $3 \div 5\frac{3}{4}$ $\frac{12}{23}$

24. $5\frac{1}{3} \div 1\frac{3}{5}$ $3\frac{1}{3}$

25. $\frac{9}{10} \div 18$ $\frac{1}{20}$

26. $3\frac{3}{8} \div 2\frac{1}{4}$ $1\frac{1}{2}$

Find each quotient where $n = \frac{3}{4}$.

27. $12 \div n$ 16

28. $n \div n$ 1

29. $n \div 1\frac{1}{3}$ $\frac{9}{16}$

30. $5\frac{1}{2} \div n$ $7\frac{1}{3}$

Standardized Testing ◀▶ **Multiple Choice**

When dividing a fraction by a lesser fraction, what will the quotient be? C

Ⓐ less than 1   Ⓑ equal to 1   Ⓒ greater than 1   Ⓓ not enough information

The Module Project

Creating Cubes

Paper folding was used in this module to help you model and understand operations with fractions. In this project, you will apply what you have learned about fractions and measurement as you make a cube by paper folding.

Step 1 Start with a square piece of paper $8\frac{1}{2}$ in. by $8\frac{1}{2}$ in. Fold the square in half as shown and then open it up again.

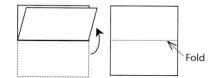
Fold

Step 2 Turn the paper over. Fold the square along one diagonal and open it up again. Then fold the square along the other diagonal and open it up.

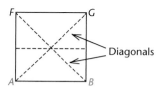
Diagonals

Step 3 Fold the paper into the shape shown at the right. a.–b. See margin.

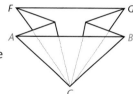

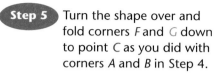
a. Use two different methods to find the area of triangle *ABC* in square inches.

b. Explain the methods you used.

Step 4 Fold the front corners *A* and *B* down to point *C* as shown.

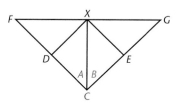

Step 5 Turn the shape over and fold corners *F* and *G* down to point *C* as you did with corners *A* and *B* in Step 4.

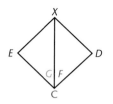

Module Project

PROJECT NOTES

The Module Project relies on students being able to follow written and visual directions to create a cube. You may want to complete steps 1 through 12 on your own first before assigning the project. Having just completed the steps yourself will allow you to more easily help any students who become stuck or make an error in one of the steps. Certain vertices are highlighted in different colors to help students identify new folds or alignments. It will help if students keep their paper oriented in the same direction as shown in each diagram.

Heavier weight paper is more difficult to inflate. Students' lined notebook paper tends to work better than copier weight paper.

1. a.–b. Answers will vary.

    Method 1: Area of triangle *ABC*

$$= \frac{1}{4} \cdot \text{Area of the square}$$

$$= \frac{1}{4} \cdot 8\frac{1}{2} \cdot 8\frac{1}{2}$$

$$= 18\frac{1}{16} \text{ in.}^2$$

    Method 2: Area of triangle *ABC*

$$= \frac{1}{2} \cdot b \cdot h$$

$$= \frac{1}{2} \cdot 8\frac{1}{8} \cdot 4\frac{1}{4}$$

$$= 18\frac{1}{16} \text{ in.}^2$$

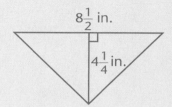

$8\frac{1}{2}$ in.

$4\frac{1}{4}$ in.

Step 6 Fold the top layer at corners *D* and *E* so they meet in the center as shown below.

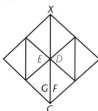

Step 7 Turn the square over and do the same for the corners on the back side as shown below.

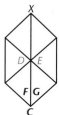

Step 8 One end of the shape in Step 7 will have loose corners. With this end pointing toward you, fold the loose corners outward on the front to form the shape shown at the right. Turn the shape over and do the same on the back.

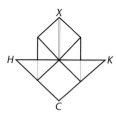

Step 9 On both sides, fold *H* and *K* in to the center as shown on the left below. The shape should now look like the one on the right.

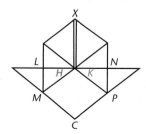

Step 10 Tuck triangle *LHM* into the slot between the layers directly underneath the triangle as shown. Then do the same for triangle *NKP*.

Step 11 Turn the shape over and do the same on the back.

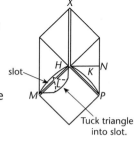

Tuck triangle into slot.

To inflate the cube, blow sharply into the small hole found at *X*. Crease the edges. *Voilà!* A cube!

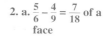

 2 Keiko decorated $1\frac{1}{2}$ of the faces blue, $1\frac{5}{9}$ of the faces red, $\frac{5}{6}$ of a face white, $\frac{4}{9}$ of a face green, and $1\frac{1}{3}$ of the faces yellow.

  a. How much more of the cube was decorated white than green?

  b. How many faces of the cube were decorated red, white, and blue?

  c. Challenge What fraction of the cube's surface was not decorated?

 3 a. The length of a side of the original square in Step 1 is how many times the length of an edge of the cube in Step 12?

  b. Write an equation to express the relationship in part (a). Let *s* = the length of a side of the square and *e* = the length of an edge of the cube.

In Questions 4 and 5, use your answer from Question 3(b) to write an equation. Then solve the equation.

 4 Masao is making cubes of different sizes to tie to a bamboo branch for *Tanabata*. How wide should his paper be to construct a cube with an edge that is $2\frac{1}{3}$ in. long? $s = 4e;\ s = 4 \cdot 2\frac{1}{3};\ s = 9\frac{1}{3}$ in.

 5 How long will the edge of Masao's cube be if he begins with a 16 in. by 16 in. square sheet of paper?
$4e = s;\ 4e = 16;\ e = 4$ in.

The Japanese use the cubes as a decoration in a summer festival called *Tanabata*. The cubes, along with other decorations such as paper dolls and colored strips, are tied to bamboo branches and then floated down the river. In ancient times this was said to bring good fortune in weaving, writing, and handicrafts. Today, some people believe that tying the cube to a bamboo branch will make a wish come true.

2. a. $\frac{5}{6} - \frac{4}{9} = \frac{7}{18}$ of a face

b. $1\frac{5}{9} + \frac{5}{6} + 1\frac{1}{2}$
$= 3\frac{8}{9}$ faces

c. $1\frac{1}{2} + 1\frac{5}{9} + \frac{5}{6} + \frac{4}{9}$
$+ 1\frac{1}{3} = 5\frac{2}{3}$ faces
are decorated

$6 - 5\frac{2}{3} = \frac{1}{3}$ face
is not decorated

$\dfrac{\left(\frac{1}{3}\right)}{6} = \frac{1}{18}$ of the
surface is not
decorated

3. a. length of edge
$= 2\frac{1}{8}$ in.

$8\frac{1}{2}$ in. $\div\ 2\frac{1}{8}$ in.
$= 4$

The length
of a side of
the square is
4 times the
length of an
edge.

b. $4e = s$

Review and Assessment

Review and Assessment

TEACHER NOTES
Students should complete the Review and Assessment independently in preparation for the Module Test.

Allow class time to discuss solutions and address any questions students may have. During this time, you may want to allow students to work in groups to share methods for solving the problems and to quiz each other on the concepts covered in this module.

You will need: • *Review and Assessment Labsheet* (Exs. 36–37) • *metric ruler* (Ex. 37)

Write the fractions in order from least to greatest. (Sec. 1, Explor. 1)

1. $\frac{4}{7}, \frac{2}{3}, \frac{5}{3}, \frac{3}{100}$ $\frac{3}{100}, \frac{4}{7}, \frac{2}{3}, \frac{5}{3}$

2. $\frac{9}{10}, \frac{4}{5}, \frac{99}{100}, \frac{19}{20}$ $\frac{4}{5}, \frac{9}{10}, \frac{19}{20}, \frac{99}{100}$

3. $\frac{7}{8}, \frac{4}{5}, \frac{1}{7}, \frac{1}{4}$ $\frac{1}{7}, \frac{1}{4}, \frac{4}{5}, \frac{7}{8}$

4. $\frac{5}{6}, \frac{2}{3}, \frac{1}{4}, \frac{1}{2}$ $\frac{1}{4}, \frac{1}{2}, \frac{2}{3}, \frac{5}{6}$

Use a common denominator to compare the fractions.
Replace each ? with >, <, or =. (Sec. 1, Explor. 2)

5. $\frac{5}{8}$ _?_ $\frac{7}{12}$ $\frac{5}{8} > \frac{7}{12}$

6. $\frac{4}{9}$ _?_ $\frac{6}{15}$ $\frac{4}{9} > \frac{6}{15}$

7. $\frac{11}{16}$ _?_ $\frac{3}{4}$ $\frac{11}{16} < \frac{3}{4}$

8. $\frac{8}{13}$ _?_ $\frac{2}{3}$ $\frac{8}{13} < \frac{2}{3}$

Write each fraction as a decimal rounded to the nearest hundredth.
Then replace each ? with >, <, or =. (Sec. 1, Explor. 2)

9. $\frac{8}{11}$ _?_ $\frac{9}{13}$ $0.73 > 0.69$

10. $\frac{15}{27}$ _?_ $\frac{68}{103}$ $0.56 < 0.66$

11. $\frac{39}{83}$ _?_ $\frac{3}{7}$ $0.47 > 0.43$

Replace each ? with a number that makes the statement true.
(Sec. 2, Explor. 2)

12. $3\frac{1}{2}$ yd = _?_ in. 126

13. 34 in. = _?_ ft $2\frac{5}{6}$

14. 6000 ft = _?_ mi $1\frac{3}{22}$

15. 26 ft = _?_ yd $8\frac{2}{3}$

16. $5\frac{1}{4}$ ft = _?_ in. 63

17. 1 mi 250 yd = _?_ ft 6030

Find each sum or difference. Write each answer in lowest terms.
(Sec. 3, Explor. 1; Sec. 4, Explors. 1 and 2) 20. $3\frac{7}{15}$ or $\frac{52}{15}$; 22. $9\frac{33}{40}$ or $\frac{393}{40}$; 28. $2\frac{1}{12}$ or $\frac{25}{12}$

18. $\frac{5}{8} + \frac{7}{8}$ $\frac{3}{2}$ or $1\frac{1}{2}$

19. $\frac{4}{7} + \frac{1}{3}$ $\frac{19}{21}$

20. $3\frac{3}{10} + \frac{1}{6}$

21. $5\frac{1}{6} + 2\frac{1}{8}$ $7\frac{7}{24}$ or $\frac{175}{24}$

22. $8\frac{1}{5} + 1\frac{5}{8}$

23. $\frac{26}{5} + \frac{13}{10}$ $6\frac{1}{2}$ or $\frac{13}{2}$

24. $\frac{5}{8} - \frac{1}{4}$ $\frac{3}{8}$

25. $8\frac{2}{3} - 2\frac{3}{5}$ $6\frac{1}{15}$ or $\frac{91}{15}$

26. $3 - \frac{2}{5}$ $2\frac{3}{5}$ or $\frac{13}{5}$

27. $\frac{7}{8} - \frac{1}{3}$ $\frac{13}{24}$

28. $8\frac{3}{4} - 6\frac{2}{3}$

29. $2\frac{3}{5} - 1\frac{5}{8}$ $\frac{39}{40}$

30. A truck driver drove from Albuquerque to Los Angeles in $15\frac{1}{2}$ hr and from Los Angeles to San Fransisco in $7\frac{2}{3}$ hr. How long did the entire trip take? (Sec. 4, Explor. 1) $23\frac{1}{6}$ hours

Use mental math or paper and pencil to find each sum or difference.
(Sec. 4, Explors. 1 and 2)

31. $9 - 2\frac{3}{4}$ $6\frac{1}{4}$

32. $2\frac{1}{2} + 1\frac{1}{2} + 4\frac{1}{2}$ $8\frac{1}{2}$

33. $10 - 4\frac{1}{16}$ $5\frac{15}{16}$

34. $\frac{1}{8} + \frac{1}{2} + \frac{3}{8} + \frac{1}{4}$ $1\frac{1}{4}$

35. Andy's house is $4\frac{1}{2}$ mi from school and Marguerite's house is $3\frac{1}{3}$ mi from school. How much farther does Andy live from school than Marguerite? (Sec. 4, Explor. 2) $1\frac{1}{6}$ mi

Use the Review and Assessment Labsheet for Exercises 36 and 37. (Sec. 5, Explors. 1–3)

36. Identify each of the *Polygons*. rectangle; triangle; parallelogram

37. Measure and label a base and the corresponding height of each of the *Polygons* to the nearest tenth of a centimeter. Then calculate the area of each polygon.

37. Answers will vary. Accept reasonable answers.
rectangle: base = 4.2 cm
height = 2.5 cm
area ≈ 10.5 cm²
triangle: base = 9.2 cm
height = 2.4 cm
area ≈ 11.0 cm²
parallelogram: base = 5.3 cm
height = 3.4 cm
area ≈ 18.0 cm²

Write and solve an equation to find the missing dimension for each figure. (Sec. 5, Explor. 3)

38.

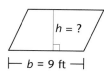

$h = ?$
$b = 9$ ft

Area = 54 ft²
$9h = 54; h = 6$ ft

39.

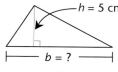

$h = 5$ cm
$b = ?$

Area = 19 cm²
$\frac{1}{2} \cdot 5b = 19; b = 7.6$ cm

Find the unknown value in each equation. (Sec. 5, Explor. 3)

40. $6x = 72$ $x = 12$

41. $\frac{2}{3}m = 12$ $m = 18$

42. $\frac{x}{4} = 12$ $x = 48$

Find each quotient. Write each answer in lowest terms.
(Sec. 6, Explors. 1 and 2) 43. $\frac{14}{9}$ or $1\frac{5}{9}$

43. $2\frac{1}{3} \div 1\frac{1}{2}$

44. $8 \div \frac{1}{3}$ 24

45. $\frac{3}{5} \div \frac{3}{7}$ $\frac{7}{5}$ or $1\frac{2}{5}$

46. $3\frac{1}{6} \div 4$ $\frac{19}{24}$

47. $3\frac{3}{8} \div 3$ $\frac{9}{8}$ or $1\frac{1}{8}$

48. $\frac{1}{4} \div \frac{9}{16}$ $\frac{4}{9}$

49. $1\frac{3}{8} \div \frac{7}{9}$ $1\frac{43}{56}$

50. $6\frac{1}{2} \div 12$ $\frac{13}{24}$

51. If Adela buys a board that is 8 ft long and 2 ft wide, how many $\frac{3}{4}$ ft by 2 ft pieces can she cut from the board? Explain. (Sec. 6, Explor. 1)
10 pieces; $8 \div \frac{3}{4} = \frac{32}{3} = 10\frac{2}{3}$.

Reflecting ◀▶ on the Module

52. Write a letter to a family member or friend describing what you have done in this module. Discuss how fractions are used to create things.
Answers will vary.

Assessment Options

TEACHER'S RESOURCE BOOK
• Module 5 Tests A and B
• Module 5 Standardized Test
• Module 5 Performance Assessment

TEST GENERATOR

MODULE 6 Comparisons and Predictions

Module 6 Overview

Situations from nature, literature, sports, art, movies, and the news provide opportunities for students to build an understanding of ratios, proportions, and percent, and to solve problems involving comparisons and predictions. Students also look at congruent and similar figures and learn to represent data in a circle graph.

Module 6 Planner

Day 1: Section 1 Setting the Stage, *pp. 364–365* Exploration 1, *pp. 365–367* Key Concepts, *p. 368*	**Day 2: Section 2** Setting the Stage, *pp. 373–374* Exploration 1 *through Question 7, pp. 374–375*	**Day 3: Section 2** Exploration 1 *from Question 8, pp. 375–376* Key Concepts, *p. 377*	**Day 4: Section 3** Setting the Stage, *p. 381* Exploration 1, *pp. 382–383*	**Day 5: Section 3** Exploration 2 *through Question 12, pp. 384–385*
Day 6: Section 3 Exploration 2 *from Example, pp. 385–386*	**Day 7: Section 3** Exploration 3, *pp. 387–388* Key Concepts, *p. 389*	**Day 8: E²** Begin E², *p. 395*	**Day 9: Review and Assessment** Mid-Module Quiz	**Day 10: Section 4** Setting the Stage, *p. 396* Exploration 1, *pp. 397–398*
Day 11: Section 4 Exploration 2, *pp. 399–400* Key Concepts, *pp. 401–402*	**Day 12: Section 5** Setting the Stage, *p. 406* Exploration 1 *through Question 7, pp. 407–409*	**Day 13: Section 5** Exploration 1 *from Example, p. 409*	**Day 14: Section 5** Exploration 2, *pp. 410–412* Key Concepts, *p. 413*	**Day 15: Section 6** Setting the Stage, *p. 419* Exploration 1 *through Question 3, p. 420*
Day 16: Section 6 Exploration 1 *from Question 4, p. 421*	**Day 17: Section 6** Exploration 2, *pp. 422–423*	**Day 18: Section 6** Exploration 3 *through Question 23, pp. 424–426*	**Day 19: Section 6** Exploration 3 *from Example, pp. 426–427* Key Concepts, *pp. 427–428*	**Day 20: Module Project** Begin Module Project, *pp. 433–435*
Day 21: Module Project Work on Module Project, *pp. 433–435*	**Day 22: Review and Assessment** Assign Review and Assessment, *pp. 436–437*	**Day 23: Review and Assessment** Discuss Review and Assessment, *pp. 436–437*	**Day 24: Assessment** Module 6 Test	

Materials List

Section	Materials
1	• Labsheet 1A, pennies
2	• Labsheet 2A, object to represent sandbag, watch or clock to time seconds, tape measure, brigade data for class, calculator, graph paper
3	• Labsheets 3A–3B, metric ruler, string, scissors, uncooked spaghetti or a clear ruler, graph paper
5	• Labsheet 5A, pattern blocks, metric ruler, tracing paper, protractor, customary ruler
6	• Labsheets 6A–6D, scissors, tape, colored markers or pencils, protractor, straightedge, compass
Project	• metric ruler, protractor, chalk or large newsprint and marker

Module 6 Objectives

Section	Objectives	NCTM Standards 2000*
1	• Use ratios to compare quantities. • Express a ratio three ways: using the word *to*, a colon, or fraction form. • Recognize and write equivalent ratios.	**1, 2, 4, 6, 7, 8, 9, 10**
2	• Find unit rates and use them to make predictions. • Make tables to represent rates and use the patterns observed to make predictions.	**1, 2, 4, 5, 6, 8, 9, 10**
3	• Use ratios to investigate measurements. • Write the decimal form of a ratio to make comparisons. • Find and use "nice" fraction forms of ratios to describe data and make predictions. • Make a scatter plot, fit a line to the data, and use the line to make predictions.	**1, 2, 3, 4, 5, 6, 8, 9, 10**
4	• Use cross products to identify equivalent ratios. • Use cross products to find a missing term in a proportion. • Write and use proportions to solve problems and make predictions. • Explore when using a proportion is or is not appropriate.	**1, 2, 4, 6, 8, 9**
5	• Identify similar and congruent figures and their corresponding parts. • Understand characteristics that make figures similar. • Apply similarity to solve problems involving scale drawings, scale models, and map scales.	**1, 2, 3, 4, 6, 8, 9, 10**
6	• Write a percent and relate fractions, decimals, and percents. • Use a fraction to estimate a percent or percent of a number. • Use a fraction to find a percent of a number. • Display data in a circle graph. • Use percents and fractions to estimate angle measures in a circle graph.	**1, 2, 3, 4, 6, 8, 9, 10**

* See page T14.

Section 1 Exploring Ratios

Section 1 Planner

Section Objectives

Exploration 1
- Use ratios to compare quantities
- Express a ratio three ways: using the word *to*, a colon, or fraction form
- Recognize and write equivalent ratios

Days for Section 1

First Day
Setting the Stage, *pp. 364–365*
Exploration 1, *pp. 365–367*
Key Concepts, *p. 368*

Teaching Resources

Teacher's Resource Book
- Warm-Up
- Labsheet 1A
- Practice and Applications
- Study Guide
See page 363 for additional teaching resources.

Materials List

Exploration 1
- Labsheet 1A
- pennies

Assessment Options

EMBEDDED ASSESSMENT
- Use ratios to compare quantities
  Exercises 8a, 8b, 11
- Express a ratio three ways: using the word *to*, a colon, or fraction form
  Exercises 11a, 11b, 12a
- Recognize and write equivalent ratios
  Exercises 3, 4, 9, 12d, 14c

PERFORMANCE TASK/PORTFOLIO
- Exercise 10 on *p. 369 (open-ended)*
- Exercise 15 on *p. 371 (language arts)*
- Exercise 16 on *p. 371 (challenge)*
- Exercise 17 on *p. 371 (research)*

QUIZZES/TESTS
- Section 1 Quick Quiz

TEST GENERATOR

Section 1 Overview

In this section, students will use literature and movies to see how ratios are used to compare measures.

Exploration 1
Following a discussion of the poem in the Setting the Stage, students will explore how props were used in the movie *The Lord of the Rings* to make the actors appear to have different statures. Students measure the heights of two mugs using pennies and write a ratio to compare the measurements. Then they measure the same two mugs using squares to find equivalent forms of the original ratio. Students learn to write a ratio in three different ways and to determine whether two ratios are equivalent. They return to Shel Silverstein's poem from the Setting the Stage to compare items in the poem using ratios.

Guide for Assigning Homework

REGULAR SCHEDULING (45 MIN CLASS PERIOD)			EXERCISES TO NOTE		
Section/ P&A Pages	**Core Assignment**	**Extended Assignment**	**Additional Practice/Review**	**Open-ended Problems**	**Extended Problems**
1 pp. 369–372	**Day 1:** 1–15, ROS 17, SR 18–29	8–16, ROS 17, SR 18–29	EP, p. 372	PA 10, 15, 17	Challenge PA 16

Key: PA = Practice & Application; ROS = Reflecting on the Section; SR = Spiral Review; TB = Toolbox; EP = Extra Skill Practice; Ext = Extension; ST = Standardized Testing

Math Background and Teaching Strategies

Classroom Notes

Bulletin board display ideas for this section include:

- a copy of *One Inch Tall* along with students' original last verses from Exercise 15

- different real world comparisons written as ratios

Visitors for this section might include:

- movie set designers

- a scale model artist

Math Strands

Topic Integration and Spiraling

Exploration 1

This exploration introduces the concepts of ratios and equivalent ratios and provides the foundation for the proportion topics that will follow this section. Students use physical objects to compare the heights of two props designed to make actors in a movie appear to be different sizes. The comparisons are written as ratios. The fact that a ratio can be written in fraction form allows students to make connections between fraction concepts studied in Module 1 and ratios, namely the concept of equivalent ratios.

In the remainder of Module 6, students will extend their work with ratios to rates and to using proportions to solve problems and make predictions. Proportional reasoning is used in problem solving situations throughout Books 1, 2, and 3. In particular, in Book 3 Module 5, ratios and proportional reasoning are used to discuss the efficiency of different sized cylindrical containers and to investigate how changes in linear dimensions affect surface area and volume.

Section 2 Rates

Section 2 Planner

Section Objectives

Exploration 1
- Use rates to make predictions
- Find unit rates
- Make tables to represent rates

Days for Section 2

First Day
Setting the Stage, *pp. 373–374*
Exploration 1 through Question 7, *pp. 374–375*

Second Day
Exploration 1 from Question 8, *pp. 375–376*
Key Concepts, *p. 377*

Teaching Resources

Teacher's Resource Book
- Warm-Up
- Labsheet 2A
- Practice and Applications
- Study Guide
See page 363 for additional teaching resources.

Materials List

Setting the Stage
- object to represent a sandbag
- watch or clock to time seconds
- tape measure

Practice and Applications
- Labsheet 2A
- your class's brigade data
- calculator
- graph paper

Assessment Options

EMBEDDED ASSESSMENT
- Use rates to make predictions
  Exercises 15, 18e, 19
- Find unit rates
  Exercises 9, 11, 13
- Make tables to represent rates
  Exercises 18a

PERFORMANCE TASK/PORTFOLIO
- Exercise 16 on *p. 378 (research)*
- Exercise 20 on *p. 379 (writing)*
- Exercise 21 on *p. 379 (journal)*
- Standardized Testing on *p. 380 (performance task)*

QUIZZES/TESTS
- Section 2 Quick Quiz

TEST GENERATOR

Section 2 Overview

In this section, students act out a problem involving rates.

Exploration 1
Students begin this exploration by using their class's sandbag brigade data to determine the units of measure for the distance and for the time it took. Then they use a ratio to compare the quantities. Students learn why a rate is a special type of ratio by identifying the units used to measure the quantities in their rates. They practice using rates to answer questions. Both tables and equivalent rates are used to solve problems involving rates. Key terms include *rate* and *unit rate*.

Guide for Assigning Homework

REGULAR SCHEDULING (45 MIN CLASS PERIOD)			EXERCISES TO NOTE		
Section/ P&A Pages	Core Assignment	Extended Assignment	Additional Practice/Review	Open-ended Problems	Extended Problems
2 pp. 377–380	**Day 1:** 1–8, 16, SR 22–27 **Day 2:** 9–15, 17, 19–20, ROS 21	1–8, 16, SR 22–27 9–17 odd, 18–20, ROS 21, Ext 28	EP, p. 380	PA 16	PA 18 Ext 28

Key: PA = Practice & Application; ROS = Reflecting on the Section; SR = Spiral Review; TB = Toolbox; EP = Extra Skill Practice; Ext = Extension; ST = Standardized Testing

Math Background and Teaching Strategies

Classroom Notes

Bulletin board displays for this section include:

- examples of rates in everyday life such as speed limit signs in mph, heart rates, rate of pay

- student work from Research Exercise 16

- a display identifying which ratios are actually rates

Math Strands

Topic Spiraling and Integration

Exploration 1

Students extend their knowledge of ratios gained in Section 1 to include rates. Tables are used to set up rates and to help students recognize equivalent rates. Unit rates are approached by writing of a rate as a fraction and finding an equivalent fraction (rate) in which the denominator is 1. In Section 4 students will work with proportions to find equivalent ratios. The use of cross products will be explored at that time.

In Exercise 18, students plot the points from a table of rates on a coordinate grid. They discover that the points lie on a line passing through the origin and use this line to make predictions. This provides an informal exposure to the connection between rates and the slopes of a line which is developed in Books 2 and 3. Extension Exercise 28 also demonstrates how rates can be represented with a coordinate graph. However, since the rates are not equivalent, the graph is not linear. In Section 4 of Module 6, students will work with graphs, using ratios and scatter plots to make predictions.

Section 3 Using Ratios

Section 3 Planner

Section Objectives

Exploration 1
- Use ratios to investigate measurements
- Write the decimal form of a ratio to make comparisons

Exploration 2
- Find and use "nice" fraction forms of ratios to describe data and make predictions

Exploration 3
- Make a scatter plot
- Fit a line to data in a scatter plot and use it to make predictions

Days for Section 3

First Day
Setting the Stage, *p. 381*
Exploration 1, *pp. 382–383*

Second Day
Exploration 2 through Question 12, *pp. 384–385*

Third Day
Exploration 2 from Example, *pp. 385–386*

Fourth Day
Exploration 3, *pp. 387–388*
Key Concepts, *p. 389*

Materials List

Exploration 1
- string and scissors
- metric ruler

Exploration 2
- Labsheet 3A
- string and scissors
- metric ruler

Exploration 3
- Labsheets 3A–3B
- uncooked spaghetti
- graph paper

Practice and Applications
- completed Labsheet 3A
- uncooked spaghetti or clear ruler
- graph paper

Teaching Resources

Teacher's Resource Book
- Warm-Up
- Labsheets 3A and 3B
- Practice and Applications
- Study Guide
See page 363 for additional teaching resources.

Assessment Options

EMBEDDED ASSESSMENT
- Use ratios to investigate measurements
   Exercises 1a, 7
- Write the decimal form of a ratio to make comparisons
   Exercises 2, 4
- Find and use "nice" fraction forms of ratios to describe data and make predictions
   Exercises 12, 13
- Make a scatter plot
   Exercises 17a, 18a
- Fit a line to data in a scatter plot and use it to make predictions
   Exercises 16, 17, 19

PERFORMANCE TASK/PORTFOLIO
- Exercise 14 on *p. 391 (home involvement)*
- Exercise 20 on *p. 393 (journal)*
- Standardized Testing on *p. 394 (open-ended)*
- Extended Exploration on *p. 395**

* indicates a problem solving task that can be assessed using the Assessment Scales

QUIZZES/TESTS
- Section 3 Quick Quiz
- Mid-Module Quiz

TEST GENERATOR

Section 3 Overview

In this section, students will use ratios to make comparisons and predictions.

Exploration 1
After reading an excerpt from *Gulliver's Travels*, students test whether the Lilliputians could accurately predict Gulliver's wrist, neck, and waist measurements using just the distance around his thumb. Students measure the distances around their thumb and wrist and compare the measurements using a ratio in decimal form. They then compare the ratio of their measures to those used by the Lilliputians in the reading. They complete the exploration by using the ratios and a person's thumb measure to predict the distance around the person's neck and waist.

Exploration 2
Students continue exploring body ratios and determining whether certain ratios are the same for different people. Data are collected and the ratios are compared by using "nice" fractions to estimate whether they are about the same.

Exploration 3
Students learn to make scatter plots and use them to make predictions based on different body ratios. Fitted lines are explored by placing a piece of uncooked spaghetti on a scatter plot and adjusting its position and orientation until it reflects the trend in the data. The fitted line is then drawn in and used to make predictions.

Guide for Assigning Homework

REGULAR SCHEDULING (45 MIN CLASS PERIOD)			EXERCISES TO NOTE		
Section/ P&A Pages	Core Assignment	Extended Assignment	Additional Practice/Review	Open-ended Problems	Extended Problems
3 pp. 390–394	**Day 1:** 1–6 **Day 2:** SR 21–24 **Day 3:** 7–15 **Day 4:** 16–19, ROS 20	1–6 SR 21–24 7–15 16–19, ROS 20	EP, p. 394	PA 1(b), 14, 20 ST, p. 394	E², p. 395

Key: PA = Practice & Application; ROS = Reflecting on the Section; SR = Spiral Review; TB = Toolbox; EP = Extra Skill Practice; Ext = Extension; ST = Standardized Testing

Math Background and Teaching Strategies

Classroom Notes

Bulletin board displays for this section include:

• a diagram of Gulliver showing the body ratios

Interest centers for this section might include:

• a copy of Gulliver's Travels to read

• skeleton to label with body ratios

Student work displays for this section might include:

• scatter plots from body ratios

• chair designs from the E²

Math Strands

Topic Spiraling and Integration

Exploration 1
Exploration 1 provides practice with writing and comparing ratios developed in Section 1 of this module. Students convert ratios written as fractions to ratios written as decimals.

Exploration 2
Students continue to measure, record, and compare ratios. "Nice" fractions are defined and used in mental comparisons and estimation. Nice fractions are common fractions that are often intuitive to students and that make mental calculations easier. Most students should be familiar with $\frac{1}{4}$, $\frac{1}{2}$, $\frac{3}{4}$, and $\frac{1}{3}$. With time students should be able to incorporate other fractions such as $\frac{2}{5}$ that are easy to visualize and easy to

compute with mentally. Module 5 of Book 2 and Module 2 of Book 3 both use "nice" fractions for estimating with percents.

Exploration 3
Students use scatter plots to compare and predict. The use of a fitted line is introduced as a way to represent a trend in the data. Fitted lines will be used again in Books 2 and 3 as students learn to write an equation based on the fitted line for a set of data. Students practice graphing skills that were introduced in Module 4 where they learned to plot ordered pairs on a coordinate grid and to make and interpret line graphs. Graphing will be extended to include ordered pairs of integers in Module 7.

Section 4 Proportions

Section 4 Planner

Section Objectives

Exploration 1
- Use cross products to identify and find equivalent ratios
- Find the missing term in a proportion

Exploration 2
- Write a proportion to solve a problem
- Use a proportion to make a prediction
- Identify when using a proportion is or is not appropriate

Days for Section 4

First Day
Setting the Stage, *p. 396*
Exploration 1, *pp. 397–398*

Second Day
Exploration 2, *pp. 399–400*
Key Concepts, *pp. 401–402*

Teaching Resources

Teacher's Resource Book
- Warm-Up
- Practice and Applications
- Study Guide
See page 363 for additional teaching resources.

Assessment Options

EMBEDDED ASSESSMENT
- Use cross products to identify and find equivalent ratios
  Exercise 2
- Find the missing term in a proportion
  Exercises 6, 7, 8
- Write a proportion to solve a problem
  Exercises 12, 13
- Use a proportion to make a prediction
  Exercises 15(b), 17
- Identify when using a proportion is or is not appropriate
  Exercises 16, 17

PERFORMANCE TASK/PORTFOLIO
- Exercise 13 on *p. 403 (writing)*
- Exercise 14 on *p. 403 (challenge)*
- Exercise 18 on *p. 404 (oral report)*

QUIZZES/TESTS
- Section 4 Quick Quiz

TEST GENERATOR

Section 4 Overview

In this section, students will learn to use proportions to compare ratios, to solve problems, and to make predictions as they explore the jumping ability of humans and animals.

Exploration 1
Students begin with a review of equivalent ratios. *Proportion* and *cross products* are then defined as key terms. Students learn to use cross products to tell whether two ratios are equivalent and to find the missing term in a proportion. They use proportions to predict how far a certain size jackrabbit can jump.

Exploration 2
Students compare the jumping ability of a frog to that of a human. Using proportions they learn how to set up a proportion and then solve it to find out how far a human with the jumping ability of a frog might be able to jump. After solving a realistic problem about a school fundraiser, students look at other situations to determine when it is or is not appropriate to use a proportion to make a prediction.

Guide for Assigning Homework

REGULAR SCHEDULING (45 MIN CLASS PERIOD)			EXERCISES TO NOTE		
Section/ P&A Pages	**Core** **Assignment**	**Extended** **Assignment**	**Additional** **Practice/Review**	**Open-ended** **Problems**	**Extended** **Problems**
4 pp. 402–405	**Day 1:** 1–11, SR 19–24 **Day 2:** 12–13, 15–17 ROS 18	1–11, SR 19–24 12–17, ROS 18	EP, p. 405	PA 18	Challenge PA 14

Key: PA = Practice & Application; ROS = Reflecting on the Section; SR = Spiral Review; TB = Toolbox; EP = Extra Skill Practice; Ext = Extension; ST = Standardized Testing

Math Background and Teaching Strategies

Classroom Notes

Bulletin board display ideas for this section include:

- animals and their record-breaking jumps

- student generated problems from Reflecting Exercise 18

- sample situations where it is or is not appropriate to use proportions to predict

Math Strands

Topic Spiraling and Integration

Exploration 1
Exploration 1 provides a review of equivalent ratios. The use of cross products to determine if two ratios are equivalent, and thus a proportion, is introduced. To students, using cross products to determine if two ratios are equivalent may seem like a "special trick", when in fact it is based on comparing fractions by converting them to equivalent fractions with a common denominator. Multiplying each numerator by the opposing denominator gives the numerators of equivalent fractions with a denominator equal to the product of the two original denominators. For example: To show that the fractions $\frac{16}{10}$ and $\frac{24}{15}$ are equivalent, you can write each fraction as an equivalent fraction with a denominator of $10 \cdot 15$ or 150.

$$\frac{16}{10} = \frac{16 \cdot 15}{10 \cdot 15} = \frac{240}{150} \text{ and}$$
$$\frac{24}{15} = \frac{24 \cdot 10}{15 \cdot 10} = \frac{240}{150}$$

On the other hand, to show that the ratios $\frac{16}{10}$ and $\frac{24}{15}$ are equivalent, you can show that the cross products $10 \cdot 24$ and $16 \cdot 15$ are equal. Notice that the cross products are simply the products used to find the numerators of the equivalent fractions. This shows that using cross products to compare ratios is the same as comparing the ratios by writing them as equivalent fractions with a common denominator.

Cross products are used to write simple equations that can then be solved to find the missing term in a proportion. The use of variables was introduced in Module 1 and students solved addition and subtraction equations in Module 4. Now variables are used to write proportions and students solve simple multiplication equations.

Exploration 2
Students learn to solve problems by setting up and solving proportions. Since not all situations involve proportions, students are exposed to situations in which it is not appropriate to use proportions to make predictions.

362J

Section 5 — Geometry and Proportions

Section 5 Planner

Section Objectives

Exploration 1
- Identify similar and congruent figures and their corresponding parts
- Understand characteristics that make figures similar

Exploration 2
- Apply similarity to solve problems involving scale drawings, scale models, and map scales

Days for Section 5

First Day
Setting the Stage, *p. 406*
Exploration 1 through Question 7, *pp. 407–409*

Second Day
Exploration 1 from Example, *p. 409*

Third Day
Exploration 2, *pp. 410–412*
Key Concepts, *p. 413*

Teaching Resources

Teacher's Resource Book
- Warm-Up
- Labsheet 5A
- Practice and Applications
- Study Guide
See page 363 for additional teaching resources.

Materials List

Exploration 1
- Labsheet 5A
- pattern blocks
- metric ruler
- tracing paper
- protractor

Exploration 2
- customary ruler

Practice and Applications
- metric ruler
- customary ruler
- protractor

Assessment Options

EMBEDDED ASSESSMENT
- Identify similar and congruent figures and their corresponding parts
  Exercises 2, 4, 6, 10
- Understand characteristics that make figures similar
  Exercises 3, 4, 5, 6, 8
- Apply similarity to solve problems involving scale drawings, scale models, and map scales
  Exercises 13, 15, 17, 19

PERFORMANCE TASK/PORTFOLIO
- Exercise 9 on *p. 415*
- Exercise 18 on *p. 416 (challenge)*
- Exercise 22 on *p. 416 (research)*
- Standardized Testing on *p. 418 (free response)*

QUIZZES/TESTS
- Section 5 Quick Quiz

TEST GENERATOR

Section 5 Overview

In this section, students will use proportions to study similarity, congruence, and scale drawings.

Exploration 1
Students look at an Escher design and its underlying geometry to see how similar figures were used to create the artwork. Corresponding parts of similar figures are identified through part of the design. Students then create similar figures using pattern blocks to explore relationships between corresponding sides and corresponding angles of similar figures. Congruent figures are also defined and the special 1 to 1 ratio of the lengths of the corresponding sides in congruent figures is explored.

Exploration 2
Students see how artists and architects use scale models to design larger works of art. They set up and solve proportions to find actual lengths from measurements on a scale drawing or scale model and vice versa.

Guide for Assigning Homework

REGULAR SCHEDULING (45 MIN CLASS PERIOD)			EXERCISES TO NOTE		
Section/ P&A Pages	Core Assignment	Extended Assignment	Additional Practice/Review	Open-ended Problems	Extended Problems
5 pp. 414–418	**Day 1:** 1–2, 9–10 **Day 2:** 3–8, SR 23–32 **Day 3:** 11–17, 19–21, ROS 22	1–2, 9–10 3–8, SR 23–32 11–21, ROS 22	EP, p. 418	PA 8, 9	Challenge PA 18 Career Connect 33–34

Key: PA = Practice & Application; ROS = Reflecting on the Section; SR = Spiral Review; TB = Toolbox; EP = Extra Skill Practice; Ext = Extension; ST = Standardized Testing

Math Background and Teaching Strategies

Classroom Notes

Bulletin board display ideas for this section include:

• scale drawings of building plans

• information on Escher and examples of his work

• pictures of Mount Rushmore or the Crazy Horse Monument

Visitors might include:

• architects

• sculptors and other artists

Interest centers might include:

• activity cards for creating Escher-like drawings

• pattern blocks for creating figures similar to a given figure

• a city or wilderness map with different distances marked for students to determine using the scale.

Math Strands

Topic Spiraling and Integration

In this section, proportions are applied to geometry concepts.

Exploration 1
Students revisit basic geometry concepts from Module 2 where they learned to describe polygons and angles. As they look more closely at polygons with the same number of sides, they learn to classify them as similar or congruent. Students should be able to make the connection from their earlier studies of triangles that an isosceles triangle cannot be similar or congruent to a scalene triangle, nor can a right triangle be similar to an equilateral triangle, etc. Ratios, equivalent ratios, and proportions are used to determine if two figures are similar and/or congruent. The application to geometry allows students to use proportions in another area of mathematics.

Exploration 2
In Exploration 2, students apply their skills with proportions and finding missing terms in real life situations involving scale models and scale drawings. Measurement concepts from Modules 4 and 5 are reinforced through the use of scale. Estimation is used to check the reasonableness of the measures in the answers.

Section 6 Planner

Section Objectives

Exploration 1
- Write a percent
- Relate fractions, decimals, and percents

Exploration 2
- Use a fraction to find a percent of a number
- Use a fraction to estimate a percent or a percent of a number

Exploration 3
- Display data in a circle graph
- Use percents and fractions to estimate angle measures

Days for Section 6

First Day
Setting the Stage, *p. 419*
Exploration 1 through Question 3, *p. 420*

Second Day
Exploration 1 from Question 4, *p. 421*

Third Day
Exploration 2, *pp. 422–423*

Fourth Day
Exploration 3 through Question 23,
pp. 424–426

Fifth Day
Exploration 3 from Example, *pp. 426–427*
Key Concepts, *pp. 427–428*

Materials List

Setting the Stage
- Labsheet 6A

Exploration 1
- Labsheet 6B

Exploration 2
- Labsheet 6C

Exploration 3
- Labsheet 6A
- scissors, tape, colored markers or pencils
- protractor, compass, straightedge

Practice and Applications
- Labsheet 6D
- protractor and compass or round object

Teaching Resources

Teacher's Resource Book
- Warm-Up
- Labsheets 6A, 6B, 6C, and 6D
- Practice and Applications
- Study Guide
See page 363 for additional teaching resources.

Assessment Options

EMBEDDED ASSESSMENT
- Write a percent
  Exercise 21
- Relate fractions, decimals, and percents
  Exercises 7, 8, 11, 13, 19
- Use a fraction to find a percent of a number
  Exercises 25, 27
- Estimate a percent or percent of a number
  Exercises 28, 31, 32
- Display data in a circle graph
  Exercise 36
- Estimate angle measures
  Exercise 37

PERFORMANCE TASK/PORTFOLIO
- Exercise 6 on *p. 429 (writing)*
- Exercise 37 on *p. 431 (visual thinking)*
- Module Project on *pp. 433–435*

QUIZZES/TESTS
- Section 6 Quick Quiz
- Module Tests A and B
- Module Standardized Test
- Module Performance Assessment

TEST GENERATOR

Section 6 Overview

In this section, students will use a class survey about Olympic sporting events to extend their understanding of ratios, fractions, and decimals to percents and to create circle graphs.

Exploration 1
Students learn to describe ratios using one-hundred grids, fractions, decimals, and percents. They complete a table of common fraction, decimal, and percent equivalents to use throughout the section.

Exploration 2
Students use fractions to find a percent of a number. They use "nice" fractions, which were discussed in Section 4, to estimate a percent or a percent of a number. The percent forms for the fractions $\frac{1}{3}$ and $\frac{2}{3}$ are explored.

Exploration 3
Students make a circle graph to display the data from their class survey. They learn to use "nice" fractions and percents to estimate the number of degrees in the central angle for sections of a circle graph. Then, using a protractor, they create the central angles and construct a circle graph.

Guide for Assigning Homework

REGULAR SCHEDULING (45 MIN CLASS PERIOD)

EXERCISES TO NOTE

Section/ P&A Pages	Core Assignment	Extended Assignment	Additional Practice/Review	Open-ended Problems	Extended Problems
6 pp. 429–432	**Day 1:** 1–6 **Day 2:** 7–21 **Day 3:** 22–34 **Day 4:** SR 38–40 **Day 3:** 36, ROS 37	1–6 7–21 odd 25–35 SR 38–40 36, ROS 37	EP, p. 432 Review & Assessment, pp. 436–437		Challenge PA 35 Mod Proj, pp. 433–435

Key: PA = Practice & Application; ROS = Reflecting on the Section; SR = Spiral Review; TB = Toolbox; EP = Extra Skill Practice; Ext = Extension; ST = Standardized Testing

Math Background and Teaching Strategies

Classroom Notes

Bulletin board displays for this section include:

- sports statistics with photographs
- a table of "nice" fractions with decimal and percent equivalents shown
- news clippings, advertisements, flyers, etc. that show the frequent use of percents in daily life

Math Strands

Topic Spiraling and Integration

Exploration 1

Exploration 1 makes the connection between fractions, decimals, and percents. Percent is introduced and students use their knowledge of equivalent fractions and decimals from Modules 1 and 3 to write fractions and decimals as percents and vice versa.

Exploration 2

Fractions and percents are used to find a percent of a number and to estimate using "nice" fractions.

In Book 2 Module 5, students will use their skills with decimals, fractions, and percents as they find a missing part or whole, estimate percents using "nice" fractions or mental math, and use percents to make predictions. Percent work is extended to include percents greater than 100%.

In Book 3 Module 2, students will apply percents in the context of surveys and shopping discounts. They will continue to estimate percents using "nice" fractions and multiples of 10%, which are briefly introduced in the Practice and Application Exercises in Book 1. Work with

percents in Book 3 is extended to include finding percents of change.

Exploration 3

Reading and constructing circle graphs bring together percent applications and the skills of measuring with a protractor, using a compass, and identifying parts of a circle. Using a strip of graph paper to create a circle graph divides the circle's circumference into the appropriate arcs which are used to divide the circle into sectors by drawing radii connecting each arc's endpoints to the circle's center. Because the central angle of a circle has the same degree measure as the arc it intersects, each sector created by the fraction of the circle's circumference represents the correct fraction of the circle's area and thus the percent of students choosing the specific sport.

OVERVIEW

Situations from nature, literature, sports, art, movies, and the news provide opportunities for students to build an understanding of ratios, proportions, and percent, and to solve problems involving comparisons and predictions. Students also look at congruent and similar figures and learn to represent data in a circle graph.

PREREQUISITE SKILLS

Warm-Up Exercises for each section are provided in the *Teacher's Resource Book.* You can use these exercises to review skills and concepts students will need for each section. In addition, the Spiral Review exercises at the end of each section in the student edition provide practice on prerequisite skills.

MODULE DIAGNOSTIC TEST

The Module Diagnostic Test in the *Teacher's Resource Book* can be used to assess students' prior knowledge of skills and concepts that will be taught in each section of this module. You can use test results to help structure your teaching to meet the diverse needs of your classroom.

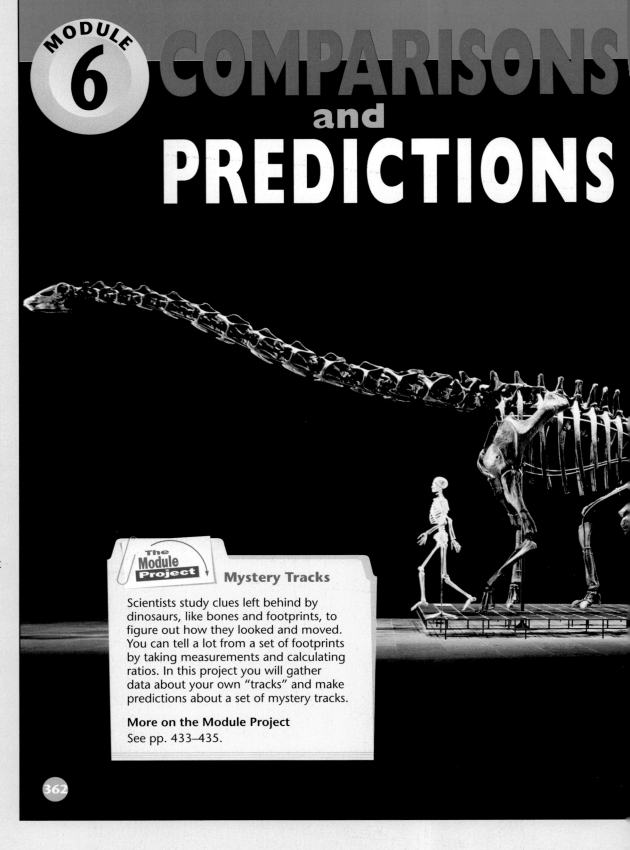

MODULE 6 COMPARISONS and PREDICTIONS

The Module Project

Mystery Tracks

Scientists study clues left behind by dinosaurs, like bones and footprints, to figure out how they looked and moved. You can tell a lot from a set of footprints by taking measurements and calculating ratios. In this project you will gather data about your own "tracks" and make predictions about a set of mystery tracks.

More on the Module Project
See pp. 433–435.

362

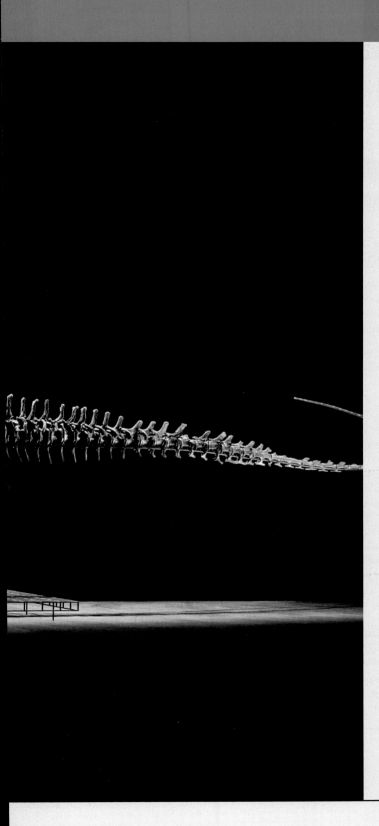

MATHMATICS
The & Theme

MODULE 6 — SECTION OVERVIEW

① Exploring Ratios

As you explore the use of props in a movie:
- ◆ Make comparisons using ratios
- ◆ Write equivalent ratios

② Rates

As you simulate a sandbag brigade:
- ◆ Use rates to make predictions
- ◆ Find unit rates

③ Using Ratios

As you find body ratios:
- ◆ Write a ratio as a decimal
- ◆ Use ratios and scatter plots to make predictions

④ Proportions

As you compare the jumping abilities of humans and animals:
- ◆ Use cross products to find equivalent ratios
- ◆ Write and use a proportion to solve a problem

⑤ Geometry and Proportions

As you look at how artists use models and scale drawings:
- ◆ Identify similar and congruent figures
- ◆ Use proportions to find missing side lengths

⑥ Percents and Circle Graphs

As you examine Olympic softball data:
- ◆ Relate fractions, decimals, and percents
- ◆ Find a percent of a number
- ◆ Display data in a circle graph

INTERNET
Resources and practice at
classzone.com

Module Resources

TEACHER'S RESOURCE BOOK
Resources
- *The Math Gazette* (parent newsletter)
- Warm-Ups
- Labsheets
- Practice and Applications
- Study Guide

Assessment
- Section Quick Quizzes
- Mid-Module Quiz
- Module 6 Diagnostic Test
- Module 6 Tests A and B
- Module 6 Standardized Test
- Module 6 Performance Assessment
- Modules 5 and 6 Cumulative Test

SPANISH RESOURCES
- *The Math Gazette* (parent newsletter)
- Practice and Applications
- Assessment
- Spanish Glossary

STUDENT WORKBOOK

TECHNOLOGY BOOK

TECHNOLOGY RESOURCES
- @Home Tutor
- Test Generator
- Activity Generator
- Professional Development DVD
- Online Activities

Setting the Stage

GETTING STARTED

Module 6 Section 1 *Warm-Up* assesses students' ability to determine equivalent fractions since equivalent ratios will be defined in terms of equivalent fractions.

You may want to read or have students take turns reading the poem out loud for students to better enjoy its rhythm and rhyme.

Section 1 Exploring Ratios

IN THIS SECTION

EXPLORATION 1
♦ Comparing Measures

Take a Closer Look

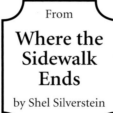

Setting the Stage

Comparing things and making predictions based on those comparisons is an important use of mathematics. In the poem *One Inch Tall*, Shel Silverstein makes comparisons to describe what the world would be like if you were only one inch tall.

From

Where the Sidewalk Ends

by Shel Silverstein

ONE INCH TALL

If you were only one inch tall, you'd ride a worm to school.
The teardrop of a crying ant would be your swimming pool.
A crumb of cake would be a feast
And last you seven days at least,
A flea would be a frightening beast
If you were one inch tall.

If you were only one inch tall, you'd walk beneath the door,
And it would take about a month to get down to the store.
A bit of fluff would be your bed,
You'd swing upon a spider's thread,
And wear a thimble on your head
If you were one inch tall.

You'd surf across the kitchen sink upon a stick of gum.
You couldn't hug your mama, you'd just have to hug her thumb.
You'd run from people's feet in fright,
To move a pen would take all night,
(This poem took fourteen years to write—
'Cause I'm just one inch tall).

 Module 6 Comparisons and Predictions

Think About It ▸▸▸ ▸

1 If the author spent the same amount of time writing each verse of the poem, about how many years did he take to write one verse?
about $4\frac{2}{3}$ years

2 If you were only one inch tall, do you think a thimble would fit on your head? Why or why not? Sample: No, a thimble is about 1 in. in height and I would not wear a hat as tall as my height. The opening would be so large that the thimble would fall right down over my head and cover my body.

Exploration 1 ▸▸▸▸ ▸

COMPARING MEASURES

SET UP *Work with a partner. You will need: • Labsheet 1A • pennies*

▸ **Shel Silverstein used comparisons with everyday objects so readers could imagine the world from the perspective of a one-inch tall person. Several movies, such as *Honey I Shrunk the Kids* and *The Lord of the Rings*, also used everyday objects to create an illusion of different sizes.**

Set designers for *The Lord of the Rings* had to make the Hobbits appear smaller than other characters in the film. To do this they created almost every prop in at least two different sizes. In one scene, two different size mugs and two different size tables were used to make Frodo appear to be smaller than Gandalf. In this exploration, you will compare the sizes of the props.

▲
Many areas in New Zealand have served as locations for scenes in *The Lord of the Rings*.

GOAL

LEARN HOW TO...
◆ make comparisons using ratios
◆ recognize and write equivalent ratios

AS YOU...
◆ explore how characters in movies can appear to be shorter or taller than their actual heights

KEY TERMS
◆ ratio
◆ equivalent ratios

TEACHING NOTES

Before students begin **Question 2**, refer them back to the first line of the poem. Explain that a common earthworm is about 5 in. long with a diameter of about $\frac{1}{4}$ in. Ask, "If you were 1 in. tall do you think this line of the poem could be true? Why or why not?" You might compare riding a worm to riding a bicycle. Riding a bicycle that is one-fourth our height (about 15 in.) would be very uncomfortable, so since a worm is about one-fourth the height of the student in the poem, it is not reasonable.

Exploration 1

TEACHER NOTES

The CD from *The Appendices to the Fellowship of the Ring* has an excellent documentary of how scale, perspective, and miniatures were used in the movie to create the illusion of different sizes. You may want to view it and show portions to your students either before or after this activity.

365

Exploration 1 *continued*

TEACHING NOTES

In **Question 4**, it is expected that most students will compare the heights of the mugs by adding or subtracting—one mug is 2 pennies taller or shorter than the other. By the time they get to **part (e)**, students should begin to see that the addition and subtraction comparisons are not the same for the squares. At this point you may want to revisit **part (a)** and discuss how multiplication or division could be used to compare the heights of the mugs and then explore whether this relationship would hold true for comparison of the heights in squares. The equivalence of 4:6 and 6:9 is addressed in **Question 7**.

Question 6 Students should realize that the numbers used in the comparisons must be written in the correct order when recording ratios, and that a different ratio results when they write the larger mug's height first. You may want to ask students to give an example of when the order of the ratio is not affected *(when the two amounts are equal)*.

4. c. Sample: Line up 6 pennies alongside the strip of squares on Labsheet 1A and then count the number of squares that are equal to the height of the pennies.
   d. 9 squares; Answers will vary depending on whether students answer 8 squares or 9 squares in part (b).
   e. Sample Response: The height of the smaller mug is $\frac{2}{3}$ the larger mug's height, or the height of the larger mug is $1\frac{1}{2}$ times the height of the smaller mug.

---

3. a. 4 pennies
   b. 6 squares

4. a. Sample Response: The larger mug is two pennies taller than the smaller mug or $1\frac{1}{2}$ times as tall.
   b. Answers will vary. Sample Responses: 8 squares, since it will be 2 squares taller than the smaller mug. OR 9 squares, since $1\frac{1}{2} \cdot 6 = 9$.

QUESTION 5

...checks that you can write a ratio to compare two quantities.

---

3 **Use Labsheet 1A.** Measure the mug shown on the labsheet.

4 **Discussion** A larger mug looks exactly like the one on Labsheet 1A, but it is 6 pennies tall.

 a. How can you compare the heights of the two mugs in pennies?

 b. *Without measuring*, predict the large mug's height in squares.

 c. Describe a way you can use pennies and squares to check your prediction in part (b). **See margin.**

 d. What is the large mug's height in squares? How does this compare with your prediction? **See margin.**

 e. How does the small mug's height in squares compare with the large mug's height in squares? **See margin.**

▶ To find the height of the large mug in squares, it can be helpful to use a special type of comparison called a *ratio*. The comparison below is an example of a ratio.

The ratio of the height of the small mug in pennies to the height of the large mug in pennies is 4 to 6.

small mug — 4 pennies

large mug — 6 pennies

▶ The **ratio** of two numbers or measures can be written several ways:

using the word "to"	with a colon	as a fraction
4 to 6	**4 : 6**	$\frac{4}{6}$

5 **✔ CHECKPOINT** Write the ratio of the small mug's height in squares to the large mug's height in squares in three ways. 6:9, 6 to 9, $\frac{6}{9}$

6 **Discussion** If you compare the large mug's height in squares to the small mug's height in squares, do you get the same ratio as in Question 5? Explain. No; $\frac{6}{9}$ is not equivalent to $\frac{9}{6}$.

▶ **Equivalent Ratios** The heights of the two mugs do not change; therefore, the two ratios used to compare their heights, 4 : 6 and 6 : 9, must be equivalent. Two ratios are **equivalent ratios** if they can be written as equivalent fractions.

7 Try This As A Class

a. Write the ratios 4 : 6 and 6 : 9 as fractions. $\frac{4}{9}, \frac{6}{9}$

b. How you can show that the ratios in part (a) are equivalent?

c. Name two more ratios that are equivalent to the ratio 6 : 9.
Sample: 12:18, 30:45

To make sure the size differences appeared correctly during the scene, it was important that the ratios of the heights of the items on Gandalf's table to the heights of the matching items on Frodo's table be equivalent.

8 a. Suppose the heights of the tables where Frodo and Gandalf sat have a ratio in inches of 18 : 27. Is this equivalent to the ratio of the heights of the mugs? Explain.

b. Gandalf is 6 ft tall. If the ratio of Frodo's height to Gandalf's height is equivalent to the ratio of the small mug's height to the large mug's height, how tall would Frodo be? 4 ft

9 Try This As A Class

a. In Shel Silverstein's poem, a person 1 in. tall surfs on a stick of gum. If a stick of gum is 3 in. long, write a ratio of *the person's height to the length of a stick of gum* in fraction form. $\frac{1}{3}$

b. Write an equivalent ratio with a numerator of 6 ft. What did you do to find the denominator? $\frac{6}{18}$; multiplied by 6

c. What do the numerators represent in the fractions in parts (a) and (b)? What do the denominators represent? a person's height; length of the gum surfboard

d. Equivalent ratios can help filmmakers decide what size to make props. Suppose you are making a movie of the poem *One Inch Tall*. If a 6-ft person plays the person in the poem, how long would you need to make the stick of gum? 18 ft

e. How does the length in part (d) compare to a typical surfboard? What other items might Mr. Silverstein have used as a realistic size surfboard for a one-inch tall person?

10 ✔ **CHECKPOINT** Which ratios are equivalent to the ratio 6 : 14?
3 to 7, 12:28

3 to 7 $\frac{21}{9}$ 12 : 28   9 : 17

HOMEWORK EXERCISES ▶ See Exs. 1–17 on pp. 369–371.

---

7. b. Write the fractions with a common denominator either by multiplying or by dividing. For example, $\frac{4}{6} = \frac{2}{3}$ and $\frac{6}{9} = \frac{2}{3}$.

8. a. Yes, in lowest terms $\frac{18}{27}$ is $\frac{2}{3}$.

9. e. It is too long. Surfboard lengths are not usually 3 times the height of the surfer. Sample items: paper clip, child's hair barrette, or other items between 1 and 2 inches in length.

✔ **QUESTION 10**

...checks that you can recognize equivalent ratios.

TEACHING NOTES
Question 9 For the comparison of a person's height to a "stick of gum" surfboard, students may think they need to perform conversions between feet and inches. Assure them that in **part (b)** they can write the equivalent ratios as $\frac{1 \text{ in.}}{3 \text{ in.}} = \frac{6 \text{ ft}}{18 \text{ ft}}$ since in both ratios, the length in the denominator is 3 times the length in the numerator.

After students complete **part (d)**, you may want to have two students use masking tape to mark off on the floor the length of the stick of gum the filmmakers would have to make. This will help students who have had little exposure to surfboards judge for **part (e)** whether they think the length is reasonable.

For **part (e)**, it is helpful to note that beginning surfers usually ride boards between 7 ft 2 in. and 9 ft 6 in. Some extreme surfers ride boards of length just over 10 ft which puts them in the category of long boards (boards over 9 ft) Originally, surfboards were often over 15 ft in length and very heavy. Today there exists a category of short boards that range from 5 ft to 7 ft in length. For answering the problem students should just find some reasonable objects of similar length. If desired you can indicate whether they are to match the length of a short board or beginner length board.

Key Concepts

CLOSURE QUESTION

Why is it important to know how to use ratios and equivalent ratios?

Sample Response: Ratios and equivalent ratios allow you to compare numbers or measures. The order that the numbers appear in a ratio is important.

ABSENT STUDENTS

For students who were absent for all or part of this section, the blackline Study Guide for Section 1 may be used to present the ideas, concepts, and skills of Section 1.

Section 1

Key Terms

ratio

equivalent ratios

Key Concepts

Ratios (p. 366)

A ratio is a special type of comparison of two numbers or measures. Ratios can be written in different ways. The order of the numbers in a ratio is important.

Example You can write the ratio of the number of cashews to the number of pretzels in three different ways.

The snack mix has 10 cashews for every 4 pretzels.

10 to 4   10 : 4 $\dfrac{10}{4}$

Equivalent Ratios (p. 367)

Sometimes a ratio can be shown another way by separating each measure into the same number of groups.

You can compare half the number of cashews with half the number of pretzels.

Example

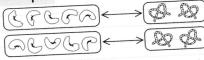

5 cashews   to   **2** pretzels

Equivalent ratios can be written as equivalent fractions.

10 : 4 is equivalent to 5 : 2 because $\dfrac{10}{4}$ and $\dfrac{5}{2}$ are equivalent fractions.

---

11 **Key Concepts Question** Suppose that in a can of mixed nuts there are 12 peanuts for every 9 cashews.

    a. Write the ratio of *the number of cashews to the number of peanuts* in each of the three forms. **9 to 12, 9:12, $\dfrac{9}{12}$**

    b. Find a ratio that is equivalent to the one in part (a).

    c. Is the ratio of *the number of peanuts to the number of cashews* equivalent to the ratio in part (a)? Explain. **No; The ratio of the number of peanuts to the number of cashews is 12 to 9 or 4 to 3.**

11. b. Sample Response: 3 to 4, 3:4, $\dfrac{3}{4}$

Section 1
Practice & Application Exercises

Tell whether the ratios are equivalent.

1. $\frac{3}{5}$ and $\frac{9}{15}$ yes

2. $\frac{5}{12}$ and $\frac{10}{8}$ no

3. $\frac{4}{3}$ and $\frac{16}{9}$ no

4. 1 : 6 and 5 : 30 yes

5. 9 : 2 and 32 : 8 no

6. 12 : 6 and 8 : 4 yes

7. **Volleyball** Before serving in the game of volleyball, players often announce the ratio of their score to the opposing team's score. Suppose Team A has 4 points and Team B has 6 points. The score ratio 6 to 4 is announced. Which team is serving the ball?
   Team B

8. Write the ratio of the number of dogs to the number of paws in each picture.

   a.
   1:4

   b.
   4:16

   c. Are the ratios you found in parts (a) and (b) equivalent? If so, explain why. Yes, $\frac{1}{4} = \frac{4}{16}$

9. For each of the following, find the number n that makes the ratios equivalent.

   a. $\frac{6}{5} = \frac{n}{20}$ 24

   b. 18 : 24 and n : 8 6

10. **Open-ended** Suppose you were one inch tall. How high would a water fountain you could drink from be? Explain how you determined your answer.

10. Sample Response: Drinking fountains are about 3 ft off the ground and I am 5 ft tall. $\frac{3}{5} = 0.6$ or a 0.6 to 1 ratio, so the water fountain would need to be about 0.6 in. or about $\frac{5}{8}$ in. high.

SUGGESTED ASSIGNMENTS
Core Course
Day 1: Exs. 1–15, 17–29

Extended Course
Day 1: Exs. 8–29

Note: Extended Course assignments can be used to differentiate within the regular classroom. In classrooms where students are grouped homogeneously, the material might be covered in fewer days. In this case assignments may be combined.

ADDITIONAL PRACTICE
See the *Teacher's Resource Book* for additional practice and application exercises for this section.

EXERCISE NOTES
Exercise 10 Students should consider the comfort and ease of reaching the water fountain. Will they have to bend over too far? Will they have to stand on their tip toes?

Practice & Applications

EXERCISE NOTES

Question 11 You may want to discuss other oversized props often seen at tourist attractions, such as giant rocking chairs that create the illusion that the person sitting in them is miniature. Some students may have visited such attractions and be able to share their observations about the ratios of their height to the object's height.

11. On the back lot of MGM Studios in Florida sits the *Honey I Shrunk the Kids* playground, where you can crawl through 30-foot blades of grass or view a dog's nose taller than a grown man.

 a. Write a ratio that compares the height of a 3-foot child to the height of the grass.
 3 to 30

 b. Suppose the height of the dog's nose is $\frac{2}{3}$ the height of a blade of grass. Write a ratio that represents the height of the dog's nose to the height of a person who is 6 feet tall.
 20 to 6

12. **Gliders** The flight performance of a glider, which is an aircraft with no engine, can be measured using a glide ratio. A glide ratio compares the gliding distance with the change in height.

change in height 500 m

gliding distance 9000 m

▲ Otto Lilienthal built the first controllable glider in the late 1800s.

a. Write the glide ratio for the glider in three ways.
 9000 to 500, 9000:500, $\frac{9000}{500}$

b. Suppose the glider's height changes half as much and it travels half as far. Write this ratio in three ways.
 4500 to 250, 4500:250, $\frac{4500}{250}$

c. Are the ratios you found in parts (a) and (b) equivalent? If so, explain why. Yes; The fractions $\frac{9000}{500}$ and $\frac{4500}{250}$ are equivalent fractions

d. Find another ratio equivalent to the ones you wrote in parts (a) and (b). Explain how you found the ratio.

12. d. Sample Response: 18 to 1; I divided the numerator and denominator of $\frac{9000}{500}$ by 500.

13. a. For every three steps Sam takes, Gandalf takes one step. Write this comparison as a ratio in three ways. 3:1, 3 to 1, $\frac{3}{1}$

 b. Suppose Gandalf takes nine steps. How many steps will Sam take? 27 steps

 c. Suppose Sam takes twelve steps. How many steps will Gandalf take? 4 steps

14. **Movie Sets** Miniatures of the Argonaths in the movie *The Lord of the Rings* were created in a ratio of 1 ft to 60 ft. That means that every 1 ft on the miniature represented 60 ft in real life.

   a. How much would 2 ft on the miniature represent in real life?
     120 ft

   b. Write a ratio for 2 ft on the miniature to the real life length in fraction form. What happens if you simplify the fraction? $\frac{2}{120}$; It equals the original ratio of 1 to 60.

   c. The miniature is 8 ft tall. Find *n* in the ratio 8 : *n* to make it equivalent to the ratio 1 : 60. How tall is the Argonath in real life? 480 ft

15. **Language Arts** Think of some things you would or would not be able to do if you were one inch tall. Then write another verse for the poem *One Inch Tall*.

16. **Challenge** The poem *One Inch Tall* says, "If you were only one inch tall, you'd walk beneath the door, and it would take about a month to get down to the store." Imagine that you are one inch tall. Estimate the distance to the store in the poem. Explain how you found your answer. See margin.

Reflecting ▶on the Section

17. Pick an object such as a pencil or a book to use as a measuring tool. Use the object as a unit of length to measure several other objects. Make sketches that compare the objects you measured and write the ratios that can be formed from the sketches.

Spiral ◀▶ Review

Find each quotient. (Module 5, p. 352)

18. $8 \div \frac{5}{6}$ $\frac{48}{5}$ or $9\frac{3}{5}$ 19. $\frac{7}{9} \div \frac{2}{3}$ $\frac{7}{6}$ or $1\frac{1}{6}$ 20. $14 \div \frac{5}{8}$ $\frac{112}{5}$ or $22\frac{2}{5}$

Choosing a Method Use mental math or paper and pencil to find each answer. (Module 3, p. 190; Module 4, p. 256)

21. $0.48 \div 0.6$ 0.8   22. $5.24 \cdot 0.01$ 0.0524   23. $43.6 \div 0.5$ 87.2

24. $27 \cdot 0.001$ 0.027   25. $3.6 \div 0.4$ 9   26. $0.76 \cdot 0.8$ 0.608

Complete each pair of equivalent fractions. (Module 1, p. 61)

27. $\frac{9}{12} = \frac{?}{4}$ 3   28. $\frac{20}{4} = \frac{?}{1}$ 5   29. $\frac{8}{10} = \frac{?}{25}$ 20

15. Sample Response: If you were only one inch tall, you couldn't ride a bike. And climbing into your bed would be a terrifying hike. You never could play basketball, Or safely stroll around the mall. A summer walk would take till fall, If you were one inch tall.

17. Answers will vary. Check students' work. Sample Response: length of pencil:length of notebook ≈ 2:1

RESEARCH

Exercise 17 checks that you can use ratios to compare.

EXERCISE NOTES
Exercise 15 Encourage students to use mathematical ratios in making the comparisons in their verses. Students may want to work on these verses over a few days or pair up with other students to combine their lines into one verse.

16. Sample Response: about 12.8 mi; I am about 60 in. tall. I think if I were $\frac{1}{60}$ as tall, I would walk $\frac{1}{60}$ as fast. Right now, I can walk about 4 mi/hr. If I planned a month-long walk, I wouldn't walk every minute of every day, but maybe about 8 hr each day, 6 days each week or about 192 hr in a month. In that time, I would be able to walk about 192 hr · 4 mi/hr = 768 mi. If I were 1 in. tall, I'd be able to walk about $\frac{768}{60}$ = 12.8 mi. in a month.

Extra Skill Practice

TEACHER NOTES
For this Section, all of the Extra Skill Practice Exercises correspond to Exploration 1.

EXTRA HELP
Teacher's Resource Book
- Practice and Applications
- Study Guide

Technology Resources
- @Home Tutor
- Test Generator

ASSESSMENT
- Section 1 Quick Quiz
- Test Generator

Section 1
Extra Skill Practice

Use the chart at the right. Write each ratio in three ways.

1. the number of pencils to the number of pens

2. the number of folders to the number of notebooks

3. the number of folders to the number of book covers

Draw a picture of the objects to show each ratio.
In Exercises 4–6, check students' pictures.

4. The ratio of the number of stars to the number of squares is five to three. **5 stars, 3 squares**

5. The ratio of the number of forks to the number of spoons is 4 : 8. **4 forks, 8 spoons**

6. The ratio of the number of cars to the number of tires is $\frac{1}{4}$. **1 car, 4 tires**

Tell whether the ratios are equivalent.

7. 6 : 5 and 24 : 20 yes   8. 13 to 5 and 10 to 26 no   9. 21 : 8 and 8 : 21 no

10. $\frac{8}{24}$ and $\frac{2}{3}$ no   11. 7 : 12 and 21 : 32 no   12. $\frac{6}{8}$ and $\frac{9}{12}$ yes

School Store Inventory Supply	
pencils	256
pens	120
erasers	60
notebooks	32
folders	37
book covers	183

1. 256 to 120, 256:120, $\frac{256}{120}$

2. 37 to 32, 37:32, $\frac{37}{32}$

3. 37 to 183, 37:183, $\frac{37}{183}$

Study Skills ◀▶ Using Mathematical Language

To read and to talk about mathematics, you need to understand the language. When you need help, use your book as a resource.

1. Find the Glossary in the book. What does the Glossary tell you that the word *ratio* means? **A ratio is a type of comparison of two numbers or measures.**

2. Find the Table of Symbols in this book. What does the table tell you about how to read 8 : 12? **"8:12" is read "the ratio of 8 to 12".**

3. Find the Table of Measures in this book. What information does the table give you about the length of 1 meter? **1 m equals 100 cm or 1000 mm.**

4. Find the Index in this book. Look up *measurement*. What ideas about measurement does this book include? **The book covers both customary and metric measurement, including length, area, volume, and capacity.**

Section ② Rates

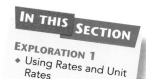

IN THIS SECTION

EXPLORATION 1
◆ Using Rates and Unit Rates

The SANDBAG BRIGADE

Setting the Stage ▶▶▶▶▶▶▶▶▶▶▶▶▶▶▶▶▶▶▶▶

SET UP *Work as a class. You will need: • object to represent a sandbag • watch or clock to time seconds • tape measure*

In the summer of 1993, one of the most costly floods in U.S. history left a wake of destruction across a nine-state region in the Midwest. Many young volunteers helped fight the floodwaters.

> **M**uddy water lapped at his shoulders, and the sky threatened rain. But Jesse Blaise, 12, stood his soggy ground. He was working hard to protect the North Lee County Historic Center in Fort Madison, Iowa, from the great Mississippi River flood of 1993. Shawn Pulis, 14, worked nearby. "Volunteers brought us boatloads of sandbags," he says. "We stacked them around the building."
>
> The volunteers worked around the clock for 13 days. It paid off. The water receded to the riverbed. The building stood. "I was so tired," says Shawn, "but I felt really good."
>
> **["The Great Flood of 1993," Barbara Brownell]**

Follow the steps to simulate a sandbag brigade.

Step 1 Line up ten students side by side.

Step 2 Hand an object representing a sandbag from one end of the line to the other.

Step 3 Record how far the object is passed and how long it takes.

373

Exploration 1

TEACHING NOTES

The ratio from **Question 3(c)** will be used in Exercise 18. Be sure all students record this ratio correctly.

Think About It

1–2. Accept reasonable estimates.

1 Suppose your class's brigade is 100 ft long. About how long will it take to pass a sandbag from one end to the other? **About 50 sec**

2 Suppose it takes one minute to pass a sandbag from one end of a brigade to the other. About how long do you expect the brigade to be? **About 120 ft**

GOAL

LEARN HOW TO...
- use rates to make predictions
- find unit rates

AS YOU...
- analyze data from your class's sandbag brigade

KEY TERMS
- rate
- unit rate

Exploration 1

Using RATES and UNIT RATES

▶ You can use ratios and the data from your class's sandbag brigade to make predictions.

3 **a.** What unit was used to measure the distance the sandbag was passed in your class? **Sample Response: feet**

b. What unit was used to measure the time it took? **Sample Response: seconds**

c. Write a ratio that compares the distance the sandbag was passed with the time it took. Label the units of measure. **Sample Response: 100 ft:50 sec**

▶ Ratios like the one you wrote in Question 3(c) that compare two quantities measured in different units are **rates**. Rates can be used to describe how one measure depends on another measure.

EXAMPLE

30 miles per gallon (mi/gal) is a rate that describes how far a car can travel on one gallon of gas.	**30.48 cm for every 12 in.** is a rate used to convert measurements from inches to centimeters and vice versa.

4 Try This as a Class Explain how you can use the rates in the Example on page 374 to answer each question.

a. How many gallons of gas does the car need to travel 60 mi?

b. How many gallons are needed to travel 80 mi?
Sample Response: 2 gallons for 60 miles with 20 miles left; $\frac{20}{30} = \frac{2}{3}$ so $2\frac{2}{3}$ gal

c. How many centimeters are in 30 in.?
Sample Response: 30 in. ÷ 12 in. = 2.5, 2.5 • 30.48 cm = 76.2 cm

d. How many centimeters are in 36 in.?
Sample Response: 36 in. ÷ 12 in. = 3, 3 • 30.48 = 91.44 cm

5 Try This as a Class Discuss which of the four answers in Question 4 were easy to find and why. Part (a) because 60 is a multiple of 30 and part (d) because 36 is a multiple of 12.

▶ **Using a Table** One way to answer questions involving rates is to make a table.

6 Suppose a brigade of students passes a sandbag 15 ft in 5 sec.

a. Make a table that predicts how far a sandbag can be passed in 5, 10, 15, 20, 25, and 30 seconds. See margin.

Distance passed (feet)	15	?	?	?	?	?
Time (seconds)	5	10	15	20	25	30

b. Explain how you predicted the distance a sandbag can be passed in 30 sec.

c. Explain two ways to predict how far a sandbag can be passed in 60 sec.

7 ✔ **CHECKPOINT** Use the rate in Question 6. Predict how long it will take to pass a sandbag 150 ft. 50 sec

The data in the table you created in Question 6(a) represent equivalent rates.

$$\frac{15 \text{ feet}}{5 \text{ seconds}} \text{ is equivalent to } \frac{30 \text{ feet}}{10 \text{ seconds}}.$$

8 Show that $\frac{15}{5}$ and $\frac{30}{10}$ are equivalent. $\frac{15}{5} = \frac{3}{1}$; $\frac{30}{10} = \frac{3}{1}$

9 Discussion Suppose a sandbag can be passed 15 feet in 5 sec. How can you use equivalent rates to predict how far the sandbag can be passed in 8 sec? $\frac{15}{5}$ and $\frac{3}{1}$ are equivalent, so $\frac{3 \cdot 8}{1 \cdot 8} = \frac{24}{8}$; 24 ft

---

4. a. Sample Response: 30 miles per gallon so divide by 30; $\frac{60}{30} = 2$ gal

6. b. Sample Response: 30 sec = 6 • 5 sec, so I predicted the sandbag could be passed 6 times as far in 30 sec as it could be passed in 5 sec.

c. Sample Response: Double the distance the sandbag could be passed in 30 sec or continue the table.

✔ **QUESTION 7**

...checks that you can use a rate to make a prediction.

375

Exploration 1 *continued*

TEACHING NOTES

In **Question 12**, encourage students to use mental math to find the unit rate for **parts (a)–(c)**.

▶ To answer Question 9, it is helpful to find a *unit rate*. A **unit rate** gives an amount per one unit. For example, 30 mi/gal is a unit rate because it gives the distance a car can travel on one gallon of gas.

EXAMPLE

To find a unit rate for the sandbag brigade in Question 6, you need to find an equivalent rate with a denominator of one second.

First Write the given rate as a fraction.

Then Set up a rate for the number of feet per one second.

$$\frac{15 \text{ feet}}{5 \text{ seconds}} = \frac{x \text{ feet}}{1 \text{ second}}$$

10 **a.** What value of x will make the rates in the Example equivalent? 3

   b. Explain how you found the value of x. $\frac{15 \div 5}{5 \div 5} = \frac{3}{1}$

   c. Use the value of x to complete the following statement:
   A sandbag can be passed __?__ feet per second. 3

   d. Show how the unit rate can be used to find the distance a sandbag can be passed in 12 sec. $\frac{3}{1} = \frac{x}{12}$; $\frac{3 \cdot 12}{1 \cdot 12} = \frac{36}{12}$; 36 ft

11 **Try This as a Class** You can also find a unit rate that shows how long it will take to pass a sandbag one foot.

Notice that the order in the rates has been changed to seconds : feet.

   a. Find a value for y so that the rates below are equivalent. $\frac{1}{3}$

   $$\frac{5 \text{ seconds}}{15 \text{ feet}} = \frac{y \text{ seconds}}{1 \text{ foot}}$$

11. d. $\frac{\left(\frac{1}{3}\right)}{1} = \frac{x}{175}$; $\frac{\frac{1}{3} \cdot 175}{1 \cdot 175}$
$= \frac{58\frac{1}{3}}{175}$; $58\frac{1}{3}$ sec

   b. Explain how you found the value for y. $\frac{5}{15} = \frac{y}{1}$; $\frac{5 \div 15}{15 \div 15} = \frac{\left(\frac{1}{3}\right)}{1}$

   c. Use the value of y to complete the following statement:
   It takes __?__ seconds to pass a sandbag one foot. $\frac{1}{3}$

   d. Show how the unit rate can be used to find how long it will take the brigade to pass a sandbag 175 ft.

✔ **QUESTION 12**

...checks that you can find a unit rate.

12 ✔ **CHECKPOINT** Find the unit rate for each rate.

   a. 250 mi in 5 hr
   50 mi/hr
   c. $4.00 for 5 pens
   $.80 per pen

   b. 56 marbles in 4 bags
   14 marbles per bag
   d. 800 turns per 60 sec
   $13\frac{1}{3}$ turns/sec

HOMEWORK EXERCISES ▶ See Exs. 1–21 on pp. 377–379.

Module 6 Comparisons and Predictions

Section 2

Key Concepts

Key Terms

Rates (pp. 374–375)

A rate is a ratio that compares two quantities measured in different units.

rate

Example $2 for 5 limes is a rate.

Rates may be equivalent.

Example

Price (dollars)	2	4	6	8
Number of limes	5	10	15	20

The pairs of numbers in the table are equivalent rates.
$$\frac{\$2}{5 \text{ limes}} = \frac{\$4}{10 \text{ limes}}$$

Unit Rates (p. 376)

A unit rate gives an amount per one unit.

unit rate

Example Find a unit rate equivalent to the rate "$2 for 5 limes."

$$\frac{\$2}{5 \text{ limes}} = \frac{x}{1 \text{ lime}}$$

$$\$2 \div 5 = \$.40$$

$$\frac{\$2}{5 \text{ limes}} = \frac{\$.40}{1 \text{ lime}}, \text{ or } \$.40 \text{ per lime}$$

13 Key Concepts Question Use the rate from the Examples. What is the cost of 25 limes? 12 limes? Explain your method.
$10; $4.80; Sample method: Multiply the cost per lime by the number of limes.

Section 2

Practice & Application Exercises

Tell whether the rates are equivalent.

1. $\frac{4.2 \text{ m}}{2 \text{ jumps}}, \frac{10.5 \text{ m}}{5 \text{ jumps}}$ Yes

2. $\frac{48 \text{ breaths}}{3 \text{ min}}, \frac{95 \text{ breaths}}{5 \text{ min}}$ No

3. $15 for 6 lb, $20 for 8 lb Yes

4. $2 for 5 pens, $8 for 20 pens Yes

5. 12 laps in 3 hr, 3 laps in 1 hr No

6. 35 mi in 2 hr, 145 mi in 4 hr No

7. $\frac{65 \text{ words}}{1 \text{ min}}, \frac{195 \text{ words}}{3 \text{ min}}$ Yes

8. $\frac{3 \text{ measures}}{12 \text{ beats}}, \frac{7 \text{ measures}}{21 \text{ beats}}$ No

> **YOU WILL NEED**
>
> For Ex. 18:
> - Labsheet 2A
> - your class's brigade data
>
> For Exs. 22–25:
> - calculator
>
> For Ex. 28:
> - graph paper

Key Concepts

CLOSURE QUESTION

How are ratios, rates, and unit rates alike? How are they different?

Sample Response: Ratios, rates, and unit rates are all comparisons between two numbers or measures. A ratio compares two numbers that are not measured or are measured with the same units. A rate compares two numbers measured with different units. And a unit rate compares two numbers with different units but gives its answer per one unit.

ABSENT STUDENTS

For students who were absent for all or part of this section, the blackline Study Guide for Section 2 may be used to present the ideas, concepts, and skills of Section 2.

Practice & Applications

SUGGESTED ASSIGNMENTS

Core Course
Day 1: Exs. 1–8, 16, 22–27
Day 2: Exs. 9–15, 17, 19–21

Extended Course
Day 1: Exs. 1–8, 16, 22–27
Day 2: Exs. 9–17 odd, 18–21, 28

Note: Extended Course assignments can be used to differentiate within the regular classroom. In classrooms where students are grouped homogeneously, the material might be covered in fewer days. In this case assignments may be combined.

Practice & Applications

ADDITIONAL PRACTICE
See the *Teacher's Resource Book* for additional practice and application exercises for this section.

EXERCISE NOTES

Exercises 9–14 Rates such as dollars per hour, miles per gallon, feet per step, and so on, are more commonly used than hours per dollar, gallons per mile, and so on. Even though one is often preferred over the other, either order is acceptable for a unit rate.

Exercise 16 If some students are unable to visit a grocery store, bring in newspaper advertisements from different stores that show the prices of various items. Students could find the unit rates from the advertisements and then determine the better buy.

Exercise 18 connects rate to the graph of a line and uses the line to predict rates. Informally students are being exposed to the concept of unit rate as the slope of a line.

Exercise 19 Many countries in Europe now use the euro as their standard currency. Students may want to research the current rate of exchange between the euro and the U.S. dollar, and then research the costs in euros of some items in Europe and use the exchange rate to determine the cost of these items in U.S. dollars.

18. a–b. See Additional Answers beginning on page A1.

---

15. $3.80 for 10 pens; Those pens cost $.38 apiece, while the other pens cost $.44 apiece.

17. 900 mi; 54,000 mi

18. e. Sample Response: 54 ft, $46\frac{2}{3}$ sec; they are similar

---

Find a unit rate for each rate.

9. $54 for 18 hr $3/hr

10. 700 mi on 20 gal   35 mi/gal

11. 150 ft in 100 steps
    1.5 ft per step

12. 500 turns in 8 min
    $62\frac{1}{2}$ turns per min

13. 17 pages in 5 min
    $3\frac{2}{5}$ pages per min

14. $3 for 5 oranges
    $.60 per orange

15. Suppose pens are packaged in two ways: $2.64 for 6 pens or $3.80 for 10 pens. Which package is the better buy? Explain.

16. **Research** Go to the grocery store. Find and record the prices for different quantities of the same item. Compare unit rates to determine which quantity is the better buy.   Answers will vary.

17.
    Science Mars travels around the sun at a rate of about 15 mi in one second. How far does Mars travel in one minute? in one hour?

    Sun

    Mars
    15 mi per second

FOR ◄HELP
with *graphing on a coordinate grid,* see
MODULE 4, p. 256

18. **Use Labsheet 2A.** You will need your class's brigade data.

    a. Complete the table of *Sandbag Brigade Data*.   See margin.

    b. Graph the data in the table. Draw segments to connect the points you graphed in order from left to right.   See margin.

    c. Use your graph to predict how far a sandbag can be passed in 18 sec.   Sample Response: about 55 ft

    d. Use a ruler to extend the line of your graph to predict how long it will take to pass a sandbag 140 ft.   Sample Response: about 46 sec

    e. Use unit rates to make the predictions in parts (c) and (d). Then compare the predictions you made using unit rates with those you made using the graph.

19. While visiting Italy, some American students found a CD that cost 15 euros. At that time, four United States dollars were worth 3 euros. How much did the CD cost in United States dollars? $20

20. Writing Gloria Jones drives 15 mi to work in about half an hour.

   a. Write her rate of travel in miles per hour. *30 mi/hr*

   b. Why do you think this rate is called her "average" speed?

Reflecting ◀▶on the Section

Write your response to Exercise 21 in your journal.

21. At top speed, a zebra can run 176 ft in 3 sec. A roadrunner can run 220 ft in 10 sec. A gray wolf can run 66 ft in one second. Which animal is the fastest? Which is the slowest? Explain.
See margin.

Spiral ◀▶Review

Calculator Write each fraction as a decimal rounded to the nearest hundredth. (Module 4, p. 225)

22. $\frac{5}{6}$ *0.83*   **23.** $\frac{12}{23}$ *0.52*   **24.** $\frac{45}{62}$ *0.73*   **25.** $\frac{84}{116}$ *0.72*

Find the mean, median, and mode(s) for each set of data.
(Module 4, p. 225)

26. 75, 86, 73, 80, 86, 80
   mean: 80; median: 80;
   modes: 80 and 86

27. 48, 52, 75, 47, 83, 48
   mean: $58\frac{5}{6}$; median: 50;
   mode: 48

Extension ▶ ▶

A Doubling Rate

28. Suppose you put $100 in a bank account where your money doubles every ten years. The table shows how it will grow. *a–b. See margin.*

Number of years	0	10	20	30	40
Money in account	$100	$200	$400	$800	$1600

a. Copy the coordinate grid and plot the data shown in the table. Connect the points in order from left to right.

b. How is the rate of growth for money in the account different from other rates in this section? (*Hint:* Are the ratios of years to money in the account equivalent?)

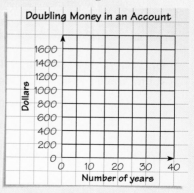
Doubling Money in an Account

Dollars (vertical axis: 200, 400, 600, 800, 1000, 1200, 1400, 1600)
Number of years (horizontal axis: 0, 10, 20, 30, 40)

Journal

Exercise 21 checks that you understand how to use rates to make comparisons.

20. b. When driving, the rate of speed is almost never constant. For example, you have to stop for lights, as well as slow down and speed up with the flow of traffic.

EXERCISE NOTES

Extension Exercise 28 shows how the doubling rate can be represented in a table (each dollar amount in the "Money in account" row of the table is twice the preceding amount) and graphically. Unlike **Exercise 18,** however, the pairs of values in the table are not equivalent rates, so the graph is not linear.

21. fastest: a gray wolf; slowest: a roadrunner; a zebra's rate is $58\frac{2}{3}$ ft/sec, a roadrunner's rate is 22 ft/sec, and a gray wolf's rate is 66 ft/sec.

28. a.

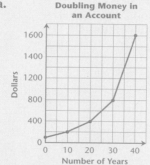
Doubling Money in an Account

b. Instead of being a constant rate of change like the rates in this section, the amount of money doubles every 10 years so the ratios of years to money are not constant. The rates are: $\frac{0}{100} = 0$, $\frac{10}{200} = \frac{1}{20}$, $\frac{20}{400} = \frac{1}{20}$, $\frac{30}{800} = \frac{3}{80}$, and $\frac{40}{1600} = \frac{1}{40}$, so the rates are not all equivalent.

Section ② Extra Skill Practice

Tell whether the rates are equivalent.

1. $\dfrac{150 \text{ words}}{3 \text{ min}}$, $\dfrac{450 \text{ words}}{9 \text{ min}}$ Yes

2. $7 for 5 lb, $16.20 for 9 lb   No

3. 204 mi on 6 gal, 68 mi on 2 gal   Yes

4. $\dfrac{212 \text{ heartbeats}}{4 \text{ min}}$, $\dfrac{343 \text{ heartbeats}}{7 \text{ min}}$ No

Find a unit rate for each rate.

5. 24 km in 3 hr
8 km/hr

6. 1500 m in 5 min
300 m/min

7. $45 for 6 books
$7.50 per book

8. 7 pages in 4 min
$1\frac{3}{4}$ pages/min

9. 84 mi on 3 gal
28 mi/gal

10. 250 ft in 200 steps
1.25 ft/step

Tell which is the better buy or if neither is the better buy.

11. $4.20 for 8 oranges or
$5.76 for 12 oranges
$5.76 for 12 oranges

12. $2.24 for 16 oz of apple juice or
$3.36 for 24 oz of apple juice
neither

13. Saturn travels around the sun at a rate of about 6 mi in one second.

   a. How far does Saturn travel in one minute?   about 360 mi

   b. How far does Saturn travel in one hour?   about 21,600 mi

14. Copy and complete the table of equivalent rates.

Number of pages read	5	10	15	20	?
Time (minutes)	8	?	?	?	40

Number of pages read	5	10	15	20	25
Time (minutes)	8	16	24	32	40

Standardized Testing ◀▶ Performance Task

On a warm day, sound travels 13,224 ft in 12 sec. On a cool day, sound travels 7140 ft in 7 sec.

1. a. Does sound travel faster through warm air or through cool air?   warm air

   b. How much faster?   82 ft/sec

2. On a warm day, how far does sound travel in 15 sec?   16,530 ft

Section ③ Using Ratios

BODY RATIOS

IN THIS SECTION

EXPLORATION 1
◆ Comparing Ratios

EXPLORATION 2
◆ Estimating Ratios

EXPLORATION 3
◆ Predicting with a Graph

Setting the Stage

In the Jonathan Swift classic *Gulliver's Travels*, Lemuel Gulliver is shipwrecked and swims to the island of Lilliput, where the people have an average height of slightly less than six inches. Since Gulliver's only clothes were those he was wearing, the Lilliputians had to make new clothing for him.

> #### GULLIVER'S TRAVELS *by Jonathan Swift*
>
> The seamstresses took my measure as I lay on the ground, one standing at my neck, and another at my mid-leg, with a strong cord extended, that each held by the end, while the third measured the length of the cord with a rule of an inch long. Then they measured my right thumb, and desired no more; for by a mathematical computation, that twice round the thumb is once round the wrist, and so on to the neck and the waist; and by the help of my old shirt, which I displayed on the ground before them for a pattern, they fitted me exactly.

Think About It

1 The height of a Lilliputian is about what fraction of your height? **Answers will vary.**

2 What two measurements did the Lilliputians take in order to make a shirt for Gulliver? **length from neck to mid-leg and the distance around his thumb**

3 **a.** What do you think Gulliver meant by "twice round the thumb is once round the wrist"? **The distance around the wrist is twice the distance around the thumb.**

   b. What do you think he meant by "and so on to the neck and the waist"?

   c. Do you think these comparisons would be true for all the students in your class? **Answers will vary.**

3. b. The distance around the neck is twice the distance around the wrist, and the distance around the waist is twice the distance around the neck.

Setting the Stage

GETTING STARTED
Module 6 Section 3 *Warm-Up* assesses student facility in comparing fractions. Students will compare ratios expressed in fraction form in this section.

To help students get an idea of the size of things on the island of Lilliput, you may wish to present some other mathematical facts from the story. You could have students estimate any of the following: the length of a Lilliputian's sword (3 in.), the tallest trees in their land (7 ft), the height of their horses (4.5 in.), the number of beds it took to make a bed for Gulliver (600), the number of tailors it took to make Gulliver's clothes (300), and the number of Lilliputians it would take to equal the length of Gulliver's dagger (5 Lilliputian men). Students may enjoy making their estimates in small groups or with a partner, then sharing their estimates with the class.

Exploration 1

CLASSROOM MANAGEMENT

Although mixed groupings are suggested for most cooperative work, you may want to consider grouping boys and girls separately for this exploration and also for Exploration 2. Some students may feel uncomfortable taking measurements of classmates of the opposite gender.

TEACHING NOTES

When measuring around the thumb in **Question 4**, caution students to be sure they wrap the string around the base of each group member's thumb so that the measurements are comparable. Also, use regular string as opposed to yarn that will stretch during use.

GOAL

LEARN HOW TO...
- use measurements to decide whether a ratio is reasonable
- write a ratio as a decimal

AS YOU...
- compare your own body ratios with those in *Gulliver's Travels*

Exploration 1

Comparing RATiOS

SET UP   *Work in a group. You will need:* • *scissors* • *string*
• *metric ruler*

▶ **In this exploration, you will test whether the ratios used by the Lilliputians can be used to accurately predict your body measurements.**

4   Have someone in your group help you measure as shown.
Check students' work.

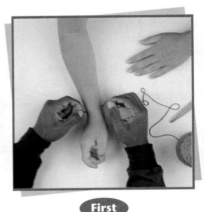

First

Cut a piece of string equal to the distance around your wrist.

Then

Wrap this string around the base of your thumb.

5 **a.** About how many times did the string go around your thumb? **Sample Response: about twice**

b. Did others in your group get about the same results? **Sample Response: They were similar.**

c. How does the relationship you observed compare with Gulliver's claim that "twice around the thumb is once around the wrist"? **Sample Response: It's the same.**

6 a. Suppose the distance around a classmate's thumb is 5 cm. What do you expect the distance around the wrist to be?
about 10 cm

b. Write the measurements from part (a) as a ratio in two ways:
5:10; $\frac{5}{10}$

(distance around thumb : distance around wrist)

$$\underline{?} \; : \; \underline{?} \; = \; \frac{?}{?}$$

▶ To compare the ratio of your body measurements to Gulliver's ratio, it may be helpful to write the ratio as a single decimal number. For example, the ratio *3 to 4* is *0.75 to 1*, or more simply, *0.75*.

7 Copy and complete the table as you answer parts (a) and (b).

Body ratio	Gulliver's ratio fraction	Gulliver's ratio decimal	Your actual ratio fraction	Your actual ratio decimal
distance around thumb / distance around wrist	?	?	?	?
distance around wrist / distance around neck	?	?	?	?

a. Use the relationship described by Gulliver on page 381 to write each body ratio as a fraction and as a decimal.

b. Wrap string to find the ratios for your body. Measure the length of the string in millimeters. Write each ratio as a fraction and as a decimal rounded to the nearest hundredth.

8 ✔ **CHECKPOINT** Look at your table from Question 7.

a. How do Gulliver's ratios compare with your ratios? Which form of the ratios did you use to compare? Explain your choice.

b. Do you think Gulliver's ratios are reasonable estimates? Explain.

9 Discussion Suppose the distance around a person's thumb is 9 cm. Explain how you can use ratios to predict the distance around the person's neck and waist. See margin.

HOMEWORK EXERCISES ▶ See Exs. 1–6 on p. 390.

---

7. Sample responses are given.

a. $\frac{\text{thumb}}{\text{wrist}}$: $\frac{1}{2}$, 0.5;

$\frac{\text{wrist}}{\text{neck}}$: $\frac{1}{2}$, 0.5

b. $\frac{\text{thumb}}{\text{wrist}}$: $\frac{96}{196}$, 0.49;

$\frac{\text{wrist}}{\text{neck}}$: $\frac{196}{384}$, 0.51

FOR ◀ HELP

with *writing a fraction as a decimal,* see
MODULE 4, p. 225

8. Sample responses are given.
a. They are similar; the decimals. They are easier to compare than the fractions.
b. Yes; They are similar to the ones I and most of my classmates got.

✔ **QUESTION 8**

...checks that you can decide whether a ratio is reasonable.

TEACHING NOTES
As students think about their answers to **Question 8**, you may want to have them share information from their completed tables from **Question 7**. Knowing some of the other ratios that were found should help them realize that the decimal form of a ratio is often the better form for making comparisons. The shared results could also help them decide in **part (b)** if Gulliver's ratios are reasonable estimates to use.

For **Question 9**, suggest that students look back at their answers to **Question 3** to remind them of the relationships between the thumb, wrist, and neck measurements. Point out how setting up equivalent ratios can help them predict the distance around the person's neck.

9. I would use Gulliver's ratios and double the distance around the person's thumb to get that the distance around his or her wrist is 18 cm, double the distance around the wrist to get that the distance around the neck is 36 cm, and double the distance around the wrist to get that the distance around the person's waist is 72 cm.

Exploration 2

TEACHING NOTES

Review the *How to Measure*
Student Resource diagram with
your students. They will use it as a
reference in completing the *Body
Measurements Table* in **Question 11**.
You may want to demonstrate the
directions for measuring the radius.
Note that students are to measure
their heights with their shoes *off*.

LEARN HOW TO...
◆ find a ratio to
describe data
◆ use a ratio to
make predictions

AS YOU...
◆ look for other
body ratios

KEY TERM
◆ "nice" fraction

Exploration 2
Estimating RATIOS

SET UP Work in a group of four. Your group will need: • Labsheet 3A
• scissors • string • metric ruler

▶ Now you will explore whether other body ratios are about the
same for most people. Use the Student Resource below to help you
measure.

10 Estimation Do you think your reach is *more* or *less* than 1 m?
more than 1 m

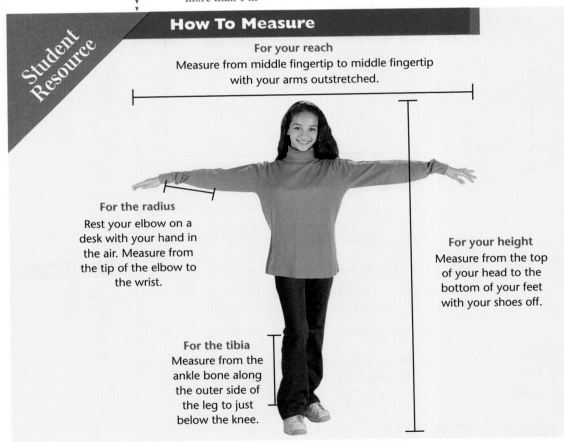

Student Resource

How To Measure

For your reach
Measure from middle fingertip to middle fingertip
with your arms outstretched.

For the radius
Rest your elbow on a
desk with your hand in
the air. Measure from
the tip of the elbow to
the wrist.

For your height
Measure from the top
of your head to the
bottom of your feet
with your shoes off.

For the tibia
Measure from the
ankle bone along
the outer side of
the leg to just
below the knee.

Use Labsheet 3A for Questions 11 and 12.

11 **a.** In the *Body Measurements Table*, record each of the given measurements for each person in your group. Round each measurement to the nearest 0.5 cm. Answers will vary. Check students' tables.

b. Include the data from two other groups in your table. (You will use these in Exploration 3.) Answers will vary. Check students' tables.

12 **a.** For each person in your group, find the decimal form of each ratio in the *Body Ratios Table*. Round to the nearest hundredth. Record your results in the table. Answers will vary. Check students' tables.

b. Which columns of your table have ratios that are about the same for everyone? Answers will vary. Check students' tables.

c. Find and record the mean of the ratios in each column. Answers will vary. Check students' work.

▶ Ratios are often expressed as fractions. **"Nice" fractions**, such as $\frac{1}{3}$, $\frac{1}{4}$, and $\frac{2}{5}$, are common fractions that are easy to visualize and easy to compute with mentally.

EXAMPLE

Find a "nice" fraction for $\frac{5}{11}$.

SAMPLE RESPONSE

Using mental math:

5 is about half of 11,

so $\frac{1}{2}$ is a "nice" fraction for $\frac{5}{11}$.

$\frac{1}{2}$ is a **"nice" fraction** because it is easy to compute with. For example, it is easier to find $\frac{1}{2}$ of 16 than $\frac{5}{11}$ of 16.

Using decimals:

$\frac{5}{11} \approx 0.45$

This is close to 0.5, or the "nice" fraction $\frac{1}{2}$.

---

13 **Try This as a Class**

a. Which of the following "nice" fractions is closest to $\frac{7}{24}$: $\frac{1}{2}$, $\frac{1}{3}$, $\frac{1}{5}$, or $\frac{1}{6}$? $\frac{1}{3}$

b. How did you decide which fraction was best in part (a)?

c. Name two fractions that the "nice" fraction $\frac{3}{4}$ could replace.

13. b. Sample Responses: $\frac{7}{24}$ is close to $\frac{8}{24} = \frac{1}{3}$, or $\frac{7}{24} \approx 0.29$ which is close to 0.33 and $0.33 \approx \frac{1}{3}$

c. Sample Responses: $\frac{74}{100}$; $\frac{17}{23}$

TEACHING NOTES

In **Question 11**, students will be rounding to the nearest 0.5 cm, so you might want to briefly review how to do this before beginning the labsheet. Completed **Labsheet 3A** is used again in Exploration 3 and again in the Practice and Application Exercises, therefore students should retain it in a secure place for future use. For any student who is absent for this exploration, you may want to make a copy of a group member's Labsheet 3A for the student to use in Exploration 3.

DEVELOPING MATH CONCEPTS

Although proportions are not formally introduced until Section 4, students may instinctively use proportional thinking as they make predictions from ratios. Therefore, this exploration is important for building a conceptual framework for students' later work with proportions. To help students understand the key term "nice" fraction, you may want to discuss why they think the fractions in **Question 13** are considered "nice" fractions while other fractions are not.

Exploration 2 *continued*

TEACHING NOTES

In **Checkpoint Question 15**, students will probably choose one of the "nice" fractions shown in **Question 14** to represent their data. All students in the group should understand and be able to explain why that particular fraction was chosen.

Question 17 Although the units are now in inches, students can use the same ratios as the ones found earlier in centimeters.

14. a. $\frac{1}{4}$; The mean is 0.23, which is close to 0.25, the decimal form of $\frac{1}{4}$.

✔ **QUESTION 15**

...checks that you can find and use a fraction to make a prediction.

As you answer Questions 14–16, record the "nice" fractions you find to describe your data in your Body Ratios Table.

14 **Use Labsheet 3A.** Sample responses are given.

a. Discussion Which ratio below is closest to the mean of your group's tibia to height ratios? Explain how you know.

$$\frac{1}{1} \quad \frac{1}{2} \quad \frac{1}{3} \quad \frac{1}{4} \quad \frac{1}{5} \quad \frac{1}{6}$$

b. Use your ratio from part (a) to predict the tibia length of a person who is 150 cm tall. *about 37.5 cm*

15 ✔ **CHECKPOINT** Sample responses are given.

a. What "nice" fraction is close to the mean of the radius to height ratios? $\frac{1}{6}$

b. Suppose a person's radius is 18 cm long. About how tall do you expect the person to be? *about 108 cm*

16 a. Write a "nice" fraction that is close to the mean of the reach to height ratios. Sample response: $\frac{1}{1}$

b. Suppose a person is 180 cm tall. About how long do you think the person's reach is? Sample Response: about 180 cm

17 Use your results from Questions 14–16. Draw and label a sketch of a 6-inch tall Lilliputian that shows the measure of the reach, the tibia, and the radius. Check students' drawings. Reach should be about 6 in., tibia 1.5 in., and radius 1 in.

HOMEWORK EXERCISES ▶ See Exs. 7–15 on pp. 390–391.

Exploration 3

Predicting with a GRAPH

SET UP Work in a group. You will need: • completed Labsheet 3A • Labsheet 3B • uncooked spaghetti • graph paper

▶ In Explorations 1 and 2 you used ratios to make predictions. You can also use a graph to make predictions from data.

Use Labsheet 3B for Questions 18–20 and 22.

18 Try This as a Class Follow the steps below to make predictions about height and reach using a graph. See margin.

Step 1

Place a piece of uncooked spaghetti on the *Reach Compared to Height Graph* so it lies close to most of the points. Try to have about the same number of points on one side of the spaghetti as on the other side.

Step 2

Draw a line segment on the *Reach Compared to Height Graph* along the edge of your spaghetti. The segment you drew on the graph is a **fitted line**. It can be used to predict unknown measurements using known ones.

19 a. How can the fitted line help you predict a person's height if you know the person's reach is 135 cm?

b. What do you expect the reach of a person 152 cm tall to be? about 152 cm

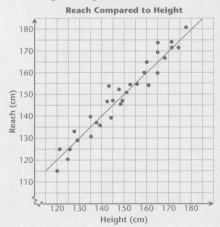

GOAL

LEARN HOW TO...
- ◆ fit a line to data in a scatter plot
- ◆ use a scatter plot to make predictions

AS YOU...
- ◆ analyze the body ratio data you collected

KEY TERMS
- ◆ fitted line
- ◆ scatter plot

19. a. Find the point where the horizontal line corresponding to a reach of 135 cm intersects the fitted line. Then find the height where a vertical line through the point intersects the Height axis.

Exploration 3

TEACHING NOTES
Before students draw their line in **Question 18**, ask them what they notice about the points on the graph. Students should notice that although the points "cluster" in the middle, they tend to fall along a line. You can model finding a fitted line by making an overhead transparency of **Labsheet 3B** and placing a piece of uncooked spaghetti or a clear ruler along the points on the graph. As you move the "line" to various places on the graph, students could tell you as a class where they think it best "fits" the data points. Students could then draw their own fitted line.

TECHNOLOGY
For a related technology activity, see the *Technology Book*.

18. Sample Response:

Reach Compared to Height

TEACHING NOTES

In **Question 20**, it is important that students understand how the scale on the graph relates to the data, as they will be choosing a scale for their own data in **Question 21(c)**. In addition to looking at the starting points on the graph, point out the two greatest values and ask students why they think the scale stops at these values. You might also want to discuss why a 10-cm interval is appropriate to represent the data.

FOR ◀HELP
with *plotting points*, see
MODULE 4, p. 256

20. Sample Response:
I think students using the graph are at least 120 cm tall and have a reach of at least 110 cm. If you begin the graph at (0,0), there will be a lot of wasted space on the graph before values are plotted.

✓ QUESTION 22

...checks that you can use a scatter plot and a fitted line to make a prediction.

20 **Discussion** Look at the scales used on the *Reach Compared to Height Graph*. Why do you think the labeling on the scales starts at a height of 120 cm and at a reach of 110 cm?

Use your data from Labsheet 3A for Questions 21 and 22.

21 Use the data on the heights and the lengths of the tibias from all three groups in your *Body Measurements Table*. You will make a graph similar to the *Reach Compared to Height Graph*.
a–d. Answers will vary. Check students' graphs.
a. Look at the height data. What are the shortest and the tallest heights?

b. Look at the tibia data. What are the shortest and the longest lengths of the tibias?

c. Use your answers from parts (a) and (b) to draw and label the scales for your graph. You do not have to start your labeling at (0, 0).

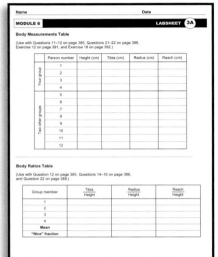

d. Plot a point representing the height and the length of the tibia for each person.

e. The type of graph you made is a **scatter plot**. What do you notice about the points in your scatter plot? Sample Response: The points are scattered, but they appear to lie close to a straight line.
f. Follow the steps in Question 18 to draw a fitted line for your scatter plot. Check students' graphs.

22 **✓ CHECKPOINT** Use your graph from Question 21.
Sample responses are given.
a. Suppose a person's tibia is 42 cm long. About how tall do you expect the person to be? about 168 cm

b. Use the fitted line on your scatter plot to complete the *Points on the Line Table* on Labsheet 3B. See margin.

c. How do the tibia to height ratios in the *Points on the Line Table* compare with the "nice" fraction you recorded in the *Body Ratios Table* on Labsheet 3A? They are similar.

HOMEWORK EXERCISES ▶ See Exs. 16–20 on pp. 392–393.

22. b. See Additional Answers beginning on page A1.

Using Ratios (pp. 382–386)

Different forms of ratios are useful in different situations.

- Using the decimal form can help you to compare ratios. To find the decimal, first write the ratio as a fraction. Then divide the numerator by the denominator.

Example   length of one step = 64 cm
height = 151 cm

$$\frac{\text{step length}}{\text{height}} = \frac{64}{151}$$

$$151\overline{)64.000} \quad 0.423$$

The ratio is about 0.42 or 0.42 to 1.

- "Nice" fractions, like $\frac{1}{2}$, $\frac{2}{3}$, or $\frac{3}{4}$, are often used to describe ratios in a simple way, making computation easier. Look to see if the decimal form is close to a "nice" fraction.

"nice" fraction

Example   The ratio 0.42 is close to 0.4, which equals the "nice" fraction $\frac{4}{10}$, or $\frac{2}{5}$. This ratio can be used to estimate the height of a person whose step length is 60 cm.

$$\frac{\text{step length}}{\text{height}} = \frac{2}{5} = \frac{60}{?} \qquad \frac{2 \times 30}{5 \times 30} = \frac{60}{150}$$

The height of the person is probably about 150 cm.

Using Scatter Plots (pp. 387–388)

A scatter plot is a graph that shows the relationship between two sets of data.

scatter plot

When the points lie close to a line, you can use a fitted line to make predictions from the data.

fitted line

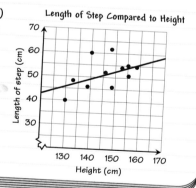

Length of Step Compared to Height

23 Key Concepts Question

a. Use the "nice" fraction in the second Example above to estimate the step length of a person 145 cm tall. **about 58 cm**

b. Use the scatter plot above and the fitted line to predict the step length of a person who is 145 cm tall. **about 51 cm**

Key Terms

Key Concepts

CLOSURE QUESTION

Why do you think estimation is useful when comparing ratios and making predictions from graphs that involve experimental data?

Sample Response: Experimental data often do not follow an exact pattern or do not produce values that can easily be calculated exactly. Using approximations, such as "nice" fractions or "nice" values, can often give a sufficient estimate for the problem.

Practice & Applications

SUGGESTED ASSIGNMENTS

Core Course

Day 1: Exs. 1–6
Day 2: Exs. 21–24
Day 3: Exs. 7–15
Day 4: Exs. 16–20

Extended Course

Day 1: Exs. 1–6
Day 2: Exs. 21–24
Day 3: Exs. 7–15
Day 4: Exs. 16–20

Note: Extended Course assignments can be used to differentiate within the regular classroom. In classrooms where students are grouped homogeneously, the material might be covered in fewer days. In this case assignments may be combined.

ADDITIONAL PRACTICE

See the *Teacher's Resource Book* for additional practice and application exercises for this section.

EXERCISE NOTES

You may wish to extend **Exercise 2** by having students apply what they have learned about width to height ratios and their effect on the shape of the ovals, to the width to height ratios for squares and rectangles. Ask, "What width to height ratio does a square have?" (*1:1*) "What would a rectangle with a width to height ratio of 0.5 look like?" "What are some possible dimensions for a rectangle with a width to height ratio of 0.25?" (*4 cm to 16 cm*)

YOU WILL NEED

For Exs. 12 and 18:
◆ completed Labsheet 3A

For Exs. 17 and 18:
◆ graph paper
◆ piece of uncooked spaghetti or a clear plastic ruler

1. a. thumb: about 10 cm; neck: about 40 cm; waist: about 80 cm

b. Check students' drawings. Collar could be 41 cm and wrist 21 cm. Students should note that shirt openings equal to the measures of Gulliver's neck (40 cm) and wrist (20 cm) would be uncomfortably tight.

41 cm

21 cm

2. b. The greater the ratio, the wider the oval. The smaller the ratio, the narrower the oval. The closer the ratio is to 1, the closer the oval is to a circle.

Section 3
Practice & Application Exercises

1. Use the ratio 1 : 2 as an estimate for the body ratios *thumb to wrist, wrist to neck,* and *neck to waist.*

   a. Suppose the distance around Gulliver's wrist is 20 cm. Estimate his thumb, neck, and waist measurements.

   b. Create Your Own Make and label a sketch of Gulliver's shirt. Select reasonable measurements for the cuffs and neckline.

2. Each oval has a vertical height of 12 mm.

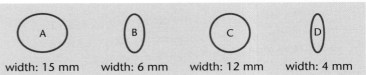

   width: 15 mm   width: 6 mm   width: 12 mm   width: 4 mm

   a. For each oval, write the ratio of the width to the height as a decimal. $\frac{15}{12} = 1.25$, $\frac{6}{12} = 0.5$, $\frac{12}{12} = 1$, $\frac{4}{12} = 0.33$

   b. What does the ratio of the width to the height tell you about the general shape of the ovals?

Write each ratio as a decimal rounded to the nearest hundredth.

3. 7 : 9 0.78   4. 6 : 11 0.55   5. 2 : 7 0.29   6. 8 : 19 0.42

7. Solve the following problems to see how an archaeologist might be able to use body ratios.

   a. A human radius 27 cm long was found. Estimate the person's height. (Use 1 : 6 as the ratio for *length of radius to height.*) about 162 cm

   b. A human tibia 46 cm long was discovered at the same site as the radius in part (a). Estimate the person's height. (Use 1 : 4 as the ratio for *length of tibia to height.*) about 184 cm

   c. Do you think both bones are from the same person? Explain. No; The estimated heights vary too greatly.

Write a "nice" fraction for each ratio.

8. 5 : 26 $\frac{1}{5}$ 9. 0.31 $\frac{3}{10}$ 10. $\frac{12}{38}$ $\frac{1}{3}$ 11. 0.6 to 1 $\frac{3}{5}$

12. **Use the data from Labsheet 3A.** Write a "nice" fraction that compares the length of the tibia with the length of the radius. $\frac{3}{2}$

13. Some students dropped a ball from different heights. They recorded how high it bounced from each drop height.

    a. The ratio of *bounce height to drop height* was about 0.81. Write a "nice" fraction close to 0.81. $\frac{4}{5}$

    b. Predict how high the ball will bounce when they drop it from a height of 5 ft. about 4 ft

    c. On one drop the ball bounced to a height of 28 in. Estimate the drop height the students used. about 35 in.

14. **Home Involvement** Find at least two other people whose ages are different from yours. Record the body measurements shown on page 384 for them. Compare the ratios of these measurements with the "nice" fractions you found for your group. Prepare a presentation of your findings. Answers will vary.

15. **Volleyball** Volleyball net heights are different for women and men. The women's net is set at 7 ft $4\frac{1}{8}$ in. The men's net is set at 7 ft $11\frac{5}{8}$ in.

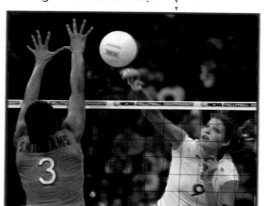

    a. Round each net height to the nearest inch. Write a ratio of *women's net height to men's net height* in inches. 88 : 96

    b. Using decimals, what "nice" fraction is the ratio in part (a) close to? $\frac{9}{10}$

    c. The average height of the top ten female volleyball players is 5 ft 9 in. The average height of the top ten male volleyball players is 6 ft 4 in. Write a ratio of the *average women's height to average men's height* in inches. 69 : 76

    d. Using decimals, what "nice" fraction is the ratio in part (c) close to? $\frac{9}{10}$

    e. How does the ratio in part (b) compare with the ratio in part (d)? They are close. The nice fractions are the same.

    f. Compare the ratio of *average women's height to women's net height* with the ratio of *average men's height to men's net height*. Describe your findings.
    69 : 88 ≈ 0.78, 76 : 96 ≈ 0.79; The ratios are very close.

Section 3   Using Ratios   391

EXERCISE NOTES CONT.

As students write their answers to **Exercise 7(b)**, encourage them to use the proportional reasoning skills they have developed in this section. You may want to have them think back to their work in Section 1 where they learned to compare the height of the two mugs by using multiplication and division instead of by using addition and subtraction. Students may be interested to know that archaeologists actually use body ratios to make estimates and predictions, and to help them piece together information about past cultures. Forensic scientists also rely on body ratios to help them uncover clues and solve crimes.

For **Exercises 8–11**, point out to students that they are not limited to just the "nice" fractions presented in this section.

Practice & Applications

DEVELOPING MATH CONCEPTS

Exercise 16 provides a good opportunity to check that all students understand the concept of a fitted line. Students having difficulty with this concept should refer to page 387.

EXERCISE NOTES

Exercise 17 Students should use their fitted line to make their predictions in **parts (b) and (c)**.

17. a. Check students' graphs.
    Sample graph:

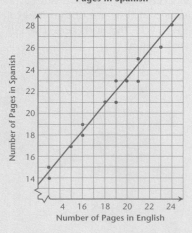

Number of Pages in English Compared to Number of Pages in Spanish

18. b. Check students' graphs for fitted line. Table at right uses 1 : 6 as the ratio for length of radius to height.

Height (cm)	Radius (cm)
120	20
150	25
180	30
144	24
192	32

16. a. Which line would you use to make predictions about the distance around a person's head or predictions about a person's height? Why? **fitted line 1; The line is close to many of the points with an equal number of points on either side.**

Distance Around the Head Compared to Height

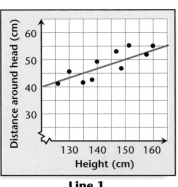

Line 1

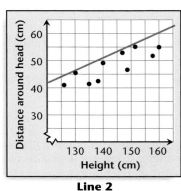

Line 2

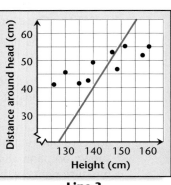

Line 3

b. Use your choice from part (a) to predict each measurement.
   about 135 cm; Answers will vary.
   • height for a distance around the head of 45 cm

   • the distance around your own head

Pages in English	Pages in Spanish
13	14
13	15
15	17
16	18
16	19
18	21
19	21
19	23
20	23
21	23
21	25
23	26
24	28

17. a. When English is translated into Spanish it takes up a different amount of space. On graph paper, make a scatter plot with a fitted line that shows the relationship between the number of pages in English and the number of pages in Spanish.
    See margin.

    b. Predict the number of pages in Spanish for an article that is 14 pages long in English. **about 16 pages**

    c. Predict the number of pages in English for an article that is 30 pages long in Spanish. **about 25 pages**

18. a. **Use the data from Labsheet 3A.**
    On graph paper, make a scatter plot that shows the relationship between the height and the length of the radius.
    Check students' graphs.

    b. Draw a fitted line on your scatter plot. Copy the table at the right. Then use your fitted line to complete it. **See margin.**

Height (cm)	Radius (cm)
120	?
150	?
180	?
?	24
?	32

19. Nearly 8000 terra-cotta warriors that are $5\frac{1}{2}$ to 6 feet tall have been found near Lintong, China. These figures were found close to the burial site of Qin Shihuangdi, the first emperor of China. Some believe that this army was built to fight the emperor's battles after death.

   a. Use your scatter plot from Exercise 18 to estimate the length of the radius of a 6-foot warrior. (1 ft is about 30.5 cm.)
   about 1 ft

   b. **Writing** A 6-foot warrior is 6 in. taller than a $5\frac{1}{2}$-foot warrior. Does this mean that the tibia of a 6-foot warrior is 6 in. longer than the tibia of a $5\frac{1}{2}$-foot warrior? Explain.

◀ The warriors are made of terra-cotta, a type of ceramic clay.

19. b. No; The tibia of a 6-ft warrior would be about $1\frac{1}{2}$ ft or 18 in. long and the tibia of a $5\frac{1}{2}$-ft warrior would be about $1\frac{3}{8}$ ft or $16\frac{1}{2}$ in. long. The difference would be about $1\frac{1}{2}$ in.

Reflecting on the Section

Write your response to Exercise 20 in your journal.

20. Think of some ratios you use in your daily life. Use sketches or descriptions to show what these ratios mean and how you could use them to find unknown values. Include different forms of ratios and explain why each form is used. **Check students' work.**

Journal

Exercise 20 checks that you understand how ratios are used.

Spiral Review

Find a unit rate for each rate. (Module 6, p. 377)

21. 99 mi on 3 gal   **22.** $17 for 6 lb   **23.** $\dfrac{265 \text{ heartbeats}}{5 \text{ min}}$
   33 mi/gal   **about $2.83 per lb**   **53 heartbeats per min**

24. Suppose heads occurred on 14 out of 30 tosses of a coin. Find the experimental probability of tossing heads. (Module 2, p. 80) $\frac{14}{30} = \frac{7}{15}$

TEACHER NOTES
For each Exploration, the corresponding Extra Skill Practice Exercises are noted.

Exploration 2: Ex. 1
Exploration 3: Ex. 2

EXTRA HELP
Teacher's Resource Book
• Practice and Applications
• Study Guide

Technology Resources
• @Home Tutor
• Test Generator

ASSESSMENT
• Section 3 Quick Quiz
• Mid-Module Quiz
• Test Generator

2. a. Sample graph:

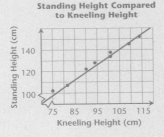

Standing Height Compared to Kneeling Height

1. d. See Additional Answers beginning on page A1.

394

Section 3
Extra Skill Practice

You will need: • *graph paper* (Ex. 2)
  • *piece of uncooked spaghetti or clear ruler* (Ex. 2)

For Exercises 1 and 2, use the data in the table.

Person	A	B	C	D	E	F	G	H
kneeling height (cm) / Standing height (cm)	$\frac{75}{102}$	$\frac{90}{122}$	$\frac{101}{137}$	$\frac{82}{108}$	$\frac{109}{145}$	$\frac{113}{152}$	$\frac{101}{135}$	$\frac{94}{128}$

1. a. Write each *kneeling height to standing height* ratio as a decimal. Round to the nearest hundredth.
   A: 0.74, B: 0.74, C: 0.74, D: 0.76, E: 0.75, F: 0.74, G: 0.75, H: 0.73

   b. Find the mean of the *kneeling height to standing height* ratios. about 0.74

   c. Write a "nice" fraction that is close to the mean. $\frac{3}{4}$

   d. Use your "nice" fraction to estimate the missing entries in the table below. See margin.

Kneeling height (cm)	94	?	?	87
Standing height (cm)	?	132	140	?

2. a. Make a scatter plot that shows the relationship between the kneeling height and the standing height of each person in the table. See margin.

   b. Use a piece of uncooked spaghetti or a clear ruler to draw a fitted line on your scatter plot. Fitted line should be close to (90,120) and (105, 140).

   c. Use your scatter plot to estimate the missing entries in the table in Exercise 1(d). How do your answers compare?
   Sample Response: The answers are close to the answers in the table.

Standardized Testing ◀▶ Open-Ended

Write a word problem that involves using ratios to make a comparison or prediction.

Solve your word problem. What form of the ratio did you use? Explain why you chose that form. Answers will vary. Check students' work.

FOR ASSESSMENT AND PORTFOLIOS

The IDEAL Chair

SET UP *You will need: • ruler • string • yardstick*

The Situation
See the *Teacher's Resource Book* for a sample solution for this Extended Exploration.

Sometimes it is hard to find a comfortable chair to sit in. Many companies manufacture wooden, polyethylene, and solid plastic classroom chairs in a range of sizes to accommodate the average size student in different grades.

The Problem

Design a chair for your classroom that has the proportions and features that make the chair comfortable not just for sitting, but for learning.

Something to Think About

- What size chair would best fit you if your feet are flat on the floor and the chair back supports your back?
- What information do you need to consider as you design a chair to fit any student in your classroom?
- How will you find and organize your data?

Present your Results

Describe your classroom chair.

- Why is it comfortable for sitting and learning?
- What other features make your design desirable?

Show the organized information you gathered.

- How did you collect the data?
- How did you use the information?

Display sketches and/or a model of your chair.

Reflect on Your Design

- What did you try that did not work?
- What did you do when you were stuck?
- What would you change if you were to design another chair?

Extended Exploration

E2 NOTES
Using an E2: Suggestions for managing and evaluating an Extended Exploration are available in the *Teacher's Resource Book* for Modules 1 and 2. See also pages T44–T45 in the *Teacher's Edition*.

Alternate E2: See the *Teacher's Resource Book* for Modules 5 and 6 for an alternate Extended Exploration that can be used after Module 6, Section 3.

INTRODUCING THE E2
Introduce the E2 by discussing a time when you have been uncomfortable in a chair, such as an airplane seat in which your feet did not touch the floor when your back was up against the seat back, or at a concert hall where your knees were bent for a period of time because the chair bottom was too short and there was no room to extend your legs. Ask students if they would be comfortable in a classroom chair in a first grade classroom. Then introduce the assignment posed by the E2.

Setting the Stage

GETTING STARTED
Module 6 Section 4 *Warm-Up* assesses students' ability to mentally find a missing numerator or denominator for a pair of equivalent fractions. The connection between equivalent fractions and proportions is introduced in Section 4 along with using equivalent fractions and other methods for finding a missing term in a proportion.

TEACHING NOTES
Questions 1 and 2 A long jumper strives for distance only and his or her height during the jump is not measured. If time allows, have students measure the distance they can long jump. The physical education department at your school may be willing to have students perform the activity as part of their regular gym class. Doing such an activity would provide students with an interesting point of reference as they think about the information shown in the table and on the graph.

Students should understand that a fair comparison of jumping ability cannot be made by considering just the length of the jump.
Questions 1(d), 2, and 11(a) indicate that a more meaningful comparison is made by using ratios to compare jumping distance to body length.

1. d. No; For example, even a fairly small person can step farther than a cricket can jump, just because of his or her size.

Section ④ Proportions

Setting the Stage

Look at the table and graph to see how the world-record long jump for a human compares to the records of several animals.

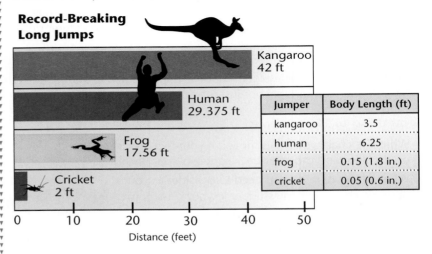

Record-Breaking Long Jumps

Kangaroo 42 ft
Human 29.375 ft
Frog 17.56 ft
Cricket 2 ft

Distance (feet)

Jumper	Body Length (ft)
kangaroo	3.5
human	6.25
frog	0.15 (1.8 in.)
cricket	0.05 (0.6 in.)

Think About It

1 a. Which of the four jumped the farthest? *the kangaroo*

b. Which of the four can jump more than 10 times its body length? *the kangaroo, the frog, and the cricket*

c. Which can jump more than 100 times its body length? *the frog*

d. Is it fair to compare jumping ability by examining just the distance jumped? Explain.

2 Describe how ratios written in decimal form can be used to identify which jumper traveled the farthest for its size. *Find the ratio of the length of each jump to the jumper's body length. Express the ratios as decimals to compare them. The best jumper is the one with the greatest ratio.*

Exploration 1

EXPLORING PROPORTIONS

▶ A black-tailed jackrabbit can jump about as far for its size as the record-breaking kangaroo. You can use this fact to estimate how far a jackrabbit 18 in. long can jump. To find out how, you will explore some properties of equivalent ratios.

3 Discussion Tell whether the ratios in each pair are equivalent. Explain how you know.

a. $\frac{10}{12}$ and $\frac{25}{30}$ **b.** $\frac{8}{24}$ and $\frac{4}{20}$ **c.** $\frac{10}{40}$ and $\frac{101}{400}$

d. $\frac{8}{6}$ and $\frac{2}{18}$ **e.** $\frac{12}{36}$ and $\frac{5}{15}$ **f.** $\frac{16}{24}$ and $\frac{27}{36}$

▶ A **proportion** is an equation stating that two ratios are equivalent. One method for determining if two ratios are equivalent is to compare **cross products**.

EXAMPLE

The equation $\frac{16}{10} = \frac{24}{15}$ is a proportion.

One cross product is 16 · 15.

The other cross product is 10 · 24.

4 Find the products 16 · 15 and 10 · 24. What do you notice? 240, 240; They are equal.

5 a. Find the cross products for each pair of equivalent ratios in Question 3. What do you notice about them? (a) 300, 300 (e) 180, 180; They are equal.

b. Find the cross products for the pairs of ratios that are not equivalent in Question 3. What do you notice? (b) 160, 96; (c) 4000, 4040; (d) 144, 12; (f) 576, 648; They are not equal.

Section 4 Proportions **397**

GOAL

LEARN HOW TO...
- Use cross products to find equivalent ratios
- find the missing term in a proportion

AS YOU...
- predict how far a jackrabbit can jump

KEY TERMS
- proportion
- cross products

3. **a.** Yes; both fractions are equivalent to $\frac{5}{6}$

b. No; $\frac{8}{24} = \frac{1}{3}$, $\frac{4}{20} = \frac{1}{5}$, and $\frac{1}{3} \neq \frac{1}{5}$.

c. No; $\frac{10}{40} = \frac{100}{400} \neq \frac{101}{400}$.

d. No; $\frac{8}{6} > 1$ and $\frac{2}{18} < 1$, so the fractions are not equivalent.

e. Yes; both fractions are equivalent to $\frac{1}{3}$

f. No; $\frac{16}{24} = \frac{2}{3}$, $\frac{27}{36} = \frac{3}{4}$, and $\frac{2}{3} \neq \frac{3}{4}$.

Exploration 1

TEACHING NOTES

Question 3 Students can use any number of approaches to determine if the ratios are equivalent, including fraction number sense, simplifying the fractions, multiplying or dividing both numerator and denominator by the same number, looking for numerator and denominator relationships, or writing the ratios as decimals.

DEVELOPING MATH CONCEPTS

Question 6 Students have seen that the cross products of two equivalent ratios are equal. From their discussion, students should realize that the converse is also true. Since the definition of proportion has now been presented, ask students which pairs of ratios in **Question 3** could be written as proportions. *(parts (a) and (e))*

The Classroom Example below can be used to further illustrate that if the cross products are equal, then the ratios are equivalent.

CLASSROOM EXAMPLE

Show that the equation $\frac{8}{14} = \frac{12}{21}$ is a proportion.

Answer:
Since $8 \cdot 21 = 168$ and $14 \cdot 12 = 168$, the cross products are equal.

Therefore, the ratios are equivalent and the equation is a proportion.

DEVELOPING MATH CONCEPTS

Question 8 Students consider two methods of solving a proportion: finding cross products and finding an equivalent fraction. Be sure they understand that the value of x in the proportion is the number that makes the cross products $9 \cdot 20$ and $12 \cdot x$ equal. To solve the equation $12 \cdot x = 180$, students should think, "12 times what number equals 180?" It may help to show students how to "check" their solution by substituting 15 for x in the proportion and showing that this is indeed the value that makes the ratios equivalent. This may be done by finding the cross products, simplifying the fractions, or finding decimal equivalents of the ratios.

11. a–b. and d. See Additional
Answers beginning on page A1.

398

✔ **QUESTION 7**

...checks that you can use cross products to tell whether two ratios are equivalent.

7. a. $66 \neq 60$, no
b. $336 \neq 256$, no
c. $900 = 900$, yes

8. a. Step 1: Find the cross products and set them equal.
Step 2: Find the product of 9 and 20.
Step 3: Divide both sides of the equation by 12.
Step 4: Find the quotient $180 \div 12$.

✔ **QUESTION 10**

...checks that you can find a missing term in a proportion.

8. b. Sample Response: Check to see if the cross products in the proportion $\frac{9}{12} = \frac{15}{20}$ are equal.

c. Yes; In simplest form, $\frac{9}{12} = \frac{3}{4}$. To find the fraction equivalent to $\frac{3}{4}$ that had the denominator 20, multiply the numerator and denominator of $\frac{3}{4}$ by 5. $\frac{3 \cdot 5}{4 \cdot 5} = \frac{15}{20}$, so $x = 15$.

 Module 6 Comparisons and Predictions

---

6 **Discussion** How do you think cross products can be used to tell whether two ratios are equivalent? **Two ratios are equivalent if the cross products are equal.**

7 ✔ **CHECKPOINT** Use cross products to tell whether the ratios are equivalent.

a. $\frac{11}{4}$ and $\frac{15}{6}$ b. $\frac{8}{14}$ and $\frac{24}{32}$ c. $\frac{12}{30}$ and $\frac{30}{75}$

8 **Try This as a Class** Cathy used cross products to help her find the missing term in the proportion $\frac{9}{12} = \frac{x}{20}$.

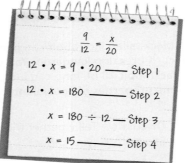

a. Explain what she did in each step.

b. How can you check whether 15 is the correct value?

c. Can you also use equivalent fractions to find the missing term in the proportion $\frac{9}{12} = \frac{x}{20}$? Explain.

9 Calculator Write a calculator key sequence to find the missing term in the proportion $\frac{12}{16} = \frac{18}{y}$. $16 \times 18 \div 12 =$

10 ✔ **CHECKPOINT** Find the missing term in each proportion.

a. $\frac{15}{20} = \frac{9}{y}$ 12   b. $\frac{18}{n} = \frac{12}{8}$ 12   c. $\frac{5}{12} = \frac{12.5}{m}$ 30

11 Now you are ready to estimate how far a jackrabbit can jump.

a. **Discussion** You were told that "A black-tailed jackrabbit can jump about as far for its size as the record-breaking kangaroo." What do you think this means? See margin.

b. Use the table on page 396. Why can the proportion below be used to estimate how far a jackrabbit with a body 18 in. long can jump? See margin.

$$\frac{42}{3.5} = \frac{d}{1.5}$$ 18 in. is equal to 1.5 ft.

c. Find the missing term in the proportion in part (b). 18 ft

d. Would you expect the jackrabbit to jump exactly the distance you found in part (c)? Explain. See margin.

HOMEWORK EXERCISES ▶ See Exs. 1–11 on p. 402.

Exploration 2

PRO**Using**POR**TIONS**

GOAL

LEARN HOW TO...
- write a proportion to solve a problem
- use a proportion to make a prediction

AS YOU...
- explore the jumping ability of a frog

▶ Frogs are much better jumpers than humans. To appreciate just how much better, you can use a proportion to explore how far someone with the jumping ability of a frog could jump.

EXAMPLE

Suppose a 6.25 foot (6 ft 3 in.) tall human has the jumping ability of the record-breaking frog that is 0.15 ft long and can jump 17.56 ft. Write a proportion to find how far this person can jump.

Step 1 Study the situation to find what measures are being compared.

$$\frac{\text{jump distance (ft)}}{\text{body length (ft)}}$$

Jump distance is being compared to body length.

Step 2 Decide what ratios to show in the proportion.

Ratio for the frog   Ratio for the human

$$\frac{\text{jump distance}}{\text{body length}} = \frac{\text{jump distance}}{\text{body length}}$$

Step 3 Fill in the information you know to write the proportion. You know the jump distance and body length of the frog and the body length of the human. Use a variable for the value you do not know.

You want to find the jump distance for the human.

$$\frac{17.56}{0.15} = \frac{d}{6.25}$$

12 **Discussion** Why was a variable used for the human jump distance? **The jump distance for the human is not known.**

13 Find the missing term in the proportion. How does the answer compare with the world record for humans given on page 396? **about 731.67 ft; about 25 times greater**

Exploration 2

TEACHING NOTES

In **Question 11(a)**, some students may have incorrectly thought that the jackrabbit is able to jump the same distance as the kangaroo. The phrase "as far for its size" was used to help students think about the comparison using proportional reasoning. In the **Example**, this point is again emphasized by writing a proportion that compares the jump distance to body size. Students should understand that a proportion is used since a fair comparison of jumping ability cannot be made by considering just the length of the jump.

Question 12 Point out that when writing a proportion to solve a problem, only one of the values will be represented by a variable. The remaining values will be given in the problem.

Question 13 Be sure students understand what is represented by the value they find. (*the distance a 6.25 foot tall human with jumping ability of a frog could jump*) The choice of the letter *d* for the variable will help remind students that the value stands for *distance*. You may want to encourage students to choose a variable that helps remind them of what the unknown represents or to record what their variable represents when setting up the proportion.

Exploration 2 *continued*

COMMON ERROR

Students may set up proportions incorrectly by putting the units in the wrong place. Remind students that each ratio must compare the units in the same "order." Writing in the units as they write each ratio will help students avoid this error.

The Classroom Example below can be used before **Checkpoint Question 15** to further illustrate the importance of order.

CLASSROOM EXAMPLE

Suppose a 5.75 ft tall person has the jumping ability of the record-breaking cricket that is 0.05 ft long and can jump 2 ft. Write a proportion to find how far this person could jump.

Answer: If we use $\dfrac{\text{jump distance}}{\text{body length}}$,

then $\dfrac{2\ \text{ft}}{0.05\ \text{ft}} = \dfrac{d\ \text{ft}}{5.75\ \text{ft}}$

$0.05 \cdot d = 2 \cdot 5.75$

$0.05 \cdot d = 11.5$

$d = 11.5 \div 0.05$

$d = 230$

The person could jump 230 ft.

TEACHING NOTE

Students may need exposure to more examples before they can confidently tell whether it is appropriate to use a proportion to solve a problem. Use the discussion of **Question 17** as an opportunity to teach students how to identify situations where proportions are not appropriate. In **part (c)**, students may think since the problem is comparing one running time to another, it is appropriate to use a proportion. Be sure they understand why sprinting times are not appropriate for predicting the times for running longer distances.

400

---

16. No; The ratio given is for the world-record holder. It isn't reasonable to assume that an average person would have a similar ratio.

17. b. Not appropriate; It isn't reasonable to assume a human and a bird have the same nutritional needs.

✔ **QUESTION 15**

...checks that you can write a proportion and use it to make a prediction.

▲ On August 30, 1991, Mike Powell set a long jump record of 29 ft $4\frac{1}{2}$ in. The record still stands today.

▶ The super-jumper problem may be a bit unrealistic, but there are many real problem situations where using a proportion is a good method for making predictions.

14 Suppose a school fundraiser makes a $1.75 profit for every 6 rolls of wrapping paper sold. One class of students sells 256 rolls.

   a. What phrase tells you the measurements that are being compared? "$1.75 profit for every 6 rolls"

   b. What two words indicate a ratio is being used? "for every"

   c. Write a proportion by filling in the values you know. Use a variable for the value you do not know. $\dfrac{1.75}{6} = \dfrac{x}{256}$

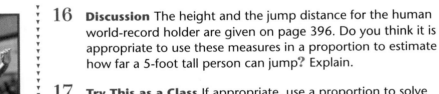

Profit ratio for 6 rolls		Profit ratio for 256 rolls
$\dfrac{\text{profit}}{\text{number of rolls sold}}$	$=$	$\dfrac{\text{profit}}{\text{number of rolls sold}}$

   d. What is the profit on 256 rolls? $74.67

15 ✔ **CHECKPOINT** Suppose a car travels 330 mi on 12 gal of gas. Use a proportion to predict how many gallons of gas it will take to travel 500 mi. Show your work. $\dfrac{330}{12} = \dfrac{500}{x}$; $330x = 12 \cdot 500$, $x \approx$ 18.2 gal

▶ In some problem situations, writing a proportion to make a prediction is not appropriate.

16 **Discussion** The height and the jump distance for the human world-record holder are given on page 396. Do you think it is appropriate to use these measures in a proportion to estimate how far a 5-foot tall person can jump? Explain.

17 **Try This as a Class** If appropriate, use a proportion to solve each problem. If it is not appropriate to use a proportion, explain why not.

   a. While resting, Tani's heart beats 11 times in 10 seconds. How many times will his heart beat during a 2-minute rest? 132 times

   b. The ratio of *body weight to daily food intake* for a bird is 10 to 4. How much will a 150-pound person eat in a day?

   c. In 1996, Gail Devers ran 100 m in 11.11 sec to win an Olympic gold medal. How long would it take her to run 1500 m? Not appropriate; It isn't reasonable to assume she could maintain the same kind of speed for such a long distance.

HOMEWORK EXERCISES ▶ See Exs. 12–18 on pp. 403–404.

Section 4 Key Concepts

Recognizing Proportions (pp. 397–398)

A proportion is an equation stating that two ratios are equivalent.

Example $\frac{4}{6} = \frac{12}{18}$ is a proportion because $\frac{4 \cdot 3}{6 \cdot 3} = \frac{12}{18}$.

The cross products in a proportion are equal.

Example

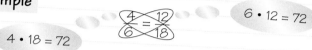

$4 \cdot 18 = 72$

$6 \cdot 12 = 72$

Finding a Missing Term in a Proportion (p. 398)

You can use cross products to find the missing term in a proportion.

Example Find the missing term in the proportion $\frac{10}{15} = \frac{x}{12}$.

Use cross products to write an equation.

$15 \cdot x = 10 \cdot 12$

$15 \cdot x = 120$

$x = 120 \div 15$

$x = 8$

Then use division to find the value of the variable.

You can check by substituting 8 for x and then checking that the ratios are equivalent.

$\frac{10}{15} \overset{?}{=} \frac{8}{12}$

$10 \cdot 12 \overset{?}{=} 15 \cdot 8$

$120 = 120$

The cross products are equal, so $x = 8$.

Key Concepts Questions

18 Use cross products to tell whether the ratios are equivalent.

a. $\frac{5}{6}$ and $\frac{17}{20}$ No
b. $\frac{48}{36}$ and $\frac{220}{165}$ Yes
c. $\frac{21}{13}$ and $\frac{189}{117}$ Yes

19 Describe two ways to find the missing term in the proportion $\frac{45}{35} = \frac{18}{n}$. Then solve the proportion using both methods. Did you get the same result?

Key Terms

proportion

cross products

Key Concepts

CLOSURE QUESTION

Is 5 the missing term in the proportion $\frac{n}{7} = \frac{15}{24}$? How can you tell?

Sample Response: No; If you substitute 5 for *n* in the proportion and check the cross products, $5 \cdot 24$ must equal $7 \cdot 15$. 140 does not equal 105, so 5 is not the solution.

---

19. Use cross products or write a fraction equivalent to $\frac{45}{35}$ with the numerator 18.
Method 1:
$45 \cdot n = 630$,
$n = 630 \div 45 = 14$;
Method 2: $\frac{45}{35} = \frac{9}{7}$,
$\frac{9 \cdot 2}{7 \cdot 2} = \frac{18}{14}$, $n = 14$;
Yes

Key Concepts continued

CLOSURE QUESTION
How can you tell if two ratios are equivalent?

Sample Response: Find the cross products of the ratios. If the cross products are equal the two ratios are equivalent. Or use one of the following approaches to determine if the ratios are equivalent: Express the ratios as fractions in lowest terms or as equivalent fractions with a common denominator and compare the fractions. Write the ratios as decimals and compare the decimals to see if they are equal.

ABSENT STUDENTS
For students who were absent for all or part of this section, the blackline Study Guide for Section 4 may be used to present the ideas, concepts, and skills of Section 4.

Practice & Applications

SUGGESTED ASSIGNMENTS

Core Course
Day 1: Exs. 1–11, 19–24
Day 2: Exs. 12–13, 15–18

Extended Course
Day 1: Exs. 1–11, 19–24
Day 2: Exs. 12–18

Note: Extended Course assignments can be used to differentiate within the regular classroom. In classrooms where students are grouped homogeneously, the material might be covered in fewer days. In this case assignments may be combined.

Section 4
Key Concepts

Writing Proportions (pp. 399–400)
When you write a proportion to solve a problem, it is important to set up the proportion correctly.

Example Suppose Miguel's dog eats 2 lb of dog food every 3 days. How many pounds of food will the dog eat in 31 days?

Ratio for 3 days   Ratio for 31 days

pounds of dog food $\dfrac{2}{3}$ = $\dfrac{x}{31}$ pounds of dog food

number of days — number of days

Key Concepts Questions

20 Use the proportion in the Example above to find how many pounds of food Miguel's dog will eat in 31 days. Would you get the same answer if you used the proportion $\dfrac{3}{2} = \dfrac{31}{x}$? Explain.
$20\frac{2}{3}$ lb; Yes; The cross products are the same.

21 It is not always appropriate to use a proportion to solve a problem involving ratios. Give an example to illustrate this.
Sample: While resting, my heart beats 11 times in 10 seconds. How many times will it beat during 1 min of running?

1. $\dfrac{15}{60}, \dfrac{75}{300}$, and $\dfrac{3.5}{14}; \dfrac{24}{32}$ and $\dfrac{21}{28}$

2. $\dfrac{6}{7}$ and $\dfrac{30}{35}; \dfrac{10}{12.5}$ and $\dfrac{16}{20}$

Section 4
Practice & Application Exercises

Find all the equivalent ratios in each list.

1. $\dfrac{15}{60}, \dfrac{24}{32}, \dfrac{75}{300}, \dfrac{21}{28}, \dfrac{3.5}{14}$ 2. $\dfrac{6}{7}, \dfrac{10}{12.5}, \dfrac{30}{35}, \dfrac{16}{20}, \dfrac{40}{45}$

In Exercises 3–11, find the missing term in each proportion.

3. $\dfrac{3}{12} = \dfrac{5}{n}$ 20   4. $\dfrac{4}{24} = \dfrac{6}{x}$ 36   5. $\dfrac{5}{15} = \dfrac{y}{24}$ 8

6. $\dfrac{s}{7} = \dfrac{3.5}{1.4}$ 17.5   7. $\dfrac{20}{8} = \dfrac{4.5}{d}$ 1.8   8. $\dfrac{5}{m} = \dfrac{2.5}{40}$ 80

9. $16 : 3 = 64 : r$ 12   10. $p : 15 = 4 : 9$ $6\frac{2}{3}$ 11. $7 : w = 56 : 40$ 5

12. Choose the proportions that have been set up correctly for solving the problem.

The *Water Arc* in Chicago, Illinois, shoots out about 21,000 gal of water over the Chicago River during each 10-minute show. How many gallons of water does it shoot in four minutes? **B and C**

A. $\dfrac{21,000}{10} = \dfrac{4}{x}$ **B.** $\dfrac{10}{21,000} = \dfrac{4}{x}$ **C.** $\dfrac{21,000}{10} = \dfrac{x}{4}$

13. a. The ratio of their shrunken size to their normal size is the same as $\dfrac{64 \text{ ft}}{3.2 \text{ mi}}$.

13. In the movie *Honey I Shrunk the Kids,* an inventor accidentally shrinks his children. They become so small that they are mistakenly thrown out with the trash and must make their way back to the house.

a. **Writing** Nicky explains to the other children, "We are exactly 64 feet from the house, which is the equivalent of 3.2 miles." What does Nicky mean?

b. Nicky can walk one mile in 20 min at his normal height. To predict how long it will take him to walk to the house at his new height, a proportion has been labeled. Fill in the values you know. Use a variable for the value you do not know. $\dfrac{1 \text{ mi}}{20 \text{ min}} = \dfrac{3.2 \text{ mi}}{x}$

Ratio for 1 mile   Ratio for 3.2 miles

$\dfrac{\text{distance}}{\text{time}} = \dfrac{\text{distance}}{\text{time}}$

c. Find the missing value in your proportion. **64 min**

14. Challenge In Exercise 13 Nicky's height was roughly $\dfrac{1}{4}$ in. Estimate Nicky's normal height. (Remember that 1 mi = 5280 ft.) **66 in. or 5 ft 6 in.**

15. Probability Connection In 5 out of 24 rolls, a number cube lands on 2.

a. Find the experimental probability of landing on 2. $\dfrac{5}{24}$

b. Use your answer to part (a) and a proportion to predict how many times out of 60 rolls a number cube will land on 2. **about 13 times**

EXERCISE NOTES
Exercise 12 is a good problem for discussing the correct way to set up proportions. After completing the exercise, show that although B and C are set up differently, they both result in the same value for the variable. It does not matter if gallons are compared to minutes or minutes to gallons, as long as each ratio in the proportion is written in the same order. Solve the proportion in A to show that the value is unreasonable.

Exercise 13 Encourage students to think back to the poem *One Inch Tall* in Section 1 where the regular sizes of objects were compared to a one-inch tall child. Suggest to students that the measures of objects in the environment did not change when the children were shrunk in the movie *Honey, I Shrunk the Kids,* but their capacity to deal with these measures changed in proportion to their decreased height.

Practice & Applications

EXERCISE NOTES

You may wish to have students save their answers to **Exercise 18** in their portfolios to show their understanding of proportions.

18. b. Sample Response:

6 min; $\dfrac{2 \text{ min}}{5 \text{ pages}} = \dfrac{x \text{ min}}{15 \text{ pages}}$;

$5 \cdot x = 2 \cdot 15; \; 5 \cdot x = 30; \; x = 6,$
or find an equivalent fraction:

$\dfrac{2}{5} \cdot \dfrac{3}{3} = \dfrac{6 \text{ min}}{15 \text{ pages}}$

24.

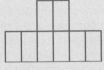

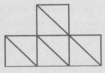

16. Not appropriate; It is not reasonable to assume Mina will continue to grow at the same rate for the next 18 years.

Oral Report

Exercise 18 checks that you know how to write a proportion to solve a problem.

20–23. Sample responses are given.

20.

21.

22.

23.

If appropriate, use a proportion to solve each problem. If it is not appropriate to use a proportion, explain why not.

16. Three year old Mina is 32 in. tall. Mina grew 4 in. in one year. How tall will Mina be in 18 years?

17. For every 4 steps Mina takes, her grandmother takes 3 steps. How many steps will Mina take if her grandmother takes 54 steps? **72 steps**

Reflecting on the Section

Be prepared to report on the following topic in class.

18. a. Write a problem about your everyday life that can be solved using a proportion. Be sure your problem is one in which it is appropriate to use a proportion. **Sample Response: It takes my printer 2 min to print 5 pages. How long will it take to print 15 pages?**

b. Solve the problem you wrote for part (a). Be sure to include an explanation of how you solved it. **See margin.**

Spiral Review

19. a. For a certain group of people, the mean of the ratios for *distance around the thumb to distance around the neck* is 0.26. Write a "nice" fraction that is close to the mean. (Module 6, p. 389) $\frac{1}{4}$

b. Predict the distance around the neck of a person whose thumb measurement is 3.75 in. (Module 6, p. 389) **about 15 in.**

Draw an example of each type of angle. (Module 2, p. 107)

20. acute   **21.** obtuse   **22.** straight   **23.** right

24. Trace the figure. Then find three ways to divide the figure into eight identical parts. (Module 1, p. 46) **See margin.**

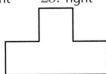

Section 4
Extra Skill Practice

Use cross products to tell whether the ratios are equivalent.

1. $\frac{12}{18}$ and $\frac{4}{6}$ Yes   2. $\frac{8}{10}$ and $\frac{12}{15}$ Yes   3. $\frac{3}{50}$ and $\frac{6}{75}$ No   4. $\frac{1.5}{3}$ and $\frac{10}{20}$ Yes

Find the missing term in each proportion.

5. $\frac{n}{8} = \frac{12}{2}$ 48   6. $\frac{8}{12} = \frac{12}{g}$ 18   7. $\frac{9}{13} = \frac{27}{r}$ 39   8. $x : 5 = 27 : 45$ 3

9. $\frac{d}{4} = \frac{13}{26}$ 2   10. $\frac{2}{n} = \frac{3}{9}$ 6   11. $\frac{2.5}{5} = \frac{c}{8}$ 4   12. $3 : 8 = k : 12$ 4.5

If appropriate, use a proportion to solve each problem. If it is not appropriate to use a proportion, explain why not.

13. Eight newspapers cost $3.60. How much will six newpapers cost? $2.70

14. Five white cars drove past Mark's house from 6:00 A.M. to 9:00 A.M. How many will pass his house in twenty-four hours?

    14. Not appropriate; It is not reasonable to assume that traffic moves past Mark's house at a steady rate all day and the ratio of white cars to other cars is always the same.

15. Janis used four yards of ribbon to make six bows. How many yards of ribbon will she need to make ten more bows? $6\frac{2}{3}$ yd

Standardized Testing ◀▶ Multiple Choice

1. For which values of x and y will the proportion $\frac{x}{25} = \frac{15}{y}$ be correct? D. II and IV

    I. $x = 20, y = 20$ II. $x = 12.5, y = 30$ III. $x = 100, y = 5$ IV. $x = 5, y = 75$

    A I only   B IV only   C I and III   D II and IV

2. For which problems is it appropriate and correct to find the solution using the proportion $\frac{x}{75} = \frac{10}{45}$? B. II only

    I. Darren read 10 pages of a book in 45 minutes. Predict how many pages he can read in 12 minutes.

    II. Sheri bought 10 tapes for the school music library for $45. If the tapes all have the same price, how many can she buy for $75?

    III. Elsa drank 10 oz of water after she finished a 45 min. exercise class. How much do you think she will drink after a 75 min. class?

    A I only   B II only   C I and III   D II and III

Section 4 Proportions **405**

Extra Skill Practice

TEACHER NOTES
For each Exploration, the corresponding Extra Skill Practice Exercises are noted.

Exploration 1: Exs. 1–12
Exploration 2: Exs. 13–15

EXTRA HELP
Teacher's Resource Book
• Practice and Applications
• Study Guide

Technology Resources
• @Home Tutor
• Test Generator

ASSESSMENT
• Section 4 Quick Quiz
• Test Generator

Section 5   Geometry and Proportions

IN THIS SECTION

EXPLORATION 1
◆ Comparing Shapes

EXPLORATION 2
◆ Models and Scale Drawings

Very SiMiLAR

Setting the Stage

Some artists use mathematics to help them design their creations. In M.C. Escher's *Square Limit* below, the fish are arranged so that there are no gaps or overlapping pieces.

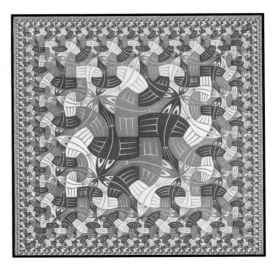

Think About It

1 **a.** How are the fish in the middle of the design and the surrounding fish alike? They have the same shape.

   b. How are they different? They are different sizes.

2 How did Escher create the impression that the design goes on forever inside the square? Sample Response: The fish pattern appears to keep shrinking so that you can imagine it getting smaller and smaller, but never stopping.

Exploration 1

COMPARING SHAPES

GOAL

LEARN HOW TO...
- identify similar and congruent figures

AS YOU...
- compare pattern block shapes

KEY TERMS
- similar figures
- corresponding parts
- congruent figures

SET UP *Work with a partner. You will need:* • *Labsheet 5A*
• *pattern blocks* • *metric ruler* • *tracing paper* • *protractor*

▶ The drawing below shows how Escher used a pattern of squares and triangles to create *Square Limit*. The drawing represents the lower right portion of Escher's work. The two outlined triangles in the drawing are *similar*. **Similar figures** have the same shape but not necessarily the same size.

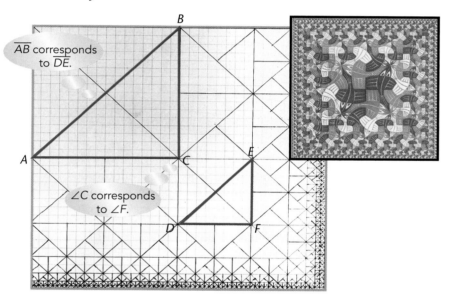

$\overline{AB}$ corresponds to $\overline{DE}$.

∠C corresponds to ∠F.

▶ When two figures are similar, for each part of one figure there is a **corresponding part** on the other figure.

3 **Discussion** Look at similar triangles *ABC* and *DEF*.

   a. Name another pair of corresponding sides.

   b. Name another pair of corresponding angles.

   c. How many pairs of corresponding angles are there? 3 pairs

   d. How many pairs of corresponding sides are there? 3 pairs

3. a. $\overline{AC}$ and $\overline{DF}$ or $\overline{BC}$ and $\overline{EF}$
   b. ∠A and ∠D or ∠B and ∠E

Exploration 1

TEACHING NOTES

After discussing **Question 3**, you may want to check students' understanding by asking them why certain sides and angles do not correspond. For example, ask, "Why does $\overline{AB}$ not correspond to $\overline{DF}$?" (*The angles at the endpoints of the segments do not have the same measure. The angles at A and B are both acute angles, but the angle at F is a right angle.*) It is important that when naming corresponding sides, students list the vertices in the correct order as they relate to the corresponding angles. However, since similar triangles *ABC* and *DEF* in the figure are isosceles triangles, there are two possible ways to name their corresponding parts. Most students will use the orientation of the triangles to match corresponding sides. A cutout of one of the triangles would help illustrate that one of the triangles could be turned so that $\overline{AB}$ corresponds to $\overline{ED}$. Drawing two similar triangles that are scalene and having students name corresponding sides can help students understand the importance of writing the endpoints of corresponding line segments in the correct order. To further test understanding, the two similar triangles can also be drawn so that corresponding sides have different orientations.

To reinforce the definition of similar figures, ask students, "Are the triangles the same shape?" (*yes*) "Are the triangles the same size?" (*no*) "If the triangles were the same size, would they still be similar triangles?" (*yes*)

407

Exploration 1 *continued*

Question 4 The two trapezoids *ABCD* and *EFGH* are isosceles, so there are two ways to match corresponding parts. After completing the question you might check students' understanding by asking them why certain sides and angles do not correspond. For example, "Why does $\overline{AB}$ not correspond to $\overline{HG}$?"

Question 5 Students should understand that the ratios of the lengths of corresponding sides are equivalent. For extra practice on this concept students could measure the lengths of the sides of the triangles in the figure on page 407 and find the ratios of the lengths of the corresponding sides. When students have completed the exploration, you may want to have them look back at Escher's *Square Limit* design in the *Setting the Stage* and discuss it in relation to what they now understand about similar and congruent figures. The discussion could also be extended to other works by Escher.

DEVELOPING MATH CONCEPTS
Use **Question 5(c)** as an opportunity to discuss the difference between the symbol for the segment from *A* to *B* ($\overline{AB}$) and the distance from *A* to *B* or the length of the segment from *A* to *B* (*AB*). Before the new notation was introduced in **part (c)**, "the length of $\overline{AB}$" had to be written out to indicate the length of the segment from *A* to *B*. Once the difference in notation is understood, **part (b)** could be written much more efficiently as "Write the ratio of *AB* to *EF* as a fraction."

4. b. See Additional Answers beginning on page A1.

408

---

5. a. $\overline{EF}$, $\overline{FG}$, and $\overline{EH}$ are each 2 units long and $\overline{GH}$ is 4 units long.

c. $\dfrac{BC}{FG} = \dfrac{1}{2}$, $\dfrac{CD}{GH} = \dfrac{2}{4}$, $\dfrac{DA}{HE} = \dfrac{1}{2}$

d. They are all equivalent.

▶ Sometimes it is hard to tell whether two figures are similar just by looking at them. To help determine if two figures are similar, you will use pattern blocks to create similar figures and explore relationships between their corresponding parts.

4 **Try This as a Class** Trapezoid *ABCD* and trapezoid *EFGH* are similar.

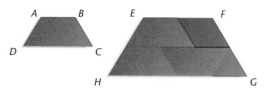

a. Use pattern blocks to build the two trapezoids. Trace around each trapezoid and label it as shown. **Check students' drawings.**

b. Copy and complete the tables. **See margin.**

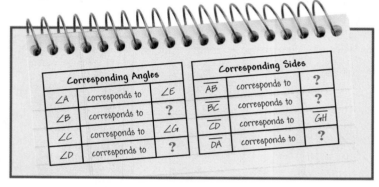

Corresponding Angles		
∠A	corresponds to	∠E
∠B	corresponds to	?
∠C	corresponds to	∠G
∠D	corresponds to	?

Corresponding Sides		
$\overline{AB}$	corresponds to	?
$\overline{BC}$	corresponds to	?
$\overline{CD}$	corresponds to	$\overline{GH}$
$\overline{DA}$	corresponds to	?

c. Place a red trapezoid pattern block on top of your tracing of trapezoid *EFGH*. Use it to compare each pair of corresponding angles. What do you notice? **Corresponding angles appear to have the same measure.**

5 Three sides of a red trapezoid are 1 unit long and one side is 2 units long.

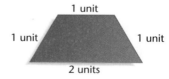

a. How many units long is each side of trapezoid *EFGH*?

b. Write the ratio of the length of $\overline{AB}$ to the length of $\overline{EF}$ as a fraction. $\dfrac{1}{2}$

c. Copy and complete the ratios of the lengths of the other pairs of corresponding sides. Write each ratio as a fraction.

BC means the length of $\overline{BC}$.

$\dfrac{BC}{FG} = \dfrac{?}{?}$ $\dfrac{CD}{GH} = \dfrac{?}{?}$ $\dfrac{DA}{HE} = \dfrac{?}{?}$

d. What do you notice about the ratios in parts (b) and (c)?

6 Discussion Think about your results in Questions 4 and 5.

    a. When two figures are similar, what do you think is true about their corresponding angles? **Corresponding angles have the same measure.**

    b. When two figures are similar, what do you think is true about the ratios of the lengths of their corresponding sides? **The ratios of the lengths of the corresponding sides are equivalent.**

7 Try This as a Class Use pattern blocks to build the trapezoid below. Is this trapezoid similar to one red trapezoid pattern block? Why or why not? **No; The ratios of the lengths of the corresponding sides are not all equivalent.**

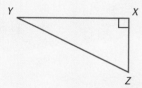

▶ **Congruent figures** are a special type of similar figures that have the same shape and the same size.

△*ABC* is congruent to △*XYZ*. Two figures are congruent even if they have different orientations.

△ABC means triangle ABC.

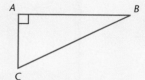

8 a. Identify the corresponding angles and corresponding sides of the two triangles in the Example.

    b. Make a tracing of one of the triangles in the Example. Place your tracing over the other triangle so that the corresponding parts match up. **Check students' work.**

    c. What is the ratio of the lengths of the corresponding sides of two congruent figures? Explain. **1:1; Corresponding sides have the same length.**

9 ✔ **CHECKPOINT** Use Labsheet 5A. Follow the directions on the labsheet to determine which of the *Polygon Pairs* are similar and which are congruent. **See margin.**

8. a. ∠A and ∠X, ∠B and ∠Y, ∠C and ∠Z; $\overline{AB}$ and $\overline{XY}$, $\overline{BC}$ and $\overline{YZ}$, $\overline{AC}$ and $\overline{XZ}$

✔ **QUESTION 9**

...checks that you can determine if two figures are similar or congruent.

HOMEWORK EXERCISES ▶ See Exs. 1–10 on pp. 414–415.

TEACHING NOTES

To check their answers to **Question 7**, students can find the ratios of the lengths of the corresponding sides of the trapezoid they build and those of a red trapezoid pattern block. Students should then see that the ratios of the corresponding sides are not equivalent.

Before completing **Labsheet 5A** in **Question 9**, you may want to have students predict which polygons they think will be similar and which polygons they think will be congruent.

9. a. not similar; The ratios of lengths of corresponding sides are not equivalent.

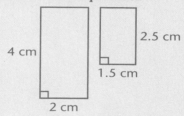

9. b–d. See Additional Answers beginning on page A1.

409

Exploration 2

TEACHING NOTES

In **Question 10**, students apply the properties of similar figures to a sculpture. In order to write the proportion in **part (b)** students will need to refer back to the opening paragraph that gives the actual sculpture's height and length.

GOAL

LEARN HOW TO...
- use proportions to find missing lengths

AS YOU...
- work with scale models and drawings

KEY TERM
- scale

Exploration 2

Models and SCALE
DRAWINGS

SET UP *You will need a customary ruler.*

In South Dakota, a model of the Sioux leader Chief Crazy Horse is being used to construct what may be the world's largest sculpture. When completed, the sculpture will measure 563 ft high by 641 ft long!

▶ **When creating a large piece of art, an artist often makes a model similar to what the completed artwork will be.**

10. a. The ratios of corresponding measurements are all equivalent. The measures of corresponding angles are equal.

10 **a.** The Crazy Horse model is similar to the sculpture. What do you know about their corresponding measurements?

b. The height of the model is 16.56 ft. Write and solve a proportion to find the length of the model. Round your answer to the nearest hundredth. $\frac{16.56}{563} = \frac{x}{641}$; about 18.85 ft

11 **Try This as a Class**

    a. Did everyone get the same answer for Question 10(b)?

    b. Did everyone use the same proportion?

12 **Discussion** Explain how you can find the length of the arm on the sculpture when you know that the arm on the model is 7.74 ft long and the height of the model is 16.56 ft.

13 ✔ **CHECKPOINT** Use a proportion to find the missing length in each pair of similar figures.

a.
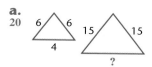

b.
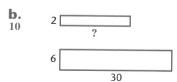

▶ The ratio of a measurement on a model or a drawing to the corresponding measurement on the actual object is the **scale**. The floor plan below uses the scale 1 in. : 14 ft.

EXAMPLE

Use the scale to find the length *a* of the actual living room.

Scale: 1 in. : 14 ft

	Bath
Living Room	
a	
Hallway	
Kitchen	Dining Room

SAMPLE RESPONSE

Measure the length of the living room in the drawing. The length is 1.25 in. Then write and solve a proportion to find the length of the actual living room.

$$\frac{\text{drawing (in.)}}{\text{actual (ft)}} \longrightarrow \frac{1}{14} = \frac{1.25}{a}$$

$$a = 17.5$$

The actual living room is 17.5 ft long.

14 **Try This as a Class** Use the floor plan above.

    a. Find the dimensions of the actual kitchen. 14 ft long, $10\frac{1}{2}$ ft wide

    b. Find the dimensions of the actual bath. 7 ft long, 7 ft wide

---

✔ **QUESTION 13**

...checks that you can use proportions to find missing lengths in similar figures.

11. a–b. Students should have gotten the same answer, but may have used different proportions, such as

$$\frac{x}{641} = \frac{16.56}{563}$$

or $\frac{563}{16.56} = \frac{641}{x}$.

12. Sample Response: Use the proportion

$$\frac{16.56}{563} = \frac{7.74}{x}$$

or $\frac{16.56}{7.74} = \frac{563}{x}$.

TEACHING NOTES

For Question 11, ask several students to put their proportions from **Question 10(b)** on the board so that you can compare and discuss them. Use these examples to emphasize the importance of writing the units in the correct places when setting up a proportion. Students can use proportions such as $\frac{\text{height 1}}{\text{length 1}} = \frac{\text{height 2}}{\text{length 2}}$ and $\frac{\text{height 1}}{\text{height 2}} = \frac{\text{length 1}}{\text{length 2}}$ but should not use $\frac{\text{height 1}}{\text{height 2}} = \frac{\text{length 2}}{\text{length 1}}$.

Question 12 Point out again that there is more than one correct way to set up the proportion. Students should be able to explain how they know their proportion is set up correctly.

Question 13 Ask students to share the proportions they used to find each missing length. Encourage students to use number sense to check the reasonableness of their result. For example, one of the incorrect proportions for **part (a)**, $\frac{6}{8} = \frac{x}{15}$ will give an answer of 11.25, but the missing length must be greater than 15, so this answer is not reasonable. In **part (b)**, $\frac{2}{x} = \frac{30}{6}$ will give a result of 0.4. Again, students should see that this answer does not make sense.

411

TEACHING NOTES

After discussing the **Example**, discuss the reason for using 1 ft instead of 16.56 ft in the scale in **Question 15(a)**.

Students will want to find a simpler scale when answering **Question 16(a)**, so you might suggest they find the scale represented by 1 ft on the drawing. Students will use their result from **part (a)** to answer **part (b)**, so you will want to make sure that students have answered **part (a)** correctly. Encourage students to use number sense to see if their answer for the height of the door in the drawing is reasonable.

15. a. 1 ft : 34 ft is easier to use when finding the actual lengths using measures on the model, since lengths on the model can be multiplied by 34 to find the actual length.

▶ The scale for the Crazy Horse model can be found by using the height of the model and the height of the monument.

EXAMPLE

Find the scale for the Crazy Horse model.

SAMPLE RESPONSE

$$\frac{\text{model height (ft)}}{\text{actual height (ft)}} \longrightarrow \frac{16.56}{563} = \frac{16.56 \div 16.56}{563 \div 16.56}$$

$$\approx \frac{1}{33.998}$$

$$\approx \frac{1}{34}$$

The scale is about 1 ft : 34 ft.

15 **a.** In the Example, why do you think the scale is written as 1 ft : 34 ft instead of 16.56 ft : 563 ft?

   b. Could 5 ft : 170 ft be used to describe the scale of the model? Explain. Yes, the ratio 5 ft : 170 ft is equivalent to 1 ft : 34 ft

✔ **QUESTION 16**

...checks that you can use a scale to find missing measurements in similar figures.

16 ✔ **CHECKPOINT**

   a. In an architect's drawing, a building is 2.5 ft tall. The actual building is 40 ft tall. What is the scale? 1 ft : 16 ft

   b. The height of the building's front door is 8 ft. What is the height of the door in the drawing of the building? 0.5 ft

HOMEWORK EXERCISES ▶ See Exs. 11–22 on pp. 415–416.

Section 5

Key Concepts

Similar and Congruent Figures (pp. 407–409)

Similar figures have the same shape, but not necessarily the same size. Congruent figures are similar figures that have the same size.

similar figures

Example Quadrilateral ABCD is congruent to quadrilateral EFGH.

$\overline{AB}$ corresponds to $\overline{EF}$.
$\angle D$ corresponds to $\angle H$.

congruent figures

Properties of Similar Figures (pp. 407–409)

corresponding parts

Example $\triangle ABC$ is similar to $\triangle DEF$.

The corresponding angles have the same measure.

$m\angle A = m\angle D$
$m\angle B = m\angle E$
$m\angle C = m\angle F$

The ratios of the lengths of the corresponding sides are equivalent.

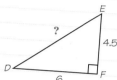

$$\frac{AB}{DE} = \frac{BC}{EF} = \frac{CA}{FD}$$

DE means the length of $\overline{DE}$.

Proportions and Scale (pp. 410–412)

scale

You can use proportions to find missing lengths in similar figures. To find DE in $\triangle DEF$ above, solve $\frac{4}{6} = \frac{5}{x}$.

You can use the scale of a drawing or a model to write a proportion to find the measurements of an actual object.

Key Concepts Questions

17 a. Solve the proportion $\frac{4}{6} = \frac{5}{x}$ to find *DE* in the second Example above. **7.5**

b. Write another proportion that you could use to find *DE*.
Sample Response: $\frac{3}{4.5} = \frac{5}{x}$

18 Suppose the scale used on a map is 1 in. : 2 mi. How long is a road that is 6 in. long on the map? **12 mi**

Key Concepts

CLOSURE QUESTION

State the difference between similar figures and congruent figures.

Sample Response: Similar figures have the same shape. Congruent figures are similar figures so they have the same shape, but they also have the same size.

ABSENT STUDENTS

For students who were absent for all or part of this section, the blackline Study Guide for Section 5 may be used to present the ideas, concepts, and skills of Section 5.

SUGGESTED ASSIGNMENTS

Core Course
Day 1: Exs. 1–2, 9–10
Day 2: Exs. 3–8, 23–32
Day 3: Exs. 11–17, 19–22

Extended Course
Day 1: Exs. 1–2, 9–10
Day 2: Exs. 3–8, 23–32
Day 3: Exs. 11–22

Note: Extended Course assignments can be used to differentiate within the regular classroom. In classrooms where students are grouped homogeneously, the material might be covered in fewer days. In this case assignments may be combined.

ADDITIONAL PRACTICE
See the *Teacher's Resource Book* for additional practice and application exercises for this section.

EXERCISE NOTES
Exercises 6–8 Students may want to make a table to record the dimensions of each rectangle for easy reference as they answer the questions.

1.

$\overline{AC}$	corresponds to	$\overline{FE}$
$\overline{AB}$	corresponds to	$\overline{FD}$
$\overline{CB}$	corresponds to	$\overline{ED}$
$\angle A$	corresponds to	$\angle F$
$\angle B$	corresponds to	$\angle D$
$\angle C$	corresponds to	$\angle E$

2. See Additional Answers beginning on page A1.

YOU WILL NEED

For Ex. 9:
♦ protractor
♦ metric or customary ruler

For Exs. 19–22:
♦ customary ruler

For Ex. 33:
♦ metric ruler

---

3. similar and congruent; Corresponding angles have the same measure and corresponding sides have the same length.

4. not similar; The figures do not have the same shape since the ratio of the lengths of the corresponding sides of the upper right triangle in the figures is 1:1 but the ratio of the lengths of the corresponding sides in the trapezoidal shapes is 1:2.

5. similar but not congruent; Corresponding angles have the same measure and the ratios of the lengths of corresponding sides are equivalent but not 1:1.

8. Sample Response:

Section 5
Practice & Application Exercises

The figures in each pair are similar. Make a table showing all the pairs of corresponding angles and corresponding sides.

1.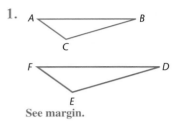

See margin.

2.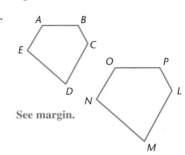

See margin.

Tell whether the figures in each pair are similar. For the similar figures, tell which are congruent. If they are not similar, explain how you know.

3.    4.   5.

Use the rectangles for Exercises 6–8.

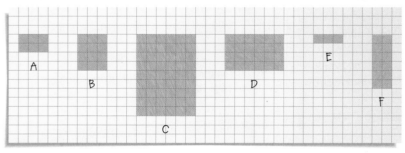

6. **a.** Name all the rectangles that are similar to rectangle A. **C and D**

   b. What is the ratio of the lengths of the corresponding sides?
   C (9:6 or 3:2) and D (6:4 or 3:2)

7. **a.** Name all the rectangles that are similar to rectangle E. **F**

   b. What is the ratio of the lengths of the corresponding sides?
   6:2 or 3:1

8. Make a sketch of a rectangle that is similar but not congruent to rectangle B. Label the length of each side.

9. Frankie thinks that any two right triangles will be similar.

   a. Sketch two right triangles that are not similar. Label the angle measures and side lengths. **See margin.**

   b. Explain to Frankie why your two triangles are not similar.

10. Which two nails are similar? Explain.

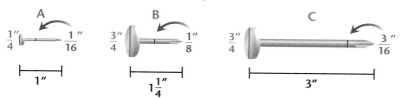

A

$\frac{1''}{4}$ ⊢▬▭▬ $\frac{1''}{16}$

⊢——————⊣
1"

B

$\frac{3''}{4}$ ⊢▭◤ $\frac{1''}{8}$

⊢——————⊣
$1\frac{1''}{4}$

C

$\frac{3''}{4}$ ⊢▭◤———— $\frac{3''}{16}$

⊢————————————⊣
3"

The figures in each pair are similar. Use proportions to find the missing lengths.

11.

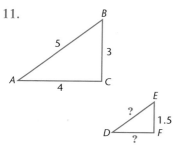

12.

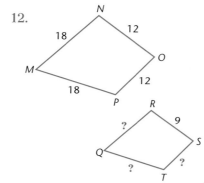

13. The Mount Rushmore sculpture of four United States Presidents was built using models of their heads with the scale 1 in. : 12 in. Each model was 5 ft tall. What is the height of each head in the sculpture? **60 ft**

Mount Rushmore ▶
near Keystone, South Dakota, was sculpted from 1927 to 1941 by artist Gutzon Borglum and almost 400 workers. An artist's studio near the site displays unique plaster models and tools related to the sculpting process.

9. Sample Response

   b. These two right triangles only have one pair of congruent angles, the right angles; the ratio of the lengths of the shorter legs is 1:2 and the ratio of the lengths of the longer legs is 2:1. Since the corresponding angles of the triangles are not congruent and the ratios of the lengths of the corresponding sides are not equivalent, the triangles are not similar.

10. A and C; The ratios of the corresponding measures are equivalent.

11. $DE = 2.5$, $DF = 2$

12. $ST = 7.2$, $TQ = 10.8$, $QR = 10.8$

9. **Sample Response**

   a.
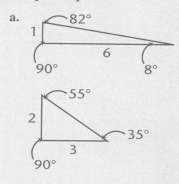

EXERCISE NOTES

Exercises 19–21 Using a map scale is an important skill in social studies courses, as well as in real life. You may want to bring some local or state maps to class to provide hands-on practice with this skill.

For each scale, find how long a measure of 3 in. on the drawing would be on the actual object.

14. 1 in. : 5 ft 15 ft   15. 2 in. : 3 ft 4.5 ft   16. $\frac{1}{2}$ in. : $2\frac{1}{2}$ ft 15 ft

17. The makers of the movie *Earthquake* made a 54-foot-long miniature of the 880-foot-long Hollywood Dam.

   a. Find the scale used to build the miniature. about 1 ft: 16.3 ft

   b. In the movie, the dam breaks and washes away buildings. The miniature buildings were built on the same scale as the miniature dam. If an actual house is 60 ft long and 40 ft wide, find the dimensions of a miniature house.
   about 3.7 ft long and about 2.5 ft wide

18. **Challenge** The model of the Death Star in *Star Wars* was built using the scale 1 ft : 2400 ft. In the movie, the Death Star was made to look like a sphere one mile in diameter. What was the diameter of the model? (1 mi = 5280 ft) 2.2 ft

Social Studies In Exercises 19–21, use the scale on the map to estimate the actual distance between each pair of cities.

19. Tete and Ndola
    400 mi

20. Tete and Harare
    200 mi

21. Lusaka and Harare
    240 mi

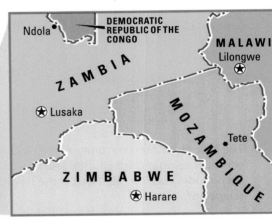

Scale: 1 in. = 160 mi

Reflecting ◀▶on the Section

22. Many miniatures are built using the scale 1 in. : 12 in. Measure the length, the width, and the height of your bed. Use the scale to find the measurements for a miniature of your bed. Then make a scale drawing of your bed. Answers will vary. Check students' work.

Spiral ◀▶Review

Use cross products to tell whether the ratios are equivalent.
(Module 6, p. 401)

23. $\frac{4}{25}$ and $\frac{5}{30}$ no   24. $\frac{21}{28}$ and $\frac{9}{12}$ yes   25. $\frac{3.5}{5}$ and $\frac{11.2}{16}$ yes

Mental Math Use mental math to add or subtract.
(Module 1, p. 11; Module 5, p. 324)

26. $6 - 2\frac{2}{5}$ $3\frac{3}{5}$ 27. $23 + 88 + 177$ 288   28. $2\frac{1}{4} + 4\frac{5}{6} + 1\frac{3}{4}$ $8\frac{5}{6}$

Write each fraction as a decimal. (Module 4, p. 225)

29. $\frac{2}{5}$ 0.4   30. $\frac{3}{10}$ 0.3   31. $\frac{3}{4}$ 0.75   32. $\frac{4}{8}$ 0.5

Exercise Notes

Exercise 33 Because of the small size of the map, the length on the map between Marotiri and Macdonald Seamount should probably be measured to the nearest tenth of a centimeter or millimeter.

Career ▪ Connection

Oceanographer: Marcia McNutt

Marcia McNutt uses sonar and satellites to create scale maps of an ocean floor. These maps can be used to locate underwater volcanoes or to show an ocean floor's depth. This map shows the Southern Austral Islands in the South Pacific Ocean.

33. **a.** The actual distance from the volcano at Marotiri to the one at Macdonald Seamount is about 264 km. Write a scale for the map. **1 cm = 132 km**

   b. Use your scale to estimate the actual distance from the volcano at Rapa to the volcano at Marotiri. **about 66 km**

34. Estimate the depth of the ocean at Marotiri. **2000 m**

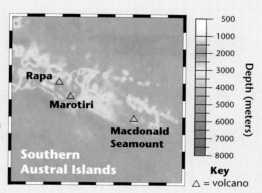

Tell whether the figures in each pair are similar. For the similar figures, tell which are congruent. If they are not similar, explain how you know.

1.

5 in.   53°   7.5 in.
53° 37°   4.5 in.
3 in.   4 in.   37°
6 in.

1. similar

2. Not similar; Corresponding angles
do not have equal measures.

2.

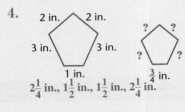

120° 3 in. 30°
2 in.   4 in.
75°   1 in. 135°

6 in. 40°
110°   8 in.
4 in.
120° 90°
2 in.

Use proportions to find the missing lengths in each pair of similar figures.

3.

6.3 cm
2.1 cm

?
32.4 cm   10.8 cm

4.

2 in.   2 in.
3 in.   3 in.
1 in.

? ?
? ?
$\frac{3}{4}$ in.

$2\frac{1}{4}$ in., $1\frac{1}{2}$ in., $1\frac{1}{2}$ in., $2\frac{1}{4}$ in.

For each scale, find how long a measure of 4 in. on the drawing would be on the actual object.

5. 1 in : 12 in. **48 in.**   6. 2 in. : 5 ft **10 ft**   7. $\frac{1}{2}$ in. : 10 ft **80 ft**

Standardized Testing ◀▶ Free Response

The parallelograms in the sketch were made with blue pattern blocks.

Parallelogram 1:   Parallelogram 2: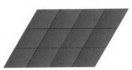

1. Explain why the parallelograms are not similar. **The ratio of lengths along the bottoms of the parallelograms is 2 to 4 (or 1 to 2), yet along the sides the ratio is 1 to 3.**

2. Make a sketch to show how you could change Parallelogram 2 so that it is similar but not congruent to Parallelogram 1. **See margin.**

Section 6 Percents and Circle Graphs

Playing the Percentages

IN THIS SECTION

EXPLORATION 1
♦ Writing Percents

EXPLORATION 2
♦ Using Fractions for Percents

EXPLORATION 3
♦ Circle Graphs

Setting the Stage

GETTING STARTED
Module 6 Section 6 *Warm-Up* assesses students' knowledge of the relationship between percents, decimals, and fractions. If students are able to work the problems correctly, they may be able to skip all of Exploration 1 except for completion of **Labsheet 6B** in Question 8.

TEACHING NOTES
Question 1 Note that on **Labsheet 6A**, the ratios in Question 3 should add up to 1.

Setting the Stage ▶▶▶▶▶▶▶▶▶▶▶▶▶▶▶▶▶▶▶▶▶▶▶▶▶▶

SET UP *You will need Labsheet 6A.*

Approximately 450 youth, representing all the nations competing in the Olympic Games, participated in the 2004 Olympic Youth Camp in Athens, Greece. The Olympic Youth Camp is a cross-cultural exchange that brings together young people ages 16–18 from around the world. They learn about other cultures, tour historic sites, observe athletes training, and attend the Opening and Closing Ceremonies and four sporting events of their choice.

Use Labsheet 6A. Complete the *Olympic Sporting Events Survey* to find out what sporting events your classmates would most like to attend if selected for an Olympic Youth Camp.

▲
Closing Ceremonies at
2004 Olympic Games

Think About It

1 Suppose your class is similar to the Youth Camp participants. Use the ratios from Question 3 on Labsheet 6A to predict how many of the 450 participants would choose each of the following sporting events as their first choice to attend.
Answers will vary. Check students' work.

  a. track and field

  b. gymnastics

  c. soccer

  d. a sport other than track and field, gymnastics, or soccer

Section 6 Percents and Circle Graphs **419**

GOAL

LEARN HOW TO...
- write a percent
- relate fractions, decimals, and percents

AS YOU...
- compare samples that have different sizes

KEY TERM
- percent

Exploration 1

Writing Percen%s

SET UP *You will need Labsheet 6B.*

▶ **Describing with Percent** If 62 out of 100 students chose to attend soccer, then 62 *percent* of the students chose soccer. **Percent** means "per hundred" or "out of 100."

EXAMPLE

You can write "62 out of 100 students chose to attend soccer" as:

$\frac{62}{100}$ of the students chose to attend soccer,

0.62 of the students chose to attend soccer, or

62% of the students chose to attend soccer.

% is the symbol for percent.

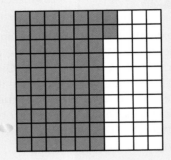

62% can be represented by shading **62** squares on a 100-square grid.

2 a. Write the number of unshaded squares in the grid above as a percent. **38%**

b. Write the percent in part (a) as a fraction and as a decimal.

c. If you combine the shaded and unshaded squares in the grid above, what percent of the grid do you have? **100%**

d. Write the percent you found in part (c) as a fraction and as a decimal. $\frac{1}{1}$; 1.0

2. b. $\frac{38}{100}$; 0.38

✔ QUESTION 3

...checks that you can write a percent as a decimal and as a fraction.

3 ✔ CHECKPOINT Write each percent as a fraction and a decimal.

a. 40% $\frac{40}{100}$, 0.4   **b.** 28% $\frac{28}{100}$, 0.28   **c.** 3% $\frac{3}{100}$, 0.03

420

4 Discussion In Class A, 3 out of 20 students were absent when the survey was taken. In Class B, 4 out of 25 students were absent. Why is it hard to tell which class surveyed has a greater fraction of students missing?

▶ Using percents or decimals can help you compare two fractions.

EXAMPLE

Look at Class A from Question 4. Write the fraction of students from Class A that were absent as a percent and as a decimal.

SAMPLE RESPONSE

You can write a fraction as a percent or as a decimal by writing an equivalent fraction in hundredths: $\frac{3}{20} = \frac{?}{100}$.

$$\frac{3}{20} = \frac{3 \cdot 5}{20 \cdot 5} = \frac{15}{100}$$

15 hundredths is **15%** or **0.15**

5 a. What is the fraction of students who were absent in Class B? $\frac{4}{25}$

b. Write the fraction from part (a) as a decimal and as a percent.
0.16, 16%

c. Which class had the greater percent of absent students? Class B

6 Replace each ? with >, <, or =.

a. 45% ? $\frac{1}{4}$ 　　　**b.** 0.7 ? 75% 　　　**c.** 3% ? 0.03
　　　>　　　　　　　　　　<　　　　　　　　　=

7 ✔ **CHECKPOINT** Write each fraction or decimal as a percent.

a. $\frac{4}{5}$ 80% 　　**b.** 0.18 18% 　　**c.** $\frac{1}{50}$ 2% 　　**d.** 0.09 9%

▶ **Recognizing Percents and Decimals** It is helpful to learn the percent and decimal forms for some common fractions.

8 Use Labsheet 6B. Follow the directions to find some *Common Fraction, Decimal, and Percent Equivalents.* See margin.

HOMEWORK EXERCISES ▶ See Exs. 1–21 on p. 429.

4. Answers will vary.
Sample Responses:
Because there is a different number of students in each class and neither class had very many students absent;
The fractions that describe the 2 ratios have different denominators, making them difficult to compare.

✔ **QUESTION 7**

...checks that you can write decimals and fractions as percents.

ALTERNATIVE APPROACH
Using the **Example** as a guide have students devise their own examples using a variety of denominators. They will quickly discover that some fractions are much easier to convert to percents than others. Eventually, they should notice what type of fraction is most easily converted to a percent or decimal (*denominators that are 100 or are a whole-number factor of 100*).

TEACHING NOTES
Question 6 Remind students they can write percents as fractions or fractions as percents to help compare.

Question 7 can be solved using the method in the **Example**.

Question 8 Encourage students to memorize the percent equivalents of the fractions on **Labsheet 6B**.

8. See Additional Answers beginning on page A1.

Exploration 2

TEACHING NOTES

You may need to quickly review finding a fraction of a whole number from Module 3 Section 5.

Remind students that a percent is the number out of 100. Discuss why the percent and the number of wins is the same for **Question 9** (*She must have played 100 games*). Throughout the exploration, make the connection between finding a fraction of a number and finding a percent of a number so students will understand how the two skills are related.

DIFFERENTIATED INSTRUCTION

Students who quickly grasp the concepts of Exploration 2 may wish to try the Challenge problem (**Exercise 35**) on page 430. They could then research other statistics from the U.S. Olympic softball team, or from another team of their choice. They could present their findings to the class, and if applicable, use fractions to determine which player had the greatest and least percent of hits. Students could create their own table similar to the one in **Question 18** on page 423, but include a fourth column labeled *Percent of hits*. Students could also vary which column they leave blank so that classmates would have to find either the number of hits, the number of at-bats, or the percent of hits. Some students may recognize that the value in the percent of hits column is the player's batting average.

GOAL

LEARN HOW TO...
- use a fraction to find a percent of a number
- use a fraction to estimate a percent of a number

AS YOU...
- examine data about the U.S. Olympic softball team

Exploration 2

USING Fractions for Percents

SET UP   *You will need Labsheet 6C.*

▶ The Olympic Games date back to 776 B.C. when the competition consisted of a single 200-yard foot race. At the 2004 Summer Olympics in Athens, there were 296 events in 28 different sports.

Some of the sports like softball, which became an official medal sport in 1996 at the Atlanta Games, are new Olympic events. In this exploration, you will use percents to examine a variety of facts and figures about players chosen for the 2004 Olympic softball team.

9   In 2004, Lisa Fernandez pitched in her third Olympic Games. While in college, she set a record by winning 93% of her games at UCLA. Lisa won 93 games. How many losses did she have? **7**

10   Amanda Freed was another athlete on the 2004 Olympic softball team. During the 2003 Pan American games, she got a hit 50% of the times she batted.

   a. What fraction in lowest terms is equivalent to 50%? $\frac{1}{2}$

   b. Amanda batted 14 times in the 2003 Pan American games. Show how to use the fraction you found in part (a) to find how many hits she got. $\frac{1}{2}$ of 14 = 7 hits

11   Write each percent as a fraction in lowest terms.

   a. 25% $\frac{1}{4}$ **b.** 10% $\frac{1}{10}$ **c.** 20% $\frac{1}{5}$

12   ✔ **CHECKPOINT**   In the 2003 Canada Cup, Amanda Freed was at bat 15 times. She had a hit 40% of the times she was at bat. Use a fraction in lowest terms to find how many hits she had. 6 hits ($\frac{2}{5}$ of 15)

FOR ◀ HELP

with *equivalent fractions,* see **MODULE 1, p. 61**

✔ **QUESTION 12**

...checks that you can use a fraction to find a percent of a number.

▶ **Estimating with Percents** You can use a "nice" fraction to estimate a percent or a percent of a number.

13. About 40% ($\approx \frac{8}{20}$)

EXAMPLE

Natasha Watley was the Most Valuable Player at the 2002 World Championships because she got a hit on 16 out of 31 times at-bat. Use a "nice" fraction to estimate the percent of hits she got.

SAMPLE RESPONSE

$\frac{16}{31}$ is close to $\frac{15}{30}$ **or** $\frac{16}{31}$ is close to $\frac{16}{32}$

$\frac{15}{30} = \frac{1}{2} = 50\%$ $\frac{16}{32} = \frac{1}{2} = 50\%$

Natasha hit about 50% of the time she was at-bat.

▲
Natasha Watley, 2004 Olympic team shortstop, was Team USA's dominant hitter during the World Championships.

13 During the 2003 Canada Cup, Leah O'Brien-Amico, an outfielder on the 2004 Olympic team, had 9 hits in 22 times at-bat. Use a "nice" fraction to estimate the percent of hits she had.

14 Cat Osterman, the youngest member of the 2004 Olympic team, won 68 out of 82 games while pitching for the University of Texas. Use a "nice" fraction to estimate the percent of games she won. About 80% ($\approx \frac{64}{80} = \frac{8}{10}$)

▶ You know the percent equivalents for many "nice" fractions. In Question 15, you will learn the percent form for $\frac{1}{3}$ and $\frac{2}{3}$.

15. a, d–e.

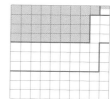

i. $66\frac{2}{3}\%$; Sample Response: I shaded another group of squares and another third of the left-over square and counted.

15 **Use Labsheet 6C.** Use the *Grid for Thirds* to write $\frac{1}{3}$ and $\frac{2}{3}$ as percents. b. 33; c. 1; f. $33\frac{1}{3}$; g. $33\frac{1}{3}$; h. $33\frac{1}{3}\%$

16 ✔ **CHECKPOINT** In the 2003 Pan American games, Natasha Watley had 7 hits in 24 at-bats. Use a fraction to estimate the percent of hits she got. See margin.

✔ **QUESTION 16**

...checks that you can use a fraction to estimate a percent.

17 Suppose a batter got a hit in 32% of her 75 at-bats. Use a "nice" fraction to estimate how many hits she got. 25 hits ($\frac{1}{3}$ of 75)

18 **Discussion** Arrange the players in the table in order from least percent of hits to greatest percent of hits. Explain your reasoning. Player C, Player A, Player B; Player C had exactly 25%, while Player A had just over 25% and Player B had an even greater number of hits out of 400 than Player A.

Player	Hits	At-Bats
A	105	400
B	120	400
C	150	600

HOMEWORK EXERCISES ▶ See Exs. 22–35 on pp. 429–430.

TEACHING NOTES
The following Classroom Example may be used prior to **Question 13** to provide additional guidance using a "nice" fraction to estimate a percent.

CLASSROOM EXAMPLE

Suppose a player stole 11 bases in 16 attempts. Use a "nice" fraction to estimate the percent of her attempts that were successful.

Answer:

$\frac{11}{16}$ is close to $\frac{12}{16}$.

$\frac{12}{16} = \frac{3}{4} = 75\%$.

A little less than 75% of her attempts were successful.

Question 15 Encourage students to memorize the percent equivalents for thirds. Having percent equivalents memorized makes it easier for students to quickly and effectively estimate using "nice" fractions. Until memorized, students may want to keep their completed copy of **Labsheet 6B** handy while working in this exploration. A table for $\frac{1}{3}$ and $\frac{2}{3}$ equivalents can be added on to the bottom of the labsheet.

Question 18 Have students share how they used the numbers in the table to find a percent.

16. Estimates may vary. Samples:
$\frac{7}{25} = 28\%$; or $\frac{8}{25} = 32\%$;
or $\frac{7}{21} = \frac{1}{3} = 33\frac{1}{3}\%$; or $\frac{8}{24} = \frac{1}{3}$
$= 33\frac{1}{3}\%$

Exploration 3

TEACHING NOTES

Discuss how using benchmarks such as $\frac{1}{4} = 25\%$ or $\frac{1}{2} = 50\%$ for fractions and percents can be helpful when making and reading circle graphs. For example, in **Questions 19 and 20**, about half the circle represents soccer, so slightly less than 50% of the students chose soccer.

LEARN HOW TO...
- display data in a circle graph
- use percents and fractions to estimate angle measures

AS YOU...
- examine the data from an *Olympic Sporting Events Survey*

KEY TERMS
- circle graph, pie chart

Exploration 3

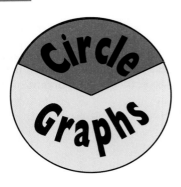

SET UP Work with a partner. You will need: • Labsheet 6A • scissors • tape • colored markers or pencils • protractor • compass • straightedge

▶ To show the part to whole relationship, data are often displayed in a **circle graph** or **pie chart**. In this exploration you will use a circle graph to display some of the data from the *Olympic Sporting Events Survey* in Labsheet 6A.

The results of a survey of 102 students are summarized in the circle graph below. Use the circle graph to answer Questions 19–21.

19 Estimate the fraction of the students that chose soccer.
about $\frac{1}{2}$

20 About what percent of the students chose soccer?
about 50%

21 a. Suppose one event on the circle graph was chosen by 24 of the 102 students. Use a "nice" fraction to estimate the percent that chose that event. $\frac{24}{102} \approx \frac{1}{4} = 25\%$

b. What event could represent 24 out of 102 on the circle graph? Track and Field

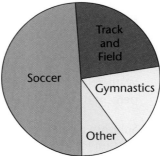

First Choice of Olympic Event to Attend

Track and Field

Soccer

Gymnastics

Other

▶ **Making a Circle Graph** Use Labsheet 6A. Follow the directions in Question 22 to make a circle graph of the results from your class survey.

22

a. Cut out the strips of paper on the right side of the labsheet. Use them to make one strip that contains one square for each student surveyed. **a–j. Check students' work.**

b. Color one square for each student that chose track and field. For example, if 5 students chose track and field, then 5 squares should be colored.

c. Repeat part (b) for gymnastics and soccer using a different color for each event.

d. Using a fourth color, color one square for each student who chose a sport other than track and field, gymnastics, or soccer.

Track   Soccer   Gymnastics   Other

e. Tape the ends of your strip together to form a loop with the colored squares on the outside. Do not overlap the ends.

f. Place the loop on a piece of paper.

g. Estimate where the center of the circle created by the loop would be and mark it. Also place a mark where each color begins and ends.

h. Remove the loop. Use a compass to draw a circle around the marks.

i. Use a straightedge to connect the mark where each color begins to the center of the circle.

j. Color and label each section with the name of the sporting event and with the fraction and the percent of the circle it represents.

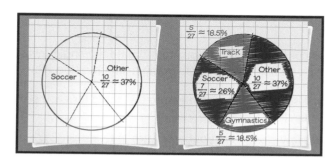

Section 6   Percents and Circle Graphs   **425**

TEACHING NOTES

Question 23 Point out that a circle graph represents 100%, or the whole data set. This makes it a good display for comparing parts of a data set to the whole set of data.

Questions 24 and 25 Remind students to use benchmarks to estimate. You may want to review how to measure an angle from Module 2 Section 4. You may also need to discuss how to measure angles greater than 180° degrees if students' circle graphs contain such angles.

23. c. Yes; The sum should be 100% since 100% is equivalent to 1, but due to rounding of percents, the sum might be a bit less or more than 100%.

23 Discussion

a. When you add the four fractions on the graph, why is the sum 1? Because the circle represents the whole class, which was split into parts, so the parts should add back up to 1 whole.

b. What is the sum of the four percents? Answers will vary. Percents should be close to 100%.

c. Will the sum of the percents always be 100%? Why?

▶ **Using Percents to Construct Circle Graphs** The circle graph shows the part to whole relationship between the number of students that chose each sporting event and the total number of students. The entire 360° circle represents the whole, or 100%. You can use percents to find the angle measure for each section of the circle graph.

EXAMPLE

Use percents and fractions to estimate the angle measure for the soccer section and the track and field section of the circle graph.

SAMPLE RESPONSE

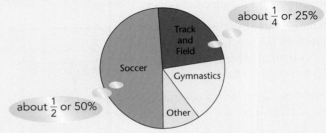

About $\frac{1}{2}$ of the circle represents soccer.

There are 360° in a circle and $\frac{1}{2}$ of 360° = 180°.

The section for soccer has an angle measure of about 180°.

Track and field is about $\frac{1}{4}$ of the circle. $\frac{1}{4}$ of 360° = 90°.

The section for track and field has an angle measure of about 90°.

24 Use percents and fractions to estimate the angle measure for each section in your circle graph from Question 22. Check students' work.

25 a. Use a protractor to measure the angle for each section of your circle graph. Check students' work.

b. How close were your estimates in Question 24? Answers will vary.

c. Does the sum of the four angle measures equal 360°? Why or why not? The sum should equal 360°, however precision in measuring and drawing the angles may cause it to be off by a few degrees.

26 ✔ **CHECKPOINT** **Use Labsheet 6A.** Use the *Olympic Sporting Events Survey* to make a circle graph that displays the data for three sports other than track and field, gymnastics, and soccer. *Note:* Your circle graph should have four sections, one for each of the sports you chose and one for all the other sports.

a–b. Check students' graphs.

a. List the sport, the fraction, the percent, and the angle measure for each section in your circle graph.

b. Title your circle graph.

HOMEWORK EXERCISES ▶ See Exs. 36–37 on pp. 430–431.

✔ **QUESTION 26**

...checks that you can use data to make and label a circle graph.

Section 6

Key Concepts

Key Terms

Understanding Percent (p. 420)

Fraction Form: $\frac{25}{100}$ or $\frac{1}{4}$

Decimal Form: 0.25

Percent Form: 25%

Percent means "per hundred" or "out of 100."

percent

Using Percents to Compare (p. 421)

Example Which is greater, $\frac{14}{25}$ or $\frac{120}{200}$?

When the denominator is greater than 100, you can divide to find an equivalent fraction with a denominator of 100.

Find equivalent fractions with denominators of 100.

$\frac{14}{25} = \frac{14 \cdot 4}{25 \cdot 4} = \frac{56}{100} = 56\%$ $\qquad$ $\frac{120}{200} = \frac{120 \div 2}{200 \div 2} = \frac{60}{100} = 60\%$

So $\frac{120}{200}$ is greater than $\frac{14}{25}$.

Key Concepts Questions

27 **a.** Write 44% as a fraction and as a decimal. $\frac{44}{100}$ or $\frac{11}{25}$; 0.44

b. Write 0.3 as a fraction and as a percent. $\frac{3}{10}$; 30%

28 Use percents to compare 0.39 and $\frac{7}{20}$. 39% > 35%, so 39% > $\frac{7}{20}$

Key Concepts

CLOSURE QUESTION

State two real-life situations where you would need to find fractions of whole numbers and two real-life situations where you need to relate percents and decimals or percents and fractions.

Sample Response:

Fractions of whole numbers: altering a recipe or building a scale model;

Percents and decimals or percents and fractions: displaying data in a book or report, or calculating a percent discount in a store.

Key Concepts continued

CLOSURE QUESTION

What is the sum of the percents in a circle graph? Why?

Sample Response: 100%, because the graph represents all or 100% of the data broken into smaller divisions.

ABSENT STUDENTS

For students who were absent for all or part of this section, the blackline Study Guide for Section 6 may be used to present the ideas, concepts, and skills of Section 6.

Key Terms

circle graph, pie chart

Section 6
Key Concepts

Using Fractions for Percents (pp. 422–423)

"Nice" fractions like $\frac{2}{5}$ and $\frac{3}{4}$ can be used to find a percent of a number. "Nice" fractions can also be used to estimate a percent or a percent of a number.

Example Use a "nice" fraction to estimate 29% of 40.

$$29\% \text{ of } 40$$
$$\frac{3}{10} \text{ of } 40$$

29% is about 30% or $\frac{3}{10}$.

Think: $\frac{1}{10}$ of 40 is 4, so $\frac{3}{10}$ of 40 is $3 \cdot 4$ or 12.

Circle Graphs (pp. 424–427)

A circle graph or pie chart can be used to compare parts of a data set with the whole. You can use percents to find the angle measure for each section of a circle graph.

Example What fraction of gift certificates are redeemed?

Holiday Season Gift Certificates

$$85\% = 85 \text{ out of } 100$$
$$= \frac{85}{100} = \frac{17}{20}$$

15%

85%

☐ redeemed   ■ not redeemed

Key Concepts Question

29 Calculate the angle measure for the *not redeemed* section in the *Holiday Season Gift Certificates* circle graph. **54°**

Section 6

Practice & Application Exercises

YOU WILL NEED

For Ex. 1:
- Labsheet 6D

For Ex. 36:
- compass or round object
- protractor

1. **Use Labsheet 6D.** Follow the directions for *Shading Percents*. Then write a fraction and a decimal for each shaded part.
   See margin.

Write each percent as a fraction and as a decimal.

2. 30%
   $\frac{30}{100}$ or $\frac{3}{10}$; 0.3

3. 54%
   $\frac{54}{100}$ or $\frac{27}{50}$; 0.54

4. 72%
   $\frac{72}{100}$ or $\frac{18}{25}$; 0.72

5. 99%
   $\frac{99}{100}$; 0.99

6. **Writing** In a raffle, Tanisha buys 4 of the 200 tickets sold. In another raffle, her friend Dustin buys 6 of the 300 tickets sold. Who is more likely to win? Why?
   Their chances are equal, since the percents are both 2%.

Write each decimal as a fraction and as a percent.

7. 0.37
   $\frac{37}{100}$; 37%

8. 0.4
   $\frac{4}{10}$ or $\frac{2}{5}$; 40%

9. 0.59
   $\frac{59}{100}$; 59%

10. 0.02
    $\frac{2}{100}$ or $\frac{1}{50}$; 2%

Write each fraction as a decimal and as a percent.

11. $\frac{3}{100}$
    0.03, 3%

12. $\frac{9}{25}$
    0.36, 36%

13. $\frac{170}{200}$
    0.85, 85%

14. $\frac{4}{5}$
    0.8, 80%

Replace each ? with >, <, or =.

15. $\frac{2}{5}$? 0.45
    <

16. 0.245 ? 23%
    >

17. 56% ? 0.18
    >

18. 72% ? $\frac{3}{4}$
    <

19. 0.9 ? 9%
    >

20. $\frac{2}{8}$? 0.18
    >

21. **Visual Thinking** Replace each ? with the number that makes the statement true. *50, 25, 12.5, 12.5*

   A is ?% of the square.

   B is ?% of the square.

   C is ?% of the square.

   D is ?% of the square.

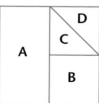

Use a fraction in lowest terms to find each value.

22. 25% of 48 12

23. 60% of 35 21

24. 10% of 90 9

25. 5% of 380 19

26. 20% of 245 49

27. 70% of 45 31.5

28. Carlos scored in 35% of his 60 soccer games.

   a. Use a "nice" fraction to estimate the number of games in which he scored. $\frac{1}{3}$ of 60 = 20

   b. Is your estimate *greater than* or *less than* the actual number of games? *less than because 35% is a little more than $\frac{1}{3}$.*

---

1. a. 1%

fraction $\frac{1}{100}$
decimal 0.01

b. 10%

fraction $\frac{10}{100} = \frac{1}{10}$
decimal 0.10

c. 25%

fraction $\frac{25}{100} = \frac{1}{4}$
decimal 0.25

d. 46%

fraction $\frac{46}{100} = \frac{23}{50}$
decimal 0.46

Practice & Applications

SUGGESTED ASSIGNMENTS

Core Course
Day 1: Exs. 1–6
Day 2: Exs. 7–21
Day 3: Exs. 22–34
Day 4: Exs. 38–40
Day 5: Exs. 36–37

Extended Course
Day 1: Exs. 1–6
Day 2: Exs. 7–21 odd
Day 3: Exs. 25–35
Day 4: Exs. 38–40
Day 5: Exs. 36–37

Note: Extended Course assignments can be used to differentiate within the regular classroom. In classrooms where students are grouped homogeneously, the material might be covered in fewer days. In this case assignments may be combined.

ADDITIONAL PRACTICE
See the *Teacher's Resource Book* for additional practice and application exercises for this section.

EXERCISE NOTES
Exercises 2–5 and 7–10
Emphasize that percent means "per hundred." Preferred answers have 100 as a denominator and it is not necessary to simplify.

Exercises 15–20 can be solved in more than one way, since all that is required is to determine the greater value. One suggested method is to change both numbers to a fraction with a common denominator of 100. Students might want to jot down under each original number the converted value to help with identifying errors.

1. e–f. See Additional Answers beginning on page A1.

429

Practice & Applications

EXERCISE NOTES

Exercise 30 Once students are comfortable finding 10% of a number mentally, they can use multiples of 10% to find common store discounts of 20%, 30%, or 40% by multiplying their 10% result by 2, 3, or 4 respectively. Students may enjoy practicing the speed at which they can mentally compute sale prices from store flyers or newspaper advertisements.

36. c–d. Check students' graphs. Sample response is shown.

World Land Area

35. c. $\frac{3}{8}$ is halfway between $\frac{2}{8}$ and $\frac{4}{8}$, or halfway between 25% and 50%, so $\frac{3}{8}$ is 37.5%.

36. a. $\frac{30}{100}, \frac{20}{100}, \frac{16}{100},$ $\frac{12}{100}, \frac{10}{100}, \frac{7}{100}, \frac{5}{100}$

▲
The All American Girls Professional Baseball League (AAGPBL) that existed from 1943 to 1954 inspired the 1992 movie *A League of Their Own*.

29. Teams in the All American Girls Professional Baseball League played games almost every night, with about 120 games a season. How many wins would a team have needed to win 75% of its games? **90 wins**

30. **Mental Math** When dining in a restaurant, some people leave a tip equal to 15% of the bill. Suppose the bill is $40.00.

   a. Use mental math to find 10% of $40.00. **$4**

   b. Use mental math to find 5% of $40.00. **$2**

   c. Use parts (a) and (b) to find 15% of $40.00. **$6**

Estimate a percent for each fraction.

31. $\frac{35}{65}$ **32.** $\frac{31}{40}$ **33.** $\frac{46}{51}$ **34.** $\frac{19}{30}$

  about 50%   about 75%   about 90%   about 66%

35. **Challenge** Kim Maher had 12 hits in 32 at-bats while playing in the Pan American games in 1995. Complete parts (a)–(c) to find the percent of times she got a hit.

   a. Write the fraction $\frac{12}{32}$ in lowest terms. $\frac{3}{8}$

   b. Find the percent equivalents of $\frac{2}{8}$ and $\frac{4}{8}$. **25%, 50%**

   c. Show how your answers from part (b) can be used to write $\frac{12}{32}$ as a percent.

36. **Displaying Data** A circle graph can be used to show the part to whole relationship between the area of each continent and the total land area on Earth.

   a. Write each percent in the table as a fraction out of 100.

   b. Use a proportion to find the angle measure in a circle graph for each continent. **108°, 72°, 58°, 43°, 36°, 25°, 18°**

World Land Area	
Continent	**Percent of total land area***
Asia	30
Africa	20
North America	16
South America	12
Antarctica	10
Europe	7
Australia	5

*Approximate percents

Example

Round to the nearest whole degree.

    Percent   Degrees

South America $\longrightarrow$ $\dfrac{12}{100}$ = $\dfrac{43.2}{360}$

Total land area $\longrightarrow$

   c. Use a compass or a round object to draw a circle and find its center. **See margin.**

   d. Use a protractor to mark off each angle you found in part (b). Label your graph with the name of each continent and write a title. **See margin.**

   e. How does a circle graph help you compare data? **Visually you can tell at a glance which parts are greater.**

Reflecting on the Section

37. Use the circle graphs and table for parts (a)–(e).
Answers may vary. Sample responses are given.

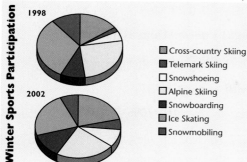

Participants (in millions)		
Sport	1998	2002
Cross-country skiing	8.8	13.5
Telemark skiing	1.3	3.3
Snowshoeing	2.9	5.9
Alpine skiing	14.8	14.3
Snowboarding	5.5	7.7
Ice Skating	18.5	14.5
Snowmobiling	6.5	4.5
Total Participants	**58.5**	**63.5**

Legend:
- Cross-country Skiing
- Telemark Skiing
- Snowshoeing
- Alpine Skiing
- Snowboarding
- Ice Skating
- Snowmobiling

a. Write a "nice" fraction for the number of participants in each of the following sports in 1998: ice skating, snowshoeing, cross-country skiing. $\frac{1}{3}, \frac{1}{20}, \frac{3}{20}$

b. Repeat part (a) for 2002. $\frac{1}{4}, \frac{1}{10}, \frac{1}{5}$

c. Use the "nice" fractions from parts (a) and (b) to estimate the percent that participated in ice skating, snowshoeing, and cross-country skiing in 1998 and in 2002.

d. Use the percents from part (c) to estimate the angle measures for ice skating, snowshoeing, and cross-country skiing in each circle graph. 1998: 120°, 18°, 54°; 2002: 90°, 36°, 72°

e. What happened to the percent of participants in ice skating from 1998 to 2002? cross-country skiing?

Spiral Review

38. The figures at the right are similar. Name all the pairs of corresponding angles and pairs of corresponding sides. (Module 6, p. 413)

For Exercises 39 and 40, choose the form of the quotient that best answers each question. (Module 1, p. 46)

39. How many 4-inch bows can be made from a 35-inch piece of ribbon? B

40. The bill for four people came to $35.00. What is each person's share of the bill? A

A. 8.75

B. 8

C. 9

D. $8\frac{3}{4}$

Visual THINKING

Exercise 37 checks that you can apply ideas about percents.

37. c. 1998: $33\frac{1}{3}\%$, 5%, 15%
2002: 25%, 10%, 20%

e. The percent of participation in ice skating decreased by 8 percentage points from 1998 to 2002 and the percent of participation in cross-country skiing increased by 5 percentage points.

38. ∠A and ∠G, ∠D and ∠F, ∠C and ∠E, ∠B and ∠H; $\overline{AD}$ and $\overline{GF}$, $\overline{DC}$ and $\overline{FE}$, $\overline{CB}$ and $\overline{EH}$, $\overline{BA}$ and $\overline{HG}$

EXERCISE NOTES

Exercise 37 Because the numerator and denominator of each ratio will be in units of millions, students do not need to write the word millions or the additional zero place holders to determine "nice" fractions for the sports in **parts (a)–(b)**.

TEACHER NOTES
For each Exploration, the corresponding Extra Skill Practice Exercises are noted.

Exploration 1: Exs. 1–14
Exploration 2: Exs. 15–27

EXTRA HELP
Teacher's Resource Book
• Practice and Applications for Section 6
• Study Guide
• Practice and Applications for Sections 1–6

Technology Resources
• @Home Tutor
• Test Generator

ASSESSMENT
• Section 6 Quick Quiz
• Test Generator

Section 6
Extra Skill Practice

Write each decimal as a percent and as a fraction.

1. 0.35 $35\%, \frac{35}{100}$ or $\frac{7}{20}$
2. 0.28 $28\%, \frac{28}{100}$ or $\frac{7}{25}$
3. 0.6 $60\%, \frac{60}{100}$ or $\frac{3}{5}$
4. 0.05 $5\%, \frac{5}{100}$ or $\frac{1}{20}$

Write each fraction as a decimal and as a percent.

5. $\frac{7}{100}$ $0.07, 7\%$
6. $\frac{8}{25}$ $0.32, 32\%$
7. $\frac{9}{10}$ $0.9, 90\%$
8. $\frac{3}{20}$ $0.15, 15\%$

Replace each ? with >, <, or =.

9. 9% ? $\frac{9}{10}$ $<$
10. 70% ? 0.07 $>$
11. 0.5 ? 52% $<$
12. 1.1 ? 100% $>$
13. 0.75 ? $\frac{3}{4}$ $=$
14. 20% ? $\frac{1}{10}$ $>$

Use a fraction in lowest terms to find each value.

15. 25% of 72 18
16. 80% of 80 64
17. 10% of 91 9.1
18. 90% of 170 153
19. 5% of 60 3
20. 75% of 104 78

Estimate a percent for each fraction.

21. $\frac{19}{61}$ about $33\frac{1}{3}\%$
22. $\frac{16}{65}$ about 25%
23. $\frac{3}{14}$ about 20%
24. $\frac{5}{49}$ about 10%

Use a "nice" fraction to estimate each value.

25. 34% of 120 about 40
26. 79% of 25 about 20
27. 48% of 90 about 45

Standardized Testing ◀▶ Multiple Choice

1. Which is the best estimate of 67% of 60? B
   - Ⓐ 42
   - Ⓑ 40
   - Ⓒ 36
   - Ⓓ 45

2. For which situation do you save the most money? C
   - Ⓐ original price: $25
     discount: 40% off
   - Ⓑ original price: $36
     discount: 25% off
   - Ⓒ original price: $40
     discount: 30% off
   - Ⓓ original price: $22
     discount: 50% off

3. For which situation is the percent you save the greatest? D
   - Ⓐ original price: $40
     discount: save $10.20
   - Ⓑ original price: $19.99
     discount: save $1.89
   - Ⓒ original price: $50
     discount: save $9
   - Ⓓ original price: $58.99
     discount: save $20

The Module Project

Mystery Tracks

Imagine searching for evidence of dinosaurs that lived millions of years ago. Do you picture finding a large bone, or even a whole skeleton? Surprisingly, some dinosaurs and other extinct animals are known only from the tracks they left behind. Footprints can provide several clues about an animal such as its height, weight, age, and running speed.

Measuring and Comparing Lengths Scientists measure dinosaur tracks in several ways. Some ways of measuring the tracks of dinosaurs that walked on two legs are shown below.

SET UP

You will need:
- *metric ruler*
- *protractor*
- *chalk, or large newspaper and marker*

length of stride

length of footprint

Since dinosaur tracks are rare, you will study your own "tracks" and learn how mathematics can be used to make predictions from them.

 1 Have someone help you find the following measurements for your "tracks." Measure to the nearest centimeter, and be sure to use your normal walking speed. **Answers will vary. Check students' work.**

   a. your height   **b.** your footprint length   **c.** your stride length

 2 Write the ratio of *your footprint length to your height* in three ways. **Answers will vary. Check students' work.**

PROJECT NOTES
Students will need a partner as they begin working on the Module Project. Enough floor space is needed so that students can walk several normal strides. Suggestions for ways to take the stride and footprint measurements include marking with chalk on the floor or using a marker on large sheets of newspaper. If convenient, you could measure outside in the sand, or by having students wet their shoes and walk on an asphalt or concrete surface. Their footprints will show up well on the pavement. Remind students to take and record the measurements carefully since they will be used as the data for several activities throughout the project.

Module Project

Module Project *continued*

PROJECT NOTES

If available, taking the measures on a tile floor may help students see how the step angle changes when running. Students may be able to see that the footprints land on (or near) one row of tiles when walking, and on a different row of tiles when running. All methods for recording steps in the stride length exercise earlier can be applied for recording steps to measure step angle. Although students do not re-measure their stride length they should pay attention to how it changes when running.

Making Predictions Now you will use your "track" data and your classmates' data to predict height.

 3 a. Write your *footprint length to height* ratio as a decimal.
   Answers will vary. Check students' work.
   b. Collect the following data from each of your classmates (including yourself):

   ◆ height

   ◆ stride length

   ◆ *footprint length to height* ratio

 4 a. Make a scatter plot that compares stride length to height. If appropriate, fit a line to the data.
   Answers will vary. Check students' work.
   b. Use your graph to predict your height from your stride length. How close is the prediction to your actual height?

 5 a. Find the mean of the *footprint length to height* ratio.
   Answers will vary, but mean decimal ratio should be close to 0.16.
   b. Write a "nice" fraction that is close to the mean.

   c. Use your result from part (b) to predict your height from your foot length.

   d. How close is the prediction to your actual height?

5. b. Answers will vary. $\frac{1}{6}$ is a reasonable "nice" fraction for 0.16.

 6 Why do you think scientists use footprint length and stride length together to predict the heights of dinosaurs? Sample Response: The combination gives the scientists a better idea of the animal's build.

Using Angles Now you will look for a method to tell whether a person was walking or running when making tracks.

 **7** The diagram shows where to measure a person's step angle. Have someone help you measure your step angle to the nearest degree. Walk at your normal speed. Answers will vary. Check students' work.

 8 a. How do you think your step angle changes when you run?
   The measure of the step angle increases.
   b. Have someone help you measure your step angle for a running speed. Answers will vary. Check students' work.

   c. Does your stride length appear to be shorter or longer when running than when walking? The stride is longer when running.

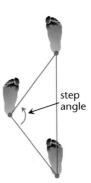

step angle

9 How can you use the measure of the step angle and stride length to tell whether tracks were made by someone walking or running?

Using Your Data Now you will use what you have learned to try to discover who may have made the mystery tracks below.

MYSTERY PERSON **1** MYSTERY PERSON **2** MYSTERY PERSON **3**

STATS	
MYSTERY PERSON 1	Height: 5 ft 1 in.
MYSTERY PERSON 2	Height: 6 ft 8 in.
MYSTERY PERSON 3	Height: 5 ft 6 in.

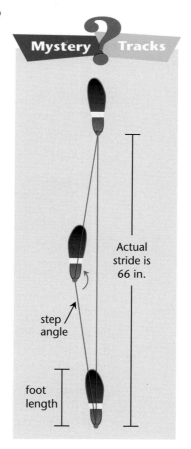

Mystery **?** Tracks

Actual stride is 66 in.

step angle

foot length

10 a. Do you think the person was walking or running when making the tracks? Why? **running; The step angle measures about 160° (nearly straight) and a larger step angle indicates running.**

b. Use the scale drawing of the mystery tracks to predict how tall the mystery person is. **about 6 ft 7 in. tall**

c. Who do you think this person may be? **Mystery Person 2**

11 Write a report that explains how you made all your predictions. Include your results from Questions 1–9 to support your prediction methods.
Answers will vary.

9. If the measure of the step angle is small, the person was probably walking. If the measure of the step angle is large, the person was probably running. The stride length will be longer if the person was running.

PROJECT NOTES
Have students share their ideas about the mystery person with a partner or in a small group. Emphasize to students that the report should explain how the predictions were made and should present evidence to support their choice of persons. If time allows, have students present their reports to the class. Students could debate the validity of each others' predictions and try to sway classmates to change their mind about the identity of the mystery person.

MODULE **6**

Review and Assessment

TEACHER NOTES
Students should complete
the Review and Assessment
independently in preparation for the
Module Test.

Allow class time to discuss solutions
and address any questions students
may have. During this time, you may
want to allow students to work in
groups to share methods for solving
the problems and to quiz each other
on the concepts covered in this
module.

7. b. $\frac{4}{7} \approx 0.57, \frac{1}{4} = 0.25, \frac{5}{6} \approx 0.83$

c. **Sample Response:** The closer
the decimal is to 1, the closer
the rectangle is to a square.

Write each ratio three ways. (Sec. 1, Explor. 1)

1. the ratio of red squares (▨) to blue squares (■)
   8 to 6, 8:6, $\frac{8}{6}$

2. the ratio of blue squares to white squares
   6 to 10, 6:10, $\frac{6}{10}$

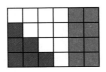

Tell whether or not the ratios are equivalent. (Sec. 1, Explor. 1)

3. $\frac{2}{5}$ and $\frac{10}{15}$
   no

4. 5 : 8 and 15 : 24
   yes

5. $\frac{3.3}{2.2}$ and $\frac{12}{8}$
   yes

6. At Super Sub, sub sandwiches are sold by the foot and you are
   charged the same amount for each foot. Suppose a 3-foot-long
   sub costs $18.00. (Sec. 2, Explor. 1)

   a. Copy and complete the table.

Length (feet)	1	2	3	4
Cost (dollars)	?	?	18	?

   6. a.
Length (feet)	1	2	3	4
Cost (dollars)	6	12	18	24

   b. How much does a 5-foot-long sub cost? $30

   c. How long is a $90.00 sub? 15 ft

7. a. Sketch three rectangles that have *height to length* ratios
   of 4 : 7, 1 : 4, and 5 : 6. (Sec. 3, Explor. 1) See margin.

   b. Write each *height to length* ratio from
   part (a) as a decimal. Round to the
   nearest hundredth. 15 ft

   c. What do the decimals you wrote for
   part (b) tell you about the general
   shape of the rectangles? See margin.

8. Use the scatter plot to estimate the missing
   entries in the table. Explain how you
   found your estimates. (Sec. 3, Explor. 3)

Latitude (°N)	25	?	44	57
Temperature (°F)	?	37	?	?

   See margin.

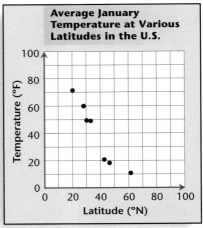

**Average January
Temperature at Various
Latitudes in the U.S.**

Find the missing term in each proportion. (Sec. 4, Explor. 1)

9. $\frac{4}{6} = \frac{10}{x}$

   $x = 15$

10. $\frac{3}{2.5} = \frac{y}{5}$

    $y = 6$

11. 21 : 3 = z : 18

    $z = 126$

7. a. and 8. See Additional Answers
beginning on page A1.

If appropriate, use a proportion to solve Exercises 12 and 13. If it is not appropriate, explain why not. (Sec. 4, Explor. 2)

12. A model of an airplane has a wingspan of 75 cm and a length of 82.5 cm. The actual airplane is 55 m long. What is its wingspan? **50 m**

13. Suppose a car's gas mileage is 30 mi/gal at a speed of 30 mi/hr. At what speed will the car get 60 mi/gal?

14. The triangles at the right are similar. Use a proportion to find the missing length. (Sec. 5, Explor. 1) **5 ft**

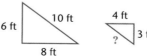

6 ft   10 ft   4 ft   3 ft   ?   8 ft

Write each fraction as a decimal and as a percent. (Sec. 6, Explor. 1)

15. $\frac{3}{5}$
0.6, 60%

16. $\frac{64}{200}$
0.32, 32%

17. $\frac{9}{20}$
0.45, 45%

18. $\frac{207}{300}$
0.69, 69%

13. Not appropriate; It is not reasonable to assume that the ratio of a car's mileage to its speed is always the same.

For Exercises 19–21, find each value. (Sec. 6, Explor. 2)

19. 25% of 84
21

20. 50% of 130
65

21. 10% of 245
24.5

22. Raphael answered 45 out of 51 questions on the math test correctly. Use a "nice" fraction to estimate what percent he answered correctly. (Sec. 6, Explor. 2)
Accept reasonable estimates; about 90%

23. A total of 70,000 lucky fans will earn a ticket to the Super Bowl. The pie chart below shows the percentages of tickets various organizations receive to distribute. (Sec. 6, Explor. 3)

a. Write each percent as a "nice" fraction.

b. About how many of the 70,000 tickets does the NFL office distribute? **17,500 tickets**

c. Find the angle measure for the 5% section. **18°**

23. a. $25.2\% \approx \frac{1}{4}$, $17.5\% \approx \frac{1}{5}$, $5\% = \frac{1}{20}$, $34.8\% \approx \frac{7}{20}$

Distribution of Tickets

Host team
5%
AFC champion
17.5%
25.2%
NFL office for distribution to fan lottery, players union, media and other associates
17.5%
NFC champion
34.8%
The 29 remaining teams (1.2% each)

Reflecting ▶on the Module

24. **Open-ended** Give at least one example of how ratios, proportions, or circle graphs help people make comparisons and predictions.
Answers will vary.

Module 6   Review and Assessment   **437**

Wonders of the World

Module 7 Overview

An exploration of intriguing or impressive structures around the world leads to work with measurement and geometric figures, including the use of formulas. Themes include the Empire State Building, the Great Pyramid at Giza, and Mesa Verde. Fraction and decimal computation skills are used to convert units and to find areas and volumes. Students also work with integers and coordinate graphs.

Module 7 Planner

Day 1: Section 1	Day 2: Section 1	Day 3: Section 1	Day 4: Section 2	Day 5: E²
Setting the Stage, p. 440 Exploration 1, pp. 441–443	Exploration 2 *through* Question 17, pp. 444–445	Exploration 2 *from* Question 18, pp. 445–446 Key Concepts, pp. 447–448	Setting the Stage, p. 452 Exploration 1, pp. 453–454 Key Concepts, p. 455	Begin E², p. 460
Day 6: Section 3	**Day 7: Section 3**	**Day 8: Section 3**	**Day 9: Review and Assessment**	**Day 10: Section 4**
Setting the Stage, p. 461 Exploration 1, pp. 462–463	Exploration 2 *through* Question 15, pp. 464–465	Exploration 2 *from* Question 16, p. 465 Key Concepts, p. 466	Mid-Module Quiz	Setting the Stage, p. 471 Exploration 1, pp. 472–474
Day 11: Section 4	**Day 12: Section 5**	**Day 13: Section 5**	**Day 14: Module Project**	**Day 15: Module Project**
Exploration 2, pp. 475–476 Key Concepts, p. 477	Setting the Stage, p. 482 Exploration 1, pp. 483–485	Exploration 2, pp. 486–488 Key Concepts, p. 489	Begin Module Project pp. 494–495	Work on Module Project pp. 494–495
Day 16: Review and Assessment	**Day 17: Review and Assessment**	**Day 18: Module Test**		
Assign Review and Assessment, pp. 496–497	Discuss Review and Assessment, pp. 496–497	Module 7 Test		

Materials List

Section	Materials
1	• Labsheets 1A–1B, tape, scissors, index cards, centimeter cubes, ruler, tracing paper
2	• Net 2 from Labsheet 1A, a scale, a coffee mug, a stapler
3	• Labsheets 3A–3B, about 30 cm of string, two pencils, compass, ruler, meter stick, 4 circular objects, calculator, clear ruler, straightedge, drawing paper, colored pencils or markers
4	• Labsheets 4A–4E, scissors, tape, rice, ruler, graph paper
5	• Labsheet 5A, metric ruler, compass (optional), graph paper, protractor
Project	• Project Labsheet A, poster board or construction paper, markers of colored pencils, ruler, scissors, tape
Rev & Assess	• scissors, tape, metric ruler, graph paper

Module 7 Objectives

Section	Objectives	NCTM Standards 2000*
1	• Identify and name prisms. • Predict the shape a net will form. • Identify vertices, edges, and faces of a polyhedron. • Draw a prism. • Understand the concept of volume. • Develop and use a formula for finding the volume of a prism.	1, 2, 3, 4, 5, 6, 7, 8, 9, 10
2	• Use appropriate customary units to estimate and measure weight. • Convert between customary units of weight.	1, 3, 4, 5, 6, 8, 9, 10
3	• Identify parts of a circle. • Use a compass to draw a circle. • Develop and use a formula for the circumference of a circle.	1, 2, 3, 4, 6, 7, 8, 9, 10
4	• Develop and use a formula for the area of a circle. • Recognize a cylinder. • Develop and use a formula for the volume of a cylinder.	1, 2, 3, 4, 6, 7, 8, 9, 10
5	• Use benchmarks to estimate Celsius and Fahrenheit temperatures. • Use integers to represent real life situations. • Compare integers. • Find solutions for simple inequalities with integers, such as $x < -3$. • Graph points with integer coordinates on a coordinate grid.	1, 3, 4, 6, 8, 9, 10

* See page T14.

438B

Section 1 Planner

Section Objectives

Exploration 1
- Identify and name prisms
- Predict the shape a net will form
- Identify vertices, edges, and faces of a polyhedron
- Draw a prism

Exploration 2
- Understand the concept of volume
- Develop and use a formula for finding the volume of a prism

Days for Section 1

First Day
Setting the Stage, *p. 440*
Exploration 1, *pp. 441–443*

Second Day
Exploration 2 through Question 17
pp. 444–445

Third Day
Exploration 2 from Question 18, *pp. 445–446*
Key Concepts, *pp. 447–448*

Teaching Resources

Teacher's Resource Book
- Warm-Up
- Labsheets 1A and 1B
- Practice and Applications
- Study Guide
See page 439 for additional teaching resources.

Materials List

Exploration 1
- Labsheet 1A
- tape and scissors
- index card

Exploration 2
- Labsheet 1B
- ruler
- tape and scissors
- centimeter cubes

Practice and Applications
- tracing paper
- metric ruler
- tape and scissors

Assessment Options

EMBEDDED ASSESSMENT
- Identify and name prisms
  Exercises 2, 3, 7, 9
- Predict the shape a net will form
  Exercises 4, 5, 10(a)
- Identify vertices, edges, and faces of a polyhedron
  Exercises 10(c), 11, 12
- Draw a prism
  Exercises 10(d), 14,
- Understand the concept of volume
  Exercises 15, 17, 24
- Develop and use a formula for finding the volume of a prism
  Exercises 19, 23, 30

PERFORMANCE TASK/PORTFOLIO
- Exercise 14 on *p. 449* (open-ended)
- Exercises 24 and 25 on *p. 450*
- Exercise 31 on *p. 450* (challenge)
- Exercise 32 on *p. 450* (research)

QUIZZES/TESTS
- Section 1 Quick Quiz

TEST GENERATOR

Section 1 Overview

In this section, students will be introduced to prisms and their volumes through a discussion of the Empire State Building. As students learn about prisms, they will study many new terms, including *cubic unit, parallel planes, polyhedron, right prism, oblique prism, net, base of a prism, face, edge, vertex,* and *volume.*

Exploration 1
Students build and use nets to explore the characteristics of different polyhedra and to learn to identify and classify prisms. The distinction between right and oblique prisms is made. So that they might better understand drawings of 3-dimensional figures, students will practice drawing their own prisms. To do this, they will learn to draw the bases of the prism first and then connect pairs of corresponding vertices with line segments.

Exploration 2
By using centimeter cubes to construct physical models of prisms and looking for patterns, students will derive the formula *volume = area of the base • height* for the volume of a right or an oblique prism. Students use nets to build both right and oblique prisms. The introduction of oblique prisms in this section helps emphasize that the height of a prism is the perpendicular distance between the two parallel bases.

Guide for Assigning Homework

REGULAR SCHEDULING (45 MIN CLASS PERIOD)			EXERCISES TO NOTE		
Section/ P&A Pages	**Core** **Assignment**	**Extended** **Assignment**	**Additional** **Practice/Review**	**Open-ended** **Problems**	**Extended** **Problems**
1 pp. 448–451	**Day 1:** 1–14 **Day 2:** 15–17, SR 33–34 **Day 3:** 18–28, 30, ROS 32	1–14 15–17, SR 33–34 18–31, ROS 32	EP, p. 451	PA 14	PA 30 Challenge, PA 31

Key: PA = Practice & Application; ROS = Reflecting on the Section; SR = Spiral Review; TB = Toolbox; EP = Extra Skill Practice; Ext = Extension; ST = Standardized Testing

Math Background and Teaching Strategies

Classroom Notes

Bulletin board display ideas for this section include:

- information about Leonhard Euler

- display of student nets for Practice and Application Exercise 31

Student interest centers for this section might include:

- materials for making nets of prisms

- volume activities with centimeter cubes such as "construct prisms that have a volume of 12 cm³."

Math Strands

Topic Integration and Spiraling

Exploration 1
Spatial visualization skills are developed through folding nets to make polyhedra and by drawing prisms on paper so they appear 3-dimensional. In the process, students learn and use vocabulary associated with 3-dimensional figures: *parallel planes*, *polyhedron*, *right prism*, *oblique prism*, *base of a prism*, *face*, *edge*, and *vertex*. The study of polyhedra leads students to look for patterns within geometric figures and helps them discover *Euler's formula* for the relationship among the number of faces (f), vertices (v), and edges (e) of a polyhedron: $e = f + v - 2$. This formula can also be written in terms of the number of faces or the number of vertices, by solving the equation for the desired unknown.

Drawing polyhedra helps build students' understanding of parallel planes and of edges as segments joining corresponding vertices. Students will need to be able to sketch and interpret drawings of polyhedra in Books 2 and 3 as they use a compass and straightedge to construct nets and calculate surface areas and volumes.

Exploration 2
The hands-on approach is continued in Exploration 2, where centimeter cubes are used to develop and explore the concept of volume. Students use patterns to develop the formula for the volume of a prism. The exposure to oblique prisms will be new to most students and may require some additional discussion.

Volumes of cylinders will be covered in Section 4 of this module. Volume will be used in Module 8 where students study the relationship between volume and metric capacity. In Book 2, volume is extended to include pyramids and cones. Book 3 includes additional work with the volumes of prisms, cylinders, pyramids, and cones, as well as volumes of combined 3-dimensional figures.

438D

Section 2 Weight in the Customary System

Section 2 Planner

Section Objectives

Exploration 1
- Use appropriate customary units to estimate and measure weight
- Convert between customary units of weight

Days for Section 2

First Day
Setting the Stage, *p. 452*
Exploration 1, *pp. 453–454*
Key Concepts, *p. 455*

Teaching Resources

Teacher's Resource Book
- Warm-Up
- Practice and Applications
- Study Guide
See page 439 for additional teaching resources.

Materials List

Setting the Stage
- Net 2 from Labsheet 1A

Exploration 1
- a scale
- a coffee mug
- a stapler

Assessment Options

EMBEDDED ASSESSMENT
- Use appropriate customary units to estimate and measure weight
  Exercises 3, 4, 6, 14
- Convert between customary units of weight
  Exercises 10, 11, 12, 17(a)

PERFORMANCE TASK/PORTFOLIO
- Exercises 5 and 6 on *p. 456 (open-ended)*
- Exercise 19 on *p. 457 (visual thinking)*
- Extended Exploration on *p. 460**

* *indicates a problem-solving task that can be assessed using the Assessment Scales*

QUIZZES/TESTS
- Section 2 Quick Quiz

TEST GENERATOR

Section 2 Overview

In this section, an exploration of the Great Pyramid at Giza will introduce students to another polyhedron, the *pyramid*, and customary units of weight.

Exploration 1
Students begin by comparing the weight in tons of the Great Pyramid with the weight of the Empire State Building. Ounces and pounds are then introduced and their relationship to tons is given. Students are given benchmarks for an ounce and a ton and then choose their own benchmark for a pound. Students practice estimating weights and choosing an appropriate unit of weight to weigh an item. Methods for converting between units of measure are reviewed and are then applied to units of weight.

Guide for Assigning Homework

REGULAR SCHEDULING (45 MIN CLASS PERIOD)			EXERCISES TO NOTE		
Section/ P&A Pages	Core Assignment	Extended Assignment	Additional Practice/Review	Open-ended Problems	Extended Problems
2 pp. 456–458	**Day 1:** 1–18, ROS 19, SR 20–23	1–18, ROS 19, SR 20–23, 24–25	EP, p. 459	PA 5, 6	Career Connect 24–25 E², p. 460

Key: PA = Practice & Application; ROS = Reflecting on the Section; SR = Spiral Review; TB = Toolbox; EP = Extra Skill Practice; Ext = Extension; ST = Standardized Testing

Math Background and Teaching Strategies

Classroom Notes

Bulletin board display ideas for this section include:

- benchmarks for ounces, pounds, and tons

- information on the Great Pyramid at Giza and the Empire State Building, showing comparisons of their weights

- Students' items for Practice and Applications Exercises 5 and 6

- Students' E² solutions

Math Strands

Topic Spiraling and Integration

Exploration 1

In this exploration students continue their study of customary units of measure by exploring customary units of weight. In Module 5, students estimated and measured using customary units of length and learned to convert between measures. Once customary units of weight are introduced, students apply the same techniques to convert between measures of weight. Skills with fraction and mixed number multiplication are employed.

Students continue to build their resource of benchmarks for estimating by including benchmarks for ounce, pound, and ton.

In Module 8, students will develop benchmarks for customary units of capacity and apply techniques for converting between the measures for capacity. Students will continue to convert between customary units of measure in Modules 3 and 7 of Book 2.

Section 3 Circles and Circumference

Section 3 Planner

Section Objectives

Exploration 1
- Identify the parts of a circle
- Use a compass to draw a circle

Exploration 2
- Develop and use a formula to find the circumference of a circle

Days for Section 3

First Day
Setting the Stage, *p. 461*
Exploration 1, *pp. 462–463*

Second Day
Exploration 2 through Question 15, *pp. 464–465*

Third Day
Exploration 2 from Question 16, *p. 465*
Key Concepts, *p. 466*

Teaching Resources

Teacher's Resource Book
- Warm-Up
- Labsheets 3A and 3B
- Practice and Applications
- Study Guide
See page 439 for additional teaching resources.

Materials List

Exploration 1
- 30-cm long piece of string
- two pencils
- compass
- ruler

Exploration 2
- Labsheet 3A
- string
- meter stick
- 4 circular objects
- calculator
- clear ruler

Practice and Applications
- Labsheet 3B
- compass
- straightedge
- drawing paper
- colored pencils or markers

Assessment Options

EMBEDDED ASSESSMENT
- Identify the parts of a circle
  Exercises 1, 2, 3
- Use a compass to draw a circle
  Exercises 4, 5
- Develop and use a formula to find the circumference of a circle
  Exercises 9, 10, 11, 14

PERFORMANCE TASK/PORTFOLIO
- Exercise 7 on *p. 467*
- Exercise 14 on *p. 468 (estimation)*
- Exercise 17 on *p. 468 (challenge)*
- Exercise 18 on *p. 468 (journal)*
- Exercise 29 on *p. 469 (extension)*

QUIZZES/TESTS
- Section 3 Quick Quiz
- Mid-Module Quiz

TEST GENERATOR

Section 3 Overview

In this section, students will explore circles using the Circus Maximus as a model.

Exploration 1
Students learn to identify the parts of a circle. Key terms include *circle, center, radius, chord,* and *diameter.* Students practice using a compass to draw circles and compare the lengths of the radii and diameters to develop the relationship that the diameter is twice the length of the radius. Students also compare the length of the diameter to other chords in a circle to discover that the diameter is the longest chord in a circle.

Exploration 2
Students gather data about the diameters and circumferences of various circular objects by measuring with a ruler and string. Then they make a scatter plot of their data and use it to estimate the circumferences of circles with given diameters. By examining the ratio of the circumference of each circle to its diameter, students discover the pi ratio and develop a formula for finding the circumference of a circle.

Guide for Assigning Homework

REGULAR SCHEDULING (45 MIN CLASS PERIOD)			EXERCISES TO NOTE		
Section/ P&A Pages	Core Assignment	Extended Assignment	Additional Practice/Review	Open-ended Problems	Extended Problems
3 pp. 467–470	**Day 1:** 1–7 **Day 2:** SR 19–27 **Day 3:** 8–16, ROS 18	1–7 SR 19–27, Ext 28–29 8–17, ROS 18	EP, p. 470	PA 16 Ext 29	PA 7 Challenge, PA 17 Ext 28–29

Key: PA = Practice & Application; ROS = Reflecting on the Section; SR = Spiral Review; TB = Toolbox; EP = Extra Skill Practice; Ext = Extension; ST = Standardized Testing

Math Background and Teaching Strategies

Classroom Notes

Bulletin board displays for this section include:

- parts of a circle and the circumference formula

- student created designs from Extension Exercise 29

Math Strands

Topic Spiraling and Integration

Exploration 1
Knowing the parts of a circle is an important prerequisite skill for Exploration 2, where students explore circumference. It is also important in Section 4, where students develop a formula for finding the area of a circle and use it to calculate the volumes of cylinders. A circle is determined by its center and radius. This fact is reinforced by the opening of the compass and placement of the compass point when drawing circles. Drawing circles with different radii helps develop the concept that the circumference of a circle is related to the length of its radius.

Exploration 2
Circumference is explored by measuring the diameters and circumferences of a variety of circular objects. The data are represented in a scatter plot and students apply the idea of a fitted line from Module 6 Section 3 to look for a relationship between the diameters and the circumferences of the circles. Because students' measurements are not exact, the data will not be exactly linear, but the points should lie very close to the fitted line. The fitted line is used to predict the circumferences of circles with given diameters and then to develop a formula for finding the circumference of a circle.

Most calculators have a π key that displays π to seven or more decimal places. This often gives students the impression that using the π key instead of 3.14 gives the exact circumference. It is important for students to understand that this is not so. Using the π key instead of 3.14 gives a more precise estimate of the circumference, but it is still not exact. Since π is an irrational number that does not terminate or repeat, any number used for π is merely an approximation. So to give the exact circumference, the π symbol must remain in the expression.

In Book 2, students will continue to study circumference and will use compasses to construct circular cipher disks. In Book 3, compass constructions are extended to include nets for polyhedra. Circumference calculations will be important in Module 4 as students find the lateral surface area of a cylinder.

Section 4 · Circles and Cylinders

Section 4 Planner

Section Objectives

Exploration 1
- Develop and use a formula for the area of a circle

Exploration 2
- Recognize a cylinder
- Develop and use a formula for the volume of a cylinder

Days for Section 4

First Day
Setting the Stage, *p. 471*
Exploration 1, *pp. 472–474*

Second Day
Exploration 2, *pp. 475–476*
Key Concepts, *p. 477*

Teaching Resources

Teacher's Resource Book
- Warm-Up
- Labsheets 4A–4E
- Practice and Applications
- Study Guide
See page 439 for additional teaching resources.

Materials List

Exploration 1
- Labsheet 4A

Exploration 2
- Labsheets 4B–4D
- scissors
- tape
- rice
- a ruler

Practice and Applications
- Labsheet 4E
- graph paper
- scissors
- tape
- rice or dry cereal
- a ruler

Assessment Options

EMBEDDED ASSESSMENT
- Find the area of a circle
  Exercises 2, 6, 7, 9
- Find the volume of a cylinder
  Exercises 16, 17, 20

PERFORMANCE TASK/PORTFOLIO
- Exercise 21 on *p. 479 (challenge)*
- Exercise 22 on *p. 479 (visual thinking)*
- Exercises 34–39 on *p. 480 (extension)*
- Standardized Testing on *p. 481 (performance task)*

QUIZZES/TESTS
- Section 4 Quick Quiz

TEST GENERATOR

Section 4 Overview

In this section, students continue working with circles. Using a special room in the Indian cliff dwellings at Mesa Verde as a model, students will learn how to calculate the area of a circle and the volume of a cylinder.

Exploration 1
Students begin by estimating the area of a circle using inscribed and circumscribed squares. Then they use the squares model to develop a formula for the area of a circle. When using the formula $A = \pi r^2$ to find the area of a circle, students use either the approximation 3.14 or the π key on a calculator to find the approximate area. They learn to write the exact area of a circle by leaving the symbol π in their answer.

Exploration 2
Students study the volumes of two cylinders by comparing their base and volume to the base and volume of two square prisms with the same height as the cylinder. Then they solve problems involving volumes of cylinders using the general formula *volume = area of base · height,* the same formula they learned for the volume of a prism.

In the Extension exercises on page 480, students investigate the volume of a cone based on its relationship to a cylinder.

Guide for Assigning Homework

Key: PA = Practice & Application; ROS = Reflecting on the Section; SR = Spiral Review; TB = Toolbox; EP = Extra Skill Practice; Ext = Extension; ST = Standardized Testing

Math Background and Teaching Strategies

Classroom Notes

Bulletin board displays for this section include:

- information on and pictures of Mesa Verde

- parts of a circle; formulas for the circumference and area of a circle and the volume of a cylinder

Interest centers for this section might include:

- books on Mesa Verde and kivas

- different size cylindrical containers that students order by their volumes and then measure to check

Math Strands

Topic Spiraling and Integration

Exploration 1
Students continue their study of circles from Section 3 of this module.

Students first estimate the area of a circle with a radius of 4 units by averaging the areas of an inscribed square and a circumscribed square. Then they generalize the method by using r for the radius. This yields the expression $3r^2$ that can be used to estimate the area of any circle. This expression is then compared to the formula $A = \pi r^2$. As was done in Section 3, the distinction between using an approximation for π and the exact value is emphasized. Areas of circles will be used in Exploration 2 to find the volumes of cylinders.

Exploration 2
In this exploration, students compare and contrast cylinders and prisms and learn how to calculate the volume of a cylinder. Students' prior exposure to cylinders has probably been limited to right cylinders, so it is important that students use the net on the labsheets to build an oblique

cylinder. They should also understand that the base of a cylinder can be any non-polygon shape, so not all cylinders are circular. Students should recognize that oblique cylinders have characteristics (such as congruent parallel bases and heights that are the perpendicular distance between the bases) similar to those of the oblique prisms they studied in Section 1.

Volumes of prisms from Section 1 are used as the basis for developing the formula for volume of a cylinder. The approach is similar to the one used to develop the formula for the area of a circle in Exploration 1, only in three dimensions instead of two.

The study of cylinders and their volumes continues in Books 2 and 3.

Section 5 Temperature, Integers, and Coordinate Graphs

Section 5 Planner

Section Objectives

Exploration 1
- Use benchmarks to estimate Celsius and Fahrenheit temperatures
- Use integers to represent real life situations
- Compare integers
- Find solutions for simple inequalities with integers, such as $x < -3$

Exploration 2
- Graph points with integer coordinates on a coordinate grid

Days for Section 5

First Day
Setting the Stage, *p. 482*
Exploration 1, *pp. 483–485*

Second Day
Exploration 2, *pp. 486–488*
Key Concepts, *p. 489*

Teaching Resources

Teacher's Resource Book
- Warm-Up
- Labsheet 5A
- Practice and Applications
- Study Guide
See page 439 for additional teaching resources.

Materials List

Exploration 2
- Labsheet 5A
- metric ruler
- compass (optional)
- graph paper

Practice and Applications
- graph paper
- protractor

Assessment Options

EMBEDDED ASSESSMENT
- Use benchmarks to estimate Celsius and Fahrenheit temperatures
  Exercises 2, 3, 4
- Use integers to represent real life situations
  Exercises 10, 11, 20, 21
- Compare Integers
  Exercises 15, 16, 17, 22(b)
- Find solutions for simple inequalities with integers
  Exercise 19
- Graph points with integer coordinates on a coordinate grid
  Exercises 24, 25(a)

PERFORMANCE TASK/PORTFOLIO
- Exercise 14 on *p. 490*
- Exercise 25(a) on *p. 492 (create your own)*
- Exercises 26–27 on *p. 492 (discussion)*
- Module Project on *pp. 494–495*

QUIZZES/TESTS
- Section 5 Quick Quiz
- Module Tests A and B
- Module Standardized Test
- Module Performance Assessment

TEST GENERATOR

Section 5 Overview

In this section, students finish their investigation of how mathematics is related to famous Wonders of the World by connecting integers to the travels of Marco Polo.

Exploration 1
Students begin their work with integers with a familiar application, temperature. They relate degrees above and below zero to positive and negative integers. Using benchmarks, they estimate temperatures in both degrees Fahrenheit and degrees Celsius. They then use a number line as a model for comparing integers.

Exploration 2
The number line is extended to a coordinate grid where students discuss location in terms of latitude and longitude. They play the game *On the Trail of Marco Polo*, which will require graphing integers in all four quadrants on a coordinate grid.

Guide for Assigning Homework

Section/ P&A Pages	Core Assignment	Extended Assignment	Additional Practice/Review	Open-ended Problems	Extended Problems
REGULAR SCHEDULING (45 MIN CLASS PERIOD)			**EXERCISES TO NOTE**		
5 pp. 490–493	**Day 1:** 1–22 **Day 2:** 24, ROS 26–27, SR 28–35	1–23 24–25, ROS 26–27, SR 28–35	EP, p. 493 Review & Assessment, pp. 496–497	PA 19, 25 ST, p. 493	Challenge, PA 23 Mod Proj, pp. 494–495

Key: PA = Practice & Application; ROS = Reflecting on the Section; SR = Spiral Review; TB = Toolbox; EP = Extra Skill Practice; Ext = Extension; ST = Standardized Testing

Math Background and Teaching Strategies

Classroom Notes

Bulletin board display ideas for this section include:

- an enlarged copy of Student Resource page (p. 483)
- additional information on Marco Polo and his travels
- a number line with negative and positive integers and zero identified

Interest centers might include:

- a copy of *The Great Travelers* or other books on Marco Polo for students to read

Math Strands

Topic Spiraling and Integration

In this section students expand their knowledge of the number system to include integers.

Exploration 1

Integers are introduced through the familiar context of temperature. Comparison of integers is introduced by comparing temperatures and extended to graphing on a number line. Students will be exposed to integer addition and subtraction in Module 8 of Book 1 and continue their studies of integer operations in Books 2 and 3 using different models to perform integer operations. Representation of integers on a number line provides an important model for adding and subtracting integers in Module 1 of Book 2. In Books 2 and 3, students will see additional real world connections to integers as they study contour maps, determine wind-chill temperatures, and explore the use of integers to create video games and special effects.

Exploration 2

In Section 4 of Module 4, students learned to graph ordered pairs in the first quadrant of a coordinate grid. Now, with the knowledge of integers gained in Exploration 1, coordinate graphing is extended to all four quadrants. Graphing in four quadrants is an important skill, used widely in Books 2 and 3 for graphing equations and for analyzing motion in transformational geometry.

Module 7

OVERVIEW

An exploration of intriguiging or impressive structures around the world leads to work with measurement and geometric figures, including the use of formulas. Themes include the Empire State Building, the Great Pyramid at Giza, and Mesa Verde. Fraction and decimal computation skills are used to convert units and to find areas and volumes. Students also work with integers and coordinate graphs.

PREREQUISITE SKILLS

Warm-Up Exercises for each section are provided in the *Teacher's Resource Book*. You can use these exercises to review skills and concepts students will need for each section. In addition, the Spiral Review exercises at the end of each section in the student edition provide practice on prerequisite skills.

MODULE DIAGNOSTIC TEST

The Module Diagnostic Test in the *Teacher's Resource Book* can be used to assess students' prior knowledge of skills and concepts that will be taught in each section of this module. You can use test results to help structure your teaching to meet the diverse needs of your classroom.

MODULE 7 WONDERS of the WORLD

438

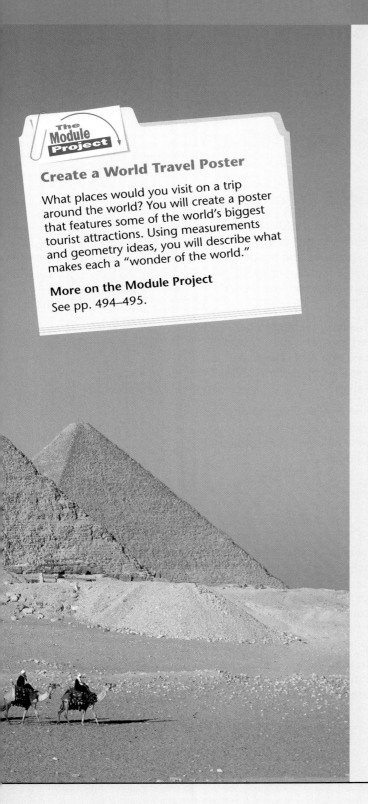

The Module Project

Create a World Travel Poster

What places would you visit on a trip around the world? You will create a poster that features some of the world's biggest tourist attractions. Using measurements and geometry ideas, you will describe what makes each a "wonder of the world."

More on the Module Project
See pp. 494–495.

CONNECTING
MATH&EMATICS
The & Theme

MODULE 7 — SECTION OVERVIEW

1 Three-Dimensional Geometry

As you study the Empire State Building:

◆ Recognize and name prisms
◆ Draw prisms
◆ Find volumes of prisms
◆ Use nets for polyhedra

2 Weight in the Customary System

As you explore the Great Pyramid:

◆ Measure weight in customary units
◆ Convert customary units of weight

3 Circles and Circumference

As you explore the Circus Maximus:

◆ Use a compass to draw a circle
◆ Identify parts of a circle
◆ Find circumference

4 Circles and Cylinders

As you learn about Mesa Verde:

◆ Find areas of circles
◆ Find volumes of cylinders

5 Temperature, Integers, and Coordinate Graphs

As you learn about Marco Polo:

◆ Measure temperature in °F and °C
◆ Compare integers
◆ Graph ordered pairs of integers

INTERNET
Resources and practice at
classzone.com

Module Resources

TEACHER'S RESOURCE BOOK
Resources
- *The Math Gazette* (parent newsletter)
- Warm-Ups
- Labsheets
- Practice and Applications
- Study Guide

Assessment
- Section Quick Quizzes
- Mid-Module Quiz
- Module 7 Diagnostic Test
- Module 7 Tests A and B
- Module 7 Standardized Test
- Module 7 Performance Assessment

SPANISH RESOURCES
- *The Math Gazette* (parent newsletter)
- Practice and Applications
- Assessment
- Spanish Glossary

STUDENT WORKBOOK

TECHNOLOGY BOOK

TECHNOLOGY RESOURCES
- @Home Tutor
- Test Generator
- Activity Generator
- Professional Development DVD
- Online Activities

Setting the Stage

About the Theme

As students explore different architectural wonders throughout the world, they will learn about the related mathematics concepts of volume, mass, circumference, area, and coordinates. In this section, students develop their spatial visualization skills by sketching 3-dimensional figures and constructing polyhedra from nets and using centimeter cubes.

Getting Started

Module 7 Section 1 *Warm-Up* assesses student facility with finding areas of rectangles and triangles. In this section, students will use the area of a prism's base to calculate its volume.

To give students an idea of the great height of the Empire State Building, you can determine an appropriate scale (such as 1 cm = 10 ft) and then model the height using blocks. Next to the model of the Empire State Building, use blocks to show the height of your school or some other building in your town. Students can compare the heights visually by looking at the models, as well as by considering the number values given in the reading.

Section 1   Three-Dimensional Geometry

IN THIS SECTION

EXPLORATION 1
♦ Figures in Space

EXPLORATION 2
♦ Volumes of Prisms

Race to the SKY

·-Setting the Stage

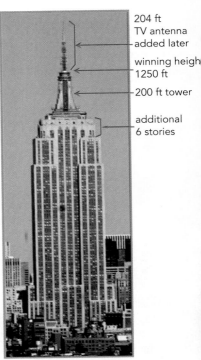

204 ft
TV antenna
added later

winning height
1250 ft

200 ft tower

additional
6 stories

Empire State Building
Tallest Building,
1931–1972

The biggest race in the 1920s and 1930s was not happening at the racetrack. In New York City, planners and builders were engaged in a frantic race to the sky. Who, everyone wondered, would build the tallest building in the world?

The Chrysler building seemed to be complete. Then a surprise spire "popped out" of the building's roof. The spire had been secretly assembled inside the building's fire shaft.

To compete, the Empire State Building added six stories and a 200 ft tower to its plans. With these changes, it became the world's tallest building.

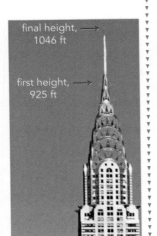

final height,
1046 ft

first height,
925 ft

Chrysler Building
Tallest Building,
1930–1931

Think About It

1 The Empire State Building has 102 stories, not including the TV antenna. About how high do you think each story is? about 12 ft

2 In the original plan, the Empire State Building contained 36 million cubic feet of space. What do you think a cubic foot is? **Sample Response:** A square foot is a square 1 ft on each side, so I think a cubic foot is a cube 1 ft on each side.

▶ The Empire State Building and the Great Pyramid at Giza are amazing structures. In this module, you will investigate the mathematics related to these and other modern *Wonders of the World*.

Exploration 1

Figures in Space

SET UP *Work with a partner. You will need: • Labsheet 1A • tape • scissors • index card*

▶ Before the 200-ft tower was added, the Empire State Building was a *polyhedron*. A **polyhedron** is a three-dimensional object made up of flat surfaces, or **faces**, shaped like polygons. For example, a cube is a polyhedron with square faces.

3 Try This as a Class Explain whether or not each object is a polyhedron.

a.

a pyramid

b.

a cylinder

▶ Models of some polyhedra can be made from *nets*. A **net** is a flat pattern that can be cut out and folded to form a three-dimensional object. Nets can provide a useful way to model large buildings.

4 a. Use Labsheet 1A. Use *Net 1* or *Net 2*. Have your partner use the other net. Follow these steps to fold the nets.

First	Next	Then
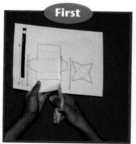		
Cut on the solid lines.	Fold on the dotted lines.	Tape the faces together.

  b. For each polyhedron, describe the shapes of the faces. Are there any pairs of faces that are congruent? If so, which ones?

GOAL

LEARN HOW TO...
◆ recognize prisms
◆ draw prisms
◆ fold a flat pattern to form a polyhedron

AS YOU...
◆ develop spatial visualization skills

KEY TERMS
◆ polyhedron (plural: polyhedra)
◆ face
◆ net
◆ parallel planes
◆ prism
◆ base of a prism
◆ edge
◆ vertex (plural: vertices)
◆ oblique prism
◆ right prism

3. a. Yes; The pyramid is a 3-dimensional object and all of its faces are flat surfaces shaped like either triangles or a square.
   b. No; A circle is not a polygon.

4. a. Check students' work.
   b. Net 1: 4 rectangles, 2 trapezoids; 3 of the rectangles are congruent and both of the trapezoids are congruent
   Net 2: a square, 4 triangles; all the triangles are congruent

---

Exploration 1

ALTERNATIVE APPROACH
Question 3 If you have access to a 3-dimensional model set or can collect various food containers or packaging, present a figure to the class and have them decide if it fits the definition of polyhedron. Alternatively, give each partner pair a figure and have them decide and then explain their decision to the class. The objects can then be used as extra practice for sketching nets, determining congruent faces, and identifying faces, vertices, and edges.

TEACHER NOTES
Students will use Net 2 from Labsheet 1A again in Section 2 of this module. If possible collect the nets for use again in Section 2.

Section 1 Three-Dimensional Geometry **441**

441

Exploration 1 continued

DEVELOPING MATH CONCEPTS

In any prism, all the faces except the bases must be parallelograms. Note that the faces in a prism are rectangles only when it is a right prism. (Students may need to be reminded that a rectangle is a parallelogram.) You may want to make the distinction between rectangular and non-rectangular parallelogram faces after students are exposed to oblique prisms in **Question 9** and again after students build an oblique prism in **Question 19** of Exploration 2.

8. b. The number of edges of a polyhedron is more than either the number of faces or the number of vertices, but it is always 2 less than the total number of faces and vertices.

5 a. Set the polyhedron made from *Net 1* on one of its trapezoidal faces. Place an index card on the other trapezoidal face.
Check that students have the polyhedron on a trapezoidal face.

b. Discussion Recall that a plane is a flat surface that extends forever. The index card models a plane. The surface the polyhedron rests on models another plane. The two planes are **parallel planes**. What does it mean for planes to be parallel?
The two planes will never intersect.

▶ A **prism** is a polyhedron in which two of the faces, the **bases**, are congruent and lie in parallel planes. The other faces are shaped like parallelograms.

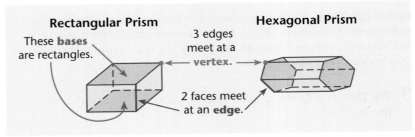

Rectangular Prism

These **bases** are rectangles.

3 edges meet at a **vertex**.

2 faces meet at an **edge**.

Hexagonal Prism

6 a. Based on the prisms shown above, how do you think prisms are named?
Prisms are named by their bases.
b. What kind of prism is shown at the right?
a triangular prism

7 Try This as a Class Explain whether or not each polyhedron is a prism. If it is, what type of prism is it?

a. the polyhedron made from *Net 1* Yes; trapezoidal prism

b. the polyhedron made from *Net 2*
No; It does not have two parallel bases, no matter which face you set it on.

8 a. Copy and complete the table for the prisms shown above and the polyhedra made from *Nets 1* and *2*. See margin.

▲
In 1750, Leonhard Euler, a Swiss mathematician, observed a relationship among the number of faces, vertices, and edges of a polyhedron. Question 8 explores this relationship.

	Number of Faces	Number of Vertices	Number of Edges
Rectangular Prism	?	?	?
Hexagonal Prism	?	?	?
Polyhedron from Net 1	?	?	?
Polyhedron from Net 2	?	?	?

b. How does the number of edges of a polyhedron appear to be related to the number of faces and vertices?

c. Write an equation for the relationship in part (b). $F + V - 2 = E$ where F is the number of faces, V is the number of vertices, and E is the number of edges.

 Module 7 Wonders of the World

8. a. See Additional Answers beginning on page A1.

9 Discussion The prisms at the right are **oblique prisms**. The prisms on page 442 are **right prisms**. How are oblique prisms and right prisms different?

▶ **Drawing Three-dimensional Objects** You may be able to understand drawings of three-dimensional objects better if you learn how to draw them yourself. Here is one way to draw a prism.

Step 1 Draw one base.

Step 2 Copy the base behind and to one side of it. The bases may overlap.

Step 3 Connect pairs of corresponding vertices. Show hidden edges with dashed segments.

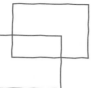 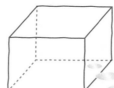 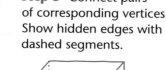

You may need to erase and redraw an edge.

10 a. Use the steps above to draw a pentagonal prism.

b. Is the relationship among the number of faces, vertices, and edges you found in Question 8(c) true for a pentagonal prism? Explain. **Yes; It has 10 vertices, 7 faces and 15 edges.**
$$10 + 7 - 2 = 15$$

11 ✔ CHECKPOINT Choose the letter of the polyhedron that can be formed from this net. **B**

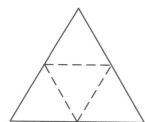

A.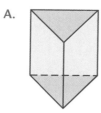

B.

HOMEWORK EXERCISES ▶ See Exs. 1–14 on pp. 448–449.

---

9. In an oblique prism, the edges joining the vertices of the bases aren't perpendicular to the bases. The prisms are slanted when sitting on one of the bases.

10. a. Check students' drawings. Sample Response:

✔ QUESTION 11

...checks that you can use a net to visualize a polyhedron.

DEVELOPING MATH CONCEPTS
It is often assumed that students do not need to be taught how to sketch what appears to many adults as simple 3-dimensional figures. In actuality, because they have never had this experience, many students have difficulty interpreting the drawings they see in textbooks. When these students need to sketch a figure, they often are not sure how to begin the sketch or how to make sure line segments are parallel and of the same length. It is important to provide opportunities for students to develop this skill and time to practice sketching. It is best if students work in pencil, since lines often need to be erased to create a 3-dimensional effect. Having drawn a figure, students then have a better visual reference when a question or exercise states, "Find the volume of a triangular prism with..." The process of drawing also helps students identify the edges, vertices, and faces of figures, as well as the parallel planes created by the faces. You might want to check with your school's art teacher to see if she or he might be able to incorporate the drawing of three-dimensional objects into art lessons.

TEACHING NOTES
For a rectangular prism like the ones drawn in Steps 1–3, point out that any pair of opposite faces can be considered the bases of the prism.

Exploration 2

TEACHING NOTES

Question 12(a) To check students' work, have them share the height and the area of the base of their prisms. List these in a table on the board, continuing until the class is convinced they have found all the possible prisms that could be built. Students who build a bottom layer of 6 cubes will not be able to stack identical layers of cubes above it as stated in the directions. These students should understand that the height of their prism is 1 cm.

TIPS FROM TEACHERS

When tracing around the base plan in **Question 12(d)**, it is helpful to remove the top layers of cubes first, then hold the bottom layer in place and trace its outline.

Some students are better able to understand the concept of a base plan if it is related to a floor plan which they may have seen for a building or house.

13. a–b. See Additional Answers beginning on page A1.

444

GOAL

LEARN HOW TO...
• find the volumes of prisms

AS YOU...
• build prisms using centimeter cubes
• fold nets to form prisms

KEY TERMS
• volume
• cubic unit
• cubic centimeter (cm³)

Exploration 2

Volumes of Prisms

SET UP Work with a partner. You will need: • Labsheet 1B • ruler • tape • scissors • centimeter cubes

▶ As the height of the Empire State Building increased, the amount of space it contained, its **volume**, also increased. Volume is measured in **cubic units**.

This is a centimeter cube. Its volume is 1 **cubic centimeter** (1 cm³).

12 a. On a sheet of paper, use centimeter cubes to build a prism with a volume of 6 cm³. Make the bottom, or *base*, in the shape of a rectangle, and stack identical layers of cubes above it.
Answers will vary.

b. How many cubes did you use? 6

c. What is the height of your prism?
Answers will vary. Heights should be either 1, 2, 3, or 6

d. Trace around the base of your prism. Use your tracing, or *base plan*, to find the area of the base.
Answers will vary. Check students' work.

13 a. Copy the table. You will fill it in as you build prisms. See margin.

Number of layers	Height (cm)	Area of base (cm²)	Volume (cm³)
1	?	6	?
2	?	6	?
3	?	6	?
4	?	6	?

Base Plan
2 cm
3 cm

b. Use the base plan shown at the left. Build a prism by stacking identical layers of centimeter cubes. Each time you add a layer, fill in a row of the table. See margin.

c. Use your completed table. How is the volume of your prism related to its height and the area of its base?
The volume is the product of the height and the area of the base.

 Module 7 Wonders of the World

14 Discussion The prisms below were made from centimeter cubes. Find the volume of each prism. Explain your method.

a.

$9 \cdot 3 = 27 \text{ cm}^3$

b.

$12 \cdot 2 = 24 \text{ cm}^3$

c.

$3 \cdot 4 = 12 \text{ cm}^3$

Use Labsheet 1B. For Exercises 15–17, use *Net 3*.

15 a. Predict what prism *Net 3* will make. **right rectangular prism**

b. Fold the net. Leave the top open. **Check students' work.**

c. Did you get the prism you expected? Explain. **Answers will vary.**

d. If you can, use centimeter cubes to find the volume of the prism you made in part (a). **24 cm³**

e. Remove any centimeter cubes from the prism and tape down the top. **Check students' work.**

16 a. Which pairs of faces are parallel and congruent?
Opposite faces are parallel and congruent.

b. Which pairs of faces could be bases for the prism?
All pairs could be bases.

17 a. How can you find the volume of the prism without using cubes?

b. Use your method to find the volume.
$(3 \cdot 4) \cdot 2 = 12 \cdot 2 = 24 \text{ cm}^3$

17. a. Measure the length, width, and height. Use the length and width to find the area of the base and multiply it by the height of the prism.

▶ **Prisms that do not have rectangular bases can also be built by beginning with a base plan and stacking identical layers of centimeter cubes.**

18 a. For each base plan below, stack identical layers of centimeter cubes until each prism is the indicated height. Record the number of cubes you used to build each prism. **15 cubes; 14 cubes**

Prism 1

height = 3 cm

Prism 2

height = 2 cm

b. What kind of polygon is used for the base of Prism 2? What do you call this prism? **octagon; octagonal prism**

c. Is the relationship you found in Question 13(c) for rectangular prisms also true for these prisms? Explain.

18. c. Yes; You can multiply the area of the base by the height.

Section 1   Three-Dimensional Geometry   445

DIFFERENTIATED INSTRUCTION
Students who need extra help understanding volume can use centimeter cubes to build more prisms. You could specify a certain volume and have students choose a height and an area for the base, or you could specify a certain area for the base and have students choose a height and determine the volume.

446

---

19 Use Labsheet 1B. Repeat Questions 15–17 using *Net 4*. **See margin.**

20 **a.** Set the prism you made from *Net 4* on one of its square faces. **Check that students have set the prism on the correct face.**

b. If the square is the base of the prism, what kind of prism did *Net 4* form? **an oblique square prism**

c. Has the volume of the prism changed from what you found in Question 19? Explain. **No; It still holds the same amount, only the orientation has changed.**

d. What is the area of the base of the prism? **16 cm²**

e. What is the height of the prism? **3 cm**

f. **Discussion** How did you measure the height of the prism? **See margin.**

g. How is the volume of the prism related to its height and the area of its base? **Volume = area of the base · height of the prism**

21 **Try This as a Class**

a. What is the height of a prism? **The height is the perpendicular distance between the bases of the prism.**

b. Explain how to find the volume of a prism without using cubes. **Volume = area of the base · height of the prism**

▶ You can find the volume of any prism if you know its height and the area of its base.

22 ✔ **CHECKPOINT** Find the volume of each prism.

a. right hexagonal prism **36 cm³**

Area = 9 cm²
4 cm

b. right trapezoidal prism **13.02 cm³**

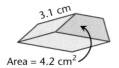
3.1 cm
Area = 4.2 cm²

c. right triangular prism **48 cm³**

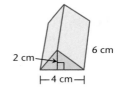
2 cm
6 cm
4 cm

23 Although the Empire State Building is not a rectangular prism, it can be approximated by one. Suppose the prism is 1000 ft tall and has a volume of 36 million cubic feet. List three possible pairs of lengths and widths for its base plan. **See margin.**

HOMEWORK EXERCISES ▶ See Exs. 15–32 on pp. 449–450.

Module 7 Wonders of the World

Section 1
Key Concepts

Parts of a Polyhedron (pp. 441–442)
A polyhedron is a three-dimensional object made up of flat surfaces, or faces, shaped like polygons. Pairs of faces meet in segments called edges. Edges meet in points called vertices.

Prisms (pp. 442–443)
A prism is a polyhedron with two bases that:
- are congruent.
- lie in parallel planes.

The other faces are parallelograms.
A prism is named by the shape of its bases.
The height of a prism is the perpendicular distance between its bases.

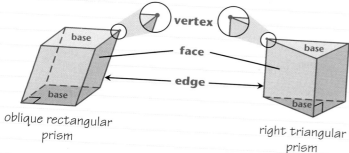

oblique rectangular prism

right triangular prism

The number of faces F, vertices V, and edges E are related by the formula $F + V - 2 = E$.

Drawing and Constructing Polyhedra (pp. 441–443)
One way to draw a prism is to draw the bases first and then connect corresponding vertices.

A net is a flat pattern that can be cut out and folded to form a three-dimensional object.

Key Terms

polyhedron (plural: polyhedra)

face

edge

vertex (plural: vertices)

prism

base of a prism

parallel planes

oblique prism

right prism

net

24. a. The net will form a right pentagonal prism. The pentagons are congruent and parallel and all the other faces are shaped like parallelograms.

Section 1   Three-Dimensional Geometry   447

24 Key Concepts Question

a. Will this net form a prism? If so, what kind of prism? Explain.

b. Describe the shapes of the faces.
Two faces, the bases, are pentagons. The other five faces are rectangles.

c. Show that the number of faces, vertices, and edges of the polyhedron satisfies the formula $F + V - 2 = E$.
7 faces, 10 vertices, and 15 edges; Yes, 7 + 10 − 2 = 15

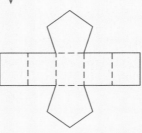

Key Concepts

CLOSURE QUESTION
Tell how to find the bases of a prism, how to name a prism, and how to find the volume of a prism.

Sample Response: The bases of a prism are two faces that are congruent and parallel to each other and leave parallelograms for all other faces. A prism is named by the shape of its bases. The volume of a prism is found by multiplying the area of a base by the height, or $V = B \cdot h$.

Key Concepts

ABSENT STUDENTS

For students who were absent for all or part of this section, the blackline Study Guide for Section 1 may be used to present the ideas, concepts, and skills of Section 1.

Practice & Applications

SUGGESTED ASSIGNMENTS

Core Course

Day 1: Exs. 1–14
Day 2: Exs. 15–17, 33–34
Day 3: Exs. 18–28, 30, 32

Extended Course

Day 1: Exs. 1–14
Day 2: Exs. 15–17, 33–34
Day 3: Exs. 18–32

Note: Extended Course assignments can be used to differentiate within the regular classroom. In classrooms where students are grouped homogeneously, the material might be covered in fewer days. In this case assignments may be combined.

ADDITIONAL PRACTICE

See the *Teacher's Resource Book* for additional practice and application exercises for this section.

Section 1

Key Terms

volume

cubic unit

cubic centimeter (cm³)

Key Concepts

Volume (pp. 444–446)

The volume of a three-dimensional object is measured in cubic units such as cubic centimeters or cubic feet.

To find the volume (V) of a prism, you can multiply the area of the base (B) by the height of the prism (h): $V = B \cdot h$

25 Key Concepts Question The area of the base of a prism is 6.25 cm². The height of the prism is 2.5 cm. What is the volume of the prism? **15.625 cm³**

Section 1

Practice & Application Exercises

YOU WILL NEED

For Ex. 10:
◆ tracing paper
◆ scissors
◆ tape

For Ex. 31:
◆ metric ruler

1. No, there are no parallel faces.

2. Yes; right hexagonal prism

3. Yes; right triangular prism

Tell whether each object is shaped like a prism. If it is, name the type of prism.

1.  **2.**  **3.**

Choose the letter of the polyhedron that can be formed with each net.

4. C **5.** B **6.** 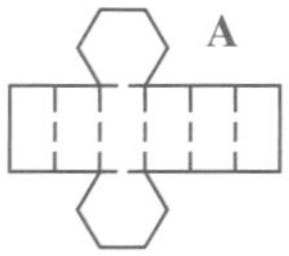 A

A.   **B.**   **C.** 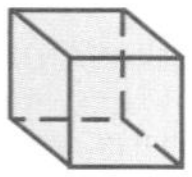 **D.**

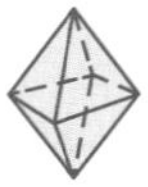

7. Name polyhedra A and C shown above. **A: right hexagonal prism; C: right square prism (or cube)**

8. Is polyhedron D shown above a prism? Why or why not? **No; It does not have a pair of parallel bases.**

448

9. Is a cube a prism? If so, what type is it? Explain.
   Yes; It is a square or rectangular prism.

10. a. Predict what shape this net will form. Trace the net.
       Then cut it out and fold it to check your prediction.
       right triangular prism
    b. Name the polyhedron you made by folding the net.
       right triangular prism
    c. How many faces, vertices, and edges does the
       polyhedron have? 5 faces, 6 vertices, 9 edges

    d. Use the methods on page 443 to draw your polyhedron.

11. A tetrahedron is a polyhedron that has 4 faces and 4 vertices.
    How many edges does a tetrahedron have?
    6 edges

12. An octahedron has 8 faces and 12 edges. How many vertices
    does an octahedron have? 6 vertices

13. Polyhedron B shown with Exercises 4–6 on page 448 is a
    tetrahedron and polyhedron D is an octahedron. Use polyhedra
    B and D to check your answers to Exercises 11 and 12.
    Check students' work.

14. **Open-ended** Find an object in your home that is shaped like a
    prism. Use the methods on page 443 to draw the object.

Find the volume of each prism built with centimeter cubes.

15.

16.

17.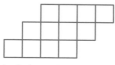

12 cm³   32 cm³   60 cm³

**Find the volume of the prism you can build with centimeter cubes
using each base plan and indicated height.**

18.
    height = 4 cm
    16 cm³

19.
    height = 5 cm
    30 cm³

20.
    height = 8 cm
    96 cm³

Find the volume of each prism.

21. right rectangular
    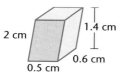
    $\frac{1}{2}$ in.
    $\frac{1}{4}$ in.
    $\frac{3}{8}$ in.

22. right triangular
    9 in.
    4 in. 6 in.

23. oblique rectangular
    2 cm
    1.4 cm
    0.6 cm
    0.5 cm

EXERCISE NOTES

Encourage students to use a
variety of methods to verify their
answers for the volume of the prisms
built in **Exercises 15–17**. They
could of course count the cubes,
accounting for those out of view.
They could find the length, width,
and height and apply the formula
for volume of a prism developed
in Exploration 2, or they could
determine the base plan and then
account for the layers of cubes
placed upon the base.

10. d. Check students'
       drawings.
       Sample
       Response:

14. Check students'
    drawings. Sample
    Response: a
    refrigerator is an
    example of a right
    rectangular prism.

21. $\frac{3}{64}$ in.³

22. 108 in.³

23. 0.42 cm³

Practice & Applications

EXERCISE NOTES

To challenge those completing the extended assignment, ask them to find 3 different ways to separate the building in **Exercise 30** into rectangular prisms. They can then compare the volumes to determine that the way the base is separated does not affect the volume of the building.

30. b. Sample Responses: Draw a line from the concave corner near the 72 ft label to the right side of the building. The two rectangular prisms are 60 ft by 180 ft by 15 ft and 108 ft by 120 ft by 15 ft.

Draw a line from the concave corner near the 72 ft label to the bottom of the building. The two rectangular prisms are 60 ft by 72 ft by 15 ft and 108 ft by 180 ft by 15 ft.

30. d. Yes; The area of the base of the building is the sum of the areas of the bases of the two rectangular prisms. Multiplying this area by the height of the building is the same as multiplying the area of the base of each rectangular prism by the height and adding the products, which is how the volume was calculated in part (c).

---

24. Volume refers to the amount of space a 3-dimensional object encloses. Area refers to the amount of surface covered by a 2-dimensional object. Height is a linear measurement.

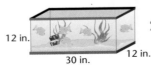
12 in.

30 in.   12 in.

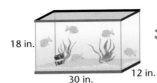
18 in.

30 in.   12 in.

25. The height of a right prism is equal to the length of an edge joining corresponding vertices of the bases; When the prism is oblique.

RESEARCH

Exercise 32 checks that you understand the meaning of volume.

31. Check students' work. Sample Response:

4 cm

2 cm   2 cm   4 cm

4 cm

---

24. Explain the differences among volume, area, and height.

25. For what type of prism is the height equal to the length of an edge joining corresponding vertices of the bases? For what type of prism is this not the case?

Replace each __?__ with the missing measurement for a prism with base area *B*, height *h*, and volume *V*.

26. $B = 40$ cm²
$h = 3$ cm
$V = $ __?__
120 cm³

27. $B = $ __?__
$h = 10$ cm
$V = 200$ cm³
20 cm²

28. $B = 18$ cm²
$h = $ __?__
$V = 72$ cm³
4 cm

29. It is recommended that pet fish be kept in tanks that hold 25 gal of water or more. Since 1 gal of water takes up 231 in.³ of space, you can divide the number of cubic inches by 231 to find the number of gallons. Does each tank at the left hold 25 gal or more?
top tank holds about 18.7 gal, no; bottom tank holds about 28.1 gal, yes

30. Visual Thinking Use the diagram.

a. The shape of this building is not a rectangular prism. Why not? The two congruent faces (the bases) are not rectangles.

b. Describe one way to separate the building into two rectangular prisms. For each prism, state the height and the length and width of a base.
See margin.

c. Find the volume of the building.
356,400 ft³

d. Is the volume of the building still the area of the base times the height? Explain.
See margin.

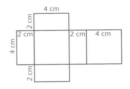
180 ft
72 ft
60 ft   180 ft
15 ft

31. Challenge Create your own net for a prism that has a volume of 32 cm³.

Reflecting ◀▶ on the Section

32. Find information about another skyscraper, including when it was built, its height, and the area of its base. Then estimate its volume. Prepare a report on your findings. Be sure to include your sources of information and the method you used to estimate the volume.
Answers will vary. Check students' work.

Spiral ◀▶ Review

33. Sketch and label a parallelogram that has a base of 4 cm and a height of 3.5 cm. Then find its area. (Module 5, p. 339)
Check students' drawings. Area = 14 cm²

34. Twelve pens cost $3.84. Use a proportion to find how much five pens cost. (Module 6, p. 401) $1.60

Section ① Extra Skill Practice

For each net, tell whether the polyhedron it will form is a prism. If it is, tell what shape the bases are and name the prism.

1.
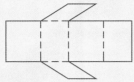

1. Yes; Possible responses: rectangles; oblique rectangular prism parallelograms; a right prism with parallelogram shaped bases

2.

2. Yes; triangles; right triangular prism

3.
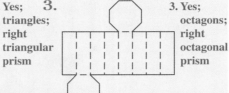

3. Yes; octagons; right octagonal prism

Find the volume of each right prism.

4.
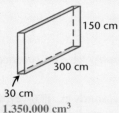
150 cm
300 cm
30 cm
1,350,000 cm³

5.

25 m
40 m
20 m
10,000 m³

6. Area = 31.7 in.²
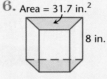
8 in.
253.6 in.³

Replace each ? with the missing measurement for a prism with a base area B, height h, and volume V.

7. $B = 17$ yd²
$h = \underline{?}$
$V = 51$ yd³
3 yd

8. $B = \underline{?}$
$h = 28$ mm
$V = 1400$ mm³
50 mm²

9. $B = 108$ cm²
$h = 21$ cm
$V = \underline{?}$
2268 cm³

Standardized Testing ◀▶ Multiple Choice

Which net will form the polyhedron shown at the right? D

A.

B.

C.

D.

Extra Skill Practice

TEACHER NOTES
For each Exploration, the corresponding Extra Skill Practice Exercises are noted.

Exploration 1: Exs. 1–3
Exploration 2: Exs. 4–9

EXTRA HELP
Teacher's Resource Book
• Practice and Applications
• Study Guide

Technology Resources
• @Home Tutor
• Test Generator

ASSESSMENT
• Section 1 Quick Quiz
• Test Generator

Setting the Stage

GETTING STARTED

Module 7 Section 2 *Warm-Up* assesses student facility with converting between customary units of length. In this section, students will employ the same methods to convert between customary units of weight.

The Great Pyramid at Giza is a major tourist attraction. It is the only one of the seven wonders of the ancient world that can still be seen today. You may want to revisit the module theme by asking, "Why do you think the Great Pyramid is classified as a Wonder of the World?" and "Why do you think it is called the *Great Pyramid*?"

TEACHING NOTES

Question 1 can be extended by asking students about how many students tall the Great Pyramid is.

Be sure students realize that in **Question 2(b)**, the given dimensions of a football field are in different units. Students should convert yards to feet before multiplying to find the area of one football field.

For **Question 3**, students will need the pyramid they folded from Net 2 on Labsheet 1A.

Section 2 — Weight in the Customary System

Setting the Stage

SET UP You will need the polyhedron from Net 2 on Labsheet 1A.

KEY TERM
◆ pyramid

The ancient Egyptians built huge stone pyramids as tombs for their rulers, or *pharaohs*. Some pyramids contained hidden rooms and secret passages. Many also held gold and other treasures.

After 4500 years, more than eighty Egyptian pyramids are still standing. The largest, the Great Pyramid at Giza, was originally about 480 ft high and has a square base with sides about 755 ft long.

▲
Some people estimate that it took about 100,000 workers twenty years to build the Great Pyramid.

Think About It

1 On a building, one story is about 10 ft high. About how many stories high was the Great Pyramid? **about 48 stories**

2 a. What is the area of the base of the Great Pyramid? **about 570,025 ft²**
   b. About how many 160 ft by 120 yd football fields would it take to cover the base of the Great Pyramid? **Accept reasonable estimates; about 10 football fields**

3 The polyhedron you folded from *Net 2* on Labsheet 1A is a **pyramid**. This polyhedron and the Great Pyramid are both square pyramids.

square base

   a. Describe the faces of a square pyramid.
      4 triangular faces and 1 square face
   b. How is a square pyramid different from a square prism? **Sample Response: A square pyramid has only 1 square base while a square prism has 2 square bases. In a square pyramid, the faces that are not bases are shaped like triangles, whereas in a square prism, the faces that are not bases are shaped like parallelograms.**

Customary U·n·i·t·s of Weight

SET UP *You will need:* • *a scale* • *a coffee mug* • *a stapler*

Building the Great Pyramid was an amazing task. The Great Pyramid is made up of two and a half million stone blocks with an average weight of about $2\frac{1}{2}$ tons each. After blocks were dug from a quarry miles away, they needed to be transported to the construction site and moved up to each layer of the pyramid.

4 a. Write a numeral for the number of stone blocks used to build the Great Pyramid. 2,500,000

   b. The Empire State Building weighs about 365,000 tons. Find the weight of the Great Pyramid in tons and compare it to the weight of the Empire State Building.

▶ To better understand how heavy the blocks were, it is helpful to become familiar with units of weight in the customary system—the **ounce** (**oz**), the **pound** (**lb**), and the **ton**. The relationships between these units are shown below:

1 lb = 16 oz   **1 ton = 2000 lb**

5 Discussion The weight of five quarters is a good benchmark for an ounce. A compact car is a good benchmark for a ton. What can you use as a benchmark for a pound? Explain your reasoning.

6 Choose an appropriate unit (*ounce*, *pound*, or *ton*) for the weight of each item.

   a. a box of cereal
   ounce or pound
   d. an orange
   ounce

   b. a person
   pound
   e. a bicycle
   pound

   c. a truck
   ton
   f. a pencil
   ounce

GOAL

LEARN HOW TO...
- measure weight in customary units
- convert customary units of weight

AS YOU...
- explore the construction of the Great Pyramid

KEY TERMS
- ounce (oz)
- pound (lb)
- ton

4. b. about 6,250,000 tons; The weight of the Great Pyramid is more than 17 times that of the Empire State Building.

5. Sample Response: Many products are sold in 1 lb packages, so I would use a 1 lb loaf of bread as a benchmark for a pound.

Exploration 1

ALTERNATIVE APPROACH
The Great Pyramid was made up of 2.5 million stone blocks, each weighing about 2.5 tons. For students to get an idea of the weight of one of these stone blocks, you could bring in a brick or a concrete block for students to weigh. They could then calculate how many of the bricks it would take to equal the weight of one of the stone blocks from the Great Pyramid.

DEVELOPING MATH CONCEPTS
After introducing the relationship between ounces, pounds, and tons, help students prepare for conversions by having them use mental math to name fractional amounts of 16 oz or 2000 lb. Ask, "What is $\frac{1}{4}$ of 16?" (*4*) This begins to get students aware that $\frac{1}{4}$ of a pound is equivalent to 4 oz. Likewise, ask, "What is $\frac{1}{8}$ of 16?" (*2*), "$\frac{1}{4}$ of 2000?" (*500*). Summarize students responses by stating that $\frac{1}{8}$ of a pound is 2 oz and that $\frac{1}{4}$ of a ton is 500 lb.

TIPS FROM TEACHERS
Tape 5 quarters together for the benchmark of an ounce mentioned in **Question 5**. The taped quarters can be passed around the class so students can get a feel for the weight of an ounce.

Exploration 1 *continued*

TEACHING NOTES

For **Question 7**, a postage scale can be used to weigh the items. If a scale is not available, items with known weights can be used. (If the weight of the item is printed on it, the weight should be covered while students make their estimates and then revealed so they can check their answers.)

Students will use the same steps for converting units of weight as they did for converting customary units of length in Module 5, Section 2. They may want to review this method before beginning **Questions 8 and 9**.

Part of the example below can be used to show students how they might approach a conversion such as that in **Question 10(c)**.

CLASSROOM EXAMPLE

A grocery store sold a carton of tortilla chips that weighed a total of 6 lb 12 oz. There were 12 bags in the carton. How many ounces did each bag weigh?

Answer: Start with the relationship between pounds and ounces.

1 lb = 16 oz

Next multiply by 6.

6 · 1 lb = 6 · 16 oz
  6 lb = 96 oz

Therefore, 6 lb 12 oz is 96 + 12 or 108 oz.

Now divide to find the weight of each bag.

108 oz ÷ 12 bags = 9 oz per bag

---

7. Answers will vary.
   Sample weights are given: pencil 0.2 oz; coffee mug 10 oz; math books 13.4 lb; stapler 6.9 oz

7 Copy the table. Use the benchmarks from Question 5 to estimate the weight of each listed item. Then weigh each item on a scale.

Item	Estimated Weight	Actual Weight
pencil	?	?
coffee mug	?	?
four math books	?	?
stapler	?	?

▶ **Converting Units** Sometimes you need to convert between different units of weight.

8 Complete the steps below to calculate how many pounds a $2\frac{1}{2}$ ton stone block weighs.

> Start with a relationship between tons and pounds.

Step 1:   1 ton = $\underline{?}$ lb $_{2000\ lb}$

Step 2: $2\frac{1}{2}$ · 1 ton = $2\frac{1}{2}$ · $\underline{?}$ lb $_{2000\ lb}$

Step 3: $2\frac{1}{2}$ tons = $\underline{?}$ lb $_{5,000\ lb}$

9 Complete the following steps to calculate how many pounds of peanut butter are in a 40-oz jar.

Step 1: Write the conversion fact for changing 1 oz to pounds.
1 oz = $\underline{?}$ lb $\frac{1}{16}$

Step 2: Multiply by 40 since you are converting 40 oz to pounds. $40 \cdot \frac{1}{16}$

Step 3: Complete the multiplication in Step 2. $2\frac{1}{2}$

✔ **QUESTION 10**

...checks that you can convert customary units of weight.

10 ✔ **CHECKPOINT** Convert each measurement to the indicated unit.

a. 1500 lb = $\underline{?}$ ton(s) $\frac{3}{4}$ ton   **b.** 36 oz = $\underline{?}$ lb $2\frac{1}{4}$ lb

c. 5 lb 6 oz = $\underline{?}$ oz 86 oz   **d.** $3\frac{1}{4}$ tons = $\underline{?}$ lb 6,500 lb

11 If the average student weighs 100 lb, how many students would weigh as much as an average stone block in the Great Pyramid?
about 50 students

HOMEWORK EXERCISES ▶ See Exs. 1–19 on pp. 456–457.

Key Terms

Pyramids (p. 452)

A pyramid is a polyhedron that has one base. All the other faces are triangular and meet at a single vertex.
Like a prism, a pyramid is named by the shape of its base.

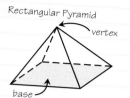

Rectangular Pyramid

vertex

base

pyramid

Customary Units of Weight (pp. 453–454)

Some commonly used units of weight in the customary system are ounce (oz), pound (lb), and ton.

- An ounce is about the weight of 5 quarters.

ounce (oz)

- A pound is about the weight of a loaf of bread.

1 lb = 16 oz

pound (lb)

- A ton is about the weight of a compact car.

1 ton = 2000 lb

ton

Key Concepts Questions

12 Choose the letter of the three-dimensional object that is a pyramid. **B**

A.   **B.**   **C.**

13 Name the pyramid in Question 12. **pentagonal pyramid**

14 Suppose a museum used two and a half million 1-oz blocks to build a scale model of the Great Pyramid at Giza.

a. Should you express the weight of the scale model in *ounces*, *pounds*, or *tons*? Explain your choice.

b. How much will the model weigh in the units from part (a)?
2,500,000 blocks ÷ 32,000 blocks per ton = 78.125 tons

14. a. tons; Sample Response: You should use the largest unit that will give a measurement that is easy to interpret or understand. Since 16 blocks weigh a pound, 32,000 blocks would weigh a ton and 2,500,000 blocks would weigh many tons. This means an answer in tons would probably be easier to understand than one in pounds.

Key Concepts

CLOSURE QUESTION

Use correct mathematical vocabulary to describe a pyramid and all its parts.

Sample Response: A pyramid is a polyhedron with one base that can be any shaped polygon. All the other faces are triangles that meet at a single vertex.

ABSENT STUDENTS

For students who were absent for all or part of this section, the blackline Study Guide for Section 2 may be used to present the ideas, concepts, and skills of Section 2.

15. a. (Ex 13) about $4.50, since 2 lb 8 oz = $2\frac{1}{2}$ lb and $2\frac{1}{2} \cdot 1.8 = 4.50$;

(Ex 14) about $3.00, since 4 lb 4 oz = $4\frac{1}{4}$ lb and $4\frac{1}{4} \cdot 0.70 \approx 3.00$

Section ② Practice & Application Exercises

Choose the best customary unit (*ounce, pound,* or *ton*) to express the weight of each object.

1. airplane ton

2. postcard ounce

3. ice skates pound

4. fork ounce

Open-ended Name something that weighs close to each amount.

5. 6 oz Sample: 30 quarters

6. 10 lb Sample: a large bag of potatoes

Replace each _?_ with the missing number.

7. 96 oz = _?_ lb 6

8. 0.75 lb = _?_ oz 12

9. 4000 lb = _?_ ton(s) 2

10. 4 oz = _?_ lb $\frac{1}{4}$

11. $5\frac{1}{2}$ tons = _?_ lb 11,000

12. 250 lb = _?_ ton(s) $\frac{1}{8}$

Give each weight using a combination of pounds and ounces.

13.

$1.79 per lb

2 lb 8 oz

14.

$.69 per lb

4 lb 4 oz

15. a. **Estimation** Estimate the cost of each purchase in Exercises 13 and 14. Describe your method.

   b. Calculate the cost of each purchase in Exercises 13 and 14.
   (Ex 13) actual cost: $4.48; (Ex 14) actual cost: $2.93

16. An apple pie recipe calls for 3 lb of apples. One apple weighs about 7 oz. About how many apples are in this pie? about 7 apples

17. **Archaeology** Tutankhamen was king of Egypt during the period 1347–1339 B.C. Most of the tombs in Egyptian pyramids have had their contents stolen, but the tomb of Tutankhamen was discovered in 1922 with its magnificent treasure still in place.

   a. The solid gold mask found on Tutankhamen's mummy weighs 22 lb. What is the mask's weight in ounces? *352 oz*

   b. Suppose gold sells for $690 per ounce. What is the value of the gold in the mummy's mask? *$242,880*

Use the shipping charge table below for Exercise 18.

18. Ramona wants to send a friend a pair of soccer cleats that weigh 2 lb 3 oz, two shin guards that weigh 6 oz each, and some pictures that weigh 2 oz altogether.

   a. **Estimation** Estimate the shipping charge. *$4.00 or $5.00*

   b. Find the total weight in pounds and ounces of the items Ramona is sending. *3 lb 1 oz*

   c. What is the shipping charge? *$5.00*

Priority Mail Shipping Charges

Shipping weight	Priority Mail 2-day shipping rate
Up to 2 lb	$3.00
Up to 3 lb	$4.00
Up to 4 lb	$5.00
Up to 5 lb	$6.00

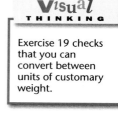

Reflecting ◀▷ on the Section

19. Suppose each block used to build this tower weighs 3 oz. What is the weight of the tower in pounds?

   $3\frac{3}{4}$ lb (Assuming the tower is solid and there aren't any blocks behind the tower that can't be seen, there are 20 blocks in all.)

V i s u a l
T H I N K I N G

Exercise 19 checks that you can convert between units of customary weight.

Although customary units are used in **Exercise 17**, the weight of gold and other precious metals is normally given in Troy units:
1 Troy oz ≈ 1.097 oz and
1 Troy lb = 0.823 lb = 12 Troy oz.

Reflecting Exercise 19 Some students may notice that the tower could have additional blocks behind it that are not noticeable from the view given. You may want to build the tower out of blocks on a table where students can walk around it to examine that there are not any additional blocks on the back side and that each block on a higher level is supported by blocks underneath it.

Practice & Applications

EXERCISE NOTES
Spiral Review Exercise 23 reviews the skill of writing an equation with variables to represent a rule, but at the same time applies to converting measurement units.

Spiral ◀▶ Review

Find the missing measurement for each prism. (Module 7, p. 448)

20. Area of base = 12 cm²

Volume = 54 cm³

Height = __?__
4.5 cm

21. Height = 6.2 cm

Volume = 155 cm³

Area of base = __?__
25 cm²

22. The volume of a rectangular box is 60 cm³. Give two possibilities for the dimensions of the box. (Module 7, p. 448)
Sample Response: 2 cm × 15 cm × 2 cm; 6 cm × 2 cm × 5 cm

23. Suppose y represents a length in yards and f represents a length in feet. Write a rule in the form of an equation for converting from yards to feet. (Module 1, p. 21; Module 5, p. 302) $f = 3 \cdot y$

Career ▪ Connection

Doctor: Darrell Mease

Darrell Mease monitors the health of children from the time they are born until they become adults. He records the weights of babies because normal growth is a sign of health.

24. A normal birth weight for boys is between 95 oz and 152 oz. Is a 9 lb 7 oz baby boy within the normal range? Explain.
Yes; 9 lb 7 oz = 151 oz and 95 oz < 151 oz < 152 oz

25. From 10 days after birth until 3 months is a time of rapid growth for infants. During this time, doctors like to see an average weight gain of close to 1 oz per day.

A baby weighs 8 lb 13 oz at her two-week check-up and 11 lb 7 oz at her two-month visit. Is she gaining at about 1 oz per day? Explain.
Yes; She has gained 42 oz in about 42 days.

▲
Pediatrician Darrell Mease works with children in his hometown of Jay, Oklahoma.

Section 2

Extra Skill Practice

Choose the best customary unit (*ounce*, *pound*, or *ton*) to express the weight of each object.

1. softball
   ounce

2. cow
   pound

3. steamship
   ton

4. bag of pretzels
   ounce

5. hammer
   ounce or pound

6. light bulb
   ounce

7. desk
   pound

8. calculator
   ounce

Replace each $?$ with the missing number.

9. 32 oz = $?$ lb 2

10. 1600 lb = $?$ ton(s) 0.8

11. 7000 lb = $?$ ton(s) 3.5

12. $3\frac{1}{2}$ lb = $?$ oz 56

13. 10 oz = $?$ lb $\frac{5}{8}$

14. 16 tons = $?$ lb 32,000

15. 2 tons = $?$ oz 64,000

16. 104 oz = $?$ lb $6\frac{1}{2}$

17. $4\frac{1}{4}$ lb = $?$ oz 68

Replace each $?$ with <, >, or =.

18. 2.5 lb $?$ 36 oz
    >

19. 64 oz $?$ 4 lb
    =

20. 32,000 oz $?$ 1 ton
    =

21. 0.5 lb $?$ 6 oz
    >

22. $4\frac{1}{2}$ lb $?$ 100 oz
    <

23. 1200 lb $?$ $\frac{1}{2}$ ton
    >

24. $5\frac{1}{4}$ lb $?$ 84 oz
    =

25. 42 oz $?$ 3 lb
    <

26. 8500 lb $?$ 5 tons
    <

Standardized Testing ▶ Free Response

1. A circus parade is shown. If each elephant weighs 2.5 tons, the clown car weighs 1 ton, and the people weigh an average of 150 lb each, should they cross the bridge together? Explain. Yes; The total weight is 13,800 lb which is less than 7 tons (14,000 lb).

2. A clown juggles a can of soup (10 oz), a golf ball ($1\frac{1}{2}$ oz), a large apple ($\frac{1}{2}$ lb), and a melon ($2\frac{3}{4}$ lb). When juggling, the clown holds two objects at a time while the rest of the objects are in the air. What is the greatest amount of weight that the clown holds? the least? Explain. greatest: 54 oz; least: 9.5 oz; The melon and the soup can weigh 54 oz together. The golf ball and apple weigh 9.5 oz together.

TEACHER NOTES

All of the Extra Skill Practice Exercises correspond to Exploration 1.

EXTRA HELP

Teacher's Resource Book
• Practice and Applications
• Study Guide

Technology Resources
• @Home Tutor
• Test Generator

ASSESSMENT
• Section 2 Quick Quiz
• Test Generator

Using an E²: Suggestions for managing and evaluating an Extended Exploration are available in the *Teacher's Resource Book* for Modules 1 and 2. See also pages T44–T45 in the *Teacher's Edition*.

Alternate E²: See the *Teacher's Resource Book* for Modules 7 and 8 for an alternate Extended Exploration that can be used after Module 7, Section 2.

FOR ASSESSMENT AND PORTFOLIOS

A Weighty Question

The Situation See the *Teacher's Resource Book* for a sample solution for this Extended Exploration.

An old balance scale is on sale at a rummage sale. Only the four weights shown are being sold with the scale. The person selling the balance claims that you can use those weights to find any weight in whole ounces from 1 oz through 40 oz.

The Problem

Prove that the seller's claim is true by showing how to measure each weight from 1 oz through 40 oz.

Something to Think About

- How can you organize your work to make sure you do not skip any weights?

- Which problem-solving strategies seem helpful for this problem?

Present your Results

Describe what you did to solve the problem. Include any tables, pictures, or charts you made to organize your data. Describe any patterns you noticed while solving the problem.

Section ③ Circles and Circumference

IN THIS SECTION

EXPLORATION 1
◆ Parts of a Circle

EXPLORATION 2
◆ Distance Around a Circle

The CIRCUS Maximus

Setting the Stage ▸▸▸▸▸▸▸▸▸▸▸▸▸▸▸▸▸▸▸▸▸▸▸▸▸▸▸▸▸▸▸

One of the wonders of the Roman Empire was the Circus Maximus. This enormous arena was the largest gathering place in ancient Rome, seating 250,000 screaming spectators. As many as 20 four-horse chariots raced around the low wall which ran down the middle of the arena.

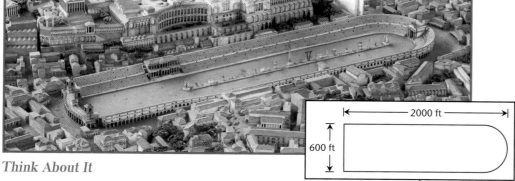

2000 ft
600 ft

Think About It

1 a. How can you estimate the perimeter of the Circus Maximus?

  b. How can you estimate the length of the curved part of the building?

2 The Astrodome in Houston, Texas, holds 60,000 people. About how many times as many people did the Circus Maximus hold?
Accept reasonable estimates. about 4 times

3 a. Estimate the area of the Circus Maximus. Explain how you estimated. Sample Response: about 1,200,000 ft²; I found the area of a rectangle with length 2000 ft and width 600 ft.

  b. How does the area of the Circus Maximus compare with the area of your classroom? Answers will vary. Check students' work.

1. a. Sample Response: You could estimate the perimeter of a rectangle with length 2000 ft and width 600 ft.

1. b. Sample Response: You could measure the curved part on the drawing with a string to find its length on the drawing, then use the scale of the drawing to estimate the length of the actual curved segment.

Setting the Stage

GETTING STARTED
In preparation for finding the circumference (perimeter) of a circle, Module 7 Section 3 *Warm-Up* assesses students' ability to find the perimeter of polygons and has students practice multiplication and division skills with decimal numbers.

TEACHING NOTES
The intended purpose of **Questions 1–3** is for students to start thinking about the length of a curve, not necessarily to come up with a value for the length of the track. The phrase *circus maximus* means "greatest circle." To give students an idea of the size of the Circus Maximus, find out how many people your school auditorium or gymnasium will hold. Then have students determine how many times as many people the Circus Maximus held. (This is similar to the development in **Question 2**.)

Exploration 1

Teaching Notes

Some students may prefer to work with a partner to accomplish the circle drawing task in **Question 4**, since the method chosen may require an extra pair of hands to turn the paper, or hold one of the pencils. Partners will need to make two circles or plan to complete **Questions 6–8** together on one paper.

In **Question 5**, students can share approaches that were unsuccessful, as well as methods that worked. Prompt students to discuss why it was important to keep the string taut when drawing the circle. Failing to create a circle when the string does not stay taut informally reinforces the definition of circle since the points will not all be the same distance from the center.

GOAL

LEARN HOW TO...
- identify the parts of a circle
- draw a circle

AS YOU...
- explore the Circus Maximus

KEY TERMS
- circle
- center
- radius (plural: radii)
- chord
- diameter

---

5. Sample Response: Use two pencils. Tie each end of the string to one of the pencils. Hold one pencil perpendicular to the paper with the point on the paper. (The mark it makes is the center of the circle.) Pull the string taut and rotate the other pencil around the center to draw the circle.

6. Sample Response:

✔ **QUESTION 8**

...checks that you can identify radii and chords of a circle.

8. a. any two of segments $\overline{AB}$, $\overline{BC}$, $\overline{BD}$, $\overline{CD}$, $\overline{AC}$, and $\overline{AD}$

Parts of a **Circle**

SET UP You will need: • *a piece of string about 30 cm long* • *two pencils* • *compass* • *ruler*

The Circus Maximus is shaped like a rectangle with a half *circle* on one end.

▶ To find distances around curved paths, it is helpful to know more about circles. A **circle** is a set of points in a plane that are all the same distance from a given point, the **center**.

4 Think about the definition of a circle. Use it to develop a way to draw a circle using only pencils and string. Then use this method to draw a circle. Label the center of your circle.
  Check students' drawings.

5 Discussion How did you draw your circle?

▶ A **radius** is a segment from the center of a circle to any point on the circle. A **chord** is a segment that connects two points on a circle.

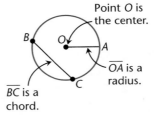

Point *O* is the center.

$\overline{OA}$ is a radius.

$\overline{BC}$ is a chord.

6 Draw a radius and a chord on your circle.

7 Is a radius a chord? Explain. No, only one endpoint of a radius is on the circle.

8 ✔ **CHECKPOINT** Look at this diagram of segments within a circle.

  a. Name two chords of the circle.

  b. Name two radii of the circle.
  any two of segments $\overline{OB}$, $\overline{OD}$, and $\overline{OE}$

▶ The term *radius* is used for length as well as for segments. Since the length of every radius of a circle is the same, this length is referred to as the *radius* of the circle.

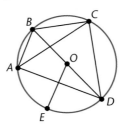

▶ **Drawing Circles** You can use a compass to draw a circle.

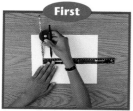
First

Next

Then

Open the compass to the desired radius.

Put the point of the compass at the center of the circle.

Draw the circle. Press down to hold the compass in place.

The circle drawn here has a 3.5 cm radius.

9 a. Draw a circle using a compass. Mark its center with a dot.
Check students' drawings.

b. How does a compass allow you to draw a set of points that are all the same distance from a center point?

c. Draw the longest possible chord. How does the length of this chord compare with the length of a radius?

▶ A **diameter** of a circle is a chord that passes through the center of the circle. Every diameter of a circle has the same length. This length is called the diameter of the circle.

10 a. How is the chord you drew in Question 9(c) related to a diameter? *The chord is a diameter.*

b. How are the lengths of other chords related to the diameter? *The length of any chord is less than or equal to the length of a diameter.*

11 ✔ **CHECKPOINT** Use the diagram of the Circus Maximus below.

a. Use what you know about circles to find the two missing dimensions. *1700 ft and 300 ft*

b. Use the scale 1 in. : 200 ft and your ruler and compass to make a scale drawing of the Circus Maximus. Label your drawing with the actual measurements given and those you found in part (a). Save your drawing for use in Exploration 2.

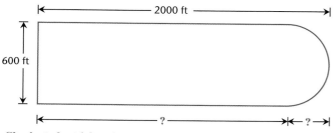

2000 ft

600 ft

? ?

Check students' drawings.

HOMEWORK EXERCISES ▶ See Exs. 1–7 on p. 467.

9. **b.** A compass is opened a set length that remains the same as you rotate the compass in a circle, producing points that are all the same distance from the center.
c. Check students' drawings. The longest possible chord is twice as long as the radius.

✔ **QUESTION 11**

...checks that you understand the relationships among parts of a circle and that you can draw a circle.

FOR ◀ HELP
with *scale drawings*, see
MODULE 6, p. 413

Section 3   Circles and Circumference   463

DIFFERENTIATED INSTRUCTION
For many students, drawing a circle with a compass without it slipping, changing the radius, or tearing a hole in the paper is difficult. Suggest that students ease up on the pressure placed on the pencil tip and compass point. Sometimes tilting the compass to the side at a slight angle instead of perpendicular to the paper will help. Also some may prefer to rotate the paper around in a circular motion instead of the compass. For students with restricted hand mobility, a flat safety compass with designated holes for the radius lengths may serve better than an upright compass.

TEACHING NOTES
After completing **Question 9**, have several students mark their longest chord on a circle you have drawn on the board or overhead projector. This way the class can compare their longest chord to those drawn and see that there are "several" longest chords but they all pass through the center of the circle; that is, they are all diameters of the circle.

COMMON ERRORS
Some students may confuse radius and diameter. An easy memory device is to notice that the word *radius* is shorter (fewer letters) than the word *diameter* and that a radius of a circle is always shorter than a diameter of the same circle.

TEACHING NOTES
Question 11 Make sure students' drawings are correct. Students will use their scale drawings in Exploration 2, so it is important that they be accurate.

Exploration 2

CLASSROOM MANAGEMENT

Question 13 Students should work in a group to measure the four objects, but each student should make a scatter plot of the data. You may want to designate which groups will share data when completing the table on **Labsheet 3A**. To help students make their estimates in **part (d)**, it may be helpful to briefly review using fitted lines to make predictions.

TEACHING NOTES

The more accurate students' measurements in **Question 13(a)** are, the closer their ratios in **Question 14** will approximate the value of π. Demonstrate how to accurately measure the diameter of the object to the nearest tenth of a centimeter and how to use string to measure the circumference.

Make sure students' answers to **Question 14** are correct, since **Question 15** uses these results.

TECHNOLOGY

For a related technology activity, see the *Technology Book*.

13. a., 14. a. See Additional
Answers beginning on page A1.

464

GOAL

LEARN HOW TO...
- find the circumference of a circle

AS YOU...
- investigate Roman chariot wheels and gather data about circles

KEY TERMS
- circumference
- pi (π)

13. b. Sample answer:

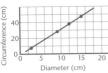

FOR◄HELP

with *scatter plots and fitted lines*, see **MODULE 6, p. 389**

Distance around a Circle

SET UP *Work in a group. You will need: • Labsheet 3A • meter stick • 4 circular objects • string • calculator • clear ruler*

▶ Using spoked wheels helped chariot racers gain speed and control. To make the rim and spokes the correct lengths to form a wheel, it was important to know how parts of a circle are related.

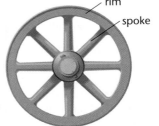

The rim of a Roman chariot ▶ wheel was made by bending a strip of wood to form a circle.

12 The distance around a circle is its **circumference**. What part of the wheel corresponds to the circumference? *the length of the outer part of the rim*

Use Labsheet 3A for Questions 13 and 14.

13 **a.** Follow the directions for the *Data Table* to find and record the circumference and diameter of circular objects. **See margin.**

b. Make a *Scatter Plot* of the data you collected in part (a).

c. Use your *Scatter Plot* to estimate the circumference of a circle with a diameter of 6 cm. *about 18 cm*

d. Use your *Scatter Plot* to estimate the diameter of a circle with a circumference of 30 cm. *about 9.5 cm*

e. The circumference is about how many times the diameter? *about 3 times*

14 Round decimal answers to the nearest hundredth.

a. Add a row to your *Data Table*. Find and record the decimal form of the ratio $\frac{\text{circumference}}{\text{diameter}}$ for each object. **See margin.**

b. What do you notice about the values of the ratios in part (a)? *All the values are a little more than 3 (about 3.14).*

c. Find the mean of the values of the ratios. *Sample Response: about 3.14*

▶ **The Ratio Pi** For any circle, the ratio of the circumference to the diameter is equal to the number represented by the Greek letter π, or **pi**. To estimate pi you can use 3.14 or the [π] key on a calculator.

15 a. Press the π key on your calculator. What value appears?

Number of digits will depend on calculator display length. 3.141592654

b. Compare the value from part (a) with your result in Question 14(c). How close are the values? How can you explain the difference?

15. b. Answers will vary. Values should be close. Differences could be due to errors in measurement with string or accuracy of measuring to the nearest tenth of a centimeter.

For answers given throughout this section, 3.14 was used for π. Answers may vary slightly if the π key is used.

16 Use Labsheet 3A. For each object named in the *Data Table*, find the product $\pi \cdot d$ to the nearest hundredth and compare it with your circumference measurement. What do you notice?
See margin.

▶ **For any circle, the circumference C equals π times the diameter d.**

$$C = \pi d$$

17 Discussion Find the exact circumference of a circle with the given measurement. (That is, leave your answer in terms of π.)

a. a diameter of 3 ft   *3π ft*

b. a radius of $\frac{1}{2}$ yd   *1π yd or π yd*

18 Use 3.14 or the π key on a calculator to estimate the circumference of each circle in Question 17. Round to the nearest hundredth.   *a. 9.42 ft; b. 3.14 yd*

▶ **If you know the circumference you can solve for the diameter.**

EXAMPLE

To find the diameter of Earth at the equator, you can use the formula for circumference and substitute the values you know.

$\approx$ means "is about equal to."

$$C = \pi d$$
$$40{,}075 \text{ km} \approx 3.14 \cdot d$$
$$40{,}075 \text{ km} \div 3.14 \approx d$$
$$12{,}763 \text{ km} \approx d$$

The circumference of Earth at the equator is 40,075 km.

The diameter rounded to the nearest kilometer is 12,763 km.

19 ✔ CHECKPOINT Replace each ? with the missing length. Round to the hundredths place.

a. $d = \frac{1}{3}$ in., $C \approx$?
1.05 in.

b. $C = 34.54$ mm, $d \approx$?
11 mm

✔ QUESTION 19

...checks that you can apply the formula for the circumference of a circle.

20 Use the information from your scale drawing in Question 11. Find the perimeter of the Circus Maximus to the nearest foot.
4942 ft

HOMEWORK EXERCISES ▶ See Exs. 8–18 on pp. 467–468.

Section 3   Circles and Circumference   **465**

TEACHING NOTES

Explain that since π is an infinite, non-repeating number, you could never write all of it out, so the Greek letter π is used to represent the number. The "approximately equal" symbol ($\approx$) is used in place of an equal sign. To represent an exact circumference, one can use the symbol π instead of an approximation.

Before students complete **Checkpoint Question 19**, you may also want to introduce $\frac{22}{7}$ as an alternative approximation for π. Using $\frac{22}{7}$ for π may be helpful for problems in which a circumference or a diameter is a multiple of 7, as in **Exercise 8** on page 467. The Classroom Example below may be used before students complete **Checkpoint Question 19** to provide additional guidance on how to use the circumference formula to find the diameter.

CLASSROOM EXAMPLE

The circumference of Mars is about 13,232 mi. Use the formula for circumference to find the approximate diameter of Mars.

Answer: $C = \pi d$
$$13{,}232 \approx 3.14 \cdot d$$
$$13{,}232 \div 3.14 \approx d$$
$$4214 \approx d$$

The diameter to the nearest mile is 4214 mi.

Question 20 If necessary, help students see that the diameter of the circle is the same measure as the width of the drawing, and that only half of the circumference is used, since one end of the Circus Maximus is a semicircle.

16. See Additional Answers beginning on page A1.

465

Key Concepts

CLOSURE QUESTIONS

Describe the relationship between a chord, a diameter, and a radius of a circle. Then describe what is meant by circumference and write a formula for circumference using symbols and words.

Sample Response: A chord is a segment that connects two points on the circle. A diameter is a chord that goes through the center of the circle. Circumference is the distance around a circle (its perimeter); $C = \pi d$. In words, the circumference of a circle equals pi times the diameter.

ABSENT STUDENTS

For students who were absent for all or part of this section, the blackline Study Guide for Section 3 may be used to present the ideas, concepts, and skills of Section 3.

Key Terms

circle

center

radius (plural: radii)

chord

diameter

circumference

pi (π)

Section ③ Key Concepts

Parts of a Circle (pp. 462–463)

You can use a compass to draw a circle.

In any circle:
- the radius (r) is one half the diameter (d).
- the diameter is the longest chord.
- all radii are the same length.
- all diameters are the same length.

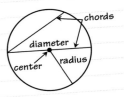
chords
diameter
center
radius

Circumference (pp. 464–465)

The circumference of a circle is the distance around the circle. The ratio of the circumference of any circle to its diameter is pi (π). To find the circumference (C), multiply π by d.

$$\frac{C}{d} = \pi, \text{ so } C = \pi d \text{ or } C = 2\pi r.$$

You can use the value 3.14 or the $\boxed{\pi}$ key on your calculator to estimate π.

Example

Find the approximate circumference of a circle that has a radius of 1.5 cm.

$\approx$ means "is about equal to."

$$C = \pi d \qquad 2r = d$$
$$C = \pi \cdot (2r)$$
$$C \approx 3.14 \cdot 2 \cdot 1.5$$
$$C \approx 9.42 \text{ cm}$$

The circumference is about 9.42 cm.

---

21 Key Concepts Question Some Roman chariot wheels had a circumference of about 113 in.

a. How can you estimate the diameter of the wheel? **Divide 113 in. by 3.**

b. Suppose the rim of the wheel is 3 in. wide and the diameter of the hub is 9 in. About how long is a spoke to the nearest inch? **Accept reasonable estimates. about 11 in.** *Note:* The length of the spoke is not equal to the radius.

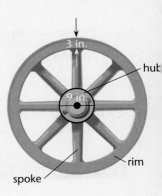
3 in.
hub
9 in.
rim
spoke

Section 3

Practice & Application Exercises

YOU WILL NEED

For Exs. 4–7:
- compass

For Ex. 7:
- Labsheet 3B

For Exs. 28–29:
- compass
- straightedge
- drawing paper
- colored pencils or markers

Practice & Applications

SUGGESTED ASSIGNMENTS

Core Course
Day 1: Exs. 1–7
Day 2: Exs. 19–27
Day 3: Exs. 8–16, 18

Extended Course
Day 1: Exs. 1–7
Day 2: Exs. 19–27, 28–29*
Day 3: Exs. 8–18

Note: Extended Course assignments can be used to differentiate within the regular classroom. In classrooms where students are grouped homogeneously, the material might be covered in fewer days. In this case assignments may be combined.

*denotes Extension Exercises

Name all the segments of each type shown on the circle with center O.

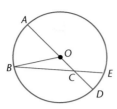

1. radii $\overline{OA}, \overline{OB}, \overline{OD}$

2. diameters $\overline{AD}$

3. chords $\overline{AD}, \overline{BE}$

Use a compass to draw a circle with each radius or diameter.

4. radius = 4 cm   5. diameter = 10 cm   6. radius = $2\frac{1}{4}$ in.
4–6. Check students' drawings.

7. **Earthquakes** A seismograph gives information about the strength and location of an earthquake. The *epicenter* of an earthquake is the point on Earth's surface directly over the place where an earthquake occurs.

   a. Readings from the seismograph at Station 1 indicate that an earthquake occurred 100 km away. What do you think the circle drawn around station 1 represents?

   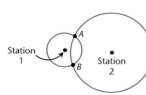

   a circle with a radius of 100 km (All of the points 100 km from Station 1.)

▲ A *seismograph* is an instrument used to record earthquake waves.

   b. A seismograph at Station 2 detected the same quake 300 km away from Station 2. Look at the two circles. Why do you think a scientist is interested in points *A* and *B*, where the two circles intersect?

   c. How do you think scientists can use circles to find the epicenter of an earthquake?

   d. **Use Labsheet 3B.** Use the seismograph locations and the distances in the table on the labsheet. Draw circles on the *Epicenter Map* to find the epicenter of an earthquake that occurred in the South Pacific on March 11, 1997.

Find the approximate circumference of each circle. Round to the nearest hundredth.

8. *d* = 21 in.
   65.94 in.

9. *d* = 5 cm
   15.7 cm

10. *r* = 6 ft
    37.68 ft

7. b. These are the points that are 100 km from Station 1 and 300 km from Station 2, so they are the possible locations for the epicenter.

7. c. Use the distance of the epicenter from a third reporting station to draw a third circle. The point of intersection of all 3 circles is the position of the epicenter.

d. Check students' drawings. The epicenter of the earthquake was located in the Philippine Islands at approximately 8° N, 127° E. (See Labsheet 3B.)

ADDITIONAL PRACTICE
See the *Teacher's Resource Book* for additional practice and application exercises for this section.

EXERCISE NOTES
Exercise 7 Students should understand that the seismograph is at the center of the circle and the radius is the distance that the epicenter is from the seismograph. This understanding is important for students to be able to answer **parts (a)–(c)**.

Practice & Applications

EXERCISE NOTES

Exercise 15 Students may be inclined to answer that the circumference is obviously twice as long and three times as long. Request that students justify their answer mathematically. They can use the original circumference to solve for the diameter and then calculate the radius. Knowing the radius they can then calculate the circumferences of the circles with radii twice and three times as long and find the ratios.

14. Accept reasonable estimates. about 17 people; The circumference of the tree is about 94 ft and a person's reach is about the same as his or her height. I estimated the average height to be about 5.5 ft, then estimated 94 ÷ 5.5 ≈ 17.

16. about 75.36 in.; about 301.44 in.; For each turn, the wheel will travel a distance equal to its circumference.

17. Sample Response: about 1779 ft; Find the mean of 620 and 513 (566.5), then find the circumference of a circle with diameter 566.5 ft.

18. Use the circumference formula to find the circumference of a circle with radius 10 mm: $C ≈ 3.14 \cdot 2 \cdot 10$ mm = 62.8 mm.

For the circle with each given circumference (C), approximate the missing radius or diameter. Replace each _?_ with the missing length. Round to the nearest hundredth.

11. $C = 69.08$ cm
   diameter ≈ _?_
   22 cm

12. $C = 28.26$ in.
   radius ≈ _?_
   4.5 in.

13. $C = 15.7$ mm
   diameter ≈ _?_
   5 mm

14. **Estimation** The trunk of an African baobab tree can grow up to 30 ft in diameter. About how many people would it take to surround the tree if the people stood with their arms fully extended and their fingertips touching? Explain your thinking.

15. **Algebra Connection** The circumference of a circle is 12.56 cm. What is the ratio of this circumference to the circumference of a circle with a radius twice as long? three times as long? $\frac{1}{2}; \frac{1}{3}$

16. Elia's bicycle wheel has a diameter of 24 in. About how far will it travel in 1 complete turn? in 4 complete turns? Explain.

17. **Challenge** The Colosseum was a large stadium in ancient Rome. Its base was shaped like an oval. Use what you know about circles to estimate the perimeter of the base. Explain how you made your estimate.

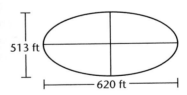

513 ft
620 ft

Journal

Exercise 18 checks that you understand the circumference formula.

Reflecting ◀▶ on the Section

Write your response to Exercise 18 in your journal.

18. The Spanish dollar was minted in Mexico during the eighteenth century. This coin had segments that allowed it to break into 8 equal sections. These bits were used as smaller coins. One-eighth of a Spanish dollar is shown. Use the measurements marked to describe two ways to find the circumference of a whole coin.
   Multiply 7.85 mm by 8: 7.85 mm · 8 = 62.8 mm.

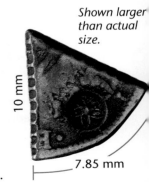

Shown larger than actual size.

10 mm

7.85 mm

Convert each measurement to pounds. (Module 7, p. 455)

19. 54 oz $3\frac{3}{8}$ lb 20. $2\frac{3}{4}$ tons 21. 35 oz $2\frac{3}{16}$ lb 22. $7\frac{1}{2}$ tons

5500 lb   15,000 lb

23. A student's scores on five tests were 84, 86, 38, 85, and 99. Which average best describes the data: the mean, the median, or the mode? Explain. (Module 4, p. 225)

23. the median; The mean is affected by the score of 38 which is unusually low in comparison to the other scores. There is no mode.

Find the value of *n*. (Module 3, p. 158)

24. $n = 3^2$ 25. $n = 2^4$ 26. $n^3 = 1$ 27. $5^n = 125$

$n = 9$ $n = 16$ $n = 1$ $n = 3$

Extension ▶ ▶

Compass Construction

You can make geometric figures called *constructions* using a compass and a straightedge.

28. Follow the steps to draw a circle and make a geometric figure.
Check students' drawings.

Step 1

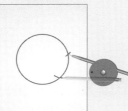
Step 2

Step 3

Use a compass to draw a circle. Keep the compass opening the same and put the point of the compass on any point on the circle. Make a small mark on the circle.

Put the point of the compass on the mark you made and make a second mark. Continue marking around the circle.

Use a straightedge to connect the marks. Name the geometric figure you made.
hexagon

29. Draw and mark another circle. Use your straightedge or compass to make a design. Some examples are shown. Answers will vary.

Exercise Notes

Exercise 29 Students should have access to unlined paper and colored pencils or crayons for making their designs. Display completed designs on a bulletin board in the classroom.

Extra Skill Practice

TEACHER NOTES

For each Exploration, the corresponding Extra Skill Practice Exercises are noted.

Exploration 1: Exs. 1–3
Exploration 2: Exs. 4–15

EXTRA HELP

Teacher's Resource Book
• Practice and Applications
• Study Guide

Technology Resources
• @Home Tutor
• Test Generator

ASSESSMENT
• Section 3 Quick Quiz
• Mid-Module Quiz
• Test Generator

Section 3
Extra Skill Practice

Name all the segments of each type shown on the circle with center O.

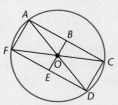

1. diameters $\overline{AD}, \overline{FC}$
2. chords $\overline{AD}, \overline{AF}, \overline{AC}, \overline{FD}, \overline{FC}, \overline{CD}$
3. radii $\overline{OA}, \overline{OF}, \overline{OD}, \overline{OC}$

For each circle in Exercises 4–9, find the approximate circumference. Round to the nearest hundredth.

4. $d = 27$ in. 84.78 in. 5. $r = 2.5$ cm 15.7 cm 6. $r = 53$ mm 332.84 mm

7. 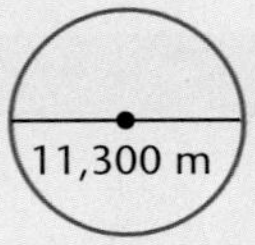 35,482 m 8. 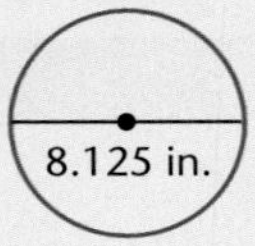 25.51 in. 9. 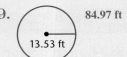 84.97 ft
   11,300 m   8.125 in.   13.53 ft

Replace each ? with the missing length. Round to the nearest hundredth.

10. $d = 5$ cm, $C \approx$?   15.7 cm   11. $C = 11$ m, $d \approx$?   3.50 m

12. $C = 117.75$ ft, $r \approx$?   18.75 ft   13. $r = 31$ in., $C \approx$?   194.68 in.

14. $C = 55$ m, $d \approx$?   17.52 m   15. $C = 175.84$ cm, $r \approx$?   28 cm

---

Standardized Testing ◀▶ Multiple Choice

1. Which statements about the circle are true? C

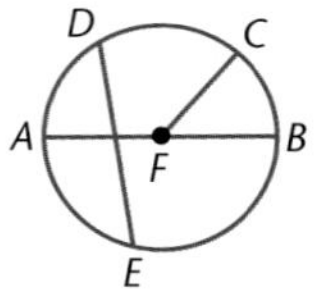

   I. $\overline{AB}$ is a radius.

   II. $\overline{DE}$ is shorter than $\overline{AB}$.

   III. FC is exactly one half of AB.

   A I and III   **B** I only   **C** II and III   **D** II only

2. Which of the equations are false? A

   I. $C = \pi d$ II. $\dfrac{C}{d} = \pi$ III. $\pi = Cd$ IV. $C = 2\pi r$

   A III only   **B** II only   **C** II and III   **D** II and IV

Section 4 Circles and Cylinders

The Mystery of Mesa Verde

Setting the Stage ▸

For many years, the ancestors of the Hopi, Zuni, and several other Native American groups lived in stone houses they built in natural caves in the cliffs of Mesa Verde, Colorado. Then something strange happened…

> "…whole villages of people left their homes. It seems that about 650 years ago, they just walked away and left most of their belongings….Why did the ancient ones build stone houses in caves?…And why did they leave?"
>
> **Ruth Shaw Radlauer,** *Mesa Verde National Park*

Although there are many theories, it is still not known for sure why the villages were abandoned.

Think About It

1 Suppose at this moment you and your classmates walked out of your classroom leaving all of your belongings behind. What do you think someone could learn about students and class activities just by looking around the room?

2 The villages contain round rooms called *kivas*. The diameter of one of the kivas is 4.3 m.

  a. What is the radius of the kiva? 2.15 m

  b. What is the circumference of the floor of the kiva? about 13.5 m

  c. How do you think the size of the kiva compares with the size of your classroom? Explain. Answers will vary.

1. Sample Response: They would learn about our clothing, our average size, and possibly our climate from the outerwear we left behind. They might learn about our language from our books and notebooks and about our forms of recreation from sports equipment or other items left in our school bags. If we left lunch bags, they would learn about our diets.

Setting the Stage

GETTING STARTED
Module 7 Section 4 *Warm-Up* assesses students' ability to identify the radius of a circle and to calculate the areas of polygons and the volumes of prisms. Areas of polygons and volumes of prisms will be used to develop formulas for the area of a circle and the volume of a cylinder.

Background Information
Mesa Verde National Park was established in 1906. The park is located in southwestern Colorado. It encompasses an area of about 210 km² (81 mi²) and is a major site of prehistoric cliff dwellings. Hundreds of ruins and artifacts document nearly 1000 years of cultural development at the site. The name Mesa Verde is Spanish for "green table." It is derived from Mesa Verde National Park's distinctive land formations of abrupt rock walls and flat tops called mesas.

TEACHING NOTES
Question 2 It will be helpful to have the classroom dimensions available to use for comparison. To give students an idea of the size of the kiva, mark a distance of 4.3 m with chalk on the floor and have students stand in a line along this length. (Make sure students understand that this length represents the diameter of the kiva.) As students stand in the line, have them make an estimate of how many people will fit inside a kiva of this diameter.

Exploration 1

DEVELOPING MATH CONCEPTS

As students complete **Labsheet 4A** in **Question 3**, they might explain that they made their estimate in **part (d)** by thinking that the area of the circle is "halfway between" the area of the inner square and the area of the outer square. Other students may have tried to actually count the squares to arrive at their estimate. Encourage these students to consider the method of averaging the areas of the inner and outer squares. Students will calculate the area of a circle with radius 4 cm in **Question 8** and compare it to their estimate in **Question 3**, so make sure students realize that the circle in **Question 3** has a radius of 4 units. Understanding how to find the area of a circle is important in Exploration 2 where volume of cylinders is developed.

The method used in **Question 4** to derive a formula that can be used to estimate the area of any circle is similar to but more abstract than the method used in **Question 3**. Be sure students fully grasp the concepts in **Question 3** before moving on.

3. e. Accept reasonable estimates. **Sample Response: about 48 units²; I found the mean of the areas of the two squares.**

GOAL

LEARN HOW TO...
◆ find the area of a circle

AS YOU...
◆ determine how many people could fit in a kiva

3. Labsheet 4A:
   a. **less than**
   b. **greater than**
   c. **64 units²; Sample Response: I counted to determine length and width, then I multiplied the length by the width.**
   d. **32 units²; Sample Response: I divided the square into 4 triangles each with an area of 8 units².**

Exploration 1

Area of a Circle

SET UP *You will need Labsheet 4A.*

In her book about Mesa Verde, Ruth Shaw Radlauer discusses the role of the kivas in the lives of people:

> "When children were old enough, they were initiated, or proclaimed adults in a ceremony. Then they could spend some of the winter in a warm kiva. The kiva was a sort of clubhouse for adults and a place for ceremonies."

▶ **To determine how many people could fit inside a kiva, you need to know the area of the floor. The floor of a kiva is shaped like a circle.**

3 **Use Labsheet 4A.** Follow the directions for *Estimating the Area of a Circle* by finding the areas of the inner and outer squares. See margin.

▶ You can use the method in Question 3 to estimate the area of any circle with radius r.

4 **Try This As A Class** The diagram below can help you see the relationship between the area of the circle and its radius r.

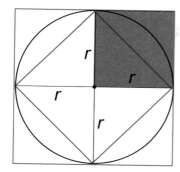

a. Use the variable r to write an expression for the area of the small red square. r^2

b. How many small red squares fit in the outer square?
4 small red squares

c. Use your answer to part (b) to write an expression for the area of the outer square. $4r^2$

d. How many of the small red squares fit in the inner square? (*Hint:* Each small red square is made up of two triangles.)
2 small red squares

e. Use your answer to part (d) to write an expression for the area of the inner square. $2r^2$

f. Use your answers to parts (c) and (e) to write an expression that can be used to estimate the area of the circle. $\frac{4r^2 + 2r^2}{2} = 3r^2$

5 **a.** Use your answer to Question 4(f) to estimate the area of a circle with a radius of 4 cm. $48\ cm^2$

b. How does your estimate compare to the estimate you found in Question 3? Sample Response: The estimates are the same.

▶ **Formula for the Area of a Circle** In Question 4, you found an expression that can be used to estimate the area of a circle. To find the actual area A of a circle with radius r, multiply pi by r to the second power.

$$A = \pi r^2$$

You can read r^2 as "r squared."

6 **Discussion** How does the formula above compare with the expression you found in Question 4(f)?

6. Since $\pi \approx 3.14$ and 3.14 is very close to 3, the areas given by the formula and the expression in Question 4(f) are very close.

Exploration 1 *continued*

TEACHING NOTES

Question 9(b) You might wish to remind students to find the radius first before using the area formula.

The example below can be used just before **Question 10** to illustrate finding the exact area of a circle.

CLASSROOM EXAMPLE

Find the exact area of a circle with radius 6.2 in.

Answer:

Use $A = \pi r^2$.

$A = \pi \cdot 6.2^2$

$A = \pi \cdot 38.44$

$A = 38.44\pi$ in.^{2}

CLASSROOM MANAGEMENT

Question 11 If you do not have enough time to find the amount of floor space an average-sized person needs to stand comfortably, 1 m^2 can be used as a reasonable estimate.

EXAMPLE

Find the approximate area of a circle with radius 8.5 cm. Round your answer to the nearest square centimeter.

SAMPLE RESPONSE

$$A = \pi r^2 = \pi \cdot (8.5)^2$$

Method 1	Method 2
To find A, use 3.14 for π.	To find A, use the π key on a calculator.
$3.14 \cdot 8.5^2 = 226.865$	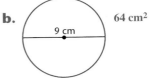 226.98...

The area is about 227 cm^2.

This key takes 8.5 to the second power.

7 a. In the Example, why aren't the answers the same? **In Method 1, the value of π is rounded to fewer decimal places.**
   b. Which answer is more accurate? Why? **Method 2 is more accurate because π on the calculator is carried out to more decimal places.**

8 a. Using 3.14 for π, find the approximate area of a circle with radius 4 cm. **50.24 cm^2**

   b. How does your answer in part (a) compare to your estimates in Question 3 and Question 5(a)? **They are about the same.**

9 ✔ CHECKPOINT Find the area of each circle to the nearest square centimeter.

a. 3 cm 28 cm^2 **b.** 9 cm 64 cm^2

▶ The area you find when you use either 3.14 or the π key on a calculator is an estimate. To find the exact area of a circle, you need to write an expression that contains the number π.

For example, to find the exact area of a circle with radius 4 cm, write $\pi \cdot 4^2$. Since $\pi \cdot 4^2 = \pi \cdot 16$, or 16π, the exact area is 16π cm^2.

10 a. What is the exact area of a kiva floor with diameter 4.3 m? **4.6225π m^2**
   b. Use 3.14 for π to estimate the area of the kiva floor. **about 14.515 m^2**

11 Estimate how much floor space an average-sized person needs to stand comfortably. How many people can stand comfortably in the kiva in Question 10? **Accept reasonable estimates. about 1 m^2; about 14 people**

HOMEWORK EXERCISES ▶ See Exs. 1–13 on pp. 478–479.

✔ QUESTION 9

...checks that you can find the area of a circle.

Exploration 2

Volume of a Cylinder

SET UP *Work in a group of four. You will need:* • *Labsheets 4B–4D* • *scissors* • *tape* • *rice* • *a ruler*

In the summer of 1891, Gustaf Nordenskiöld of Sweden and his team began to uncover the ruins at Mesa Verde. Part of their task was to remove the layers of dust and rubbish that had piled up over the centuries. After digging to a depth of $\frac{1}{2}$ m at one location, they began to see a kiva take shape.

12 How do you think Nordenskiöld could have estimated the amount of dust and rubbish in the kiva without removing it?

A kiva is shaped like a *cylinder*. A 3-dimensional figure that has a curved surface and two congruent parallel bases that are circles is a **cylinder**.

The **bases** are parallel and congruent.

13 **Use Labsheets 4B–4D.** Cut out the nets for the open-topped *Prisms* and *Cylinders*. Fold and tape each net. **Check students' work.**

14 **Try This as a Class**

a. How are the two cylinders like prisms? How are they different from prisms?

b. Cylinder 1 is a **right cylinder** and Cylinder 2 is an **oblique cylinder**. How are right and oblique cylinders different?
See margin.

c. How would you measure the height of each cylinder?
See margin.

d. Which cylinder do you think has the greater volume? Why?
Answers will vary.

e. Fill Cylinder 2 with rice and then pour the rice into Cylinder 1. Does the rice completely fill Cylinder 1, or is there too much or not enough rice? **Sample Response: The amount of rice is almost exactly the same for both cylinders.**

f. What can you conclude about the volumes of the cylinders?
The volumes are the same.

15 Which has the greater volume, Prism A or Prism B? Explain.
See margin.

GOAL

LEARN HOW TO...
• recognize a cylinder
• find the volume of a cylinder

AS YOU...
• explore the size and shape of a kiva

KEY TERMS
• cylinder
• right cylinder
• oblique cylinder

---

12. Sample Response: He could have found the volume of the region containing the dust and rubbish.

14. a. Sample Response: Cylinders and prisms both have two congruent, parallel bases.; The surface that joins the bases of a cylinder is curved. The faces that join the bases of a prism are polygons.

Exploration 2

TEACHING NOTES

This exploration builds on students' knowledge of how to find the volume of a rectangular prism from Section 1, so you may want to review this skill. Remind students that volume = area of base x height.

Question 13 Before cutting out the prisms on **Labsheets 4B–4D**, you may want to have students glue the nets on tag board in order to make sturdier models. When taping Prism B and the cylinders, instruct students to tape the tabs to the *outside* of the figure and put tape all the way around the base of each figure to keep rice from coming out the bottom in **Question 14(e)**. When students fill the models, the contents should be flush with the top. You may want to make the models ahead of time to demonstrate this. As students pour the rice, point out "how full" each model is after pouring. By using the increments marked on the models, students should see that Prism B fills Cylinder 1 about $\frac{2}{3}$ full and that Cylinder 1 fills Prism A about $\frac{2}{3}$ full. Students will verify this observation in **Question 18(c)**.

MANAGING MATERIALS

Question 14(e) To avoid spills, have students make a paper funnel for pouring the rice. Paper cups or plastic bowls work well for passing out the rice. Students will need this container to pour the rice back into as they pour back and forth between models. Placing a newspaper under the pouring area will make cleaning up any spilled rice easier.

14. b.–c., 15. See Additional Answers beginning on page A1.

Exploration 2 *continued*

TEACHING NOTES

While the base of a cylinder can be any non-polygon shape, all of the cylinders in this book are cylinders with *circular* bases.

The following Classroom Example can be used to provide additional practice finding the volume of a cylinder before students complete **Checkpoint Question 19**.

CLASSROOM EXAMPLE

Find the volume of the cylinder shown to the nearest cubic millimeter. Use 3.14 for π.

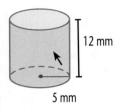

12 mm

5 mm

Answer:

$V = \pi r^2 h$

$\approx 3.14 \cdot 5^2 \cdot 12$

$\approx 942 \text{ mm}^3$

---

16. a. Sample Response: Prism A holds more; It looks like Cylinder 1 will fit inside Prism A.

b. Sample Response: Cylinder 1 holds more; It looks like Prism B will fit inside Cylinder 1.

17. b. The volume of Cylinder 1 is less than the volume of Prism A and greater than the volume of Prism B.

---

18. a. See the table in Question 17 for the volumes of Prisms A and B.; To find the volumes of the prisms, I multiplied the area of the base by the height.

---

16 a. Which do you think holds more, Cylinder 1 or Prism A? Why?

b. Which do you think holds more, Cylinder 1 or Prism B? Why?

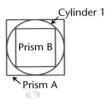

Cylinder 1

Prism B

Prism A

top view

17 a. Place Cylinder 1 inside the larger prism. Then place the smaller prism inside Cylinder 1. **Check students' work.**

b. What can you conclude about the volume of Cylinder 1?

c. For each of the prisms and cylinders, find the area of the base and the height. Make a table to record your results. **See margin.**

18 Discussion Add on to the table you completed in Question 17.

a. Find the volumes of Prism A and Prism B. Explain your method. **See margin.**

b. Use the same method you used in part (a) to find the volumes of Cylinder 1 and Cylinder 2. **See the table in Question 17 for the volumes of Cylinders 1 and 2.**

c. Use your models to decide whether the volume you found for Cylinder 1 is reasonable. **It is reasonable. It is close to the mean of the volumes of Prisms A and B.**

▶ You can find the volume *V* of a cylinder with height *h* and a base with area *B* in the same way you find the volume of a prism.

$$V = Bh, \text{ or } V = \pi r^2 h.$$

 area of circular base

EXAMPLE

Find the volume of the right cylinder shown to the nearest cubic centimeter. Use 3.14 for π.

4 cm

5.3 cm

SAMPLE RESPONSE

$V = \pi r^2 h$

$\approx 3.14 \cdot 4^2 \cdot 5.3 = 266.272$

The volume is about 266 cm³.

Volume is measured in cubic units.

✔ **QUESTION 19**

...checks that you can find the volume of a cylinder.

19 ✔ **CHECKPOINT** Find the volume of the right cylinder at the right to the nearest cubic meter. Use 3.14 for π. **550 m³**

10 m

7 m

20 Gustaf Nordenskiöld reported that one of the kivas he uncovered had a diameter of 4.3 m and walls 2 m high. If this kiva was completely full of dust and rubbish, about how much material did Nordenskiöld have to remove? **about 29 m³.**

HOMEWORK EXERCISES ▶ See Exs. 14–22 on p. 479.

---

17. c. See Additional Answers beginning on page A1.

Section 4

Key Concepts

Key Terms

Area of a Circle (pp. 472–474)

To find the area (A) of a circle, multiply π by the **radius squared**.

$$A = \pi r^2$$

Using π (pp. 473–474)

- To estimate the answer: Use π on a calculator or use 3.14 for π.
- To find the exact answer: Write an expression using the number π.

Cylinders (p. 475)

A 3-dimensional figure that has a curved surface and two congruent parallel bases that are circles is a cylinder.

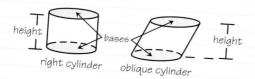

height   bases   height

right cylinder   oblique cylinder

cylinder

right cylinder

oblique cylinder

Volume of a Cylinder (pp. 475–476)

To find the volume (V) of a cylinder, multiply the **area of the base** (B) by the **height** (h).

$$V = Bh$$

For a circular base, $B = \pi r^2$.

$$V = \pi r^2 h$$

Example

Find the volume of the right cylinder shown to the nearest cubic inch. Use 3.14 for π.

$V = \pi r^2 h$

$\approx 3.14 \cdot 1.5^2 \cdot 4.5$

≈ 31.793

The volume is about 32 in.³

1.5 in.

4.5 in.

Key Concepts Questions

21 Find the volume to the nearest cubic centimeter of a cylinder that has a diameter of 16 cm and a height of 10 cm. Use 3.14 for π. **2010 cm³**

22 What happens to the volume of the cylinder in Question 21 if the diameter is doubled? **The volume is multiplied by 4.**

Key Concepts

CLOSURE QUESTION

Why is knowing the formula for the area of a circle important for finding the volume of a cylinder? Use the formulas for area and volume in your answer.

Sample Response: The bases of a cylinder are circles. Since the volume of a cylinder is the area of the base times the height, you need to know how to find the area of a circle in order to find the volume of the cylinder. The volume of a cylinder is given by the formula $V = Bh$ where V is the volume, B is the area of the base, and h is the height. The area (A) of a circle with radius r is given by $A = \pi r^2$ and since the base of the cylinder is a circle, $B = \pi r^2$. Thus, the volume of the cylinder is given by $V = \pi r^2 h$.

ABSENT STUDENTS

For students who were absent for all or part of this section, the blackline Study Guide for Section 4 may be used to present the ideas, concepts, and skills of Section 4.

Section 4
Practice & Application Exercises

Unless you are asked to find exact areas or volumes, use the π key on a calculator or 3.14 for the value of pi. Round to the nearest hundredth.

Find the area of the circle with the given radius (r) or diameter (d).

1. $r = 2\frac{1}{2}$ in. **19.63 in.²**
2. $d = 6$ ft **28.26 ft²**
3. $d = 4.2$ m **13.85 m²**

4. 2 cm **12.56 cm²**
5. 3 in. **7.07 in.²**
6. 1.4 mm **6.15 mm²**

Find the exact area of the circle with the given radius (r) or diameter (d).

7. $r = 25$ mm
 625π mm²

8. $d = 3$ in. **2.25π in.²**

9. $r = 4.6$ cm
 21.16π cm²

10. The circumference of a circle is about 28.26 cm. Find the approximate area of the circle. **about 63.59 cm²**

11. **Archaeology** Gustav Nordenskiöld found a piece of broken pottery at Mesa Verde. The drawing shows a whole bowl based on the broken piece. The top of the bowl is circular with a 14 cm diameter.

 broken piece

 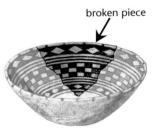

 If you made a flat, circular cover for a bowl this size, what would its area be? **about 153.86 cm²**

12. **Weather** One of the largest tropical storms ever recorded occurred in the Northwest Pacific on October 12, 1979. This storm, a circular typhoon named Tip, had a radius of 1100 km.

 a. What is the approximate area that Tip covered? **3,799,400 km²**

 b. **Estimation** The area of Australia is 7,614,500 km². Suppose Tip had reached Australia. About what fraction of this continent could Tip have covered? **about $\frac{1}{2}$**

◄ A severe rotating wind storm that forms in the western Pacific Ocean or Indian Ocean is called a typhoon. Similar storms in the Atlantic Ocean or Caribbean Sea are called hurricanes.

13. Challenge Figure *ABCD* is a square. Find the area of the shaded region.
about 3.93 in.²

A   B

3 in.   2 in.

D   C

Find the volume of each right cylinder. Use 3.14 for π.

14.
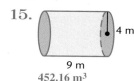

5m

3 m

141.3 m³

15.

4 m

9 m

452.16 m³

16.
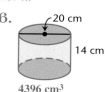

20 cm

14 cm

4396 cm³

For each right cylinder, replace the _?_ with the missing measurement.

17. *r* = 2 in.
h = 6 in.
V ≈ _?_
75.36 in.³

18. *d* = 3.5 cm
h ≈ _?_
V = 57.7 cm³
6 cm

19. *d* = 5.4 m
h = 8 m
V ≈ _?_
183.12 m³

20. Which swimming pool holds more water? A

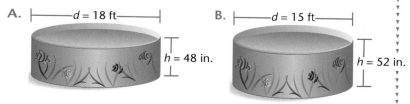

A. |— *d* = 18 ft —|

h = 48 in.

B. |— *d* = 15 ft —|

h = 52 in.

21. Challenge Mugs come in many different shapes and sizes.

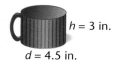

h = 3 in.

d = 4.5 in.

a. What three-dimensional figure are most mugs shaped like?
cylinder

b. Design a mug that will hold about the same amount of liquid as the one shown, but with different dimensions. Sketch your mug and label its height and diameter. **Sample Response:**

h = 3.8 in.

d = 4 in.

Reflecting ◀▶on the Section

22. Make a concept map that pulls together what you have learned about circles, prisms, and cylinders. Include ideas about the following: Answers will vary. Check students' work.

• parts of a prism, a circle, and a cylinder

• formulas for area, volume, and circumference

FOR◀HELP
with concept maps, see
MODULE 5, p. 344

Visual THINKING

Exercise 22 checks that you can make connections between prisms and cylinders and the methods used to find their volumes.

Challenge Exercise 13 may require some hints for students to get started. Ask questions such as, "Can you find the area of the square?" (*Yes, 3 in. • 3 in. = 9 in.²*) "Can you find the area of the small circle?" (*Yes, the radius = 1 in., so the area is π • 1² or about 3.14 in.²*) "How could you find the diameter of the larger circle?" (*It is the same length as one side of the square, so d = 3 in.*) Then give students time to try to figure out how they could use the three areas to find the area of the shaded region. It might help if they cut out a similar square, and two circles, so they could overlay the pieces to see which areas need to be subtracted and which areas remain. (*The area of the shaded region can be found by subtracting the area of the smaller circle from the area of the larger. The area of the square is not needed; only the length of one side is needed to find the diameter of the larger circle.*)

Reflecting Exercise 22 If students are not familiar with concept maps, you may want to draw an example using another topic. One strategy for helping students organize their maps is to have them write the various concepts and information on adhesive notes. Students can arrange the content in different categories or groupings by arranging the adhesive notes on a piece of paper. Using the adhesive notes allows students to easily rearrange or reorganize to see where content "fits" best. Students can then use tape to secure the adhesive notes permanently to the paper, or recopy the map on a separate sheet of paper.

Practice & Applications

EXERCISE NOTES

For **Extension Exercise 35**, students will need access to rice to fill their cones and cylinders. Transparent commercial sets of solids containing a cone and a cylinder with the same size base and height can also be used with water (if there is an opening) to complete **Exercises 34–35**. If used, you may want students to try to sketch the net of the cone and cylinder before looking at **Labsheet 4E**.

34. b. Sample Response: A cone and a cylinder both have a curved surface and at least one circular base. A cone and a pyramid both have one base and the faces that are not bases meet at one vertex.

c. A cone has only one base while a cylinder has two.; A cone has a curved surface and its base is a circle, while the faces and the base of a pyramid are flat polygon-shaped surfaces.

Spiral ◀▶ **Review**

Find the circumference of each circle to the nearest hundredth. Use 3.14 for π. (Module 7, p. 466)

23. diameter = 13 ft   **24.** radius = 6 in.   **25.** diameter = 4.5 m
40.82 ft   37.68 in.   14.13 m

Write each percent as a fraction in lowest terms and as a decimal. (Module 6, p. 427)

26. 40% $\frac{2}{5}$, 0.4 **27.** 9% $\frac{9}{100}$, 0.09 **28.** 15% $\frac{3}{20}$, 0.15 **29.** 63% $\frac{63}{100}$, 0.63

Graph each ordered pair on a coordinate grid. (Module 4, p. 256)

30. (5, 4)   **31.** (0, 7)   **32.** (2, 6)   **33.** (7, 3)

30–33.

(0,7)
(2,6)
(5,4)
(7,3)

Extension ▶ ▶

Volume of a Cone

Home Involvement Use the *Cone and Cylinder Nets* on Labsheet 4E to find the relationship between the volume of a cone and the volume of a cylinder.

34. a. Cut out and fold the nets.
Check students' work.
b. How is the cone like a cylinder? like a pyramid?
See margin.
c. How is a cone different from a cylinder? from a pyramid?
See margin.
d. How do the heights of the cone and cylinder compare?
The heights of the cone and cylinder are the same.
e. How do the shapes and sizes of the bases of the cone and cylinder compare?
The bases of the cone and cylinder have the same shape and size.

> The cones you will work with are *circular* cones because their bases are shaped like circles.

35. a. Fill the cone with rice and pour the rice into the cylinder. Repeat until the cylinder is full. Check students' work.

b. How many of the cones filled with rice did it take to fill the cylinder? 3 cones of rice

36. Write a formula for the volume of a cone.

36. $V = \frac{1}{3}Bh$ where
V = volume of cone,
B = area of the base,
and h = height or, since the base is a circle, $V = \frac{1}{3}\pi r^2 h$
where r is the radius of the base.

Find the volume of each cone. Round to the nearest hundredth.

37.
h = 30 cm
r = 8 cm
2009.60 cm³

38.
h = 13 ft
r = 16 ft
3483.31 ft³

39.
h = 5 in.
d = 3 in.
11.78 in.³

Extra Skill Practice

Find the area of the circle with the given radius (*r*) or diameter (*d*). Use the π key on a calculator or 3.14 for π. Round to the nearest hundredth.

1. $r = 26.3$ mm   2171.91 mm²   2. 5407.87 in.²   3. $r = \frac{1}{2}$ ft   0.79 ft²

Find the exact area of the circle with the given radius (*r*) or diameter (*d*).

4.  225π cm²   5. $d = 49$ yd   600.25π yd²   6. 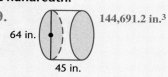 81π m²

Find the volume of each right cylinder. Round to the nearest hundredth.

7. 137,858.56 ft³   56 ft   56 ft

8. 4069.44 cm³   16 cm   9 cm

9. 144,691.2 in.³   64 in.   45 in.

For each right cylinder, replace the ? with the missing measurement. Round to the nearest tenth in Exercises 10 and 11 and to the nearest whole number in Exercise 12.

10. $r = 4.7$ m
$h \approx$?
$V = 458$ m³
6.6 m

11. $d = 2.5$ ft
$h = 4.5$ ft
$V \approx$?
22.1 ft³

12. $r = 10$ cm
$h \approx$?
$V = 1885$ cm³
6 cm

Standardized Testing ◄ Performance Task

Suppose Cylinder 1 is full of sand. If you pour the sand from Cylinder 1 into Cylinder 2, can you fill Cylinder 2 to the top? If not, then how much more sand is needed? If so, what volume of sand is left over in Cylinder 1?
No; about 63.59 cm³ more sand is needed.

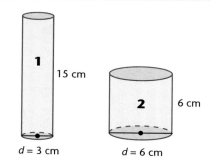

1   15 cm

2   6 cm

$d = 3$ cm $d = 6$ cm

Extra Skill Practice

TEACHER NOTES
For each Exploration, the corresponding Extra Skill Practice Exercises are noted.

Exploration 1: 1–6
Exploration 2: 7–12

EXTRA HELP
Teacher's Resource Book
• Practice and Applications
• Study Guide

Technology Resources
• @Home Tutor
• Test Generator

ASSESSMENT
• Section 4 Quick Quiz
• Test Generator

GETTING STARTED

In preparation for working with integers and graphing in all four quadrants of the coordinate plane, Module 7 Section 5 *Warm-Up* assesses student facility with rounding to the nearest whole number and writing ordered pairs for points in the first quadrant.

Section 5 — Temperature, Integers, and Coordinate Graphs

IN THIS SECTION

EXPLORATION 1
♦ Temperature and Integers

EXPLORATION 2
♦ Graphing Ordered Pairs

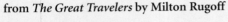
World Traveler

Setting the Stage

from *The Great Travelers* by Milton Rugoff

"Of all the travelers the world has known, there is none whose name conjures up [brings to mind] more images of the exotic, of the wonder of unknown places, than that of Marco Polo.

It was in 1271 that the seventeen-year-old Marco set out from Venice with his father and uncle. ...it took the Polos more than three years to reach China and the fabulous court of [its ruler] Kublai Khan... . Eventually [Marco] visited nearly every part of the vast empire... . The Polos finally arrived in Venice after an absence of almost twenty-six years."

Marco Polo ► in a Tartar costume

Think About It

1 How many years ago did Marco Polo begin his trip? **Check student responses for current school year.**

2 Use the map of the Polos' route. What different kinds of weather do you think the Polos experienced along the way? **Sample Response: I think the Polos met with extremes of both warm and cold weather, as well as moderate climates.**

Exploration 1

Temperature and Integers

Marco Polo's travels took him to places with a wide variety of weather conditions. During the first summer of his trip, he visited the city of Hormuz on the Persian Gulf. In Hormuz, the desert wind, or *simoom*, was so hot that the people spent all morning covered up to their chins in the water of a nearby river.

3 What do you think the high temperature was on a hot day in Hormuz during Marco Polo's visit? **Sample Response: 110°F**

GOAL

LEARN HOW TO...
- measure temperature
- compare integers

AS YOU...
- explore the climate and geography along Marco Polo's route

KEY TERMS
- Celsius (°C)
- Fahrenheit (°F)
- positive
- negative
- integer

Interpreting Temperature Scales

Student Resource

The thermometers show two different ways to measure temperature.

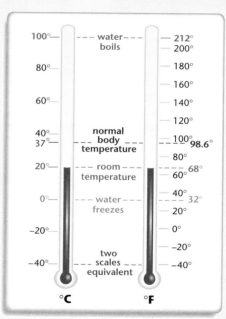

Celsius Temperature Scale

In **degrees Celsius (°C),** water freezes at 0°C and boils at 100°C.

Temperatures *above zero* are **positive.** For example, you write 5 *degrees above zero* as +5° or 5°.

Fahrenheit Temperature Scale

In **degrees Fahrenheit (°F),** water freezes at 32°F and boils at 212°F.

Temperatures *below zero* are **negative.** For example, you write 5 *degrees below zero* as –5°.

Labels on thermometers:
- water boils
- normal body temperature
- room temperature
- water freezes
- two scales equivalent

Exploration 1

DEVELOPING MATH CONCEPTS

This exploration introduces students to positive and negative integers using the context of temperature. As students work through the exploration they should develop meaningful benchmarks for both the Celsius and Fahrenheit temperature scales. You may want to discuss other areas where integers are useful (*recording elevation above and below sea level, recording scores in games, income gain or loss*). As students first learn to compare integers, you may want to relate the comparison to a real life situation. When comparing –3 and –8, you might ask, "Which is colder, –3° or –8°?"

ALTERNATIVE APPROACH

To help students develop benchmarks for Fahrenheit and Celsius temperatures, and to provide practice measuring temperature, you could set up thermometers both inside and outside the classroom. Students could estimate the temperature each day and then take turns recording the actual temperature from the thermometers.

COMMON ERROR
Caution students to read –7 as "negative seven" and not "minus seven".

TEACHING NOTES
To distinguish between positive and negative integers, a negative sign (–) is written in front of a number to indicate the opposite of that whole number. Sometimes students will also see a positive sign (+) written to emphasize positive integers. Since, up to this point, students have been working with positive integers without writing the + sign in front of each number, it is not used with the positive integers in this text. It is important when using signs for negative and positive integers, to be sure students understand that 0 is neither positive nor negative.

4 a. What temperature on the Celsius scale is about the same as 0°F? Accept reasonable estimates; about –20°C

b. Will water freeze at this temperature? Explain.
Yes; –20°C is below 0°C, the temperature at which water freezes.

▶ The benchmark temperatures shown on the Student Resource on page 483 can help you to estimate other temperatures.

5 Estimation Estimate the temperature in each scene in degrees Celsius and in degrees Fahrenheit. Accept reasonable estimates.

a.

about 102°F or about 40°C

b.

about 25°F or about –5°C

c.

about 85°F or about 30°C

d.

about 212°F or about 100°C

6 Select the warmer temperature in each pair.

a. 30°F, 32°F
32°F

b. –5°F, 5°F
5°F

c. –8°F, –21°F
–8°F

▶ Many of the numbers you have been using to describe temperature are *integers*. The **integers** are the numbers ..., –3, –2, –1, 0, 1, 2, 3, ... You can show integers on a number line.

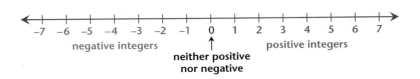

7 a. List the next three integers to the right of 7 on the number line. Are they *positive* or *negative* integers? 8, 9, 10; positive

b. List the next three integers to the left of –7 on the number line. Are they *positive* or *negative* integers? –8, –9, –10; negative

8 Integers are used to describe more than just temperatures. In the diagram, tell which elevations are represented by the given number(s).

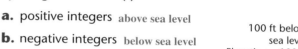

←100 ft above
sea level
Elevation: 100 ft

100 ft below→
sea level
Elevation: −100 ft

a. positive integers *above sea level*

b. negative integers *below sea level*

c. zero *at sea level*

9 The Dead Sea has an elevation of 1312 ft below sea level. Write an integer for the elevation of the Dead Sea. −1312

10 Write an integer to represent each measurement.

a. 40° below zero
−40
b. 10,200 ft above sea level
10,200
c. a profit of $752
752
d. a $50 drop in price
−50

▶ **Comparing Integers** When you want to compare temperatures or elevations, you can think about comparing integers on a number line.

EXAMPLE

Use a number line to compare −2 and −6.

SAMPLE RESPONSE

Since −2 is to the right of −6 on the number line, −2 > −6 or −6 < −2.

11 a. List three integers that are greater than −6.
Answers will vary. Sample Response: −5, 0, 12
b. The integers you listed in part (a) are three solutions of the inequality $x > -6$. List three solutions of the inequality $x < -6$.
Answers will vary. Sample Response: −7, −12, −10
c. List three integer solutions of the inequality $x < 2$.
Answers will vary. Sample Response: 0, 1, −5

12 ✔ **CHECKPOINT** Replace each _?_ with > or <.

a. 3 _?_ −4
>
b. −8 _?_ −2
<
c. 0 _?_ 4
<
d. 8 _?_ −9
>
e. −5 _?_ −13
>
f. 4 _?_ −4
>

✔ **QUESTION 12**

...checks that you can compare integers.

13 **Discussion** After leaving Hormuz, the Polos started their long trek northeast to China. Their route crossed the Pamir Plateau, which has an elevation of 15,600 ft above sea level. How much does the elevation increase from the Dead Sea 1312 ft below sea level to the Pamir Plateau? 16,912 ft

HOMEWORK EXERCISES ▶ See Exs. 1–23 on pp. 490–491.

DIFFERENTIATED INSTRUCTION
Some students may need to use a number line as a visual aid for comparing integers. You might consider displaying a number line across the top of the chalkboard or in some other easily visible place for students to use for reference.

TEACHING NOTES
Checkpoint Question 12 At first, it may be difficult for students to conceptualize inequalities such as 3 > −4 and −8 < −2, since without the negative signs, the inequality would be reversed. Encourage students having difficulty to refer to the number line and to identify the number in each pair that is farther to the right. Point out that the number farther to the right is always greater than the other number in the pair.

Since students have not done addition and subtraction of integers, they should rely on their number sense to answer **Question 13** rather than trying to use an algorithm. To help students do this, sketch roughly to scale the Pamir Plateau as 15,600 ft, sea level as 0 ft, and the Dead Sea as −1312 ft. Students can more easily visualize the increase in elevation.

Exploration 2

DEVELOPING MATH CONCEPTS

This exploration builds on students' previous knowledge of graphing ordered pairs with positive coordinates, so you may want to briefly review this topic from Module 4. The idea of extending the axes system from one quadrant to four is approached through lines of latitude and longitude and directions in relation to the equator and the prime meridian. This concept is then transferred to a coordinate grid system of four quadrants and can be tied to the idea of intersecting a horizontal number line and a vertical number line at the point 0, which becomes the origin.

GOAL

LEARN HOW TO...
* graph points with integer coordinates on a coordinate grid

AS YOU...
* play the game *On the Trail of Marco Polo*

KEY TERM
* quadrant

Exploration 2

GRAPHING Ordered Pairs

SET UP *Work with a partner. You will need:* • *Labsheet 5A* • *metric ruler* • *compass to draw circles (optional)* • *graph paper*

If you were to take a trip to visit all the wonders of the world, you would probably want to pack a world map.

In the thirteenth century, many parts of the world were still unknown. World travelers like Marco Polo had incomplete maps. Today's world maps show a system of lines that you can use to locate any place on Earth.

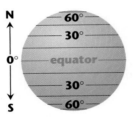

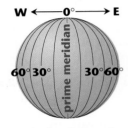

Latitude tells how far north or south of the **equator**.

Longitude tells how far east or west of the **prime meridian**.

The prime meridian is the line of longitude that runs through Greenwich, England.

▶ **Latitude and longitude lines form a coordinate grid.**

14 a. Is the United States *north* or *south* of the equator? north

b. Is the United States *east* or *west* of the prime meridian? west

15 Explain how two distinct locations can both be at 30° latitude on the same line of longitude. The locations are on opposite sides of the equator.

▶ In this exploration, you will play the game *On the Trail of Marco Polo*. To play the game, you need to be able to graph ordered pairs of integers on a coordinate grid.

The grid below extends the one you used in Module 4 to include points with coordinates that are negative integers. The axes divide the grid into four parts called **quadrants**.

EXAMPLE

Graph the ordered pair (–2, 3) on a coordinate grid.

SAMPLE RESPONSE

* Start at the origin, (0, 0).

* Since the first coordinate is **negative**, the horizontal move is to the **left**.

* Since the second coordinate is **positive**, the vertical move is **up**.

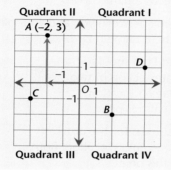

Quadrant II   Quadrant I
Quadrant III   Quadrant IV

16. Quadrant I; Both coordinates are positive so you move to the right, then up. That puts you in Quadrant I.

16 In Module 4 you graphed ordered pairs in which both coordinates were positive numbers. In which quadrant are the graphs of those ordered pairs located? Why?

17 What are the ordered pairs for points *B*, *C*, and *D* on the coordinate grid in the Example above? *B*(2, –2); *C*(–3, –1); *D*(4, 1)

18 Identify the quadrant in which the graph of an ordered pair is located under the given conditions.

   a. Both coordinates are negative. Quadrant III

   b. The first coordinate is negative, and the second coordinate is positive. Quadrant II

   c. The first coordinate is positive, and the second coordinate is negative. Quadrant IV

19 Plot each point on a coordinate grid.

   a. (1, –5)   **b.** (–6, 9)   **c.** (–4, –8)

   d. (4, 0)   **e.** (–7, 7)   **f.** (0, –10)

20 ✔ **CHECKPOINT** If you plot the point with coordinates (–3, 0) on the coordinate grid in the Example above, which point on the grid—*A*, *B*, *C*, or *D*—will be closest to the new point? C

FOR ◀ HELP
with *coordinate graphing*, see
MODULE 4, p. 256

19.
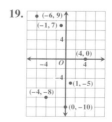

✔ **QUESTION 20**
...checks that you can locate a point on a coordinate grid.

TEACHING NOTES
Remind students to always start at the origin when plotting points on a coordinate grid. To help students summarize movement on the grid, point out that a positive coordinate indicates movement to the right or up, and a negative coordinate indicates movement to the left or down.

COMMON ERROR
Students may be confused when graphing ordered pairs that have 0 as one of the coordinates. Explain that a coordinate of 0 means there is no movement along the corresponding axis.

TEACHING NOTES
The Classroom Example below can be used to show students how to set up a coordinate grid and graph points before they do so on their own in **Question 19**. The distinction between points (3, –2) and (–3, 2) is also made.

CLASSROOM EXAMPLE

Plot points *A*(3, –2) and *B*(–3, 2) on a coordinate grid.

Answer: Point *A*: Start at 0. The first coordinate is positive, so the horizontal move is to the right 3. The second coordinate is negative, so the vertical move is down 2.

Point *B*: Start at 0. The first coordinate is negative, so the horizontal move is to the left 3. The second coordinate is positive, so the vertical move is up 2.

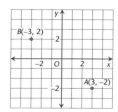

TEACHING NOTES
Before students play *On the Trail of Marco Polo* in **Question 21**, have them read **Question 22**. This will help students focus on what they are to learn from playing the game and be better prepared to discuss their strategies.

As students discuss the game in **Question 22**, you may want to present a sample guess (and distance from Marco's location) and have students share with the class what their next move would be and why.

22. **a.** Yes; I used a compass to draw a circle with center X and radius the given distance, then checked where that circle crossed an intersection of two grid lines. That helped me choose my next guess.
   b. I used points near the edges of the grid for my first guess because the directions from those points are limited.

---

21 **Use Labsheet 5A.** The object of the game *On the Trail of Marco Polo* is to find the ordered pair of integers that represents Marco Polo's location. Read the rules. Then play the game twice with your partner, so each of you has a chance to be Marco Polo.
Observe students playing the game.

On the Trail of Marco Polo

◆ Decide which player will be Marco Polo. The other player is the Searcher. Each player needs a game board.

◆ Place an upright notebook between you and your partner so that you cannot see each other's game board.

◆ The player who is Marco Polo should choose a point at the intersection of two grid lines to indicate Marco's location, and then mark a dot (•) at this point.

◆ The Searcher calls out a guess for the ordered pair that represents Marco Polo's location. Both players draw an "X" at this point.

◆ The player who is Marco Polo should use a metric ruler to measure how far the "X" is from the dot to the nearest millimeter, and call out the measurement.

◆ The Searcher has four more chances to guess the ordered pair. The game ends when the Searcher either finds Marco Polo or has no guesses left.

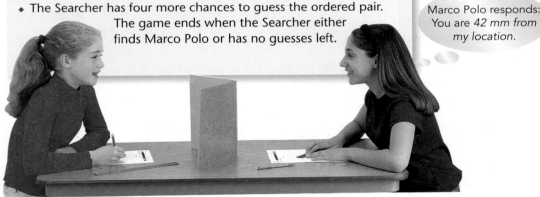

Marco Polo's location is at (–1, 1).

The Searcher calls out the ordered pair (3, –2).

Marco Polo responds: You are *42 mm from my location.*

22 **Discussion** Think about how you played the game.
Sample responses are given. See margin.
   a. When you were the Searcher, was it helpful to know how far your guess was from Marco Polo's location? Explain.
   b. What strategies did you use to play the game?

HOMEWORK EXERCISES ▶ See Exs. 24–27 on p. 492.

Key Concepts

Temperature and Integers (pp. 483–485)

You can measure temperature in degrees Celsius or degrees Fahrenheit. You can use integers to represent temperatures, elevations, and other measurements.

negative integers   zero   positive integers

..., –4, –3, –2, –1,   0,   1,   2,   3,   4,   ...

Comparing Integers:

• A positive integer is always greater than a negative integer.
5 > –6 or –6 < 5

• A negative integer that is closer to zero on a number line is always greater than a negative integer that is farther from zero.
–3 > –6 or –6 < –3

Graphing Ordered Pairs of Integers (pp. 486–488)

A coordinate grid for graphing points where coordinates are integers has four quadrants, I, II, III, and IV as shown.

Example

Write the coordinates of point A.

Move along the horizontal axis to read the first coordinate.

Move along the vertical axis to read the second coordinate.

Point A is at (3, –2).

Key Terms

Celsius (°C)

Fahrenheit (°F)

integers

positive integers

negative integers

quadrant

Key Concepts

CLOSURE QUESTIONS

Describe how you can use positive and negative integers to model temperature. Then describe how you can use a coordinate grid to graph ordered pairs.

Sample Response: For temperatures that are greater than 0°, use positive integers. For temperatures that are less than 0°, use negative integers.

To graph ordered pairs on a coordinate grid, begin at the origin, then move horizontally the distance and direction that the first number in the ordered pair indicates, and from there move vertically the distance and direction that the second number in the ordered pair indicates.

ABSENT STUDENTS

For students who were absent for all or part of this section, the blackline Study Guide for Section 5 may be used to present the ideas, concepts, and skills of Section 5.

Key Concepts Questions

23 One day a thermometer read 8°F at 10 A.M. At 10 P.M. on the same day, the thermometer read –13°F.

  a. Was the temperature reading higher at 10 A.M. or 10 P.M.?
  10 A.M.

  b. Was the temperature at 10 A.M. *above* or *below* freezing?
  below freezing

24 Explain how you would graph (–5, –1) on a coordinate grid.

24. Start at the origin. Move five units to the left on the horizontal axis and 1 unit down from the horizontal axis.

Practice & Applications

SUGGESTED ASSIGNMENTS

Core Course
Day 1: Exs. 1–22
Day 2: Exs. 24, 26–35

Extended Course
Day 1: Exs. 1–23
Day 2: Exs. 24–35

Note: Extended Course assignments can be used to differentiate within the regular classroom. In classrooms where students are grouped homogeneously, the material might be covered in fewer days. In this case assignments may be combined.

ADDITIONAL PRACTICE
See the *Teacher's Resource Book* for additional practice and application exercises for this section.

4. Sample Response: heavy clothing such as a winter coat, hat, scarf, gloves, boots; no outdoor activities; It is too cold to be outdoors for any length of time.

8. February, March, January, December, April, November, October, May, September, June, August, July

---

YOU WILL NEED

For Ex. 25:
♦ graph paper

For Exs. 31–34:
♦ protractor

1. Sample Response: light weight clothing such as long pants and a shirt; tennis, jogging, hiking; It is warm but not hot.

2. Sample Response: very light clothing; swimming, sailing; It is very hot.

3. Sample Response: heavy clothing such as a winter coat, hat, scarf, gloves, boots; ice skating, skiing; It is quite cold.

Section ⑤
Practice & Application Exercises

Writing For each average daily temperature, describe the clothing it is reasonable to wear and the outdoor activities it is reasonable to participate in. Explain your choices.

1. 63°F   2. 32°C   3. 27°F   4. –15°C
See margin.

5. While in Russia Marco Polo experienced "the greatest cold that is to be found anywhere, so great as to be scarcely bearable." Give Fahrenheit and Celsius temperatures to match this condition.
Sample Response: –60°F or –50°C

Interpreting Data Use the graph for Exercises 6–9.

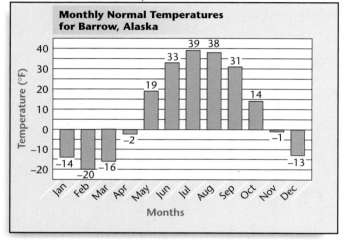

6. a. Which month shown is the coldest? February

   b. Which month shown is the warmest? July

7. a. How are the temperatures for January and October alike?
   The number of degrees is the same.
   b. How are the temperatures for January and October different?
   One is negative and one is positive.

8. List the months in order from coldest to warmest. See margin.

9. How many degrees greater is the monthly normal temperature in July than in October? April than in January? October than in March? 25°F; 12°F; 30°F

Write an integer to represent each measurement.

10. a 25 yd gain in football
    25

11. a debt of $349
    –349

12. 823 ft below sea level
    –823

13. a credit of $10
    10

14. a. Draw a number line, and use a dot to locate each of the following integers on it: 7, –1, –9, 3, 5, –5, 2, 4, –7.

    b. List the integers in part (a) from least to greatest.

14. a.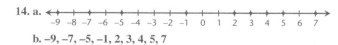

b. –9, –7, –5, –1, 2, 3, 4, 5, 7

Replace each ? with > or <.

15. –5 ? 4
    <

16. –9 ? –5
    <

17. 0 ? –3
    >

18. –7 ? –20
    >

19. **Algebra Connection** On a number line, show two positive and two negative solutions of the inequality $x < 10$.

Social Studies *The Diving Bell* by Todd Strasser is a historical novel set in sixteenth century Mexico. In the story, a Spanish ship loaded with gold is sunk off the Mexican coast. The ship, the *Santo Cristo*, lies so deep that even the best divers cannot bring up the treasure. A young girl named Culca finds a way to do it:

..."If the great [church] bell were lowered into the water a diver could swim under it and breathe new air," Culca explained. [A diver] could go deeper and stay down longer...."

20. **Estimation** The sides of a ship sent to pick up the recovered treasure rise "the height of five men" above the surface. Estimate this height in feet. Then write an integer for this measurement.

21. The bell was lowered 10 fathoms below the surface to where the *Santo Cristo* was believed to be. Write an integer for this depth below the surface in feet. (1 fathom = 6 ft) –60

22. a. In 1733 a real Spanish ship, the *San Pedro*, sank in 18 ft of water. Write an integer for the depth of the water in feet. –18

    b. Write an inequality that compares the depth of this real wreck with the depth of the wreck in the story.
    –18 > –60 or –60 < –18

23. **Challenge** Order the numbers from least to greatest.

    $-23, 56, -12\frac{3}{4}, 2.4, -35, 25\frac{1}{3}, 25.48, 0, 13, -12.25, 25.5$

    $-35, -23, -12\frac{3}{4}, -12.25, 0, 2.4, 13, 25\frac{1}{3}, 25.48, 25.5, 56$

20. Accept reasonable estimates.
    25 ft–30 ft; Possible answers: 25, 26, 27, 28, 29, or 30

19. Sample Response:

    <+—+—+—+—+—+—+—+—+—+—+—+—+—+—+—+>
    　　　–4　　–2　　0　　2　　4　　6　　8　　10

Practice & Applications

EXERCISE NOTES

Exercise 25 Students may enjoy coloring their designs and presenting them on a bulletin board. Students could describe how they constructed their design on a note card and staple the card next to their design.

26. **Sample Response:** The horizontal and vertical axes on a coordinate grid are number lines that are positioned perpendicular to each other, intersecting at 0. Then lines parallel to these axes are drawn through each integer on both axes.

Discussion

Exercises 26 and 27 check your understanding of integers on a number line and on a coordinate grid.

35. **Sample Response:** I would use estimation. I could round $2.29 up to $2.50 and 1.7 up to 2. Then 2 · $2.50 = $5. Since both numbers are rounded up, I know the estimate is higher than the actual cost and I have enough money.

24. Write the coordinates of each of the labeled points *A–F*. $A(1,2)$; $B(-3,-2)$; $C(-1,1)$; $D(1,-3)$; $E(-3,-5)$; $F(4,-1)$

25. a. **Create Your Own** Draw a coordinate grid on graph paper. Plot points and draw segments connecting these points to create your own design. List the ordered pairs for your design in the order they need to be connected. Check students' work.

   b. **Home Involvement** Without showing the figure, ask a friend or family member to plot your points and connect them to try to make your design. Answers will vary.

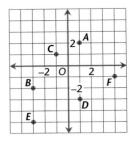

Reflecting ◀▶ on the Section

Be prepared to discuss your responses to Exercises 26 and 27 in class.

26. Explain how number lines are used to form a coordinate grid. Include a sketch in your answer.

27. Tell how the integers in the ordered pair for a point on a coordinate grid change if the point is moved in the given direction.

   a. to the right
      The first coordinate increases.

   b. to the left
      The first coordinate decreases.

   c. up
      The second coordinate increases.

   d. down
      The second coordinate decreases.

Spiral ◀▶ Review

Approximate the area of each circle. Use 3.14 for π. Round to the nearest hundredth. (Module 7, p. 477)

28. diameter = 6 in.
    28.26 in.²

29. radius = 8 cm
    200.96 cm²

30. diameter = 3.5 m
    9.62 m²

Use a protractor to draw each angle. (Module 2, p. 119)

31. 35°   32. 175°   33. 92°   34. 58°
31–34. Check students' drawings.

35. **Choose a Method** Cherries cost $2.29 per pound. A bag of cherries weighs 1.7 lb. Would you use mental math, paper and pencil, or estimation to decide if $5 is enough money to buy the bag of cherries? Explain. (Module 1, pp. 10–11; Module 3, p. 190)

Section 5

Extra Skill Practice

You will need: • *graph paper* (Exs. 12–19)

For each situation, give a possible temperature in degrees Fahrenheit and in degrees Celsius.

1. The snow on the ground is starting to melt. **Sample Response: 41°F or 5°C**

2. The beach is crowded with swimmers. **Sample Response: 86°F or 30°C**

3. People are wearing light sweaters or jackets. **Sample Response: 59°F or 15°C**

Replace each ? with > or <.

4. 5 ? –14   5. –8 ? –4   6. –7 ? 0
  >   **<**   **<**

7. 6 ? 18   8. –6 ? –18   9. 23 ? –24
  <   **>**   **>**

Use the coordinate grid for Exercises 10–11.

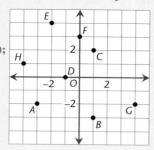

10. Write the coordinates of each of the labeled points A–H. **A(–3,–2); B(1, –3); C(1,2); D(–1,0); E(–2,4); F(0,3); G(4, –2); H(–4, 1)**

11. If you plot the point with the coordinates (–3, 1), which labeled point will be closest to the new point? **H**

Make a coordinate grid on graph paper. The integers on each axis should range from –10 to 10. Then plot and label each point on your grid.

12. R (–10, 0)   13. S (5, –3)   14. T (2, 4)   15. U (–3, 5)

16. V (0, –6)   17. W (–2, 2)   18. X (–7, –4)   19. Y (8, –9)

12–19.

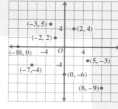

Standardized Testing ◀▶ Open-Ended

1. On a weekend afternoon in the summer, which temperature would you prefer, 20°C or 32°C? Explain why. **Sample Response: I would prefer 32°C because it is hot enough to go swimming.**

2. Here is an example of an inequality for which –5 is a solution:

$$x < -2$$

Write two more inequalities for which –5 is a solution.
Sample Responses: $x < 0, x > -10$

Module Project

INTRODUCING THE PROJECT
If possible bring in a brochure or poster from a travel agency that is promoting a travel opportunity. Use this pamphlet to motivate the discussion about creating a travel poster.

Labsheet: Each student needs a copy of Project Labsheet A, which is found in the *Teacher's Resource Book*.

The Module Project

Create a World Travel Poster

In this module, you learned about some of the most fascinating places in the world. You will use what you have learned to create a travel poster promoting a trip around the world. To make your poster informative and attractive, you may include photographs, diagrams, and 3-dimensional objects as well as interesting facts.

What places would you visit on a trip around the world? You will need to decide on four sites that you would like to feature on your poster and then gather information about each one. Your poster should highlight three of the wonders described in this module. As you choose your sites, think about how you would like to display each one.

Answers to Questions 1–3 and 5–9 will vary. Check students' work.

Gathering Data Select the four sites for your poster.

1. Visit a travel agent or a library, or search the Internet to help find photos and information about the sites.

2. The Empire State Building is world famous because it once was the world's tallest skyscraper, standing 1472 ft high. Explain why each site you chose is considered "wondrous." In particular, find out whether there is an incredible measurement that makes it world famous. If so, tell whether the measurement is related to length, area, or volume.

3. Gather information on the geography and climate of the places where the sites for your poster are located.

   a. For each site, write an integer to represent what you might experience as an average temperature if you traveled there in January, or write an integer to represent the elevation of each site.

   b. Write an inequality comparing two of the values (two temperatures or two elevations) in part (a).

Nets for 3-dimensional Objects To make your poster more attractive, you can attach 3-dimensional models of some of the sites you plan to feature.

 4 a. **Use Project Labsheet A.** Follow the directions on the labsheet to create a net for a *Model of the Great Pyramid at Giza*.

b. How many faces, vertices, and edges does a square pyramid have?
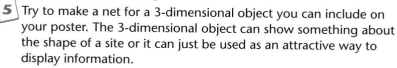
5 faces, 5 vertices, 8 edges

 5 Try to make a net for a 3-dimensional object you can include on your poster. The 3-dimensional object can show something about the shape of a site or it can just be used as an attractive way to display information.

Finishing and Sharing Your Poster To finish the project, you will use the information you have gathered to complete your poster. You will also decide which of the four sites you would most like to see.

6 Create your poster. Include the following:

◆ the name and location of each site

◆ visuals that you have made or collected to help others see details of the site

◆ a "Did you know?" fact for each site that applies at least one of the mathematical ideas you learned in the module and uses information you have gathered

7 Look back at your poster and the information you gathered. Which site would you most like to visit? Explain in a brief summary what there is about the site that attracts you.

8 Display your poster in class along with your classmates' posters. Then look back at the *Presentation Scale* of the *Assessment Scales* in Module 2. What types of things make each poster unique? Is there any one poster that you found especially attractive? If so, explain why.

9 Think about each poster you saw. Name something you learned about a different part of the world or about one of the "world wonders" presented.

PROJECT NOTES

Question 5 Students may need help or teacher guidance as they draw their nets. You may want to have them draw their nets on graph paper to be sure the bases are congruent and in the correct position. Encourage students to keep trying if their first attempt does not work, and to modify previous attempts instead of starting completely over each time. Before cutting out the nets, students could glue them onto stiffer paper such as tag board. After completing their nets, you may want students to record how many faces, edges, and vertices there are for each polyhedron they make. You might also want to have students make two copies of each net so other students can see what the net looked like before it was cut out and folded. If time allows, suggest that students complete more than one net. Students can attach the nets to their poster with glue or tape.

MODULE 7 Review and Assessment

You will need: • *scissors and tape* (Ex. 1) • *metric ruler* (Exs. 4 and 11)
• *graph paper* (Ex. 18)

Use the net shown for Exercises 1–4. (Sec. 1, Explors. 1 and 2)

1. a. Predict what polyhedron
   the net will form.
   Answers will vary. an oblique pentagonal prism
   b. Trace the net. Then cut
   out the tracing and fold it
   to check your prediction.
   Check students' work.

2. a. Describe the shapes of the
   faces.

   b. Name the polyhedron.
   an oblique pentagonal prism

3. How many faces, vertices,
   and edges does the figure
   have? 7 faces, 10 vertices, 15 edges

4. a. Decide the dimensions you
   need to find the volume. Then
   find these measurements to the
   nearest millimeter.

   b. Find the volume. 19,610 mm^3

2. a. two of the faces
   are pentagons, five
   are parallelograms
   of which one is a
   rectangle

5. A flower planter is in the shape of a right
   rectangular prism 18 in. long, $5\frac{1}{2}$ in. high,
   and $6\frac{1}{2}$ in. wide. Estimate the volume of soil
   the planter can hold. (Sec. 1, Explor. 2)
   Accept reasonable estimates. The exact volume is 643.5 in.^{3}

6. Dick bought a 7-lb bag of apples for $4.97. (Sec. 2, Explor. 1)

   a. What was the cost per pound of the apples?
   $.71 per pound
   b. Each apple weighed about 12 oz. About how
   many apples were in the bag?
   about 9 apples

4. a. area of the
   pentagonal base =
   20 mm • 18 mm + $\frac{1}{2}$
   (20 mm • 17 mm) =
   530 mm^2,
   height of the prism
   = 37 mm

Replace each ? with the missing number. (Sec. 2, Explor. 1)

7. 3 lb = __?__ oz 48   8. 80 oz = __?__ lb 5   9. 3500 lb = __?__ tons $1\frac{3}{4}$

Use the circle at the right for Exercises 10–12.

10. Name parts of the circle as described.
    (Sec. 3, Explor. 1)

    a. the center
       O
    b. two radii
       any two of $\overline{OE}$, $\overline{OB}$, and $\overline{OD}$
    c. two chords
       $\overline{AC}$, $\overline{BE}$
    d. a diameter
       $\overline{BE}$

11. Measure the radius of the circle to the nearest tenth of a centimeter. (Sec. 3, Explor. 1)
    2.5 cm

12. a. Find the approximate circumference of the circle. (Sec. 3, Explor. 2) about 15.7 cm

    b. Find the approximate area of the circle. (Sec. 4, Explor. 1) about 19.6 cm²

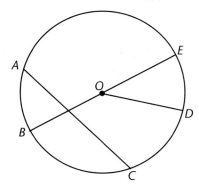

13. The Temple of Artemis in ancient Greece was regarded as one of the Seven Ancient Wonders of the World. It dated back to 550 B.C. and was thought to be the most beautiful structure on Earth. The structure had right cylindrical columns 60 ft high. If the diameter of each column was about 15 ft, what was the approximate volume of one of the columns? (Sec. 4, Explor. 2)
    10,597.5 ft³

18. a–b.

14. On February 21, 1918, the temperature in Granville, North Dakota, changed from –33°F to 50°F. Did the weather get warmer or cooler? By how many degrees did the temperature change? Explain. (Sec. 5, Explor. 1) warmer; 83°F; The difference between 33° below 0 and 50° above 0 on the Fahrenheit scale is 83 degrees.

Replace each ? with > or < to make each a true statement. (Sec. 5, Explor. 1)

15. –5 ? 3
    <

16. –10 ? –2
    <

17. –5 ? –6
    >

18. Make a coordinate grid on graph paper. (Sec. 5, Explor. 2)

    a. Label the axes and the origin.

    b. Plot the points (–2, 8) and (5, –4) on the grid.

Reflecting ◀▶ **on the Module**

19. a. Find a container that is shaped like a prism and find its volume.

    b. Find the dimensions of a right cylinder that has about the same volume as the container you found. Sketch it and label its height and the diameter of a base.

    c. Find and label the circumference of a base of the cylinder in part (b).

19. Sample Response:
    A box that holds ten 3.5 in. computer diskettes is a rectangular prism that is about 9.5 cm long, 4.7 cm wide, and 9.8 cm high. Its volume is about 437.57 cm³. A cylinder that has a base diameter of 8 cm and height 8.7 cm has about the same volume. Its volume is about 437.09 cm³.

Assessment Options

TEACHER'S RESOURCE BOOK
• Module 7 Tests A and B
• Module 7 Standardized Test
• Module 7 Performance Assessment

TEST GENERATOR

Module 8 Overview

This module presents new material while revisiting each of the themes from Modules 1 through 6. Activities include estimating capacities of containers, building cubic centimeter and one-liter cubes, investigating a math-magic trick, playing an integer game, making quilt squares, modeling our solar system, and predicting by tossing a globe.

Module 8 Planner

Day 1: Section 1	Day 2: Section 1	Day 3: Section 1	Day 4: Section 2	Day 5: Section 2
Setting the Stage, p. 500 Exploration 1 *through* *Question 6, p. 501*	Exploration 1 *from* *Question 7, p. 502*	Exploration 2, *pp. 503–505* Key Concepts, p. 506	Setting the Stage, p. 512 Exploration 1 *through* *Question 7, pp. 513–514*	Exploration 1 *from* *Example, p. 515* Key Concepts, p. 516
Day 6: Section 3	**Day 7: Section 3**	**Day 8: Section 3**	**Day 9: E²**	**Day 10: Review and Assessment**
Setting the Stage, p. 520 Exploration 1, *pp. 521–523*	Exploration 2 *through* *Question 18,* *pp. 523–525*	Exploration 2 *from* *Question 19,* *pp. 525–526* Key Concepts, p. 527	Begin E², p. 533	Mid-Module Quiz
Day 11: Section 4	**Day 12: Section 5**	**Day 13: Section 5**	**Day 14: Section 5**	**Day 15: Section 6**
Setting the Stage, p. 534 Exploration 1, *pp. 535–536* Key Concepts, p. 537	Setting the Stage, *pp. 542–543* Exploration 1 *through* *Question 7, pp. 543–544*	Exploration 1 *from* *Example, p. 545*	Exploration 2, *pp. 546–547* Key Concepts, p. 548	Setting the Stage, p. 553 Exploration 1 *through* *Question 7, p. 554*
Day 16: Section 6	**Day 17: Module Project**	**Day 18: Module Project**	**Day 19: Review and Assessment**	**Day 20: Review and Assessment**
Exploration 1 *from* *Example, p. 555* Key Concepts, p. 556	Begin Module Project, *pp. 560–561*	Play Module Project Game	Assign Review and Assessment, *pp. 562–563*	Discuss Review and Assessment, *pp. 562–563*
Day 21: Assessment				
Module 8 Test				

Materials List

Section	Materials
1	• Labsheet 1A, various size containers, milk containers in pint, quart, and gallon sizes, tape, scissors, water in a cup, eyedropper, metric ruler, 12 straws, 24 paper clips, one graduated cylinder for the class
3	• Labsheet 3A, 12 beans each marked with a "+" on one side and a "−" on the other side for each pair of students, paper cups, game pieces, graph paper
4	• an inflatable globe
5	• Labsheets 5A–5D, tracing paper, index card, scissors, ruler, clear tape, construction paper, triangle from Exploration 1, glue, decorative paper, drawing software (optional)
6	• Labsheet 6A, sticky notes, calculators, index cards or planet cutouts, scissors
Project	• 8 index cards or 8 overhead transparencies, markers
Rev & Assess	• tracing paper

Module 8 Objectives

Section	Objectives	NCTM Standards 2000*
1	• Use benchmarks to estimate capacity in customary units. • Convert between customary units of capacity. • Relate metric units of capacity to metric units of volume. • Estimate capacity in metric units. • Convert between metric units of capacity.	1, 3, 4, 6, 7, 8, 9, 10
2	• Use trading off to find a whole number or decimal sum. • Use front-end estimation to approximate a whole number or decimal sum.	1, 6, 7, 8, 9, 10
3	• Use a model to represent integers and sums of integers. • Add integers. • Use a model to represent integer subtraction. • Subtract integers.	1, 2, 6, 7, 8, 9, 10
4	• Find geometric probabilities. • Use probability to make predictions.	1, 5, 6, 7, 8, 9, 10
5	• Perform a translation, a rotation, and a reflection. • Use transformations to make designs.	3, 4, 6, 7, 8, 9, 10
6	• Write numbers in scientific notation using positive exponents. • Write numbers that are in scientific notation in standard form.	1, 4, 6, 8, 9, 10

* See page T14.

Section 1 Customary and Metric Capacity

Section 1 Planner

Section Objectives

Exploration 1
- Use benchmarks to estimate capacity in customary units
- Convert between customary units of capacity

Exploration 2
- Relate metric units of capacity to metric units of volume
- Estimate capacity in metric units
- Convert between metric units of capacity

Days for Section 1

First Day
Setting the Stage, *p. 500*
Exploration 1 through Question 6, *p. 501*

Second Day
Exploration 1 from Question 7, *p. 502*

Third Day
Exploration 2, *pp. 503–505*
Key Concepts, *p. 506*

Teaching Resources

Teacher's Resource Book
- Warm-Up
- Labsheet 1A
- Practice and Applications
- Study Guide
See page 499 for additional teaching resources.

Materials List

Setting the Stage
- various size containers
- milk containers in pint, quart, and gallon sizes

Exploration 2
- Labsheet 1A
- scissors and tape
- water in a cup
- eyedropper
- metric ruler
- 12 straws
- 24 paper clips
- one graduated cylinder for the class

Assessment Options

EMBEDDED ASSESSMENT
- Use benchmarks to estimate capacity in customary units
    Exercises 2, 3, 4
- Convert between customary units of capacity
    Exercises 6, 8, 10
- Relate metric units of capacity to metric units of volume
    Exercises 17, 19
- Estimate capacity in metric units
    Exercises 27, 28, 29
- Convert between metric units of capacity
    Exercises 23, 24, 25

PERFORMANCE TASK/PORTFOLIO
- Exercise 12 on *p. 507 (writing)*
- Exercise 14 on *p. 508 (create your own)*
- Exercise 20 on *p. 508 (visual thinking)*
- Exercise 32 on *p. 509 (challenge)*
- Exercise 33 on *p. 509 (visual thinking)*

QUIZZES/TESTS
- Section 1 Quick Quiz

TEST GENERATOR

Section 1 Overview

In this section, students will work with customary and metric units of capacity. The section begins with an estimation activity in which students use milk containers as benchmarks for estimating the customary capacity of various containers.

Exploration 1
Students are introduced to a visual pattern to help them understand and remember the relationships between the customary units of measure necessary for conversions.

Exploration 2
Students explore the connection between metric volume (1 cm^3) and metric capacity (1 mL) by constructing a cubic centimeter model and filling it with water. New vocabulary for this exploration includes *milliliter, liter,* and *kiloliter.* The prefixes *milli-* and *kilo-* were originally presented in Module 4, Section 1 and can be reviewed if necessary.

Guide for Assigning Homework

REGULAR SCHEDULING (45 MIN CLASS PERIOD)			EXERCISES TO NOTE		
Section/ P&A Pages	Core Assignment	Extended Assignment	Additional Practice/Review	Open-ended Problems	Extended Problems
1 pp. 507–511	**Day 1:** 1–5, SR 34–42 **Day 2:** 6–15, 43 **Day 3:** 16–31, ROS 33	1–5, SR 34–42 6–15, 43 16–32, ROS 33	EP, p. 511	PA 14	Challenge, PA 32 Career Connection 43

Key: PA = Practice & Application; ROS = Reflecting on the Section; SR = Spiral Review; TB = Toolbox; EP = Extra Skill Practice; Ext = Extension; ST = Standardized Testing

Math Background and Teaching Strategies

Classroom Notes

Bulletin board display ideas for this section include:

- pictures of gallon, quart, pint, and cup size containers

- a capacity visual diagram similar to the one on page 501

- relationships between 1 cm³, a milliliter, a liter, and a kiloliter

- student created capacity problems (see Exercise 14 on page 508)

Math Strands

Topic Integration and Spiraling

Exploration 1

Exploration 1 focuses on developing students' intuitive understanding of conversions between customary units of capacity. At this point, students should feel comfortable with conversions between units since conversions for length and for weight were developed in Modules 5 and 7 respectively. Estimation skills are developed through a hands-on activity that allows students to use containers of known capacity as a basis for improving their estimates. Fraction multiplication skills from Module 3 are used in making conversions. Students will continue work with customary conversions in Modules 3 and 7 of Book 2.

Exploration 2

Students explore the connections between a cubic centimeter and a milliliter by filling cubic centimeters with water, pouring them into a graduated cylinder, and reading the capacity in milliliters. The centimeter cube is then compared to the size of a liter cube to develop relationships between capacities. The visual models serve as guides for students to estimate the capacity of several items. Students were exposed to metric measures of length and mass in Module 4. When they study volume in Book 2, Module 7, students will return to metric units of capacity and apply relationships between volume, mass, and capacity.

Section 2 Estimation and Mental Math

Section 2 Planner

Section Objectives

Exploration 1
- Use trading off to find a whole number or decimal sum
- Use front-end estimation to approximate a whole number or decimal sum

Days for Section 2

First Day
Setting the Stage, *p. 512*
Exploration 1 through Question 7, *pp. 513–514*

Second Day
Exploration 1 from Example, *p. 515*
Key Concepts, *p. 516*

Teaching Resources

Teacher's Resource Book
- Warm-Up
- Practice and Applications
- Study Guide
See page 499 for additional teaching resources.

Assessment Options

EMBEDDED ASSESSMENT
- Use trading off to find a whole number or decimal sum
  Exercises 3, 4, 5
- Use front-end estimation to approximate a whole number or decimal sum
  Exercises 8, 9, 11

PERFORMANCE TASK/PORTFOLIO
- Exercise 7 on *p. 517*
- Exercise 14 on *p. 518 (journal)*
- Standardized Testing on *p. 519 (open-ended)*

QUIZZES/TESTS
- Section 2 Quick Quiz

TEST GENERATOR

Section 2 Overview

In this section, students will learn how to use the *trading off* mental math technique to find the sum of a set of numbers and *front-end estimation* to estimate sums.

Exploration 1
Students begin by performing a math-magic trick in the *Setting the Stage*. During Exploration 1, students investigate the mathematics behind the trick and learn how to use trading off in both tricks and in everyday computations. Students use front-end estimation to estimate sums. They learn how front-end estimation focuses on the digits with the greatest value and how trading off balances rounding up with subtraction.

Guide for Assigning Homework

REGULAR SCHEDULING (45 MIN CLASS PERIOD)			EXERCISES TO NOTE		
Section/ P&A Pages	Core Assignment	Extended Assignment	Additional Practice/Review	Open-ended Problems	Extended Problems
2 pp. 517–519	**Day 1:** 1–7, SR 15–23 **Day 2:** 8–12, ROS 14, SR 24–28	1–7, SR 15–23 8–13, ROS 14, SR 24–28	EP, p. 519 TB, p. 567	PA 14 ST, p. 519	PA 13

Key: PA = Practice & Application; ROS = Reflecting on the Section; SR = Spiral Review; TB = Toolbox; EP = Extra Skill Practice; Ext = Extension; ST = Standardized Testing

Math Background and Teaching Strategies

Classroom Notes

Bulletin board display ideas for this section include:

- examples showing how to use trading off and front-end estimation
- student explanations for the magic trick in Exercise 7 (page 517)
- student responses to *Standardized Testing* (page 519)

Math Strands

Topic Spiraling and Integration

Exploration 1

The goal of this Exploration is for students to improve their mental math and estimation skills. The magic trick motivates the lesson by showing how being able to compute quickly mentally can be used in recreational puzzles. Often students think there is some magic to being able to compute sums mentally, when in fact, it usually is the result of knowing particular strategies and how to apply them. It also takes practice. Students should not limit their use of the trading off strategy just to this section, but continue to use it in other contexts when they have the opportunity. Encourage students to try it at stores with prices of items or with numbers they read in the newspaper.

Estimation is an important skill that will be used throughout Books 2 and 3. There is no one set technique for estimating, though many times rounding is favored. Front-end estimation gives students another possible strategy to employ. The clustering strategy is addressed in the *Practice and Application Exercises*. Clustering is a valuable strategy for estimation when numbers are all close to one value.

Section 3   Adding and Subtracting Integers

Section 3 Planner

Section Objectives

Exploration 1
• Add integers

Exploration 2
• Subtract integers

Days for Section 3

First Day
Setting the Stage, *p. 520*
Exploration 1, *pp. 521–523*

Second Day
Exploration 2 through Question 18,
pp. 523–525

Third Day
Exploration 2 from Question 19, *pp. 525–526*
Key Concepts, *p. 527*

Materials List

Setting the Stage
• Labsheet 3A
• 12 beans, each marked with a "+" on one side and a "–" on the other side for each pair of students
• paper cups
• game pieces

Exploration 1
• 12 beans from Setting the Stage

Exploration 2
• 12 beans from Setting the Stage

Practice and Applications
• graph paper

Teaching Resources

Teacher's Resource Book
• Warm-Up
• Labsheet 3A
• Practice and Applications
• Study Guide
See page 499 for additional teaching resources.

Assessment Options

EMBEDDED ASSESSMENT
• Use a model to represent integers and sums of integers
 Exercises 4, 5, 6
• Add integers
 Exercises 9, 11, 12 ,14, 18
• Use a model to represent integer subtraction
 Exercises 22, 25
• Subtract integers
 Exercises 30, 32, 37, 40

PERFORMANCE TASK/PORTFOLIO
• Exercise 7 on *p. 528 (writing)*
• Exercise 21 on *p. 529 (challenge)*
• Exercise 44 on *p. 530 (oral report)*
• Extended Exploration on *p. 533**

* indicates a problem-solving task that can be assessed using the Assessment Scales

QUIZZES/TESTS
• Section 3 Quick Quiz
• Mid-Module Quiz

TEST GENERATOR

Section 3 Overview

In this section, students will play the game *Charge-O-Meter* which models the addition of integers representing positive and negative electrical charges. Then students will apply the concepts developed in the game to add and subtract integers.

Exploration 1
Students first learn to add a positive integer and a negative integer by combining as many opposite units as possible from the models of the integers and then counting the remaining units. Then they formulate informal rules for adding integers. The only new term in this section is *opposites*.

Exploration 2
The "take away" model is used to help students understand subtraction of integers. In the "take away" model, beans representing positive and negative integers are physically removed from a group of beans. Students will determine how many positive or negative beans remain. After modeling subtraction, students discuss how subtraction of an integer is related to addition of the opposite of that integer. Then they formulate a rule for subtracting integers.

Guide for Assigning Homework

REGULAR SCHEDULING (45 MIN CLASS PERIOD)			EXERCISES TO NOTE		
Section/ P&A Pages	Core Assignment	Extended Assignment	Additional Practice/Review	Open-ended Problems	Extended Problems
3 pp. 528–532	**Day 1:** 1–20 **Day 2:** 22–25, SR 45–60 **Day 3:** 26–42, ROS 44	1–21 22–25, SR 45–60 26–42 even, 43, ROS 44, Ext 61–71	EP, p. 532	PA 44 E² , p. 533	Challenge, PA 21, 43 Ext 61–71 E² , p. 533

Key: PA = Practice & Application; ROS = Reflecting on the Section; SR = Spiral Review; TB = Toolbox; EP = Extra Skill Practice; Ext = Extension; ST = Standardized Testing

Math Background and Teaching Strategies

Classroom Notes

Bulletin board display ideas for this section include:

- representations of different integers using beans
- students' summaries of rules for addition and subtraction of integers
- students' E² solutions

Math Strands

Topic Spiraling and Integration

In this section, students use the charged particle model for integers to discover how to add and subtract integers.

Exploration 1

Students were introduced to integers and the number line model in Section 5 of Module 7. By using beans marked with positive and negative signs to represent charged particles, students are introduced to a different model for integers. The idea of pairing opposite charges in the *Charge-O-Meter* game helps students understand that the sum of opposites is equal to zero. Students use the beans for several calculations before developing rules for addition of integers. Use of the beans to model addition helps students understand why sums of certain numbers are negative or positive. For those students not quite ready for abstract rules, the experience with beans helps them in transitioning towards the abstract by providing a way for students to think about the numbers concretely even though they are not physically using the beans. When writing rules for addition, students are still encouraged to use the beans to explain why the sum is positive or negative.

Exploration 2

Subtraction of integers is also modeled using beans. After work with the concrete model, students look for a connection between addition and subtraction of integers to develop a method for subtracting integers by using addition.

The concept of absolute value is developed in Module 1 of Book 2, where students will continue their work with addition and subtraction of integers. Multiplication and division of integers are not addressed in Book 1, but they will be taught in Book 2 and applied in Books 2 and 3 to solve equations, find the slopes of lines, and write expressions for translations on a coordinate grid. In Module 2 of Book 3 integer operations are extended to the real numbers, including addition and subtraction of positive and negative fractions and mixed numbers.

Section 4   Geometric Probability

Section 4 Planner

Section Objectives

Exploration 1
- Find geometric probabilities
- Use probability to make predictions

Days for Section 4

First Day
Setting the Stage, *p. 534*
Exploration 1, *pp. 535–536*
Key Concepts, *p. 537*

Teaching Resources

Teacher's Resource Book
- Warm-Up
- Practice and Applications
- Study Guide

See page 499 for additional teaching resources.

Materials List

Exploration 1
- an inflatable globe

Assessment Options

EMBEDDED ASSESSMENT
- Find geometric probabilities
  Exercises 1, 3, 4, 8(a)
- Use probability to make predictions
  Exercises 8(c), 10

PERFORMANCE TASK/PORTFOLIO
- Exercise 7 on *p. 539 (create your own)*
- Exercise 8 on *p. 539 (estimation)*
- Exercise 12 on *p. 540 (journal)*
- Standardized Testing on *p. 541 (performance task)*

QUIZZES/TESTS
- Section 4 Quick Quiz

TEST GENERATOR

Section 4 Overview

In this section, students revisit the Module 4 theme of *Statistical Safari* by examining the theory that dinosaur extinction was the result of a meteorite hitting Earth.

Exploration 1
Students use geometric probability to study the chance of a meteorite hitting a particular place on Earth. They begin by conducting an experiment using an inflatable globe. Students record the number of times their left index finger is touching water and the number of times it is touching land when the globe is tossed among students. This information is then used to calculate the probability of a meteorite randomly hitting land. The experiment is then related to geometric figures for which areas can be computed and geometric probability is defined.

Guide for Assigning Homework

REGULAR SCHEDULING (45 MIN CLASS PERIOD)			EXERCISES TO NOTE		
Section/ P&A Pages	Core Assignment	Extended Assignment	Additional Practice/Review	Open-ended Problems	Extended Problems
4 pp. 538–541	**Day 1:** 1–10, ROS 12, SR 13–26	1–11, ROS 12, SR 13–26	EP, p. 541	PA 7	Challenge, PA 11(b)

Key: PA = Practice & Application; ROS = Reflecting on the Section; SR = Spiral Review; TB = Toolbox; EP = Extra Skill Practice; Ext = Extension; ST = Standardized Testing

Math Background and Teaching Strategies

Classroom Notes

Bulletin board display ideas for this section include:

- information on the Chicxulub crater

- a list of area and volume formulas for computing geometric probabilities

- student created targets from Practice and Applications Exercise 7

Math Strands

Topic Spiraling and Integration

In this section students will extend their knowledge of probability to include geometric probability.

Exploration 1

This exploration relies heavily on students' prior acquisition of skills in performing experiments, collecting data, and using percents and probabilities to make predictions based on the data collected.

The contrast between an event occurring or not occurring is used to define complementary events. The sum of the probabilities of two complementary events will always equal 1. If Events A and B are complementary events, then the probability that A or B occurs is 1 and the probability that both A and B occur is 0.

In calculating the probability of an object hitting a target or not hitting the target, students are required to find the areas of shaded and unshaded regions of a geometric figure. Students will need to use formulas developed in Module 5, Section 5 to find areas of parallelograms and triangles and in Module 7, Section 4 to find areas of circles.

Students will revisit geometric probability and complementary events in Module 6 of Book 2. Probabilities based on more complicated geometric areas are covered in Module 8 of Book 3.

Section 5 Transformations

Section 5 Planner

Section Objectives

Exploration 1
- Perform a translation, a rotation, and a reflection

Exploration 2
- Use transformations to make designs

Days for Section 5

First Day
Setting the Stage, *pp. 542–543*
Exploration 1 through Question 7, *pp. 543–544*

Second Day
Exploration 1 from Example, *p. 545*

Third Day
Exploration 2, *pp. 546–547*
Key Concepts, *p. 548*

Teaching Resources

Teacher's Resource Book
- Warm-Up
- Labsheets 5A, 5B, 5C, and 5D
- Practice and Applications
- Study Guide
See page 499 for additional teaching resources.

Materials List

Exploration 1
- Labsheets 5A–5B
- tracing paper
- index card or cardboard
- scissors
- ruler

Exploration 2
- Labsheet 5C
- construction paper
- scissors
- clear tape
- triangle from Exploration 1

Practice and Applications
- Labsheet 5D
- glue
- decorative paper
- scissors
- ruler
- drawing software (optional)

Assessment Options

EMBEDDED ASSESSMENT
- Perform a translation, a rotation, and a reflection
  Exercises 5, 7, 9, 11
- Use transformations to make designs
  Exercise 15

PERFORMANCE TASK/PORTFOLIO
- Exercise 9 on *p. 549 (arts)*
- Exercise 15 on *p. 550 (create your own)*
- Exercise 18 on *p. 551 (home involvement)*
- Exercise 20 on *p. 551 (research)*

QUIZZES/TESTS
- Section 5 Quick Quiz

TEST GENERATOR

Section 5 Overview

In this section, students will investigate the characteristics of geometric designs using translations, rotations, and reflections.

Exploration 1
After studying a quilt pattern, students cut out their own isosceles triangle and use it to create three different patches, one by translation, one by rotation, and one by reflection. The exploration culminates with students using at least two transformations with their triangle to create a patch of their own.

Exploration 2
Students continue to look at transformations in quilting. They use a small square patch of two colors and transformations to make zigzag patterns.

Guide for Assigning Homework

REGULAR SCHEDULING (45 MIN CLASS PERIOD)			EXERCISES TO NOTE		
Section/ P&A Pages	Core Assignment	Extended Assignment	Additional Practice/Review	Open-ended Problems	Extended Problems
5 pp. 549–552	**Day 1:** 1–5, SR 21–30 **Day 2:** 6–11 **Day 3:** 12–18, ROS 20	1–5, SR 21–30 6–11 12–19, ROS 20	EP, p. 552	PA 15, 18, 20 ST, p. 552	Challenge, PA 19

Key: PA = Practice & Application; ROS = Reflecting on the Section; SR = Spiral Review; TB = Toolbox; EP = Extra Skill Practice; Ext = Extension; ST = Standardized Testing

Math Background and Teaching Strategies

Classroom Notes

Bulletin board display ideas for this section include:

- various pictures of quilt patterns that illustrate use of transformations

- student work display of quilt designs from Question 11 on page 545

- a description and an example of each type of transformation

- student collected logos from Reflecting Exercise 20 on page 551

Visitors might include:

- a quilter

- an artist who uses transformations in his or her work

Math Strands

Topic Spiraling and Integration

In this section students study transformational geometry.

Exploration 1
In this exploration, the transformations translations, rotations, and reflections are introduced by using a triangle and having students physically perform the transformation using the triangle.

Students revisit transformations in Module 4 of Book 2. Translations are extended to the coordinate plane, where students learn to use coordinates to describe translations. Then, in Module 6 of Book 3, students use algorithms to transform geometric shapes using translations, reflections, and rotations on a coordinate plane. In Module 8 of Book 3, rotations are extended to

include identifying the degree measures of the rotational symmetries of a figure.

Exploration 2
Exploration 2 continues to develop students' understanding of the transformations learned in Exploration 1. Students apply visualization skills as they study a design and then attempt to use transformations to recreate the design.

Section 6 Scientific Notation

Section 6 Planner

Section Objectives

Exploration 1
- Write numbers in scientific notation using positive exponents
- Write numbers that are in scientific notation in standard form

Days for Section 6

First Day
Setting the Stage, *p. 553*
Exploration 1 through Question 7, *p. 554*

Second Day
Exploration 1 from Example, *p. 555*
Key Concepts, *p. 556*

Teaching Resources

Teacher's Resource Book
- Warm-Up
- Labsheet 6A
- Practice and Applications
- Study Guide
See page 499 for additional teaching resources.

Materials List

Setting Stage
- Labsheet 6A
- sticky notes
- calculators
- index cards or planet cutouts
- scissors

Exploration 1
- completed Labsheet 6A

Assessment Options

EMBEDDED ASSESSMENT
- Write numbers in scientific notation using positive exponents
  Exercises 4, 5, 6, 14
- Write numbers that are in scientific notation in standard form
  Exercises 10, 11, 12, 16

PERFORMANCE TASK/PORTFOLIO
- Exercise 20 on *p. 558 (research)*

QUIZZES/TESTS
- Section 6 Quick Quiz
- Module Tests A and B
- Module Standardized Test
- Module Performance Assessment

TEST GENERATOR

Section 6 Overview

In this section, students will examine the use of scientific notation to represent numbers. In the *Setting the Stage* the students will use toilet paper squares to construct a scale model of the distances from the Sun to different planets.

Exploration 1
In the *Setting the Stage* the students expressed distances greater than 100,000,000 km by using powers of 10. In Exploration 1, these distances are related to scientific notation. Following the definition, students look at numbers to determine whether or not they are written in scientific notation. They practice converting between scientific notation and standard form and examine how different calculators display a number in scientific notation. Students return to the model of the planets and use the distances written in scientific notation to order the planets' distances from the Sun from greatest to least.

Guide for Assigning Homework

REGULAR SCHEDULING (45 MIN CLASS PERIOD)			EXERCISES TO NOTE		
Section/ P&A Pages	Core Assignment	Extended Assignment	Additional Practice/Review	Open-ended Problems	Extended Problems
6 pp. 556–559	**Day 1:** 1–6, 13–15, SR 21–33 **Day 2:** 7–12, 16–19, ROS 20	1–6, 13–15, SR 21–33 7–12, 16–19, ROS 20	EP, p. 559 Review & Assessment, pp. 562–563	ROS 20	

Key: PA = Practice & Application; ROS = Reflecting on the Section; SR = Spiral Review; TB = Toolbox; EP = Extra Skill Practice; Ext = Extension; ST = Standardized Testing

Math Background and Teaching Strategies

Classroom Notes

Bulletin board displays for this section include:

• facts about the planets

• information on Mars Exploration Rovers

• student work from Reflecting Exercise 20

Math Strands

Topic Spiraling and Integration

Exploration 1
When writing numbers in scientific notation, students make use of their skills with decimal place value, decimal multiplication, exponents, and powers of 10, all studied previously in Module 3. Students will continue to be exposed to scientific notation, especially when computing with numbers that produce extremely large products with several digits since these are typically displayed in scientific notation on their calculators.

Students will work with scientific notation again in Module 2 of Book 2. At this point negative integers will be introduced as exponents and then applied to representing decimal numbers less than 1 in scientific notation. In Book 3 of Module 3, scientific notation with positive powers of 10 is applied to carbon dating. Use of negative exponents with scientific notation is revisited in Module 7 of Book 3.

Module 8

OVERVIEW

This module presents new material while revisiting each of the themes from Modules 1 through 6. Activities include estimating capacities of containers, building cubic centimeter and one-liter cubes, investigating a math-magic trick, playing an integer game, making quilt squares, modeling our solar system, and predicting by tossing a globe.

PREREQUISITE SKILLS

Warm-Up Exercises for each section are provided in the *Teacher's Resource Book*. You can use these exercises to review skills and concepts students will need for each section. In addition, the Spiral Review exercises at the end of each section in the student edition provide practice on prerequisite skills.

MODULE DIAGNOSTIC TEST

The Module Diagnostic Test in the *Teacher's Resource Book* can be used to assess students' prior knowledge of skills and concepts that will be taught in each section of this module. You can use test results to help structure your teaching to meet the diverse needs of your classroom.

MODULE 8

MATH-Thematical MIX

498

Play *The Math is Right!*

A quiz game is a fun way to test your knowledge. You will work as a team to create questions that relate to a theme and to the mathematics you have learned this year. Will your questions stump the other teams in your class? Find out when you play *The Math is Right!*

More on the Module Project
See pp. 560–561.

CONNECTING
MATHEMATICS & The Theme

MODULE 8 — SECTION OVERVIEW

1 Customary and Metric Capacity

As you revisit Patterns and Problem Solving:
- ◆ Convert between customary units of capacity
- ◆ Relate volume and metric capacity
- ◆ Estimate capacity in metric units

2 Estimation and Mental Math

As you revisit Math Detectives:
- ◆ Use estimation and mental math strategies

3 Adding and Subtracting Integers

As you revisit Mind Games:
- ◆ Add and subtract integers

4 Geometric Probability

As you revisit Statistical Safari:
- ◆ Find geometric probabilities
- ◆ Use probability to make predictions

5 Transformations

As you revisit Creating Things:
- ◆ Perform translations, rotations, and reflections

6 Scientific Notation

As you revisit Comparisons and Predictions:
- ◆ Write large numbers in scientific notation

INTERNET
Resources and practice at
classzone.com

 499

Module Resources

TEACHER'S RESOURCE BOOK
Resources
- *The Math Gazette* (parent newsletter)
- Warm-Ups
- Labsheets
- Practice and Applications
- Study Guide

Assessment
- Section Quick Quizzes
- Mid-Module Quiz
- Module 8 Diagnostic Test
- Module 8 Tests A and B
- Module 8 Standardized Test
- Module 8 Performance Assessment
- Modules 7 and 8 Cumulative Test
- End-of-Year Test

SPANISH RESOURCES
- *The Math Gazette* (parent newsletter)
- Practice and Applications
- Assessment
- Spanish Glossary

STUDENT WORKBOOK

TECHNOLOGY BOOK

TECHNOLOGY RESOURCES
- @Home Tutor
- Test Generator
- Activity Generator
- Professional Development DVD
- Online Activities

Setting the Stage

GETTING STARTED

Module 8 Section 1 *Warm-Up* assesses student facility with ordering metric units of length and weight in preparation for the connection to metric capacity.

ABOUT THE MATERIALS

Collect, or ask students to bring in, empty milk containers and other containers during the weeks prior to the activity. It would be helpful to have one set with a cup, a pint, a quart, a half-gallon, and a gallon milk container for each group of students.

TEACHING NOTES

After students have practiced estimating, you can use a game show format for estimating the capacities of the last few containers. Call four students (names chosen from a hat) to bid on the next item. The student closest to the capacity of the item without going over wins the item. Consider using items such as sports drinks, chocolate milk, or yogurt. If the capacity of the container is shown on its label, be sure students cannot see it as you display the container (masking tape works well). Be sure you know the capacity of each container presented.

Section 1 Customary and Metric Capacity

PATTERNS & PROBLEM SOLVING

Setting the Stage

SET UP *You will need containers of various sizes.*

The average teen consumes over 7 gallons of soda a month! To compare this to drinking one can, bottle, or fountain drink a day, you need to know the *capacity* of each container. The **capacity** of a container is the amount of liquid it can hold. In the customary system, capacity is measured in **gallons (gal)**, **quarts (qt)**, **pints (pt)**, **cups (c)**, or **fluid ounces (fl oz)**.

Milk containers are good benchmarks for estimating capacity. In this activity you will use milk containers to help estimate the capacity of various containers.

ESTIMATING CAPACITY

♦ Your teacher will hold up an item and ask you to estimate its capacity in either gallons, quarts, pints, cups, or fluid ounces.

♦ Record the item and your estimate. Then record the actual capacity when your teacher tells it to you.

♦ Use the previous items and the milk containers to help improve your estimates each time.

Think About It

1. a. not reasonable; Sample Response: The pint container appears to hold twice as much as the cup container, so one cup is the same as a half pint.

b. not reasonable; Sample Response: I think a car's fuel tank holds about 15 gallons, and the gallon container is much bigger than the pint container.

1 Think about the milk containers and other items to decide whether each statement is reasonable.

   a. I have to fill a cup four times to make a pint.

   b. The maximum capacity of a car's fuel tank is 15 pt.

   c. Some tea kettles can hold about $1\frac{1}{2}$ qt of water. reasonable

2 You go to the store to buy 1 qt of buttermilk, but it is sold only in pints. How many pints should you purchase? 2

▶ In this module, you will revisit themes from earlier modules as you continue to learn new mathematics. In Module 1, you used patterns to learn about fractions. In this section you will use patterns to investigate units of capacity and solve problems related to capacity.

Exploration 1

TEACHING NOTES
Once students complete **Questions 3 and 4** they should realize that to recreate the diagram on their own all they need to be able to replicate is the pattern inside one "Q", which they can then repeat four times inside the "G".

4. b. The diagram indicates that
$1 \text{ c} = 8 \text{ fl oz}$, $2 \text{ c} = 1 \text{ pt}$,
$2 \text{ pt} = 1 \text{ qt}$, and $4 \text{ qt} = 1 \text{ gal}$.
Some of the other relationships
indicated are $1 \text{ fl oz} = \frac{1}{8} \text{ c}$,
$1 \text{ c} = \frac{1}{2} \text{ pt}$, $1 \text{ pt} = \frac{1}{2} \text{ qt}$, and
$1 \text{ qt} = \frac{1}{4} \text{ gal}$.

Exploration 1

Customary Capacity

GOAL

LEARN HOW TO...
◆ convert between customary units of capacity

AS YOU...
◆ examine a visual pattern for capacity

Use the diagram to answer Questions 3–11.

3 a. How many Cs are inside one P? 2

b. How many Ps are inside one Q? 2

4 Try This as a Class

a. What do you think the G, Q, P, C, and 8 in the diagram represent? gallon, quart, pint, cup and 8 fluid ounces in a cup

b. Explain how the diagram shows the relationships among customary units of capacity. (*Hint*: 8 fl oz = 1 c) See margin.

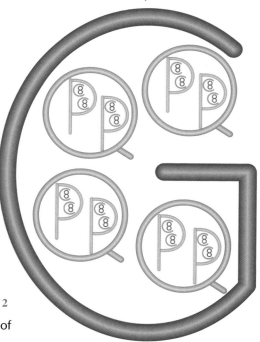

5 A recipe needs 2 c of tomato sauce. Will a 12 fl oz can of sauce be enough? Explain. No, 2 c = 16 fl oz, so you will be short 4 fl oz.

6 Place your hand or a sheet of paper over two of the Qs inside the big G. The uncovered part represents half of a gallon.

a. How many quarts are in half of a gallon? 2

b. How many cups are needed to make half of a gallon? 8

c. Are 3 pt *more than* or *less than* half of a gallon? less than

d. How many Qs would you have to cover to show the number of quarts, pints, cups, and fluid ounces in one fourth of a gallon? 3

TEACHING NOTES
While working through
Question 9 as a class, it may be
helpful to discuss how the same
rules for converting units of length
presented in Module 5 Section 2
apply to converting units of
capacity, once the relationship fact
is known. Encourage students to use
their estimation skills to check the
reasonableness of their answers in
Questions 10 and 11.

7 **Discussion** Explain how you could use the diagram on the preceding page to find the following.

   a. the number of pints in half of a quart **Cover up half of a Q, which entails covering one of two P's in a Q.**

   b. the number of cups in one fourth of a quart
    Choose one of the Q's and select one of the four C's for $\frac{1}{4}$ of the quart.

   c. the number of fluid ounces in 5 pints
    The diagram shows 16 fl oz in 1 pt, so multiply by 5.

✔ **QUESTION 8**

...checks that you understand the relationships between customary units of capacity.

8 ✔ **CHECKPOINT** Replace each _?_ with the number that makes the statement true. Use the diagram on the preceding page.

   a. _?_ pt = $\frac{1}{2}$ qt 1   **b.** 3 qt = _?_ gal $\frac{3}{4}$ **c.** _?_ pt = 1 c $\frac{1}{2}$

   d. _?_ pt = $\frac{1}{4}$ gal 2   **e.** 16 fl oz = _?_ c 2   **f.** $\frac{1}{8}$ qt = _?_ c $\frac{1}{2}$

FOR ◄ HELP

with *converting
units of measure,*
see

MODULE 5, p. 302

9 **Try This as a Class** Suppose you need about 100 cups of juice for a party. The juice is sold in half-gallon bottles.

   a. How many cups are in $\frac{1}{2}$ gal? 8

   b. Complete the relationship fact below. 8; $\frac{1}{8}$

     _?_ c = 1 half-gallon bottle, so 1 c = _?_ half-gallon bottle.

   c. Using the fact from part (b), complete the steps below to find the number of half-gallon size bottles equal to 100 c.

     Step 1:   1 c = _?_ half-gallon bottle $\frac{1}{8}$; $\frac{1}{8}$; $12\frac{1}{2}$

     Step 2: 100 · 1 c = 100 · _?_ half-gallon bottle

     Step 3:   100 c = _?_ half-gallon bottles

✔ **QUESTION 10**

...checks that you can convert between customary units of capacity.

10 ✔ **CHECKPOINT** Replace each _?_ with the number that makes the statement true.

   a. 15 qt = _?_ pt 30 **b.** 26 fl oz = _?_ c $3\frac{1}{4}$ **c.** 22 qt = _?_ gal $5\frac{1}{2}$

11 In the *Setting the Stage*, you learned that the average teen consumes 7 gal of soda per month.

Container	Capacity
Can	12 fl oz
Bottle	20 fl oz
Super-size Fountain Drink	32 fl oz

   a. On average, how many cans of soda would you have to drink each day to consume the same amount as the average teen?

   b. Make a statement about the number of bottles of soda the average teen consumes in one month. **Sample Response: The average teen consumes nearly 45 bottles of soda each month.**

   c. On average, how many fluid ounces of soda does the average teen drink per week? How many super-size fountain drinks is this? **about 224 fl oz; about 7**

11. a. About $2\frac{1}{2}$ cans a day

HOMEWORK EXERCISES ▶ See Exs. 1–15 on pp. 507–508.

 502   **Module 8**   MATH-Thematical Mix

Exploration 2

 **Capacity**

GOAL

LEARN HOW TO...
- relate volume and metric capacity
- estimate capacity in metric units

AS YOU...
- create benchmarks

KEY TERMS
- milliliter (mL)
- liter (L)
- kiloliter (kL)

SET UP | *Work with a partner. You will need:* • *Labsheet 1A* • *tape* • *scissors* • *eyedropper* • *metric ruler* • *12 straws* • *one graduated cylinder for the class* • *water in a cup* • *24 paper clips*

▶ Although soda cans and other single serving size drinks are usually measured in fluid ounces, larger soda containers, such as 1 *liter* and 2 *liter* bottles, are measured in metric units. To get an idea of how metric units of capacity are related you will first look at a more familiar unit—a cubic centimeter.

12 **Use Labsheet 1A.** Follow the steps below to construct a cubic centimeter from a net. **Check students' work.**

Step 1 Place a layer of tape on both sides to reinforce the paper.

Step 2 Cut out the cube net.

Step 3 Fold the net along the dashed lines and tape the tabs to the faces to form a cube that is open on one face.

13 **a.** How do you know that the volume of the cube you made is 1 cm³ (one cubic centimeter)?

b. Use an eyedropper to fill your cube with water.
b–c. Observe students' work.
c. Pour your cubic centimeter of water into the graduated cylinder.

d. How many cubic centimeters of water did your class pour into the cylinder? **Answers will vary.**

13. a. Each face of the figure is a square 1 cm on a side and the volume of the cube is 1 cm • 1 cm • 1 cm = 1 cm³.

Exploration 2

CLASSROOM MANAGEMENT
Students should work in groups of 2 or 4 for this Exploration. Each group needs only one net **from Labsheet 1A**. Copy the labsheet and cut apart the nets prior to the lesson. For **Question 12**, give each group one net. The clear tape is necessary so that in **Question 13** the cubes will be able to hold water (salt or rice may be used instead of water). The graduated cylinder is needed for the class, not for each group.

TIPS FROM TEACHERS
Commercially produced base-ten blocks can also serve as models for Exploration 2. The smallest block (1 cm³) is a 1 mL cube, and the largest block (usually used to represent one thousand) is a 1 L cube.

ALTERNATIVE APPROACH
Setting up a class rain gauge outside in the schoolyard is an interesting way to explore a real life application of capacity. Students could estimate, then measure the amount of rainwater in the gauge after each rain. You could pour the amount collected after each rain into a liter container so that students can continue to make connections between metric units of capacity. Rain gauges can be purchased inexpensively at most discount or home supply stores.

Exploration 2 *continued*

Teaching Notes

To stimulate students' thinking in **Question 16**, you might ask: "How many centimeter cubes would it take to cover just the bottom layer of the liter-sized cube?" (*100*) "How many layers would it take to reach the top?" (*10*) Check student answers since the dimensions are needed to complete **Question 18**.

In building the cube for **Question 17**, it is easiest if students connect the paper clips for each vertex together in a group of three before inserting them into the straws.

14. a. For all classes the milliliters of water are expected to be equal to the number of cubic centimeters poured into the graduated cylinder.
c. Differences might be due to cubes that were not measured, cut, or folded exactly, or water that may have been absorbed into the paper cubes or spilled.

> **FOR ◄HELP**
> with *metric measures and prefixes*, see
> **MODULE 4, p. 208**

> ✔ **QUESTION 16**
> ...checks that you understand how to determine the dimensions of a liter-size cube.

> ► In the metric system, a container that can hold 1 cm³ of liquid has a capacity of **1 milliliter (mL)**.

14 a. How many milliliters of water should there be in the class's graduated cylinder?

b. How many milliliters of water are in the class's graduated cylinder?
Answers will vary.

c. Are your answers to parts (a) and (b) the same? If not, why might they be different?

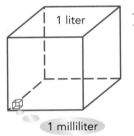

Volume
1 cm³

Capacity
1 mL

> ► Since a milliliter (mL) is such a small amount, many liquids, such as juice and soda, are measured in *liters*. The picture below shows the size difference between a cube that could hold a **liter (L)** of fluid and one that could hold a milliliter.

1 liter

1 milliliter

15 a. What does the prefix "milli" mean?
one thousandth

b. How many milliliters are there in a liter? *1000 mL*

c. How many centimeter cubes filled with water would you need to make a liter of water? *1000 centimeter cubes*

16 ✔ CHECKPOINT Determine the dimensions of a liter-size cube.
10 cm on a side

17 Follow the steps below to create a liter-size cube.
Check students' work.

First

Measure and cut your straws. Use the dimensions you found in Question 16.

Then

Form a liter-size cube by using paper clips to connect the straws.

18 a. Place your centimeter cube inside your liter-size cube to visually compare the sizes of these two benchmarks.
Observe students' work.

b. Give a different set of dimensions that could be used to create a liter-size rectangular box. *Sample Response: 5 cm by 10 cm by 20 cm*

19 **Try This as a Class**

   a. What does the prefix "kilo" mean? *one thousand*

   b. How many liters are there in a **kiloliter (kL)**? *1000 L*

   c. Give a set of dimensions that could be used to create a kiloliter-size rectangular box. *Sample Response: 100 cm by 100 cm by 100 cm*

20 ✔ **CHECKPOINT** Use your liter and milliliter cubes to help choose the best estimate.

   a. capacity of a can of soup   300 mL   3 mL   300 L *300 mL*

   b. capacity of a bathtub   1.8 kL   800 L   180 L *180 L*

   c. a dose of children's   5 mL   100 mL   1 L *5 mL*
        liquid medicine

21 Tell whether or not each container could hold a liter of water. Explain your reasoning.

   a.   **b.**   **c.**

22 **a.** Besides the cube you made in Question 17, what type of container could you use as a benchmark to estimate 1 L? *Sample Response: A one-quart milk container, a one liter soda bottle*

   b. What benchmark could you use for 1 kL? *Sample Response: a cubic meter*

23 It has been estimated that a person can survive comfortably with as little as 100 L of water each day. This includes water for washing, drinking, and cooking.

   a. Would 100 L fill a *pond*, an *outdoor swimming pool*, a *large fish tank*, or a *sink*? Explain.

   b. Do you think that 100 L of water per day is a good estimate of *your* needs? Explain. *Sample Response: No; I think I use nearly that much to shower each day.*

HOMEWORK EXERCISES ▶ See Exs. 16–33 on pp. 508–509.

DEVELOPING MATH CONCEPTS
You could connect the new learning in **Question 19** to the previous development by asking, "How many centimeter cubes filled with water would you need in order to have a kiloliter of water?" (*1,000,000*)

To provide more practice with metric capacity estimation, you could repeat the capacity activity from the *Setting the Stage*, having students estimate the number of milliliters and liters that the various containers hold.

✔ **QUESTION 20**

...checks that you can estimate capacity in metric units.

21. a. Yes; The volume is about 1769 cm³.
   b. No; The volume is about 528 cm³.
   c. Yes; The volume is about 1489 cm³.

23. a. 100 L of water would be too much to fill a sink and too little to fill a pond or an outdoor swimming pool.

CLOSURE QUESTION

Explain the meaning of capacity and how it is related to metric units of volume.

Sample Response: Capacity is the amount of fluid a container can hold. A volume of one cubic centimeter has a capacity of one milliliter.

Key Terms

capacity

fluid ounce (fl oz)

cup (c)

pint (pt)

quart (qt)

gallon (gal)

milliliter (mL)

liter (L)

kiloliter (kL)

Section ① Key Concepts

Customary Capacity (pp. 501–502)

You can use customary units of capacity to measure how much liquid a container can hold.

1 cup = 8 fluid ounces
1 pint = 2 cups
1 quart = 2 pints
1 gallon = 4 quarts

Example $2\frac{1}{2}$ qt = _?_ c

Begin by stating a relationship between quarts and cups.

Step 1:   1 qt = 4 c

Step 2: $2\frac{1}{2} \cdot 1$ qt = $2\frac{1}{2} \cdot 4$ c

Step 3: $2\frac{1}{2}$ qt = 10 c

Metric Capacity (pp. 503–505)

Volume and capacity are related in the metric system. One cubic centimeter of water has a capacity of one milliliter.

Unit of Measure	Symbol	Relationship to other units
milliliter	mL	$1 \text{ mL} = \frac{1}{1000} \text{ L} = 0.001 \text{ L}$
liter	L	$1 \text{ L} = 1000 \text{ mL}$ $1 \text{ L} = \frac{1}{1000} \text{ kL} = 0.001 \text{ kL}$
kiloliter	kL	1 kL = 1000 L

Volume
1 cm³

Capacity
1 mL

Key Concepts Questions

24 A recipe calls for $3\frac{1}{4}$ c of water.

   a. How many fluid ounces is this? **26 fl oz**

   b. How many pints of water do you need to make 4 times as much as the original recipe? $6\frac{1}{2}$ **pt**

25 A 40 cm by 20 cm by 20 cm rectangular fish tank is filled with water. What is its capacity in liters? **16 L**

Section 1

Practice & Application Exercises

Choose the letter of the most reasonable measurement for the capacity of each object.

1.   2.    3.   4.   5.

A. 4 gal D   B. 1 fl oz A   C. 1 pt C   D. 10 fl oz B   E. 3 qt E

Replace each _?_ with the number that makes the statement true.

6. 6 pt = _?_ qt 3   7. $5\frac{1}{2}$ gal = _?_ qt 22   8. 5 c = _?_ qt $1\frac{1}{4}$

9. $2\frac{1}{2}$ pt = _?_ c 5   10. 20 fl oz = _?_ c $2\frac{1}{2}$ 11. 6 c = _?_ pt 3

12. **Writing** Below are the ingredients for making paper-sculpture figures. You have only a one-cup measuring cup. Explain how you can measure the correct amount for each ingredient.

Measure 12 c of pulp, 2 c of paste, and 2 c of plaster of Paris.

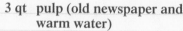

3 qt	pulp (old newspaper and warm water)
1 pt	paste
2 c	plaster of Paris

SUGGESTED ASSIGNMENTS

Core Course
Day 1: Exs. 1–5, 34–42
Day 2: Exs. 6–15, 43
Day 3: Exs. 16–31, 33

Extended Course
Day 1: Exs. 1–5, 34–42
Day 2: Exs. 6–15, 43
Day 3: Exs. 16–33

Note: Extended Course assignments can be used to differentiate within the regular classroom. In classrooms where students are grouped homogeneously, the material might be covered in fewer days. In this case assignments may be combined.

ADDITIONAL PRACTICE
See the *Teacher's Resource Book* for additional practice and application exercises for this section.

14. **Answers will vary.**
Sample Response:
Each empty half-gallon supports
4 lb of weight. How many pounds can the *Speed Racer 27* support? (560 pounds)

15. It has grown by more than $1\frac{1}{2}$ cups of soda.

20. **Answers will vary.**
Sample Response:
A sketch of three nested cubes, the largest marked with edges of 100 cm each to represent 1 kL, the next with 10 cm edges to represent 1 L, and then 1 cm edges to represent 1 cm³ or 1 mL.

Growing Size of Single Serving Containers

$6\frac{1}{2}$ fl oz   12 fl oz   20 fl oz

13. The *Aquatennial Milk Carton Boat Race* in Minneapolis, Minnesota, is an annual contest among boats that are constructed from milk cartons. In 1993, a Minneapolis company entered the largest milk carton boat in the history of the contest. The boat was made from 25,000 milk cartons and was shaped like an aircraft.

a. How many 8 fl oz glasses of milk would you have to drink to empty 25,000 half-gallon milk cartons? 200,000 glasses

b. Each empty half-gallon carton will support 4 lb. Assume that the boat described above was made only from half-gallon cartons. About how many pounds would it support? 100,000 lb

c. Assume that an empty one-gallon carton can support twice as much weight as an empty half-gallon carton. How would your answers to parts (a) and (b) change if the milk cartons were each one-gallon size? It would double the number of glasses to 400,000 and the number of pounds the boat can support to 200,000.

14. **Create Your Own** Create your own capacity problem using some of the information given below. Be sure to include the solution.

The Seafair Milk Carton Derby is held every summer in Seattle, Washington. One of the boats in 2006 was the *Speed Racer 27*, which was constructed from 65 one-gallon cartons and 10 half-gallon cartons.

15. In the 1950s, a 6.5 fl oz bottle was the standard serving of soda. That has now grown to a 20 fl oz bottle. Compare the size change in cups. By about how many cups has the serving size grown?

Find the capacity, in milliliters and in liters, of the rectangular container with the given dimensions.

16. 5 cm × 20 cm × 10 cm
1000 mL, 1 L

17. 2 cm × 5 cm × 2 cm
20 mL, 0.02 L

18. 25 cm × 20 cm × 8 cm
4000 mL, 4 L

19. 8.5 cm × 10 cm × 12.3 cm
1045.5 mL, 1.0455 L

20. **Visual Thinking** Design a visual diagram that represents the relationship between kL, L, mL, and cm³.

Replace each ? with the number that makes the statement true.

21. 1800 L = ? kL
1.8

22. 3 kL = ? L
3000

23. 892 mL = ? L
0.892

24. 0.62 kL = ? L
620

25. 2.5 L = ? mL
2500

26. 0.002 kL = ? mL
2,000

Choose the best estimate for each capacity.

27. capacity of a kitchen sink: 60 mL   30 L   300 L   30 L

28. amount of water you can hold in your hands: 100 mL   1 L   100 L
    100 mL

29. capacity of a small carton of milk: 250 mL   250 L   250 kL   250 mL

30. **Home Involvement** Have a friend or relative help you find a
    container at home. Estimate the metric capacity of the container.
    How can you check your estimate?

31. **Geography** The Baltic Sea has a surface
    area of about 381,705 km². The average
    depth of this sea is about 55 m. Estimate
    the capacity of the Baltic Sea in kiloliters.
    Explain how you made your estimate.

32. **Challenge** A soda can has a capacity of
    355 mL. Soda is also packaged in 2-liter
    bottles. Which is a better value: a 2-liter
    bottle of soda for $1.20 or a can of soda
    for $.30? Explain. the 2-liter bottle; Sample
    Response: The soda in the can costs about $.00085
    per mL while the soda in the bottle costs $.0006
    per mL.

Reflecting ◀▶ on the Section

33. When experimenting with the cells in proteins, chemists create
    buffer solutions. A buffer solution is a liquid that is close to the
    normal environment of the cell.

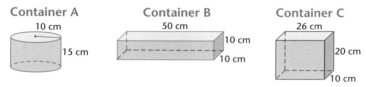

Container A   Container B   Container C
10 cm   50 cm   26 cm
15 cm   10 cm   20 cm
               10 cm   10 cm

   a. Which container should a chemist use for mixing 5 L of a
      buffer solution? Explain your choice.

   b. Once the buffer solution is mixed, the experiment may only
      require 300 mL of the solution. How many liters is this? How
      many liters of the solution will be left? 0.3 L; 4.7 L

33. a. C; A is too small and since B holds exactly 5 L, there won't be any room for
    stirring so the liquid will probably spill over the container.

---

30. Answers will
    vary. To check
    the estimate,
    you can measure
    the container
    and calculate its
    volume in cubic
    centimeters.

Visual
THINKING

Exercise 33 checks
that you understand
metric capacity.

31. Accept reasonable
    estimates; about
    21,000,000,000,000
    kL; I estimated
    the volume in
    cubic meters by
    converting the
    surface area from
    km² to m² and
    then multiplying
    the surface area by
    the depth. Then I
    used the fact that
    a container with
    volume 1 m³ has a
    capacity of 1 kL.

Find each value. (Module 6, p. 428)

34. 23% of 80 18.4   **35.** 35% of 42 14.7   **36.** 6% of 18 1.08

Evaluate each expression when $x = 4$ and $y = 9$. (Module 1, p. 21; Module 3, p. 143; Module 5, p. 352)

37. $7 \cdot x$ 28   **38.** $y - 3.4$ 5.6   **39.** $8\frac{5}{6} \div x$ $2\frac{5}{24}$

40. Suppose a coin is tossed 50 times and lands with a head showing 29 times. What is the experimental probability of heads? of tails? (Module 2, p. 80) $\frac{29}{50}, \frac{21}{50}$

Find the volume of each right cylinder with the given radius and height. Use 3.14 for π. (Module 7, p. 477)

41. $r = 5$ in., $h = 11$ in.
about 863.5 in.³

42. $r = 2.1$ cm, $h = 3.4$ cm
about 47.1 cm³

Career ▪ Connection

Chef: Bobby Flay

Bobby Flay became interested in cooking as a teenager. He impressed his first employers so much that they paid for him to study at the French Culinary Institute in New York City.

Chefs learn to test recipes in small batches, adjust them to taste, and then prepare large amounts.

43. A recipe for pie crust for one pie calls for $1\frac{1}{2}$ c flour, $\frac{1}{2}$ c butter, and $\frac{1}{4}$ c water.

a. Suppose you decide to replace $\frac{1}{2}$ of the flour with whole wheat flour, $\frac{2}{3}$ of the butter with shortening, and $\frac{1}{2}$ of the water with cider. Write the new recipe.

b. If you buy a half gallon of cider, how many cups will be left after making 6 pies? $7\frac{1}{4}$ cups

43. a. $\frac{3}{4}$ c flour,
$\frac{3}{4}$ c whole wheat
flour, $\frac{1}{6}$ c butter,
$\frac{1}{3}$ c shortening,
$\frac{1}{8}$ c water, $\frac{1}{8}$ c cider

Section 1

Extra Skill Practice

Replace each ? with the number that makes the statement true.

1. _?_ pt = 2 gal 16

2. 1 gal = _?_ fl oz 128

3. _?_ qt = 2 c $\frac{1}{2}$

4. _?_ qt = 96 fl oz 3

5. _?_ qt = 7 pt $3\frac{1}{2}$

6. $1\frac{1}{2}$ c = _?_ fl oz 12

7. 28 fl oz = _?_ pt $1\frac{3}{4}$

8. $\frac{1}{2}$ gal = _?_ c 8

9. 16 c = _?_ pt 8

10. 3400 L = _?_ kL 3.4

11. 4200 mL = _?_ L 4.2

12. 12 kL = _?_ L 12,000

13. 750 mL = _?_ L 0.75

14. 14 L = _?_ mL 14,000

15. 628 L = _?_ kL 0.628

Choose the best estimate for each capacity.

16. capacity of a bathtub 40 gal   4 gal   40 gal   400 gal

17. capacity of a tea cup 6 fl oz   1 pt   2 c   6 fl oz

18. capacity of a dog bowl $\frac{1}{2}$ qt   4 fl oz $\frac{1}{2}$ gal $\frac{1}{2}$ qt

19. capacity of a beach pail 2 L   2 L   200 mL   20 L

20. capacity of a swimming pool 16 kL   10 L   16 kL   600 mL

21. capacity of a flower vase 700 mL   700 mL   5 L   20 mL

Standardized Testing ◀▶ Free Response

Angelique had a cubic centimeter filled with water. Stacey had a larger container filled with water. Stacey said her container held more than 1000% of what Angelique's held. For Stacey to be correct, how large must her container be? Give your answer in liters. greater than 0.01 L

1 cm³

Extra Skill Practice

TEACHER NOTES

For each Exploration, the corresponding Extra Skill Practice Exercises are noted.

Exploration 1: Exs. 1–9, 16–18
Exploration 2: Exs. 10–15, 19–21

EXTRA HELP
Teacher's Resource Book
• Practice and Applications
• Study Guide

Technology Resources
• @Home Tutor
• Test Generator

ASSESSMENT
• Section 1 Quick Quiz
• Test Generator

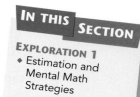
Setting the Stage

GETTING STARTED

Module 8 Section 2 *Warm-Up* has students evaluate expressions in preparation for the mental math techniques in this section. Discussion of the *Warm-Up* solutions should help draw attention to those pairs of numbers equal to zero and can be connected to the method of trading off in Exploration 1.

TEACHING NOTES

At this point, it is not necessary that students understand why this trick works, only that they are able to perform it successfully. The "why" provides the motivation for understanding *trading off*, which is taught in Exploration 1. If any students' tricks do not work, suggest they return to steps 2 and 3 and check that they followed the instructions correctly and that the sum of the digits they chose in each column is 18. If time allows, students might enjoy trying the trick a second time.

Section ② Estimation and Mental Math

MATH Detectives

--‹Setting the Stage

Most of us love being entertained by magic tricks. Here is a trick for you to try. Once you learn the trick, you can try it on your friends.

Magic Sum

	I	II
A		
B		
C		

Step 1: Make a table like the one shown. Be sure to label the columns I and II, and label the rows A, B, and C.

Step 2: Choose three single-digit numbers whose sum is 18. Write one of the numbers in each row of column I.

Step 3: Repeat step 2 for column II. You may use the same or different numbers as long as the column has a sum of 18.

Step 4: Add a fourth row, D. Write a 2-digit "mystery number" in row D with one digit in each column. You now have four 2-digit numbers, one in row A, one in row B, and so on.

Step 5: Subtract 2 from your mystery number and write a 2 in front of this new number. This is the sum of your four numbers!

Think About It

1 Check that this trick works by adding your four 2-digit numbers.
Answers will vary.

2 **a.** Did each of your classmates write the same numbers in rows A, B, and C? no

b. What is the sum of the three 2-digit numbers in rows A, B, and C? 198

c. How does the sum in part (b) compare to your classmates' sums? They are all the same.

▶ As a math detective, you will uncover how mathematics makes the magic trick work. You will begin by learning the skill of *trading off.*

Estimation and Mental Math Strategies

Exploration 1

TEACHING NOTES
Question 4 is designated as a discussion question so that students can hear the thought processes for deciding the amount to "trade off".
Part (d) shows that there is more than one way to trade off. Be sure students understand why trading off works and how it uses the concept of adding zero. Since they are adding and subtracting an equal amount, they have added 0 and therefore the sum is not affected.

▶ **Trading off** is a technique that uses addition and subtraction to help find the sum of a group of numbers mentally.

3 **a.** Find the sum 57 + 68. 125

  b. Add 3 to the sum, and then subtract 3 from this new total. How does the result compare to your sum in part (a)?
  It is the same.

  c. Add 3 to 57 and subtract 3 from 68. Now add these new numbers. 60 + 65 = 125

  d. Why were the numbers in part (c) easier to add than the original numbers in part (a)? Because one of them ended in a zero.

4 **Discussion**

  a. To find the sum 76 + 45, what number can you add to 76 so that the sum will be easier to find? 4

  b. If you add the number in part (a) to 76, how much will you need to subtract from 45? Why?

  c. Use trading off to find the sum 76 + 45. 80 + 41 = 121

  d. Describe another way to add 76 and 45 by trading off.
  Sample Response: Add 5 to 45 and subtract 5 from 76 to get 71 + 50 = 121

4. b. 4; In order to keep the problem the same, you must take away the same amount as was added since adding 4 and then subtracting 4 is equal to adding zero.

▶ Trading off can also be used to find the sum of three or more numbers, as shown in the example below.

EXAMPLE

Use trading off to find the sum of 73, 98, and 23.

SAMPLE RESPONSE

Add a total of 3 to the other numbers to make up for subtracting 3.

Subtract 3 from 73 to make 70.

$$
\begin{array}{ccc}
73 & \xrightarrow{-3} & 70 \\
98 & \xrightarrow{+2} & 100 \\
+\,23 & \xrightarrow{+1} & 24
\end{array}
\quad
\begin{array}{c}
170 \\
+\,24 \\
\hline
194
\end{array}
$$

The sum is 194.

Exploration 1 *continued*

TEACHING NOTES

Remind students that the goal of trading off is to change the numbers to ones that can be easily added mentally. Most of the time this entails getting a 2-digit number to the nearest ten or a 3-digit number to the nearest hundred if possible.

7. c. Add 2000 to the mystery number and then subtract 2. Since 1998 is added to the mystery number you are taking two off of the mystery number and adding it to 1998 to make it easier to find the sum.

Mystery number: 549 − 2 = 547
3 number sum: 1998 + 2 = 2000
                             2547

---

5. a. Adding 2 to 98 makes it an even 100, and then 70 and 100 can be added to 24 easily.

✔ **QUESTION 6**

...checks that you can use trading off to find a sum.

---

5 a. In the Example on page 513, why do you think 3 was split into 2 and 1 to add to the numbers 98 and 23?

b. Show another way to use trading off to add the three numbers mentally. Sample Response: (73 + 1) + (98 − 8) + (23 + 7) = 74 + 90 + 30 = 194

6 ✔ **CHECKPOINT** Use trading off to find each sum.

a.   121 **220**
        + 99

b.   53 **225**
          75
        + 97

c.   84 **198**
          37
        + 77

▶ In the *Setting the Stage*, you discovered that the mystery number is always added to a sum of 198. Suppose someone has a mystery number of 46. Then according to the trick, the magic sum will be 244. Here's how trading off is used to find the final answer.

EXAMPLE

Use trading off to find the sum of 198 and the mystery number 46.

$$198 \xrightarrow{+2} 200$$

$$+46 \xrightarrow{-2} +44$$

$$244$$

The sum is 244.

---

7 Follow the steps below to adapt the *Magic Sum* trick for 3-digit numbers.

a. Add a third column to the original table to make three 3-digit numbers. Be sure the digits in the new column also add up to 18. Answers will vary.

b. What will the sum of your three 3-digit numbers always be? 1998

c. Show how you could use trading off to quickly tell someone the magic sum of the four numbers when they give you a 3-digit mystery number. See margin.

▶ Estimation can be used to determine if your mental math answer is reasonable. When adding or subtracting numbers, *front-end estimation* is a quick way to estimate the answer. **Front-end estimation** focuses on the leftmost digits of the numbers, since they have the greatest value.

EXAMPLE

Estimate the number of cans of food collected for the food drive.

Step 1: Add the digits representing the highest place value (tens).

$5 + 2 + 6 = 13$ so the total number of cans is greater than 130.

Week	Cans
1	54
2	29
3	68

Step 2: Estimate the sum of the remaining digits.

$4 + 9 + 8$ Is it greater than 10? *Yes*
Is it greater than 20? *Yes*

Step 3: Combine the results from each step to estimate the number of cans.

$130 + 20 = 150$

More than 150 cans of food were collected.

---

8 Try This As a Class Use front-end estimation to approximate each sum.

a. $\begin{array}{r} 38 \\ 46 \\ + 29 \\ \hline \end{array}$ 110

b. $\begin{array}{r} 2.56 \\ 3.42 \\ 7.78 \\ + 5.30 \\ \hline \end{array}$ 19

c. $\begin{array}{r} 2{,}432 \\ 1{,}119 \\ + 3{,}287 \\ \hline \end{array}$ 6800

9 Discussion Front-end estimation can be used to estimate the difference of two numbers, like 641 and 218.

a. Find the front-end difference of 641 and 218. 4 (400)

b. Compare the remaining numbers. Is 41 *more* or *less* than 18?
more

c. Will the difference of 641 and 218 be *more* or *less* than your answer in part (a)? How can you tell?
more, since 41 is greater than 18.

d. Use front-end estimation to approximate 641 − 218.
about 420

e. Make up a subtraction problem where the estimate will be less than the amount first found by the front-end subtraction.
Sample Response: 4367 − 1712

10 ✔ **CHECKPOINT** Use front-end estimation to approximate each answer.

a. $\begin{array}{r} 5{,}452 \\ - 3{,}709 \\ \hline \end{array}$ 2000

b. $\begin{array}{r} 389 \\ + 116 \\ \hline \end{array}$ 500

c. $\begin{array}{r} 14.62 \\ - 8.40 \\ \hline \end{array}$ 6 or 6.2

✔ **QUESTION 10**

...checks that you can use front-end estimation to approximate sums and differences.

HOMEWORK EXERCISES ▶ See Exs. 1–14 on pp. 517–518.

DEVELOPING MATH CONCEPTS
Some students may have difficulty understanding why front-end estimation is needed when they could just round and get an estimate. You may want to present an example such as:
$2{,}441 + 1{,}206 + 2{,}429$ where rounding gives $2{,}000 + 1{,}000 + 2{,}000 = 5{,}000$, but with front-end estimation you get $2 + 1 + 2 = 5$ or 5,000 with an end estimate greater than 1,000 ($441 + 206 + 429$), so the total estimate is closer to 6,000 than 5,000. Knowing more than one method of estimating gives students choices for varying situations.

Key Concepts

CLOSURE QUESTIONS

Explain the basic steps and purpose of using trading off to add numbers mentally. Explain the basic steps and purpose of using front-end estimation.

Sample Response:

Trading off: When adding numbers, take an amount from one number and add it to another number(s) to make the numbers easier to add, so the sum can be found mentally.

Front-end: When estimating a sum , add the digits of the greatest place value. This gives a rough estimate. Then refine the estimate by approximating the sum of the remaining numbers beneath that place value and adding them onto your first estimate. Front-end estimation can be a bit more precise than rounding.

ABSENT STUDENTS

For students who were absent for all or part of this section, the blackline Study Guide for Section 2 may be used to present the ideas, concepts, and skills of Section 2.

Section 2
Key Concepts

Key Terms

trading off

front-end estimation

Trading Off (pp. 513–514)

One way to find a sum using mental math is by trading off.

Example Find the sum 1.95 + 2.37.

$$1.95 \xrightarrow{+0.05} 2.00 \qquad \text{Add 0.05 to 1.95 to get 2.00.}$$

$$+ 2.37 \xrightarrow{-0.05} 2.32 \qquad \begin{array}{l}\text{Subtract 0.05 from 2.37 to make}\\ \text{up for what you added to 1.95.}\end{array}$$

$$4.32 \qquad \text{Add the two new numbers.}$$

The sum is 4.32.

Front-end Estimation (pp. 514–515)

Front-end estimation focuses on the leftmost digits for a first estimate. The other digits help you adjust the estimate.

Example Estimate the sum of 135 and 278.

The sum is greater than 300.

$$\begin{array}{r}135\\ + 278\\ \hline 3\end{array}$$

35 + 78 is about 100.

The sum 135 + 278 is about 300 + 100, or 400.

Key Concepts Questions

11. d. The subtraction is done after the sum of the two numbers is found, but essentially you are doing the same thing, adding 0.05 and subtracting 0.05, just at a different step.

11 Rework the *Trading Off* Example above by following steps (a)–(c).

  a. Add 0.05 to 1.95. **2**

  b. Add 2.37 to the result in part (a). **4.37**

  c. Subtract 0.05 from the sum in part (b). **4.32**

  d. How is this method different from the method in the Example? How are the methods similar?

12 a. Use front-end estimation to estimate the sum of 12.9, 20.5, and 3.6. **about 37**

  b. Use trading off to find the exact sum of 12.9, 20.5, and 3.6. How close was your estimate in part (a)? **37; Answers will vary.**

Section 2

Practice & Application Exercises

Mental Math Use trading off to find each sum.

1. $36 + 48$ 84

2. $0.24 + 0.31$ 0.55

3. $79 + 36$ 115

4. $3.4 + 5.8$ 9.2

5. $18 + 23 + 37$ 78

6. $\$1.26 + \$2.69$ $3.95

7. The magic sum trick below can be explained by trading off.

   ♦ A volunteer writes a 3-digit number.   8 3 2

   ♦ A second volunteer writes a 3-digit number.   3 9 4

   ♦ You write a third 3-digit number that makes   + 6 0 5
   999 when added to the second number.

   ♦ Announce that you predict the sum of the three numbers is
   1831!

   a. Use trading off to show that the sum of 832 and 999 is 1831.
   Sample Response: $(832 - 1) + (999 + 1) = 831 + 1000 = 1831$

   b. Try the trick again with different numbers and use trading off
   to check your prediction. **Check student work.**

   c. Write an explanation of how you can use the first volunteer's
   number to "magically" get the sum. **Add 1000 and subtract 1.**
   (That way you have added 999 to the first volunteer's number.)

Estimation Use front-end estimation to estimate each sum.

8. $1324 + 2235$ about 3500

9. $13.2 + 17.4 + 24.2$ about 54

10. $312 + 560 + 125$ about 1000

11. $12 + 84 + 73 + 56$ about 220

12. **Estimation** Use front-end estimation to decide whether each sum
    or difference is *greater than* or *less than* 400.

    a. $134 + 161 + 125$ b. $1,646 - 1,238$ c. $987 - 589$
       greater than   greater than   less than

13. *Clustering* is another strategy that can be used to estimate a sum.
    The amounts collected for ticket sales for Thursday's talent show
    all cluster around $250, meaning they are all "close" to $250.
    You can estimate the sum of Thursday's ticket sales by multiplying
    $250 by 3.

    a. Use clustering to estimate the total amount
    of money collected for Thursday's show.
    $750

    b. What number do the sales for Friday's show
    cluster around? **$400**

    c. Estimate the total amount of money
    collected for Friday's show. Explain your method.
    $1200; $400 · 3 = $1200.

Talent Show Ticket Sales	6th Grade	7th Grade	8th Grade
Thursday's Show	$258	$244	$261
Friday's Show	$416	$385	$420

Section 2   Estimation and Mental Math   517

Practice & Applications

SUGGESTED ASSIGNMENTS

Core Course
Day 1: Exs. 1–7, 15–23
Day 2: Exs. 8–12, 14, 24–28

Extended Course
Day 1: Exs. 1–7, 15–23
Day 2: Exs. 8–14, 24–28

Note: Extended Course assignments
can be used to differentiate within
the regular classroom. In classrooms
where students are grouped
homogeneously, the material might
be covered in fewer days. In this
case assignments may be combined.

ADDITIONAL PRACTICE
See the *Teacher's Resource Book* for
additional practice and application
exercises for this section.

EXERCISE NOTES
Exercise 13 Clustering is a
new technique not introduced
in the exploration. The concept
of clustering is similar to that of
estimating the mean of the numbers
and multiplying it by the number
of numbers. For example, the value
of $250 is used as the number that
Thursday's sales cluster around.
$250 is close enough to the actual
mean of $254\frac{1}{3}$ and it is easier to
multiply by 3.

517

Practice & Applications

EXERCISE NOTES

Exercise 14 Have students share their responses with a classmate to see if they agree on **parts (d)–(f)**. They can then share ideas about when to use front-end estimation and when to use rounding.

Journal

Exercise 14 checks that you understand front-end estimation.

FOR ▶ HELP

with *rounding*, see
TOOLBOX, p. 567;
MODULE 1, p. 10;
and **MODULE 4,**
p. 225

Reflecting ◀▶ on the Section

14. It is helpful to know more than one method for estimating. Rounding and front-end estimation are both good strategies to know. **Answers will vary, check student work.**

   a. Make up two numbers. Use rounding to estimate their sum.

   b. Use front-end estimation to estimate the sum of the numbers in part (a).

   c. Repeat parts (a) and (b) several times using different numbers until you feel prepared to answer parts (d) and (e).

   d. In which situations did rounding give you a better estimate?

   e. In which situations was front-end estimation easier than rounding?

   f. Are your findings in parts (d) and (e) true for subtraction? Explain.

Spiral ◀▶ Review

Find the missing term in each proportion. (Module 6, p. 401)

15. $\frac{8}{15} = \frac{x}{27}$ 14.4   16. $\frac{3}{n} = \frac{22.5}{60}$ 8   17. $a : 42 = 2 : 3$ 28

Replace each ? with the number that makes the statement true.
(Module 8, p. 506)

18. 25 qt = ? gal $6\frac{1}{4}$ 19. 3 pt = ? c 6   20. 32 fl oz = ? gal $\frac{1}{4}$

21. 3 L = ? mL 3000   22. 70 mL = ? cm³ 70   23. 2300 L = ? kL 2.3

Find the volume of each right cylinder with the given dimensions.
Use 3.14 for π. (Module 7, p. 477)

24. $r = 40$ cm, $h = 23$ cm   25. $d = 46$ cm, $h = 40$ cm
   115,552 cm³   66,442.4 cm³

Find each quotient. Write your answer in lowest terms.
(Module 5, p. 352)

26. $\frac{5}{8} \div \frac{3}{8}$ $1\frac{2}{3}$ 27. $1\frac{1}{3} \div \frac{6}{11}$ $2\frac{4}{9}$ 28. $\frac{3}{14} \div 3\frac{3}{7}$ $\frac{1}{16}$

Section ② Extra Skill Practice

Estimation Use front-end estimation to estimate each sum or difference.

1. 2130 + 1225 + 1410 *about 5000*

2. 2.6 + 3.7 + 1.2 + 4.3 *about 12*

3. 12.42 + 10.53 + 7.08 *about 30*

4. 210 + 150 + 140 + 305 *about 800*

5. 5.7 + 2.3 + 3.2 + 0.2 *about 11*

6. 576 – 238 *about 340*

7. 817 – 356 *about 450*

8. 1234 – 821 *about 400*

Mental Math Use trading off to find each sum.

9. 24 + 68 *92*

10. 0.72 + 0.31 *1.03*

11. 98 + 207 *305*

12. 3.6 + 2.3 *5.9*

13. 71 + 33 + 48 *152*

14. 1.4 + 1.7 + 3.6 *6.7*

15. 86 + 42 + 58 *186*

16. 0.12 + 0.28 + 0.3 *0.7*

17. 21.2 + 32.4 + 11.7 *65.3*

18. 235 + 999 *1234*

19. 12 + 87 + 11 *110*

20. 63.4 + 23.8 *87.2*

Standardized Testing ◀▶ Open-ended

None of the amounts shown is a whole number of dollars. The cents are hidden behind the rectangle. *Sample responses are given.*

$3.
$4.
$5.

1. Complete each dollar amount so that an estimate of the sum made by front-end estimation would be the given value.

   a. $15.00
   $3.95 + $4.91 + $5.83

   b. $14.00
   $3.65 + $4.61 + $5.73

   c. $13.00
   $3.15 + $4.01 + $5.83

2. Complete each dollar amount so that an estimate of the sum made by rounding would be the given value.

   a. $15.00
   $3.86 + $4.97 + $5.88

   b. $14.00
   $3.42 + $4.71 + $5.83

   c. $13.00
   $3.74 + $4.01 + $5.26

Extra Skill Practice

TEACHER NOTES
All of the Extra Skill Practice Exercises correspond to Exploration 1.

EXTRA HELP
Teacher's Resource Book
• Practice and Applications
• Study Guide

Technology Resources
• @Home Tutor
• Test Generator

ASSESSMENT
• Section 2 Quick Quiz
• Test Generator

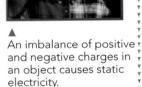

▲
An imbalance of positive and negative charges in an object causes static electricity.

Section 3

Adding and Subtracting Integers

IN THIS SECTION

EXPLORATION 1
♦ Adding Integers

EXPLORATION 2
♦ Subtracting Integers

Mind Games

SET UP *Work with a partner. You will need:* • *Labsheet 3A* • *paper cup* • *12 beans, each marked with a "+" on one side and a "–" on the other side* • *2 game pieces*

Setting the Stage

In Module 3 you used games to learn about whole numbers, decimals, and fractions. In this section, you will play *Charge-O-Meter*, a game where beans represent positive and negative electrical charges similar to the ones that cause lightning and static electricity in your hair. As you play the game, you will learn about addition and subtraction of integers.

▶ **Use Labsheet 3A.** Follow the directions on the labsheet to play *Charge-O-Meter*. Play the game two times.

Think About It

1 **a.** Did you find a way to quickly determine where to place your game piece after a bean toss? Explain. See margin.

   b. At the end of a turn, can your game piece ever be an even number of units away from where it was at the start of your turn? Why?

   c. At the end of a turn, can your game piece ever be in the same place it was when you started the turn? Why? No; As indicated in part (b), the number of units moved must be 7, 5, 3, or 1.

2 **a.** If you played *Charge-O-Meter* with only six beans, what moves would be possible? Moves of 0, 2, 4, or 6 units left or right

   b. Would playing with only six beans change your answers to Questions 1(b) and 1(c)? Explain.

Adding + Integers

GOAL

LEARN HOW TO...
◆ add integers

AS YOU...
◆ analyze the game Charge-O-Meter

KEY TERM
◆ opposites

▶ One strategy for quickly finding how far to move your game piece is to pair positive beans with negative beans. This strategy can also be used to model addition of integers.

EXAMPLE

Suppose you tossed 5 positive beans and 2 negative beans.

2 positive beans can be paired with 2 negative beans to cancel each other out.

+5 + −2 = __?__

3 Discussion Look at the addition in the Example.

a. Why do the paired beans cancel each other out?

b. If you tossed the combination of beans shown, how far and in what direction would you move your game piece?
3 units to the right

c. What integer is represented by the combination of beans? +3

d. +5 + (−2) = __?__ +3

This is read "5 plus negative 2."

To avoid confusion negative integers can be written in parentheses.

3. a. The two beans indicate moves of 1 unit in opposite directions, so the piece ends up where it started.

Section 3 Adding and Subtracting Integers (521)

Exploration 1

COMMON ERROR

Students may incorrectly think the parentheses written around a negative integer indicate multiplication. Provide examples to illustrate the difference in meanings: 7 + (−2) means 7 plus −2, while 7(−2) means 7 times −2.

Also, when students explain how to determine the sign of the sum, they may incorrectly say, "use the sign of the greater number," when in fact the number may not be greater. For example, in the addition sentence, 12 + (−17) = −5, the sum has the same sign as −17, but −17 is less than 12. Encourage students to explain how they get the sign of their answer in terms of the number of beans "left over" when modeling the sum using beans.

Exploration 1 continued

TEACHING NOTES

Question 6 Review the term *addend* before beginning **part (a)**. Have students give several examples for **part (a)**. Write these on the board for students to refer to during the discussion in **Questions 8–10**. You may want to help the class summarize their responses to **part (c)** with statements such as Negative + Negative = Negative. Ignore the signs and add the numbers, then make the sum negative.

Remind students they can check that their examples in **Question 7** are correct by using beans to find each sum. You may want to have students work on this question with a partner. Students can each write an example and then check each other's work to be sure they agree.

The example below can be used to make sure students grasped the concepts in **Question 7 and 8**.

CLASSROOM EXAMPLE

Without finding the sum, determine if the sum will be positive, negative, or zero.

a) $-84 + (-3)$ b) $41 + (-37)$

c) $-50 + 35$ d) $314 + (-314)$

Answer:
a) negative   b) positive
c) negative   d) zero

✔ **QUESTION 4**

...checks that you can represent integer addition using a bean model.

7. Sample responses are given.

 a. $+4 + (-3) = +1$;
    $+5 + (-2) = +3$

 b. $+2 + (-3) = -1$;
    $+6 + (-8) = -2$

 c. $+7 + (-7) = 0$;
    $+2 + (-2) = 0$

8. First, ignore the signs of the numbers and think of the numbers as whole numbers.

 a. The sum is positive if the greater whole number started out as a positive integer.

 b. The sum is negative if the greater whole number started out as a negative integer.

 c. The sum is equal to 0 if the whole numbers are the same.

9. Sample Response: Ignore the signs of the numbers. Subtract the number of lesser value from the number with greater value. Give the result the sign of the greater number.

---

4 ✔ **CHECKPOINT**

 a. Suppose you had 24 beans in your cup and you tossed 10 positive beans and 14 negative beans. How would you move your game piece? **4 units to the left**

 b. Write an integer addition equation for the combination of beans in part (a). $-14 + 10 = -4$

5 Use a bean model to find each sum.

 a. $+1 + (-5)$ **−4**   **b.** $+6 + (-4)$ **+2** **c.** $+3 + (-3)$ **0** **d.** $-5 + (-2)$ **−7**

Use bean models to help answer Questions 6–8.

6 **Try This as a Class**

 a. Write two different addition equations where both addends (the numbers that are added) are negative.
 Sample Response: $-7 + (-1) = -8$; $-2 + (-3) = -5$

 b. Is the sum of two negative numbers *positive* or *negative*? **negative**

 c. How can you find the sum of two negative numbers without using a bean model? **Sample Response: Ignore the signs and add the numbers. Then make the sum negative.**

7 Write two different examples for each case below.

Case	Examples

a. one addend is positive, one addend is negative, the sum is a positive integer

b. one addend is positive, one addend is negative, the sum is a negative integer

c. one addend is positive, one addend is negative, the sum is zero

8 **Discussion** Explain when the sum of a positive integer and a negative integer will be the given number.

 a. a positive number   **b.** a negative number   **c.** 0

9 Describe a general method for finding the sum of a positive and a negative integer.

10 Try This as a Class The numbers you used to answer Question 8(c) are *opposites*. What do you think it means for two numbers to be **opposites**?

▶ It is not necessary to label positive integers with a "+" sign. For example, +3 is the same as 3.

11 ✔ **CHECKPOINT** Find each sum.

a. −17 + 25 8   b. 13 + (−7) 6   c. −36 + (−9) −45

d. −11 + 11 0   e. −24 + 19 −5   f. 12 + (−17) −5

HOMEWORK EXERCISES ▶ See Exs. 1–21 on pp. 528–529.

See Exs. 1–21 on pp. 528–529.

10. Sample Response: The numbers are named by the same numeral with opposite signs.

✔ **QUESTION 11**

...checks that you can add integers.

Exploration 2

Subtracting — Integers

GOAL

LEARN HOW TO...
◆ subtract integers

AS YOU...
◆ model thundercloud charges with bean models

SET UP *Work in a group. You will need the 12 beans from Exploration 1.*

Though it is not known for certain how thunderclouds become charged, scientists do know that lightning is the movement of electrical charges from a cloud.

▶ Integer subtraction can be modeled in a similar way by taking away beans representing positive or negative charges.

Exploration 2

TIPS FROM TEACHERS

As students work through the questions using the bean model, it helps if they use a sheet of paper as their workspace, removing from the paper any beans that have been "taken away". This makes it easier to tell which beans are still part of the problem and which beans have been "taken away."

As students use beans to model the subtraction of two integers, be sure they understand that the number of ways to model an integer is only limited by the number of beans they have. For example, to model –1, students may simply show one negative bean. To model –1 a different way, students could use 3 negative beans and 2 positive beans, or 4 negative beans and 3 positive beans. This understanding is essential for students, since to show subtraction, they must find ways to model integers so that a given number of beans can be taken away.

In **Question 13**, be sure students understand how +2 can be modeled by 7 positive beans and 5 negative beans. Then ask, "Would the result of +2 – (–3) still be 5 if you had modeled +2 in a different way?" (*Yes*)

---

12 What integer is represented by this combination of beans? Explain. **2; Of the 12 beans, 7 are positive and 5 are negative, so 7 + (–5) = 2.**

13 **Try This as a Class** Use the bean model for 2 – (–3) shown below.

The combination of beans below represents +2.

3 negative beans are being taken away, making the expression +2 – (–3).

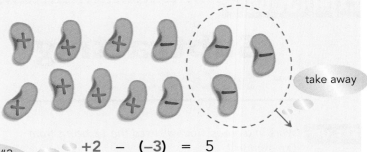

take away

This is read "2 minus negative 3."

$$+2 \; - \; (-3) \; = \; 5$$

a. How is subtracting –3 shown in the model? **The circle shows 3 negative beans being taken away.**

b. The difference is 5. How was this found? **Of the remaining 9 beans, 7 are positive and 2 are negative. 7 + (–2) = 5**

14 Write the subtraction equation shown by each bean model.

a. **b.** **c.**

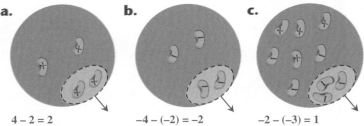

$4 - 2 = 2$ $-4 - (-2) = -2$ $-2 - (-3) = 1$

15 Use a bean model to find each difference.

a. $-6 - (-3)$ **–3** **b.** $-7 - (-2)$ **–5** **c.** $-4 - (-4)$ **0**

16 **Discussion** Think about finding the difference 3 – 6.

    a. If you modeled 3 as shown below, why would it be hard to subtract 6? There are not 6 positive beans to remove.

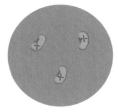

    b. You can also model 3 like this. Why can this model be used to subtract 6? Now there are 6 positive beans to remove.

    c. Use the model of 3 from part (b) to find 3 – 6. –3

17 **Try This as a Class** Use a bean model to find each difference.

    a. 1 – 2 –1   **b.** –5 – (–7) 2

    c. 4 – (–2) 6   **d.** –3 – (–1) –2

18 ✔ **CHECKPOINT** Use a bean model to find each difference.

    a. 1 – 4 –3   **b.** –2 – (–4) 2

    c. 3 – (–2) 5   **d.** 0 – (–5) 5

19 Find each sum.

    a. 1 + (–4) –3   **b.** –2 + 4 2

    c. 3 + 2 5   **d.** 0 + 5 5

20 **Discussion**

    a. How do the problems in Questions 18 and 19 compare?

    b. How do the answers compare? The answer for each pair of problems is the same.

✔ **QUESTION 18**

...checks that you can use a bean model to subtract integers.

20. a. The problems in Question 18 are subtraction and the problems in Question 19 are addition. In Question 19, each subtraction problem from Question 18 is rewritten as the addition of its opposite.

TEACHING NOTES

Question 16(b) Ask students why 7 and –4 were chosen to model 3 rather than a different combination of beans. (*Although other combinations could work, there is a minimum number of beans that must be used for the model. Since positive 6 is taken away, the model you begin with must have at least 6 positive beans.*)

Question 17 Because there is more than one model for each subtraction problem, discuss with students how they would represent each situation and why the model they chose can be used to complete the subtraction.

Discussion in **Question 20** will be an important reference for students as they write a rule for subtraction in **Question 22**.

COMMON ERROR
When changing a subtraction problem to an addition problem, students may incorrectly change the signs of both numbers. Remind them to only change the sign of the number that is being subtracted.

21. a. You need 3 negative beans to take away, and the combination of 8 positive beans and 3 negative beans equals 5.
c. One involves 5 and –3, one involves 5 and 3; one is a subtraction expression, and the other is an addition expression.

▶ The bean models in the Example below show the relationship between the expressions 5 – (–3) and 5 + 3.

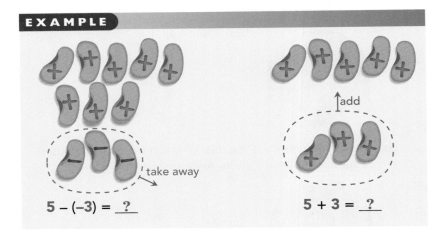

EXAMPLE

add

take away

5 – (–3) = ___?___   5 + 3 = ___?___

21 **a.** In the Example, why are 8 positive beans and 3 negative beans used to model 5?

b. How are the expressions 5 – (–3) and 5 + 3 similar?
Both contain the numerals 5 and 3.
c. How are the expressions different?

d. Use the beans to find 5 – (–3) and 5 + 3. How do their values compare? 8; 8; They are the same.

22 **Try This as a Class**

a. Use your answers from Questions 20 and 21 to describe a method for changing a subtraction problem to an addition problem. Rewrite subtracting a number as adding its opposite.

b. Use your method to find –2 – 3 by rewriting it as an addition problem. –2 + (–3) = –5

c. Check your answer to part (b) by using beans to find –2 – 3.
–5 is the correct answer.

23 Use your method from Question 22(a) to find each difference. Show your steps.

a. 22 – (–12)   **b.** 15 – 72   **c.** –18 – 7
22 + 12 = 34   15 + (–72) = –57   –18 + (–7) = –25

✔ QUESTION 24

...checks that you can subtract integers.

24 **✔ CHECKPOINT** Find each difference.

a. –17 – (–25) 8   **b.** 13 – (–7) 20   **c.** –36 – (–19) –17

d. –11 – 11 –22   **e.** 49 – 78 –29   **f.** 0 – (–13) 13

HOMEWORK EXERCISES ▶ See Exs. 22–44 on pp. 529–530.

Section 3
Key Concepts

Integer Addition (pp. 521–523)

Key Term

The sum of two positive integers is a positive integer.

$1 + 2 = 3$

The sum of two negative integers is a negative integer.

$-2 + (-3) = -5$

The sum of a positive and a negative integer can be positive, negative, or zero.

$3 + (-2) = 1$
$2 + (-4) = -2$
$-2 + 2 = 0$

−2 and 2 are opposites.

The sum of an integer and 0 is that integer.

$-2 + 0 = -2$

opposites

Integer Subtraction (pp. 523–526)

Subtraction of an integer can be rewritten as an addition of the opposite of the integer.

Example Subtracting a negative:

The opposite of −8 is −(−8) = 8.

$5 - (-8) = 5 + 8$
$= 13$

Example Subtracting a positive:

−7 is the opposite of 7.

$-3 - 7 = -3 + (-7)$
$= -10$

Key Concepts

CLOSURE QUESTION

Explain how to add and subtract two integers when the integers being added are both positive, both negative, and when one is positive and the other is negative.

Sample Responses:

For addition: When both integers are positive, add the integers and the result is positive. When both integers are negative, ignore the signs and add the integers. The result is negative. When one integer is positive and the other is negative, ignore the signs and subtract the integers, then give the result the sign of the integer that is farther from 0 on a number line. If the integers are opposites, the result is zero.

For subtraction: Rewrite the expression as addition of the opposite of the integer being subtracted and follow the rules of addition.

ABSENT STUDENTS

For students who were absent for all or part of this section, the blackline Study Guide for Section 3 may be used to present the ideas, concepts, and skills of Section 3.

Key Concepts Questions

25 Find each sum.

   a. −152 + 37 −115   **b.** 17 + (−41) −24   **c.** −23 + (−15) −38

26 Describe the integers that can be subtracted from −5 so that the difference is the given number.

   a. a positive number
      integers less than −5

   b. a negative number
      integers greater than −5

   c. 0
      −5

Section 3
Practice & Application Exercises

YOU WILL NEED

For Exs. 45–48:
♦ graph paper

Write the integer represented by each combination of algebra tiles.

1.  –2

2. 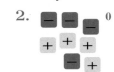 0

3. 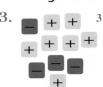 3

4. Draw a model that represents 4 and uses exactly two negative tiles.

5. Draw a model that represents –6 and uses a total of eight tiles.

6. Draw a model that represents 0 and uses a total of six tiles.

7. **Writing** Is it possible to model 5 using ten tiles? Explain.
No; 5 of the tiles would have to total 0 and that is not possible.

Find each sum.

8. 24 + (–16) 8   9. –12 + (–32) –44   10. 0 + (–17) –17

11. –19 + 4 –15   12. –8 + 22 14   13. 5 + (–15) –10

14. 12 + (–12) 0   15. –26 + (–6) –32   16. 20 + (–55) –35

17. Three game show contestants are about to answer a question. They will earn 800 points if they answer correctly and lose 800 points if they answer incorrectly.

  a. How many points will each contestant have if they answer correctly? 1300, 450, 1575

  b. How many points will each have if they answer incorrectly?
  –300, –1150, –25

528

Algebra Connection For each expression, describe the possible values for x.

18. The sum $10 + x$ is a positive integer. *integers greater than −10*

19. The sum $-3 + x$ is a negative integer. *integers less than 3*

20. The sum $x + 6$ is zero. *−6*

21. **Challenge** In a magic square, the sum of the numbers in each row, column, and main diagonal is the same. Copy and complete the magic square using −10, −6, −4, 0, 2, 4, and 6.

21.

−8	6	−4
2	−2	−6
0	−10	4

Magic Square

−8	?	?
?	−2	?
?	?	?

Write the subtraction equation shown by each model.

22.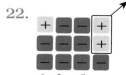

$-6 - 2 = -8$

23.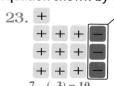

$7 - (-3) = 10$

24.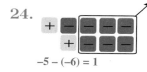

$-5 - (-6) = 1$

25.

25. Draw a model of 3 that can be used to show the subtraction $3 - (-2)$.

Write an equivalent addition expression for each subtraction expression. Then find the sum.

26. $18 - (-33)$
$18 + 33 = 51$

27. $-12 - 9$
$-12 + (-9) = -21$

28. $0 - (-28)$
$0 + 28 = 28$

29. **Temperature** The greatest 24-hour temperature change in the United States was recorded in Loma, Montana, on January 14–15, 1972. The temperature rose from −54°F to 49°F.

29. b. $49 + 54 = 103$;
The thermometer shows that there are 49 degrees between 49°F and 0°F and there are 54 degrees between 0° and −54°F, for a total of 103 degrees.

a. Write a subtraction expression to find the change in temperature. $49 - (-54) = 103$

b. Write an addition expression to find the change in temperature. Use the thermometer above to help explain why this expression gives the same answer as your expression from part (a).

EXERCISE NOTES

Exercise 21 may take some students a long time to solve using guess and check. It helps if students use reasoning such as, it would not make sense to have −10 in a row, column, or diagonal with −8 since this will be difficult to balance with the other spaces and remaining integers.

Exercise 29 Extend this problem by having students record the high and low temperatures for a few days, then calculate the range in temperature in your locality. Students could use a thermometer to measure the temperature, or they could use weather statistics from a local newspaper or the internet.

Practice & Applications

EXERCISE NOTE

Exercise 42 Make sure students understand the definition of *par* given in **part (a)**, and that a negative integer means *the number of strokes below (or less than) par.*

Find the sum or difference.

30. 27 – 55 –28   **31.** 23 + (–18) 5   **32.** –8 – (–17) 9

33. –10 – 0 –10   **34.** –29 – (–50) 21   **35.** –7 + 24 17

36. –19 – (–19) 0   **37.** –5 – 8 –13   **38.** 0 – 25 –25

39. –19 + (–19) –38   **40.** 0 – (–25) 25   **41.** 26 – (–55) 81

42. **Golf** In 1997, twenty-one-year-old Tiger Woods became the youngest winner of the Masters Tournament.

a. *Par* is the number of strokes it should take a very good golfer to get the ball from the tee into the hole. Of the players in the table, who took the most strokes? the fewest? Tom Watson, Tiger Woods

b. By how many strokes did Tiger Woods beat Tom Kite? 12 strokes

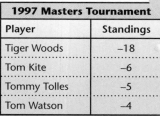

−18 means 18 strokes less than par.

1997 Masters Tournament	
Player	**Standings**
Tiger Woods	–18
Tom Kite	–6
Tommy Tolles	–5
Tom Watson	–4

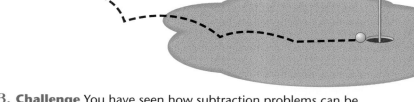

43. **Challenge** You have seen how subtraction problems can be changed to addition problems. Addition problems can also be changed to subtraction problems. Change each addition problem to a subtraction problem. Then find the difference.

a. –17 + 17
  –17 – (–17) = 0

b. 23 + (–8)
  23 – 8 = 15

c. 14 + (–22)
  14 – 22 = –8

Oral Report

Exercise 44 checks that you understand integer addition and subtraction.

Reflecting ◀▶on the Section

Be prepared to report on the following in class.

44. Draw a model and write an equation to show how each situation could occur. Check students' models.

a. adding an integer to a number and getting a sum that is less than the original number when the integer that is added is negative; Sample Response: 5 + (–1) = 4

b. subtracting an integer from a number and getting a difference that is greater than the original number when the integer that is subtracted is negative; Sample Response: –10 – (–7) = –3

Spiral ▶Review

Plot each pair of coordinates on a grid. (Module 7, p. 489)

45. (4, –7) **46.** (0, 5) **47.** (–3, –3) **48.** (–2, 0)

Estimation Estimate each sum or difference. (Module 1, p. 10; Module 5, p. 324; Module 8, p. 516)

49. $5\frac{7}{8} + 7\frac{1}{5}$ **50.** 2763 + 1287 **51.** $9 - 6\frac{8}{11}$

52. $2\frac{2}{7} + 3\frac{1}{8}$ **53.** $16\frac{5}{9} - 4\frac{3}{4}$ **54.** 15.8 + 9.2 + 7.9

Mental Math Use mental math to multiply. (Toolbox, p. 574)

55. 0.137 · 1000
137
56. 4.23 · 100
423
57. 3.59 · 10,000
35,900

58. 0.2 · 10
2
59. 2.213 · 1000
2,213
60. 75 · 100,000
7,500,000

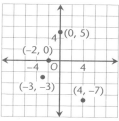

45.–48.

49. about 13

50. about 4000

51. about 2

52. about 5

53. about 12

54. about 33

Extension ▶ ▶

Commutative and Associative Properties

Find the sums for each pair of expressions.

61. 2 + (–4) –2, –2
–4 + 2
62. –3 + (–2) –5, –5
–2 + (–3)
63. –8 + 15 7, 7
15 + (–8)

64. [5 + (–6)] + 2 1, 1
5 + (–6 + 2)
65. (–7 + 3) + (–5) –9, –9
–7 + [3 + (–5)]
66. 13 + [–1 + (–9)] 3, 3
[13 + (–1)] + (–9)

67. Addition of integers is *commutative*. The order in which the integers are added does not change the result. Explain which pairs of sums in Exercises 61–66 show this property.

68. The addition of integers is also *associative*. The grouping of the integers does not change the result. Explain which pairs of sums in Exercises 61–66 show this property.

Add the integers mentally. Explain the method you used.

69. –21 + 15 + (–9) + 5
See margin.
70. –8 + 13 + (–3) + (–13)
See margin.

71. **a.** Is subtraction of integers commutative? no

b. Is subtraction of integers associative? no

c. Give examples to support your answers to parts (a) and (b).
Sample Response: part (a): 5 – 7 = –2 and 7 – 5 = 2; part (b): 10 – (8 – 3) = 5 and (10 – 8) – 3 = –1

67. Exercises 61–63 include a pair of expressions in which the same addends are added in different orders and the answers are the same.

68. Exercises 64–66 include a pair of expressions in which the same three addends are grouped differently and the answers are the same.

EXERCISE NOTES
Extension Exercises 61–71 Once students discover the commutative and associative properties for addition of integers, they can use them with the methods learned in Section 2 to perform calculations using mental math.

69. –10; group –21 with (–9) and 15 with 5 to get –30 + 20 = –10

70. –11; group 13 with (–13) and –8 with (–3) to get 0 + (–11) = –11

TEACHER NOTES
For each Exploration, the corresponding Extra Skill Practice Exercises are noted.

Exploration 1: Exs. 1–9, 21, 23, 27, 28

Exploration 2: Exs. 10–20, 22, 24–26, 29–30

EXTRA HELP
Teacher's Resource Book
- Practice and Applications
- Study Guide

Technology Resources
- @Home Tutor
- Test Generator

ASSESSMENT
- Section 3 Quick Quiz
- Mid-Module Quiz
- Test Generator

Section 3
Extra Skill Practice

Find each sum.

1. $-10 + (-7)$ −17
2. $21 + (-3)$ 18
3. $-34 + (-6)$ −40
4. $7 + (-14)$ −7
5. $-45 + 61$ 16
6. $15 + (-15)$ 0
7. $-21 + (-5)$ −26
8. $16 + (-52)$ −36
9. $-7 + 3$ −4

Find each difference.

10. $6 - (-4)$ 10
11. $-22 - (-13)$ −9
12. $-12 - (-7)$ −5
13. $15 - 19$ −4
14. $-16 - 7$ −23
15. $10 - (-12)$ 22
16. $0 - (-72)$ 72
17. $-51 - 12$ −63
18. $-5 - (-5)$ 0

For each expression, describe the possible values for x.

19. The difference $-4 - x$ is a positive integer. integers less than −4

20. The difference $x - 6$ is a negative integer. integers less than 6

21. The sum $12 + x$ is zero. −12

Find each sum or difference.

22. $51 - 73$ −22
23. $29 + (-35)$ −6
24. $-96 - (-8)$ −88
25. $0 - (-16)$ 16
26. $-1 - (-5)$ 4
27. $-14 + 62$ 48
28. $-91 + (-35)$ −126
29. $-13 - 18$ −31
30. $12 - 44$ −32

Study Skills ◀▶ Listening

Listening to the thoughts and ideas of other people can help clarify your own thoughts. It can also spark new ideas you might not have thought of otherwise.

Look at Discussion Questions 16 and 20 on page 525. Try to remember your class discussion of these questions.

1. What were some of the comments and answers from your classmates? 1–2. Answers will vary.

2. Did any of the ideas from the discussion make you think in a new way? Explain.

EXTENDED EXPLORATION

E2

Extended Exploration

E² Notes

Using an E²: Suggestions for managing and evaluating an Extended Exploration are available in the *Teacher's Resource Book* for Modules 1 and 2. See also pages T44–T45 in the *Teacher's Edition*.

Mix It Up

The Situation See the *Teacher's Resource Book* for a sample solution for this Extended Exploration.

Trail mix is a mixture of different types of nuts, dried fruits, and sweets that can be eaten on the go. *Mix It Up* is a new store in town that has several items you can choose from to create your own trail mix.

The Problem

Create several different trail mixes that have one type of nut, one type of fruit, and one type of sweet. Each mix must fill a quart size bag and cost about $5.

▲
A mix of raisins and peanuts is a common snack.

Typically, mixes like the one above have extra ingredients to please individual tastes.

Mix It Up

Nuts	Cost/Cup
Almonds	$1.29
Cashews	$1.34
Peanuts	$.81
Fruits	**Cost/Cup**
Apples	$.23
Banana chips	$.37
Raisins	$.43
Sweets	**Cost/Cup**
Chocolate covered cranberries	$2.84
Candy covered chocolate	$2.75
Chocolate chips	$1.38

Something to Think About

◆ How many cups are in one quart?

◆ Fractions of a cup can be used.

◆ What combinations of three ingredients do you think would taste good?

◆ What percent of each mix should be nuts? What percent fruits? What percent sweets?

Present Your Results

How many different combinations of nuts, fruits, and sweets are possible?

Name the trail mixes you created.

For each of your trail mixes, list the three ingredients, the amount of each ingredient, the total cost of each ingredient, and the cost of a quart of the trail mix.

Choose one of your trail mixes to be the *Mix of the Month* for the *Mix It Up* store. Explain why you chose it.

Setting the Stage

GETTING STARTED

Module 8 Section 4 *Warm-Up* assesses students' facility with calculating probability. Students will use previously learned probability skills to compute geometric probabilities.

Students may be interested in knowing that an asteroid is a rocky body that orbits the Sun. Most asteroids are located between the orbits of Mars and Jupiter. *Meteoroids* are small pieces of asteroids. A *meteorite* is a meteoroid that survives the passage through the atmosphere and hits the surface of Earth before burning up completely.

Section 4 Geometric Probability

Setting the Stage

In Module 4, you analyzed data about dinosaurs. After dominating the land for 130 million years, dinosaurs disappeared from the face of the Earth at the end of the Cretaceous Period, about 65 million years ago. "Why did the dinosaurs become extinct?" The answer is that nobody knows for sure.

Many scientists believe that a huge asteroid that crashed into the Yucatán Peninsula at a site known as Chicxulub (pronounced CHEEK-shoo-loob) caused the extinction of 70% of the living species, including the dinosaurs, on the planet. The impact blasted a crater 180 km wide and 900 m deep.

◀ Location of the Chicxulub crater (circle) on Mexico's Yucatán Peninsula

Think About It

1 The Chicxulub crater is about how many times as wide as it is deep? **about 200 times**

2 If an asteroid strikes Earth, is it more likely to hit land or water? Why? **water; There is more water than land on Earth.**

Exploration 1

Predicting with Geometric Probability

SET UP   *Work as a class. You will need an inflatable globe.*

GOAL

LEARN HOW TO...
- find geometric probabilities
- use probability to make predictions

AS YOU...
- describe the chance of an object falling in a particular area

KEY TERMS
- complementary events
- geometric probability

▶ Since the orbits of most asteroids do not intersect Earth's orbit, it isn't likely that one will strike Earth. However, about 500 meteorites do strike Earth each year. Each meteorite has an equally likely chance of hitting anywhere on Earth. To find the probability that a meteorite will hit land you will conduct an experiment with a globe.

3 **Try This as a Class** Follow the steps below to simulate a meteorite falling to Earth. **Check students' work.**

First   Make a table like the one below to record the results of your experiment.

Next   Carefully toss an inflated globe from one person to another. Each time the globe is caught, make a tally mark to record whether the tip of your left index finger is touching land or touching water before tossing it again. Record the results of 30 tosses.

Then   Complete your table by calculating the percent of the tosses that hit land and the percent that hit water.

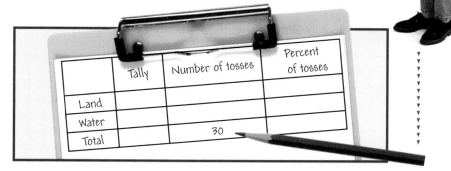

	Tally	Number of tosses	Percent of tosses
Land			
Water			
Total		30	

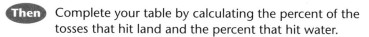

Exploration 1

CLASSROOM MANAGEMENT

If an inflatable globe is not available, you could use a ball that is 20% shaded. Be sure the shading is placed randomly around the ball and students understand that the shaded areas represent land. One way to keep track of the number of tosses is to have students shout out the toss number and where their finger lands. For example, on the fifth toss the students would say either "5 water" or "5 land". Before beginning the activity, have students make a prediction about the percent of tosses that will hit land and the percent that will hit water.

You may want to stop after every 5 or 10 catches to have students estimate the percents and explain how they made their estimates. Students may observe that after a few tosses their estimates were not very good, but that the estimates got better as the number of catches increased.

DEVELOPING MATH CONCEPTS

Be sure students understand how the globe tossing simulates the probability that a meteorite will hit land. Emphasize that when the globe is caught, there is an equally likely chance of the tip of a student's finger landing anywhere on the globe. The probability that a meteorite will "hit land" is the number of times the tip of the index finger hits land divided by the total number of catches.

TEACHING NOTES

Students may want to look more carefully at the globe to help them answer **Question 4(a)**. You may want to ask students to think about how the amount of land available to "land on" affects the probability. This will set the stage for the development of geometric probability that follows.

The example below provides another opportunity for students to see how geometric probability is calculated prior to completing **Checkpoint Question 7**.

CLASSROOM EXAMPLE

Find the probability that a randomly thrown dart that hits the target below lands in one of the shaded regions. Then find the probability that it lands in the unshaded region.

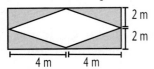

Answer: Probability that the dart lands in one of the shaded regions

$$= \frac{\text{total area of shaded region}}{\text{total area of rectangle}}$$

$$= \frac{4 \cdot \left(\frac{1}{2} \cdot 2 \cdot 4\right)}{4 \cdot 8}$$

$$= \frac{16}{32} \text{ or } \frac{1}{2}$$

To find the probability that the dart hits the unshaded region:

= 1 – Probability that the dart lands in one of the shaded regions

$$= 1 - \frac{1}{2}$$

$$= \frac{1}{2}$$

FOR ◄ HELP

with *finding probabilities*, see **MODULE 2, p. 80**

▲

Objects in space travel at great speeds. An aluminum sphere 1 cm in diameter orbiting Earth can cause the same damage to a spacecraft as a 40 lb object traveling 60 mi/hr on Earth!

6. a. Divide the area of the sensor by the area of the panel; 10%

b. 90%; Sample Response: I subtracted the probability of the space junk hitting the sensor, 10%, from 100%.

✔ QUESTION 7

...checks that you can find geometric probabilities and use them to make predictions.

---

4 Discussion Use the results of the globe-tossing experiment.
Sample responses are given.

a. What percent of Earth do you think is covered by water? *about 80%*

b. Estimate the probability that a meteorite will hit water. *about 80%*

c. Estimate the probability that it will hit land. *about 20%*

d. What is the probability a meteorite will hit either land or water? *100%*

▶ When a meteorite strikes Earth, it either hits water or it hits land. The events *a meteorite hits water* and *a meteorite hits land* are **complementary events**. Two events are complementary if one or the other must occur, but they cannot both happen at the same time.

5 Try This as a Class Use the probabilities you found in Question 4.

a. If two events are complementary, what must be true about their probabilities? *One or the other of the events must occur, and the sum of the probabilities must be 1, or 100%.*

b. It is estimated that 500 meteorites hit Earth each year. About how many meteorites would you expect to hit water each year? About how many meteorites would you expect to hit land each year? *Sample Response: about 400 meteorites; about 100 meteorites*

▶ In addition to meteoroids, space junk—such as pieces of satellites and rockets—can be harmful to orbiting spacecraft.

6 Try This as a Class Suppose a rectangular sensor is placed in the middle of a rectangular panel on a spacecraft as shown.

a. If a piece of space junk randomly hits the panel, how can you find the probability that it hits the sensor? Find the probability.

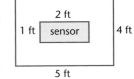

b. What is the probability that a piece of space junk hits the panel but not the sensor? How did you find the probability?

▶ In Question 6, you used areas to find a probability. Probabilities that are based on lengths, areas, or volumes are **geometric probabilities**.

7 ✔ CHECKPOINT Suppose an object randomly hits within the circle at the right.

a. What is the probability that it will hit within the square? *about 32%*

b. If 200 objects randomly hit within the circle, about how many would you expect to hit within the square? *about 64 objects*

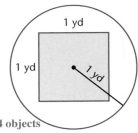

HOMEWORK EXERCISES ▶ See Exs. 1–12 on pp. 538–540.

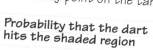
Geometric Probability (pp. 535–536)

A probability that is based on lengths, areas, or volumes is a geometric probability.

Example

A dart that hits the target is equally likely to hit any point on the target.

Probability that the dart hits the shaded region $= \dfrac{\text{Area of shaded region}}{\text{Total area of target}}$

$= \dfrac{\pi \cdot 6^2}{\pi \cdot 12^2} = \dfrac{36\pi}{144\pi} = \dfrac{1}{4}$

Probability that the dart hits the white region $= 1 - \dfrac{1}{4}$

$= \dfrac{3}{4}$

1 minus the probability that the dart hits the shaded region.

Since a dart can hit the white region or the shaded region, but not both, the events *the dart hits the white region* and **the dart hits the shaded region** are complementary events.

You can use the probability $\dfrac{3}{4}$ to predict the number of times a dart will hit the white region when it hits the target 80 times.

$\dfrac{3}{4}$ of the 80 hits are in the white region.

$\dfrac{3}{4}$ of 80 hits = 60 hits

Key Terms

geometric probability

complementary events

Key Concepts Questions

8 A dart that hits the square target at the right is equally likely to hit any point on the target. What is the probability that the dart hits the shaded region? $\dfrac{1}{6}$

9 In the Example above, why does the probability that the dart hits the white region equal 1 minus the probability that the dart hits the shaded region?

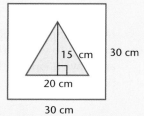

15 cm   30 cm

20 cm

30 cm

9. For a dart that hits the target, the probability of hitting the target is 1, so the sum of the two indicated probabilities is 1.

Key Concepts

CLOSURE QUESTIONS

Describe geometric probability and explain how it is different from probability you have studied previously.

Sample Response: Geometric probability is probability based on lengths, areas, or volumes. Probability studied previously was based on data values. Both are ratios that compare a part to a whole.

ABSENT STUDENTS

For students who were absent for all or part of this section, the blackline Study Guide for Section 4 may be used to present the ideas, concepts, and skills of Section 4.

Practice & Applications

Section ④
Practice & Application Exercises

Suppose an object falls at random onto each target shown below. For each target, find the probability that the object will land in a shaded region.

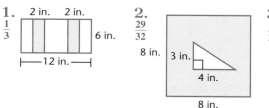 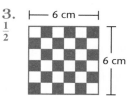

1. $\frac{1}{3}$ 2 in. 2 in. 6 in. 12 in.

2. $\frac{29}{32}$ 8 in. 3 in. 4 in. 8 in.

3. $\frac{1}{2}$ 6 cm 6 cm

Shuffleboard In a game of shuffleboard, players take turns sliding plastic disks onto a scoring area. Players gain or lose the number of points marked on the space their disk is on.

4. If you randomly slide your disk so that it lands somewhere on the green court shown, what is the probability that it will land within the triangle that is outlined in black? $\frac{1}{3}$

5. If you randomly slide your disk so that it lands within the black triangle, what is the probability that you will score 10 points? $\frac{1}{9}$

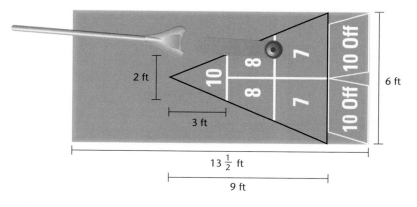

6. At a fair there is a jug filled with water with a small glass at the bottom. To win a prize you must drop a quarter into the jug and have it land in the glass. If the quarter falls randomly to the bottom, what is the probability of winning a prize? $\frac{1}{36}$

7. **Create Your Own** Draw and shade a target. Include at least two different geometric shapes in your design. Find the probability of a dart hitting a shaded part of your target. **Check students' work.**

8. **Estimation** Suppose an object falls at random within the rectangle shown.

   a. Estimate the probability the object will land within the shaded circle. Explain how you made your estimate.

   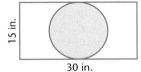

   b. Estimate the probability the object will land within the white area around the circle. How did you make your estimate? **about 0.6; 1 – 0.4 = 0.6**

   c. Suppose 250 objects are dropped at random onto the rectangle. About how many objects would you expect to land within the circle? **about 100**

8. a. about 0.4; The area of the circle is about $3.14(7.5^2)$ $= 176.625$ in.^{2} and the area of the rectangle is about 450 in.^{2}, so the probability is about $\frac{176.625}{450} \approx 0.4.$

9. **Ballooning** The balloon festival held in Albuquerque, New Mexico, has a target event where people drop objects from their balloons onto a target area. Suppose an object is randomly dropped onto the target area at the right. What is the probability that the object lands within the 6 in. by 6 in. blue square region? $\frac{1}{40}$

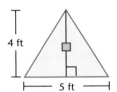

10. The land area of the United States is about 1.8% of the area of the surface of Earth. If 500 meteorites hit Earth each year, about how many meteorites would you expect to hit the United States each year? **about 9 meteorites**

11. a. An object dropped from an airplane is equally likely to land anywhere in the rectangular region below. The area of the rectangular region is approximately 75 mi^2. The probability that an object will land within the circular region is $\frac{1}{6}$. What is the area of the circular region? **12.5 mi^2**

   b. **Challenge** What is the radius of the circular region? Round to the nearest tenth of a mile. **about 2.0 mi**

Practice & Applications

EXERCISE NOTES

Exercise 12 This is an excellent discussion question because of all the variables to consider (people on land and water, standing, sitting, or laying down, population density, etc.). The point is that the probability of a person being hit by a meteorite is extremely low.

12. about 0.00001; Sample Response: I looked in an almanac and on the internet and found that the surface area of Earth is about 200 million square miles, and the population is about 6.4 billion. I allowed about 1 yd² per person, converted 1 mi² to 1760² yd², and divided 6,400,000,000 by (200,000,000 · 1760²).

20 a.

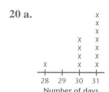

28 29 30 31
Number of days

Reflecting on the Section

Write your response to Exercise 12 in your journal.

12. In 1954, Ann Hodges was resting on a sofa when a 4 kg meteorite broke through her roof, ricocheted off a radio, and hit her leg. The probability of a person being hit by a meteorite is actually very low because of the small fraction of Earth that is covered with people. Estimate this probability and explain how you found your answer.

Spiral Review

Convert each measurement to liters. (Module 8, p. 506)

13. 3425 mL 3.425 L   14. 97 kL 97,000 L

15. 250 cm³ 0.25 L   16. 0.84 kL 840 L

For the circle with each given measurement, replace each ? with the missing diameter or circumference. Round to the nearest hundredth. (Module 7, p. 466)

17. $C = 105.6$ cm   18. $r = 4\frac{1}{5}$ in.   19. $d = 70$ ft

    $d \approx$ _?_ $C \approx$ _?_ $C \approx$ _?_

    33.63 cm   26.38 in.   219.80 ft

20. a. Make a line plot for the data in the table. (Module 4, p. 224)

Month	Jan	Feb	Mar	Apr	May	Jun	Jul	Aug	Sep	Oct	Nov	Dec
Number of days	31	28	31	30	31	30	31	31	30	31	30	31

   b. Use your line plot to find the mode and the median for the number of days in the twelve months. 31; 31

Find each product or quotient. Then use estimation to check that your answer is reasonable. (Module 3, p. 190; Module 4, p. 256)

21. 0.5 · 0.41   22. 10.06 · 0.2   23. 15 ÷ 0.3
0.205; half of 0.4 = 0.2   2.012; 0.2 · 10 = 2   50; 1 ÷ 0.3 ≈ 3, so 15 · 3 = 45

Order the numbers from least to greatest. (Module 3, p. 134)

24. 7, 0.7, 0.57, 7.4, 7.29   25. 45.2, 43.5, 45.02, 4.569
0.57, 0.7, 7, 7.29, 7.4   4.569, 43.5, 45.02, 45.2

26. Find the least common multiple of 15 and 9. (Module 3, p. 168) 45

Section 4

Suppose a dart thrown at random hits each target. What is the probability that it hits the white region?

1.

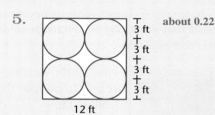

80 cm

$\frac{1}{7}$

60 cm   80 cm   60 cm

area of white square = 1600 cm²

2.

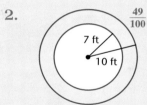

7 ft

10 ft

$\frac{49}{100}$

3.

6 m

$\frac{1}{4}$

18 m

side length of each square is 3 m

4.

60 cm

5 cm

40 cm

about 0.14

5.

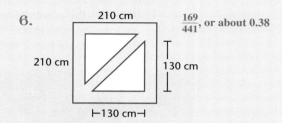

3 ft
3 ft
3 ft
3 ft

12 ft

about 0.22

6.

210 cm

210 cm

130 cm

130 cm

$\frac{169}{441}$, or about 0.38

Standardized Testing ▶ Performance Task

You are designing a dart game where a player will throw darts at a 1 ft by 1 ft board with three to five separate squares drawn on it. Suppose that the squares are all the same size and that a dart thrown at random hits the board.

1. If there are three squares and each has a side length of 2 in., what is the probability that a dart hits a square? Round your answer to the nearest whole percent. about 8%

2. Suppose you want players to have about a 30% chance of hitting one of the squares. How many squares would you include and how long would you make each side? Explain. Answers will vary. Sample Response: The combined area of the squares should be about 44 in.² For example: 4 squares, each 3.3 in. on a side.

TEACHER NOTES

All of the Extra Skill Practice Exercises correspond to Exploration 1.

EXTRA HELP

Teacher's Resource Book
• Practice and Applications
• Study Guide

Technology Resources
• @Home Tutor
• Test Generator

ASSESSMENT
• Section 4 Quick Quiz
• Test Generator

GETTING STARTED
Module 8 Section 5 *Warm-Up* assesses students' understanding of the words *slide, flip, turn*. In this section these movements will be formalized to *translation, reflection*, and *rotation*.

Have students bring in small quilts, quilted pillows, or photos of quilts for a show-and-tell session in class. Discuss the patterns and geometric shapes that can be found in the various quilts.

TECHNOLOGY
For related technology activity, see the *Technology Book*.

Section 5 Transformations

IN THIS SECTION

EXPLORATION 1
◆ Translations, Rotations, and Reflections

EXPLORATION 2
◆ Transformations in Quilting

CREATING THINGS

Setting the Stage

Patchwork quilts are made from scraps of material or old clothing that are cut into shapes and sewn together into a pattern. Ideas for patterns and their names come from people's everyday experiences—the tools they use, the plants or animals they see, and the events or people that are important to them. Patchwork was especially important in colonial times, because fabric was scarce and expensive.

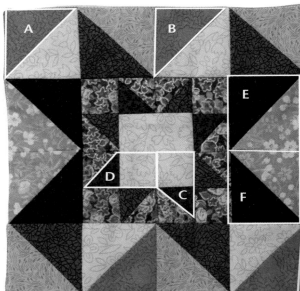

In the 1800s, quilting became so popular that an entire family would often work together to make a quilt.

◀ This quilt pattern, called Eight Hands Round, is named for a movement in square dancing.

▶ A quilter can experiment with patterns by sewing a copy of part of a design and moving it to different positions.

Think About It ▶▶▶▶▶▶▶▶▶▶▶▶▶▶▶▶▶▶▶▶▶▶▶▶▶▶▶▶▶▶▶

1 Give directions for *sliding, flipping,* or *turning* the outlined quilt patches on page 542 to make each move.

a. Move the triangle labeled A onto the triangle labeled B.
Slide triangle A to the right.

b. Move the group of patches labeled C to D. Turn group C 90° clockwise around the upper left corner of C.

c. Move the group of patches labeled E to F. Flip group E across its bottom edge.

2 Can any of the moves in Question 1 be done in more than one way? Discuss your ideas. Yes; for example, to move triangle A onto triangle B, first flip triangle A across the vertical seam of the triangle to its right, then flip it again across the left edge of B. To move group C onto group D, turn C 270° counterclockwise around the upper left corner of C.

Exploration 1 ▶▶▶▶▶▶▶▶▶▶▶▶▶▶▶▶▶▶▶▶▶▶▶▶

Translations, Rotations, and Reflections

SET UP You will need: • Labsheets 5A and 5B • tracing paper
• index card or cardboard • scissors • ruler

3 Follow the steps below to make an isosceles right triangle. Later you will use your triangle to make quilt patch designs.
Check students' work.

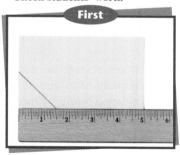

First

Then

Side A   Side B
Side C

Draw an isosceles right triangle on an index card. The sides forming the right angle should each be $1\frac{1}{2}$ in. long.

Cut out the triangle and label the sides as shown.

TEACHING NOTES
Before beginning **Question 3**, review with students the definition of *isosceles right triangle*. Make sure students use an index card or other sturdy material so they will be able to trace their triangle without tearing or bending it. The triangle constructed is needed for **Questions 5, 7, 9, 11** and again in Exploration 2 for **Question 12**.

GOAL

LEARN HOW TO...
◆ perform a translation, a rotation, and a reflection

AS YOU...
◆ create quilt patch designs

KEY TERMS
◆ translation
◆ rotation
◆ reflection
◆ transformation

FOR ◀HELP
with *classifying triangles*, see
MODULE 2, pp. 106–107

Exploration 1 *continued*

TEACHING NOTES

As students complete
Labsheets 5A and 5B, check their
progress to make sure that they are
following the directions given. It is
important that students realize a
translation can be in any direction,
not just vertically up and down, or
horizontally right and left. Some
students may believe that a point
of rotation has to be on or inside
the figure being rotated. Provide
examples to show that the point of
rotation may lie outside the figure.

▶ A **translation** (slide) moves a figure by sliding it. Every point moves
the same distance in the same direction in a plane.

EXAMPLE

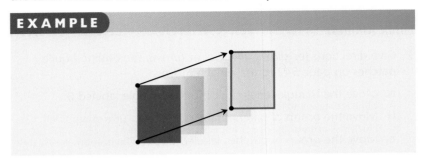

4 **a.** Place tracing paper over the Example above and trace the
shaded rectangle. Slide your tracing along the arrows until it
covers the unshaded rectangle. Check students' work.

b. Did you have to flip or turn the rectangle in part (a)? No.

c. What do the arrows tell you about the translation?
the direction and extent of the translation

5 **Use Labsheet 5A.** Follow the directions on the labsheet and use
your triangle from Question 3 to create a *Translation Patch*.

▶ A **rotation** (turn) moves a figure by turning it either clockwise or
counterclockwise around a fixed point.

EXAMPLE

The **point of rotation**
can be any fixed point
outside, inside, or on
the figure.

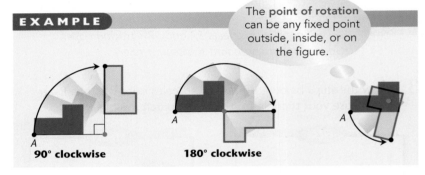

90° clockwise   180° clockwise

6 **a.** Place tracing paper over one of the rotations above. Trace the
shaded figure. Put your pencil tip on the point of rotation.
Rotate the tracing until it covers the unshaded figure by moving
point *A* along the arrow. Check students' work.

b. What does the arrow tell you about the rotation?
the direction and extent of the rotation

c. Could you get the same result by translating the figure? No.

7 **Use Labsheet 5A.** Follow the directions on the labsheet and use
your triangle from Question 3 to create a *Rotation Patch*.

5.

7.

▶ A **reflection** (flip) moves a figure by flipping it across a line.

EXAMPLE

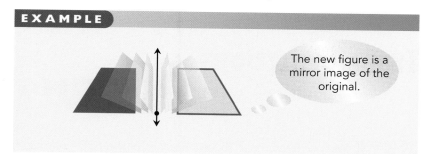

The new figure is a mirror image of the original.

8 a. Place tracing paper over the shaded trapezoid in the Example. Trace the shaded figure, the line, and the point on the line. Flip your paper over so that the tracing covers the unshaded figure. Check students' work.

b. How did the line and the point on the line help you to flip the figure? It helped to position the image correctly.

c. Could you get the same result by translating or rotating the trapezoid? No.

9 Use Labsheet 5B. Follow the directions on the labsheet and use your triangle from Question 3 to create a *Reflection Patch.* e. Yes; the triangle could be rotated to its position in the bottom right square.

▶ A **transformation** is a change made to a figure or to its position. Translations, rotations, and reflections are transformations that change the position of a figure but not its size or shape.

10 ✔ CHECKPOINT Name the transformation that will move each shaded trapezoid onto the unshaded trapezoid.

a.

translation

b.

reflection

c.

rotation

11 Use Labsheet 5B. Follow the directions on the labsheet and use your triangle from Question 3 to *Create Your Own Patch.*

HOMEWORK EXERCISES ▶ See Exs. 1–10 on pp. 549–550.

9. a.–d.

11. a. Sample Response:

b. Sample Response: I positioned my triangle with side A on Line 1 and side B on Line 2. I flipped the triangle across Line 1, then slid it down along Line 1. Finally, I flipped it across Line 1 again.

TEACHING NOTES
Question 11 After students have created their own patch, and if time allows, have them use colors and designs to personalize their patches. The patches can then be glued onto a piece of poster board and put on display for the rest of Module 8.

✔ QUESTION 10

…checks that you can recognize translations, rotations, and reflections.

Exploration 2

Exploration 2

CLASSROOM MANAGEMENT
For **Question 12**, have one student in the partner pair draw and cut out the light triangles while the other person draws and cuts out the dark triangles.

LEARN HOW TO...
◆ use transformations to make designs

AS YOU...
◆ create a zigzag quilt

Exploration 2

Transformations
in QUILTING

SET UP   *Work with a partner. You will need: • Labsheet 5C • scissors • clear tape • construction paper • your triangle from Exploration 1*

▶ **This zigzag design is made entirely from isosceles right triangles using two colors of material.**

You will make the section of the design outlined on the quilt.

12 Follow the steps below to make triangles for a zigzag quilt.
Check students' work.

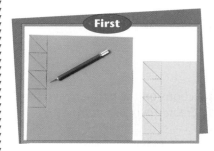

First

Choose one light and one dark color of construction paper. Use your triangle from Exploration 1 to trace 8 triangles of each color.

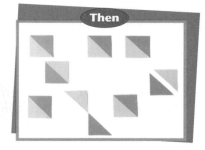

Then

Cut out the triangles. Tape one triangle of each color together to make a square. Make 8 squares.

Use Labsheet 5C for Questions 13–17.

13 a. Place a square patch on the square labeled A on the *Zigzag Design*. Match the triangles and the light and dark colors. Tape the patch in place. Check students' work.

b. Place another patch on top of the patch taped over A, matching the triangles and colors. Use a transformation, or a series of transformations, to move the top patch to square B so that it follows the zigzag pattern shown. Tape the patch in place. Check students' work.

c. Describe the transformation or transformations you used in part (b).

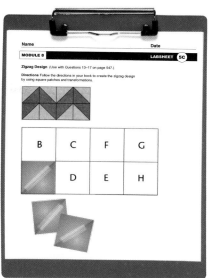

14 Discussion Compare answers for Question 13(c). Did everyone use the same transformations? If not, is one way better than another? Why? There are several ways to move the patch to square B. No one way is necessarily better than the others.

15 ✔ **CHECKPOINT**

a. Place another patch on top of the patch taped over B on the *Zigzag Design*. Match the triangles and colors. Check students' work.

b. Find two different transformations that will move the top patch to C in just one move and continue the zigzag pattern. Tape the patch in place and describe the transformations.

16 a. Place a patch on top of the patch taped over C. Check students' work.

b. Use a transformation or a series of transformations to move the top patch to D so that it follows the zigzag pattern. Tape the patch in place. What transformation or series of transformations did you use?

17 a. Tape the four remaining patches together to make a separate copy of the large square formed by the patches on A, B, C, and D. Check students' work.

b. Place the copy over the large square so that the patterns match. Use a transformation to move the copy to cover the squares E, F, G, and H, and continue the zigzag pattern. Describe the transformation you used. Translate the patch covering squares A, B, C, and D to the right, or reflect it across its right edge.

HOMEWORK EXERCISES ▶ See Exs. 11–20 on pp. 550–551.

Section 5 Transformations 547

✔ **QUESTION 15**

...checks that you can identify and describe transformations.

13. c. Sample Response: I slid the square up, then reflected it across the diagonal.

15. b. Reflect the patch on square B across its right edge, or rotate it 90° clockwise around its lower right corner.

16. b. Sample response: Rotate the patch on square C 180° clockwise around its lower right corner, then translate it to the left.

Key Concepts

CLOSURE QUESTIONS

Name three types of transformations defined in this section. Then discuss the similarities and differences among them.

Sample Response: translations, rotations, and reflections; They all move a figure without changing its size or shape. Translations slide every part of a figure the same direction and distance on a flat surface, rotations turn a figure around a fixed point, and reflections flip a figure over a line.

ABSENT STUDENTS

For students who were absent for all or part of this section, the blackline Study Guide for Section 5 may be used to present the ideas, concepts, and skills of Section 5.

Key Terms

transformation

translation

rotation

reflection

Section 5
Key Concepts

Transformations (pp. 543–547)

A transformation is a change made to a figure or its position. Translations, rotations, and reflections are transformations that change the position of a figure but not the size or the shape of the figure.

Examples

Translation (slide)

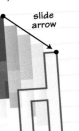

slide arrow

Rotation (turn)

point of rotation

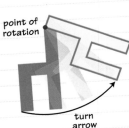

turn arrow

Reflection (flip)

reflecting line

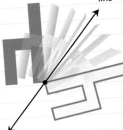

A translation moves every point the same distance in the same direction in a plane. The slide arrow tells the distance and direction to move.

A rotation turns a figure around a fixed point. The turn arrow tells which direction and how many degrees to turn.

A reflection flips a figure across a line. The new figure is a mirror image of the original.

Key Concepts Questions

18 Use transformations to describe how the figure on the screen changes from view to view. **The figure is reflected, then rotated, then translated.**

19. Sample drawing:

a: translation;
b: rotation;
c: reflection

19 Make a simple drawing of an object. Now draw a translation, a rotation, and a reflection of the object. Label each drawing with the transformation you used.

Section 5

Practice & Application Exercises

YOU WILL NEED

For Exs. 11 and 19:
- Labsheet 5D

For Exs. 15 and 18:
- scissors
- glue
- decorative paper
- ruler
- drawing software (optional)

Name the transformation shown in each photo.

1.

reflection

2.

rotation

Name the transformation that will move each shaded figure onto the unshaded figure.

3.

translation

4.

rotation

5.

translation

6.

rotation

7.

reflection

8.

reflection

9. **Arts** The Pennsylvania Dutch hex signs below contain several transformations. Dividing the signs into quarters makes it easier to see the transformations.

Sun, Star, and Rain Hex

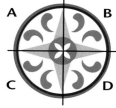
Double Rain Hex and Luck Symbol

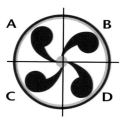
Hex Sign for Rain

▲ Hex signs are painted on barns in Pennsylvania.

a. For each hex sign, name the transformation needed to move quarter A to quarter B. reflection; rotation or reflection; rotation

b. For one of the hex signs, you can move quarter A to quarter B in two ways. Name the hex sign and describe the two transformations. Quarter A can be moved to Quarter B in the middle Hex symbol by rotation or reflection.

Practice & Applications

SUGGESTED ASSIGNMENTS

Core Course
Day 1: Exs. 1–5, 21–30
Day 2: Exs. 6–11
Day 3: Exs. 12–18, 20

Extended Course
Day 1: Exs. 1–5, 21–30
Day 2: Exs. 6–11
Day 3: Exs. 12–20

Note: Extended Course assignments can be used to differentiate within the regular classroom. In classrooms where students are grouped homogeneously, the material might be covered in fewer days. In this case assignments may be combined.

ADDITIONAL PRACTICE

See the *Teacher's Resource Book* for additional practice and application exercises for this section.

EXERCISE NOTES

After students have finished **Exercise 9**, ask them to name the transformation that moves quarter A to quarter D. (*clockwise or counterclockwise rotation through 180°*) After they have completed **Exercise 19**, return to this question and ask students to find another way to use transformations to move quarter A to quarter D. (*First reflect quarter A over the vertical line. Then reflect the result over the horizontal line. The two steps may also be done in the reverse order.*)

Practice & Applications

EXERCISE NOTES

Allow students extra time to complete their designs in **Exercise 15**. Then display students' designs along with explanations in the classroom. To obtain free materials for students to use, check with a home decorating store. Such stores will often donate old wallpaper sample books. Used wrapping paper or greeting cards and old brochures can also serve as free materials for use in designs.

12.

13.

14.

16.

17.

10. Use transformations to describe how the position of the airplane changes from view to view. *translation, rotation, reflection*

11. Use Labsheet 5D. Follow the directions on the labsheet to sketch transformations on the *Grid for Transformations.*

Visual Thinking Sketch the next three terms in each sequence.

12. 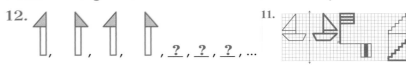 , ? , ? , ? , ...

13. , , , , ? , ? , ? , ...

14.  , ? , ? , ? , ...

15. a. Create Your Own Make a design that is 40 cm by 40 cm using a combination of at least two transformations. Your original shape or shapes can be no larger than 10 cm by 10 cm. You may cut your shapes from construction paper, wrapping paper, or wallpaper, or you can use computer drawing software. a.–b. Check students' work.

b. Describe the transformations used. Show a drawing of your original shape or shapes and any other diagrams that would help someone understand what you did.

In Exercises 16 and 17, A changes to B in the same way that C changes to D. Sketch figure D.

16.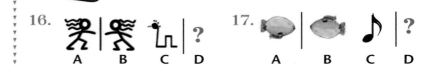
A   B   C   D

17.
A   B   C   D

18. **Home Involvement** Many families treasure quilts that represent their family history and heritage. You can create your own quilt square that displays something about your family's history.
Check students' work.

a. To get ideas for your quilt square, discuss the following with your family:

♦ where your family originally came from

♦ people or places that have been important to your family

♦ objects or patterns that are associated with your family or culture

b. Make a sketch of a design for your square.

c. Create your quilt square. Use convenient materials such as colored paper, pieces of fabric, or white paper and fabric crayons.

d. Share your quilt square with your class. Explain how your design relates to your family's heritage.

19. a.

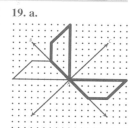

19. **Challenge** Use the *Double Reflection Grid* on Labsheet 5D.

a. Follow the directions on the labsheet to draw two reflections of a trapezoid.

b. What single transformation has the same result as reflecting the trapezoid across $\overleftrightarrow{AB}$ and then reflecting it across $\overleftrightarrow{AC}$?
180° rotation (clockwise or counterclockwise) around point A

 **Reflecting ◀▶on the Section**

20. Look for examples of company or product logos that use translations, rotations, or reflections. Sketch or copy the designs and describe the transformations.

Logo of the Sarajevo Winter Olympics (1984)

Recycling Logo

 **Spiral ◀▶Review**

Write each fraction in lowest terms. (Module 1, p. 61)

21. $\frac{6}{18}$ $\frac{1}{3}$ 22. $\frac{24}{30}$ $\frac{4}{5}$ 23. $\frac{15}{25}$ $\frac{3}{5}$ 24. $\frac{9}{27}$ $\frac{1}{3}$

Replace each ? with > or <. (Module 7, p. 489)

25. 34 ? 43
    <
26. –3 ? 3
    <
27. –55 ? –56
    >
28. –658 ? 0
    <
29. –7 ? –9
    >
30. 24 ? –2
    >

RESEARCH

Exercise 20 checks that you can recognize translations, rotations, and reflections.

20. **Sample Response:** The symbol for the Mercedes Benz automobile company can be produced by rotating a sector of a circle 120° and 240° around the point of the sector.

Section 5
Extra Skill Practice

Name the transformation or transformations that will move each shaded figure onto the unshaded figure.

1.
reflection

2.
rotation

3.
translation

4.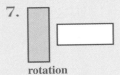
reflection followed by translation

5.
translation

6.
reflection followed by rotation

7.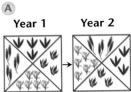
rotation

8.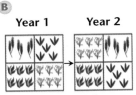
reflection

9.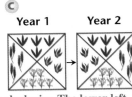
translation

Match each situation with the transformation that best describes it. Choices may be used more than once.

10. Opening a sliding glass door C

11. Closing a bureau drawer C

12. Flipping a page in a book B

13. Turning the minute hand of a clock to adjust the time A

A. rotation   B. reflection   C. translation

Standardized Testing ◀▶ Open-ended

Which farmer really "rotates" the crops? Describe how the other farmers "transform" their fields.

A
Year 1   Year 2

B
Year 1   Year 2

C
Year 1   Year 2

A; B: The crops in the two upper sections are rotated one section clockwise. The lower left crop is replanted in the same section, while the lower right crop is moved to the upper left; C: reflection across a vertical line dividing the field

COMPARISONS and PREDICTIONS

Setting the Stage ▶▶▶▶▶▶▶▶▶▶▶▶▶▶▶▶▶▶▶▶▶▶▶▶

SET UP *Work as a class. You will need:* • *Labsheet 6A* • *calculator* • *sticky notes* • *index cards or planet cutouts* • *scissors*

In the summer of 2003, NASA launched spacecraft carrying twin robot geologists, the *Mars Exploration Rovers*. Six months later, in January 2004, the rovers landed on Mars and began collecting data in an effort to learn more about the history of Mars.

To better relate to the long trip the rovers took, you will build a model of the planets and compare their distances from the sun.

Use Labsheet 6A. Follow the directions to build the *Planet Distance Model*. See margin.

Think About It

1 List the planets in order from least to greatest distance from the sun. Mercury, Venus, Earth, Mars, Jupiter, Saturn, Uranus, Neptune

2 Look at the far right column of the table on the labsheet. The distances for Venus, Earth, Jupiter, and Mars were written in a form called *scientific notation*.

  a. What do these numbers have in common?

  b. How do these numbers differ from the other planets' distances that are not written in *scientific notation*?

2. a. All have only one digit in the one's place and a decimal part, and this number is multiplied by 10^8.
   b. The numbers not written in scientific notation all have a two-digit number multiplied by 10^8, except Mercury, which has a number less than 1 multiplied by 10^8.

Setting the Stage

GETTING STARTED

Module 8 Section 6 *Warm-Up* assesses students' ability to multiply and divide by factors that are powers of 10. These skills will be essential in understanding scientific notation and converting numbers between scientific notation and standard form.

Before students build the *Planet Distance Model*, check with the science teacher for pictures of the planets to place at the end of each line of sticky notes. These can be used instead of index cards marked with the names of the planets.

Labsheet 6A. See Additional Answers beginning on page A1.

TEACHING NOTES

Point out to students that some of the definition of *scientific notation* is contained within the bubbles of the two samples shown just above **Question 3**.

After completing **Question 9**, have students revisit **Question 4** to rewrite those numbers not in scientific notation in scientific notation. Most students will convert each number to standard form and then to scientific notation. Advanced students may try to determine some patterns with the exponents when rewriting a number with powers of 10 in scientific notation.

You may want to discuss the following Classroom Example before students complete **Question 5**.

CLASSROOM EXAMPLE

Write 605,000 in scientific notation.

Answer: First write 605,000 as the product of a number that is greater than or equal to 1 and less than 10, (deleting any unnecessary zeros) and a power of 10.

$6.05 \cdot 100{,}000$

Then rewrite 100,000 using an exponent and a base of 10.

$6.05 \cdot 10^5$

When discussing **Question 6**, ask students "What do you think the *e* in the first two displays represents?" (*the exponent of the power of 10*) Also ask why the displays only show the exponent of each power of 10, but do not display the base number 10. (*In scientific notation the base number is always 10. By not showing the number 10, the format allows you to see more digits of the first number since most displays have a limited number of digits that can be shown.*)

554

GOAL

LEARN HOW TO...
◆ write large numbers in scientific notation

AS YOU...
◆ work with statistics about the planets

KEY TERM
◆ scientific notation

Exploration 1

Writing Numbers in Scientific Notation

▶ To make reading and writing large numbers easier, they are often written in *scientific notation*. **Scientific notation** uses powers of 10 to express the value of a number. You may have noticed that the numbers you wrote in scientific notation, such as $1.082 \cdot 10^8$ and $7.7833 \cdot 10^8$, have two parts.

The first part is a number greater than or equal to 1 but less than 10.

$1.082 \cdot 10^8$

The second part is a **power of 10.**

$7.7833 \cdot 10^8$

3 **Discussion** Explain why $7 \cdot 10^3$ is in scientific notation, but $70 \cdot 10^5$ is not.

✔ **QUESTION 4**

...checks that you can recognize numbers written in scientific notation.

4 ✔ **CHECKPOINT** Tell whether each number is written in scientific notation. If a number is not in scientific notation, explain why not.

a. $60 \cdot 10^3$
no; 60 is not less than 10

b. $6 \cdot 10^3$
yes

c. $0.6 \cdot 10^3$
no; 0.6 < 1

d. $35 \cdot 10^1$
no; 35 is not less than 10

e. $3.5 \cdot 2^3$
no, 2^3 is not a power of 10

f. $7.48 \cdot 10^6$
yes

5 Write each number in scientific notation.

a. 54,000,000
$5.4 \cdot 10^7$

b. 1,245,000,000
$1.245 \cdot 10^9$

c. 99,900
$9.99 \cdot 10^4$

6 **Calculator** Three of the ways calculators display a number in scientific notation are shown below.

| 4 E 12 | 4.e + 12 | 4 12 |

a. Write the number represented in the displays in standard form. 4,000,000,000,000

b. Write the number in scientific notation. $4 \cdot 10^{12}$

c. How does your calculator display numbers in scientific notation? Answers will vary.

7 How would the number 789,000,000 appear in scientific notation on each of the three calculators in Question 6?

3. $7 \cdot 10^3$ has a number greater than 1 but less than 10 multiplied by a power of 10, whereas $70 \cdot 10^5$ has a number multiplied by a power of 10, but 70 is not greater than or equal to 1 and less than 10.

7. 7.89 E8;
   7.89e + 8; 7.89 8

▶ So far you have used powers of 10 to write numbers in scientific notation. You can also use powers of 10 to change a number from scientific notation to standard form.

EXAMPLE

Write $8.1 \cdot 10^3$ in standard form.

SAMPLE RESPONSE

$$10^3 = 10 \cdot 10 \cdot 10$$
$$= 1000$$

$$8.1 \cdot 10^3 = 8.1 \cdot 1000 = 8100$$

8 Write each number in standard form.

a. $2.38 \cdot 10^1$ **23.8** b. $2.38 \cdot 10^2$ **238** c. $2.38 \cdot 10^3$ **2380**

d. $2.38 \cdot 10^4$ **23,800** e. $2.38 \cdot 10^5$ **238,000** f. $2.38 \cdot 10^6$ **2,380,000**

9 **Discussion** Look for a pattern in the problems and answers from Question 8.

a. What happened to the decimal point in the product when 2.38 was multiplied by 10^3? by 10^2? by 10^4? **It moved 3 places to the right; 2 places to the right; 4 places to the right**

b. What happens to the decimal point of a number when it is multiplied by 10^9? Test your prediction by writing $2.38 \cdot 10^9$ in standard form. **It moves 9 places to the right; 2,380,000,000**

c. How can you use the exponent on the power of 10 to change a number from scientific notation to standard form?

d. What is the exponent on the power of 10 when 23,800,000 is written in scientific notation? **7**

10 a. **Use Labsheet 6A.** Write the distance from the sun for Mercury, Neptune, Saturn, and Uranus in scientific notation.

b. Using scientific notation, list all 8 planets in order from greatest distance to least distance from the sun.
Neptune, Uranus, Saturn, Jupiter, Mars, Earth, Venus, Mercury

c. How did you use scientific notation to put the planets in order?

d. If you lay the sticky notes for Mars and Earth on top of each other, by how many notes do they differ? How many kilometers does this represent? **About 1 note; 100,000,000 kilometers**

HOMEWORK EXERCISES ▶ See Exs. 1–20 on pp. 556–558.

See Exs. 1–20 on pp. 556–558.

---

9. c. Write the number with enough zeros at the end to allow you to move the decimal place to the right the number of places indicated by the power of 10.

10. a. Mercury $5.791 \cdot 10^7$; Neptune $4.504 \cdot 10^9$; Saturn $1.4294 \cdot 10^9$; Uranus $2.87099 \cdot 10^9$

c. Sample answer: First I compared the numbers multiplied by 10^9, since 10^9 is greater than 10^8, and arranged them in order. Then I did the same with the numbers multiplied by 10^8, and arranged them in order. Finally there was only one number multiplied by 10^7, so it was last.

TEACHING NOTES

Question 8(a) The power of 10 is emphasized by showing the exponent of 1. Students should understand that $2.38 \cdot 10$ is also in scientific notation. Only positive exponents are introduced at this level. Negative and zero exponents will be addressed in Book 2.

Key Concepts

CLOSURE QUESTIONS

What are the advantages of writing a number in scientific notation? How does the exponent give the reader an idea of the number's value?

Sample Response: For very large numbers with lots of zeros, scientific notation can shorten the number of characters used on a calculator display or reduce the number of digits written by hand, making it easier to read the number and quicker to write. Two numbers can often be compared quickly by comparing the exponents instead of having to count the digits in the number. The exponent indicates how many places to move the decimal to get the number in standard form, so the reader can look at the exponents first to get an idea if the number is in the millions, billions, ten-thousands, etc. and then look at the first number for a more precise value.

Practice & Applications

SUGGESTED ASSIGNMENTS

Core Course
Day 1: Exs. 1–6, 13–15, 21–33
Day 2: Exs. 7–12, 16–20

Extended Course
Day 1: Exs. 1–6, 13–15, 21–33
Day 2: Exs. 7–12, 16–20

Note: Extended Course assignments can be used to differentiate within the regular classroom. In classrooms where students are grouped homogeneously, the material might be covered in fewer days. In this case assignments may be combined.

Key Term

scientific notation

11. The 7 indicates the number of places the decimal point is moved to the right, not the number of digits in the standard form of the number.

Section 6
Key Concepts

Scientific Notation (pp. 554–555)

To write a number in scientific notation, write it as a number greater than or equal to 1 but less than 10, times a power of ten.

> Make the first part a number greater than or equal to 1 but less than 10.

$$9{,}800{,}000{,}000 = 9.8 \cdot 1{,}000{,}000{,}000 = 9.8 \cdot 10^9$$

To change a number in scientific notation to standard form, multiply by the power of ten.

> The second part is a power of 10.

$$5.32 \cdot 10^7 = 5.32 \cdot 10{,}000{,}000 = 53{,}200{,}000$$

11 Key Concepts Question When $5.32 \cdot 10^7$ is written in standard form there are eight digits in the answer. Why is the 10 raised to only the 7th power?

Section 6
Practice & Application Exercises

Write each number in scientific notation.

1. 157,000
   $1.57 \cdot 10^5$

2. 7000
   $7 \cdot 10^3$

3. 56,000,000
   $5.6 \cdot 10^7$

4. 10.2
   $1.02 \cdot 10^1$

5. 5600
   $5.6 \cdot 10^3$

6. 9 billion
   $9 \cdot 10^9$

Write each number in standard form.

7. $5.9 \cdot 10^4$
   59,000

8. $1 \cdot 10^2$
   100

9. $9.82 \cdot 10^5$
   982,000

10. $8.1 \cdot 10^7$
    81,000,000

11. $6 \cdot 10^1$
    60

12. $3.5 \cdot 10^8$
    350,000,000

Use scientific notation to express each fact.

13. The temperature of volcanic lava can reach 1500°F. $1.5 \cdot 10^3$

14. The temperature on the surface of the sun is about 10,000°F. $1 \cdot 10^4$

15. Lightning reaches temperatures of up to 50,000°F. $5 \cdot 10^4$

16. Write the world population for each year in standard form.
310,000,000; 500,000,000; 1,650,000,000; 4,450,000,000; 6,840,000,000

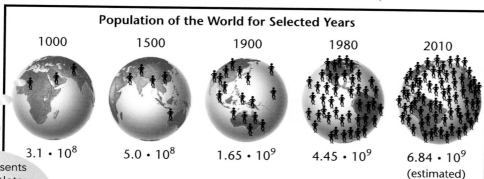

Population of the World for Selected Years

| 1000 | 1500 | 1900 | 1980 | 2010 |

$3.1 \cdot 10^8$ $5.0 \cdot 10^8$ $1.65 \cdot 10^9$ $4.45 \cdot 10^9$ $6.84 \cdot 10^9$
(estimated)

1 figure represents 10^8 people. (Note: Numbers have been rounded to show only whole figures.)

ADDITIONAL PRACTICE
See the *Teacher's Resource Book* for additional practice and application exercises for this section.

EXERCISE NOTES

Exercise 17 Students will have to convert the measures of Olympus Mons to standard form or put the measures of Mauna Loa in scientific notation to make the comparisons.

17. The largest volcano on Mars is Olympus Mons. It is $3.74 \cdot 10^2$ mi in diameter and $1.6 \cdot 10^1$ mi high. The largest volcano on Earth is Mauna Loa in Hawaii. It is 75 mi in diameter and 6.3 mi high.

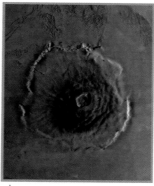

a. Compare the heights of the two volcanoes. Which is taller, and by how many miles? Olympus Mons is 9.7 mi higher.

b. Compare the diameters. Which volcano is wider, and by how many miles? Olympus Mons is 299 mi wider in diameter.

▲
Aerial view of Olympus Mons on Mars

18. In 2005, a group of scientists discovered an object in our solar system that was estimated to be about one-and-a-half times the size of Pluto. The object, nicknamed Xena, is approximately 9 billion miles from the sun.

a. Write the distance of Xena from the sun in scientific notation. $9 \cdot 10^9$

b. Earth is approximately $9.3 \cdot 10^7$ mi from the sun. Write this distance in standard form. 93,000,000 mi

c. Xena is about how many miles farther from the sun than Earth is from the sun? 8,907,000,000 mi

19. a. Without changing the numbers to standard form, tell whether the tons of plastic collected in the United States *increased* or *decreased* from 2004 to 2005. increased

Recyclable Materials Collected in the United States

Material	Amount collected for recycling in 2004	Amount collected for recycling in 2005
plastic	$2.73 \cdot 10^6$ tons	$2.76 \cdot 10^6$ tons
glass	$1.6 \cdot 10^6$ tons	$1.65 \cdot 10^6$ tons

b. How did the number of tons of glass collected from 2004 to 2005 change? Explain. The tons of glass collected increased. It was previously $1.6 \cdot 10^6$ and then changed to 1.65 times the same power of 10.

RESEARCH

Exercise 20 checks that you understand how to write numbers in both scientific notation and standard form.

Reflecting ◀▶on the Section

20. a. Look in magazines or newspapers to find three examples of articles including numbers greater than 100,000.
a–c. Answers will vary. Check students' work.

b. Tell what each number represents.

c. For each example, write the number in both standard form and scientific notation.

Spiral ◀▶Review

Find each sum or difference. (Module 8, p. 527)

21. $-18 + 7$ –11   **22.** $-26 + (-17)$ –43 **23.** $15 + (-8)$ 7

24. $25 - (-18)$ 43   **25.** $-36 - 13$ –49   **26.** $-12 - (-3)$ –9

27. A dart thrown at random hits the square target shown at the right. Find the probability that it hits the shaded area. (Module 8, p. 537)
about 72%

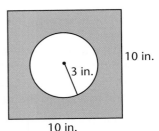

10 in.

3 in.

10 in.

Find each product or quotient. (Module 3, p. 178; Module 5, p. 352)

28. $5 \cdot 2\frac{1}{3}$ $11\frac{2}{3}$ **29.** $6\frac{3}{5} \div 4$ $1\frac{13}{20}$ **30.** $\frac{5}{12} \cdot 2\frac{3}{8}$ $\frac{95}{96}$

31. $8 \div 2\frac{1}{4}$ $3\frac{5}{9}$ **32.** $3\frac{2}{7} \cdot 5\frac{1}{2}$ $18\frac{1}{14}$ **33.** $10\frac{2}{5} \div 4\frac{1}{4}$ $2\frac{38}{85}$

Section 6

Extra Skill Practice

Write each number in scientific notation.

1. 49,800,000 $4.98 \cdot 10^7$ 2. 16.34 $1.634 \cdot 10^1$ 3. 32 billion $3.2 \cdot 10^{10}$

4. 958 $9.58 \cdot 10^2$ 5. 2,500,000 $2.5 \cdot 10^6$ 6. 326,000 $3.26 \cdot 10^5$

7. 76,300 $7.63 \cdot 10^4$ 8. 2 million $2 \cdot 10^6$ 9. 24 $2.4 \cdot 10^1$

Write each number in standard form.

10. $1.1 \cdot 10^3$ 1100   11. $6.08 \cdot 10^1$ 60.8   12. $5.03 \cdot 10^6$ 5,030,000

13. $4.14 \cdot 10^3$ 4140   14. $2 \cdot 10^9$ 2,000,000,000   15. $4.1 \cdot 10^2$ 410

16. $3.041 \cdot 10^5$ 304,100   17. $1.9 \cdot 10^9$ 1,900,000,000   18. $9.9 \cdot 10^4$ 99,000

Without changing the numbers to standard form, order the numbers from least to greatest.

19. $2 \cdot 10^2, 3.5 \cdot 10^1, 1.3 \cdot 10^3$ $3.5 \cdot 10^1, 2 \cdot 10^2, 1.3 \cdot 10^3$

20. $4.53 \cdot 10^6, 4.3 \cdot 10^7, 4.682 \cdot 10^5$ $4.682 \cdot 10^5, 4.53 \cdot 10^6, 4.3 \cdot 10^7$

21. $5.5 \cdot 10^3, 5.5 \cdot 10^6, 5.5 \cdot 10^2$ $5.5 \cdot 10^2, 5.5 \cdot 10^3, 5.5 \cdot 10^6$

Standardized Testing ◀▶ Multiple Choice

Write: Ⓐ   if the amount in column A is greater.

Ⓑ   if the amount in column B is greater.

Ⓒ   if the amounts in column A and column B are equal.

Ⓓ   if there is no way to tell which amount is greater.

Column A	Column B
1. $1.735 \cdot 10^6$	$17.35 \cdot 10^5$ C
2. 120	$1.2 \cdot 10^1$ A
3. $1.8 \cdot 10^4$	$1.7 \cdot 10^5$ B

Teacher Notes

All of the Extra Skill Practice Exercises correspond to Exploration 1.

Extra Help

Teacher's Resource Book

- Practice and Applications for Section 6
- Study Guide
- Practice and Applications for Sections 1–6

Technology Resources

- @Home Tutor
- Test Generator

Assessment

- Section 6 Quick Quiz
- Test Generator

Module Project

PROJECT NOTES

Although there are only 7 themes, students will be writing 8 questions. Therefore, they will choose one theme twice. For this eighth question, encourage them to choose a concept from Module 8 that relates back to one of the seven themes. Also encourage students to consider how much the question makes them think and apply their knowledge, as opposed to a question that simply involves a difficult or lengthy series of computations.

Revising You may want to use peer editing before students read their questions out loud to their team for a final edit. Edit questions for clarity, completeness, correctness, difficulty, and appropriateness (whether the question relates to the chosen theme and assesses the chosen mathematical concept).

The Module Project

The Math is Right!

Have you ever watched a quiz show on TV? A quiz game can be a fun way to test your knowledge. You will work as a team to create questions for a math quiz game. Will your questions stump the other teams in your class? You'll find out when you play *The Math is Right*!

Getting Started Your team is responsible for writing a set of eight questions. The set should include at least one question related to each of the first seven module themes and use mathematics you have studied this year. **1–8.Answers will vary.**

1 Decide for which module themes each team member will write questions.

2 Choose a mathematical concept for each question.

Game Format In *The Math is Right!*, your team's questions will be read aloud or shown on an overhead projector. Each of the other teams will work together to agree on an answer. No team is allowed to answer its own questions!

3 Write each question so it relates to the module theme and uses mathematical concepts you studied this year.

4 Make sure your questions are clear and ask for specific answers.

Revising Your Questions Now that you have written your questions, you can test them out on your teammates.

5 Take turns reading your quiz questions to your teammates. Make sure that everyone understands each question and agrees on an answer.

6 Rewrite any questions that are not clear.

7 Write each question on an index card or overhead transparency. Write your team number at the top of the card and the answer on the bottom.

SET UP

Work in a team of four.

You will need:
- *8 index cards or 8 overhead transparencies*
- *markers*

Module Themes

1. Patterns and Problem Solving
2. Math Detectives
3. Mind Games
4. Statistical Safari
5. Creating Things
6. Comparing and Predicting
7. Wonders of the World

8 Review your team's questions and decide which one you think is the most challenging. Mark this question with a star. This will be used as a bonus question in *The Math is Right!*

Play *The Math is Right!*

Get Ready

Your teacher should have each team's questions in separate, shuffled piles.

- Sit in a group with your team.
- Make sure each player has paper and pencil.

Play the Game

- Your teacher picks a card from Team 1's pile, reads it out loud, and then sets a timer for two minutes.
- Team 1 is not allowed to answer the question.
- When time is up the teams put their pencils down and then show their answers. All answers must be written down.
- Each team gets 10 points for a correct answer.
- The next question read is from Team 2's pile and Team 2 is not allowed to answer.
- Continue reading questions in this manner.

Bonus Question

If a bonus question is drawn, teams answering the question decide how many points they want to risk on the question before it is read.

- Each team writes the point value on a piece of paper and turns it over. A team without any points can risk up to 10 points.
- Each team gets the number of points it risked for a correct answer to a bonus question.
- Teams with incorrect answers to bonus questions lose the number of points they risked.

Winning the Game

The team with the most points when all the questions have been read or the class period ends wins.

For an alternative to playing *The Math is Right*,

- Organize the cards by the theme. Shuffle the cards in each theme.
- Have Team 1 choose a theme.
- Pick a card from the chosen theme pile.
- Announce the team number on the card so that team knows they may not answer the question.
- Read the question out loud and set a timer for two minutes.
- When time is up, the teams put their pencils down and then show their answers. All answers must be written down.
- Each team gets 10 points for a correct answer.
- Team 2 chooses a theme.
- Continue reading questions in this manner.

MODULE **8**

Review and Assessment

TEACHER NOTES
Students should complete
the Review and Assessment
independently in preparation for the
Module Test.

Allow class time to discuss solutions
and address any questions students
may have. During this time, you may
want to allow students to work in
groups to share methods for solving
the problems and to quiz each other
on the concepts covered in this
module.

You will need: • *tracing paper* (Exs. 19–22)

1. A recipe calls for $\frac{1}{2}$ c of cooking oil. Choose the letter of each amount that will supply enough oil for the recipe. (Sec. 1, Explor. 1) A, C, D

   A. $\frac{1}{4}$ pt   B. $\frac{1}{3}$ c   C. 5 fl oz   D. $\frac{1}{16}$ gal

2. To make 1 chicken loaf you need $1\frac{1}{3}$ c of chicken broth. Suppose you want to make 7 loaves to freeze. (Sec. 1, Explor. 1)

   a. How many cups of broth do you need? $9\frac{1}{3}$ c

   b. How many pints do you need? $4\frac{2}{3}$ pt

   c. How many fluid ounces do you need? $74\frac{2}{3}$ fl oz

3. It is recommended that people drink about 4 L of water a day. Give the dimensions of a rectangular container that has a capacity of exactly 4 L. (Sec. 1, Explor. 2) Sample answer: 10 cm by 10 cm by 40 cm

Mental Math Explain how to use trading off to find each sum. (Sec. 2, Explor. 1)

4. 23 + 79
   22 + 80 = 102

5. 1.06 + 4.98
   1.04 + 5.00 = 6.04

6. 0.75 + 0.24 + 0.86
   0.75 + 0.25 + 0.85 = 1.85

Explain how to use front-end estimation to estimate each sum. (Sec. 2, Explor. 1)

7. 146 + 609 + 234
   900 + 100; about 1000

8. $15.13 + $24.49
   $15 + $25; about $40.00

9. 3.3 + 8.15 + 6.65
   17 + 1; about 18

Find each sum or difference. (Sec. 3, Explors. 1 and 2)

10. −19 + 25   6

11. −36 − 3   −39

12. 0 − (−18)   18

13. −12 + (−12)   −24

14. 42 − 68   −26

15. −21 + 15   −6

For each target, a dart that hits the target is equally likely to hit any point on the target. Find the probability that the dart hits the shaded area. (Sec. 4, Explor. 1)

16.

area of rectangle = 5 cm²
diameter of circle = 7 cm
about 87%

17.

The four small triangles
are all the same size.
$\frac{1}{4}$

18.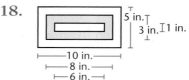

5 in.
3 in. 1 in.
10 in.
8 in.
6 in.
$\frac{9}{25}$

Sketch each flower and show how one part of the flower is a reflection or a rotation of another part. (Sec. 5, Explors. 1 and 2) 19–22. Check students' sketches.

19.

reflection

20.

reflection or rotation

21.

reflection or rotation

22.

reflection

Write each number in standard form. (Sec. 6, Explor. 1)

23. $5.67 \cdot 10^3$
5,670

24. $1.002 \cdot 10^5$
100,200

25. $7 \cdot 10^8$
700,000,000

26. $2.3 \cdot 10^1$
23

27. $9.11 \cdot 10^2$
911

28. $1.833 \cdot 10^4$
18,330

Write each number in scientific notation. (Sec. 6, Explor. 1)

29. 4,400,000
$4.4 \cdot 10^6$

30. 7700
$7.7 \cdot 10^3$

31. 789
$7.89 \cdot 10^2$

32. 62,000
$6.2 \cdot 10^4$

33. 5,000,000,000
$5 \cdot 10^9$

34. 377,125
$3.77125 \cdot 10^5$

Reflecting ◀▶on the Module

35. Each section in this module connects to the theme of a previous module. For example, Section 5 connects to *Creating Things*, the theme of Module 5. Choose one section in this module and explain how the mathematics connects to the mathematics in the module with the same theme. Answers will vary.

Assessment Options

TEACHER'S RESOURCE BOOK
• Module 8 Tests A and B
• Module 8 Standardized Test
• Module 8 Performance Assessment
• Modules 7 and 8 Cumulative Test
• End-of-Year Test

TEST GENERATOR

CONTENTS

STUDENT RESOURCES

▶▶▶▶▶▶▶▶▶▶▶▶▶▶▶▶▶▶▶▶▶▶▶▶▶▶▶▶▶▶▶▶▶▶▶▶ **STUDENT RESOURCES**

TOOLBOX

Whole Number Place Value

Each digit in a number has a place. To find the value of a digit, multiply the digit by the value of the place.

Millions			Thousands			Ones		
Hundreds	Tens	Ones	Hundreds	Tens	Ones	Hundreds	Tens	Ones
	8	3	2	9	5	0	4	1

The places are grouped into periods.

Period: millions
Place: one millions
Value: **3,000,000**

83,295,041 ← standard form

In expanded form 83,295,041 is written as:
80,000,000 + 3,000,000 + 200,000 + 90,000 + 5,000 + 40 + 1

In words, 83,295,041 is expressed as:
eighty-three million, two hundred ninety-five thousand, forty-one

EXAMPLE

Write the place and the value of each underlined digit.

1,248,630   225,000   85,699

SOLUTION   place: **one millions**   place: **ten thousands**   place: **tens**

value: **1,000,000**   value: **20,000**   value: **90**

Write the place and the value of each underlined digit.

1. 841,670   place: one hundred thousands   value: 800,000
2. 335,928   place: one thousands   value: 5,000
3. 56,831,000   place: ten millions   value: 50,000,000
4. 28   place: ones   value: 8
5. 993,671   place: ten thousands   value: 90,000
6. 403,200   place: hundreds   value: 200

Give the following information about the number 469,224.

7. the place of the 6   ten thousands
8. the value of the digit in the tens place   20

Write each number in standard form.

9. fifteen million, nine hundred forty-six thousand, six hundred nineteen   15,946,619

10. two hundred twenty thousand, nine   220,009

Write each number in words.

11. 518   five hundred eighteen

12. 23,400   twenty-three thousand, four hundred

13. 70,000,624   seventy million, six hundred twenty-four

14. 450,672   four hundred fifty thousand, six hundred seventy-two

Comparing Whole Numbers

The symbols below are used to compare numbers:

> (is greater than)　　　< (is less than)　　　= (is equal to)

Thinking about place value will help you compare two numbers and put a list of numbers in order.

EXAMPLE

To compare 23,760 and 23,748, first line up the digits of each number by place value. Then compare the digits in each place, starting at the left. If the digits are equal, compare the digits in the next place to the right, and so on until you come to different digits.

23,760 is greater than 23,748 because it has a greater digit in the first place that is different, the tens place.

> Compare digits from left to right since the leftmost place has the greatest value.

2	3	7	6	0
2	3	7	4	8

same　same　same　different: 6 > 4

EXAMPLE

Write the list of numbers in order from greatest to least.

2,227　　　21,237　　　20,080　　　1,919　　　450,900　　　34,888

SOLUTION　Compare the digits in each place starting with the greatest place value.

		2	2	2	7
	2	1	2	3	7
	2	0	0	8	0
		1	9	1	9
4	5	0	9	0	0
	3	4	8	8	8

hundred thousands: The only number with a digit in the hundred thousands place is 450,900, so 450,900 is the greatest number.

ten thousands: 3 > 2 so 34,888 is greater than both 21,237 and 20,080. Check the next digit of 21,237 and 20,080. 1 > 0 so 21,237 > 20,080.

thousands: 2 > 1 so 2,227 > 1,919.

450,900 > 34,888 > 21,237 > 20,080 > 2,227 > 1,919

Replace each ? with >, <, or =.

1. 2224 __?__ 1810　>　　　2. 20,111 __?__ 19,991　>　　3. 3,201,999 __?__ 419,963　>

4. 37,011 __?__ 370,110　<　5. 897,500 __?__ 190,001　>　6. 5,402,320 __?__ 5,410,320　<

7. 198,999 __?__ 199,000　<　8. 891,450 __?__ 340,232　>　9. 50,777,760 __?__ 51,666,700　<

Write each list of numbers in order from greatest to least.

10. 239,400; 47,777; 24,000; 79,899　　11. 6,150,762; 892,570; 7,902,500; 937,400
239,400; 79,899; 47,777; 24,000　　　　7,902,500; 6,150,762; 937,400; 892,570

566

Rounding Whole Numbers and Money

To round a number to a given place, look at the digit to the right of that place to decide whether the number is greater or less than the halfway point.

If the digit in the place to the right is less than 5 (0, 1, 2, 3, or 4), round down.

If the digit in the place to the right is 5 or greater (5, 6, 7, 8, or 9), round up.

EXAMPLE

Round 5839 to the nearest hundred.

SOLUTION   5839 is between 5800 and 5900.

Look at the digit to the right of the hundreds place: 5839
the 3 in the tens place. 3 is less than 5, so 39 is less than half
of 100. Round down to the nearest hundred, 5800.

5839 rounded to the nearest hundred is 5800.

The halfway number.

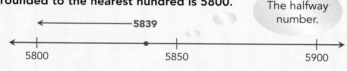

EXAMPLE

Round $42.61 to the nearest one dollar.

SOLUTION $42.61 is between $42 and $43.

6 is the digit to the right of the dollars place. $42.61
6 is greater than 5, so 61 cents is greater than half
of a dollar. Round up to the nearest dollar, $43.

$42.61 rounded to the nearest one dollar is $43.

Round each number to the given place.

1. 888 (nearest ten) 890

2. 94,575 (nearest hundred) 94,600

3. 85,920 (nearest thousand) 86,000

4. 27,380,573 (nearest million) 27,000,000

5. 602 (nearest hundred) 600

6. 43 (nearest ten) 40

7. 298,722 (nearest ten thousand) 300,000

8. 68,274 (nearest hundred) 68,300

Round each amount to the given place.

9. $949.50 (nearest dollar) $950.00

10. $4369.75 (nearest ten dollars) $4370.00

11. $52.05 (nearest dollar) $52.00

12. $644.00 (nearest hundred dollars) $600.00

Adding Whole Numbers and Money

To add whole numbers, add place by place. First add the ones, then the tens, then the hundreds, then the thousands, and so on.

EXAMPLE

Find 206 + 58.

SOLUTION   Rewrite the numbers, lining up the ones, the tens, and the hundreds.

Add the ones and trade if needed.	Add the tens and trade if needed.	Add the hundreds.

Trade 14 ones for 1 ten and 4 ones.

```
    1              1              1
  206            206            206
+  58          +  58          +  58
————           ————           ————
    4             64            264
```

206 + 58 = 264

Money amounts can be expressed in dollars using a dollar sign ($) and a dot. The dot separates the whole dollars and the parts of a dollar. Money amounts can also be expressed in cents using a cents sign (¢) and no dot. No matter which way the number is written, you add money place by place. First add the pennies, then the dimes, then the one dollars, then the ten dollars, and so on.

EXAMPLE

Find $3.80 + $9.44 + $.75.

$.75 means 75 cents, or 7 dimes and 5 pennies.

SOLUTION   Line up the pennies, the dimes, and the dollars.

Add the pennies, dimes, and dollars separately. Trade as needed.

Trade 19 dimes for 1 dollar and 9 dimes.

```
     1
   $3.80
   $9.44
+   $.75
————————
  $13.99
```

Add.

1. 2767 + 465 3232
2. 8219 + 4499 12,718
3. 66,405 + 35,511 101,916
4. 2,082 + 58,875 60,957
5. 35,294 + 62,472 97,766
6. 77,996 + 5,687 + 5,434 89,117
7. $8.14 + $3.97 $12.11
8. $20.87 + $18.17 $39.04
9. $27.40 + $16.75 $44.15
10. $54.25 + $66.65 $120.90
11. $31.24 + $11.83 $43.07
12. $26.50 + $88.95 $115.45

Mental Math

When you want to use mental math to add, it helps to break numbers into parts.

To add two-digit numbers, you can break up at least one of the numbers you are adding into tens and ones and add on these parts separately.

EXAMPLE

Find 38 + 15.

SOLUTION   Break 15 into tens and ones: 15 = 10 + 5

$$38 + 10 = 48 \quad \leftarrow \text{Add the tens to 38.}$$
$$48 + 5 = 53 \quad \leftarrow \text{Add the ones to the result.}$$

38 + 15 = 53

Sometimes it is helpful to add enough to reach a number that ends in 0 and then add the rest.

EXAMPLE

Find $5.75 + $1.50.

SOLUTION   You need $.25 to get $5.75 to reach $6.00, so break $1.50 into $.25 + $1.25.

$$\$5.75 + \$.25 = \$6.00 \quad \leftarrow \text{Add the \$.25 to the \$5.75.}$$
$$\$6.00 + \$1.25 = \$7.25 \quad \leftarrow \text{Add the remaining \$1.25 to the result.}$$

$5.75 + $1.50 = $7.25

Use mental math to find each sum.

1. 56 + 67 123
2. 35 + 47 82
3. 452 + 29 481
4. 253 + 68 321
5. 49 + 322 371
6. 796 + 35 831
7. 428 + 67 495
8. 634 + 157 791
9. 181 + 494 675
10. $6.90 + $5.35 $12.25
11. $4.20 + $14.37 $18.57
12. $6.28 + $4.10 $10.38
13. $8.35 + $5.00 $13.35
14. $2.45 + $11.95 $14.40
15. $3.99 + $4.98 $8.97
16. $15.50 + $4.75 $20.25
17. $9.84 + $3.56 $13.40
18. $17.69 + $5.36 $23.05

Subtracting Whole Numbers and Money

To subtract whole numbers, subtract the ones, then the tens, then the hundreds, and so on. Trade before each step if necessary.

EXAMPLE

Find 3001 – 1953.

SOLUTION Rewrite the numbers, lining up the ones, the tens, and so on.

Since there are no tens or hundreds, trade 1 thousand for 9 hundreds, 9 tens, and 10 ones to get more ones.

You need to trade to get more ones.

```
  29911
  3̶0̶0̶1̶
– 1953
```

Now you can subtract.

```
  29911
  3̶0̶0̶1̶
– 1953
  1048  ← difference
```

3001 – 1953 = 1048

Check your answer with addition. The difference plus the number subtracted should equal the number you started with: 1048 + 1953 = 3001.

When you subtract money, first subtract the pennies, then the dimes, then the one dollars, then the ten dollars, and so on.

EXAMPLE

Find $5.45 – $2.86.

SOLUTION Line up the dollars and cents.

Subtract the pennies. Trade first if needed.

```
   3 15
  $5.4̶5̶
– $2.86
       9
```

Subtract the dimes. Trade first if needed.

```
  41315
  $5̶.4̶5̶
– $2.86
      59
```

Subtract the dollars.

```
  41315
  $5̶.4̶5̶
– $2.86
  $2.59
```

Put in a dot to separate dollars and cents.

$5.45 – $2.86 = $2.59

Your answer can be checked with addition.
$2.59 + $2.86 = $5.45

Subtract.

1. 8712 – 134 8578
2. 506 – 318 188
3. 9501 – 4688 4813
4. 2500 – 379 2121
5. 7211 – 709 6502
6. 6040 – 2199 3841
7. $46.26 – $17.18 $29.08
8. $401.40 – $13.00 $388.40
9. $183.50 – $119.42 $64.08
10. $333.25 – $299.86 $33.39
11. $501.00 – $180.67 $320.33

Multiplying Whole Numbers and Money

To multiply whole numbers, begin by lining up the numbers you are multiplying. Multiply the entire first number by the ones of the second number, by the tens of the second number, and so on.

EXAMPLE

Find 583 × 304.

SOLUTION Rewrite the numbers, lining up the ones, the tens, and the hundreds.

0 tens × 583 = 0, so no product is written.

$$
\begin{array}{r}
583 \\
\times\ 304 \\
\hline
2332 \\
+\ 174900 \\
\hline
177{,}232 \\
\end{array}
$$

← 4 × 583   ← Multiply by **4** ones.
← 300 × 583   ← Multiply by **3** hundreds.
product → 177,232   ← 304 × 583

Zeros are used to hold the ones and tens place.

When multiplying with money, you can think of dollars and cents as just cents and multiply as you do with whole numbers.

EXAMPLE

Find 7 × $3.25.

SOLUTION $3.25 is equal to 325 cents.

$$
\begin{array}{r}
325¢ \\
\times\ 7 \\
\hline
2275¢ \\
\end{array}
$$
← Multiply 325 by 7.

Think of 2275 cents as 22 hundred cents and another 75 cents. Each hundred cents is worth one dollar so you have 22 dollars and 75 cents.

7 × $3.25 = $22.75

Multiply.

1. 25 × 38 950
2. 96 × 504 48,384
3. 146 × 260 37,960
4. 655 × 337 220,735
5. 158 × 29 4582
6. 14 × 2048 28,672
7. 6 × $38.18 $229.08
8. 22 × $16.01 $352.22
9. 41 × $2.72 $111.52
10. 60 × $31.50 $1890.00
11. 2 × $54.82 $109.64
12. 303 × $9.95 $3014.85

Dividing Whole Numbers

Dividing whole numbers is the same as finding how many times the divisor goes into the dividend.

Sometimes when you divide there will be a remainder. The remainder is a number that is leftover after the divisor goes into the dividend as many times as possible.

$$9 \leftarrow \text{quotient}$$
$$\text{divisor} \rightarrow 5\overline{)45} \leftarrow \text{dividend}$$

EXAMPLE

Find 968 ÷ 27.

SOLUTION Rewrite the division in columns to organize your work. Try to divide 27 into each place or combination of places in 968, starting at the left.

You will need to multiply and subtract each time you write a digit in the quotient. Be careful to keep columns lined up.

hundreds place	tens place	ones place
27 does not go into 9.	Divide 27 into 96. It goes in 3 times.	Divide 27 into 158. It goes in 5 times.

$$27\overline{)968}$$

$$\begin{array}{r} 3 \\ 27\overline{)968} \\ -81 \\ \hline 15 \end{array}$$

27 × 3 = 81
Subtracting 81 from 96 gives a remainder of **15**.

$$\begin{array}{r} 35 \text{ R}23 \\ 27\overline{)968} \\ -81 \downarrow \\ \hline 158 \\ -135 \\ \hline 23 \end{array}$$

Combine the **15** tens remaining and the **8** ones from the dividend to get **158**.

27 × 5 = 135
Subtracting 135 from 158 gives a remainder of **23**.

968 ÷ 27 = 35 R23 (35 remainder 23)

To check the answer, multiply the quotient by the divisor and add the remainder. The result should equal the dividend.

$$35 \times 27 = 945 \qquad 945 + 23 = 968$$

Divide.

1. 3205 ÷ 8 400 R5
2. 500 ÷ 64 7 R52
3. 9875 ÷ 4 2468 R3
4. 269 ÷ 21 12 R17
5. 7852 ÷ 26 302
6. 8080 ÷ 15 538 R10
7. 741 ÷ 36 20 R21
8. 520 ÷ 45 11 R25 ,
9. 6800 ÷ 42 161 R38
10. 350 ÷ 102 3 R44
11. 1208 ÷ 34 35 R18
12. 344 ÷ 26 13 R6

Number Fact Families

The following is an example of a number fact family for addition and subtraction:

$$7 + 9 = 16 \qquad 9 + 7 = 16 \qquad 16 - 7 = 9 \qquad 16 - 9 = 7$$

You can use a number fact family to find missing numbers. For example, suppose you want to find the missing number in $7 + \underline{?} = 16$. If you know that $16 - 7$ will give you the same number, you can subtract to find the missing number.

A number fact family for multiplication and division is given below:

$$6 \times 2 = 12 \qquad 2 \times 6 = 12 \qquad 12 \div 6 = 2 \qquad 12 \div 2 = 6$$

You can use this family to complete the number sentence $12 \div \underline{?} = 2$.

EXAMPLE

addends sum

Complete the number fact family for 3 + 5 = 8.

SOLUTION You can write the other addition fact in the family by switching the order of the addends. You can write the related subtraction facts by starting with the sum and taking away each addend.

$$3 + 5 = 8 \qquad\qquad 5 + 3 = 8 \qquad\qquad 8 - 3 = 5 \qquad\qquad 8 - 5 = 3$$

EXAMPLE

Find the missing number: $18 \div \underline{?} = 2$

SOLUTION You know from the multiplication and division number fact families that the missing number is the same for $18 \div \underline{?} = 2$ as for $18 \div 2 = \underline{?}$.

$18 \div 2 = 9$. **Therefore $18 \div 9 = 2$.**

Complete each number fact family.

1. $6 + 3 = 9$ $3 + \underline{?} = 9$ $9 - \underline{?} = 6$ $9 - \underline{?} = \underline{?}$ _{6; 3; 6, 3}

2. $16 \div 2 = \underline{?}$ $\underline{?} \div \underline{?} = 2$ $\underline{?} \times 8 = 16$ $\underline{?} \times \underline{?} = 16$
                                                                          _{8; 16, 8; 2; 8, 2}

Find each missing number.

3. $23 + \underline{?} = 35$ ₁₂   4. $344 - \underline{?} = 320$ ₂₄   5. $\underline{?} + 12 = 65$ ₅₃

6. $62 - \underline{?} = 37$ ₂₅   7. $\underline{?} - 4 = 77$ ₈₁   8. $\underline{?} + 51 = 83$ ₃₂

9. $\underline{?} - 8 = 95$ ₁₀₃   10. $\underline{?} \times 4 = 52$ ₁₃   11. $\underline{?} \div 7 = 9$ ₆₃

12. $7 \times \underline{?} = 56$ ₈   13. $\underline{?} \div 3 = 13$ ₃₉   14. $6 \times \underline{?} = 72$ ₁₂

15. $\underline{?} \div 4 = 12$ ₄₈   16. $28 \div \underline{?} = 7$ ₄   17. $\underline{?} \times 3 = 42$ ₁₄

Multiplying and Dividing by Tens

You can use mental math to multiply by 10, 100, 1000, and so on, by thinking about place value.

EXAMPLE

To find 100×23, think: 1 hundred taken 23 times is 23 hundreds.

$100 \times 23 = 2300$

You can use what you know about multiplying by 10, 100, or 1000 to multiply other numbers that end in one or more zeros.

EXAMPLE

To find 200×80, first multiply the non-zero digits and then put on the extra zeros.

$200 \times 80 = 2 \times 100 \times 8 \times 10 = 16 \times 1000 = 16,000$

$2 \times 8 = 16$

$100 \times 10 = 1000$, so you need 3 zeros at the end.

The mental math strategies shown for multiplying numbers ending in zeros can also help you to divide numbers ending in zeros. Think about the relationship between division and multiplication.

EXAMPLE

To find $670,000 \div 1000$, think: $\underline{?} \times 1000 = 670,000$.

$670,000 \div 1000 = 670$

To find $48,000 \div 60$, think about the zeros and the non-zero digits separately.

$48,000 \div 60 = 800$

Think: $\underline{?} \times 6 = 48$

Think: $\underline{?} \times 10 = 1000$

Multiply or divide.

1. 100×500 50,000
2. 200×30 6000
3. 5000×300 1,500,000
4. 400×4000 1,600,000
5. 3000×200 600,000
6. 5000×100 500,000
7. $200 \times 60,000$ 12,000,000
8. $10,000 \times 2,000$ 20,000,000
9. $8,000 \times 40,000$ 320,000,000
10. $800,000 \div 2$ 400,000
11. $10,000 \div 1,000$ 10
12. $10,000 \div 200$ 50
13. $3900 \div 30$ 130
14. $20,000 \div 400$ 50
15. $250,000 \div 50$ 5000

Perimeter and Using a Ruler

The perimeter (*P*) of a figure is the distance around it. You can find
the perimeter by adding the lengths of the sides together.

EXAMPLE

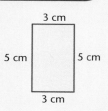

$$3 + 5 + 3 + 5 = 16$$
$$P = 16 \text{ cm}$$

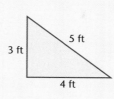

$$4 + 2 + 2 + 6 + 6 + 4 = 24$$
$$P = 24 \text{ m}$$

$$3 + 5 + 4 = 12$$
$$P = 12 \text{ ft}$$

A ruler is a tool that is used to measure length. A United States
customary ruler shows measurements in inches.

The other end of
the pencil is between
3 in. and 4 in. It does not
reach the halfway mark,
so round down.

EXAMPLE

Use a ruler to measure the pencil to the nearest inch.

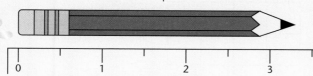

Line up one
end of the pencil
with the 0 mark
on the ruler.

The pencil is about 3 in. long.

For Exercises 1–5, find the perimeter of each figure.

1.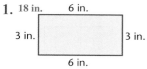

2.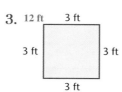

3.
12 ft	3 ft

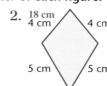

4. a square with sides 5 cm long 20 cm

5. a triangle with sides 3 in., 5 in., and 6 in. long 14 in.

Use a ruler to measure each nail to the nearest inch.

6.  1 in.

7.  2 in.

Toolbox 575

575

Area

The area of a figure is the amount of surface it covers. Area is measured in square units. The square units used may be square inches, square centimeters, square feet, or squares of any other size.

EXAMPLE

This square is a square inch.

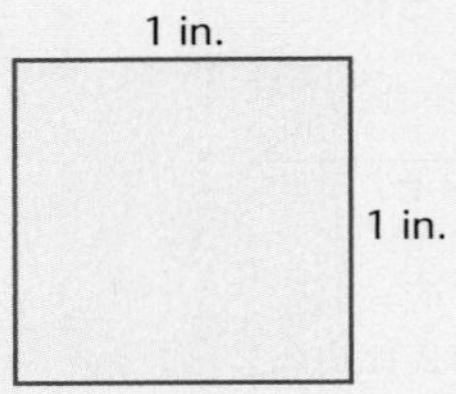

1 in.

1 in.

You can count the number of square inches to find the area.

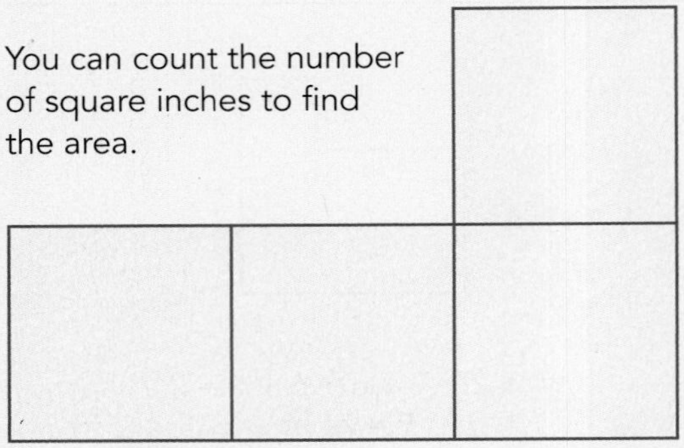

The area of the figure on the right is 4 square inches.

EXAMPLE

The square on the left is a square centimeter.

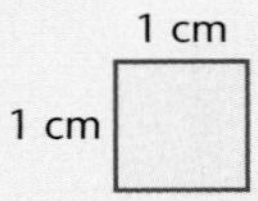

1 cm

1 cm

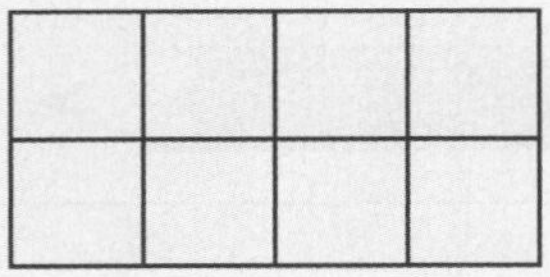

Add 4 square centimeters in each row to get 8 square centimeters.

The area of the figure on the right is 8 square centimeters.

Find the area of each figure. Each small square is 1 centimeter by 1 centimeter.

1. 6 cm^2

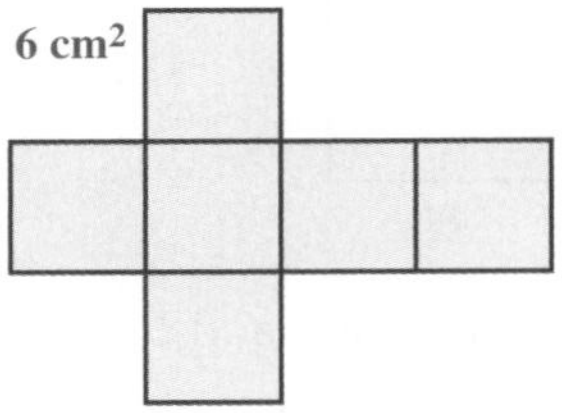

2. 5 cm^2

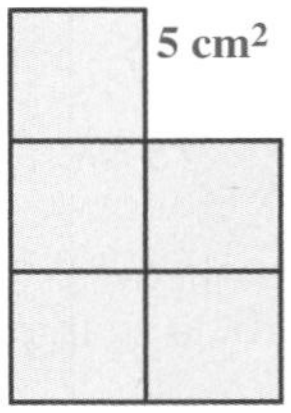

3. 7 cm^2

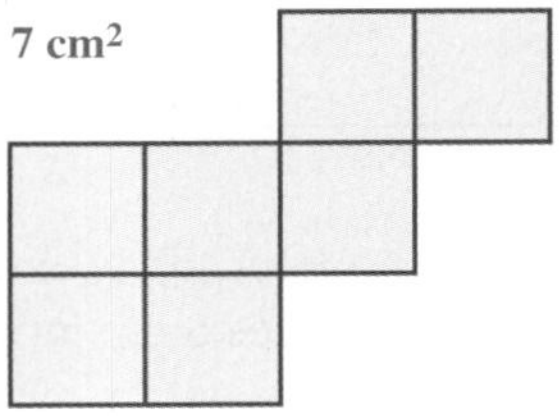

Time Conversions and Elapsed Time

The chart below can help you convert time measurements. You can also use these relationships when you subtract to find elapsed time.

60 seconds (sec) = 1 minute (min)
60 minutes (min) = 1 hour (hr)
24 hours (hr) = 1 day
7 days = 1 week

EXAMPLE

Find the missing number: 20 min = _?_ seconds

SOLUTION   Every 1 min equals 60 seconds.
20 min = 20 × 60 seconds = **1200 seconds**

EXAMPLE

How much time has elapsed between 8:30 A.M. and 10:15 A.M.?

SOLUTION

$$\begin{array}{r} 9 \quad 75 \\ 10:15 \text{ A.M.} \rightarrow \cancel{10} \text{ hr } \cancel{15} \text{ min} \\ - \; 8:30 \text{ A.M.} \rightarrow - \; 8 \text{ hr } 30 \text{ min} \\ \hline 1 \text{ hr } 45 \text{ min} \end{array}$$

Trade 1 hr for 60 min. Then combine the 60 min with the 15 min already there.

EXAMPLE

How much time has elapsed between 3:00 P.M. and 1:30 A.M.?

To get to 1:30 A.M. you need to go another hour and a half past 12:00 midnight. Add 1 hr 30 min to 12 hr to get 13 hr 30 min.

SOLUTION

$$\begin{array}{r} 1:30 \text{ A.M.} \rightarrow 13 \text{ hr } 30 \text{ min} \\ - \; 3:00 \text{ P.M.} \rightarrow - \; 3 \text{ hr } 00 \text{ min} \\ \hline 10 \text{ hr } 30 \text{ min} \end{array}$$

Change each time measurement to the given unit of time.

1. 8 hr to minutes 480 min
2. 72 hr to days 3 days
3. 180 seconds to minutes 3 min

Find how much time has elapsed between the given times.

4. 12:40 P.M. and 5:35 P.M. 4 hr 55 min
5. 9:30 A.M. and 11:23 P.M. 13 hr 53 min
6. 6:10 P.M. and 9:06 P.M. 2 hr 56 min
7. 10:45 P.M. and 12:20 A.M. 1 hr 35 min

Reading a Graph

A graph is a visual display of data. Different types of graphs are used depending on the type of data and the relationship you are showing.

EXAMPLE

To read a bar graph, find the bar that represents the information you are looking for. Think of extending a line from the end of the bar to the numbers on the scale.

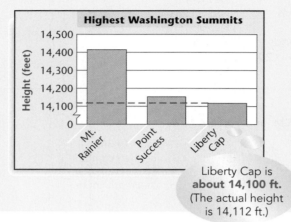

Liberty Cap is **about 14,100 ft.** (The actual height is 14,112 ft.)

To see what each point represents on a line graph, think of drawing a line across or down to each of the scales.

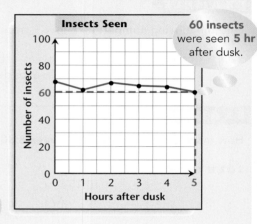

60 insects were seen **5 hr** after dusk.

Use the graph to estimate each value.

1. By the end of 1998, how many World Cup tourneys had Brazil played? had France played?

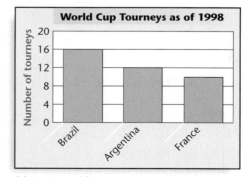

16 tourneys, 10 tourneys

2. What was the population of Birmingham, Alabama, in 1990? in 1994? about 840,000 people, about 870,000 people

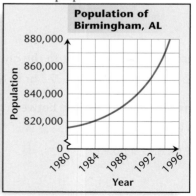

Making a Pictograph

A pictograph can be used to display data. Usually a symbol is used to represent a given number of items.

EXAMPLE

Make a pictograph to represent the number of campers each summer.

Year	1993	1994	1995	1996	1997	1998
Campers	600	640	690	655	700	750

SOLUTION You can use 1 triangle for each 100 campers. You can also use part of a triangle to show part of 100.

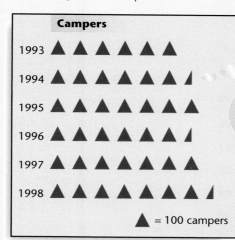

There are 6 hundreds in 600, so use 6 full triangles to show 600 campers. There are 40 campers left and 40 is almost half of 100, so you can show half of another triangle.

▲ = 100 campers

1. Make a pictograph to represent the students studying music in each grade.

Grade	6th	7th	8th
Students studying music	71	90	85

6th grade ● ● ● ● ● ● ●
7th grade ● ● ● ● ● ● ● ● ●
8th grade ● ● ● ● ● ● ● ● (
● = 10 students

2. Make a pictograph to represent the money spent on advertising in 1994. The dollar amounts have been rounded to the nearest billion.

Advertising medium	newspapers	magazines	television	radio	direct mail
Billions of dollars	34	8	34	10	29

Newspapers ● ● ● ● ● ● ●
Magazines ● ●
Television ● ● ● ● ● ●
Radio ● ●
Direct Mail ● ● ● ● ● ●

● = 5 billion dollars

TABLE OF SYMBOLS

SYMBOL		Page	SYMBOL		Page
+	plus	3	2^3	3rd power of 2	156
−	minus	3	$\frac{3}{4}$	3 divided by 4	222
×	times	3	≥	is greater than or equal to	225
•	times	3	≈	is about equal to	225
÷	divided by	3	(x, y)	ordered pair of numbers	254
=	equals	3	1 : 2	ratio of 1 to 2	366
( )	parentheses—grouping symbol	4	AB	length of $\overline{AB}$	408
...	and so on	16	$\triangle ABC$	triangle ABC	409
$\frac{3}{4}$	3 parts of 4	40	%	percent	420
$\overline{)}$	divided into	44	π	pi, a number approximately equal to 3.14	464
R	remainder	44	−1	negative 1	483
{ }	braces, enclose objects of a set	78	−1	the opposite of 1	527
$\overleftrightarrow{AB}$	line AB	99			
$\overline{AB}$	segment AB	99			
$\overrightarrow{AB}$	ray AB	99			
‖	is parallel to	100			
⊥	is perpendicular to	100			
⌐	right angle	100			
∠A	angle A	103			
°	degree(s)	103			
1.2	decimal point, separates whole numbers from parts of a whole number	131			
<	is less than	133			
>	is greater than	133			

TABLE OF MEASURES

Time

60 seconds (sec) = 1 minute (min)	
60 minutes = 1 hour (hr)	
24 hours = 1 day	
7 days = 1 week	
4 weeks (approx.) = 1 month	

$\left.\begin{array}{c}\text{365 days}\\ \text{52 weeks (approx.)}\\ \text{12 months}\end{array}\right\} = 1 \text{ year}$

10 years = 1 decade
100 years = 1 century

METRIC

Length

10 millimeters (mm) = 1 centimeter (cm)

$\left.\begin{array}{c}\text{100 cm}\\ \text{1000 mm}\end{array}\right\} = 1 \text{ meter (m)}$

1000 m = 1 kilometer (km)

Area

$\begin{array}{c}\text{100 square millimeters}\\ \text{(mm}^2)\end{array} = \begin{array}{c}\text{1 square centimeter}\\ \text{(cm}^2)\end{array}$

$10,000 \text{ cm}^2 = 1 \text{ square meter (m}^2)$

$10,000 \text{ m}^2 = 1 \text{ hectare (ha)}$

Volume

$\begin{array}{c}\text{1000 cubic millimeters}\\ \text{(mm}^3)\end{array} = \begin{array}{c}\text{1 cubic centimeter}\\ \text{(cm}^3)\end{array}$

$1,000,000 \text{ cm}^3 = 1 \text{ cubic meter (m}^3)$

Liquid Capacity

1000 milliliters (mL) = 1 liter (L)

1000 L = 1 kiloliter (kL)

Mass

1000 milligrams (mg) = 1 gram (g)

1000 g = 1 kilogram (kg)

1000 kg = 1 metric ton (t)

Temperature — **Degrees Celsius (°C)**

0°C = freezing point of water

37°C = normal body temperature

100°C = boiling point of water

UNITED STATES CUSTOMARY

Length

12 inches (in.) = 1 foot (ft)

$\left.\begin{array}{c}\text{36 in.}\\ \text{3 ft}\end{array}\right\} = 1 \text{ yard (yd)}$

$\left.\begin{array}{c}\text{5280 ft}\\ \text{1760 yd}\end{array}\right\} = 1 \text{ mile (mi)}$

Area

$144 \text{ square inches (in.}^2) = 1 \text{ square foot (ft}^2)$

$9 \text{ ft}^2 = 1 \text{ square yard (yd}^2)$

$\left.\begin{array}{c}43,560 \text{ ft}^2\\ 4840 \text{ yd}^2\end{array}\right\} = 1 \text{ acre (A)}$

Volume

$1728 \text{ cubic inches (in.}^3) = 1 \text{ cubic foot (ft}^3)$

$27 \text{ ft}^3 = 1 \text{ cubic yard (yd}^3)$

Liquid Capacity

8 fluid ounces (fl oz) = 1 cup (c)

2 c = 1 pint (pt)

2 pt = 1 quart (qt)

4 qt = 1 gallon (gal)

Weight

16 ounces (oz) = 1 pound (lb)

2000 lb = 1 ton (t)

Temperature — **Degrees Fahrenheit (°F)**

32°F = freezing point of water

98.6°F = normal body temperature

212°F = boiling point of water

GLOSSARY

acute angle (p. 104) An angle with a measure greater than 0° but less than 90°. *See also* angle.

acute triangle (p. 104) A triangle with three acute angles.

angle (p. 103) A figure formed by two rays that have a common endpoint.

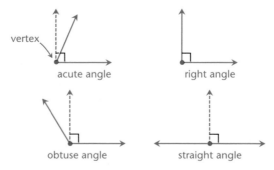

area (p. 331) The number of square units of surface a figure covers.

average (p. 218) A single number used to describe what is typical of a set of data. *See* mean, median, *and* mode.

axes (p. 255) *See* coordinate grid.

back-to-back stem-and-leaf plot (p. 262) A stem-and-leaf plot that compares two related sets of data.

bar graph (p. 578) A graph used to compare data by comparing the lengths of bars.

base (p. 156) *See* power.

base of a polygon (pp. 334, 335) *See* parallelogram *and* triangle.

base of a 3-dimensional figure (pp. 442, 452, 475) *See* prism, pyramid, *and* cylinder.

benchmark (p. 203) An item whose measure you know that can be used to estimate lengths. For example, you could use your height to estimate the height of a doorway.

capacity (p. 500) The amount of liquid a container can hold.

center (p. 462) *See* circle.

certain event (p. 79) An event that must happen. It has a probability of 1.

chord (p. 462) A segment that connects two points on a circle. *See also* circle.

circle (p. 462) The set of points in a plane that are all the same distance from a given point, the center.

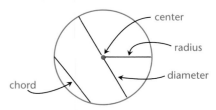

circle graph (p. 424) A circular-shaped graph that shows the part to whole relationship between data. A whole circle represents 100%. Also called a *pie chart*.

circumference (p. 464) The distance around a circle.

cluster (p. 217) A group of numerical data items that are bunched closely together.

common denominator (p. 287) A common multiple of the denominators of two or more fractions.

compatible numbers (p. 8) Numbers that have sums, products, or quotients that are easy to find and compute with.

complementary events (p. 536) Two events are complementary if one or the other must occur, but they cannot both happen at the same time.

composite number (p. 153) A whole number greater than 1 that has more than two factors.

congruent (p. 409) Having the same size and shape.

congruent figures (p. 409) Figures that have the same shape and the same size.

connections (p. 90) Similarities that relate two patterns, problems, ideas, or applications.

coordinate grid (p. 255) A grid formed using two number lines as axes. The axes intersect at the point (0, 0) called the *origin*.

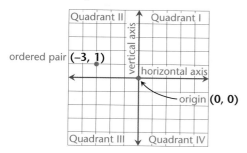

corresponding parts (p. 407) A pair of sides or angles that have the same relative position in two similar or congruent figures.

cross products (p. 397) Equal products formed from a pair of equivalent ratios by multiplying the numerator of each fraction by the denominator of the other fraction.

proportion	cross products
$\frac{2}{3} = \frac{4}{6}$	$2 \cdot 6$
	$3 \cdot 4$

cubic unit (p. 444) A unit for measuring volume.

cylinder (p. 475) A 3-dimensional figure that has a curved surface and two parallel, congruent bases that are circles.

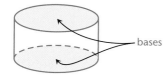
cylinder
bases

D ▸

decimal system (p. 131) A system of numbers based on 10.

degree (p. 103) A unit of measurement for angles. The symbol for degrees is °.

denominator (p. 40) The bottom number in a fraction that tells how many equal-sized parts the whole is divided into.

diameter (p. 463) A chord that passes through the center of a circle and the length of such a chord. *See also* circle.

difference (p. 570) The result when two numbers are subtracted.

distributive property (p. 176) Each addend inside a set of parentheses can be multiplied by a factor outside the parentheses. For example, $3 \cdot (4 + 2) = 3 \cdot 4 + 3 \cdot 2$.

divisible (p. 149) When a number can be evenly divided by another number, it is divisible by that number.

dot plot (p. 216) *See* line plot.

E ▸

edge (p. 442) A segment on a polyhedron where two faces meet. *See also* prism.

empty set (p. 202) A set with no objects in it.

equally likely (p. 76) Outcomes are equally likely if they have the same chance of occurring.

equation (p. 19) A mathematical sentence that uses the symbol "=" between two expressions to show that they have the same value.

equilateral triangle (p. 101) A triangle with three sides of equal length.

equivalent decimals (p. 133)
Two decimals that represent the same amount.

equivalent fractions (p. 55) Fractions that name the same part of a whole.

equivalent ratios (p. 367) Ratios that can be written as equivalent fractions.

estimate (p. 5) An answer that is not exact.

evaluate an expression (p. 19) To substitute a number for each variable, then carry out any operations in the expression.

event (p. 78) A set of outcomes for a particular experiment.

experiment (p. 75) An activity whose results can be observed and recorded.

experimental probability (p. 75) The experimental probability of an outcome is the ratio of the number of times the outcome happened to the number of times the experiment was repeated.

exponent (p. 156) A raised number that tells how many times a base is used as a factor. *See also* power.

expression (p. 2) A mathematical phrase that can contain numbers, variables, and operations.

F ▶

face (p. 441) A flat surface of a polyhedron. *See also* prism.

factor (p. 150) When a whole number is divisible by a second whole number, the second number is a factor of the first.

factor tree (p. 153) *See* prime factorization.

fitted line (p. 387) A line that passes near to most of the data points in a scatter plot, so that close to half of the data points fall above the line and close to half fall below the line.

fraction (p. 40) A number that compares a part with a whole.

front-end estimation (p. 514) A method of estimation that focuses on the leftmost digits, since they have the greatest value.

G ▶

gap (p. 217) When numerical data are plotted on a number line (as in a line plot), a large interval in which there are no data items is a *gap* in the data.

general case (p. 91) When you solve a problem for one situation and extend it to any such situation, you are extending the solution to the general case.

geometric probability (p. 536) A probability that is based on length, area, or volume.

greatest common factor (GCF) (p. 151) The greatest number that is a factor of each of two or more numbers.

H ▶

height of a polygon (pp. 334, 335) *See* parallelogram, triangle.

I ▶

impossible event (p. 79) An event that cannot happen. It has a probability of 0.

inequality (p. 285) A mathematical sentence that uses symbols such as > (greater than) or < (less than) to compare values.

integer (p. 484) Any number in the set {…, −3, −2, −1, 0, 1, 2, 3, …}.

intersect (p. 334) Two segments or figures that meet at a common point intersect.

inverse operations (p. 238) Operations that "undo" each other. For example, addition and subtraction are inverse operations.

isosceles triangle (p. 101) A triangle with two or more sides of equal length.

L ▶

least common denominator (p. 287) The least common multiple of the denominators of two or more fractions.

least common multiple (LCM) (p. 167) For two or more whole numbers, the least number in the list of their common multiples.

line (p. 99) A straight arrangement of points that extends forever in opposite directions.

←————————→

line graph (p. 265) A graph on which the plotted points are connected with line segments. It may show changes that take place over time.

line plot (p. 216) A plot displaying data above the appropriate points along a scale. The scale must include the greatest and least values of the data. Also called a *dot plot*.

lowest terms (p. 58) A fraction is in lowest terms when 1 is the greatest whole number that will divide both the numerator and the denominator evenly.

M ▶

mean (p. 220) The sum of a set of numerical data divided by the number of data items.

median (p. 219) The middle data item in a set of data in numerical order. If there is no single middle item, the number halfway between the two data items closest to the middle.

mixed number (p. 42) The sum of a whole number and a nonzero fraction.

mode (p. 218) The data item or items that occur most often in a set of data.

multiple (p. 166) A multiple of a whole number is the product of that number and any nonzero whole number.

N ▶

negative (p. 483) Less than zero.

net (p. 441) A flat pattern that can be cut out and folded to form a 3-dimensional object.

"nice" fraction (p. 385) A fraction like $\frac{1}{3}$, $\frac{1}{4}$, or $\frac{2}{5}$ that can be used to estimate a ratio or percent, making computation easier.

numerator (p. 40) The top number in a fraction that tells how many parts of the whole to consider.

O ▸

oblique cylinder (p. 475) A cylinder whose curved surface is not perpendicular to the bases.

oblique prism (p. 443) A prism such that each edge joining a vertex of one base and a vertex of the other base is not perpendicular to the bases.

obtuse angle (p. 104) An angle with a measure greater than 90° but less than 180°. *See also* angle.

obtuse triangle (p. 104) A triangle with one obtuse angle.

opposites (p. 521) Two numbers whose sum is equal to 0; one addend is positive, one addend is negative.

order of operations (p. 3) The order to follow when performing operations: simplify inside parentheses, multiply or divide left to right, and finally add or subtract left to right.

ordered pair (p. 254) The numbers that give the location of a point on a coordinate grid. The first number gives the horizontal position and the second number gives the vertical position. *See also* coordinate grid.

origin (p. 255) *See* coordinate grid.

outcome (p. 75) The result of an experiment.

P ▸

parallel lines (p. 100) Lines on a flat surface that do not meet.

parallel planes (p. 442) Planes that do not intersect.

parallelogram (p. 115) A quadrilateral with two pairs of parallel sides.

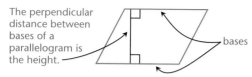

The perpendicular distance between bases of a parallelogram is the height.

bases

percent (p. 420) "per hundred" or "out of 100."

perimeter (p. 575) The distance around a figure.

perpendicular (p. 100) The relationship between lines or segments that meet at a right angle.

pi (π) (p. 464) The ratio of circumference to diameter for any circle. The value of π is approximately equal to 3.14.

pie chart (p. 424) *See* circle graph.

place value (p. 131) The numerical value assigned to the different positions of digits in a number that is written in decimal form.

plane (p. 100) A flat surface that extends forever.

point (p. 99) A specific location in space.

polygon (p. 112) A closed plane figure made from segments, called sides, that do not cross.

vertex
side

A polygon can have 3 or more sides. Some types of polygons are:

| pentagon (5 sides) | hexagon (6 sides) |
| octagon (8 sides) | decagon (10 sides) |

polyhedron (plural: polyhedra) (p. 441) A 3-dimensional object made up of flat surfaces, called faces, shaped like polygons.

population (p. 59) A whole set of objects being studied.

positive (p. 483) Greater than zero.

power (p. 156) An expression that represents repeated multiplication of the same factor.

8 is a power of 2

$$\text{standard form} \quad 8 = 2 \cdot 2 \cdot 2 = 2^3$$

exponent
power
base

prime factorization (p. 153) A number written as the product of prime factors. A factor tree helps to find the prime factorization.

factor tree

The prime factorization of 12 is $2 \cdot 2 \cdot 3$.

prime number (p. 153) A whole number greater than 1 that has exactly two factors, 1 and the number itself.

prism (p. 442) A polyhedron with two congruent bases that lie in parallel planes, and whose other faces are parallelograms.

rectangular prism

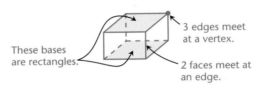

These bases are rectangles.

3 edges meet at a vertex.

2 faces meet at an edge.

probability (p. 75) A number from 0 to 1 that tells you how likely something is to happen.

product (p. 571) The result when two or more numbers are multiplied.

proportion (p. 397) An equation stating that two ratios are equivalent.

protractor (p. 117) A tool used to measure an angle.

pyramid (p. 452) A space figure that has one polygon-shaped base. All the other faces are triangles that meet at a single vertex.

rectangular pyramid

vertex

base

Q ▸▸▸▸▸▸▸▸▸▸▸▸▸▸▸▸▸▸▸▸▸▸▸▸▸▸▸▸▸▸▸▸▸

quadrant (p. 487) The four parts of a coordinate grid divided by the axes. *See also* coordinate grid.

quadrilateral (p. 114) A polygon with four sides.

quotient (p. 572) The result when two numbers are divided.

R ▸▸▸▸▸▸▸▸▸▸▸▸▸▸▸▸▸▸▸▸▸▸▸▸▸▸▸▸▸▸▸▸

radius (plural: radii) (p. 462) A segment from the center of a circle to any point on the circle and the length of such a segment. *See also* circle.

range (p. 216) The difference between the greatest and the least values of a set of numerical data.

rate (p. 374) A ratio that compares two quantities measured in different units. Rates describe how one measure depends on another measure.

ratio (p. 366) A type of comparison of two numbers or measures. Ratios can be written several ways. For example, the ratio of 8 and 12 can be expressed as 8 to 12, 8 : 12, or $\frac{8}{12}$.

ray (p. 99) A part of a line that starts at a point and extends forever in one direction.

endpoint ➔

reciprocals (p. 346) Two numbers whose product is equal to 1.

reflection (p. 545) A change made to a figure by flipping it across a line.

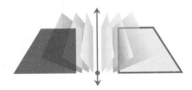

regular polygon (p. 113) A polygon that has sides that are all of equal length and angles that are all of equal measure.

representations (p. 89) Diagrams, tables, graphs, and other visual means to help you solve problems and explain your solutions.

rhombus (p. 115) A parallelogram with all sides the same length.

right angle (p. 104) An angle with a measure of 90°. *See also* angle.

right cylinder (p. 475) A cylinder whose curved surface is perpendicular to the bases.

right prism (p. 443) A prism such that each edge joining a vertex of one base and a vertex of the other base is perpendicular to the bases.

right triangle (p. 104) A triangle that has one right angle.

rotation (p. 544) A change made to a figure by turning it around a fixed point. The point of rotation can be any fixed point outside, inside, or on the figure.

A

round (p. 5) To approximate a number to a given place. For example, 28 rounded to the nearest ten is 30.

rule (p. 16) An explanation of how to create or extend a pattern.

S ▸▸▸▸▸▸▸▸▸▸▸▸▸▸▸▸▸▸▸▸▸▸▸▸▸▸▸▸▸▸

sample (p. 59) Part of a whole set of objects being studied.

scale (p. 411) The ratio of a measurement on a model or a drawing to the corresponding measurement on the actual object.

scalene triangle (p. 101) A triangle with no sides of equal length.

scatter plot (p. 388) A graph that shows the relationship between two sets of data. The data are represented by points, and a fitted line can be drawn based on the pattern in the points.

scientific notation (p. 554) A form of writing a number using a number greater than or equal to 1 but less than 10 and a power of 10.

segment (p. 99) Two points on a line and all points between them.

endpoints

sequence (p. 15) An ordered list of numbers or objects.

set (p. 78) Any collection of objects.

similar figures (p. 407) Figures that have the same shape but not necessarily the same size.

solution of an equation (p. 236) A value of a variable that makes an equation true.

solving an equation (p. 236) The process of finding solutions of an equation.

standard form (p. 153) A number written without using exponents. *See also* power.

stem-and-leaf plot (p. 249) A display of data where each number is represented by a *stem* (the leftmost digits) and a *leaf* (the rightmost digits).

straight angle (p. 104) An angle with a measure of 180°. *See also* angle.

sum (p. 569) The result when two or more numbers are added.

T ▸▸▸▸▸▸▸▸▸▸▸▸▸▸▸▸▸▸▸▸▸▸▸▸▸▸▸▸▸▸

term of a sequence (p. 17) An individual number or object in a sequence.

term number (p. 17) Indicates the order or position of a term in a sequence.

theoretical probability (p. 78) The ratio of the number of outcomes in the event to the total number of possible outcomes.

trading off (p. 513) A method that involves taking away from one number and adding the same amount to another number, to have numbers that are easier to add using mental math.

transformation (p. 545) A change made to a figure or its position.

translation (p. 544) A change made to a figure by sliding every point of it the same distance in the same direction.

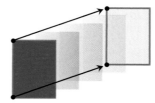

trapezoid (p. 115) A quadrilateral with exactly one pair of parallel sides.

triangle (pp. 101, 112) A polygon with three sides.

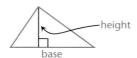
height
base

U ▸▸▸▸▸▸▸▸▸▸▸▸▸▸▸▸▸▸▸▸▸▸▸▸▸▸▸▸▸▸

unit rate (p. 376) A form of a rate that gives an amount per one unit.

V ▸▸▸▸▸▸▸▸▸▸▸▸▸▸▸▸▸▸▸▸▸▸▸▸▸▸▸▸▸▸

variable (p. 19) A letter or symbol that represents a quantity that is unknown or that can change.

Venn diagram (p. 115) A diagram that uses a drawing to show how sets are related.

vertex of an angle (p. 103) The endpoint of the rays of an angle. *See also* angle.

vertex (plural: vertices) of a polygon (p. 112) Each endpoint of a side of a polygon. *See also* polygon.

vertex of a prism (p. 442) A point where three edges meet. *See also* prism.

volume (p. 444) The amount of space an object contains.

INDEX

594

596

597

CREDITS

ACKNOWLEDGMENTS

108 Graphic and text from *Puzzles and Brain Twisters* by Fred Walls. Copyright © 1970 by Franklin Watts, Inc. Reprinted by permission of Franklin Watts, an imprint of Scholastic Library Publishing, Inc. **181** Excerpt and illustration from *Justin and the Best Biscuits in the World* by Mildred Pitts Walter. Text copyright © 1986 by Mildred Pitts Walter. Illustrations copyright © 1986 by Catherine Stock. Used by permission of HarperCollins Publishers. **214** Excerpts and illustrations from *The Phantom Tollbooth* by Norton Juster and illustrated by Jules Feiffer, copyright © 1961 and renewed by Norton Juster, illustrations copyright © 1961 and renewed 1989 by Jules Feiffer. Used by permission of Random House Children's Books, a division of Random House, Inc. **282** Excerpt and illustration from *Sadako and the Thousand Paper Cranes* by Eleanor Coerr, illustrated by Ronald Himler, text copyright © 1977 by Eleanor Coerr, copyright © 1977 by Ronald Himler, illustrations. Used by permission of G.P. Putnam's Sons, A Division of Penguin Young Readers Group, A Member of Penguin Group (USA) Inc., 345 Hudson Street, New York, NY 10014. All rights reserved. **364** "One Inch Tall," from *Where the Sidewalk Ends* by Shel Silverstein. Copyright © 2004 by Evil Eye Music, Inc. Reprinted with permission from the Estate of Shel Silverstein and HarperCollins Children's Books. **373** Excerpt from "The Great Flood of 1993" by Barbara Brownell, *National Geographic World,* October 1993. Copyright © 1993 National Geographic Society. Reprinted by permission of National Geographic Society.

PHOTOGRAPHY

See copyright page for additional acknowledgments.
1 © Settimio Cipriani/Grand Tour/Corbis; **15** © Araldo de Luca/Corbis; **22** *all* © Kent Wood/Photo Researchers, Inc.; **27, 28, 30** *all* RMIP/Richard Haynes/McDougal Littell/Houghton Mifflin Co.; **34** © Royalty-Free/Corbis; **35** © Tami Dawson/Alamy; **38** © Fridmar Damm/zefa/Corbis; **39** *all* HeritageAuctions.com; **40** *top* Courtesy of William Eckberg; *bottom* © Dinodia/The Image Works; **53** © Alessandro D'Amico/AAD Worldwide Travel Images/Alamy; **54** *all* RMIP/Richard Haynes/McDougal Littell/Houghton Mifflin Co.; **62** © Walter Bibikow/Index Stock Photography; **63** *all* © PhotoDisc; **65** © Peter Menzel/Stock Boston; **68, 69** *all* © Artville; **72–73** © Skyscan Photolibrary/Alamy; **74** *left* © David Young-Wolff/PhotoEdit; *right* Courtesy of The American Numismatic Association; **83** RMIP/Richard Haynes/McDougal Littell/Houghton Mifflin Co.; **85** *top* © Artville; *bottom* © Paul C. Chauncey/Corbis;

86 © Stephanie Reix/For Picture/Corbis; **89** Ken Karp/McDougal Littell/Houghton Mifflin Co.; **94** RMIP/Richard Haynes/McDougal Littell/Houghton Mifflin Co.; **95** *top* © Karl Kinne/zefa/Corbis; *center* © Atlantide Phototravel/Corbis; *bottom* © Anders Blomqvist/Getty Images; **97** RMIP/Richard Haynes/McDougal Littell/Houghton Mifflin Co.; **100** © Royalty-Free/Corbis; **103** *left* © David Sanger/Getty Images; *right* © Momatiuk-Eastcott/Corbis; **116** © Don Hammond/Design Pics/Corbis; **117** *all* RMIP/Richard Haynes/McDougal Littell/Houghton Mifflin Co.; **124, 125** *all* Bonnie Spence/McDougal Littell/Houghton Mifflin Co.; **128–129** © Phil Schermeister/Corbis; **130** Tracey Wheeler McDougal Littell/Houghton Mifflin Co.; **135** © Ariadne Van Zandbergen/Getty Images; **144** *all* RMIP/Richard Haynes/McDougal Littell/Houghton Mifflin Co.; **160** © Peter Johnson/Corbis; **164** *top* © Artville; *bottom* © Michael Newman/PhotoEdit; **165** RMIP/Richard Haynes/McDougal Littell/Houghton Mifflin Co.; **169** © Paul A. Souders/Corbis; **170** *top* © National Portrait Gallery, Smithsonian Institution/Art Resource, NY; *bottom* Courtesy of Emiko Tokunaga; **189** RMIP/Richard Haynes/McDougal Littell/Houghton Mifflin Co.; **198–199** © Frans Lanting/Minden Pictures; **200** *left* © DLILLC/Corbis; *center* © David Hosking/Photo Researchers, Inc.; *right* © franzfoto.com/Alamy; **203** © Douglas Hill/Beatworks/Corbis; **204** © Joe McDonald/Corbis; **206** *left* © Peter Burian/Corbis; *right* © Colin Seddon/Alamy; **212** © Kevin Schafer/Getty Images; **215** Lyle Andersen/McDougal Littell/Houghton Mifflin Co.; **218** © altrendo nature/Getty Images; **220** © Digital Vision/Getty Images; **223** © Tom Brakefield/Getty Images; **226** © Chris Birck/NBAE/Getty Images; **227** School Division/Houghton Mifflin Co.; **228** © AFP/Getty Images; **231** *left* © John Bracegirdle/Getty Images; *center* © George D. Lepp/Corbis; *right* © Joseph Van Os/Getty Images; **232** © Konrad Wothe/Getty Images; **235** © Gerard Lacz/Animals Animals; **241** © Don S. Montgomery/Corbis; **242** *top left* © Bettmann/Corbis; *right* © AP Images; *bottom left* © Ed Clark/Time Life Pictures/Getty Images; **254** RMIP/Richard Haynes/McDougal Littell/Houghton Mifflin Co.; **259** © Justin Lane/epa/Corbis; **260** © Jeremy Spiegel **265** © Dani/Jeske/Animals Animals; **267** © DLILLC/Corbis; **273** © David M. Dennis/Animals Animals; **274, 276** *all* RMIP/Richard Haynes/McDougal Littell/Houghton Mifflin Co.; **280–281** © Jim West/The Image Works; **282** School Division/Houghton Mifflin Co.; **283** *all* Bonnie Spence/McDougal Littell/Houghton Mifflin Co.; **284, 286** *all* RMIP/Richard Haynes/McDougal Littell/Houghton Mifflin Co.; **295** © D.E.

Cox/Stone/Getty Images; **296** School Division/ Houghton Mifflin Co.; **299** © Dean Conger/Corbis; **300** © Charles E. Rotkin/Corbis; **303** RMIP/Richard Haynes/McDougal Littell/Houghton Mifflin Co.; **304** © Amos Nachoum/Corbis; **307, 308** *all* Bonnie Spence/ McDougal Littell/Houghton Mifflin Co.; **310** RMIP/ Richard Haynes/McDougal Littell/Houghton Mifflin Co.; **318** © Charles Bennett/AP Images; **319** School Division/ Houghton Mifflin Co.; **321** *left* RMIP/Richard Haynes/ McDougal Littell/Houghton Mifflin Co.; *center* School Division/Houghton Mifflin Co.; *right* © Lowe Art Museum/SuperStock; **325** Allan Penn/McDougal Littell/ Houghton Mifflin Co.; **327** © AP Images/Rusty Kennedy; **330** © Riccardo Spila/Grand Tour/Corbis; **333** © Walter Bibikow/The Image Bank/Getty Images; **334** RMIP/ Richard Haynes/McDougal Littell/Houghton Mifflin Co.; **335** © Photosindia/Getty Images; **345** © Peter Guttman/Corbis; **346** RMIP/Richard Haynes/McDougal Littell/Houghton Mifflin Co.; **354** *left* © William Leaman/ Alamy; *right* © Roger Tidman/Corbis; **359** © Goro Uno/ HAGA/The Image Works; **362–363** © Louie Psihoyos/ Corbis; **365** © Andrew Bain/Lonely Planet Images; **366** *left, center right* Bonnie Spence/McDougal Littell/ Houghton Mifflin Co.; *center left, right* © Artville; **369** *top right* © FAN travelstock/Alamy; *dogs* © PhotoDisc; **370** *grass* © D. Hurst/Alamy; *person* © Comstock; *basset hound* © Comstock; *bottom* © Bettmann/Corbis; **373** © Elaine Thompson/AP Images; **374** RMIP/Richard Haynes/ McDougal Littell/Houghton Mifflin Co.; **378** © Brand X Pictures; **382** *all* RMIP/Richard Haynes/McDougal Littell/ Houghton Mifflin Co.; **384** *top* RMIP/Richard Haynes/ McDougal Littell/Houghton Mifflin Co.; *bottom* Allan Penn/McDougal Littell/Houghton Mifflin Co.; **386** © Popperfoto/Alamy; **387** *all* RMIP/Richard Haynes/ McDougal Littell/Houghton Mifflin Co.; **391** © Tony Gutierrez/AP Images; **393** © O. Louis Mazzatenta/ National Geographic Image Collection; **395** © Barry Rosenthal/Getty Images; **400** © AFB/Stringer/Getty Images; **403** © Kim Karpeles/Alamy; **404** © Jack Hollingsworth/Corbis; **406, 407** M.C. Escher's *Square Limit* © 2007 The M.C. Escher Company-Holland. All rights reserved. www.mcescher.com; **410** © Nik Wheeler/Corbis; **412** © Rhoda Sidney/PhotoEdit; **415** © PhotoDisc; **417** *all* Courtesy of Marcia McNutt; **419** © Andreas Rentz/Bongarts/Getty Images; **422** © AFP/Getty Images; **423** © Getty Images; **430** © Bettman/Corbis; **433, 435** *all* RMIP/Richard Haynes/McDougal Littell/ Houghton Mifflin Co.; **438–439** © Jose Fuste Raga/ Corbis; **440** *left* © Simon McBride/AA World Travel/ Topfoto/The Image Works; *right* © Reuters/Corbis; **441** *all* Bala Mullur/McDougal Littell/Houghton Mifflin Co.; **442** © mediacolor's/Alamy; **444, 445, 448, 449** *all* School Division/Houghton Mifflin Co.; **452** © Rick Strange/AA World Travel/Topfoto/The Image Works; **453** © Richard T. Nowitz/Corbis; **457** *all* School Division/Houghton Mifflin Co.; **458** Courtesy of Dr. Darrell Mease; **461** © Scala/Art Resource, NY; **463** *all* RMIP/Richard Haynes/McDougal Littell/Houghton

Mifflin Co.; **465** School Division/Houghton Mifflin Company Co.; **467** © Reuters/Corbis; **468** *top* © Atlantide Phototravel/Corbis; *center* © Charles E. Rotkin/ Corbis; *bottom* Courtesy of the American Numismatic Society; **472** © Richard Broadwell/Corbis; **475** © Craig Lovell/Eagle Visions Photography/Alamy; **478** © NOAA/ AP Images; **482** *top* © PhotoDisc; *bottom* © Roger-Viollet/The Image Works; **488** RMIP/Richard Haynes/ McDougal Littell/Houghton Mifflin Co.; **494** *pyramids, Taj Mahal* © Goodshoot/Corbis; *bottom* RMIP/Richard Haynes/McDougal Littell/Houghton Mifflin Co.; **498–499** © Chuck Place/Alamy; **503** Bonnie Spence/ McDougal Littell/Houghton Mifflin Co.; **504** *all* RMIP/ Richard Haynes/McDougal Littell/Houghton Mifflin Co.; **505** *all* School Division/Houghton Mifflin Co.; **507** *bottom left* RMIP/Richard Haynes/McDougal Littell/ Houghton Mifflin Co.; *right* School Division/Houghton Mifflin Co.; **508** © Ron Wurzer/AP Images; **510** © Jim Cooper/AP Images; **520** *left* © Paul A. Souders/Corbis; *right* School Division/Houghton Mifflin Co.; **523** © Aaron Horowitz/Corbis; **528** *all* © Jupiterimages; **530** © Leo Mason/Corbis; **533** © Purestock/Getty Images; **535** *all* RMIP/Richard Haynes/McDougal Littell/ Houghton Mifflin Co.; **536** NASA Johnson Space Center (NASA-JSC); **539** © Vince Streano/Corbis; **542** *left* School Division/Houghton Mifflin Co.; *right* © Peter Hvizdak/The Image Works; **543, 546** *all* School Division/ Houghton Mifflin Co.; **549** *top left* © Bruno Barbier/ Robert Harding World Imagery/Corbis; *top right* © Duomo/Corbis; *bottom* © Superstock, Inc./Superstock; **551** © Bob Daemmrich/The Image Works; **553, 557** NASA Jet Propulsion Laboratory (NASA-JPL); NASA Jet Propulsion Laboratory (NASA-JPL); **560** RMIP/Richard Haynes/McDougal Littell/Houghton Mifflin Co.; **563** *all* © PhotoDisc.

ILLUSTRATION

15, 63 Robin Storesund/McDougal Littell/Houghton Mifflin Co.; **63** Robin Storesund/McDougal Littell/ Houghton Mifflin Co.; **172, 295** David Ballard; **332** Chris Costello; **367** Jeremy Spiegel/McDougal Littell/Houghton Mifflin Co.; **381, 390** Hannah Bonner; **396** Robin Storesund/McDougal Littell/Houghton Mifflin Co.; **472** Chris Costello; **478** Matthew Pippin; **482** Chris Costello; **508, 529** Robin Storesund/McDougal Littell/ Houghton Mifflin Co.

All other illustrations by McDougal Littell/Houghton Mifflin Co. or School Division/Houghton Mifflin Co.

SELECTED ANSWERS

MODULE 1

Section 1, Practice and Application (p. 11)

1. a. 355; The answer is not reasonable because the first hurdle would be at 45 m and, since 45 m + 355 m = 400 m, the second hurdle would be at the finish line.
b. $(400 - 40 - 45) \div 9$ **c.** 35 meters **3.** 36 **5.** 10 **7.** 7
9. 3 **11.** $(11 + 5) \div 4$ **13.** $50 - (4 \cdot 6)$ **17.** about 14,000; not possible to tell whether estimate is greater than or less than exact product **19.** about 200; less than **21.** about 9,700; less than **23.** 40 **25.** 120
27. 600 **29. a.** 4,941 **b.** 240 **c.** 364 **d.** 580
31. $26 \cdot 200$ is $26 \cdot 2 = 52$ greater than the exact answer. $25 \cdot 200$ is $198 - 25 \cdot 2 = 148$ less than the exact answer. So $26 \cdot 200$ is closer.
33. $25 \cdot 400 = 10,000$

Spiral Review (p. 13)
36. < **37.** > **38.** 3,000 **39.** 180

Extra Skill Practice (p. 14)
1. 26 **3.** 13 **5.** 15 **7.** 5 **9.** 37 **11.** 14 **13.** about 300, greater than **15.** about 100, less than **17.** about 1800, not possible to tell **19.** about 280, not possible to tell **21.** about 2,600, greater than **23.** about 4,500, greater than **25.** 40 **27.** 90 **29.** 1,200 **31.** 1,800

Standardized Testing (p. 14)
1. A **2.** C

Section 2, Practice and Application (p. 22)
1.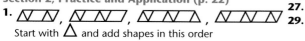
Start with △ and add shapes in this order
 to continue pattern.
3. 63, 54, 45, 36; Start with 99 and subtract 9 from each term to get the next term. **5.** end of August
7. a.

Term Number	1	2	3	4
Term	1	2	4	8

b. Each term is twice the preceding term. **c.** 32 cells

11. $t = 3 \cdot n$
13. a.

Term Number	5	6	7	8
Term	60	72	84	96

b. The term is 12 times the term number. **c.** $t = 12 \cdot n$
d. $t = 12 \cdot 30 = 360$
15. a.
b.

Term Number	1	2	3	4	5	6
Term	2	5	8	11	14	17

c. Make rectangle 10 squares tall and 3 squares wide. Remove the square from the top right corner.
d. Start with 2 and add 3 to each term to get the next term. Multiply the term number by 3 and subtract 1.
e. $t = 3n - 1$; t = term; n = term number
f. $t = 3 \cdot 25 - 1 = 74$

Spiral Review (p. 25)
20. three thousand six hundred seventy-two
21. six hundred seventy-one thousand five hundred ninety-eight **22.** twenty-three thousand eight hundred fifty-six **23.** 1216 **24.** 135 **25.** 8129 **26.** 4875
27. 23,328 **28.** 502
29.
30.

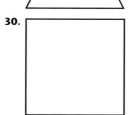

31.

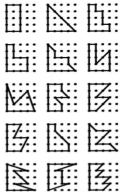

Extra Skill Practice (p. 26)
1. 125, 150, 175, 200, 225; Multiply the term number by 25. Or, start with 25 and add 25 to each term to get the next term. **3.** 96, 84, 72, 60, 48; Multiply the term number by 12 and subtract the product from 156. Or, start with 144 and subtract 12 from each term to get the next term. **5.** 81, 243, 729, 2187, 6561; Multiply each term by 3 to get the next term.
7. a.

Term Number	14	15	16	17
Term	140	150	160	170

b. $t = 10n$ **c.** $t = 10 \cdot 40 = 400$

Study Skills (p. 26)
1. Answers will vary. **2.** Toolbox, Tables, Glossary, Index, Selected Answers **3.** page 567

Section 3, Practice and Application (p. 34)
1. a. Which of two monthly service contracts for 8 to 10 hours a month on-line is a better buy? **b.** the monthly fee, number of included hours, and hourly rate for hours beyond the number included **c.** whether there are limits on the total number of hours or available times, and whether either has cheaper telephone access
3. a. How many times does a given event occur? **b.** the time periods over which the tour runs, and the frequency and length of the trips **c.** whether there is more than one double-hulled canoe (If not, the times given could not be exact. There would need to be time to load and unload.) **5.** too much information; Jon had $25.00 **7.** If you are online 8 hr, the standard contract is cheaper. For 9 hr the costs are the same. For 10 hr the frequent user contract is cheaper. **9.** Try a simpler problem, make a table, look for a pattern; Draw chains with 1, 2, 3, and 4 triangles. Find the perimeters. Enter the values in a table. Make a prediction. **11.** 25 times
13. No later than 6:45 AM

Spiral Review (p. 36)
16. 5,600 **17.** $40 **18.** $7 **19.** 35,000 **20.** 900
21. 45,000 **22.** 10,000 **23.** 100,000 **24.** 6,000
25. 560 **26.** 21,000 **27.** 72,600 **28.** 32,000
29. 1,000,000 **30.** 63,000,000 **31.** 12 **32.** 1600
33. 70

34.

Term Number	1	2	3	4	5	6
Term	4	8	12	16	20	24

$t = 4n$ where n is the term number and t is the term

Extra Skill Practice (p. 37)
1. too much; the cost of markers and pens **3.** not enough; Jose's age, ticket price **5.** 4 mi; make a picture or diagram **7.** $83.50; work backward

Standardized Testing (p. 37)
Answers will vary.

Section 4, Practice and Application (p. 47)
1. $\frac{1}{2}$ **3.** $\frac{4}{12}$ **5. a.** $\frac{3}{8}$ **b.** $\frac{5}{8}$ **c.** 1; the two fractions together represent the whole. **7.** $\frac{4}{3}$, $1\frac{1}{3}$ **9.** $\frac{5}{2}$, $2\frac{1}{2}$ **11.** $\frac{3}{4}$, $\frac{5}{9}$, $\frac{7}{16}$, $\frac{9}{25}$, $\frac{11}{36}$ **13. c.** $\frac{1}{2}$ **d.** Answers will vary. Sample Responses:

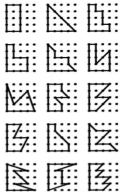

15. The figures are congruent because they have the same size and shape. **17.** The figures are congruent because they have the same size and shape.
21. $1\frac{7}{8}$ **23.** $4\frac{2}{3}$ **25.** $\frac{19}{12}$ **27.** $\frac{8}{3}$ **29.** $\frac{25}{8}$ **31.** $\frac{108}{11}$
32–35.

$$\begin{array}{c} \\ \xleftarrow{}\underset{0}{|}\underset{1}{|}\underset{1\frac{2}{3}}{\overset{\frac{9}{6}}{\bullet}}\underset{2}{|}\underset{\frac{14}{6}}{\overset{2\frac{1}{6}}{\bullet}}\underset{3}{|}\xrightarrow{} \end{array}$$

37. $7\frac{3}{7}$ **39. a.** Let t = the term and n = the term number; $t = \frac{3 \cdot n}{6}$ **b.** $\frac{3}{6}$, 1, $1\frac{3}{6}$, 2, $2\frac{3}{6}$ **c.** 5 more turns
41. b (1.50); Half of a dollar is $0.50.

Spiral Review (p. 51)
44. Add 3 and 2, then multiply the sum by 4.
45. Divide 10 by 2, then add the quotient to 7.
46. Multiply 3 by 2, then subtract the product from 8.
47. $1.55 **48.** 11 postcards and 19 letters **49.** 340
50. 15,900 **51.** 43,890,000

Extra Skill Practice (p. 52)
1. False; The two parts of the triangle are not the same size. **3.** True **5.** $\frac{5}{2}$, $2\frac{1}{2}$ **7.** $3\frac{1}{3}$ **9.** $4\frac{1}{4}$ **11.** $10\frac{1}{2}$ **13.** $\frac{49}{9}$

15. $\frac{24}{7}$ **17.** $2\frac{1}{5}$ **19.** $4\frac{2}{4}$ **21.** $4.50

Standardized Testing (p. 52)

1. a. **b.** **c.**

2. $1\frac{3}{9}$, $2\frac{6}{9}$, $3\frac{1}{9}$, $4\frac{4}{9}$; Sample Response: To get the next term, add 4 to the numerator of the previous term and use the same denominator. Then rewrite any improper fractions to mixed numbers or whole numbers.

Section 5, Practice and Application (p. 62)

1. a. $\frac{1}{2}$ **b.** $\frac{4}{8}$ **3.** $\frac{2}{5}$, $\frac{4}{10}$ **5.** $\frac{2}{3}$, $\frac{4}{6}$ **7.** $\frac{1}{3}$, $\frac{2}{6}$ **9. a.** Samples: $\frac{4}{16}$, $\frac{2}{8}$, $\frac{1}{4}$. **b.** 208¢ **c.** $\frac{52}{208}$ **d.** It is equivalent because each stamp has the same value. **11.** 21 **13.** 2 **15.** 9

17. $\frac{10}{15}$, $\frac{12}{18}$, $\frac{14}{21}$ **19.** $\frac{3}{20}$ **21.** $\frac{4}{9}$ **23.** $\frac{2}{3}$ **25.** $\frac{1}{12}$

27. a. $\frac{18}{24}$ **b.** $\frac{9}{12}$; divided both numerator and denominator by 2. **c.** $\frac{3}{4}$; divided the numerator and denominator of $\frac{9}{12}$ by 3. **d.** $\frac{3}{4}$; the fraction is in lowest terms.

29. a. No **b.** Yes **c.** Yes **31.** 15 **33.** 9 **35.** 6 **37.** 15 **39.** 8 triangles **41.** 14 triangles **43.** pine: 216 grains; grass: 162 grains; oak: 135 grains; cactus: 27 grains **45.** about 4

Spiral Review (p. 66)

50. 350, greater than **51.** 14,000, not possible to tell **52.** 1600, not possible to tell **53.** 400, greater than **54.** 4, less than **55.** 7800, less than **56.** 58 **57.** 480 **58.** 280 **59.** 1200 **60.** The term is 7 times the term number. **61.** 420 **62.** No, the circle is not divided into 4 equal parts. **63.** 135 **64.** 8,497 **65.** 1,293

Extra Skill Practice (p. 67)

1. $\frac{2}{10}$, $\frac{1}{5}$ **3.** $\frac{4}{8}$, $\frac{1}{2}$ **5.** $\frac{8}{18}$, $\frac{12}{27}$, $\frac{16}{36}$ **7.** $\frac{6}{16}$, $\frac{9}{24}$, $\frac{12}{32}$ **9.** $\frac{2}{12}$, $\frac{3}{18}$, $\frac{4}{24}$ **11.** $\frac{1}{8}$, $\frac{2}{16}$, $\frac{3}{24}$ **13.** $\frac{2}{5}$, $\frac{12}{30}$, $\frac{18}{45}$ **15.** 42 **17.** 12 **19.** 1 **21.** 120 **23.** $\frac{1}{6}$ **25.** $\frac{1}{5}$ **27.** $\frac{7}{16}$ **29.** $\frac{4}{15}$ **31.** $\frac{3}{8}$ **33.** 12 **35.** 6 **37.** 24 **39.** 15

Standardized Testing (p. 67)

1. B **2.** B

Review & Assessment (pp. 70–71)

1. 45 **2.** 47 **3.** 6 **4.** 21 **5.** 12 **6.** 19 **7.** about $40 \cdot 70 = 2,800$ **8.** about $250 - 190 = 60$ **9.** about $3,100 + 900 = 4,000$ **10.** about $260 + 30 + 90 = 380$ **11.** about $200 \cdot 10 = 2,000$ **12.** about $3,500 - 2,100 = 1,400$ **13.** greater than; He rounded $47.98 up and $22.31 down, so he increased the difference.

14. $67 + 143 = 210$
$19 + 31 = 50$
$210 + 50 = 260$
16. $5 \cdot 2 = 10$
$10 \cdot 46 = 460$

15. $4 \cdot 25 = 100$
$7 \cdot 5 = 35$
$100 \cdot 35 = 3,500$
17. $34 + 66 = 100$
$100 + 158 = 258$

18. 176, 173, 170; Start with 188. Subtract 3 from each term to get the next term, or subtract 3 times the term number from 191 to find the term. **19.** 75, 90, 105; The term is 15 times the term number, or start with 15 and add 15 to each term to get the next term.

20.

Term No.	5	6	7
Term	9	10	11

$t = n + 4$ where t = term and n = term number
$t = 50 + 4 = 54$

21.

Term No.	5	6	7
Term	20	24	28

$t = 4n$ where t = term and n = term number
$t = 4(50) = 200$

22.

Pres.	VP	Sec.
G	L	B
G	B	L
L	G	B
L	B	G
B	G	L
B	L	G

G = Gail
B = Ben
L = Lita

23. page 130; $130 \cdot 131 = 17,030$ **24.** False; The square is not divided into two equal-sized parts.
25. False; The circle is divided into 4 equal-sized pieces, so $\frac{1}{4}$ of the circle is shaded. **26.** True **27.** 33 **28.** 3
29. 7 **30.** 7 **31.** Answers will vary. $\frac{1}{5}$, $\frac{4}{20}$, $\frac{2}{10}$
32. b and c. Multiplying or dividing both the numerator and denominator of a fraction by the same number yields an equivalent fraction. **33.** $\frac{1}{4}$ **34.** $\frac{3}{4}$ **35.** $\frac{5}{6}$
36. $\frac{3}{8}$ **37.** $\frac{7}{8}$ **38.** 9 **39.** 20 **40.** 50 **41.** 49

MODULE 2

Section 1, Practice and Application (p. 81)

1. $\frac{25}{60}$ or $\frac{5}{12}$ **3. a.**

Experimental Probability of Heads
$\frac{4}{10}$ or $\frac{2}{5}$
$\frac{44}{100}$ or $\frac{11}{25}$
$\frac{502}{1000}$ or $\frac{251}{500}$
$\frac{5067}{10000}$

b. 4,933 tails **c.** $\frac{4933}{10000}$ **5. a.** $\frac{8}{25}$ **b.** 17; $\frac{17}{25}$ **c.** The probabilities have a sum of $\frac{8}{25} + \frac{17}{25} = \frac{25}{25}$, or 1. **d.** about 32 (25 × 4 = 100, so 8 × 4 = 32); about 68 (100 – 32) **7.** Yes, all outcomes have the same chance of occurring because each specific numbered card or face card does not appear more than once. **9. a.** $\frac{11}{66}$ or $\frac{1}{6}$; $\frac{5}{66}$

Spiral Review (p. 83)

12. six ways

Quarters	Dimes	Nickels
1	1	0
1	0	2
0	3	1
0	2	3
0	1	5
0	0	7

13. 25, 29 **14.** 20, 27 **15.** Exercise 13: Begin with 9 as the first term. Add 4 to the previous term to get the next term; Exercise 14: Begin with 2 as the first term, then add 3, then 4, then 5, increasing the amount you add to the previous term by one each time.

Extra Skill Practice (p. 84)

1. $\frac{15}{80}$ or $\frac{3}{16}$ **3.** $\frac{50}{80}$ or $\frac{5}{8}$ **5. a.** {A, I, E, G, D, C, F, H}
b. Yes, each outcome has the same chance of occurring because the circle is divided into equal partitions and each outcome appears on the spinner once.

7. $\frac{0}{8}$ or 0 **9.** $\frac{3}{8}$ **11.** "The spinner stops on B" is impossible since there is no B on the spinner. None are certain.

Study Skills (p. 84)

1–2. Answers will vary.

Section 2, Practice and Application (p. 93)

1. Student scores will vary. 8 days since on the 8th day the snail advances 3 ft and is out of the well before night when he usually slips back. **3. a.** $C = 2$, $E = 5$, $D = 7$, $G = 1$, $K = 3$ **b.** Multiply 257 by 13 and check your solution. **5. a.** Not correct. This line divides the square into one right triangle and one pentagon. **b.** Correct. The square figure is broken into two three sided polygons that each have a right angle, since the line only affected two of the four right angles in the square. **c.** Not correct. Although there are two right triangles, the figure is not a square. **7.** Answers vary. Sample Response: How many ways can the lower star reach the upper star through left and up moves only? **9. a.** least is 5 games; greatest is 11 games; Explanations will vary. This problem is similar to the first round of the World Cup Problem. **b.** Scores will vary.

Spiral Review (p. 95)

11. 43 **12.** 45 **13.** 36

14.

Term Number	1	2	3	4	5	6
Term in the sequence	5	9	13	17	21	**25**

Begin the first term with 5, then add 4 to obtain each succeeding term.

Extra Skill Practice (p. 96)

1. 2 blocks north; 6 blocks west

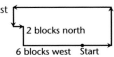

2 blocks north

6 blocks west   Start

3. Sue is the president.

	Pres	VP	Sec	Treas
John	No	Yes	No	No
Sue	Yes	No	No	No
Lisa	No	No	No	Yes
Fernando	No	No	Yes	No

5.

Tables of 4	Tables of 2
7	0
6	2
5	4
4	6
3	8
2	10
1	12
0	14

Standardized Testing (p. 96)

Yes; Each person can carry 31 lb. There are a number of ways to divide the weight. Sample: Caroline carries clothing 10 lb, food 14 lb, first-aid kit 1 lb, camping stove 6 lb. Juanita carries the tent 7 lb, lantern 3 lb, water 15 lb, two sleeping bags 6 lb.

Section 3, Practice and Application (p. 108)

1. Sample Response: $\overline{XY}$, $\overline{YZ}$, $\overline{XZ}$; They differ in length and endpoints. **3.** $\overleftrightarrow{XY}$, $\overleftrightarrow{XZ}$, $\overleftrightarrow{YZ}$, $\overleftrightarrow{YX}$, $\overleftrightarrow{ZX}$, $\overleftrightarrow{ZY}$ **5.** ray
7. parallel **9.** 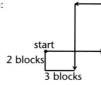 **11.** can **13.** cannot

15. The segments won't form a triangle since the sum of the lengths of the two shorter sides is not greater than the length of the third side. There could be no such triangle-shaped piece of land. **17.** The ray pictured has A as an endpoint and goes in the direction opposite of $\overrightarrow{CB}$. **19.** obtuse **21.** straight **23.** acute isosceles **25.** acute scalene **27.** acute equilateral **29. a.** No; Give the type of triangles and whether the vertex or side of the triangle is touching the watch face. Give the size of the circular face and whether the face has all numbers 1-12 or just 12, 3, 6, and 9. **b.** 2 or 3: The owner used triangles to describe the watch, but they were not specific enough to identify the watch.

Spiral Review (p. 110)

32. $\frac{1}{3}$ **33.** $\frac{4}{5}$ **34.** $\frac{3}{5}$ **35.** $\frac{2}{3}$ **36.** 7 **37.** 40 **38.** 16
39. red, blue, and white ball **40. a.** $\frac{2}{10}$ or $\frac{1}{5}$ **b.** $\frac{0}{10}$ or 0
c. $\frac{7}{10}$ **d.** $\frac{5}{10}$ or $\frac{1}{2}$ **41.** 6 times because the probability the ball is blue is $\frac{3}{10}$. 20 is twice 10, so 6 would be twice 3.

Extra Skill Practice (p. 111)

1. C **3.** D **5.** can **7.** cannot **9.** true **11.** true
13. straight **15.** obtuse

Standardized Testing (p. 111)

Sample responses are given. A. 2, 5, 6; B. 4, 5; C. 1, 2; D. 1, 4; E. 1, 3, 4; F. 2, 5

Section 4, Practice and Application (p. 120)

1. a. Not regular. Angles are not of equal measure.
b. Not regular. Angles are not of equal measure. **c.** Not regular. Side lengths are not equal. **d.** Regular **e.** Regular
f. Not regular. Side lengths are not equal; angles are not of equal measure. **3. a.** $\frac{1}{6}$ **b.** $\frac{6}{6}$ or 1 **c.** $\frac{4}{6}$ or $\frac{2}{3}$
5. $m\angle Z = 35°$ **7.** $m\angle G = 75°$ **11. a–b.** Scores will vary.

Spiral Review (p. 121)

13. Right; Isosceles **14.** Obtuse; Scalene **15.** Acute; Equilateral **16.** 2 cm, 5 cm or 3 cm, 4 cm **17.** Red, green, blue, yellow

Extra Skill Practice (p. 122)

1. Yes **3.** Yes **5.** Yes **7.** No; angles have different measures. **9.** Rectangle **11.** Regular pentagon

Study Skills (p. 122)

1. It illustrates the classifications of quadrilaterals according to the number of pairs of parallel sides, the number of sides of equal length, and the number of right angles.

2. Answers will vary. Sample Response:

Angle Name	Measure
Acute	greater than 0°, less than 90°
Right	90°
Obtuse	Greater than 90°, less than 180°
Straight	180°

Review & Assessment (pp. 126–127)

1. $\frac{18}{75}$ or $\frac{6}{25}$ **2.** $\frac{37}{75}$ **3.** $\frac{0}{75}$ or 0
4. probability of rolling a 2 $= \frac{1}{4}$

probability of rolling an even number $= \frac{1}{2}$

probability of rolling a number greater than 4 $= 0$

5. Answers will vary. Possible answers are shown. Each path represents a path of 5 blocks to get home.

Original path:

Possible paths home:

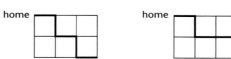

6. a. 36 squares **b.** Sample: Make a table and notice that the sequence of perimeters increases by 4 while the number of squares is the sequence of triangular numbers.

term number	1	2	3	4	5	6	7	8
number of squares	1	3	6	10	15	21	28	36
perimeter	4	8	12	16	20	24	28	32

So for any perimeter, divide the perimeter by 4 and find the corresponding triangular number. For example, for a perimeter of 24, divide 24 by 4 and find the 6th triangular number, 21.

7. Answers will vary. Sample Response:

8. Not possible; the angles in an equilateral triangle all have the same measure. But if a triangle had two right angles, it would have two parallel sides, which is impossible.

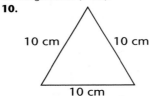

9. Not possible since the sum of the lengths of the two shortest sides (4 cm) is not greater than the length of the longest side (7 cm).

10.

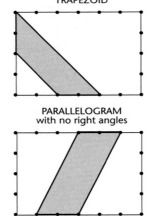
10 cm   10 cm
10 cm

11. $\angle ADB$ **12.** $\overrightarrow{GF}$ **13.** $\overrightarrow{DB}$ **14.** $\overleftrightarrow{GH} \perp \overleftrightarrow{FE}$ **15.** $\angle ADF$ **16.** $\angle CDB$ **17.** $\overleftrightarrow{GH}$ **18.** H **19.** $\overleftrightarrow{GH} \parallel \overleftrightarrow{AC}$

20. Answers will vary. Sample responses are given.

TRAPEZOID

PARALLELOGRAM
with no right angles

SQUARE

RHOMBUS
with no right angles

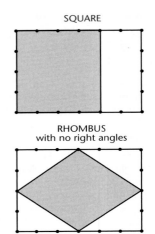

21. green and yellow vegetables, sweet potatoes, butter, liver, fish liver, milk, eggs, and oils **22.** 4 (fish liver, milk, eggs, and oils) **23.** Nuts and citrus fruits are not sources of either vitamin A or vitamin D, so they are not in either set. **24.** Estimates will vary.

25. a.   **b.**

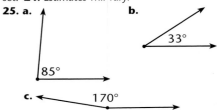
85°   33°

c. ← 170°

MODULE 3

Section 1, Practice and Application (p. 135)
1. tens **3.** tenths **5.** thousandths **7.** eight and three tenths, $\frac{83}{10}$ or $8\frac{3}{10}$ **9.** one and two thousandths, $\frac{1002}{1000}$ or $1\frac{2}{1000}$ **11.** 0.03 **13.** 0.0205 **15. a.** dime **b.** penny **17.** Show that 40 pennies is equal in value to 4 dimes. **19.** $\frac{1}{10}$ **21.** 0.03, 0.16, 0.3, 0.51 **23.** 0.008, 0.105, 0.17, 0.717 **25.** < **27.** >

Spiral Review (p. 136)
30. about $20 **31.** about $123 **32.** about $9
33. line, $\overleftrightarrow{AB}$ or $\overleftrightarrow{BA}$ **34.** segment, $\overline{CD}$ or $\overline{DC}$
35. ray, $\overrightarrow{FE}$ **36.** regular pentagon; All angles are equal in measure and the five sides are the same length.
37. parallelogram; Opposite sides are parallel and equal in length. **38.** trapezoid; It has exactly one pair of parallel sides.

Extra Skill Practice (p. 137)
1. thousandths **3.** tenths **5.** ones **7.** tenths
9. 0.2, $\frac{2}{10}$ **11.** 4000.6, $\frac{40006}{10}$ or $4000\frac{6}{10}$
13. 356.40, $\frac{35640}{100}$ or $356\frac{40}{100}$ **15.** twenty-six thousandths **17.** ten and two hundred five thousandths **19.** one and four thousandths **21.** eleven and one hundred thousandths **23.** > **25.** > **27.** < **29.** 0.123, 1.233, 12.3, 123.1, 124 **31.** 7.0652, 7.526, 75.024, 75.24

Standardized Testing (p. 137)
1. D **2.** B

Section 2, Practice and Application (p. 143)
1. 13.841 **3.** 78.91 **5.** 20.692 **7.** $9.51 **9.** 0.63, 0.74, 0.85 **11.** 0.75 + 0.25 = 1; 2 + 3 + 1 = 6 **13.** 0.35 + 0.65 = 1; 1 + 5 + 2 + 1 = 9; 9 + 0.8 = 9.8 **15.** 3.138 + 0.002 = 3.140; 3.140 + 0.045 = 3.185; 3.185 − 0.002 = 3.183
17. a. 7.7 **b.** one decimal place; since 7.700 = 7.7, the calculator does not display the additional zeros.
19. 29.27 **21.** 2.2 **23.** 0.0046 **25.** 2 **27.** It appears that the whole numbers were subtracted and the decimal parts were added. The correct answer is 4.259.
29. The problem solved was 11.689 − 0.689. The correct answer is 116.201. **31.** Difference 0.017; No, 0.017 > 0.005 **33.** Difference 0.221; No, 0.221 > 0.205

Spiral Review (p. 146)
38. one and twelve hundredths **39.** eight hundred three thousandths **40.** three and four tenths
41. fifty and twenty-eight hundredths **42.** 69 or 87
43. 8 • 5 = 40; 40 ÷ 8 = 5; 40 ÷ 5 = 8 **44.** 6 • 7 = 42; 7 • 6 = 42; 42 ÷ 7 = 6; 42 ÷ 6 = 7 **45.** 18 ÷ 9 = 2; 18 ÷ 2 = 9; 9 • 2 = 18; 2 • 9 = 18

Extension (p. 146)
47. 0.00001, 0.00009, 0.00015, 0.0008, 1.00002
49. 0.99993

Extra Skill Practice (p. 147)
1. 21.46 **3.** 51.423 **5.** 245.97 **7.** 31.617 **9.** 0.075
11. 33.959 **13.** 0.77 **15.** 34.72 **17.** 71.685
19. 141.886 **21.** 8.5 **23.** 71.08 **25.** 34.196
27. $33.10 **29.** 6.4, 6.9, 7.5 **31.** 1.42, 1.52, 1.62

Standardized Testing (p. 147)
The first three terms of the sequence of payments are $0.10, $0.20, and $0.40. Jim interprets this as a sequence in which each term is twice that of the previous term. Jim's dad intends it to be a sequence in which the increase from term to term goes up by an additional $0.10 each time. The payments in dollars for each plan are shown in the table.

Time mowed	1	2	3	4	5
Pay: Jim's plan	0.10	0.20	0.40	0.80	1.60
Pay: Dad's plan	0.10	0.20	0.40	0.70	1.10

Time mowed	6	7	8	9	10
Pay: Jim's plan	3.20	6.40	12.80	25.60	51.20
Pay: Dad's plan	1.60	2.20	2.90	3.70	4.60

Section 3, Practice and Application (p. 147)
1. 2, 3 **3.** none **5.** 2, 3 **7.** 3 **9. a.** Yes, 9 is a multiple of 3. **b.** Sometimes, but not all multiples of 3 are a multiple of 9. **11.** 1, 3, 17, 51 **13.** 1, 2, 3, 4, 6, 8, 9, 12, 18, 24, 36, 72 **15.** 14 **17.** 3 **19.** 18 **21.** $\frac{3}{8}$ **23.** $\frac{2}{3}$
25. 25 • 48 = 25 • 4 • 12 = 100 • 12 = 1200
27. 16 • 125 = 4 • 4 • 5 • 25 = 4 • 5 • 4 • 25 = 20 • 100 = 2000 **29. a.** common factors of 18, 90, and 48 or 1, 2, 3, and 6.
b.   Endangered Plant Species
Namibia |❋ ❋ ❋
Portugal |❋ ❋ ❋ ❋ ❋ ❋ ❋ ❋ ❋ ❋ ❋ ❋ ❋
Sicily |❋ ❋ ❋ ❋ ❋ ❋ ❋
           Key: ❋ = 6 species
31. composite **33.** composite **35.** composite
37. 2 • 3 • 7 **39.** 53 **41.** $2^2 \cdot 11^2$ **43. a.** Prime factorization of each number is in a box with the common factors in the overlapping region. **b.** The GCF is the product of the numbers in the overlapping region.
GCF = 2 • 2 = 4. **c.**

$$\boxed{2 \cdot 2 \cdot \boxed{2 \cdot 3} \cdot 5}$$

GCF = 2 • 3 = 6
45. 2401 **47.** 216 **49.** $2^3 \cdot 3^2 \cdot 5^2$ **51.** 2^3

53. 5^3 **55.** 3^{15} **57.** equal **59. a.** Answers will vary. Sample Response:

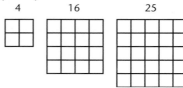

b. $9 = 3^2$; $4 = 2^2$; $16 = 4^2$; $25 = 5^2$; Yes; Each square number can be represented by a square made with that number of square tiles. Since the number of tiles in the square equals the length of the square times its width, and since the length and width are equal, the square number equals the length of a side of the square raised to the 2nd power.

Spiral Review (p. 162)

62. $\frac{1}{10}$; 0 **63.** Possible. **64.** No; $3 + 2 = 5 < 6$
65. Yes; $4 + 22 = 26 > 25$ **66.** $t = 3 + n$ **67.** $t = 4 \cdot n$
68. $t = 3 \cdot n + 2$ **69.** $t = n^3$ **70.** (66) 4, 5, 6, 7;
(67) 4, 8, 12, 16; (68) 5, 8, 11, 14; (69) 1, 8, 27, 64

Extra Skill Practice (p. 163)

1. 2 **3.** 2, 3 **5.** 3 **7.** 1 **9.** 9 **11.** 8 **13.** $\frac{8}{15}$ **15.** $\frac{5}{7}$
17. composite **19.** composite **21.** $3^2 \cdot 2$ **23.** 3^3
25. $2^2 \cdot 5^2$ **27.** 343 **29.** 256 **31.** <; $8 < 9$ **33.** >;
$81 > 64$ **35.** $2^2 \cdot 3 \cdot 5^2$ **37.** 2^8 **39.** 5^2 **41.** 10^3
43. 11^2

Standardized Testing (p. 163)
1. a. Sample: 20, 40, 60, 80, 100, 120, 140, 160, 180, 200 **b.** Sample: The last digit must be zero, the other digits must represent an even number. **2. a.** $2 \cdot 5$; $2^2 \cdot 5^2$; $2^3 \cdot 5^3$ **b.** $2^8 \cdot 5^8$

Section 4, Practice and Application (p. 169)
1. 7, 14, 21, 28, 35, 42, 49 **3.** 99, 198, 297, 396, 495, 594, 693 **5.** 8, 16, 24, 32, 40, 48, 56 **7.** a, c, d
9. 70 **11.** 80 **13.** 48 **15.** 105 **17. a.** 24 seconds
b. 24 seconds

Spiral Review (p. 170)
21. 1 **22.** 40 **23.** 2 **24.** $3\frac{1}{4}$ **25.** $5\frac{3}{5}$ **26.** $3\frac{5}{8}$
27. a. $\frac{1}{2}, \frac{1}{4}, \frac{1}{8}, \frac{1}{16}$ **b.** triangle, quadrilateral, trapezoid, rhombus, pentagon, hexagon, heptagon, octagon

Extra Skill Practice (p. 171)
1. 4, 8, 12, 16, 20, 24, 28 **3.** 33, 66, 99, 132, 165, 198, 231 **5.** 27 **7.** 150 **9.** 120 **11.** 30, 60, 90

Standardized Testing (p. 171)
1. B **2.** A **3.** C

Section 5, Practice and Application (p. 179)
1. a. $\frac{5}{24}$ **b.** $\frac{5}{24}$ **c.** They are the same. **3.** $\frac{10}{27}$ **5.** $\frac{1}{144}$ **7.** $\frac{3}{8}$
9. $\frac{4}{7}$ **11.** No, the farmer multiplied $\frac{1}{3} \cdot \frac{1}{5}$, but it is really $\frac{1}{3} \cdot \frac{4}{5}$ since $\frac{1}{3}$ of the remaining $\frac{4}{5}$ was eaten by insects. So, $\frac{4}{15}$ of the entire crop was eaten by insects. **15.** $\frac{1}{64}$
17. 7 **19.** 10 **21.** 49 **23.** $4\frac{1}{3}$ **25.** $2\frac{14}{15}$ **27.** $\frac{3}{8}$ **29. a.** $\frac{1}{3}$
b. $\frac{7}{12}$ cup **c.** $4\frac{3}{8}$ cups **31.** greater than **33.** less than

Spiral Review (p. 182)
36. $2^2 \cdot 11$ **37.** 5^3 **38.** $2^3 \cdot 7$ **39.** $13 \cdot 3^2$
40. about $4000 **41.** about $120 **42.** about $52
43. 3.759 **44.** 2.65 **45.** 17.345

Extension (p. 182)

47. $\dfrac{\overset{1}{\cancel{8}} \cdot \overset{1}{\cancel{4}}}{3 \; \underset{3}{\cancel{12} \cdot \cancel{15}}} = \dfrac{1}{9}$; Sample: Dividing by a common factor before multiplying is easier because you don't have to multiply larger factors such as $12 \cdot 15$, or reduce the answer to lowest terms after multiplying.

Extra Skill Practice (p. 183)
1. $\frac{1}{3}$ **3.** $\frac{1}{10}$ **5.** $\frac{7}{15}$ **7.** $\frac{7}{18}$ **9. a.** $\frac{2}{15}$ **b.** $\frac{6}{15}$ or $\frac{2}{5}$ **11.** $12\frac{4}{5}$
13. $\frac{15}{16}$ **15.** $11\frac{23}{27}$

Standardized Testing (p. 183)
$8\frac{1}{3}$ cups of apple juice

Section 6, Practice and Application (p. 190)
1. 53.55 **3.** 1.029 **5.** 0.036; $0.3 \cdot 0.1 = 0.03$
7. 4.68; $8 \cdot 0.6 = 4.8$ **9.** 8.928 **13.** 0.67 **15.** 2.635
17. about $510 **19.** Less than; N is multiplied by a number less than 1. **21.** Greater than; N is multiplied by a number greater than 1.

Spiral Review (p. 192)
26. $\frac{3}{32}$ **27.** $\frac{2}{15}$ **28.** $\frac{1}{3}$ **29.** A rhombus that is not a square. **30.** a trapezoid **31.** 16 **32.** 92 **33.** 32

Extra Skill Practice (p. 193)
1. 198.74 **3.** 0.092 **5.** 2.76 **7.** 5.34 **9.** 8.37 **11.** 2.349
13. 0.0504 **15.** 0.75 **17.** 0.35; $100 \cdot 0.35 = 35$
19. 6.31; $28 \cdot 6 = 168$ and $28 \cdot 7 = 196$

Standardized Testing (p. 193)
1. Sample: Sam bought 2.5 lb of fish at $8.99 per pound. How much did Sam pay for the fish?
2. Sample: 0.75 (Any number between 0.5 and 1 is an acceptable answer.) **3.** Sample: $0.5 \cdot 0.1 = 0.05$

Review & Assessment (pp. 196–197)

1. six and fifty-six hundredths **2.** seven ten-thousandths
3. one thousand two hundred eight and three tenths
4. thirty-five and one tenth **5.** one hundred twenty-three thousandths **6.** twenty-five thousand one and five hundredths **7.** five hundred twenty-one and sixty-three hundredths **8.** one and twenty-two thousandths
9. six hundred and seven hundredths **10.** < **11.** <
12. = **13.** > **14.** < **15.** = **16.** 500.92 **17.** 11
18. 6.103 **19.** 15.17 **20.** 2.212 **21.** 5.217
22. a. Max $3.85, Rachel $1.51, Alisha $2.98 **b.** $8.34
23. 0, 2, 4, 6, 8 **24.** 0, 5 **25.** 0, 3, 6, 9 **26.** 3 **27.** No; he missed 6 × 18; Sample Response: I tried all the factors from 1 to 11 and checked for each matching factor so that the pairs produce a product of 108. **28.** 12
29. 1 **30.** 26 **31.** composite **32.** composite **33.** prime
34. composite **35.** >; 32 > 25 **36.** =; 4 • 4 • 4 = (2 • 2) • (2 • 2) • (2 • 2) = 64 **37.** <; $3^3 < 3^4$
38. 2^5 **39.** 97 **40.** $2^2 • 3 • 5^2$ **41.** 3 • 7 • 11
42. Sunday **43.** $\frac{1}{10}$ **44.** $\frac{10}{21}$ **45.** $\frac{5}{18}$ **46.** $\frac{3}{8}$ **47.** $\frac{45}{4}$ or $11\frac{1}{4}$ **48.** $\frac{50}{6}$ or $8\frac{1}{3}$ **49.** $\frac{13}{24}$ **50.** $\frac{29}{10}$ or $2\frac{9}{10}$ **51.** 7 **52.** 34
53. 16 **54.** 26 **55.** 0.128 **56.** 1851.3 **57.** 0.0282

MODULE 4

Section 1, Practice and Application (p. 209)
1. a. The bear is an omnivore. **b.** The bear eats both meat and plants. **c.** If a bear is an omnivore and eats both meat and plants, then an omnivore eats both meat and plants. **3.** Horse and pronghorn antelope; Set F
5. a. Cheetah, Lion, Gray wolf, Coyote, Jaguar **b.** The animals in Set D are carnivores that have a maximum speed greater than or equal to 60 km/hr. **7. a.** meat
b. Answers will vary. Sample Response: Yes. Carnivores use speed to catch other animals. **9.** Nearest millimeter; measuring to the smaller unit provides a more exact measurement. **11.** millimeter **13.** 7 m **15.** 1 mm
17. gram or kilogram **19.** 15 kg **21.** 0.5 g
23. a. 25–30 mm **b.** 2.5–3.0 cm **29.** 0.0034 **31.** 0.07
33. 0.0001 **35.** 650 **37.** 2.54 or 2.540 **39.** 720
41. Spectacled Bear; Thomson's Gazelle (It is possible for human infants to survive at birth weights as low as those of an infant lion or gorilla.) **43.** > **45.** >

Spiral Review (p. 212)
47. a. 8 **b.** 7 **c.** 20 **48.** 7 **49.** 12 **50.** They were found in both Alberta and Colorado. **51. a.** inside rectangles, but outside rhombuses **b.** inside rhombuses, but outside rectangles **c.** inside the overlap area of rectangles and rhombuses **d.** outside of rectangles and rhombuses, but inside quadrilaterals

Extra Skill Practice (p. 213)
1. Vampire Bat, Pika, Koala, Gorilla, Guinea Pig, Orangutan; Set C **3.** 3 **5.** Set C; chimpanzees live on land and do not have tails **7.** 0.0025 **9.** 348 **11.** 2.93 or 2.930 **13.** 400

Study Skills (p. 213)
1. The example on page 204 shows how to use decimals to record measurements. The example on page 207 shows how to convert a measurement from millimeters to meters. **2. a.** empty set, benchmark, kilometer, meter, centimeter, millimeter, metric ton, kilogram, gram, milligram **b.** Answers will vary. Sample Response: A set with no objects is an empty set.

Section 2, Practice and Application (p. 226)
1. Range: 90 – 72 = 18 **3.** 79 in. and 80 in.
5. a. Range = 5 **b.**

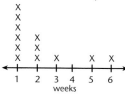

Time Fish Was Kept
weeks

7. Yes; 6 years **9.** Answers vary. Sample Response: They are spread out over a wide range. **11.** Mean = 7; Median = 5; Modes = 5 and 12 **13.** Mean =20; Median = 20; No mode **19. a.** The mode **b.** No; The mode implies Thom will probably get an A. The mean (about 82) and the median (80) are better descriptions of his scores. The teacher will probably use the mean.
21. 0.73 **23.** 0.83 **25.** 1.13 **27.** 1.75
29.

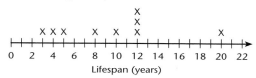

31. 0.396 **33.** 4.3 **35.** 102.34

Spiral Review (p. 229)
38. Royal Albatross; arctic tern **39.** about 225 cm
40. about 20 cm **41.** $\frac{1}{2}$ **42.** $\frac{19}{10}$ **43.** $\frac{3}{4}$ **44.** $\frac{1}{25}$ **45.** 5
46. 53 **47.** 57

Extra Skill Practice (p. 230)
1. Average Lifespans of Selected Animals

Lifespan (years)

3. 5 **5.** Sample Response: Median, because that is about the center of where the data are clustered and the mean is affected by the extreme (20). **7.** Mean = 4; Median = 4; Mode = 4 **9.** Mean = 345; Median = 283.5; no mode

Selected Answers SA9

11. 12.46 **13.** 367.13 **15.** 0.19 **17.** 1.33 **19.** 0.81

Standardized Testing (p. 230)
Answers will vary. Sample Response: 2 2 3 6 7

Section 3, Practice and Application (p. 241)
1. incorrect; $800 \div 4 = 200$; 195.8 **3.** incorrect; $21 \div 7 = 3$; 3.02 **5.** 0.08; $0.6 \div 6 = 0.1$ **7.** 1.09; $12 \div 12 = 1$
9. 9.325; $36 \div 4 = 9$ **11.** 1.3075 cm **13.** 0.875
15. 1.8 **17.** $x + 4 = 8$

21.
$x = 2$

23.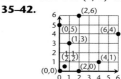
$x = 6$

25. $1973 + y = 1979$ **27.** $m + 2 = 20$; m = number of
existing members **29.** $m + 3 = 17$; m = number of
medals Alice had before **31.** $B - 5.75 = 4.25$;
B = amount of money John had originally **33.** $a = 28$
35. $q = 63$ **37.** $b = 43$ **39.** $x = 1.74$ **41.** $n = 4.5$
43. $n = 3.94$ **45.** no, $0.2 + 6 = 6.2$, not 8 **47.** $B - 165 = 357.49$; B = balance before the withdrawal; $522.49
49. $1450.24 + I = 1453.95$; I = interest; $3.71
51. $a = 44.8$; paper and pencil **53.** $y = 291$; paper and
pencil **55.** $s = 5$; mental math

Spiral Review (p. 244)
58. 64 **59.** 13.40 **60.** 3.0 **61.** 0.361 **62.** $2 + 6 > 7$; yes
63. $5 + 3 = 8$; no **64.** $2 + 13 < 35$; no **65.** $0.4 + 0.7 > 1$; yes **66.** 21 **67.** 72 **68.** 21 **69.** $\frac{21}{45} = \frac{7}{15}$
70. $\frac{3}{2} = 1\frac{1}{2}$ **71.** $\frac{99}{32} = 3\frac{3}{32}$ **72.** 3, 5 **73.** 2, 3, 5, 9, 10
74. none **75.** 5 **76.** 16 **77.** 11.5 **78. a.** 12 hours
b. Answers will vary; Sample Response: make a table,
guess and check

Extension (p. 245)
79. Remove one [+] tile from each side of the
equation. **81.** Remove two [+] tiles from each side
of the equation. **83.** $n = 1$, check $1 + 1 \overset{?}{=} 2 \cdot 1$, $2 = 2$;
$n = 4$, check $4 + 6 \overset{?}{=} 2 + 2 \cdot 4$, $10 = 10$; $n = 3$, check
$2 \cdot 3 + 3 \overset{?}{=} 3 \cdot 3$, $9 = 9$; $n = 2$, check $2 + 5 \overset{?}{=} 3 + 2 \cdot 2$,
$7 = 7$

Extra Skill Practice (p. 246)
1. 0.09; $0.5 \div 5 = 0.1$ **3.** 3.115; $12 \div 4 = 3$ **5.** 3.454;
$27 \div 9 = 3$ **7.** no, 7.22 **9.** correct **11.** $6 = 1 + n$
13. $53 + b = 85$; b = number of apples Jill's brother
picked **15.** $q = 50$

Standardized Testing (p. 246)
1. B **2.** D

Section 4, Practice and Application (p. 257)
1. 62; 100 **3.** Mean = 84, Median = 86, Mode = 86
5. They represent the integers in the tens place between
the least value and the greatest value in the table. The
0 is included to represent the digit in the tens place of a
one-digit number.

7.   Meat Consumption by Small and
         Medium-Sized Predatory Dinosaurs

0	4
1	9
2	1 1 6 7
3	
4	6 7 8

4 | 8 means 4.8 kg per day

9. 30 years; Answers may vary. Sample Response: The
bar graph because it is easy to see the tallest bar
11. Gray Wolf; Sample Response: The bar graph
because the stem-and-leaf plot doesn't identify individual animals **13.** 15.9 years; Sample Response: The
stem-and-leaf plot because the numbers would have to
be estimated from the bar graph **15.** 60 **17.** 2.8
19. 18.75 **21.** 285.5 **23.** 0.902 **25. a.** $36 \times 0.12 = 4.32$; yes it is correct **b.** $1.2 \times 0.05 = 0.06$; it is incorrect
c. $50 \times 0.003 = 0.15$; it is incorrect **27.** 6.25 lb
29. 5.4 min **31.** (1, 5) **33.** (8, 26)
35–42.

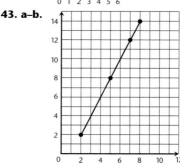

c. 7, 6 **d.** (2, 2), (5, 8), (7, 12), (8, 14); Sample
Response: For every increase of 1 in the input, the output increases by 2. To find the output for $4\frac{1}{2}$, notice that
$4\frac{1}{2} - 2 = 2\frac{1}{2}$ and $2\frac{1}{2} \cdot 2 = 5$; $2 + 5 = 7$.

43. a–b.

45. a–b. **c.** square

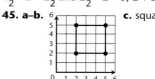

47. a. $2 \cdot t$ **b.** $3 \cdot p$ **c.** $4 \cdot q$ **d.** $2 \cdot t + 3 \cdot p + 4 \cdot q$

49. a. Sample Response:

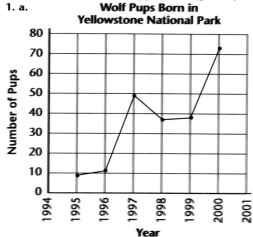

Length of a side (cm)	Area (cm^2)	Perimeter (cm)
1	1	4
2	4	8
3	9	12
4	16	16

b. Let s = the length of a side and A = the area. $A = s^2$
c. Let s = the length of a side and P = the perimeter. $P = 4 \cdot s$

Spiral Review (p. 262)
52. 0.09 **53.** 5.27184 **54.** 9.423 **55.** 3 quarters and 4 dimes **56.** $\frac{13}{8}$; $1\frac{5}{8}$

57. range: 145

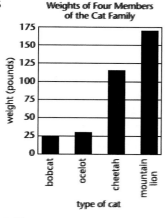

Weights of Four Members of the Cat Family

Extension (p. 262)
59. men: mean: 10.1; median: 10.0; modes: 9.9, 10.0, and 10.1; women: mean: 11.1, median: 11.1; mode: 11.1 **61.** Sample Response: Because the plots line up according to stems, you can easily compare the data. For example, it is clear that the median for the men's winning times is lower than the median for the women's winning times and that more men than women had winning times between 10 sec and 11 sec.

Extra Skill Practice (p. 263)
1. 77 **3.** 2 tests **5.** 70 **7.** 3.4 **9.** 29.35 **11.** 5.7
13. G **15.** A **17.** (5, 0) **19. a.** $t = 18 \cdot x$ where t = number of T-shirts made and x = hours a machine runs **b.** 4 hr: 72 T-shirts; 20 hr: 360 T-shirts

Standardized Testing (p. 263)
Sample Response: The product of the divisor and the quotient equals the dividend. Because the divisor is between 0 and 1, the product of the divisor and the quotient is less than the quotient, and therefore the quotient is greater than the dividend. For example, $12 \div 0.5 = 24$, and you can see that the quotient, 24, is greater than the dividend, 12.

Section 5, Practice and Application (p. 271)
1. a.

Wolf Pups Born in Yellowstone National Park

[Line graph with vertical axis "Number of Pups" ranging 0 to 80 in increments of 10, horizontal axis "Year" from 1994 to 2001. Data points: 1995 ≈ 8, 1996 ≈ 11, 1997 ≈ 49, 1998 ≈ 37, 1999 ≈ 38, 2000 ≈ 72]

b. Sample Response: The number of pups born increased slightly from 1995 to 1996 and then made a big jump from 1996 to 1997. From 1997 to 1998, the number of pups born decreased by about 12 pups and then increased slightly the next year. The number increased rapidly from 1999 to 2000. **3. a.** Florida **b.** Estimates will vary. Sample responses are given. Alaska: about 26, California: about 45, Florida: about 47, Kentucky: about 40, Vermont: about 30; Florida **5.** Sample responses are given. **a.** No, graph 1 appears to show this relationship, but in graph 2 the bar for public transit and carpoolers is about one-fifth of the bar for those that drive alone. **c.** Graph 1; The bars for commuters who carpool or use public transit are longer than the corresponding bars in graph 2 and in comparison to the bars for commuters who drive alone. **d.** On graph 1, the vertical scale goes from 0 to 100 in increments of 10. On graph 2, the vertical scale goes from 20 to 70 in increments of 5. **7.** Stem-and-leaf plot (A bar graph would get too crowded for more than 10 contestants) **9.** Bar graph; a double bar graph can show the difference between male and female numbers. **11.** Sample Response: The median; There is no mode and the mean will be affected by extreme data values. **13.** Sample Response: The median; The mean is affected by the extreme values 52 and 61. The mode could be used, but the mode usually is only used with categorical data.

15. mode; The data are categorical. **17.** mean; The mode has to be a whole number. The median has to be a whole number or the mean of two whole numbers, which would have a 5 in the tenths place.

Spiral Review (p. 274)

19. $\overline{WT}$, $\overline{TW}$ **20.** $\overrightarrow{CA}$, A ray must be named with its endpoint first. **21.** $\angle PAY$, $\angle YAP$, or $\angle A$ **22. a.** $\frac{2}{6}$ or $\frac{1}{3}$ **b.** $\frac{0}{6}$ or 0 **c.** $\frac{4}{6}$ or $\frac{2}{3}$ **d.** $\frac{5}{6}$ **23.** $2 \cdot 2 \cdot 3 \cdot 7$

Extra Skill Practice (p. 275)
1. The number of grizzlies being removed was on the rise in the late 60's and early 70's. Then the number dropped drastically after 1972. **3.** Answers will vary. **5.** Answers will vary. Before 1972: mean = 6.25, mode = 3, and median = 5.5; After 1972 the mean, mode and median are all 2.

Standardized Testing (p. 275)
1. median; It is 200 and fairly represents four of the five data values. There is no mode and the mean is affected by the large number of elephants in Laos. **2.** mean; The extreme data value for Laos gives a mean of about 341 elephants. Without that data value the mean for the four countries is about 189.

Review & Assessment (pp. 278–279)
1. 8000 **2.** 23 **3.** 1.3 **4.** 2300 **5.** 500 **6.** 4000 **7.** 42
8. Maximum Speed of Some Yellowstone Park Mammals

speed (mi/hr)

9. 4 animals **10.** yes, clusters appear from 6 to 15 mi/hr, 30 to 35 mi/hr, and 42 to 48 mi/hr. There is a large gap from 16 to 29. **11. a.** approximately 30–35 mi/hr **b.** approximately 6–15 mi/hr
12. modes = 30 and 35, median = 32.5, mean ≈ 29.1
13. Answers will vary. Sample Response: The median since the data are grouped in three clusters and the median falls in the middle of the middle cluster. There is a large gap between the lower cluster and the rest of the data, and this affects the mean. Since there are two modes, the mode is not an appropriate average to use for the data. **14.** 3.505 **15.** 19.705 **16.** 0.7
17. Sample: $b + 45 = 315$; b = number of baseball cards Jon had before the purchase. **18.** $d = 51$ **19.** $f = 22$
20. $k = 4.7$ **21.** $s = 5.55$ **22.** $x = 7.9$ **23.** $w = 21$
24. 1181.1 **25.** 0.97888 **26.** 1.224 **27.** 91 cm
28. 30 cm **29.** median: 79.5 cm; modes: 77 cm and 86 cm

30. a–b.

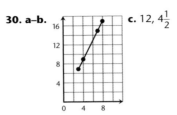

c. 12, $4\frac{1}{2}$

31. Graph 2 is easier to read. It clearly shows that there were two years (1983 and 1988) when cereal production was less than 1.8 billion metric tons and two years (1985 and 1986) when production was greater than 1.8 billion metric tons. So the median is the mean of the production in 1984 and 1987 which appears to be about 1.8 billion metric tons. **32.** Graph 1; The line appears almost flat, indicating very little change.
33. The scale on the vertical axis was changed so it started at 1600 (instead of 0) and was divided into increments of 50 (instead of 350).

MODULE 5

Section 1, Practice and Application (p. 291)
1. No; The sections of the strip are not equal in length. **3.** $\frac{2}{4} = \frac{1}{2}$ **5.** $\frac{5}{12} < \frac{1}{2}$ **7.** $\frac{2}{3}, \frac{9}{10}, \frac{49}{50}, \frac{99}{100}$ **9.** > **11.** > **13.** > **17.** < **19.** > **21.** = **23.** > **25.** > **27.** > **29.** Trinja

Spiral Review (p. 293)

33. $5\frac{1}{2}$ **34.** $2\frac{3}{12}$ **35.** $4\frac{3}{7}$ **36.** $4\frac{1}{3}$
37.
Daily High Temperatures
in a Midwest City in July

```
 5 | 6 9
 6 | 1 4 8 9 9
 7 | 1 2 2 7 7 8 8 8 8
 8 | 0 2 2 2 4 5 5 7 7 9
 9 | 0 1 1 8
10 | 1
```
7 | 1 means 71 degrees Fahrenheit

Extension (p. 293)
39. $\frac{1}{2}$ **41.** $\frac{1}{2}$

Extra Skill Practice (p. 294)
1. > **3.** > **5.** > **7.** > **9.** < **11.** > **13.** < **15.** > **17.** < **19.** < **21.** <

Study Skills (p. 294)
1. Pages 287–288

Section 2, Practice and Application (p. 302)
1. Sample Response: about 6 in. **3.** Sample Response: about 2 ft **5.** Sample Response: an unsharpened pencil

7. Sample Response: the length of my living room
9. feet **11.** inches **13. a.** $1\frac{1}{2}$ in. **b.** $1\frac{2}{4}$ in. **c.** $1\frac{3}{8}$ in.
15. 198 **17.** $4\frac{1}{2}$ **19.** 99 **21.** $\frac{2}{3}$ yd **23.** $\frac{18}{36}$ yd or $\frac{1}{2}$ yd
25. 6 yd 2 ft 1 in. **27.** 1 mi 1198 yd **29.** 1 yd 1 ft 10 in.
31. 7 yd 1 ft

Spiral Review (p. 305)
34. < **35.** < **36.** > **37.** 10 ways. (2 quarters; 1 quarter
2 dimes 1 nickel; 1 quarter 1 dime 3 nickels; 1 quarter
5 nickels; 5 dimes; 4 dimes 2 nickels; 3 dimes 4 nickels;
2 dimes 6 nickels; 1 dime 8 nickels; 10 nickels)

Extra Skill Practice (p. 306)
1. 2 in. **3.** $1\frac{3}{4}$ in. **5.** 27 **7.** $4\frac{1}{6}$ **9.** $\frac{1}{2}$ **11.** $11\frac{1}{4}$
13. 180 **15.** $\frac{2}{3}$ **17.** 5 yd 1 ft 7 in. **19.** 2 ft **21.** 11 yd
2 ft **23.** 1 mi 71 yd **25.** 2 yd 1 in.

Standardized Testing (p. 306)
Sample Response: To measure 1 in., place the longest
strip on top of the midsize strip with the left ends meeting. Mark the right end of the midsize strip on the longest strip. The mark will be 2 in. from the end. Fold the
2 in. strip in half. You now have a 1 in. measure. You can
use it to mark off a 3 in. piece or any combination that
adds to 3 in. to overlap the strips. The total length will
be 3 ft 2 in. + 2 ft 9 in. + 3 ft 4 in. – 3 in. = 3 yd.

Section 3, Practice and Application (p. 313)
1. $\frac{7}{9}$ **3.** $\frac{21}{20} = 1\frac{1}{20}$ **5.** $\frac{7}{9}$ **7.** $\frac{4}{7}$ **9.** $\frac{1}{8}$ **11.** $\frac{7}{45}$ **13. a.** $\frac{3}{2}$ or
$1\frac{1}{2}$ **b.** $\frac{5}{16}$ **c.** $\frac{11}{24}$ **15. a.** Subtract $\frac{1}{3}$ from each side of the
equation. To do this you would need to rewrite $\frac{1}{3}$ as $\frac{7}{21}$
and $\frac{5}{7}$ as $\frac{15}{21}$. **b.** $\frac{8}{21}$

Spiral Review (p. 315)
20. $1\frac{3}{4}$ **21.** 3520 **22.** $5\frac{1}{3}$ **23.** 2 yd 1 ft 6 in.
24. 3 mi 1320 yd 2 ft **25.** 2 yd 2 ft 7 in. **26. a.** 4 **b.** 8
c. 3 **d.** 9 **e.** 1 **27.** 35 **28.** 85 **29.** 49 **30.** 83 **31.** 9
32. 12 **33.** 37 **34.** 153 **35.** 15 **36.** 23

Extra Skill Practice (p. 316)
1. $\frac{7}{15}$ **3.** $\frac{17}{18}$ **5.** $\frac{35}{33} = 1\frac{2}{33}$ **7.** $\frac{11}{13}$ **9.** $\frac{2}{5}$ **11.** $\frac{9}{28}$
13. $\frac{37}{30} = 1\frac{7}{30}$ **15.** $\frac{11}{12}$ **17.** $\frac{7}{6} = 1\frac{1}{6}$ **19.** $\frac{27}{20} = 1\frac{7}{20}$
21. $\frac{139}{126} = 1\frac{13}{126}$ **23.** $\frac{59}{90}$ **25.** $\frac{13}{8} = 1\frac{5}{8}$ **27.** $\frac{7}{12}$

Standardized Testing (p. 316)
1–2. Answers will vary.

Section 4, Practice and Application (p. 325)
1. about 10 **3.** about 5 **5.** $10\frac{1}{6}$ **7.** $8\frac{23}{24}$ **9.** $5\frac{13}{18}$
11. $8\frac{4}{5} + 1\frac{1}{5} = 10$ and $4\frac{3}{8} + 2\frac{5}{8} = 7$; $10 + 7 + 6\frac{1}{3} = 23\frac{1}{3}$

13. a. $3\frac{3}{8}$ is closer to $3\frac{1}{2}$ than to 3. **b.** high; Both numbers were rounded up. **c.** $8\frac{7}{40}$; The sum is lower than the
estimate. **15.** $1\frac{3}{20}$ **17.** $\frac{3}{8}$ **19.** $7\frac{6}{11}$ **21.** $3\frac{2}{3}$; $3\frac{1}{3} + \frac{2}{3} = 4$,
so $3\frac{1}{3} + 3\frac{2}{3} = 7$ **23.** $1\frac{3}{4}$; $1\frac{1}{4} + \frac{3}{4} = 2$, so $1\frac{1}{4} + 1\frac{3}{4} = 3$
25. a. Sharon; $\frac{1}{4}$ in. **b.** $3\frac{1}{8}$ in. **27.** $2\frac{1}{4}$ ft **29.** $1\frac{1}{4}$ in.

Spiral Review (p. 328)
32. $\frac{9}{25}$ **33.** $\frac{1}{12}$ **34.** $\frac{41}{30}$ or $1\frac{11}{30}$ **35.** 0.52 **36.** 0.57
37. 0.63 **38.** $2 \times 3^2 \times 7$ **39.** 2×7^2 **40.** $3^2 \times 17$
41. neither **42.** impossible **43.** certain **44.** 9 **45.** 6
46. 40

Extension (p. 328)
47. a. $4:16 – 1:37 = 3:76 – 1:37 = 2:39$; 2 hr 39 min
b. Sample Response: The regrouping is the same
because I had to change a whole (1 hour) into parts
(60 minutes). The regrouping is different because the
parts (minutes) can be represented by whole numbers.

Extra Skill Practice (p. 329)
1. $8\frac{1}{4}$ **3.** $10\frac{1}{10}$ **5.** $4\frac{7}{60}$ **7.** $2\frac{1}{18}$ **9.** $4\frac{17}{28}$ **11.** $8\frac{11}{18}$
13. $3\frac{1}{4}$ **15.** $2\frac{5}{16}$ **17.** $18\frac{1}{2}$ **19.** $16\frac{5}{6}$ **21.** $\frac{17}{20}$ **23.** $2\frac{43}{45}$

Standardized Testing (p. 329)
1. D **2.** E

Section 5, Practice and Application (p. 340)
1. Answers will vary. **3.** 9 **5.** 2394 **7.** 1,000,000;
1 km = 1000 m, so 1 km^2 = 1 km · 1 km =
1000 m · 1000 m = 1,000,000 m^2 **9.** 20 cm^2
11. 2600 yd^2 **13.** Answers will vary. E: 12.5 cm^2;
F: 3.38 cm^2; G: 5.2 cm^2; H: 5.46 cm^2 **15. d.** Yes; They
represent the area of the same figure. **17.** 120 cm^2
19. $24 = \frac{1}{2} \cdot 8 \cdot h$; 6 ft **21.** $14 = 2 + 3 + 3 + 2 + x$; 4
in. **23.** 4 **25.** 32
27. Sample Response:

Spiral Review (p. 342)
30. 17.7 **31.** $\frac{5}{24}$ **32.** 4.2

33. a.

Input	2	5	6	10
Output	1	7	9	17

b. (2, 1), (5, 7), (6, 9), (10, 17)

Selected Answers SA13

33. c.

d. 2.5

Extension (p. 343)

37. a. 16 cm²; Sample Response: I estimated the average width at about 2 cm and the length at about 8 cm and multiplied. **b.** 40,000 km² **c.** about 64,000 km²

Extra Skill Practice (p. 344)

1. 24,192 **3.** $\frac{2}{3}$ **5.** $40\frac{1}{2}$ **7.** 916.8 mm² **9.** $22\frac{3}{4}$ cm²

11. 80 cm² **13.** $148 = 34 + 34 + 58 + x$; $x = 22$ in.
15. $12.5 = 2.5 \cdot h$; $h = 5$ ft

Study Skills (p. 344)

Section 6, Practice and Application (p. 353)

1. $\frac{1}{10}$ **3.** $\frac{3}{2}$ **5.** 3 **7.** 2 **9.** $13\frac{1}{3}$ **11.** 3 **13.** $1\frac{1}{8}$ **15. a.** 13 pieces **b.** Yes, $\frac{1}{3}$ of a piece **17.** $2\frac{2}{9}$ **19.** $2\frac{1}{6}$ **21.** $1\frac{1}{4}$

23. 9 **25.** 1 **27. a.** $-\frac{15}{16}$ **b.** Monday - 96; Tuesday - 105

29. a. less than; Sample Response: $2 \cdot 6 = 12$ and $\frac{3}{4} > \frac{1}{2}$, so $2 \cdot 6\frac{3}{4} > 13$ **b.** $1\frac{23}{27}$

Spiral Review (p. 355)

32. 21 **33.** $20\frac{2}{5}$ **34.** $1\frac{1}{6}$ **35.** (4, 6) **36.** (1, 3) **37.** (6, 0)
38. 14 **39.** 15 **40.** 5

Extra Skill Practice (p. 356)

1. 6 **3.** $\frac{1}{32}$ **5.** 6 **7.** 9 **9.** $4\frac{1}{2}$ **11.** $3\frac{1}{7}$ **13.** $4\frac{5}{32}$ **15.** $3\frac{3}{5}$
17. $1\frac{1}{2}$ **19.** $9\frac{1}{3}$ **21.** $2\frac{1}{4}$ **23.** $\frac{12}{23}$ **25.** $\frac{1}{20}$ **27.** 16
29. $\frac{9}{16}$

C

Review & Assessment (pp. 360–361)

1. $\frac{3}{100}, \frac{4}{7}, \frac{2}{3}, \frac{5}{3}$ **2.** $\frac{4}{5}, \frac{9}{10}, \frac{19}{20}, \frac{99}{100}$ **3.** $\frac{1}{7}, \frac{1}{4}, \frac{4}{5}, \frac{7}{8}$
4. $\frac{1}{4}, \frac{1}{2}, \frac{2}{3}, \frac{5}{6}$ **5.** $\frac{5}{8} > \frac{7}{12}$ **6.** $\frac{4}{9} > \frac{6}{15}$ **7.** $\frac{11}{16} < \frac{3}{4}$ **8.** $\frac{8}{13} < \frac{2}{3}$
9. $0.73 > 0.69$ **10.** $0.56 < 0.66$ **11.** $0.47 > 0.43$

12. 126 **13.** $2\frac{5}{6}$ **14.** $1\frac{3}{22}$ **15.** $8\frac{2}{3}$ **16.** 63 **17.** 6030

18. $\frac{3}{2}$ or $1\frac{1}{2}$ **19.** $\frac{19}{21}$ **20.** $3\frac{7}{15}$ or $\frac{52}{15}$ **21.** $7\frac{7}{24}$ or $\frac{175}{24}$
22. $9\frac{33}{40}$ or $\frac{393}{40}$ **23.** $6\frac{1}{2}$ or $\frac{13}{2}$ **24.** $\frac{3}{8}$ **25.** $6\frac{1}{15}$ or $\frac{91}{15}$
26. $2\frac{3}{5}$ or $\frac{13}{5}$ **27.** $\frac{13}{24}$ **28.** $2\frac{1}{12}$ or $\frac{25}{12}$ **29.** $\frac{39}{40}$
30. $23\frac{1}{6}$ hours **31.** $6\frac{1}{4}$ **32.** $8\frac{1}{2}$ **33.** $5\frac{15}{16}$ **34.** $1\frac{1}{4}$

35. $1\frac{1}{6}$ mi **36.** rectangle; triangle; parallelogram

37. Answers will vary.
rectangle: base = 4.2 cm
         height = 2.5 cm
         area ≈ 10.5 cm²
triangle: base = 9.2 cm
        height = 2.4 cm
        area ≈ 11.0 cm²
parallelogram: base = 5.3 cm
            height = 3.4 cm
            area ≈ 18.0 cm²

38. $9h = 54$; $h = 6$ ft **39.** $\frac{1}{2} \cdot 5b = 19$; $b = 7.6$ cm
40. $x = 12$ **41.** $m = 18$ **42.** $x = 48$ **43.** $\frac{14}{9}$ or $1\frac{5}{9}$ **44.** 24
45. $\frac{7}{5}$ or $1\frac{2}{5}$ **46.** $\frac{19}{24}$ **47.** $\frac{9}{8}$ or $1\frac{1}{8}$ **48.** $\frac{4}{9}$ **49.** $1\frac{43}{56}$ **50.** $\frac{13}{24}$
51. 10 pieces; $8 \div \frac{3}{4} = \frac{32}{3} = 10\frac{2}{3}$.

MODULE 6

Section 1, Practice and Application (p. 369)
1. yes **3.** no **5.** no **7.** Team B **9. a.** 24 **b.** 6
11. a. 3 to 30 **b.** 20 to 6 **13. a.** 3:1, 3 to 1, $\frac{3}{1}$

b. 27 steps **c.** 4 steps **15.** Sample Response: If you were only one inch tall, you couldn't ride a bike. And climbing into your bed would be a terrifying hike. You never could play basketball, Or safely stroll around the mall. A summer walk would take till fall, If you were one inch tall.

Spiral Review (p. 371)

18. $\frac{48}{5}$ or $9\frac{3}{5}$ **19.** $\frac{7}{6}$ or $1\frac{1}{6}$ **20.** $\frac{112}{5}$ or $22\frac{2}{5}$ **21.** 0.8
22. 0.0524 **23.** 87.2 **24.** 0.027 **25.** 9 **26.** 0.608
27. 3 **28.** 5 **29.** 20

Extra Skill Practice (p. 372)
1. 256 to 120, 256:120, $\frac{256}{120}$ **3.** 37 to 183, 37:183, $\frac{37}{183}$
5. 4 forks, 8 spoons **7.** yes **9.** no **11.** no

Study Skills (p. 372)
1. A ratio is a type of comparison of two numbers or measures. **2.** "8:12" is read "the ratio of 8 to 12."
3. 1 m equals 100 cm or 1000 mm. **4.** The book covers both customary and metric measurement, including length, area, volume, and capacity.

Section 2, Practice and Application (p. 377)
1. Yes **3.** Yes **5.** No **7.** Yes **9.** \$3/hr **11.** 1.5 ft per
step **13.** $3\frac{2}{5}$ pages per min **15.** \$3.80 for 10 pens;
Those pens cost \$.38 apiece, while the other pens cost \$.44 apiece. **17.** 900 mi; 54,000 mi **19.** \$20

Spiral Review (p. 379)
22. 0.83 **23.** 0.52 **24.** 0.73 **25.** 0.72 **26.** mean: 80; median: 80; modes: 80 and 86 **27.** mean: $58\frac{5}{6}$; median: 50; mode: 48

Extra Skill Practice (p. 380)
1. Yes **3.** Yes **5.** 8 km/hr **7.** \$7.50 per book
9. 28 mi/gal **11.** \$5.76 for 12 oranges **13. a.** about 360 mi **b.** about 21,600 mi

Standardized Testing (p. 380)
1. a. warm air **b.** 82 ft/sec **2.** 16,530 ft

Section 3, Practice and Application (p. 390)
1. a. thumb: about 10 cm; neck: about 40 cm; waist: about 80 cm **b.** Collar could be 41 cm and wrist 21 cm. Students should note that shirt openings equal to the measures of Gulliver's neck (40 cm) and wrist (20 cm) would be uncomfortably tight.

41 cm
21 cm

3. 0.78 **5.** 0.29 **7. a.** about 162 cm **b.** about 184 cm
c. No; The estimated heights vary too greatly.
9. $\frac{3}{10}$ **11.** $\frac{3}{5}$ **13. a.** $\frac{4}{5}$ **b.** about 4 ft **c.** about 35 in.
15. a. 88 : 96 **b.** $\frac{9}{10}$ **c.** 69 : 76 **d.** $\frac{9}{10}$ **e.** They are close.
The nice fractions are the same. **f.** 69 : 88 ≈ 0.78,
76 : 96 ≈ 0.79; The ratios are very close.

17. a. Sample graph:
b. about 16 pages
c. about 25 pages

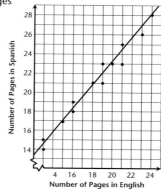

Number of Pages in English Compared to Number of Pages in Spanish

Number of Pages in Spanish (vertical axis)
Number of Pages in English (horizontal axis)

19. a. about 1 ft

Spiral Review (p. 393)
21. 33 mi/gal **22.** about \$2.83 per lb **23.** 53 heart-
beats per min **24.** $\frac{14}{30} = \frac{7}{15}$

Extra Skill Practice (p. 394)
1. a. A: 0.74, B: 0.74, C: 0.74, D: 0.76, E: 0.75, F: 0.74,
G: 0.75, H: 0.73 **b.** about 0.74 **c.** $\frac{3}{4}$
d.

Kneeling height (cm)	94	**99**	**105**	87
Standing height (cm)	**125**	132	140	**116**

Standardized Testing (p. 394)
Answers will vary.

Section 4, Practice and Application (p. 402)
1. $\frac{15}{60}$, $\frac{75}{300}$, and $\frac{3.5}{14}$; $\frac{24}{32}$ and $\frac{21}{28}$ **3.** 20 **5.** 8 **7.** 1.8
9. 12 **11.** 5 **13. b.** $\frac{1 \text{ mi}}{20 \text{ min}} = \frac{3.2 \text{ mi}}{x}$ **c.** 64 min
15. a. $\frac{5}{24}$ **b.** about 13 times **17.** 72 steps

Spiral Review (p. 404)
19. a. $\frac{1}{4}$ **b.** about 15 in. **20.**
21. **22.** **23.**
24.

Extra Skill Practice (p. 405)
1. Yes **3.** No **5.** 48 **7.** 39 **9.** 2 **11.** 4 **13.** \$2.70
15. $6\frac{2}{3}$ yd

Section 5, Practice and Application (p. 414)

1.

$\overline{AC}$	corresponds to	$\overline{FE}$
$\overline{AB}$	corresponds to	$\overline{FD}$
$\overline{CB}$	corresponds to	$\overline{ED}$
$\angle A$	corresponds to	$\angle F$
$\angle B$	corresponds to	$\angle D$
$\angle C$	corresponds to	$\angle E$

3. similar and congruent; Corresponding angles have the same measure and corresponding sides have the same length. **5.** similar but not congruent; Corresponding angles have the same measure and the ratios of the lengths of corresponding sides are equivalent but not 1:1. **7. a.** F **b.** 6:2 or 3:1
9. Sample Responses:

a.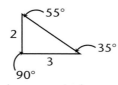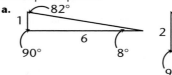

b. These two right triangles only have one pair of congruent angles, the right angles; the ratio of the lengths of the shorter legs is 1:2 and the ratio of the lengths of the longer legs is 2:1. Since the corresponding angles of the triangles are not congruent and the ratios of the lengths of the corresponding sides are not equivalent, the triangles are not similar. **11.** $DE = 2.5$, $DF = 2$
13. 60 ft **15.** 4.5 ft **17. a.** about 1 ft: 16.3 ft
b. about 3.7 ft long and about 2.5 ft wide **19.** 400 mi
21. 240 mi

Spiral Review (p. 417)

23. no **24.** yes **25.** yes **26.** $3\frac{3}{5}$ **27.** 288 **28.** $8\frac{5}{6}$
29. 0.4 **30.** 0.3 **31.** 0.75 **32.** 0.5

Career Connection (p. 417)

33. a. 1 cm = 132 km **b.** about 66 km

Extra Skill Practice (p. 418)

1. similar **3.** 32.4 cm **5.** 48 in. **7.** 80 ft

Standardized Testing (p. 418)

1. The ratio of lengths along the bottoms of the parallelograms is 2 to 4 (or 1 to 2), yet along the sides the ratio is 1 to 3.

2. Sample responses:

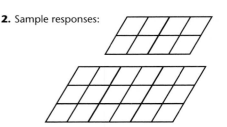

Section 6, Practice and Application (p. 429)

1. a. 1% 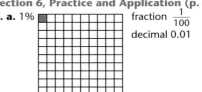 fraction $\frac{1}{100}$ decimal 0.01

b. 10% 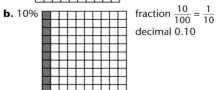 fraction $\frac{10}{100} = \frac{1}{10}$ decimal 0.10

c. 25% 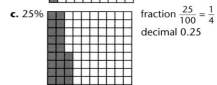 fraction $\frac{25}{100} = \frac{1}{4}$ decimal 0.25

d. 46% 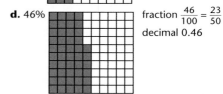 fraction $\frac{46}{100} = \frac{23}{50}$ decimal 0.46

e. 67% 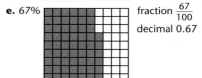 fraction $\frac{67}{100}$ decimal 0.67

f. 100% 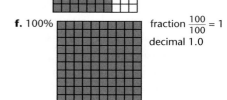 fraction $\frac{100}{100} = 1$ decimal 1.0

3. $\frac{54}{100}$ or $\frac{27}{50}$; 0.54 **5.** $\frac{99}{100}$; 0.99 **7.** $\frac{37}{100}$; 37%
9. $\frac{59}{100}$; 59% **11.** 0.03, 3% **13.** 0.85, 85% **15.** < **17.** >
19. > **21.** 50, 25, 12.5, 12.5 **23.** 21 **25.** 19

SELECTED ANSWERS

27. 31.5 **29.** 90 wins **31.** about 50% **33.** about 90%

Spiral Review (p. 431)
38. ∠A and ∠G, ∠D and ∠F, ∠C and ∠E, ∠B and ∠H;
$\overline{AD}$ and $\overline{GF}$, $\overline{DC}$ and $\overline{FE}$, $\overline{CB}$ and $\overline{EH}$, $\overline{BA}$ and $\overline{HG}$ **39.** B
40. A

Extra Skill Practice (p. 432)
1. 35%, $\frac{35}{100}$ or $\frac{7}{20}$ **3.** 60%, $\frac{60}{100}$ or $\frac{3}{5}$ **5.** 0.07, 7%
7. 0.9, 90% **9.** < **11.** < **13.** = **15.** 18 **17.** 9.1 **19.** 3
21. about $33\frac{1}{3}$% **23.** about 20% **25.** about 40
27. about 45

Standardized Testing (p. 432)
1. B **2.** C **3.** D

Review & Assessment (pp. 436–437)
1. 8 to 6, 8:6, $\frac{8}{6}$ **2.** 6 to 10, 6:10, $\frac{6}{10}$ **3.** no **4.** yes
5. yes
6. a.

Length (feet)	1	2	3	4
Cost (dollars)	6	12	18	24

b. $30
c. 15 ft

7. a.
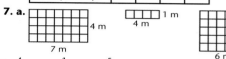

b. $\frac{4}{7} \approx 0.57$, $\frac{1}{4} = 0.25$, $\frac{5}{6} \approx 0.83$ **c.** Sample Response: The closer the decimal is to 1, the closer the rectangle is to a square. **8.** I drew a fitted line for the scatter plot, and I used the line to make my estimates.

Latitude (°N)	25	40	44	57
Temperature (°F)	65	37	25	5

9. x = 15 **10.** y = 6 **11.** z = 126 **12.** 50 m **13.** Not appropriate; It is not reasonable to assume that the ratio of a car's mileage to its speed is always the same.
14. 5 ft **15.** 0.6, 60% **16.** 0.32, 32% **17.** 0.45, 45%
18. 0.69, 69% **19.** 21 **20.** 65 **21.** 24.5 **22.** about 90%
23. a. 25.2% ≈ $\frac{1}{4}$, 17.5% ≈ $\frac{1}{5}$, 5% = $\frac{1}{20}$, 34.8% ≈ $\frac{7}{20}$
b. 17,500 tickets **c.** 18°

MODULE 7

Section 1, Practice and Application (p. 448)
1. No, there are no parallel faces. **3.** Yes; right triangular prism **5.** B **7.** A: right hexagonal prism; C: right square prism (or cube) **9.** Yes; It is a square or rectangular prism. **11.** 6 edges **15.** 12 cm³ **17.** 60 cm³
19. 30 cm³ **21.** $\frac{3}{64}$ in.³ **23.** 0.42 cm³ **25.** The height of a right prism is equal to the length of an edge joining corresponding vertices of the bases; When the prism is oblique. **27.** 20 cm² **29.** top tank holds about 18.7 gal, no; bottom tank holds about 28.1 gal, yes

Spiral Review (p. 450)
33. Area = 14 cm² **34.** $1.60

Extra Skill Practice (p. 451)
1. Yes; Possible responses: rectangles; oblique rectangular prism parallelograms; a right prism with parallelogram shaped bases **3.** Yes; octagons; right octagonal prism **5.** 10,000 m³ **7.** 3 yd **9.** 2268 cm³

Standardized Testing (p. 451)
D

Section 2, Practice and Application (p. 456)
1. ton **3.** pound **5.** Sample: 30 quarters **7.** 6 **9.** 2
11. 11,000 **13.** 2 lb 8 oz **15. a.** (Ex 13) about $4.50,
since 2 lb 8 oz = $2\frac{1}{2}$ lb and $2\frac{1}{2}$ · 1.8 = 4.50;
(Ex 14) about $3.00, since 4 lb 4 oz = $4\frac{1}{4}$ lb and
$4\frac{1}{4}$ · 0.70 ≈ 3.00 **b.** (Ex 13) actual cost: $4.48; (Ex 14)
actual cost: $2.93 **17. a.** 352 oz **b.** $242,880

Spiral Review (p. 458)
20. 4.5 cm **21.** 25 cm² **22.** Sample Response:
2 cm × 15 cm × 2 cm; 6 cm × 2 cm × 5 cm
23. f = 3 · y

Career Connection (p. 458)
25. Yes; She has gained 42 oz in about 42 days.

Extra Skill Practice (p. 459)
1. ounce **3.** ton **5.** ounce or pound **7.** pound **9.** 2
11. 3.5 **13.** $\frac{5}{8}$ **15.** 64,000 **17.** 68 **19.** = **21.** > **23.** >
25. <

Standardized Testing (p. 459)
1. Yes; The total weight is 13,800 lb which is less than 7 tons (14,000 lb). **2.** greatest: 54 oz; least: 9.5 oz; The melon and the soup can weigh 54 oz together. The golf ball and apple weigh 9.5 oz together.

Section 3, Practice and Application (p. 467)
1. $\overline{OA}$, $\overline{OB}$, $\overline{OD}$ **3.** $\overline{AD}$, $\overline{BE}$ **7. a.** a circle with a radius of 100 km (All of the points 100 km from Station 1.)
b. These are the points that are 100 km from Station 1 and 300 km from Station 2, so they are the possible locations for the epicenter. **c.** Use the distance of the epicenter from a third reporting station to draw a third circle. The point of intersection of all 3 circles is the position of the epicenter. **d.** The epicenter of the earthquake was located in the Philippine Islands at approximately 8° N, 127° E. (See Labsheet 3B.) **9.** 15.7 cm **11.** 22 cm
13. 5 mm **15.** $\frac{1}{2}$, $\frac{1}{3}$

Spiral Review (p. 469)

19. $3\frac{3}{8}$ lb **20.** 5500 lb **21.** $2\frac{3}{16}$ lb **22.** 15,000 lb

23. the median; The mean is affected by the score of 38 which is unusually low in comparison to the other scores. There is no mode. **24.** $n = 9$ **25.** $n = 16$
26. $n = 1$ **27.** $n = 3$

Extension (p. 469)
29. Answers will vary.

Extra Skill Practice (p. 470)
1. $\overline{AD}$, $\overline{FC}$ **3.** $\overline{OA}$, $\overline{OF}$, $\overline{OD}$, $\overline{OC}$ **5.** 15.7 cm **7.** 35,482 m
9. 84.97 ft **11.** 3.50 m **13.** 194.68 in. **15.** 28 cm

Standardized Testing (p. 470)
1. C **2.** A

Section 4, Practice and Application (p. 478)
1. 19.63 in.^{2} **3.** 13.85 m^2 **5.** 7.07 in.^{2} **7.** 625π mm^2
9. 21.16π cm^2 **11.** about 153.86 cm^2
15. 452.16 m^3 **17.** 75.36 in.^{3} **19.** 183.12 m^3

Spiral Review (p. 480)
23. 40.82 ft **24.** 37.68 in. **25.** 14.13 m **26.** $\frac{2}{5}$, 0.4
27. $\frac{9}{100}$, 0.09 **28.** $\frac{3}{20}$, 0.15 **29.** $\frac{63}{100}$, 0.63
30–33.

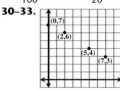

Extension (p. 480)
35. b. 3 cones of rice **37.** 2009.60 cm^3 **39.** 11.78 in.^{3}

Extra Skill Practice (p. 481)
1. 2171.91 mm^2 **3.** 0.79 ft^2 **5.** 600.25π yd^2
7. 137,858.56 ft^3 **9.** 144,691.2 in.^{3} **11.** 22.1 ft^3

Standardized Testing (p. 481)
No; about 63.59 cm^3 more sand is needed.

Section 5, Practice and Application (p. 490)
1. Sample Response: light weight clothing such as long pants and a shirt; tennis, jogging, hiking; It is warm but not hot. **3.** Sample Response: heavy clothing such as a winter coat, hat, scarf, gloves, boots; ice skating, skiing; It is quite cold. **5.** Sample Response: –60°F or –50°C
7. a. The number of degrees is the same. **b.** One is negative and one is positive. **9.** 25°F; 12°F; 30°F
11. –349 **13.** 10 **15.** <. **17.** >
19. Sample Response:

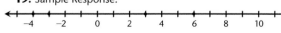

21. –60 **25. b.** Answers will vary.

Spiral Review (p. 492)
28. 28.26 in.^{2} **29.** 200.96 cm^2 **30.** 9.62 m^2
35. Sample Response: I would use estimation. I could round $2.29 up to $2.50 and 1.7 up to 2. Then $2 \cdot \$2.50 = \$5$. Since both numbers are rounded up, I know the estimate is higher than the actual cost and I have enough money.

Extra Skill Practice (p. 493)
1. Sample Response: 41°F or 5°C **3.** Sample Response: 59°F or 15°C **5.** < **7.** < **9.** > **11.** H
12–19.

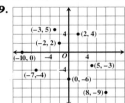

Standardized Testing (p. 493)
1. Sample Response: I would prefer 32°C because it is hot enough to go swimming. **2.** Sample Responses: $x < 0$, $x > -10$

Review & Assessment (pp. 496–497)
1. a. Answers will vary. an oblique pentagonal prism
2. a. two of the faces are pentagons, five are parallelograms of which one is a rectangle **b.** an oblique pentagonal prism **3.** 7 faces, 10 vertices, 15 edges
4. a. area of the pentagonal base = 20 mm · 18 mm + $\frac{1}{2}$ (20 mm · 17 mm) = 530 mm^2, height of the prism = 37 mm **b.** 19,610 mm^3 **5.** The exact volume is 643.5 in.^{3} **6. a.** $.71 per pound **b.** about 9 apples **7.** 48
8. 5 **9.** $1\frac{3}{4}$ **10. a.** O **b.** any two of $\overline{OE}$, $\overline{OB}$, and $\overline{OD}$
c. $\overline{AE}$, $\overline{BE}$ **d.** $\overline{BE}$ **11.** 2.5 cm **12. a.** about 15.7 cm
b. about 19.6 cm^2 **13.** 10,597.5 ft^3 **14.** warmer; 83°F; The difference between 33° below 0 and 50° above 0 on the Fahrenheit scale is 83 degrees. **15.** < **16.** < **17.** >
18. a–b.

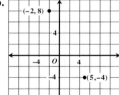

MODULE 8

Section 1, Practice and Application (p. 507)
1. D **3.** C **5.** E **7.** 22 **9.** 5 **11.** 3 **13. a.** 200,000 glasses **b.** 100,000 lb **c.** It would double the number of

glasses to 400,000 and the number of pounds the boat can support to 200,000. **15.** It has grown by more than $1\frac{1}{2}$ cups of soda. **17.** 20 mL, 0.02 L **19.** 1045.5 mL, 1.0455 L **21.** 1.8 **23.** 0.892 **25.** 2500 **27.** 30 L **29.** 250 mL **31.** about 21,000,000,000,000 kL; I estimated the volume in cubic meters by converting the surface area from km² to m² and then multiplying the surface area by the depth. Then I used the fact that a container with volume 1 m³ has a capacity of 1 kL.

Spiral Review (p. 510)
34. 18.4 **35.** 14.7 **36.** 1.08 **37.** 28 **38.** 5.6
39. $2\frac{5}{24}$ **40.** $\frac{29}{50}, \frac{21}{50}$ **41.** about 863.5 in.³ **42.** about 47.1 cm³

Career Connection (p. 510)
43. a. $\frac{3}{4}$ c flour, $\frac{3}{4}$ c whole wheat flour, $\frac{1}{6}$ c butter, $\frac{1}{3}$ c shortening, $\frac{1}{8}$ c water, $\frac{1}{8}$ c cider **b.** $7\frac{1}{4}$ cups

Extra Skill Practice (p. 511)
1. 16 **3.** $\frac{1}{2}$ **5.** $3\frac{1}{2}$ **7.** $1\frac{3}{4}$ **9.** 8 **11.** 4.2 **13.** 0.75
15. 0.628 **17.** 6 fl oz **19.** 2 L **21.** 700 mL

Standardized Testing (p. 511)
greater than 0.01 L

Section 2, Practice and Application (p. 517)
1. 84 **3.** 115 **5.** 78 **7. a.** Sample Response:
$(832 − 1) + (999 + 1) = 831 + 1000 = 1831$ **c.** Add 1000 and subtract 1. (That way you have added 999 to the first volunteer's number.) **9.** about 54 **11.** about 220 **13. a.** $750 **b.** $400 **c.** $1200; $400 • 3 = $1200.

Spiral Review (p. 518)
15. 14.4 **16.** 8 **17.** 28 **18.** $6\frac{1}{4}$ **19.** 6 **20.** $\frac{1}{4}$
21. 3000 **22.** 70 **23.** 2.3 **24.** 115,552 cm³
25. 66,442.4 cm³ **26.** $1\frac{2}{3}$ **27.** $2\frac{4}{9}$ **28.** $\frac{1}{16}$

Extra Skill Practice (p. 519)
1. about 5000 **3.** about 30 **5.** about 11 **7.** about 450
9. 92 **11.** 305 **13.** 152 **15.** 186 **17.** 65.3 **19.** 110

Standardized Testing (p. 519)
1. Sample responses are given. **a.** $3.95 + $4.91 + $5.83 **b.** $3.65 + $4.61 + $5.73 **c.** $3.15 + $4.01 + $5.83 **2. a.** $3.86 + $4.97 + $5.88 **b.** $3.42 + $4.71 + $5.83 **c.** $3.74 + $4.01 + $5.26

Section 3, Practice and Application (p. 528)
1. – 2 **3.** 3 **5.**

7. No; 5 of the tiles would have to total 0 and that is not possible. **9.** – 44 **11.** –15 **13.** –10 **15.** –32

17. a. 1300, 450, 1575 **b.** –300, –1150, –25
19. integers less than 3 **23.** 7 – (–3) = 10
25. 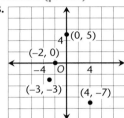 **27.** –12 + (–9) = –21

29. a. 49 – (–54) = 103 **b.** 49 + 54 = 103; The thermometer shows that there are 49 degrees between 49°F and 0°F and there are 54 degrees between 0° and –54°F, for a total of 103 degrees. **31.** 5 **33.** –10 **35.** 17
37. –13 **39.** –38 **41.** 81

Spiral Review (p. 531)
45–48.

49. about 13 **50.** about 4000 **51.** about 2 **52.** about 5
53. about 12 **54.** about 33 **55.** 137 **56.** 423
57. 35,900 **58.** 2 **59.** 2,213 **60.** 7,500,000

Extension (p. 531)
61. –2, –2 **63.** 7, 7 **65.** –9, –9 **67.** Exercises 61–63 include a pair of expressions in which the same addends are added in different orders and the answers are the same. **69.** –10; group –21 with (–9) and 15 with 5 to get –30 + 20 = –10 **71. a.** no **b.** no **c.** Sample Response: part (a): 5 – 7 = –2 and 7 – 5 = 2; part (b): 10 – (8 – 3) = 5 and (10 – 8) – 3 = –1

Extra Skill Practice (p. 532)
1. –17 **3.** –40 **5.** 16 **7.** –26 **9.** –4 **11.** –9 **13.** –4
15. 22 **17.** –63 **19.** integers less than –4 **21.** –12
23. –6 **25.** 16 **27.** 48 **29.** –31

Study Skills (p. 532)
1–2. Answers will vary.

Section 4, Practice and Application (p. 538)
1. $\frac{1}{3}$ **3.** $\frac{1}{2}$ **5.** $\frac{1}{9}$ **9.** $\frac{1}{40}$ **11. a.** 12.5 mi²

Spiral Review (p. 540)
13. 3.425 L **14.** 97,000 L **15.** 0.25 L **16.** 840 L
17. 33.63 cm **18.** 26.38 in. **19.** 219.80 ft
20. a.   **b.** 31; 31

21. 0.205; half of 0.4 = 0.2 **22.** 2.012; 0.2 • 10 = 2

23. 50; $1 \div 0.3 \approx 3$, so $15 \cdot 3 = 45$ **24.** 0.57, 0.7, 7, 7.29, 7.4 **25.** 4.569, 43.5, 45.02, 45.2 **26.** 45

Extra Skill Practice (p. 541)

1. $\frac{1}{7}$ **3.** $\frac{1}{4}$ **5.** about 0.22

Standardized Testing (p. 541)

1. about 8% **2.** Answers will vary. Sample Response: The combined area of the squares should be about 44 in.^{2} For example: 4 squares, each 3.3 in. on a side.

Section 5, Practice and Application (p. 549)

1. reflection **3.** translation **5.** translation **7.** reflection
9. a. reflection; rotation or reflection; rotation
b. Quarter A can be moved to Quarter B in the middle Hex symbol by rotation or reflection.
11.

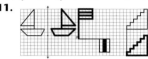

13.    **17.** ♩

Spiral Review (p. 551)

21. $\frac{1}{3}$ **22.** $\frac{4}{5}$ **23.** $\frac{3}{5}$ **24.** $\frac{1}{3}$ **25.** < **26.** < **27.** > **28.** <
29. > **30.** >

Extra Skill Practice (p. 552)

1. reflection **3.** translation **5.** translation **7.** rotation
9. translation **11.** C **13.** A

Standardized Testing (p. 552)

A; B: The crops in the two upper sections are rotated one section clockwise. The lower left crop is replanted in the same section, while the lower right crop is moved to the upper left; C: reflection across a vertical line dividing the field

Section 6, Practice and Application (p. 556)

1. $1.57 \cdot 10^5$ **3.** $5.6 \cdot 10^7$ **5.** $5.6 \cdot 10^3$ **7.** 59,000
9. 982,000 **11.** 60 **13.** $1.5 \cdot 10^3$ **15.** $5 \cdot 10^4$
17. a. Olympus Mons is 9.7 mi higher. **b.** Olympus Mons is 299 mi wider in diameter. **19. a.** increased
b. The tons of glass collected increased. It was previously $1.6 \cdot 10^6$ and then changed to 1.65 times the same power of 10.

Spiral Review (p. 558)

21. −11 **22.** −43 **23.** 7 **24.** 43 **25.** −49 **26.** −9
27. about 72% **28.** $11\frac{2}{3}$ **29.** $1\frac{13}{20}$ **30.** $\frac{95}{96}$ **31.** $3\frac{5}{9}$
32. $18\frac{1}{14}$ **33.** $2\frac{38}{85}$

Extra Skill Practice (p. 559)

1. $4.98 \cdot 10^7$ **3.** $3.2 \cdot 10^{10}$ **5.** $2.5 \cdot 10^6$ **7.** $7.63 \cdot 10^4$
9. $2.4 \cdot 10^1$ **11.** 60.8 **13.** 4140 **15.** 410
17. 1,900,000,000 **19.** $3.5 \cdot 10^1$, $2 \cdot 10^2$, $1.3 \cdot 10^3$
21. $5.5 \cdot 10^2$, $5.5 \cdot 10^3$, $5.5 \cdot 10^6$

Standardized Testing (p. 559)

1. C **2.** A **3.** B

Review & Assessment (pp. 562–563)

1. A, C, D **2. a.** $9\frac{1}{3}$ c **b.** $4\frac{2}{3}$ pt **c.** $74\frac{2}{3}$ fl oz **3.** Sample answer: 10 cm by 10 cm by 40 cm **4.** $22 + 80 = 102$
5. $1.04 + 5.00 = 6.04$ **6.** $0.75 + 0.25 + 0.85 = 1.85$
7. $900 + 100$; about 1000 **8.** $15 + 25; about $40.00
9. $17 + 1$; about 18 **10.** 6 **11.** −39 **12.** 18 **13.** −24
14. −26 **15.** −6 **16.** about 87% **17.** $\frac{1}{4}$ **18.** $\frac{9}{25}$
19. reflection **20.** reflection or rotation **21.** reflection or rotation **22.** reflection **23.** 5,670 **24.** 100,200
25. 700,000,000 **26.** 23 **27.** 911 **28.** 18,330
29. $4.4 \cdot 10^6$ **30.** $7.7 \cdot 10^3$ **31.** $7.89 \cdot 10^2$
32. $6.2 \cdot 10^4$ **33.** $5 \cdot 10^9$ **34.** $3.77125 \cdot 10^5$

TOOLBOX ANSWERS

NUMBERS AND OPERATIONS

Whole Number Place Value (p. 565)
1. place: one hundred thousands; value: 800,000
2. place: one thousands; value: 5,000 **3.** place: ten millions; value: 50,000,000 **4.** place: ones; value: 8
5. place: ten thousands; value: 90,000 **6.** place: hundreds; value: 200 **7.** ten thousands **8.** 20
9. 15,946,619 **10.** 220,009 **11.** five hundred eighteen **12.** twenty-three thousand, four hundred
13. seventy million, six hundred twenty-four **14.** four hundred fifty thousand, six hundred seventy-two

Comparing Whole Numbers (p. 566)
1. > **2.** > **3.** > **4.** < **5.** > **6.** < **7.** < **8.** > **9.** <
10. 239,400; 79,899; 47,777; 24,000 **11.** 7,902,500; 6,150,762; 937,400; 892,570

Rounding Whole Numbers and Money (p. 567)
1. 890 **2.** 94,600 **3.** 86,000 **4.** 27,000,000 **5.** 600
6. 40 **7.** 300,000 **8.** 68,300 **9.** $950.00
10. $4370.00 **11.** $52.00 **12.** $600.00

Adding Whole Numbers and Money (p. 568)
1. 3232 **2.** 12,718 **3.** 101,916 **4.** 60,957
5. 97,766 **6.** 89,117 **7.** $12.11 **8.** $39.04 **9.** $44.15
10. $120.90 **11.** $43.07 **12.** $115.45

Mental Math (p. 569)
1. 123 **2.** 82 **3.** 481 **4.** 321 **5.** 371 **6.** 831 **7.** 495
8. 791 **9.** 675 **10.** $12.25 **11.** $18.57 **12.** $10.38
13. $13.35 **14.** $14.40 **15.** $8.97 **16.** $20.25
17. $13.40 **18.** $23.05

Subtracting Whole Numbers and Money (p. 570)
1. 8578 **2.** 188 **3.** 4813 **4.** 2121 **5.** 6502 **6.** 3841
7. $29.08 **8.** $388.40 **9.** $64.08 **10.** $33.39
11. $320.33

Multiplying Whole Numbers and Money (p. 571)
1. 950 **2.** 48,384 **3.** 37,960 **4.** 220,735 **5.** 4582
6. 28,672 **7.** $229.08 **8.** $352.22 **9.** $111.52
10. $1890.00 **11.** $109.64 **12.** $3014.85

Dividing Whole Numbers (p. 572)
1. 400 R5 **2.** 7 R52 **3.** 2468 R3 **4.** 12 R17 **5.** 302
6. 538 R10 **7.** 20 R21 **8.** 11 R25 **9.** 161 R38 **10.** 3 R44
11. 35 R18 **12.** 13 R6

Number Fact Families (p. 573)
1. 6; 3; 6, 3 **2.** 8; 16, 8; 2; 8, 2 **3.** 12 **4.** 24 **5.** 53
6. 25 **7.** 81 **8.** 32 **9.** 103 **10.** 13 **11.** 63 **12.** 8
13. 39 **14.** 12 **15.** 48 **16.** 4 **17.** 14

Multiplying and Dividing by Tens (p. 574)
1. 50,000 **2.** 6000 **3.** 1,500,000 **4.** 1,600,000
5. 600,000 **6.** 500,000 **7.** 12,000,000
8. 20,000,000 **9.** 320,000,000 **10.** 400,000 **11.** 10
12. 50 **13.** 130 **14.** 50 **15.** 5000

MEASUREMENT

Perimeter and Using a Ruler (p. 575)
1. 18 in. **2.** 18 cm **3.** 12 ft **4.** 20 cm **5.** 14 in. **6.** 1 in.
7. 2 in.

Area (p. 576)
1. 6 cm^2 **2.** 5 cm^2 **3.** 7 cm^2

Time Conversions and Elapsed Time (p. 577)
1. 480 min **2.** 3 days **3.** 3 min **4.** 4 hr 55 min
5. 13 hr 53 min **6.** 2 hr 56 min **7.** 1 hr 35 min

DATA DISPLAYS

Reading a Graph (p. 578)
1. 16 tourneys, 10 tourneys **2.** about 840,000 people, about 870,000 people

Making a Pictograph (p. 579)
1.
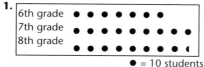

2.
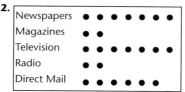

ADDITIONAL ANSWERS

Managing Extended Explorations (Teacher's Edition, pp. T44–T45)

1. *How might you introduce the* Estimating Animal Populations E^2?

You could begin by having students share their ideas about why wildlife biologists might want to know the population of a particular kind of animal in a region, the methods researchers might use to count the animals, and what problems they might encounter taking a count. This discussion could provide a lead into estimating the number from a photograph. After introducing the problem, discuss the due date and the format students should use for their presentation.

2. *What approaches do you think would work best?*

The best approach to the problem may be to randomly select a small region on the photo and count the geese in that region. The ratio of the area of the photo to the area of the small region can then be used to predict the number of geese in the photo. If this process is repeated 3 or 4 times, the mean of the estimates from the individual samples should give a good estimate of the number of geese in the photo.

Students often use some variation of the "count the geese in a smaller region" method to make their estimates, but they usually do not select the regions randomly or repeat the sampling to verify their result or to find an average.

6. *Read, assess, and grade the students' sample work.*

Michael's Solution

Michael's solution would score at Level 4 on the *Problem Solving Scale*. He understood the problem well enough to make a plan and find a solution, but he did not attempt to verify his solution or check that it was reasonable.

This E^2 does not provide an opportunity for students to use much mathematical vocabulary, so you may decide not to score their solutions on the *Mathematical Language Scale*. Michael's solution would score at Level 3 on the scale. He did use appropriate terms like *grid* and *multiplying* correctly, but he could have used other mathematical terms to describe his estimate (the *product*) and the grid (*rectangular* sections). He also used the term *line* when he meant *segment*. You could also legitimately score this solution at Level 1 since, with the exception of *multiplying*, no mathematical language was used, or at Level 5 because the other uses indicated would not have made the solution any clearer.

Michael's solution would score at Level 5 on the *Representations Scale*. The equation and drawing that he used were appropriate and helped explain his solution.

Michael *explained* how his method of solving the problem is related to the problem of estimating the population of a city. His explanation of the connections could have been clearer, so his solution would score at Level 4 on the *Connections Scale*.

Michael's presentation of his solution can be understood by others, but he did not clearly explain his reasoning. Why is it appropriate to estimate the number of geese by multiplying the number in one section by the number of sections? Would this method work for any section (in particular, Sections 1 or 17)? How does he know his estimate is reasonable? Because his reasoning is not clear or necessarily correct, his solution would score at Level 3 on the *Presentation Scale*.

Michael's solution would be considered a **Good Response.** He is a little lower on the *Mathematical Language Scale* than shown on the Good Response Profile, but this problem did not provide much opportunity to use mathematical terms or symbols. He is also lower than the Profile on the *Presentation Scale*, but this is the first E^2 in the book, so that is not unusual. Also, his high score on the *Representations Scale* tends to balance this out.

Annie's Solution

Annie's solution would score at Level 5 on the *Problem Solving Scale*. Not only did she understand the problem well enough to make a plan and find a solution, but she checked that it was reasonable when she decided that the estimate was too high and used a new approach to find another estimate. She apparently decided the second estimate was too low and averaged the results to get her final estimate.

Annie's solution would score at Level 4 on the *Mathematical Language Scale*. She used terms like *square, multiplied, product,* and *averaged* where they were appropriate, and she used them correctly. She used *line* instead of *segment* and could have used *area* if she had explained why she multiplied by 12.75.

Annie's solution would score at Level 5 on the *Representations Scale*. The drawings and table she used were appropriate and helped explain her solution.

Annie *recognized* that this problem is related to other types of problems but did not try to explain how they are related. It would also have been nice if Annie had explained how her second approach relates to her understanding of multiplication (the array model). Her solution would score at Level 3 on the *Connections Scale*.

Annie did not explain how she found the 12.75 or why she would multiply the number of geese in the square by it. Annie also needed to explain whether her second estimate was reasonable or not and why she decided to average the two estimates. Other than this, the presentation of her solution is clear and can be understood by others. She also did not recognize or did not explain the need to do a random sample with both of her methods. Her solution would score at Level 4 on the *Presentation Scale*.

Annie's solution would be considered an **Excellent Response,** especially for her first E^2. She is a little lower on the *Mathematical Language Scale* than shown on the Excellent Response Profile, but considering that this problem did not provide much opportunity to use mathematical terms or symbols she did very well. She is also lower than the Profile on the *Connections* and *Presentation Scales*, but this is a difficult problem for which to find connections and her solution did display considerable thought and originality.

Pre-Course Test (pp. xxii–xxiii), (Teacher's Edition, pp. T58–T59)

39.

Basketball	● ◖
Football	● ● ● ◖
Soccer	● ● ◗
Baseball	● ●

● = 10 players

Practicing Test-Taking Skills (p. xxxi), (Teacher's Edition, p. T67)
1. 18; Brian gave $\frac{1}{4}$ of 48 brownies = 12 brownies to his grandmother. 48 – 12 = 36 brownies left. Then he gave $\frac{1}{2}$ of 36 brownies = 18 brownies to his father. 36 – 18 = 18 brownies left. **2.** mean = 7.9 hours, median = 8 hours, mode = 9 hours; the mean = (6 + 6 + 7 + 8 + 8 + 8 + 9 + 9 + 9 + 9) ÷ 10 = 7.9 hours. The two middle values in the line plot are 8 and 8, so the median is 8 hours. The mode is the data value with the most Xs, 9 hours **3.** $2x - 5$; 25 years old; Let x represent Laura's age. An expression for Mark's age is $2x - 5$. Evaluate $2x - 5$ when $x = 15$ to find Mark's age. 2(15) – 5 = 30 – 5 = 25. Mark is 25 years old. **4.** 30 cm; 1.8 m ÷ 6 = 0.3 m, 0.3 m × 100 = 30 cm. **5.** 1 group of 30, 2 groups of 15, 3 groups of 10, 10 groups of 3, 5 groups of 6, or 6 groups of 5; Use the fact that the factors of 30 are 1, 2, 3, 5, 6, 10, 15, and 30. **6.** 45; The first digit is even so it has to be 2, 4, 6, or 8. The number is divisible by 5, so the second digit is either 0 or 5. Combining these two facts gives the numbers 20, 25, 40, 45, 60, 65, 80, and 85. Of these, 45 is the only number divisible by 9. **7.** mean = 77, median = 83, mode = 93; The mean is $\frac{74 + 31 + 85 + 80 + 93 + 83 + 93}{7}$, or 77. If the numbers are listed from least to greatest, the middle number, 83, is the median. The mode, 93, is the number that occurs most often. Sample Response: median, the particularly low score of 31 makes the mean too low to be representative and the mode is too high. **8.** $22.42; The cost of the hamburger is 4.75 × $3.40 = $16.15. Alvin needs 3 packages of buns, so the cost is 3 × $2.09 = $6.27. The total cost is $16.15 + $6.27 = $22.42. **9.** from the *MISSISSIPPI* bag; The probability of drawing an *I* from the *MISSISSIPPI* bag is $\frac{4}{11}$, or about 36%. The probability of drawing an *I* from the *OHIO* bag is $\frac{1}{4}$, or 25%. **10.** soccer: 27, basketball: 18, track: 42; number of girls on the soccer team = 18 + 2 + 3 + 4 = 27, number of girls on the basketball team = 12 + 2 + 3 + 1 = 18, number of girls on the track team = 34 + 4 + 3 + 1 = 42

Practicing Test-Taking Skills (p. xxxvii), (Teacher's Edition, p. T73)
1. Volume of prism A = 5 • 4 • 6 = 120 in.³, volume of prism B = 5 • 3 • 10 = 150 in.³; Sample Response: To make the volume of prism A equal to 150 in.³, you can change the width from 4 inches to 5 inches. Then the volume of prism A = 5 • 5 • 6 = 150 in.³. **2.** $3.40; The unit price for macaroni salad is $8.16 ÷ 3 lb = $2.72 per lb. Since there are 16 oz in 1 lb, 4 oz = $\frac{1}{4}$ lb. The cost of $1\frac{1}{4}$ lb of macaroni salad = $2.72 + $2.72 ÷ 4 = $2.72 + $.68 = $3.40. **3.** mean = 7°F, median = 6°F, mode = –2°F; mean = (–2 +28 + 6 + 0 + 9 + 10+ (–2)) ÷ 7 = 7°F, median (middle value) = 6°F, mode = –2°F; mode because it is the least value. **4.** target A; area of shaded circle on target A = πr² = 3.14 • (1)² = 3.14 ft²; area of square on target A = 3 • 3 = 9 ft²; probability of landing within the shaded circle = 3.14 ÷ 9 = 0.35 = 35%; area of shaded square on target B = 1.5 • 1.5 = 2.25 ft²; area of circle on target B = πr² = 3.14 • (1.5)² = 7.065 ft ²; probability of landing within the shaded square = 2.25 ÷ 7.065 = 0.32 = 32% **5.** 20; To find the number of students who said that playing sports was their favorite after-school activity, find 35% of 400 = 0.35 • 400 = 140. To find the number of students who said that playing video games is their favorite activity, find 30% of 400 = 0.3 • 400 = 120; 140 – 120 = 20.

6.

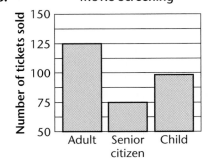

The scale used for the vertical axis creates the impression that the number of tickets sold to children was double the number of tickets sold to senior citizens.

MODULE 1

Section 1, Exploration 2 (p. 8)
22. a. about 600; less than; Both numbers were rounded own. **b.** about 24,000; it is not possible to tell whether the estimate is greater than or less than the exact product because one number was rounded up and the other down. **c.** about 2,200; it is not possible to tell whether the estimate is greater than or less than the exact product because one number was rounded up and the other down. **d.** about 5,500; greater than; 99 was rounded up. **e.** about 70,000; less than; Both numbers were rounded down. **f.** about 1,600,000; it is not possible to tell whether the estimate is greater than or less than the exact product because one number was rounded up and the other down.

Section 1, Exploration 3 (p. 8)
24. a. 17 and 31 are not compatible since their sum, 48, is not easy to use in computations. **b.** 31 and 19 are compatible because their sum, 50, is easy to use in computations. **c.** 31 + 19 = 50 and 17 + 8 = 25, so the sum is 25 + 50 + 25 = 100.

Section 2, Exploration 1 (p. 17)

10. a.

Term Number	1	2	3	4	5	6	7
Term	1	3	7	13	21	31	43

b.

Term Number	1	2	3	4	5	6
Term	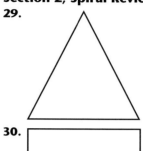					

Section 2, Exploration 2 (p. 20)

15.

Term Number	. . .	5	6	. . .
Shape	. . .			. . .
Number	. . .	9	11	. . .

Section 2, Key Concepts (p. 21)

18.

Term Number	1	2	3	4	5	6	7
Term	3	5	7	9	11	13	15

$t = 2n + 1$ where t = term and n = term number
Start with 3 and add 2 to each term to get the next term.

Section 2, Practice and Application (pp. 22–25)

1.

Start with △ and add shapes in this order

▽, ▱, △ to continue pattern.

6. b.

Term Number	1	2	3	4
Term	7:40 AM	8:30 AM	9:20 AM	10:10 AM

Term Number	5	6	7	
Term	11:00 AM	11:50 AM	12:40 PM	

The 7th period will begin at 12:40 P.M.

7. a.

Term Number	1	2	3	4
Term	1	2	4	8

13. a.

Term Number	5	6	7	8
Term	60	72	84	96

14. a.

Term Number	5	6	7	8
Term	95	94	93	92

15. b.

Term Number	1	2	3	4	5	6
Term	2	5	8	11	14	17

16. a.

Term Number	1	2	3	4	5
Term	6	11	16	21	26

Section 2, Spiral Review (p. 25)

29.

30.

31.

Section 2, Extra Skills Practice (p. 26)

6. a.

Term Number	5	6	7	8
Term	495	494	493	492

b. $t = 500 - n$ **c.** $t = 500 - 40 = 460$

7. a.

Term Number	14	15	16	17
Term	140	150	160	170

b. $t = 10n$ **c.** $t = 10 \cdot 40 = 400$

8. a.

Term Number	5	6	7	8
Term	22	24	26	28

b. $t = 2n + 12$ **c.** $t = 2 \cdot 40 + 12 = 92$

Section 3, Practice and Application (p. 34)

1. a. Which of two monthly service contracts for 8 to 10 hours a month on-line is a better buy? **b.** the monthly fee, number of included hours, and hourly rate for hours beyond the number included **c.** whether there are limits on the total number of hours or available times, and whether either has cheaper telephone access **2. a.** Are you able to attend all five events offered at a cultural center in a given time period? **b.** the starting times of all five events and how long they last **c.** how long it takes to get from one event to another
3. a. How many times does a given event occur? **b.** the time periods over which the tour runs, and the frequency and length of the trips **c.** whether there is more than one double-hulled canoe (If not, the times given could not be exact. There would need to be time to load and unload.)

Section 4, Practice and Application (pp. 49–50)

14. b. Check students' work. Seven possible answers are shown for parts b, d, and e.

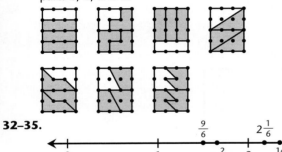

32–35.

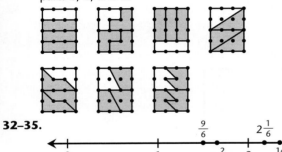

Section 5, Exploration 3 (p. 59)

20. a. 36
b. 12

c. See diagram in part (b); 24
d. 24 **e.** 24

21. a.

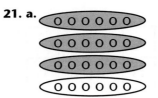

b. 18 **c.** 18

Module Project (p. 68)

1. b. (2) Replace the second penny and every second penny after it with a nickel. (3) Replace the third coin and every third coin after it with a dime. (4) Replace the fourth coin and every fourth coin after it with a quarter. (5) Replace the fifth coin and every fifth coin with a fifty-cent piece.

2. a.

	Term Number	1	2	3	4	5
Step 1	Term	P	P	P	P	P
Step 2	Term	P	N	P	N	P
Step 3	Term	P	N	D	N	P
Step 4	Term	P	N	D	Q	P
Step 5	Term	P	N	D	Q	F

	Term Number	6	7	8	9	10
Step 1	Term	P	P	P	P	P
Step 2	Term	N	P	N	P	N
Step 3	Term	D	P	N	D	N
Step 4	Term	D	P	Q	D	N
Step 5	Term	D	P	Q	D	F

b. Each odd numbered term is P; each even numbered term is N.
c. If the term number is odd and not divisible by 3, the term is P. If the term number is even and not divisible by 3, the term is N. If the term number is divisible by 3, the term is D.
d. (4) If the term number is odd and not divisible by 3 the term is P. If the term number is even and not divisible by 3 or 4, the term is N. If the term number is divisible by 3 but not 4, the term is D. If the term number is divisible by 4, the term is Q.
(5) If the term number is not divisible by 2, 3, 4, or 5, the term is P. If the term number is even but is not divisible by 3, 4, or 5, the term is N. If the term number is divisible by 3 but not 4 or 5, the term is D. If the term number is divisible by 4 but not 5, the term is Q. If the term number is divisible by 5, the term is F.

MODULE 2

Section 1, Exploration 1 (p. 76)

9. a. Methods may vary. Sample: Multiply the number of student pairs in the class by 20 and then calculate the part of this amount that would most closely match the fraction of heads for 100 flips. Figure out how many groups of 100 are in the total number of flips made by the class. Then multiply the number of heads from the 100 flips by this number of groups. Then do the same for tails. **b.** Answers will vary based on student data for Exercise 8. Predictions may be close to $\frac{1}{2}$ for each outcome. **11.** The class's total flips should give the best idea of the chances since the experiment was repeated more times. However, there are groups that may have achieved heads 50% of the time with only 20 flips. **13. c.** Answers will vary. Sample Responses: a spinner with two colors that each cover half the circle, the numbers 1, 2, 3, 4, 5, and 6 on a number cube

Section 1, Practice and Application (p. 82)

8. e.

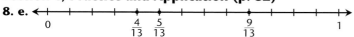

Section 2, Setting the Stage (p. 85)

2. He means that sometimes things that may appear unlike can really be related to each other, and that the cases that he has solved before can be used to help solve current crimes. **3.** Answers will vary. Sample Responses: breaking the problem into smaller problems, using diagrams, pictures, tables, or equations, acting out the problem, guess and check.

Section 2, Exploration 1 (p. 86)

4. Team explanations will vary. There will be 48 games played. Sample Explanation:

Understand the Problem "Given 32 teams divided into eight groups of four, each team in a group plays three other teams once, what's the total number of games played?"

Make a Plan Determine number of games played in one group and then multiply by eight groups.

Carry out the Plan Within one group of four teams there will be six games played. If teams are labeled A, B, C, D, then all games played would be {(A, B), (A, C), (A, D), (B, C), (B, D), (C, D)}. There are eight groups so this makes eight groups of six games or 48 games played in the first round of the finals.

Look Back Check for reasonableness of number of games for 32 teams.

5. Team answers will vary. Sample responses are given. **a.** We each read the problem on our own. Then one student read it out loud. We discussed the problem and answered questions to be sure we all agreed on what the problem was asking and that we understood the facts that were given. We decided "Every four years" had no bearing on the problem asked. **b.** Our plan was to figure out how many games were played in just one group and apply that to all eight groups. **c.** We made a diagram with team numbers and counted the number of games played by one group (6 games) and then multiplied that by eight groups for a total of 48 games played. **d.** We rechecked the number of

games to be sure it sounded reasonable for the number of teams. We also reread the problem and checked that we answered all questions that were asked. **8.** For a 5: Make a plan, use it to solve the problem, and verify your solution; Sample for a 4: Make a plan, and use it to solve the problem, but get an incorrect solution or fail to verify your solution.

Section 2, Exploration 3 (pp. 90–91)

17. Answers will vary. Sample Response: In both the World Cup Problem and the Handshake Problem teams/people were paired up two at a time. The pattern can be extended from:

4 teams taken 2 at a time = 6 games (add 4 to get next number)
5 teams taken 2 at a time = 10 (add 5 to get next number)
6 teams taken 2 at a time = 15 (add 6 to get next number)
7 teams taken 2 at a time = 21 (add 7 to get next number)

21.

Number of pegs	1	2	3	4	5	6	7
Number of linkups	0	1	3	6	10	15	21

Section 2, Key Concepts (p. 92)

24. Sample Responses:

Labsheet 2A:

Team 1 would score 2 on the *Problem Solving* scale. They understood the problem well enough to make a plan, but not well enough to make a plan that would lead to the correct solution. Because they didn't try to verify their solution, they did not recognize the errors in their analysis. As a result every handshake was counted twice in their solution.

Team 1 would score 3 on the *Representations* scale. The diagram appropriately represents the first person's handshakes, but different diagrams are needed to represent the rest of the handshakes.

Team 1 would score 2 on the *Connections* scale. They recognized that the *Handshake Problem* is similar to the *World Cup Problem*, but they did not recognize the difference between the problems.

Labsheet 2B:

Team 2 would score 4 on the *Problem Solving* scale. They understood the problem, made a plan to solve it, carried out the plan, and found the correct solution, but they did not try to verify their solution. They could verify the solution by solving the problem another way. For example, each person shakes hands with 4 other people, so there would appear to be 5 × 4 = 20 handshakes. But, this counts "A shakes with B" and "B shakes with A" as different handshakes. In fact it counts every handshake twice, so the solution is 20 ÷ 2 = 10 handshakes.

Team 2 would score 5 on the *Representations* scale. They used appropriate and correct representations that helped them explain their solution.

Team 2 would score 5 on the *Connections* scale. They explained how the *Handshake Problem* is like the *String Art Problem*. If they had also shown how to generalize the solution for any number of people, they would have received a star.

Section 2, Practice and Application (p. 94)

6. a. Positions 1, 2, 3, 4, 10, 11, 13, 14, 15, 17, 20, 21, 25, 28, and 29 are women.

Positions 5, 6, 7, 8, 9, 12, 16, 18, 19, 22, 23, 24, 26, 27, and 30 are men.

$$\frac{\ }{W}\ \frac{\ }{W}\ \frac{\ }{W}\ \frac{\ }{W}\ \frac{X}{M}\ \frac{X}{M}\ \frac{X}{M}\ \frac{X}{M}\ \frac{X}{M}\ \frac{\ }{W}\ \frac{\ }{W}\ \frac{X}{M}\ \frac{\ }{W}\ \frac{\ }{W}\ \frac{\ }{W}\ \frac{X}{M}\ \frac{\ }{W}\ \frac{X}{M}\ \frac{X}{M}\ \frac{\ }{W}\ \frac{\ }{W}\ \frac{X}{M}\ \frac{X}{M}\ \frac{X}{M}\ \frac{\ }{W}\ \frac{X}{M}\ \frac{X}{M}\ \frac{\ }{W}\ \frac{\ }{W}\ \frac{X}{M}$$

Section 2, Spiral Review (p. 95)

14.

Term Number	1	2	3	4	5	6
Term in the sequence	5	9	13	17	21	25

Begin the first term with 5, then add 4 to obtain each succeeding term.

Section 2, Extra Skills Practice (p. 96)

3. Sue is the president.

	Pres	VP	Sec	Treas
John	No	Yes	No	No
Sue	Yes	No	No	No
Lisa	No	No	No	Yes
Fernando	No	No	Yes	No

5.

Tables of 4	Tables of 2
7	0
6	2
5	4
4	6
3	8
2	10
1	12
0	14

6. 17 student tickets; Use guess and check and make a table to organize the results. Sample Response:

Number of students	29	20	15	17
Others	20	29	34	32
$8 × Number of students	$232	$160	$120	$136
$12 × Others	$240	$348	$408	$384
Total ticket sales	$472	$508	$528	$520

Section 3, Exploration 2 (p. 102)

14.

Stick Combination	Sketch of triangle	Type of triangle	Length of the longest side	Length of the other sides
3 in. 4 in. 5 in.		scalene	5 in.	3 in., 4 in.
2 in. 2 in. 5 in.		not possible		
3 in. 5 in. 5 in.		isosceles	2 sides are 5 in.	3 in.
6 in. 6 in. 6 in.		equilateral	all sides are 6 in.	all sides are 6 in.
2 in. 3 in. 4 in.		scalene	4 in.	2 in., 3 in.
2 in. 3 in. 6 in.		not possible		
3 in. 5 in. 8 in.		not possible		
5 in. 5 in. 8 in.		isosceles	8 in.	both are 5 in.
4 in. 4 in. 8 in.		not possible		

Section 3, Exploration 3 (p. 104)

20.

Triangle	Acute angles	Right angles	Obtuse angles	Type of triangle
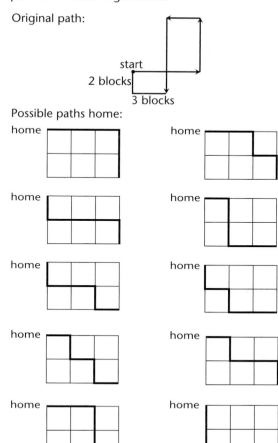 Triangle A,B,C	∠A, ∠C	∠B	(none)	right
Triangle D,E,F	∠D, ∠F	(none)	∠E	obtuse
Triangle G,H,I	∠G, ∠H, ∠I	(none)	(none)	acute
Triangle J,K,L	∠J, ∠K, ∠L	(none)	(none)	acute
Triangle M,N,O	∠M, ∠N	∠O	(none)	right
Triangle P,Q,R	∠P, ∠Q, ∠R	(none)	(none)	acute

Section 4, Setting the Stage (p. 112)

1.

Type	Names	Score
Triangle	ABH, BCI, CDI, DEF, BCD, ACE, ACG, CEG	8
4-sided polygon	ABIG, ABDF, ABDE, HBDE, HBDF, HBIG, GIDF, GIDE, ACDF, HBCE, HBCG, GCDF	24
5-sided polygon	HBCDF, ACIDF, ECIBH, ACDIG, ECBIG, ACIDE, ECIBA	21
6-sided polygon	ABICDF, EDICBH, HBICDF, HBCIDF, HBCDIG, FDCBIG	30

Section 4, Extra Skill Practice (p. 122)

2. Answers will vary. Sample Response:

Angle Name	Measure
Acute	greater than 0°, less than 90°
Right	90°
Obtuse	Greater than 90°, less than 180°
Straight	180°

Review and Assessment (pp. 126–127)

5. Answers will vary. Possible answers are shown. Each path represents a path of 5 blocks to get home.

Original path:

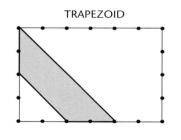

start

2 blocks

3 blocks

Possible paths home:

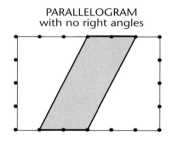

6. b. Sample: Make a table and notice that the sequence of perimeters increases by 4 while the number of squares is the sequence of triangular numbers.

term number	1	2	3	4	5	6	7	8
number of squares	1	3	6	10	15	21	28	36
perimeter	4	8	12	16	20	24	28	32

So for any perimeter, divide the perimeter by 4 and find the corresponding triangular number. For example, for a perimeter of 24, divide 24 by 4 and find the 6th triangular number, 21.

20. Answers will vary. Sample responses are given.

TRAPEZOID

PARALLELOGRAM with no right angles

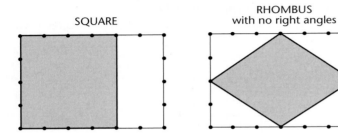

SQUARE

RHOMBUS
with no right angles

MODULE 3

Section 1, Exploration 1 (pp. 131–132)

4.

Place Value of the Digits	ten thousands	thousands	hundreds		tens	ones			
Number	2	5	4	3	6	.	9	8	

7. a.

Place Value of the Digits	ten thousands	thousands	hundreds		tens	ones		tenths	hundredths
Number	2	5	4	3	6	.	9	8	

8. a.

	Words	Fraction	Decimal
Value of the 9	nine tenths	$\frac{9}{10}$	0.9
Value of the 8	eight hundredths	$\frac{8}{100}$	0.08

The zero between the decimal point and the 8 in 0.08 is a place holder. The number includes no tenths.

The zero to the left of the decimal point in 0.08 shows that the whole number part of the decimal is 0 and that what follows is a decimal fraction.

b.

9 complete rods
8 extra squares
98 of the 100 blocks are shaded, which

is $\frac{98}{100}$ or 0.98, so 0.98 is read ninety-eight

hundredths.

9. a.

Number in words	Sketch of base-ten blocks	Fraction	Decimal
one and eighteen hundredths		$1\frac{18}{100}$	1.18
four tenths		$\frac{4}{10}$	0.4
one and three tenths		$1\frac{3}{10}$	1.3
one and three hundredths		$1\frac{3}{100}$	1.03
twenty-seven hundredths		$\frac{27}{100}$	0.27
thirty-four hundredths		$\frac{34}{100}$	0.34
seven tenths		$\frac{7}{10}$	0.7

Section 2, Standardized Testing (p. 147)

The first three terms of the sequence of payments are $0.10, $0.20, and $0.40. Jim interprets this as a sequence in which each term is twice that of the previous term. Jim's dad intends it to be a sequence in which the increase from term to term goes up by an additional $0.10 each time. The payments in dollars for each plan are shown in the table.

Time mowed	1	2	3	4	5
Pay: Jim's plan	0.10	0.20	0.40	0.80	1.60
Pay: Dad's plan	0.10	0.20	0.40	0.70	1.10

Time mowed	6	7	8	9	10
Pay: Jim's plan	3.20	6.40	12.80	25.60	51.20
Pay: Dad's plan	1.60	2.20	2.90	3.70	4.60

Section 3, Exploration 1 (p. 150)

7.

Number	1	2	3	4	5	6	13	27
Multiply by 3	3	6	9	12	15	18	39	81
Sum of the Digits	3	6	9	3	6	9	12	9

Number	55	456	659	2260
Multiply by 3	165	1368	1977	6780
Sum of the Digits	12	18	24	21

7. a. Yes, the first row was multiplied by 3 in order to produce the second row. **b.** All the numbers in the third row are divisible by 3. **c.** A number is divisible by 3 if the sum of its digits is divisible by 3. **d.** Answers will vary. Students should state that the test seems to work.

Section 3, Exploration 3 (p. 156)

34. a.

Number of folds	Number of sections	Rewritten form	Power of 2
1	2	2	2^1
2	4	$2 \cdot 2$	2^2
3	8	$2 \cdot 2 \cdot 2$	2^3
4	16	$2 \cdot 2 \cdot 2 \cdot 2$	2^4
5	32	$2 \cdot 2 \cdot 2 \cdot 2 \cdot 2$	2^5
6	64	$2 \cdot 2 \cdot 2 \cdot 2 \cdot 2 \cdot 2$	2^6
7	128	$2 \cdot 2 \cdot 2 \cdot 2 \cdot 2 \cdot 2 \cdot 2$	2^7
8	256	$2 \cdot 2 \cdot 2 \cdot 2 \cdot 2 \cdot 2 \cdot 2 \cdot 2$	2^8

Section 3, Practice and Application (p. 160)

29. b.

Endangered Plant Species

Namibia	❀❀❀
Portugal	❀❀❀❀❀❀❀❀❀❀❀❀❀❀❀❀
Sicily	❀❀❀❀❀❀❀❀

Key: ❀ = 6 species

Section 4, Exploration 1 (p. 166)

7. a.

Term Number	1	2	3	4	5	6	7	8	9	...	n
Term	5	10	15	20	25	30	35	40	45	...	$5 \cdot n$

50th term = 250

b. Multiples of 13

Term Number	1	2	3	4	5	6	7
Term	13	26	39	52	65	78	91

Term Number	8	9	10	...	n
Term	104	117	130	...	$13 \cdot n$

50th term = 650

c. Multiples of 8

Term Number	1	2	3	4	5	6	7	...	n
Term	8	16	24	32	40	48	56	...	$8 \cdot n$

50th term = 400

d. Multiples of 9

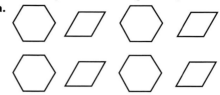

Term Number	1	2	3	4	5	6	7	...	n
Term	9	18	27	36	45	54	63	...	$9 \cdot n$

50th term = 450

Section 5, Exploration 2 (p. 176)

13. a.

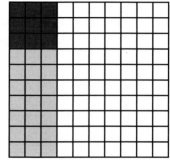

Section 6, Exploration 1 (p. 186)

5.

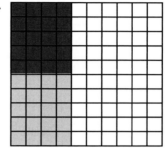

$\dfrac{5}{10} \cdot \dfrac{4}{10} = \dfrac{20}{100}$; $0.5 \cdot 0.4 = 0.20$ $\dfrac{3}{10} \cdot \dfrac{3}{10} = \dfrac{9}{100}$; $0.3 \cdot 0.3 = 0.09$

6.

Decimal Multiplication problem	Equivalent fraction problem	Fraction product	Decimal product
$0.6 \cdot 4$	$\dfrac{6}{10} \cdot \dfrac{4}{1}$	$\dfrac{24}{10}$	2.4
$0.3 \cdot 0.2$	$\dfrac{3}{10} \cdot \dfrac{2}{10}$	$\dfrac{6}{100}$	0.06
$0.8 \cdot 0.19$	$\dfrac{8}{10} \cdot \dfrac{19}{100}$	$\dfrac{152}{1000}$	0.152
$0.05 \cdot 0.07$	$\dfrac{5}{100} \cdot \dfrac{7}{100}$	$\dfrac{35}{10000}$	0.0035
$6 \cdot 0.03$	$\dfrac{6}{1} \cdot \dfrac{3}{100}$	$\dfrac{18}{100}$	0.18

MODULE 4

Section 1, Exploration 1 (p. 201)

3. b.

Set A (Kilograms)	Set B (Grams)
Bighorn Sheep	Dwarf Shrew
Bison	Deer Mouse
Black Bear	Little Brown Bat
Bobcat	Northern Flying Squirrel
Grizzly Bear	Pika
Coyote	Least Chipmunk
Gray Wolf	Red Squirrel
Porcupine	Water Vole
Marten	
Striped Skunk	

Section 1, Exploration 3 (p. 207)

22.

•	0.001	0.01	0.1	1	10	100	1000
3	0.003	0.03	0.3	3	30	300	3000
0.6	0.0006	0.006	0.06	0.6	6	60	600
4.9	0.0049	0.049	0.49	4.9	49	490	4900
0.002	0.000002	0.00002	0.0002	0.002	0.02	0.2	2

a. When you multiply by 1, the number stays the same.

When you multiply by a special multiplier greater than 1, the decimal point moves to the right, so the number increases.

When you multiply by a special multiplier less than 1, the decimal point moves to the left, so the number decreases.

b. When I multiply by 1000, the decimal point moves 3 places to the right.

When I multiply by 100, the decimal point moves 2 places to the right.

When I multiply by 10, the decimal point moves 1 place to the right.

When I multiply by 1, the decimal point stays in the same place.

When I multiply by 0.1, the decimal point moves 1 place to the left.

When I multiply by 0.01, the decimal point moves 2 places to the left.

When I multiply by 0.001, the decimal point moves 3 places to the left.

23.

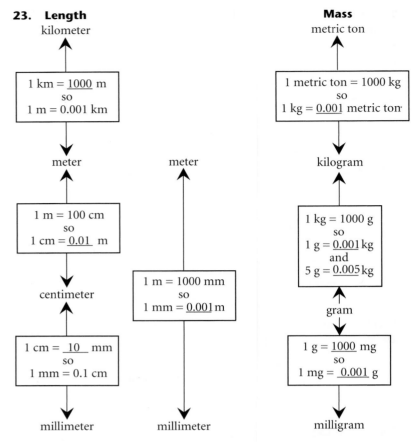

Section 2, Exploration 1 (p. 217)

7. b.

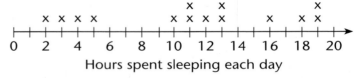

Sleeping Habits of Selected Animals

Hours spent sleeping each day

Section 2, Exploration 2 (p. 218)

10. a.

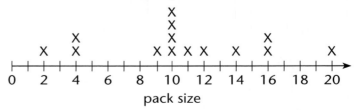

2002 Yellowstone National Park
Wolf Population

pack size

Section 2, Exploration 3 (p. 222)

24. a.

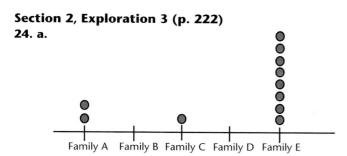

Section 2, Practice and Application (p. 226)

6.

Average Lifespans of Some Yellowstone Park Mammals

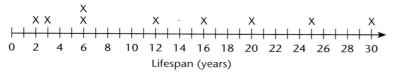

Lifespan (years)

Section 2, Extra Skill Practice (p. 230)

1.

Average Lifespans of Selected Animals

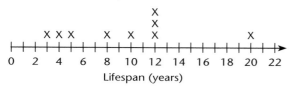

Lifespan (years)

Section 3, Exploration 1 (p. 232)

4. b–c.

5. a–b.

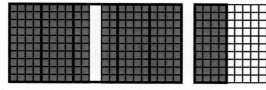

6. a. 0.02   **b.** 0.04

c. 0.65

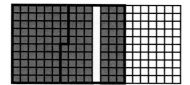

Section 3, Practice and Application (p. 242)

21.  ; $x = 2$

22. ; $x = 8$

23. ; $x = 6$

Section 4, Exploration 1 (pp. 249–250)

3. c. They represent the integers in the tens place between the least value and the greatest value in the table. The 0 is included to represent the digit in the tens place of a one digit number.

5. Weights of Some Plant-Eating Dinosaurs

```
0 | 1
1 |
2 | 0 2 6 7 7
3 | 0 0 5 5 7 9 9
4 | 0 0
5 | 0 0 3
```

Key: 2 | 6 means 2.6 tons (Keys will vary.)

6. a. A leaf with stem 1 would indicate a weight with 1 in the ones place. There are no weights in the table with a 1 in the ones place.

d. Sample Response: The weight of the Euoplocephalus is about in the center of the weights of the plant-eating dinosaurs.

e. Sample Response: Both have a similar number of stems and 18 leaves. The stem-and-leaf plot for the lengths is almost symmetrical (there are about the same number of leaves for 0 and 4 and for 1 and 3) but the weights plot is not. All of the stems on the lengths plot have at least one leaf; that is not true for the weights plot.

Section 4, Exploration 2 (p. 251)

10. a. 4

b. 7

c. 2

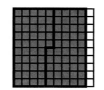

Section 4, Exploration 3 (p. 255)

20.

Rule Table

Input	Applying the Rule	Output	Ordered pair
3	3 · 2 + 1	7	(3, 7)
4	4 · 2 + 1	9	(4, 9)
0	0 · 2 + 1	1	(0, 1)
2	2 · 2 + 1	5	(2, 5)
1	1 · 2 + 1	3	(1, 3)

Section 4, Practice and Application (pp. 257–261)

6.   Masses of Small and Medium-Sized
Predatory Dinosaurs

```
 0 | 6
 1 |
 2 |
 3 |
 4 | 5
 5 | 0  0
 6 | 8
 7 | 3
 8 |
 9 |
10 |
11 |
12 |
13 |
14 | 4
15 | 0  3
```

7 | 3 means 73 kg

7.   Meat Consumption by Small and
Medium-Sized Predatory Dinosaurs

```
0 | 4
1 | 9
2 | 1  1  6  7
3 |
4 | 6  7  8
```

4 | 8 means 4.8 kg per day

8. Sample Response: Yes; In both plots, there are 3 clusters of data (in both plots one of the clusters contains only one value); Masses: 6 kg, 45 kg to 73 kg, and 144 kg to 153 kg; Meat Consumption: 0.4 kg, 1.9 kg to 2.7 kg, and 4.6 kg to 4.8 kg. I think this makes sense because it indicates that the bigger the dinosaur, the greater the daily meat consumption. There are no large gaps in the consumption stem-and-leaf plot as there are in the mass stem-and-leaf plot. This doesn't affect my original conclusion.

49. a. Sample Response:

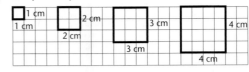

Length of a side (cm)	Area (cm²)	Perimeter (cm)
1	1	4
2	4	8
3	9	12
4	16	16

Section 5, Exploration 1 (pp. 265–266)

5.

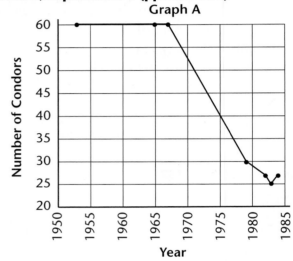

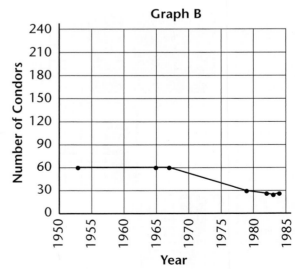

8. a–b.

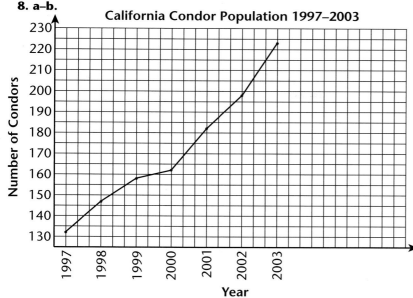

California Condor Population 1997–2003

(graph: y-axis "Number of Condors" from 130 to 230, x-axis "Year" from 1997 to 2003)

Section 5, Practice and Application (p. 271)

1. a.

Wolf Pups Born in Yellowstone National Park

(graph: y-axis "Number of Pups" from 0 to 80, x-axis "Year" from 1994 to 2001)

4.

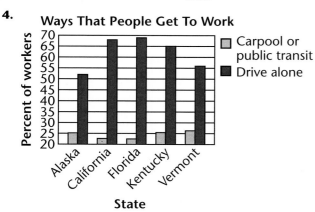

Ways That People Get To Work

(bar graph: y-axis "Percent of workers" from 20 to 70, x-axis "State" with Alaska, California, Florida, Kentucky, Vermont; legend: Carpool or public transit, Drive alone)

Section 5, Extra Skill Practice (p. 275)

4. Bar graph: A bar graph is appropriate. For each period, the number of grizzlies removed would be represented by a bar.

Circle graph: A circle graph is not appropriate since the data shown in the line graph do not represent a percent of all grizzlies in the park. For the 29 bears removed since 1931, each group of data could be made into the percent of bears removed and represented in a circle graph, with the years on each pie piece.

Line plot: A line plot would show the modes and clusters and gaps.

Stem-and-Leaf plot: A stem-and-leaf plot is possible, but there would only be two stems: 0 and 1.

Neither the line plot nor the stem-and-leaf plot would show the changes since the 1972 campaign began.

Review and Assessment (p. 278)

8.

Maximum Speed of Some Yellowstone Park Mammals

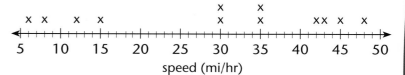

speed (mi/hr)

MODULE 5

Section 1, Spiral Review (p. 293)

37.   Daily High Temperatures
            in a Midwest City in July

```
 5 | 6 9
 6 | 1 4 8 9 9
 7 | 1 2 2 7 7 8 8 8 8
 8 | 0 2 2 2 4 5 5 7 7 9
 9 | 0 1 1 8
10 | 1
```

7 | 1 means 71 degrees Fahrenheit

Section 2, Exploration 1 (p. 297)

7. b. How good a measurement is depends on the person doing the measuring and the quality of the measuring device. If you measured to the nearest 32nd of an inch, it is possible to measure to the nearest 64th and then the nearest 128th, 256th of an inch and so on as the preciseness never ends.

ADDITIONAL ANSWERS

Section 5, Study Skills (p. 344)

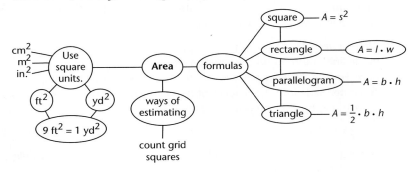

MODULE 6

Section 2, Practice and Application (p. 378)

18. Sample Responses:

a.

Number of Students	Length of brigade (ft)	Time to pass sandbag (sec)
10	30	10
20	60	20
30	90	30
40	120	40

b.

Sandbag Brigade

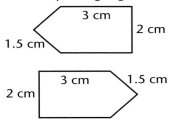

Section 3, Exploration 3 (p. 388)

22. b.

Tibia (cm)	32	35	38	40	45
Height (cm)	130	140	150	160	180
$\dfrac{\text{Tibia}}{\text{Height}}$	$\dfrac{32}{130}$	$\dfrac{35}{140}$	$\dfrac{38}{150}$	$\dfrac{40}{160}$	$\dfrac{45}{180}$

Section 3, Extra Skill Practice (p. 394)

1. d.

Kneeling height (cm)	94	**99**	**105**	87
Standing height (cm)	**125**	132	140	**116**

Section 4, Exploration 1 (p. 398)

11. a. The ratio $\dfrac{\text{distance jumped}}{\text{body length}}$ is about the same for the jackrabbit and the kangaroo. **b.** The ratio $\dfrac{\text{distance jumped}}{\text{body length}}$ for the kangaroo is $\dfrac{42}{3.5}$, and the ratios for the jackrabbit and kangaroo are about the same. **d.** Not necessarily; the ratios are about the same, and the distance given for the kangaroo was a record. The kangaroo probably didn't jump that far every time; the jackrabbit probably wouldn't jump 18 ft every time.

Section 5, Exploration 1 (pp. 408–409)

4. b.

Corresponding Angles			Corresponding Sides		
$\angle A$	corresponds to	$\angle E$	$\overline{AB}$	corresponds to	$\overline{EF}$
$\angle B$	corresponds to	$\angle F$	$\overline{BC}$	corresponds to	$\overline{FG}$
$\angle C$	corresponds to	$\angle G$	$\overline{CD}$	corresponds to	$\overline{GH}$
$\angle D$	corresponds to	$\angle H$	$\overline{DA}$	corresponds to	$\overline{HE}$

9. b. similar; corresponding angles have equal measures and the ratios of the lengths of corresponding sides are all equivalent to a ratio of 2:1

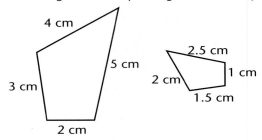

c. not similar; one triangle is a right scalene and the other is a right isosceles, so they are not the same shape.

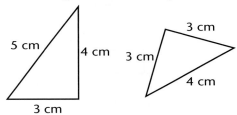

d. similar and congruent; corresponding sides have a 1:1 ratio and corresponding angles are congruent. Same shape and size.

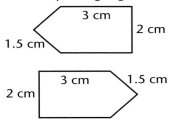

Section 5, Practice and Application (p. 414)

2.

$\overline{AB}$	corresponds to	$\overline{OP}$
$\overline{BC}$	corresponds to	$\overline{PL}$
$\overline{CD}$	corresponds to	$\overline{LM}$
$\overline{DE}$	corresponds to	$\overline{MN}$
$\overline{EA}$	corresponds to	$\overline{NO}$
$\angle A$	corresponds to	$\angle O$
$\angle B$	corresponds to	$\angle P$
$\angle C$	corresponds to	$\angle L$
$\angle D$	corresponds to	$\angle M$
$\angle E$	corresponds to	$\angle N$

Section 6, Exploration 1 (p. 421)

8.

Fraction	Equivalent Fraction in Hundredths	Percent	Decimal
$\frac{1}{2}$	$\frac{50}{100}$	50%	0.5
$\frac{2}{2}=1$	$\frac{100}{100}$	100%	1.0

Fraction	Equivalent Fraction in Hundredths	Percent	Decimal
$\frac{1}{4}$	$\frac{25}{100}$	25%	0.25
$\frac{2}{4}=\frac{1}{2}$	$\frac{50}{100}$	50%	0.5
$\frac{3}{4}$	$\frac{75}{100}$	75%	0.75
$\frac{4}{4}=1$	$\frac{100}{100}$	100%	1.0

Fraction	Equivalent Fraction in Hundredths	Percent	Decimal
$\frac{1}{10}$	$\frac{10}{100}$	10%	0.1
$\frac{2}{10}=\frac{1}{5}$	$\frac{20}{100}$	20%	0.2
$\frac{3}{10}$	$\frac{30}{100}$	30%	0.3
$\frac{4}{10}=\frac{2}{5}$	$\frac{40}{100}$	40%	0.4
$\frac{5}{10}=\frac{1}{2}$	$\frac{50}{100}$	50%	0.5
$\frac{6}{10}=\frac{3}{5}$	$\frac{60}{100}$	60%	0.6
$\frac{7}{10}$	$\frac{70}{100}$	70%	0.7
$\frac{8}{10}=\frac{4}{5}$	$\frac{80}{100}$	80%	0.8
$\frac{9}{10}$	$\frac{90}{100}$	90%	0.9
$\frac{10}{10}=1$	$\frac{100}{100}$	100%	1.0

Fraction	Equivalent Fraction in Hundredths	Percent	Decimal
$\frac{1}{5}$	$\frac{20}{100}$	20%	0.2
$\frac{2}{5}$	$\frac{40}{100}$	40%	0.4
$\frac{3}{5}$	$\frac{60}{100}$	60%	0.6
$\frac{4}{5}$	$\frac{80}{100}$	80%	0.8
$\frac{5}{5}=1$	$\frac{100}{100}$	100%	1.0

Section 6, Practice and Application (p. 429)

1. e. 67% fraction $\frac{67}{100}$
decimal 0.67

f. 100% fraction $\frac{100}{100}=1$
decimal 1.0

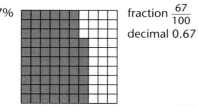

Review and Assessment (p. 436)

7. a.

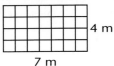

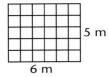

8. I drew a fitted line for the scatter plot, and I used the line to make my estimates.

Latitude (°N)	25	**40**	44	57
Temperature (°F)	**65**	37	**25**	**5**

MODULE 7

Section 1, Exploration 1 (p. 442)

8. a.

	Number of Faces	Number of Vertices	Number of Edges
Rectangular Prism	6	8	12
Hexagonal Prism	8	12	18
Polyhedron from Net 1	6	8	12
Polyhedron from Net 2	5	5	8

Section 1, Exploration 2 (pp. 444–446)

13. a–b.

Number of Layers	Height (cm)	Area of Base (cm²)	Volume (cm³)
1	1	6	6
2	2	6	12
3	3	6	18
4	4	6	24

20. f. I measured the height of the parallelogram, which is the perpendicular distance between the two parallel bases (the two square faces) of the prism.

23. Sample Responses:

length	width	height
36	1000	1000
360	100	1000
900	40	1000

Section 3, Exploration 2 (pp. 464–465)

13. a. Sample answers:

Object	quarter	drinking glass	CD	cereal bowl
Circumference (C)	7.5 cm	26.1 cm	37.7 cm	47 cm
Diameter (d)	2.4 cm	8.3 cm	12 cm	15 cm

14. a. Sample answers:

Object	quarter	drinking glass	CD	cereal bowl
Circumference (C) / Diameter (D)	3.13	3.14	3.14	3.13

16. Sample answers:

Object	quarter	drinking glass	CD	cereal bowl
π · diameter	7.54 cm	26.06 cm	37.68 cm	47.10 cm

The products are very close to the measured circumference.

Section 4, Exploration 2 (pp. 475–476)

14. b. Sample Response: The curved surface of the right cylinder is perpendicular to the bases and the net has a rectangle and a circle. The curved surface of the oblique cylinder is not perpendicular to the bases and the net has a "wavy" shape and a circle. **c.** Sample Response: Measure the perpendicular distance from one base to the other.

15. Prism A; The prisms are the same height. But the area of the base of Prism A is greater than area of the base of Prism B.

17. c.

Figure	Area of base (cm²)	Height (cm)	Volume (cm³)
Prism A	20.25	6	121.5
Prism B	9	6	54
Cylinder 1	about 15.9	6	about 95.4
Cylinder 2	about 15.9	6	about 95.4

MODULE 8

Section 6, Setting The Stage (p. 553)

Labsheet 6A

Planet	Distance from the sun		
	in km	expressed as the number of sticky notes × 100,000,000	expressed as the number of sticky notes × a power of 10
Earth	149,600,000	1.496 × 100,000,000	$1.496 \cdot 10^8$
Jupiter	778,330,000	7.7833 × 100,000,000	$7.7833 \cdot 10^8$
Mars	227,940,000	2.2794 × 100,000,000	$2.2794 \cdot 10^8$
Mercury	57,910,000	0.5791 × 100,000,000	$0.5791 \cdot 10^8$
Neptune	4,504,000,000	45.04 × 100,000,000	$45.04 \cdot 10^8$
Saturn	1,429,400,000	14.294 × 100,000,000	$14.294 \cdot 10^8$
Uranus	2,870,990,000	28.7099 × 100,000,000	$28.7099 \cdot 10^8$
Venus	108,200,000	1.082 × 100,000,000	$1.082 \cdot 10^8$